# LAROUSSE
## ENCYCLOPEDIA OF WORLD

# GEO
# GRA
# PHY

Adapted *from* GEOGRAPHIE UNIVERSELLE LAROUSSE,
*edited by Pierre Deffontaines, Director of the French Institute, Barcelona*

*Foreword by* L. DUDLEY STAMP, C.B.E.

# PAUL HAMLYN
LONDON · NEW YORK · SYDNEY · TORONTO

Other titles in this series

Larousse Encyclopedia of Astronomy
Larousse Encyclopedia of Prehistoric and Ancient Art
Larousse Encyclopedia of Byzantine and Medieval Art
Larousse Encyclopedia of Renaissance and Baroque Art
Larousse Encyclopedia of Modern Art
Larousse Encyclopedia of Ancient and Medieval History
Larousse Encyclopedia of Modern History
Larousse Encyclopedia of the Earth
Larousse World Mythology
Larousse Encyclopedia of Animal Life

Published by
THE HAMLYN PUBLISHING GROUP LIMITED
LONDON · NEW YORK · SYDNEY · TORONTO
Hamlyn House, Feltham, Middlesex, England

Larousse Encyclopedia of World Geography translated from
LAROUSSE GEOGRAPHIE UNIVERSELLE

Second impression 1969.

Printed by O.G.A.M., Verona, Italy.

LAROUSSE ENCYCLOPEDIA OF WORLD GEOGRAPHY
is adapted from Géographie Universelle Larousse

edited by **Pierre Deffontaines**

assisted by **Mariel Jean-Brunhes Delamarre**

editorial advisers (English edition): **M. Kidron, Alan B. Mountjoy, W. G. Moore, Alice Taylor**

## The Contributors are

**Paul Akamatsu (with**
**V. Elisseeff):** Japan
**Edgar Aubert de la Rüe:** Thailand, Saint-Pierre and
Miquelon
**Georges Azambre:** Vietnam
**Edouard Berlan:** Ethiopia, The Somalilands
**Jean-Jacques Berreby:** Arabia
**Jacques Besançon:** Egypt
**Pierre Birot:** Portugal, Portuguese
Islands of the North
Atlantic
**André Blanc:** Hungary, Yugoslavia,
Albania
**Antoine Bon:** Greece, Cyprus
**Jean Borde:** Chile
**André Cailleux:** Scandinavia (Denmark,
Norway, Sweden)
**Eila M. Campbell:** The Philippines
**Jean Canu:** Alaska, The United States
**Robert Capot-Rey:** The Sahara
**Auguste Cauneille:** Libya
**Jean Chardonnet:** Poland
**Jean Chesneaux:** China (1959), Mongolia
**André Chouraqui:** Israel
**Pierre Deffontaines:** Canada, Paraguay,
**(with Jean-Francois** Uruguay
**Gravier):** France
**Claude Collin Delavaud:** Afghanistan
**Jean Delvert:** Cambodia
**Jean Demangeot:** Italy, Vatican City, San
Marino
**Jean Dollfus:** Germany
**Jean-Pierre Dufourg:** Jordan
**Frans Dussart:** Belgium, Netherlands,
Luxembourg, Congo
Brazzaville, Congo
Kinshasa, Rwanda,
Burundi
**Vadime Elisseeff:** Korea
**Maurice Fevret:** Syria
**Alfred Fichelle:** Czechoslovakia, Bulgaria
**Robert Ficheux:** Rumania
**Pierre Flatrès:** Ireland
**Joseph Grelier:** Colombia, Venezuela
**Francisco**
**Hernández-Pacheco:** Spanish West Africa
**Alain Huetz de Lemps:** The Archipelagos of
Oceania, New Zealand,
Australia

**Hildebert Isnard:** North Africa (Algeria,
Tunisia, Morocco),
Zambia, Rhodesia,
The Republic of
South Africa, Madagascar,
The Comoro Islands
Réunion, Mauritius
**Louis C. D. Joos:** Spanish Guinea,
Portuguese Islands of the
Gulf of Guinea, Angola,
Mozambique
**Georges Jorré:** U.S.S.R.
**Guy Lasserre:** The West Indies
**Jean Malaurie:** Greenland
**Pierre Meile:** India, Nepal, Ceylon,
Pakistan
**André Meynier:** The British Isles
**Jean Michéa:** The Arctic Regions
**W. G. Moore:** Mexico
**Robert Nollet (with**
**Dr. S. Farzami):** Iran
**Gabriel Ollivier:** Monaco
**Henri Onde:** The Alps (Switzerland,
Liechtenstein, Austria)
**André Pauly:** Malta
**Eugène Pépin:** St. Helena, Ascension,
Tristan da Cunha,
Formosa, Hong Kong,
Macao, Bermuda, The
Guianas, Peru, Bolivia
**Marie-Magdeleine del**
**Perugia:** Iceland
**Paul Poumaillou:** Ecuador
**Pierre Rondot:** Turkey, The Lebanon,
Iraq, Oil and the Middle
East
**Gabriel Rougerie:** West Africa
**Jean Sermet:** Andorra, Spain
**Jean Sirol:** Guatemala, British
Honduras, Honduras, El
Salvador, Nicaragua, Costa
Rica, The Republic of
Panama
**Joseph Earle Spencer:** The East Indies
**L. Dudley Stamp:** Burma, Malaya
**François and Michel**
**Tabuteau:** Antarctica
**François Taillefer:** Finland
**Jules Vidal:** Laos
**Mariano Zamorano:** Argentina

# CONTENTS

# COLOUR PLATES

# LIST OF MAPS

# FOREWORD

Published by Librairie Larousse of Paris in three large quarto volumes, GEOGRAPHIE UNIVERSELLE LAROUSSE forms a comprehensive, scholarly and magnificently presented account of the world's surface which it would be hard to equal in any language. But in English editions the name Larousse is now firmly associated in the public mind with the single-volume encyclopedias — *The Earth, Mythology* and *Astronomy* — which have brought achievement in their respective fields right up to date and are available in a most attractive form to a large public. It was accordingly a logical step to condense the three volumes of the French GEOGRAPHIE UNIVERSELLE into this single-volume encyclopedia, at the same time taking the opportunity to make certain that illustrations were up to date, that maps showed the latest changes in the kaleidoscopic political situation, and that equally rapid developments in economic geography received due attention.

The result is this fine volume, for which I am happy to write the Foreword. To my mind it bears the indelible stamp of the General Editor, my good friend, Pierre Deffontaines. He has that rare quality of being able to detach himself from his surroundings and see the world in perspective as from afar. Perhaps it is because he is both poet and geographer, perhaps it is because he has for so long, as head of the French Institute in Barcelona, been able to serve his own country from outside and to uphold French culture beyond his homeland. In the pages which follow we in the English-speaking world see ourselves presented as others see us, and the point of view is sometimes an unusual one. We see the countries of the world considered logically, in sequence and each given a weight in words roughly commensurate with world importance. At the same time the emergent countries are each given their own specific recognition in an individual treatment, however brief, and so are the older units such as the Vatican City, Monaco and Andorra.

Geography has been defined in many and varied ways, but most geographers would agree today on the essential unity of their subject. Whether or not one accepts the concept of human ecology — the relationship between man and his environment considered in time and space — most would agree that it is important to look carefully at the physical background, and then to see how man has adapted it, or has adapted himself to it through the ages. In physical geography we may restrict ourselves to a study simply of the environment or some part thereof, but to attempt to consider 'human' or 'economic' geography apart from the environmental background and natural resources is indefensible. In this encyclopedia such a holistic view of geography, to use the word favourably, is naturally and effortlessly used throughout; the illustrations too range from the great works of Nature little touched by the hand of man to the great works of man almost entirely his own. The illustrations in this book have been selected with marked care. Many will be appreciated for their pictorial beauty and effectiveness, but all tell their part of the complex story which is the geography of the world. Geography used to be dismissed as that dull subject from which one suffered in junior forms at school and from which, in due course, one was fortunately allowed to escape. In large measure the dullness resulted from the almost meaningless collection of facts which used to pass for geography. But we are all interested in ourselves; we like to compare ourselves with the people of other nations; it becomes fascinating when we see how our lives have links with the conditions in which we live. We see adaptations of homes to mountain and plain, to the vagaries of the seasons; we see our villages and towns clustering around some eminence our ancestors fought to defend; we see our very latest factories arising where they have the advantages afforded by favourable physical conditions — a sheltered harbour, a source of power, a conveniently available supply of raw material. Through its text, its maps and its pictures this encyclopedia enables us to see these causal relationships manifested at every stage. There are the intimate details of family life, there are the activities in field and factory, the settlements large and small in village, town and city. Some magnificent aerial views enable us to take the broad view. Colour has been used where needed to emphasise contrasts both in the natural landscape and in the works of man.

Surely no one, young or old, into whose hands this encyclopedia may come, can fail to be stirred to a deeper appreciation and understanding of the varied and fascinating world in which we live. It is a world which modern communications have rendered one whole, and in which we are inevitably all world citizens. Nothing is more important than an appreciation, founded on sound knowledge, of the other man's problems and his point of view — so often the direct or indirect result of the circumstances in which he lives. And that is what we learn, painlessly and with pleasure, from the pages which follow.

L. DUDLEY STAMP

# THE EARTH

What is the Earth? The planet inhabited by mankind?
We are not even sure if that is an accurate definition.
Let us begin by taking stock of what we do know.

Our knowledge of the Earth is comparatively recent.
Human history and prehistory have lasted for several
millions of years, but we have known that the Earth is
round and mapped its regions only during the last few
centuries.

Space projects apart, we human beings cling to the
tiny pinhead of the planet which remains our terrestrial
prison somewhere in the midst of an enormous universe.
There are a number of special features about the Earth
which fundamentally effect our behaviour and our
way of living. The most important is the tilting of the
Earth's axis. The Earth both rotates on its own axis daily
and revolves in its orbit around the sun annually, tilted
at an angle of $66\frac{1}{2}°$ to the plane of the path it traces
during its revolution. Without this marked tilting the
Earth would be infinitely more regular, with the sun
rising and setting at the same time throughout the
year: climates, too, would be invariable.

The tilting of the Earth's axis is responsible for the
seasons, in particular those periods of bad weather which
regularly affect all forms of life. These periods, which
we call *winters,* differ regionally in duration and
severity, but they endow the whole of life with a
cyclic aspect which has enabled us to measure and define
time more accurately. The season of growth and
abundance after winter which we call *summer* once
served to measure age, and the longest day of the year
was celebrated accordingly. The return of winter brings
great hardship in its train. In the vegetable world many
plants disappear from the surface of the Earth to
escape the cold — annual plants contrasting with
perennial plants. There is a vital distinction between two
types of tree — the deciduous species, which are bare
in winter, and the non-deciduous (conifers and evergreens).

Animals' behaviour in winter is largely determined
by their mobility. Many of them undertake periodic
migrations to escape, others have lives as ephemeral as
those of certain plants, while still others undergo
physical changes enabling them to withstand the
rigours of the winter. A distinction as fundamental as
that between deciduous and non-deciduous trees divides
the animal world into cold- and warm-blooded species.

Man, on the other hand, is not particularly well
equipped to face the inclement weather with his relatively
high body temperature. His skin is a poor insulator and
he has no protective fur. The regular recurrence of
cold weather sets him one of his most difficult problems.
In many regions he has concentrated all his forces on
combating the weather. He has been driven to invent
a series of devices: first clothing, then increasingly
elaborate houses. He is the only living being who has
had to make clothes, just as he is the sole genus to have
used fire — a mysterious discovery whose use is taken
by archaeologists as a defining characteristic of man.

But man has not been daunted by the winter; with
the help of better clothing, housing, heating and food, he
has done his utmost to overcome the cold and has
become one of the most ubiquitous of living
beings, despite the severe handicaps of his constitution.

In spite of multiple protective devices, marked variations
in temperature constitute a severe test for man. Isotherm
maps marking off the zones with the severest winters
also define the regions where he finds it hardest to
survive. The Earth undergoes only relatively minor
changes in temperature, yet these differences are enough
to have a marked effect on mankind's distribution
on the Earth. As far as possible men have avoided
regions with lengthy winters. Since these regions are
situated in the interior of continental land masses where
the modifying influence of the oceans cannot affect
the seasons, humanity was driven towards the edges of
the continents. This phenomenon is particularly striking
in Eurasia, where there are two zones of high density
separated by a desert zone: the Far East, extending
from Japan to the Indies, with the shores of the China
Sea and the Indian Ocean alone containing more than
half the world's population (one milliard three hundred
millions), and the West, linked with the North
Atlantic and Mediterranean littorals, which has a
population of more than half a milliard.

But the distribution of the population still presents
many anomalies; nearly three-quarters of the continents
have less than one inhabitant to the square mile, while
some regions have densities of more than 1,000
inhabitants for the same area.

However, it is possible that man's settlement on the
Earth is as yet in its early stages. The rapid growth of
world population is a comparatively recent phenomenon.
In 1800 it was estimated at about seven hundred
million; it exceeded one milliard around 1850, two
milliards towards 1900, and today the Earth supports
over three milliards. In one hundred and fifty years
the number of men has more than trebled. This is a

sensational event in world history, with consequences which are only beginning to make themselves felt. It challenges mankind to take new measures and perhaps to adopt a more systematic demographic policy.

We must take into account not only the men who live, work and consume today, but also the men of the past who have contributed to the progressively better living conditions which we now enjoy. Geographers find it useful to establish the value of the past which blends so intimately with the present and weighs so heavily on it, and their work is thus linked with that of historians and archaeologists. Countries which have supported an ancient human civilisation look very different from those with a short human history.

There are certain zones of the Earth which have had the privilege of being cradles of civilisation. These pioneer regions are mainly found grouped around those semi-closed seas which we call 'mediterranean'. Physically they are relatively unstable, with marine deeps cheek by jowl with high reliefs, and they exhibit considerable evidence of the effects of vulcanism and earthquakes. In addition, relief is broken and peninsulas numerous.

The most ancient human peoples did not live in these zones — they are, in fact, poor in prehistoric remains — but history began in them. Here for the first time civilisation emerged from primitive anonymity; every product of the human mind appeared in these regions astonishingly early. The Mediterranean saw the beginnings of philosophy, religion, political systems, art, law and science. If a map could be made showing where the greatest works of mankind were concentrated, the Mediterranean zone would easily be the richest, during antiquity at least. The names of the cities built around it make an impressive list: Thebes, Memphis, Carthage, Rome, Syracuse, Alexandria and Constantinople.

This tiny Mediterranean region was the point of departure for man's first reconnaissance of the Earth, as if the rest of the globe (forty-nine fiftieths) was but an appendage. Around it the continents of Europe, Asia and Africa were born; in their infancy they existed only as the hinterland of this sea.

So perhaps it is not surprising that another roughly similar advance post existed in the New World in and around the other 'mediterranean' formed by the Caribbean Sea. Here, too, appeared the most ancient political systems of the American continents, the oldest towns and monuments. The most prosperous European colonies were maintained around the Caribbean until

the beginning of the nineteenth century. In 1789, New York had only 16,000 inhabitants, whereas Mexico contained more than 100,000. In both 'mediterraneans' the violence of physical features was coupled with an equally dynamic human outburst.

If we find it hard to understand the reasons why this intensive human activity was concentrated as it was, it is just as difficult for us to find a logical way of differentiating between the various groups making up the human species.

The concept of race is vey deceptive; what criterion are we to adopt to classify the different types of men? The most obvious distinction, the colour of the skin, must be discarded. We do not even know whether it is a racial characteristic or an acquired quality. In addition, the distribution of men according to their colour is singularly complicated. To allot the white races to Europe, black races to Africa and yellow races to Asia is a common but greatly oversimplified distinction. Asia has its whites: the Iranians, a number of Indians and undoubtedly the ancient Ainus of Japan. Africa, too, has hers: the peoples of North Africa and the Tuaregs in the Sahara. It is the same in Oceania, where the Polynesians and perhaps the Malays should be classified among the whites. As for the yellow races, they have descendants in Europe: the Turks and the Tatars. The great majority of American Indians are also of yellow origin. The black races have many representatives in Asia or Oceania: the Dravidians in the Indies and the Melanesians in the Pacific archipelagos. And what are we to make of the even more primitive races still existing: the Pygmies, Hottentots and Australian aborigines? What colour are they to be assigned? And what was the colour of the skin of the most ancient Palaeolithic men whose remains have been discovered?

The classification of men by their language does not give any better results, for languages do not correspond to races but jump from continent to continent in a remark-able way. The distinction of languages today is frankly disconcerting. Fortunately, in the midst of this tangled forest, certain major tongues stand out, some because they are the mother tongues of a vast number of people, such as Russian or Chinese (although there are many dialects of Chinese), others because they serve as the vehicles for certain needs of expression and are spoken in addition to their mother tongues by the inhabitants of widely varied regions. English, for example, is the language of trade, Latin the language of the Catholic liturgy and French the language of diplomacy and culture.

Nor can religions well be used for classification, on account of their dispersion and their astonishing variety.

How then are we to conduct this study of mankind and the present-day world? We propose here to abandon the classical division into continents, which appears increasingly arbitrary and inapt.

Europe was never able to define its eastern frontier precisely in the past. It is still less able to do so today when the vast Eurasian plains are farmed in a fairly uniform collective system from the Oder and the Vistula to the shores of the Seas of Japan and China. We have felt it indispensable to treat these vast flat expanses as a single unit, since they have no natural barriers, overlap into Europe and Asia and have been the scene of large-scale migrations of people for so long. Moreover, why separate the European peninsula from the Asiatic land mass any more than the Indian or Indo-Chinese peninsula? It would undoubtedly be easier to define an Indian continent than a European continent. from physical and human geographical points of view.

In addition, the traditional division into continents has the serious drawback of destroying the unity of the Mediterranean basin which is so obvious to the physical geographer at least. For the human geographer, too, the types of farming and ways of life in the basin have more in common with each other than they have with the continental regions behind them.

No doubt the Mediterranean basin varies considerably within itself, but the elements which separate its regions do not correspond to the continental divisions; the Muslim world straddles Africa and Asia and even overlaps a little into Europe; the Latin world overflowed into North Africa and at one time into the Middle East; the ancient Greek world, in common with the most ancient Phoenician and Aegean civilisations, occupied the Asian as well as the African and European shores.

As for the Americas, for so long centred on the other mediterranean, the Caribbean Sea, they were also the meeting-place for the Latin and Anglo-Saxon worlds. Here again we shall not restrict ourselves to continental divisions. South America is not south in the way that North America is north; rather, it is central, more so than Central America, since it is crossed at its widest point by the equator.

We have, then, attempted to establish groupings in relation to the human problems they pose.

Our geographical picture of the present-day world must be a realistic, positive picture, alive to the modern situation, and we must discard outmoded divisions.

Some may object that there has never been so much talk of continents as now. A United States of Europe is planned. Successful slogans are coined: Asia for the Asians, Africa for the Africans. But this should not be considered as a reassertion of traditional continental divisions so much as the symptom of new aspirations which have not yet found their real name.

Human geography inevitably faces the question of the destiny of the human race. No doubt *homo sapiens* has reached a high level today, but the process of evolution is not finished. Perhaps we are entering on a phase when the individual human being will be transcended by society. Already men are moving towards a gregarious way of life. In contradistinction to other species which live exclusively together (bees, ants, etc.) or as individuals, mankind has always had the choice. It seems that in the past dispersion won the day, but today a gregarious impulse of unknown force is driving men into larger and larger agglomerations, some becoming so vast that they have more than ten million inhabitants. Is humanity going to opt for the life of the hive? Could not current tendencies also lead to a new 'charitable' order which might finally integrate humanity into a single community? No doubt we are still a long way from that!

Will the population of the Earth increase indefinitely? It has been said that in Asia, with its destructive monsoons, that vast swarms of men are necessary to keep pace with the forces of nature. Is there then a struggle between man and nature? The new sources of power which are increasing so rapidly in number may change the whole nature of the world population problem. The growing of food may be revolutionised at short notice; already there is talk of irradiated seeds, of hydroponic crops grown in ionised solutions of water and needing no earth. Should we not also envisage a far more extensive agricultural use of the seas? And for how much longer will human geography remain confined to the planet Earth?

We hear a great deal about the difficulties facing the future of the human race, but despite present demographic and political trends, there is some hope that technological discoveries may be applied for the benefit of mankind rather than for its destruction.

PIERRE DEFFONTAINES

# NORTHERN EUROPE

# SCANDINAVIA

Scandinavia today consists of Denmark, Sweden and Norway. It has rarely formed a single state in the whole course of history, yet the three countries are closely allied by ties of soil, language, customs and common interest as well as by general outlook. The Scandinavian family also includes two more distant members: Iceland and Finland.

*On the edge of Europe.* On a map Scandinavia proper emerges as the north-west flank of Europe, with only about 900 miles separating Lapland from the Urals. On the other side is the Skandik, the Scandinavian (Norwegian) sea, an extension of the North Atlantic opening to the Arctic Ocean. Beyond it, less than 900 miles to the north-west, Greenland marks the beginning of the American continent. The distance by sea to Spitsbergen, to the north, is barely 400 miles, to Iceland 650 miles, and to Scotland 300 miles. Thus the Scandinavians' vocation as a seafaring people was encouraged from earliest times, and was further emphasised by the deep penetration of the Baltic Sea, which is linked with the North Sea by the Great and Little Belts and by the Sound, the Kattegat and the

Skagerrak. These waters separate two very different peninsulas: to the north, the Scandinavian peninsula proper, composed of Norway and Sweden, measuring 1,185 miles from Scania (Skåne) to the North Cape in latitude 71°, and connected with Finland and Russia by a frozen and sparsely inhabited isthmus; and to the south of the straits, the Jutland peninsula, which with the neighbouring archipelago makes up Denmark and is separated from Germany rather than connected to it by the rather narrow isthmus of Schleswig-Holstein. Thus Scandinavia is bounded by the sea on nearly all sides; including the indentations of its fiords and archipelagos, its total coastline length is nearly 22,000 miles, inclusive of the many indentations.

The land surface of Scandinavia is extremely varied, with rugged moutains in Norway, low hills in Denmark and undulating broken plains in Sweden. This variety is paralleled in the sea itself: the giant breakers and heavy tides of the Atlantic and the North Sea in the west; the limpid mirrors of the Norwegian fiords; the calm grey waters of the homely Baltic, which are tideless and only slightly saline. Salinity falls from 35 grams per litre in the Atlantic to 24 in the Kattegat, 14 in the Danish archipelago, and a mere 4 in the Gulf of Bothnia. Oceanic species disappear one by one, the further one penetrates the straits and the Baltic, until most of the fish in the furthest parts of the Gulf of Bothnia are freshwater species.

The Baltic is shallow, generally less than 300 feet deep, although there is one deep of 1,540 feet north of the island of Gotland, and another of 970 feet in the Gulf of Bothnia. The two Belts are less than 164 feet deep, and in the Sound there is a shelf less than 26 feet below sea level that is a hazard to ships of heavy tonnage. The Baltic Sea and the straits as a whole are classified as epi-continental seas, and geophysical samples taken in their southern waters reveal the same strata that are found in Sweden and Denmark.

*A region of early glaciation.* The geological structure of Scandinavia is simple: an ancient rock shield on which other strata have since been deposited and which was subjected to Quaternary glaciation several times in the last million years.

The ancient shield is composed of barren siliceous rocks, gneiss, mica schists and granite; it also includes some strata of metalliferous deposits, notably iron, which is a source of wealth. It is between 500 and 3,500 million years old. The whole of its surface underwent several vigorous foldings with the result that its rocks are steeply inclined. Subsequently they have been worn down into a peneplain. Schists, sandstone and limestone were deposited on top of the peneplain, and when a pedestrian walks through a Swedish town, he is treading on stones full of *Orthoceras,* 420 million-year-old shells.

Some 400 million years ago, the west of Scandinavia underwent one last violent folding, and the rock formations of Norway were moved from west to east. Today, towards Sweden, the glint-line and a number of mountains still mark the limit of the erosion of the ancient *nappes.* From then until the Quaternary era, the heart of the Scandinavian peninsula remained above sea level, while the sea made frequent inroads into the Baltic and Danish coastline. This was the time of the chalk deposits which even now, worn down

The sulphate works at Husun, in Northern Ångermanland, where first-quality wood pulp is made.

by sea and ice, can be found in the dazzling white cliffs at Moen in Denmark. Fossil remains of the period bear witness to climates considerably warmer than those of present-day Danish waters.

Then, at the end of the Tertiary and the beginning of the Quaternary era — about a million years ago — the climate gradually grew very much colder, although there were occasional violent fluctuations. In the west, which had risen progressively in the meantime, glaciers formed on the Norwegian mountains. To the west, they flowed into the Scandinavian sea where they broke up; towards the east, they spread out over the high Swedish and Finnish plains, meeting in a piedmont glacier which gradually rose higher. The snow was transformed into firn; the glacier bulged, becoming an enormous dome of ice covering the whole of the interior of the country, whence its name *inlandsis* (*is,* ice, and *inland,* interior of the country). Soon the *inlandsis* crossed the Baltic and invaded Denmark, Germany, Poland and Russia. Then, as the climate grew warmer, it receded and disappeared or was confined to the highest mountains.

There were several successive glacial periods, separated by interglacial phases, and they have left cirques, glaciated valleys, and fiords in Norway; countless lakes in Sweden; lines of moraines marking the ice sheet's final recession from Denmark to Sweden, Norway and Lapland; ancient shore-lines around the Baltic and vast expanses of sand and gravel from the ancient deltas. Other features are the *eskers,* deposits from the ancient subglacial watercourses which dominate the plains with their strange, sinuous, elongated ridges; covering the low plains there is boulder clay deposited in the lakes, with thin parallel layers (*varves*) dating the history of the final recession of the ice sheet. Towards 18,000 B.C. the glacial front cut Jutland in two; towards 11,000 B.C. it freed the south and towards 6,000 B.C moved to the north of Sweden.

Glacial and allied deposits, except in Denmark, are mostly siliceous and naturally rather infertile, and the blocks of stone with which they are dotted are a hindrance to cultivation. But the lush, well-cultivated fields of Denmark, southern Sweden and some Norwegian valleys are a tribute to the tenacity of the Scandinavian farmer.

As the ice sheet retreated and grew narrower, it exposed the rocky shield which has tended to rise. Thus the north of Sweden is already about 900 feet higher than it was once, and the land still continues to rise in relation to sea level. The uplift is 10–15 inches a century at Stockholm, and 3 feet at the bottom of the Gulf of Bothnia. Harbour installations rapidly become inadequate in such a situation and have to be moved to remain of practical use. This explains the curious siting of the commercial port of Stockholm, which today lies far from the old city. Copenhagen has been luckier: uplift there does not exceed 4 inches in the course of a century, and the port has been able to expand normally.

*A wet region of many rivers.* Since 6,000 B.C. the climate of Scandinavia has been, apart from a few fluctuations, the same as it is today: cool temperate verging on cold in the north. The mean annual temperature varies from 8°C. (46°F.) in the south to –2°C. (28°F.) in the north. The high latitudes (from 55° to 71°) would normally impose a genuinely cold climate, but Scandinavia has a western façade, most of which is open to maritime influences, and Norway is washed by the warm waters of the Gulf Stream. This has a modifying influence on temperature and causes heavy rainfall, particularly in the west. The east and north are drier and colder than the west in winter and hotter in summer. But of all the areas in these latitudes, Scandinavia is the most habitable and the most densely populated.

Its rivers and countless lakes occupy six per cent of

The Naero Valley, Norway, seen from Stalheim. The harsh rocks and rugged mountains with wooded slopes are typical of Norway's landscape.

A young Norwegian lumberjack. As in the rest of Scandinavia, the timber industry is important, for forest covers one quarter of the country.

its surface, an excessively high proportion that is exceeded only in Finland and certain districts of Canada. The lakes are a legacy of recent glaciations; in the past they provided natural routes for sledges and boats, but they have impeded modern road-building. This inconvenience is slightly compensated for by the fishing they offer; they have also fostered the Scandinavians' love of sailing.

The rivers are extremely numerous, but their basins are small: the largest and most navigable, that of the Klar-Väner-Göta, does not exceed 19,300 square miles On the Lapland plateaus watercourses are the only natural landmarks, and the River Torne separates Sweden from Finland for 250 miles. The river systems of the peninsula are usually regular, most courses flowing down from the mountains to the sea in parallel lines. In the plains, the systems have varied according to the vicissitudes of the glacial retreat.

In the north and in the mountains most of the precipitation is snow, which forms a permanent blanket during the winter, accumulating and melting little, if at all. Skiing was invented here as a means of everyday communication. The thaw takes place in the spring, bringing belated floods in its train.

In the plains of Denmark and the south of Sweden, rainfall plays a more important part in feeding the

The ice cascades of a frozen waterfall in the province of Jämtland, Sweden.

rivers; evaporation is more marked owing to the summer heat; the waters are low in summer, and the main floods take place in winter and at the beginning of the spring. The proportion of water carried away in relation to the total precipitation is 40 to 50 per cent even in the southern plains. In the mountains and the north it reaches 80 to 85 per cent. This proportion accounts for the great volume of the rivers; in conjunction with heavy precipitation it assures Norway and Sweden of large resources of hydro-electric power. In Norway an annual average of 10,350 kWh. per head is produced, in Sweden 5,370 but in Denmark a mere 550, almost all thermal.

*Fine forests.* To judge by those forests which have been preserved in more or less their original state, the region's woodland scenery must have been magnificent when the first men arrived in Scandinavia. There are fine forests of beech trees in Denmark and south-west Sweden. Farther north, more and more conifers are mixed with the deciduous trees. Still farther north there are pines, with spruces on the increase. In the far north, the desolate treeless stretches of the tundra predominate. Similar graduations may be observed on the mountains. The upper limit of forest lies at 3,600 feet in the south of Norway and falls to 1,200 feet in Lapland. In the south of Sweden it takes 90 years for a tree to reach a height of 60 feet and a diameter of 1 foot; in the north it takes 150 to 180 years.

Wild animals include the reindeer in the north, and the elk in Sweden and Norway. In other parts of Scandinavia wolves, foxes, lynxes, otters and beavers can be found, although they are becoming rarer. Prominent among the birds is the capercailzie, a game-bird with magnificent plumage. The lemming, a kind of miniature guinea-pig, is common in the mountains. Scandinavia is one of the best regions for the study of the phenomena of variation in the abundance of flora and fauna in relation to latitude and the resulting climatic zones.

*The arrival of man.* We know that man appeared some hundreds of millennia ago, but it is improbable that he reached Scandinavia in those distant epochs. If he did, subsequent glaciations which scoured the surface of the country destroyed any evidence of his presence. In about 18,000 B.C. the ice sheet still covered the whole of the peninsula. It is known that towards 13,000 B.C. Magdalenian reindeer hunters were pitching their tents near Hamburg, which was then as cold as present-day Lapland. Their only tools were made of chipped stone or bone. Later, as the climate grew milder, the ice-cap receded from the Danish islands and then from the south of Sweden. Towards 7,000 B.C. Stockholm was freed, and during the same epoch men entered Denmark. Between 7,000 and 6,000 B.C. men lived by hunting and picking nuts in the forests of Denmark and southern Sweden, or by gathering shellfish if they inhabited the coast. The mounds of piles of shells known as *kjökkenmöddings* (kitchen middens) are their culinary remains — valuable as evidence of early man's way of life.

Between 5,000 and 4,000 B.C. some progress was made. The dog, the first domestic animal, was introduced — probably for hunting — and man learned to polish stone and make pots. Then, towards 3,500 B.C. came primitive cultivation of wheat and barley with the hoe, the rearing of cows, pigs and sheep; and soon, between 2,400 and 2,000 B.C., the megalithic monuments, the tumuli, dolmens, covered ways and lines of menhirs. Next came the domestic horse, and towards 1,800 B.C. copper, bronze, oats and the first swingploughs. Their late arrival in Scandinavia was the penalty for isolation.

The types of skeletons and the evolution of the burial-places in Denmark around 2,200 B.C. have been taken as evidence that Indo-European invaders speaking a Germanic tongue mingled with the ancient farming people; farther south their cousins, the Celts, invaded Gaul and the British Isles, many settling there permanently.

Technical and artistic progress continued in Scandinavia: in 700 B.C. there were rock engravings; in 500 B.C. iron was being extracted from ore taken from the marshes; the first ploughs and the first ships were in use. Towards the beginning of the Christian era came the introduction of rye, and the first attempts at manuring land and at marling, a technique which originated in Gaul. About 300 B.C. windmills with revolving millstones were used on the land. At about the same period the runic alphabet appeared.

*Who are the Scandinavians?* The Scandinavians belong to the white Nordic race. They are tall (average height 5 ft. 8 in.), slim and broad-shouldered, with pinkish-white skins. Their hair is fair, their eyes blue, their faces and skulls long. They have thin, prominent noses, thin-set lips and prominent chins. By nature they are serious, even taciturn. The type is purest in central Sweden.

There are exceptions of course — notably the Lapps, who display totally different features. A minority resident in the north, they are short (a little over 5 feet) and dark-complexioned, with small heads and round skulls.

The Scandinavians have known many changes in sovereignty in the course of history. At first they were ruled by minor chieftains; after 872 Norway became a kingdom, followed by Denmark and Sweden. From 1375 Denmark was the dominant nation, and even effected a union of the three countries under its government from 1389 to 1523. In 1520 Sweden revolted and itself became a great European power during the reigns of Gustavus Adolphus and Charles XII. After 1720 it began to decline again. Norway, under the Danish monarchy from 1375 to 1814 and afterwards ceded to Sweden, finally regained its independence in 1905 and established sovereignty over bases in the Arctic and Antarctic.

The sea has fostered remarkable unity, and down the centuries has been a tremendously powerful force in the lives of the people, inspiring the expeditions of the Vikings from the eighth to the tenth centuries, the conquests of Normandy in 911 and of England in 1013, the discovery of Iceland in 874, and of Greenland and North America towards 1000. Even before the Christian era the Goths and the Suevi crossed the Baltic, while in the thirteenth century the Danes gained a foothold in Estonia. The Swedes established themselves in Finland from the ninth to the fourteenth century and, advancing from there, founded Novgorod. They played an important part among the peoples who were to become the Russians and they even gave their name to them: Rus. In the seventeenth century

the Swedes settled in Pomerania. In the eighteenth century the Danes colonised Greenland again.

The persistence of maritime enterprises in the course of Scandinavian history explains the importance of shipping in the region's life today. Tonnage per head of population is 0.52 tons in Denmark; 0.55 in Sweden; and 3.7 in Norway, figures which no other power in the world can equal. External trade also reaches record heights per head of population. Commerce on such a large scale, made possible by the large merchant fleet, is necessary because of the lack of natural resources. Many foodstuffs have to be imported.

The only important activity connected with the soil common to all the Scandinavian countries is the raising of livestock. There are approximately 340 cattle per 1,000 inhabitants in Sweden, 310 in Norway, and 720 in Denmark.

Isolation accounts for other features peculiar to Scandinavian life. Roman influence was slight and indirect. Christianity was a late arrival, slowly penetrating from the ninth to the twelfth century. On the other hand, no other countries accepted the Reformation so easily or so unanimously; according to official statistics Lutherans form 92 per cent of the population in Sweden, 97 per cent in Norway, and 99 per cent

A minority resident in northern Scandinavia, the short, dark-complexioned Lapps display features that are quite different from the tall, fair Nordic type found throughout the peninsular. Traditionally nomads, fishermen and keepers of reindeer, their way of life is changing under new social and commercial contacts.

Gutting cod at the Norwegian port of Svolvaer, in the Lofoten Islands. Fishing and whaling have always played an important rôle in the country's economy, and Norway's merchant fleet is the third largest in the world.

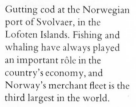

Houses in Smogen, on the west coast of Sweden. Scandinavia has one of the highest standards of living in Europe.
Substantial aid for education, rigorous campaigning against alcoholism and a generous social insurance plan are some of the provisions for general welfare.

in Denmark, though there are few regularly practising members in any of the three countries.

*A high standard of living.* In the country areas the tendency is towards dispersed communities, the principal exception being the oldest Danish villages, established under early influences. Elsewhere farms are isolated.

Small towns all offer the same delightful prospect. The most careful observer will see at first only one or two houses tucked unobtrusively behind a clump of trees. But behind that clump another house is hidden and behind it more trees. The little town is one big garden.

Social and political development is curious in that it has never kept in step with the rest of Europe; sometimes it has lagged behind, sometimes it has set the pace. Europe's oldest democracy was established in Iceland in 874, yet today Sweden, Norway and Denmark are still monarchies. Sweden has had a parliament since 1435, and neither she nor Norway experienced the oppression of the feudal system, but it was only in 1907–9 that universal male suffrage was introduced. Norway extended it to women in 1919 and Sweden in 1918. From 1920 on, a wave of enthusiasm for socialism produced a programme of economic and social legislation. It included social and unemployment insurance; legislation to foster good industrial relations; old age pensions; encouragement of co-operatives; aid for schools and adult education; a strict campaign against alcoholism. Similar liberal legislation began in Denmark in the 1890's; Scandinavia today has one of the highest standards of living in Europe, and, indeed, in the world.

The amount of power used annually per head of the population provides interesting evidence of the national wealth. Expressed in weight of coal per head and per annum, total power, including electricity and paraffin but excluding wood, amounts to more than 2 tons in Denmark, 4 in Sweden and 5 in Norway. This is considerably in excess of the global average of 1·5 and means that the Scandinavians are well provided with electrical appliances.

Large sums have been devoted to education, before World War II, and especially in the 1950's and 1960's.

The whole population attaches the utmost importance to the teaching profession, and this creates an atmosphere favourable to education and work in the schools. The Danish industrialist, Jacobsen, donated all the income from his Carlsberg brewery to scientific research. Denmark publishes over 3,100 books a year, Sweden 3,200 and Norway 2,800. The dissemination of news is more widespread than in most countries; one newspaper is sold for every two inhabitants in Sweden, and almost as many in Denmark and Norway.

*A thriving population.* A high general standard of living, a balanced but strict campaign against alcoholism, a high level of medical care and organisation, and constant regard for public health contribute to general longevity. The Scandinavian mortality rate is the lowest in the world: 0·8 per cent annually. The population is increasing by almost 1 per cent per annum. As resources are growing even more rapidly, the standard of living should go on rising, and the Scandinavians can face the future with confidence. Development has made enormous strides, especially in the last half-century. The reason lies not so much in individual initiative as in the way in which it is co-ordinated in the common effort, in the nation's wisdom and in its conception of the State.

# DENMARK

The kingdom of Denmark, smallest of the Scandinavian states and only a little larger than Belgium, is low-lying and made up of fragments of land. Including the irregular peninsula of Jylland (Jutland), it comprises about 500 islands, of which about 100 are inhabited. The largest are grouped in the straits: Zealand, Funen, Lolland and Falster. Bornholm, which is appreciably further away, is the sunniest island, and the only one where there is good building stone. Danish houses are usually made of brick, less often wood roofs are tiled.

The population in 1960 was just over 4,500,000; its density, at 274 to the square mile, is by far the highest of the Scandinavian states. While the Lutheran church (the State religion) claims 99 per cent of the population, there is freedom of worship.

A constitutional monarchy, Denmark has a one-chamber parliament, dominated at present by the Social Democrats. Denmark is a member of the European Free Trade Association, of the Council of Europe and of the Nordic Council, which established reciprocal economic and social measures between the five Scandinavian countries. Neutral, and despite national service virtually without an army in 1940, Denmark joined NATO in 1949. The army is kept up to strength by compulsory military service of sixteen months, and there is a well developed Home Guard.

*A wide-awake economy.* The Danes are simple people. In a country where agricultural production is industrialised and more standardised than anywhere else, many women, even in the towns, make it a point of honour to maintain the traditional domestic arts, especially baking. Most Danes have a bicycle, a machine well suited to the gently undulating countryside; even in Copenhagen, when the offices and factories cease work, the streets are jammed with hordes of cyclists.

The Danes have always exhibited great economic activity and for a long time their vocation was agricultural and maritime. Though Denmark never had a feudal system, peasant copyholders were dominated by the medieval manor; however, reform legislation starting in 1760 prompted freeholdings and small rather than large properties. The compact village centre was not abandoned but tended to play a new rôle, as an administration unit and a craft centre. The Land Fund, set up in 1919, enables the government to assist smallholders to buy their farms, and to procure extra land for them where the holdings are uneconomically small. Since 1938 government loans have helped agricultural workers to build their own houses.

Agricultural production, as well as the distribution of land, has been developed by intelligent adaptation to changing circumstances. Until 1860, cereals had predominated. Towards 1870 the competition of the United States was felt, and rather than introduce protective tariffs and risk stagnation the Danes preferred to make a radical change and concentrate on dairy farming or mixed farming.

It was realised that products would have to be standardised to build up and maintain high sales. Co-operatives have contributed largely to this end. They centralise nine-tenths of the milk produced and slaughter 85 per cent of the pigs. Eggs are graded in screening machines to less than a millimetre. This uniformity has many advantages so that it is being increasingly developed by the Danish authorities in most areas of production.

Co-operatives also encourage and subsidise scientific and technical research.

Apart from arable and stock-farming, fishing has always been one of Scandinavia's resources, and its growth has been particularly rapid in Denmark in the last twenty years.

Mineral resources are negligible. There is a little lignite. Prospecting for petroleum continues, but so far unsuccessfully. Large reserves of limestone and marl support a flourishing cement industry, and an abundance of clay in the glacial deposits provides the material for Denmark's famous pottery. Copenhagen

Denmark, the smallest of the Scandinavian states, is a low-lying country made up of fragments of land including the irregular peninsular of Jutland. Of the 500 islands making up the national territory, about 100 are inhabited.

A landscape in the rich cereal-growing district of North Zealand, Denmark. Until 1860 grain was the principal crop; today imports exceed exports.

Preparing bacon in a Danish factory. Denmark is an agricultural country, exporting much of its produce to provide a large part of the national revenue. Scrupulous maintenance of quality has ensured continued demand abroad.

The fishing port of Esbjerg. The town has been growing rapidly in importance with the great increase in the export trade to Britain.
Other customers for Danish fish are Western Germany, Sweden, and France. Denmark has a fishing fleet of 8,387 motor boats and 5,692 sailing boats.

A fishwife skinning an eel in the old fish-market of Copenhagen. The recognised hub of all Danish activities and trade, Copenhagen's port is by far the busiest in Denmark, as its name indicates—København: merchants' harbour.

porcelain is noted for its elegance and the sobriety of its design.

The deficiencies of the soil are compensated for by the proximity of the sea, which has encouraged commerce and processing industries. Iron, coal and other imported raw materials are transported by sea and processed in the factories. Shipbuilding is the most important industry.

Lying between Sweden, the islands and Jutland, the Danish straits, with their shores devoted to commerce, are the key to the Baltic. By value, half Denmark's exports are farm produce: cattle and meat, eggs, cheese and butter. Increasingly exports include manufactured products and, quite recently, fresh fish. Great Britain is the principal customer, followed by Western Germany, Sweden and the U.S.A.

Now another trading channel has acquired importance: the Schleswig-Holstein isthmus. An agricultural region, it was for long a source of dispute between its neighbours Germany and Denmark. Today the two countries are connected by two rail routes and two main roads. There is very heavy traffic through the small frontier town of Krusa.

From time to time there are acute crises in Denmark's export trade, exceptionally sensitive to foreign trends. Balance of payments difficulties mean that a keen eye on the general economy will be needed to ensure continued prosperity and to maintain the present standard of living.

COPENHAGEN. The hub of all Danish activities and trade is the capital, Copenhagen. Today it houses about one-fifth of the population of Denmark, and is the biggest city in Scandinavia. Bishop Absalon founded it in the twelfth century; a tiny, easily fortified islet between the large islands of Zealand and Amager became the heart of the city. It rapidly earned the name of København (*havn*, harbour, and *køben*, merchants) and was chosen as the capital in 1443, when it lay in the geographical centre of the country, which then included what is now southern Sweden. The university was founded in 1478. A library was built in the sixteenth century, and several academic establishments were founded in the eighteenth. Theatres and museums play their part in making Copenhagen the intellectual capital. Also at Copenhagen are the Royal Palace, and the headquarters of civil service departments and important commercial associations. The town is criss-crossed with canals, and the port is by far the busiest in Denmark. The population total has followed an ascending curve: 130,000 inhabitants in 1850, 380,000 in 1900, and, still increasing, 923,000 in 1960.

Copenhagen today is a charming, hospitable city of handsome monuments and well-kept streets, tasteful window displays, peaceful parks and cheerful church bells. In the calm waters of the port Hans Andersen's Little Mermaid, well known to tourists, still dreams of immortality.

No other town in Denmark is more than one-eighth the size of the capital. Aarhus, in Jutland, is the seat of a university founded in 1933 and boasts a remarkable folklore museum. There are many small towns of historic interest, buildings dating from the Middle Ages to the eighteenth century. The castle at Elsinore, the setting of Shakespeare's *Hamlet,* still guards the entrance to the Sound.

The Danish countryside is a medley of gentle hills, fields and meadows dotted with smiling farms and copses, through which countless meandering country roads twist and turn. Far from the main towns, there are places where the traveller can follow tracks dating from neolithic times, and where the silhouettes of ancient tumuli stand out serene against the sky.

THE FAEROE ISLANDS. A province of Denmark, like Greenland, the Faeroe Islands are situated in the North Atlantic, halfway between Scotland and Iceland. They are entirely volcanic, and trees on the islands are now rare. The 32,000 inhabitants live mainly by fishing and sheepfarming. Their language is similar to Icelandic. Some foster dreams of independence, but the majority are satisfied with the internal autonomy Denmark granted them in 1948. The Faeroes have their own parliament and their own flag. The capital is Thorshavn.

*An imaginative social and cultural policy.* Denmark's social development is as distinguished as its economic development. There are free school canteens and hospitals for everyone; maternity benefits; free medicine for all but the very rich; and a vastly expanded programme of adult education.

Both the arts and science are actively and widely cultivated; scholarship is appreciated and respected. Notable contributions have been made to linguistics, oceanography, philosophy, physics and also applied arts. Though small in size, Denmark has made its mark as a source of ingenuity and wisdom.

# NORWAY

Norway's is the loveliest and the most varied of the Scandinavian landscapes, the rockiest and the most precipitous, with regal mountains divided by lush green valleys and intersected by majestic, sheer-sided fiords some as deep as 4,000 feet. The length of the country from north to south is 1,100 miles; its width varies considerably, from about 270 miles in the central part of the South Country to a narrow 4–mile strip separating fiord from Swedish frontier at a point near Narvik. Its area is 124,556 square miles.

Norway is surrounded by sea on all sides except the east, where it is bounded by Sweden for 1,021 miles, by Finland for 445 miles, and by the U.S.S.R. for 122 miles. Seven per cent of the country's area is occupied by 150,000 islands, the largest of which is Hinnöy (about 850 square miles), one of the Lofoten Islands lying north of the Artic Circle. The small coastal islands, often eroded almost to sea-level, form the skjaergard, or 'skerry guard'. The 200,000 lakes are all very small; the largest, Lake Mjösa, is only about 140 square miles in area. The rivers are impetuous torrents rushing down from the mountains and, with the exception of the 365–mile–long Glomma, are all very short. Their courses are frequently broken by magnificent waterfalls; Vettisfoss, the highest, has a fall of 853 feet. Altogether, lakes and rivers cover about 4 per cent of the country's surface, and glaciers 1 per cent.

The population of Norway is about 3,680,000, including 10,440 speaking Lappish. Density is 30 inhabitants per square mile, a relatively high figure

Copenhagen's Rådhuspladsen (Town Hall Square), the busiest square in the capital, is dominated by the Rådhuset (Town Hall) on the right of the photograph. Concentration of population and industry in the city is unparalleled elsewhere.

Norway, surrounded by sea on all except the east side, has a mainland coastline of 1,650 miles, not including fiords and bays.

for a country that is both mountainous and sub-arctic. Over two-thirds of the population lives in villages or on isolated farms. A factor vital to the full settlement and development of Norway was that until 1940 the country had not been invaded since the Middle Ages. Today, though farms may be far-flung, the government tries to ensure that they are not isolated.

The ancient language was Old Norse, but under Danish rule it became heavily modified by Danish literary influence. The mid-nineteenth century brought the development of two more genuinely Norwegian literary languages, *nynorsk* and *bokmål*, based on spoken dialects. Efforts are now being made to merge these into a common tongue, *samnorsk*.

Lutheran Protestantism has been the State religion since 1537. The Norwegians are very proud of their independence, recovered peacefully in 1905, when they chose as king a Danish prince who assumed the name of Haakon VII (the reign of Haakon VI had ended 525 years earlier). On 9 April, 1940, Norway was invaded by Germany without warning. For two months it put up a valiant defence before being forced to submit to occupation. In 1949 it signed the North Atlantic Pact. Its national defence budget is the largest of all the Scandinavian countries. Norway is a member of the European Free Trade Association.

*The Merchant Navy.* Heirs of the Viking tradition, the Norwegians have a merchant navy that ranks third in the world tonnage, and an easy first in relation to the number of inhabitants, with 3 tons per head of population.

Fishing has always played an important rôle; until the fourteenth century it paid for all imports. Today Norway's total catch is a million tons a year. The areas fished are mainly along the coasts of Norway and Iceland, but some are in the North Sea, others off Greenland and Bear Island. The fishing grounds change according to the season, with catches of cod off the Lofoten Islands from December to April and in the Norwegian Sea from April to November. Mackerel is sought along the southern coasts from May to October, and still farther south, in the North Sea, from July to October. Sprats are caught from

May to February in the fiords and gulfs of southern Norway. On the west coast the height of the herring fishing season comes in February and March between Trondheim and Stavanger, but herring is caught practically throughout the year along the coast, up to the far north. In spring and summer parts of the herring fleet also operate in the North Sea and off the coast of Iceland.

Whaling is another of Norway's traditional occupations. The harpoon gun was invented by a Norwegian, Sven Foyn, in 1872, and Norwegian crews man more than half the world's whaling fleet. The catch is about 5,000 whales a year, from which 43,000 tons of oil are extracted in the factory ships.

The merchant navy earns 35 per cent of Norway's foreign currency, fish and fish products 6 per cent, pulp, paper and paper products 8 per cent, ores and metals 11 per cent, chemicals and fertilizers 4 per cent, and manufactured goods most of the rest. The main customers are Great Britain, West Germany, Sweden and the U.S.A.

*Three per cent agricultural land.* Mountains, forests and lakes make up two-thirds of the country. Half of the farms have less than 25 acres of arable land, and Norway has to import large quantities of cereals, as well as some fruit and vegetables. Stock-farming is widespread, especially sheep (525 head per 1,000 inhabitants). Fur farming also flourishes, with 1961 production of 1,900 silver fox, 94,000 blue fox and 860,000 mink. These products play an extremely important part in the country's economy.

Forests cover almost a quarter of the country and in 1962–63 supplied 7.2 million cubic metres of wood, mostly from conifers.

*Power to spare.* Nature provides Norway with numerous waterfalls, heavy falls of rain and snow, high mountains and abrupt slopes. These are optimum conditions for hydro-electric power. In 1962 total production of electricity was 37,470 million kWh, 99 per cent of which was produced by hydro-electric plant, and it supplied 99.3 per cent of all homes.

Industry long existed on a small scale only, being limited to saw-milling, mining and quarrying. In the

A waterfall between Steinkjen and Levanger. Heavy rain and snow, high mountains and precipitous slopes assure Norway and Sweden of exceptionally large resources of hydro-electric power.

1840's textile and engineering and later pulp and paper industries were introduced. The coming of hydro-electric power initiated about 1900 further development and diversification of manufacturing industries, especially electro-chemical (e.g. nitrates) and electro-metallurgical (e.g. aluminium, iron, steel and ferro-alloys). Shipyards and other engineering industries also play an important rôle. Industrial production is increasing by about 3 per cent per annum.

*Communications.* In a few parts of the country the sea is still the most practical means of communication. There are several motorways, though in sparsely settled inland districts roads are often poor and narrow. Some are snowbound in winter, and in spring often suffer badly from the thawing of the frozen ground. Snow ploughs are kept busy clearing the routes in winter. The rail system covers 3,000 miles. Air traffic is of increasing importance. Oslo, Stavanger and Kristiansand have international airports.

*Towns, ports and countryside.* The countryside is dotted with trim wooden houses, roofed with slate, tiles, and even sods of turf. The old farmhouses of each valley are distinguished by some special stylistic feature. The traditional *stabbur,* a special isolated building used as a store-house for grain and other foods and decorated with beautifully carved woodwork, is still in use.

The Östland, the south eastern district, is relatively low and open on its east side. It stretches across the border into Sweden, for the frontier is a historical not a natural one. The climate is more or less continental, and agriculture is better developed here than in any other part of Norway. Oslo is situated at the head of the area's most sheltered fiord. Founded towards the ninth century, it was rapidly raised to a bishopric, burnt down in 1624, and reconstructed immediately afterwards by the Danes as Kristiania. It has been Norway's capital ever since. In 1815 it had only 14,000 inhabitants, compared with today's figure nearing the half-million mark.

Today Oslo is the seat of a lively university, the main port for imports and an industrial centre. The islets in Oslo fiord and the surrounding wooded hills make it particularly attractive.

The west has one of the heaviest rainfalls in all Europe. It is mountainous, except for a narrow strip in the south-west. There, in Jaeren, in the vicinity of Stavanger, rich pasturelands fostered the development of a dairy-farming district. The region is also noted for its various manufacturing industries. Bergen, farther north, was founded in 1070, and is an important fishing centre. In the fourteenth century the German Hanseatic merchants established themselves there and claimed a monopoly of the commerce. Later, the Hanseatic League declined, and from 1750 onwards Bergen became a completely integral part of the country.

Farther north still, there is an expanse of flat, comparatively agricultural land, with Trondheim as its principal town. Founded in 995, and originally called Nidaros, this was the country's capital for many years.

Northern Norway extends between latitudes 65° and 71°. Wheat is not found above latitude 65°, nor rye above latitude 70°. At latitude 66° population density is still 16 per square mile; then towards 70° N. it falls to 3–5 per square mile. Straddling the seventieth degree of latitude, the extreme north (or

Ålesund, an attractive fishing port with a population of nearly 20,000 people.
Norway's total annual catch, mainly of cod and herring, is one million tons.

Reindeer in the Jotunheimen Mountains. Invaluable in the forest and mountain areas, they provide meat, leather, skins and milk; they are also used to draw sledges where other forms of transport cannot be used.

Cod drying at Henningvaer, strung up on *kjell* (raised wooden poles).

Oslo, the administrative capital, lies at the head of the Oslo fiord, which is 65 miles wide and free from ice throughout the year.
Founded towards the ninth century, it developed rapidly after the introduction of rail communications from 1854 onwards. It is an active port and an industrial centre.

A typical landscape in the agricultural region, Namdalseid. Rocks, hills and marshland cover two-thirds of the country. Only four per cent is crop-bearing, and heavy imports of cereals are needed.

Finnmark) is a hummocky, violently windswept plateau rising from 900 feet up to about 1,500 feet. The mean January temperature is $-6°C.$ ($22°F.$) and may drop as low as $-16°C.$ ($2°F.$). The tundra reigns supreme, a dreary expanse of moss, dwarf willows and lichens. The only centre in which the Lapps are in the majority is Kautokeino. The region's only real towns are ports: Narvik, which handles Swedish iron ore exports from Kiruna in the winter, and Tromsö and Hammerfest. This last, a town of about 4,000 inhabitants, is the most northerly town in Europe. The area's main resource lies in the fisheries. The waters around the Lofoten Islands attract, in addition to the permanent inhabitants, a seasonal population of fishermen who come from other parts of northern Norway to occupy the 25,000 chalets or *rorbodars* from February to April.

SVALBARD AND NORWAY'S OTHER ARCTIC POSSESSIONS. The Norwegians have established sovereignty over a certain number of territories, most of them uninhabited: in the southern hemisphere, they have Bouvet Island and Peter I Island, and a sector of the Antarctic continent; in the north, Svalbard (Spitsbergen, Bear I. etc.) and Jan Mayen. Svalbard, a group of islands north of Norway, was known even in the times of the medieval sagas; in 1596 the Dutchman Barents rediscovered them and rechristened two of the islands Spitsbergen and Bear Island.

Svalbard, about 360 miles north of Norway, extends from latitude 74° to latitude 81°, and has a surface area of 23,957 square miles. Warmed by the Gulf Stream, it enjoys an exceptionally mild climate. Mountainous and rugged, Svalbard has some glaciers, and in many parts bare rock or tundra. Coal has been mined there by Norway since 1899. In 1925 Norwegian sovereignty was established after an agreement with the U.S.S.R. Some mines are leased to Russia, who has proceeded to develop their resources with tremendous energy.

Bear Island, situated halfway between Norway and Spitsbergen, and the small islands of Kvitöya and Hopen, near Spitsbergen, also belong to Svalbard.

Jan Mayen Island, in latitude 71° north, between Greenland and the North Cape, is a hideous black mountain of purely volcanic origin. It has a surface area of 144 square miles, with its highest point in the ice-capped Beerenberg (8,347 feet). It is cold: $5°C.$ ($41°F.$) in July, and $-6°C.$ ($21°F.$) in January. In the past the only living creature on the island was the Arctic fox. In 1921 the Norwegians set up a permanent meteorological station, and in 1929 annexed the whole island. The station plays an essential rôle in forecasting weather conditions in the Arctic.

BOLDNESS AND ORIGINALITY. Norway has supplied the world with many men of brilliance: Abel, the mathematician; Amundsen, discoverer of the South Pole; Nansen, another explorer, and a benefactor of refugees and prisoners-of-war. Meteorology has made marked progress with the work of Bjerknes; Birkeland discovered how to produce nitrates from the nitrogen content of the atmosphere. Oceanography is, not surprisingly, a respected study. The arts, too, are encouraged: this is the country of the composer Grieg and the dramatist and poet Ibsen. Here Vigeland sculpted his *Obelisk of life*, which constitutes a symbol of mankind's aspiration.

# SWEDEN

Sweden is the largest of the Scandinavian countries and the third largest in Europe. Vast plains covering the south and east gradually give way to mountains in the north-west. The highest, Kebnekaise (6,965 feet), still has small glaciers on its slopes. The country teems with lakes — 96,000 of them; together with the rivers, they occupy almost one-tenth of the country's surface. The largest, Lake Väner, cover 2,141 square miles, more than most English counties. The largest island, Gotland, covers 1,225 square miles. There are three main natural divisions: the south or Götaland, the centre or Svealand, and the north or Norrland.

In 1964 Sweden's population was 7,626,978, including about 10,000 Lapps. About 25,000 immigrants arrive in Sweden each year, of which 10,000 are Finns. Ninety-two per cent of the population belong to the Lutheran State Church; about 7 per cent are Nonconformist.

Sweden is a constitutional monarchy. Local self-government is based on very old traditions among the independent farmers in Sweden. Central government has been in force since the 1520's, when Gustavus Vasa broke the Church's power, conquered rebellious provinces and united the country. Today, the government (for over thirty years Social Democratic) has allowed 95 per cent of the means of production to remain in private hands, while expanding public activities in fields such as social welfare, education, communications and hydro-electric power. The living standard is high and the economy is expanding. Sweden remained neutral during the two World Wars and has pursued a policy of non-alliance while earmarking 15 per cent of the national budget for a modern defence system.

## SWEDEN'S NATURAL RESOURCES

*Wood and paper.* Sweden is the most heavily wooded of the Scandinavian countries. On average there are 600 pines, 720 fir trees, 270 birches and a few oaks and beeches per inhabitant (these figures are for trees with a minimum diameter of 4 inches). The trunks, felled and stripped in autumn and winter, are towed down to the river banks by tractor and piled up on the banks or on the ice. In spring, when the heavy thaw comes, loggers armed with hooked poles manoeuvre the trunks into the water. The current does the rest. They make an impressive sight, these expanses of water covered as far as the eye can see with tightly packed logs making their way down to the sea or the lakes. Cheapness apart, an additional advantage of floating the logs is that parasites, fungi and insects are destroyed by contact with the water.

Saw-mills and factories are installed at the termini of rivers and canals, frequently on the very edge of the Baltic. In their vast open areas piles of logs and planks dry out of doors; in their well-lit buildings the most up-to-date machinery turns the timber into planks, beams, wood pulp or various other products, depending on the nature of the factory. The timber may also be treated chemically, for the products extracted from it become more varied and abundant every year: plastics, dyes, artificial leather, synthetic

Rolls of newsprint ready for despatch at a Norwegian paper mill.

An Oslo fisherman. Heirs of the Viking tradition, the Norwegians still look to the sea for their livelihood.

Svalbard, a group of islands 360 miles north of Norway. Bare rock and tundra predominate and in the north-east glaciers force their way to the sea, Yet Svalbard has a mild climate warmed by the Gulf Stream.

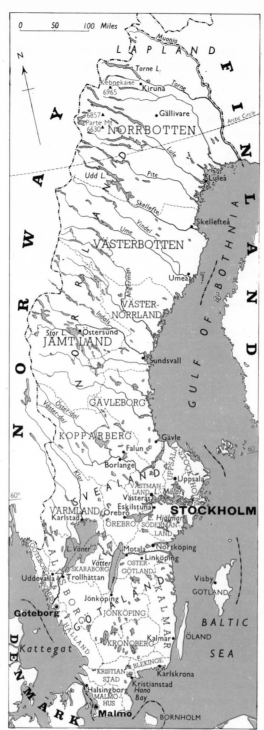

Sweden is the largest of the Scandinavian countries and the third largest in Europe. This map shows how south and central Sweden, the two historic regions of the country, have been influenced by easy communications to the west with Denmark. They contrast with the much more extensive but sparsely settled region of north Sweden with its series of almost parallel rivers flowing east into the Gulf of Bothnia.

deposits were exploited, and the mining districts in Bergslagen in central Sweden developed.

Bergslagen consists of scattered mines and factories hidden amid luxuriant forests. The other large mining district, Kiruna, in the extreme north of Lapland and on the edge of the forest zone, is highly concentrated. It is a mountain of iron worked on the open-cast principle and also, more recently, by shaft system. Almost all the ore from these districts is exported, in summer via the Baltic, in winter via the Norwegian port of Narvik. The quantity of pure iron extracted annually throughout Sweden is about one-tenth of world production.

Tungsten, vanadium and zinc production meets home demands; lead and copper very nearly so. Production represents 1 per cent or more of the world total of zinc, lead, tungsten and silver; 0.6 per cent to 0.3 per cent copper and gold. These valuable mineral resources have allowed Sweden a degree of economic independence in the past.

Metallurgy has always been an active industry. In the past smelting was done by charcoal, and this is still so for one-third of the production; the rest is treated by coal (imported) or by electro-metallurgy. Natural resources of water power are responsible for rapid expansion in electro-metallurgical techniques, particularly in the production of the world renowned high-grade steels of which the Swedes are legitimately proud.

*Water power and increasing productivity.* The main industrial power is water. Since the fifteenth century an ingenious system of headraces has been developed in the Bergslagen mines to operate the hydraulic machinery. During the twentieth century large hydro-electric dams have been built. The Harspranget waterfall centre, very near the Arctic Circle, and the centre at Stornorrfoss are the most powerful.

Sweden has no petroleum deposits, and practically no coal. Peat-bogs cover vast expanses, but their exploitation is uneconomical. To compensate for the lack of petroleum, the Swedes have tried to utilise the bituminous schists of Kvarntorp near Örebro. The schists contain 5 to 6 per cent hydrocarbons.

Factories avoid concentration in grim industrial areas, and ultramodern workshops are cleverly and unobtrusively sited in a green landscape. Sweden still manages to look like a vast park.

*Agriculture.* The arable area of Sweden (12 per cent of the total) meets all the country's requirements for agricultural products, and farming employs under 20 per cent of the population. Farms are small but productive; the highly developed co-operatives handle milk and butter, cheese, meat, cereals and eggs.

*Communications and commerce.* As a vast industrialised country, Sweden has an extensive railway network that is particularly comfortable. All the main lines are electrified.

A system of good highways is almost completed. Right-hand driving will be introduced in 1967. In winter, sledges carry timber on snowbound roads.

Sweden's shipyards supply about 10 per cent of world production, which puts them in fourth place. Timber and wood pulp and its derivatives represent 28 per cent of all exports. Steel, iron ore and manufactured products account for about 50 per cent. There are many customers, headed by West Germany taking 15

rubber and cellulose. The waste products are made into wood, alcohol and turpentine. Sweden supplies about 7 per cent of the world's annual total of wood pulp. The volume of wood felled every year represents one-quarter of world production. This high proportion threatens to decimate the forests of the future, and the State has had to take measures to protect young plantations, and to put in hand a programme of research with the ultimate object of introducing and acclimatising species more productive than the present trees.

*Iron ore.* Sweden's second largest natural resource is iron. Here, as elsewhere, prehistoric man used the iron ore he found in the marshes. In the Middle Ages, rock

A pile-up of logs being blasted free at Umeå, in eastern Sweden. Sweden is the most extensively wooded of the Scandinavian countries; the forests are its richest resource. The state has had to introduce measures to prevent their decimation under the heavy annual felling required to produce timber, wood pulp, plastics, dyes, cellulose products, synthetic rubber and an ever-increasing variety of by-products.

per cent of the total, followed by Great Britain (13 per cent), the Benelux countries and the other Scandinavian countries, each taking about 10 per cent.

## THE RURAL LANDSCAPE

*The south: Götaland.* The south, or Götaland, is one magnificent garden of cornfields, hillocks, plains and woods. In Scania (Skåne), in the extreme south, grapes ripen. This is the country of clear skies, with long sandy beaches where holidaymakers bask in the sun. The beaches in the west are rockier, but offer the additional attraction of fishing.

The mouth of the River Göta is the only point on the west coast that has always been under Swedish sovereignty. The town of Gothenburg (Göteborg) was founded there in the seventeenth century with the help of Dutch settlers. In the nineteenth century the waterway connecting Gothenburg with Lake Väner was made navigable. It is today the headquarters of the ocean shipping lines, the largest port in Sweden, and the second largest town, with shipyards and a wide variety of industries.

Farther south, in Scania, Malmö is the port serving Germany and Western Europe. Scania, which was Danish for many years, boasts some beautiful Renaissance castles.

Oland is the island of sun and windmills, while Gotland is the island of roses and ruins. Thirteenth-century ramparts still stand guard over Visby, its

The iron ore deposits at Kiruna, in Lapland. Further rich deposits are found in the Bergslagen district in central Sweden, where there is a heavy concentration of metallurgical industries.

The harbour at Gothenburg. Founded at the mouth of the River Göta in the seventeenth century, it is today the most important port in Sweden, and—with a population of over 500,000—its second town. As well as shipyards, Gothenburg has a wide variety of industries.

Operation is continuous day and night in this sulphate works manufacturing pulp for use in the production of rayon.

Calves in Swedish Lapland. This is a cold region of sparse population, colonised only about 150 years ago. Cereals can be grown with only little success.
At low and middle altitudes forest predominates.
Other resources are iron ore and four-fifths of the country's hydro-electric power.

modest capital. Not far away, on the mainland, the Rök stone bears the longest runic inscription so far discovered.

*The centre: Svealand.* The central region, the country of the Suevi, embraces the mining district of Bergslagen. In Dalecarlia the system of *faebods* prospered for many years. The old villages were established, as might be expected, on the best land. In the summer, the farmers used to leave the villages to graze their flocks on inferior marshy or morain land about five or ten miles away. Here they built wooden chalets, or *faebods*. Some of these later became permanent. Half the permanent chalets have now been abandoned because flocks are now kept in the richer pasturage even in summer.

*Stockholm.* The capital of Svealand ultimately became the capital of Sweden and the second largest town in Scandinavia. It occupies a magnificent site on the strait linking Lake Mälar with the Baltic. Because the land has risen, the lake is eighteen inches higher than the Baltic. As a result new harbour installations have had to be built, for Stockholm is second only to Gothenburg as a port. The open sea is is separated from the town by the Stockholm archipelago. This consists of 10,000 wooded islands and grassy islets surrounded by calm water and dotted with pretty, brightly painted week-end cottages. The water's edge is gay with small craft.

Stockholm is a modern city which still preserves its historic associations in the old quarter. With numerous well-kept parks it is the residence of the King and the administrative headquarters, as well as being the banking and commercial capital and an important industrial centre. Uppsala, a little farther away, is the old capital, a cathedral town and the seat of the oldest and most important university in Sweden.

*Norrland and Swedish Lapland.* There is a gradual transition from the milder lands of Svealand to the Norrland, the country of the north. It was settled much later than the others, and is still sparsely inhabited; according to a popular saying, it is where 'oaks, crayfish and noblemen cease'. Wheat is cultivated only in the south-east district; rye is planted right up to the Arctic Circle.

Some Norrland farmers still own *faebods*. Along the coast the Baltic herring is caught. Winter sports are practised in Jämtland from January to March, and in Lapland from March to May.

The Lapps, about 10,000 in number, differ widely from the Scandinavians racially, linguistically (they speak an Uralo-altaic language), and in their way of life. They are nomads, fishermen, and keepers of reindeer, which supply them with meat, skins, and dairy produce. The herds are also used to pull sledges. Loaded, a reindeer can carry from 60 to 70 lb. One family can live off a hundred head. The forest Lapps and the mountain Lapps raise different kinds of reindeer. Their traditional way of life is currently undergoing vast changes as they come into contact with new techniques and as they establish commercial relations.

Part of Lapland lies outside the forest zone. This is the country of long bluish twilights, the land where the midnight sun lasts for forty days.

CULTURAL AND SOCIAL SENSE. The Swedes have a well-developed sense of social responsibility. They took certain measures in the field of welfare long in advance of many other civilised countries. Economic plans have been worked out in advance against a time of possible unemployment. State loans and allowances encourage the construction of roomy, well-equipped houses. The sale of alcohol, while not illegal, carries a very high tax as a deterrent to alcoholism.

If there is another side of the coin, it is uniformity throughout the country. From north to south, the farms are painted the same maroon colour, with the same white door frames and the same white window frames. Nor is there any relief in the large towns, where all the buildings are faced with the same sort of stucco.

Attention to detail and organising ability emerge in the talent of national celebrities: the chemists Scheele and Berzelius, the explorer Andree and Nordenskjöld, the industrialist Nobel, who founded the dynamite industry and then devoted his fortune to monetary awards for science, literature and peace. The eighteenth-century botanist Linnaeus substituted the order of his own classification method for the chaos of the existing systems. Celsius invented the centigrade temperature scale, and Gerhard de Geer produced the first absolute chronological scale in geology.

Sweden can offer the world an example of precision and orderliness and sound planning in the social and economic fields.

Stockholm, capital of Sweden and the second largest town in Scandinavia, linking Lake Mälar with the Baltic.
The curious siting of its commercial port, far removed from the old city, is the result of continued uplift since the retreat of the ice sheet.
There is a rise of 10–15 inches a century at Stockholm; in such conditions harbour installations had to be moved to remain of practical use.

# FINLAND

Known to its inhabitants as Suomi, Finland extends beyond the 60th parallel and about a third of the country lies beyond the Arctic Circle. With Iceland, it is the most northerly country in the world.

*The northern edge of the inhabited world.* In Lapland the sun shines for 57 days without setting. But the winter nights are interminable. Helsinki sees a total of 17 hours of sunshine in December. The rivers in the north are frozen from mid-October onwards, while even further south they freeze at the end of November and remains frozen until May. By mid-December at the latest ice covers even the largest lakes, and a rim of ice lines the sea shores and connects the islands with the mainland. Between January and April it is possible to reach the Ahvenanmaa Islands and, in some winters, the Swedish coast across a bridge of ice.

Snow, which is permanent in certain parts of Lapland, begins to fall towards the middle of September. By Christmas Finland has donned the white cloak of winter that will not be shed until early April in the south-west and late in May in Lapland. The snow is thickest towards the middle of March, with 12 inches in the south-west, and from 20 to 30 inches on the higher ground of the eastern ridges. It rarely exceeds 23 inches in Lapland.

Precipitation is comparatively light, for Finland is sheltered from rainy oceanic winds by Scandinavia. Snow accounts for 30 per cent of it in the south-west and 40 per cent in the north. It rains frequently but only a little at a time. Summer is the rainiest season. Fairly high evaporation means that the rain is barely sufficient to meet the needs of the crops and vegetation. In Lapland, some places receive only 8 inches a year.

In north-east Finland, the mean annual temperature is less than 0°C. (32°F.). The growing season, during which the daily mean is 5°C. (41°F.) or higher, is very short. In June or July, Helsinki has 300 hours of sunshine, and the lengthening days in the northern regions mean that they receive almost as much solar heat as the rest of the country. Vegetation in the north grows with surprising speed and strength, but the late frosts of spring (until early June) and early autumn frosts (from the end of August onwards) are often fatal.

Finland's climate is said to be one of the most temperate in the world, in relation to its latitude. January is 10°C. to 14°C. warmer than the average for the same latitude. The lowest mean monthly temperatures never fall below –15°C. (5°F.), even in Lapland; nor below –2°C. (28°F.) in the south-west.

Drought and cold prevent trees from flourishing in the most northerly latitudes. The birch is the most northerly specimen, while the dark pines and spruces have withdrawn to southern Lapland. The bare heights of the *tunturi* (similar to the Scandinavian *fjell*), are a wasteland of dwarf bushes broken only by light-coloured patches of lichens.

Finland's population, too, is sparser towards the north. Lapland has barely one inhabitant per square mile.

*Between East and West.* On the very edge of the inhabited world, Finland is also the meeting place of Western and Eastern civilisations. This halfway

Finland is one of the most northerly countries in the world. Note the extremely broken topography, particularly in the south and east, where the coastline is deeply and closely indented and hundreds of morainic ridges enclose a myriad of lakes covering 20–50 per cent of the surface. The 55,000 lakes of Finland comprise 8 per cent of its total area.

position, commercially advantageous in times of peace, is also at the root of the country's misfortunes. Linked with Sweden until 1809, Finland was then annexed to the Tsarist empire and became an autonomous Grand Duchy. Having proclaimed its independence after the October Revolution (1917), it has been able to preserve it only at the cost of heavy territorial losses and an unstable frontier line. By the Treaty of Paris (1947) it had to cede 17,698 square miles to the U.S.S.R. The ceded land included the region around the nickel mines of Petsamo (and thus Finland's outlet to the Arctic Ocean) and Karelia, with the town of Viipuri (Viborg). The naval base of Porkkala, also occupied by the Russians, was recovered in 1956. Finland had to pay enormous war reparations, and to rehabilitate 420,000 refugees from its ceded territory. It maintains normal commercial and diplomatic relations with both East and West, but has not adhered to any of the blocs.

*A land from the sea.* Finland is a low-lying country, with mountains only in the north-west. The Haltia *tunturi* (4,344 feet) is a fragment of Norwegian *fjell*. The Gulfs of Bothnia and Finland are bordered by a coastal plain rising gently towards the interior in the regions of the lakes, some of which are more than 200 feet above sea-level. The coastline is so deeply and closely indented, especially in the south west, that certain parts of the country are inextricable tangles of strips of land and strips of water.

The lakes cover 8 per cent of the country's surface, are shallow, and very unevenly distributed. Comparatively rare in the coastal plains and in Lapland, though it contains Inari — one of the biggest — they abound in the south-east. The figure of 55,000 lakes is given for the whole of Finland, but in fact they defy counting. The largest, Lake Saimaa (1,698 square miles), is also more accurately called *Satanen* (the Hundred Lakes).

Finnish rivers flow from lake to lake without any definite direction and have no attendant alluvial plains. In the centre, a north-west to south-east orientation prevails in rivers and most of the lakes, following the long chain of hills called *harju*.

A layer of alluvial soil covers the greater part of Finland, but it lies on an extremely ancient granite shield for Finland is a fragment of one of the oldest known lands, Finnoscandia. In the strata formed by the granites and other hard rocks of the Archaean epoch, before the Primary era, geologists have identified the roots of two very old mountain chains, long since levelled down by erosion. Finland has none of the mineral wealth — coal, petroleum, bauxite — associated with sedimentary rocks.

Ten thousand years ago, at the end of the glacial period, the whole country, except for a few summits, was covered by the sea. Karelia was the first to emerge, then the upthrust continued progressively from south-east to north-west. New rocks emerged along the coasts. Channels became shallower. The islands increased in size and gradually joined up with the mainland. Towns situated on the edge of the sea, such as Vaasa, have had to be moved to keep pace with the sea's withdrawal. It is estimated that the country's surface area is increasing in this way by 390 square miles a century.

The thrust, which is not uniform throughout the country, involves a buckling of the surface sufficient to modify the outlets of some lakes. The formation of the Inari rapids in 1604 is an example of this action. *The northern forest.* The recent disappearance of the glaciers explains the vast expanse of peat-bogs covering one-third of Finland. Their hillocks of turf are particularly common in the north and elsewhere many of them are wooded or even cultivated. Birches began to spread even when the glacier still reached down to the Salpausselkä. The subsequently warmer climate encouraged the introduction of pine trees, with hazels, elms and alders. Later still, the climate became more severe, and the pine abandoned Lapland to bushy scrub and the birch, which makes up 19 per cent of the forests today. Meanwhile the spruce, encouraged by the cold, advanced from the east; today it forms more than a quarter of the forests, and its progress would have been even greater if man had not regained some of the best land from it.

Finland is the most densely wooded country in Europe. The northern forests are older than those in the south, for their trees are slower to develop. Seven per cent of the northern forests contains trees 200 years old, and more than fifty per cent is 100 years old or more.

The exploitation of the forests supplies timber for building and fuel, and produces the woods in greatest demand on world markets. About two-thirds of the forests belong to private individuals or industrial undertakings; the remainder belong to the State. The main occupations in winter are the felling and transport of timber. The tree trunks, usually made into rafts to avoid losses, are assembled and transported along 25,000 miles of waterways. In spring and summer floating timber gives work to thousands of people.

A winter landscape at Vuokatti, in northern Finland. The old insular shelf, worn down by glaciers, is now covered by lakes and vast forests.

Timber being towed across a lake in bundle rafts. Tree trunks are collected and transported on 25,000 miles of navigable waterways, usually grouped into rafts so as to minimise losses. During recent years, timber products have accounted for more than 90 per cent of the total export figures.

Undeterred by the solid ice of winter. Finnish fishermen make their catch through holes cut in the frozen lakes.

Timber processing and allied industries employ 70,000 workers. The paper industry was a little later to develop. It utilises trees of smaller diameter whose stripped and crushed trunks are used in the preparation of wood pulp. Finland is the third largest exporter of paper, after Canada and Sweden. More recently new industries have begun to flourish: the manufacture of prefabricated houses (now one of the major export industries), plywood, furniture and man-made cellulose textiles.

The forest is Finland's most precious possession. All owners are legally bound to ensure the continuous regeneration their forests, and in all the rural parishes they are members of a forestry association. The institute for Forestry Research at Helsinki, the Forestry School of Helsinki University and six national Forestry Schools are dedicated to the study and improvement of the land's most valuable asset.

*Agricultural activity.* A line drawn from the north-east of Lake Ladoga to Kemi on the Gulf of Bothnia separates populated Finland from the Far North, the civilised from the uninhabited. The former contains nearly all the cultivated land, all the towns except Rovaniemi, and all except two of the railways. The line from Joensuu to Oulu and Tornio roughly follows the dividing line between the two Finlands.

The regions which have been longest occupied are the fertile plains of marine clay along the coast and on the shores of certain lakes. Behind this coastal zone, pioneers, scattered here and there along the waterways or along the sprawling bank of the *harju,* burnt a few strips of forest and sowed the land enriched by the ashes. Their wooden houses, each with its barn, its granary, its *sauna* bath, its covered threshing floor, are grey, the natural colour the wood acquires with age. Each is arranged round two or three sides of a fenced-in courtyard. Near the towns, the houses are painted in brighter colours: light brown, light yellow, or white predominate.

The slow encroachment into inland forest areas has accelerated with the growth of Finland's population. After 1945 the need to settle over 400,000 refugees entailed further land clearance in the centre and east.

Finland can still be regarded as a country of colonisation.

Even so, crops cover only 8.5 per cent of Finland's area. On most farms, the principal activity is the exploitation of the forest. This, together with the poor natural conditions — short summers that make it impossible to cultivate plants with a long growing season, and August rains delaying the ripening of cereals and interfering with the harvest — explains, in part, the nature of Finnish agriculture.

Its main purpose is to feed the inhabitants. Until 1940 winter rye was the main cereal for bread. Sown on unploughed land, it ripens as far as the south of Lapland. Today it has almost been overtaken by spring wheat. Winter wheat, which gives a better yield and ripens earlier, is more or less confined to the clay plains of the south-west. In spite of imported fertilizers, yields remain low. Nevertheless, before the Second World War, Finland had almost succeeded in winning the battle for bread. But since then she has had to start importing again. Potatoes are a valuable supplementary crop.

Finnish agriculture is turning more and more towards stock-farming, and more than two-thirds of the area under cultivation produces food for livestock. Oats, grown on the acid soil of the peat-bogs, covers one-fifth of the arable land, as much as all the other cereals put together. North of Oulu it does not ripen, but is harvested while still green.

About 500 dairies turn half the milk yield into butter. Before the Second World War, Finland managed to export butter, a little cheese, meat and eggs. Since 1930 she has developed fur-farming (mink, silver fox and blue fox). Lapland has about 100,000 reindeer. Coastal waters are not very rich in fish.

Since the end of the eighteenth century Finland has been a country with heavy rural emigration, particularly to America. New activities have had to be developed on the national territory.

*The new Finland.* The Finns have been able to consolidate the industries which they developed to pay off their heavy war reparations to the U.S.S.R. The food industries, the flour mills and sugar refineries of Helsinki and Turku, process national agricultural products and imported produce. Flax and some wool for the textile industry are home products, though the main textile demand is for fibres bought abroad. The principal textile centres are Helsinki, Tampere and Turku. The most remarkable advance of all has been made by the metallurgical industry.

In spite of recent progress in prospecting, Finland is not an important mining country and is even less so since the loss of Petsamo. The Outokumpu Company extracts copper, iron and sulphur, and produces small amounts of lead, zinc, nickel and silver. The ores are smelted at Harjavalta, and refined in Pori.

Mechanical engineering employs the largest number of workers (slightly more than the timber industry) at Helsinki, Tampere, Turku, Pori and Kotka. This success is all the more meritorious in view of the number of obstacles: scarcity of raw materials; no coal; rapids with gentle gradients, and power per head of population half that of Sweden, shortage of ready capital and a comparatively small internal market. The interference of climate with traffic also had to be overcome.

These efforts in the field of production have not delayed completion of railways begun in 1858, using the Russian gauge of 1.524 metres. Two reach as far as the Arctic Circle. More than half the railway goods traffic is timber. Ice-breakers keep the channels leading to the principal ports, Helsinki, and Turku, clear, while the government has built a large winter port at Hangö, at the nearest point to the open sea.

Helsinki absorbs more than half of Finnish imports, followed by Turku; Kotka comes an easy first for exports. Exports consist primarily of timber products and paper. Imports are more varied: fuel, fertilizers, cereals and foodstuffs, textiles, metal, factory plant and motor vehicles. The balance of payments, which displayed a marked deficit after 1940, is showing a tendency to redress itself. The United Kingdom used to be Finland's main supplier and also its best customer, but the first place has been taken by the U.S.S.R. in recent years.

*Expansion of the towns.* In 1930 only one Finn in six lived in a town. Today the proportion is two in five. The majority of Finnish towns are small; with their wooden single-storey houses, separated from each other by gardens, and their wide streets, which are not always surfaced or lined with pavements, they preserve a rural aspect. Only three have more than 100,000 inhabitants: Tampere (133,406), the main inland centre; Turku (130,844), the old capital, which has become an industrial port; and, of course, Helsinki, the only large town in the country (477,000 inhabitants). Almost unique among Finnish towns, it has some tall modern stone and cement buildings, and an enormous stadium in which the 1952 Olympic Games were held. The economic, religious and intellectual capital (the old university of Turku has been moved to Helsinki), it is even better known as the political

A general view of Helsinki, capital of Finland and the only large city in the country (477,000 inhabitants).

The church at Rajamäki:
an example of modern Finnish
architecture. Scandinavian
designers have had spectacular
successes in recent years,
particularly in the field of
domestic furniture, furnishings
and utensils.

Lake Thingvellir, one of the
numerous inland lakes.
Population distribution has been
determined by two physical
factors: the island's
twenty volcanoes and
the central glaciers covering
almost an eighth of the
country's area.
Exploitation of pastureland
has tended to disperse settlement.

capital. The President of the Republic holds the
executive power and shares the legislative power with
a single Chamber of Representatives (Eduskunta)
elected every three years by direct universal suffrage.

Anthropological research has shown that the Finns
are closely allied to the European peoples surrounding
them; the principal stocks derive from Nordic and
East Baltic races. Linguistically they belong to the
Finno-Ugrian group. Although Swedish, the cultural
language, is still an official language in addition to
Finnish, only certain districts are officially bilingual,
and the Åland Islands are the sole region where
Swedish alone is spoken. The Lapps number scarcely
more than 2,000. Religious freedom has existed since
1923, though 95.7 per cent of the population are
members of the Evangelical Lutheran Church, the
national church.

Total population is 4,446,222 (1960); density of
population is 34 per square mile. The birth-rate,
which was very high until the beginning of the century, fell to an average of 19.6 per thousand during
the years 1930–40. In 1964 it was 17.6 per thousand.
The death rate is 9.3 per thousand.

The Finnish people can ensure a safe future for themselves by making even better use of their country's
limited potentialities, by improving still further their
agricultural techniques, by mastering their inland
waters more completely, and by introducing a still
greater variety of industries.

# ICELAND

Iceland — *Ultima Thule* — is primarily distinguished
by its geographical isolation. This Arctic island
with an area of 39,758 square miles appeared at the
end of the Tertiary era on the volcanic fault which
fissured the Atlantic from Jan Mayen to St Helena.
It consists of a young basaltic shield, with very little
metallic intrusion and a tough, nourishing grass as its
only natural resource.

A very ancient civilisation has been in continuous
existence there since 870 or 874. The Icelanders'
complete isolation has enabled them to preserve a
language similar to that of the sagas of the late
Middle Ages. The re-establishment of complete independence in 1944, after centuries of Danish rule,
followed a period since 1918 during which Iceland
was a sovereign state but recognised the Danish king.
Iceland is governed by one of the rare legal codes
owing nothing to Roman Law.

*Obstacles surmounted.* The temperature is alternately
lowered by the action of the Arctic current and raised
by that of the Gulf Stream, two opposing influences
which gave Reykjavik, the capital of the Republic,
an annual temperature of 3.9°C. (39°F.), with a mean
monthly temperature of –1.02°C. (30.1°F.) in January
and 10.9°C. (51.6°F.) in July. Such conditions make
the island a seasonal meeting place for many species of
birds and fish; its seas teem with cod in the winter
and herring in the summer. The forests have been
extensively destroyed by the combined efforts of
man and the island's sheep.

The population is made up of a Norse nucleus,

NORWAY: View over Bergen, one of many fishing ports on Norway's indented coastline. FINLAND: Timber poo

Settlers who arrived from 870 onwards, often bringing Celtic slaves. The first settlements were situated inland: the parliament of Thingvellir, which met in 930, was twenty-five miles from the Atlantic. The distribution of the population was determined by the twenty volcanoes aligned along a north-south axis, and the central glaciers; extensive exploitations of pasture land has tended to disperse the settlements. Stock-farming is conducted from a central farm, or *boer*, and makes use of remote communal pasture lands.

The *boer* is a conglomeration of small buildings with steeply pitched roofs, generally situated on a hillside near a peat-bog. Its walls of violet dolerite and earth are cleft with narrow windows, and its roof is covered with sods of green turf. The stables are set apart. Above the rooftops, mill sails turn in the strong winds. Gradually, the traditional *boer* is being replaced by modern farm buildings.

*Urban growth and economic activity.* In 1880 there were only three agglomerations, with a total of 3,630 inhabitants. For half a century now the industrialisation of fishing has been draining the countryside of its manpower, and the figures for 1962 showed a total of 81 per cent urban dwellers.

Towns and hamlets are connected by a network of horse tracks across expanses of pumice stone and moraine, signposted by cairns (*varda*) which often have legendary significance. Until quite recently transport was by caravans of pack horses; it has passed directly from horse-drawn traffic to aircraft. It is not uncommon for the farmer to fly to his hayfields behind the glacier line although weather conditions occasionally constitute a hazard.

Country economy depends on stock-farming and bird-catching. In spring, the eggs of migrant birds are collected in their thousands on the high cliffs, while the birds are caught in nets to supplement the food reserves. The herds and flocks are of great importance. Iceland raises more horses than any country in Europe per head of population. Sheep supply meat, skins and valuable wool, which is considered a symbol of wealth: the Icelandic word for it is synonymous with 'silver'.

*Economic change.* After the mid-nineteenth century, Iceland, freed from the Danish colonial monopoly, was able to sell wool direct for gold. It bought its first flotilla of old trawlers and its economy underwent a rapid change. In 1958 it protected its fishing industry by proclaiming a 12-mile limit for foreign fishermen fishing near its coasts. Today more than nine-tenths of all exports come from fishing, while two-thirds of the imports are for fuels and building materials, and the rest for coffee, sugar and textiles.

The new fleet gained a sizeable share of Mediterranean markets. Iceland produces its own margarine, fish meal, fertilizers and canned goods, and is already industrially well equipped with canning factories, cold storage factories and electrical centres.

During the Second World War, Iceland, occupied first by the British and then by the Americans, still managed to preserve neutrality. Today it is one of the few countries which have no standing Army. It is a sort of aircraft carrier for N.A.T.O., situated halfway between Moscow and New York. Air and sea links are rapidly helping to modify the economy and even the old-age culture of this Arctic republic.

An old Icelandic fisherman. Herrings hang drying from the walls behind him.

A general view of Reykjavik, the world's most northerly capital.

Volcanic lava in Lake Myvatn. Iceland is built up almost wholly of volcanic rock.

OCEANIC EUROPE

# THE BRITISH ISLES

European, but separated from the Continent, the British Isles consist in the main of two large islands: Great Britain with an area of 89,034 square miles, and Ireland with an area of 31,842 square miles. Small archipelagos are scattered between them and round their coasts. The country is 780 miles long from north to south, and tends to be narrow — there is no point more than 75 miles from the sea. In the west the deep waters of the Atlantic bring rains and storms; in the east the North Sea with its shallow continental shelf, though theoretically separating Great Britain from Scandinavia and Central Europe, in fact serves to link them.

The British Isles belong to north-west Europe; they do not possess a single important Mediterranean or Alpine characteristic. Their landscape often recalls the Dutch polders, the Danish grasslands, and the mountains and fiords of Norway, and the population has traits that recall the tall, blond people of Scandinavia. This connection is of great antiquity; the oldest mountains, the Caledonians, which date from the middle of the Primary era, once covered the British Isles and Scandinavia without a break. During the cold Quaternary era, vast glaciers spread across the present site of the North Sea and over almost the whole of the British Isles.

The geography of Great Britain is explained by its dual association with a maritime and with a continental world.

*A series of blocks.* The British Isles have not been fundamentally upfolded since the end of the Primary era (600 million years ago). Over such a long period the ravages of erosion would have reduced them to nothing but a monotonous plateau today, had not three factors intervened.

First, the rocks of which they are composed are not uniform. Apart from the usual granites and gneiss, large areas are covered by extremely hard red sandstone, softer schists, soluble limestone pitted with caves, and complex volcanic lava. These different types have put up unequal resistance to erosion.

The second original feature is that sediment has accumulated at the foot of the mountains in straits, lakes or seas. Throughout south-east England and in the broad depressed region of the Midlands, the old shield is marked by Secondary and Tertiary limestone and clay.

Thirdly and lastly, the ancient massifs would no longer be mountains if they had not undergone comparatively recent minor upfolding into isolated blocks separated by regions which remained flat. What was the driving force behind this last act of structural history? A remote after-effect of the Alpine folding, or an unknown force issuing from the Atlantic, since the most elevated points are situated mainly in the north and west?

More recently (between 1 million and 10,000 years ago) glaciers from Scandinavia twice covered the North Sea and, with a few rare exceptions, swallowed up mountains and plains, making their mark in the form of valleys and leaving behind thick deposits of clay and sand (*drift*) when they melted. After they finally retreated isolated summits still had small glaciers which formed ridges and slopes. Most of the lakes in England and Scotland were formed in this period.

*An oceanic climate.* The British Isles are generally reputed to have a mild climate, distinguished by frequent rain and much cloud. Extreme temperatures do not rise above 31°C. (88°F.) at Liverpool, or fall below –3°C. (26°F.) in the Scilly Isles; Krakow in the same latitude as the latter often registers –30°C. (–22°F.). London's mean January temperature of 4°C. (39°F.) seems delightfully mild in comparison with the –19°C. (–2°F.) of Winnipeg in Canada. Variations between winter and summer are small. Rain, which is more frequent than abundant, falls throughout the year locally with a maximum in autumn and at the beginning of winter, and a fairly pronounced minimum from February to April. Fogs occur for an average of 24 days in London during November, December and January. In the south, the sun shines for about one hour in two on average (one in four in winter); in Scotland the average is one in three in summer, and one in seven or eight in winter.

But the pattern is by no means uniform. The mountains in the west condense the rains, which exceed 80 inches on the most exposed heights in the south-west of Ireland and the Highlands of Scotland, with a maximum of 150 inches near Ben Nevis. A moderate proportion of the precipitation falls in the form of snow. In the plains of the east, the dry winds reduce the rainfall significantly, to under 20 inches. There is considerable local variation.

The mean or annual totals do not accurately reflect the situation. The British Isles are situated in the path of disturbances along the 'Polar front'. In summer the disturbances may withdraw farther north, leaving the whole of the south open to warmer and drier air. In winter, on the other hand, the zone of disturbance may move southwards to France or even Spain, allowing icy winds to dry up the islands. Drought is occasionally a feature of the complex British climate.

No description of the English climate would be complete without a reference to its notorious fog. Its distribution, heaviest in industrial towns, bears witness to the role which man and man-made smoke have played in its formation. Measures have been taken to combat it, and the classical London 'pea-soup' fog has been practically non-existent for thirty years.

Such a climate excludes those types of vegetation needing heat, but encourages plants thriving in cool, moist conditions. Grass grows rapidly and animal husbandry is more successful than crop growing; but on the cold and humid heights the proportion of moors or peat-bogs to grassland is often excessive.

The heavy precipitation in the mountains feeds numerous rivers. In January two-thirds of the rainfall finds its way into the rivers, but in summer evaporation and vegetation absorb four-fifths of it in the mountains and nine-tenths in the plain. The July and September minima virtually deprive the rivers of water. Thus the volume remains low and if the rivers were harnessed they would give little power.

The Giant's Causeway, on the
north coat of County
Antrim, Northern Ireland.
The formation is of volcanic
origin. The basalt pillars are
mostly irregular hexagons
15 to 20 inches in diameter and
reaching 20 feet in height.

The shipyards and docks of
Newcastle-on-Tyne,
Northumberland.
Situated in the middle of the rich
Northumberland coalfield,
Newcastle is a coal port,
and a shipbuilding and
engineering centre.
The threat of an uncertain future
for both coal and shipbuilding
made the introduction
of new industries
in the north-east imperative.

Ullapool harbour, in Wester
Ross, northern Scotland.
The sea has always played
an important rôle in Great
Britain's history and economy,
and fishing for herring
and cod is an important
industry in Scotland.

*Political organisation and racial origins.* The British cannot be understood without reference to the sea which
brought Britain's heterogeneous inhabitants to the
archipelago: Celts from Central Europe, Romans from
Gaul, Angles, Saxons, Scandinavians and, lastly, the
Normans who arrived in the eleventh century.

A major part of medieval and even modern British
history revolves around the conflict between these
races and their tongues. The Normans and Saxons
finally merged, and the English language has roots
from both sources; but Cornish was not ousted for
more than four centuries, and English still has not
entirely conquered Wales, where a language similar
to Breton is spoken. Wales still hankers for independence and puts up a spirited fight to preserve its native
tongue. The Scandinavians managed to take root
especially in the Orkneys, Shetlands and Hebrides. The
union of England and Scotland in 1707 was never
universally accepted and the Gaelic language, of Celtic
origin is still spoken by some Highlanders. Across the
Irish Sea, even centuries of war and three hundred
years of alien rule did not overcome Irish resistance
to English political rule.

Three-quarters of Ireland (the Catholic South) has
now left the British Commonwealth and forms the
independent Republic of Ireland. Protestant Northern
Ireland, together with England, Wales and Scotland,
make up the United Kingdom, but a separate parliament for Northern Ireland (the Stormont) sits in Belfast. Scotland keeps its own institutions and has its own
legal system; the Isle of Man in the Irish Sea, and
Jersey and Guernsey in the Channel Islands have their
own special forms of government. The great bond
between these territories, except in the Republic of
Ireland, is the Crown, and few countries exhibit such
loyalty to the sovereign. This is all the more remarkable when we recall that the English were, historically,
the first people to limit monarchical power and establish the prototype of constitutional and later parliamentary government.

*Economic history.* England began to trade with the
Continent at a very early date. In the Middle Ages,
the fortunes of the feudal system linked her lot with
that of Guienne, and the Hundred Years' War arose
partly from the English commercial difficulties in Flanders. Time passed and the English ranged the seas and
established colonies. Their merchant navy originally
developed because of their geographical situation and
soon expanded far beyond the needs which brought it
into being.

This commercial success was the reason for the early
influx of foreign capital, which was available for investment in new industries precisely when technical
advances called for additional capital. England possessed mechanised factories long before other countries, and introduced the first textile machinery. The
first railways, the first locomotives worthy of the
name, and the first metal bridge were also of English
origin.

The profits derived from commerce were put to
good use by the property-owning middle classes.
Farm labourers flocked to the towns where ample
employment in industry awaited them. Landed proprietors then acquired the plots and strips of land into
which the open fields had formerly been divided. They
enclosed them and supressed the poorer hamlets; and

since an archaic electoral system gave them practically unlimited rights, they were able to evict smallholders whenever they wished. Begun in the sixteenth century, this movement flourished best in the eighteenth and was completed in the nineteenth.

One-half of the land in England is owned by 8,000 proprietors; 91 of the biggest proprietors account for one-sixth. The big landowner tends to reduce his labour costs by keeping most of his land under grass. There are relatively few farm workers: in England only 6 per cent of the population live on the land, and 9 per cent in Scotland.

The remainder are packed into enormous towns, sixty of which have more than 100,000 inhabitants. Red brick fights a losing battle with industrial grime. The towns are composed of endless streets of identical houses with the same ground plan, the same roofs, and the same doors. They are often surrounded by uninhabited areas and within a few miles of the town centre the overpopulated, smoky, urban agglomerations have given way to the absolute solitude of hills and moors.

In this way Great Britain remains typically European, with small regional units displaying individual characteristics, often with their own vernacular, features of which the New World is ignorant, at least on this restricted scale.

# GREAT BRITAIN

## SOUTH-EAST PLAINS AND PLATEAUS

A line from Newcastle to Exeter separates the plains, hills and plateaus of south-east England from the mountainous regions of the north and west.

The beds decline gently from the hills towards the heart of the basin. Hard (limestone and chalk) and soft (clay, sand) in turn, they appear alternately as hills and plains. These escarpments are markedly asymmetrical, rising steeply towards the mountains of the north-west but sloping gently down towards the south-east. Of the five structural belts of this type that can be identified, two are almost continuous: an escarpment of Jurassic limestone known as the Cotswolds in the south and the Lincoln Edge farther north, and a chalk escarpment — the Chiltern Hills.

The main rivers hesitate between a course following the general slope of the strata (the Thames, for example, cuts through the Chiltern Hills in this way), and the path of least resistance which, over the centuries, has turned them aside into the softer and more easily eroded beds. Thus at the foot of the Cotswolds-Lincoln Edge, the Severn flows southwards and the Trent northwards. These vacillations produce elbows and strange courses, even including a diffluence. The Waveney escapes from a tributary of the Ouse and reaches the North Sea, where its estuary is blocked by a long spit of sand. It is a river without a source and without a mouth.

Structual arrangement is somewhat disturbed by geological foldings. The region south of London was upfolded as a consequence of Alpine movements and its crest was attacked by erosion, with the result that it now consists of a depression, the Weald, flanked by

two chalk escarpments, the Downs. The Isle of Wight and adjacent areas were upfolded in a narrower anticline which is an extension of the Bray axis in France.

The English Plain is only a half-basin. Its strata descend from Wales towards the North Sea but do not rise again on the other side. The lowest points towards which the rivers converge are therefore situated near the sea. The Scandinavian glaciers once covered most of the plain, depositing boulder clay which often modifies the characteristics of the plain's subsoil.

*The agricultural landscape.* The south-east, the region south of a line running from the Cotswolds to the Wash, exhibits a subtle and complete adaptation of agronomy to topography. With the aid of Dudley Stamp's excellent land utilisation maps, a very accurate reconstruction of the geological structure can be made. The clay plains, largely devoted to stock-farming, contrast with the limestone escarpments where mixed farming is practised. The originally wooded and marshy clay has gradually been transformed into

The bold cliffs of the Sussex coast viewed from Beachy Head. East of this point, Wealden clay and Hastings beds form the south coast; westwards it is mainly chalk.

Rock strata exposed by wave action on the coast of Pembrokeshire.

grassland. Stock-farming, especially dairy farming, has swallowed up whole parishes, and arable land sometimes occupies less than one-tenth of the whole farming area.

On limestone and chalk, rich grassland, dairy farms, cereal crops and fruit are found alongside each other in every parish. The farmer follows the dictates of the soil down to the very last detail, abandoning completely as waste land only relatively small barren areas. Wheat and oats are the essential produce. The high grade specimens of seeds and breeding stock which English farmers have succeeded in producing are in worldwide demand.

During the fifty years before the Second World War, arable land in England and Wales fell from 13,250,000 acres to 8,935,000 acres whereas pasture land increased from 14,560,000 acres to 15,709,000 acres. The war reversed this tendency: arable land again spread at the expense of grassland and in many cases this appears to be a permanent feature.

*Specialised agricultural districts.* To the south and south-east of London extend two strips of land devoted almost exclusively to fruit and vegetables, one between the North Downs and the Thames, the other at the southern foot of the North downs, in the Weald of Kent.

East Anglia, a vast protuberance sticking out into the North Sea between the Thames estuary and the Wash, is characterised by its flatness, its clayey soil, and its dry climate. Comparatively isolated from the main commercial routes and also from the paths of early invaders, it has known nine centuries of peace — a history undoubtedly unique in Europe. It has retained open fields and compact villages, and the area under crops is more than double the area devoted to grassland. The Norfolk system of crop rotation revolutionised European agriculture in the eighteenth century by introducing root crops on land which had previously lain fallow. East Anglia alone produces one-quarter of England's wheat. Faced with economic difficulties, the large-scale farmers are developing the raising of livestock, while the smallholder prefers to grow more remunerative crops (vegetables such as

peas and Brussel sprouts, seeds and fruit). The towns serve as a market for agricultural produce, whilst their manufactured products are sold in the surrounding countryside. Norwich is a financial centre for insurance companies, and a major manufacturer of agricultural machinery and shoes.

The Fens occupy an ancient marsh which was an extension of the Wash. Their drainage involves constant use of the world's biggest pumping station, which clears 2,595 tons of water a minute. It is the richest, most densely populated and most specialised of all the English agricultural regions. The crops, especially potatoes and sugar-beet, are all grown commercially.

*Towns and industrialisation.* Before the First World War, south-east England had the reputation of being rural and non-industrial. Its towns, often extremely picturesque — Canterbury and Salisbury spring to mind — were generally little more than large market towns and county capitals. The most distinctive were the ancient university towns, Oxford on the Thames and Cambridge on the Cam, with their handsome colleges and quadrangles.

The last twenty years have wrought changes in this age-old state of affairs. Crises elsewhere in England drove industrialists to seek fresh prosperity in a region which they had previously neglected. Nearly all the old towns have doubled in size and their populations have increased considerably. Oxford, for instance, where the population has risen sharply from 50,000 to 110,000, has become an important motor vehicle manufacturing centre.

Lastly, since 1945, a start has been made on building 'New Towns', which are playing an essential part in the move to relieve congestion in the overgrown cities.

*The coasts and ports.* The English coastline follows the country's physical structure fairly closely. The chalk escarpments end at the sea's edge in vertical cliffs, indented and broken by dry clefts; the clay plains terminate in a low flat coastline lashed by the waves. Often they have receded — in East Anglia as much as four miles since Roman times — leaving villages

Hop-picking in Kent. Beer is the national drink in England, and every summer casual labour is employed to gather the hop harvest.

Salisbury Cathedral, Wiltshire.

and even towns high and dry. A general submerging movement has transformed the mouths of many rivers into estuaries and gulfs, and the south coast is losing ground fractionally but steadily every year. This movement is counterbalanced by river and marine alluvial deposits.

In the extreme west, the clay plain which stretches along the foot of the limestone escarpment has been much encroached upon by the sea in the Bristol Channel, the huge estuary of the Severn. For a long time Gloucester served as a port for the estuary. But it is accessible only to ships under 800 tons, and all the main traffic now passes through Bristol, where a bridge was completed in 1966 to ease the pressure of transport using the five-mile-long rail tunnel under the Severn. The city has sent out a constant stream of expeditions and ships: to Guienne in the Middle Ages and later to the New World. John and Sebastion Cabot, the first to explore the North American coast, sailed from the quays of Bristol. Bristol men founded the Society of Merchant Adventurers in the fifteenth century and established a colony in Maine in 1620. Enriched by the slave trade, Bristol's fortunes declined when it was suppressed. The city assumed great importance again when Britain became industrialised. Half a million people live within its limits, and another six million within a radius of 75 miles. Since 1909 Bristol has had its own university.

The south coast engages in two types of activity: tourism and trade. The first is encouraged by the fact that is one of the sunniest regions in England, and by its proximity to London. Cross-channel trade keeps a few medium sized ports busy. Channel Island traffic sails from Weymouth; Dieppe is served by Newhaven. Southampton, one of the main centres of maritime trade, already combined the ideal conditions for establishing a port, and its proximity to London (less than two hours by train) ensured its development. Today Southampton is the chief passenger port and the sixth cargo port in the country. A few miles further down on the mainland side of Spithead is Portsmouth; its functions are exclusively naval. Fishing has developed and makes a welcome addition to the cross-channel passenger traffic which is the main activity of the ports of Folkestone and Dover.

On the North Sea coast, fishing has become the principal activity of Yarmouth and Lowestoft, both important herring ports. Their commercial activity, on the other hand, has been on the decline since silting up of the estuaries prevented ships from using them. Ipswich retains its commercial importance as a port, in spite of its position twelve miles inland. Passengers for Belgium and Holland embark at Harwich, at the end of the same estuary.

LONDON. *A political and economic capital.* The relative stagnation of the towns and ports in the east is partly due to London's excessive size (population of Greater London is over 9 million). The city was built at the lowest crossing point of the Thames above the estuary. London's early development was as a commercial centre, but very soon it assumed political importance because it was the centre of monarchical government and of the noble or popular resistance that established parliamentary government. Today London is known chiefly as the political capital, embracing the Royal

Tulip fields near Spalding, Lincolnshire. The area is noted for its bulb fields, with 3,000 acres given over to daffodils and tulips. Lincolnshire is one of the principal arable counties of England; 86 per cent of its 1,700,000 acres is cultivated.

A view of Canterbury, the cathedral city of England's Primate.

Magdalen College, Oxford.

Palaces, the Houses of Parliament, the Ministries, and the offices of the Commonwealth representatives. It is also a cultural capital, with its famous museums and galleries (the British Museum which is both museum and national library, the National Gallery, Tate Gallery, and countless specialised museums), and the biggest university in England (31,600 students and a teaching staff of 3,000).

London is also the leading industrial centre in England, employing 21 per cent of British workers. Its industries are of the sort that need few raw materials and plenty of manpower. The capital's commercial and financial functions are even more important. All the wholesale houses have their head offices there. Futures markets deal in all kinds of goods, and the Stock Exchange in securities. There are centres for trading, and the major banks and insurance companies are without serious rival on the Continent.

*England's chief port.* The port is the basis of all London's activity. As the water is not deep enough in the heart of the city to take the largest vessels, it has been necessary to organise an extensive lighter service between the stretch downstream where the big ships moor and the wharves and warehouses up river. Canals and docks have had to be built. At certain times of the year fogs downstream interfere with the regularity of the traffic. Lastly, the actual position of the Thames estuary adds considerable extra distance to the voyages of the transatlantic liners.

In spite of these inconveniences, London remains the busiest of all English ports, importing half the country's raw materials and exporting half its manufactured goods, handling 33 per cent of British external trade and 16 per cent of its coastal trade. Imports outweigh exports by nearly 50 per cent in terms of value.

The port is one of the foremost in the world, though not as active as formerly in handling the entrepôt and re-export trade. Liverpool has taken over much of the work of supplying English industry. London owes its importance today rather to its own industrial and commercial activities and to the extensive needs of its population.

*The first town in Europe.* Until the outbreak of war in 1939 London was the first city in the world. More than eight million people lived in this enormous city. Very few today live in the old, medieval 'City', almost exclusively an office sector with a permanent population of only 5,000; after six o'clock in the afternoon activity in the area ceases. But the City, as it is known, retains the prestige of history. Its numerous historic buildings include the Tower; it preserves its administrative traditions, and elects its Lord Mayor, from whom the Queen must seek permission before entering the ancient precinct.

All round it, cities and boroughs have linked up as the capital grew and only a token municipal autonomy exists within the County of London, which embraces about $3\frac{1}{2}$ million inhabitants. Although it stretches for $12\frac{1}{2}$ miles from north to south and 15 miles from east to west, the county itself is now simply the heart of the built-up area.

London has extended far beyond these limits. Houses stretch in unbroken lines along the main roads for 15 miles north and south of the city, and for 25 miles to the west. Most isolated suburbs lie even farther out, and a vast transport system of buses, underground trains and suburban electric trains is necessary to cope with the tremendous sprawl.

As in most other cities, the different quarters are associated with specialised economic and social activities: Westminster with the Ministries and public services, the Strand and its vicinity with the law, Fleet Street with newspaper offices, and the City with finance and insurance. The residential West End houses a wealthier population than the industrial quarters of the East End, which even today have not entirely lost their poverty-stricken character. London's distinctive quality seems to consist, first, in a dense general plan, secondly, in the minor rôle played by the Thames in the city's aesthetic appearance, and lastly in the many public gardens. As soon as one leaves the centre, calm reigns over all; even people who are in a hurry do not show it. Patient queues stand at stations, bus stops, theatres, cinemas, and sometimes even restaurants. The Hyde Park orators

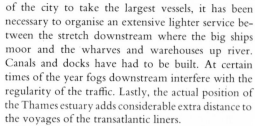

The clock tower of the Houses of Parliament, London. The capital is the hub of England's political, commercial and industrial life. Its port is the busiest in England and its population (now over 9 million) is by far the largest urban population in Britain.

are symbolic of this social discipline, well aware that few of the crowd listening to their harangues would dream of expressing disagreement in a violent or boisterous way.

## CENTRAL ENGLAND

To the north, the English Plain extends by swallowing up the Pennine upland, pushing its way between the Pennines and the North Sea on the one side, and between the Pennines and Wales on the other, as well as along the coastline of the Irish Sea. It is flanked by mountains where the seams of coal basic to all industry and the salt strata indispensable to the chemical industry are found, The mountains are also the sources of springs of low limestone content that give the 'soft' water particularly suitable for the textile industry. Rainfall is heavier here because of the proximity of the mountains. Natural humidity in the textile factories is adequate at all seasons of the year, whereas in the south-east the atmosphere has to be artificially humidified to prevent dry threads from breaking during spinning and weaving.

No other British region is so rich in historical memories: York, Chester, Lincoln, and Nottingham are names with a special place in history. The introduction of heavy industry promoted the well-known 'Manchester School' of economics, and Rochdale was the cradle of the worldwide consumers' co-operative movement.

YORKSHIRE AND LINCOLNSHIRE. In Yorkshire the two lines of the main chalk and limestone escarpments join. They are intersected by two gaps which connect the long north-south depression of the Vale of York with the sea. Only the more southerly contains a watercourse, the Humber, which receives the waters carried down from the Pennines and those of the Ouse and the Trent. The present course of all these rivers is the result of a series of captures. The wanderings of the Don and Trent, which are now under control, have left the name of the Isle of Axholme as a souvenir of an area no longer an island. The last glaciation to fill the valleys deposited clay and moraines, and caused a westerly diversion of the waters of the Vale of Pickering which is separated from the sea by a moraine no more than a few yards wide.

*An extensive crop-growing district.* The tops of the limestone escarpments (the North Yorkshire Moors and the Yorkshire Wolds) are often uncultivated, the plains sometimes peaty. But many of the marshes have been drained, many of the rivers embanked, and the soil of the uplands improved by manuring. The climate is relatively dry, especially in summer. The area of arable land exceeds 55 per cent, a proportion rarely reached in England. In 1874 Yorkshire produced 7.6 per cent of England's wheat, in 1938, 10 per cent. The establishment of two large sugar refineries has stimulated the cultivation of sugar-beet. The Trent valley specialises in raising cattle for beef and veal, and in milch cows. The southern part of the region produces early new potatoes, while mustard is grown on the banks of the Humber.

*The coal and wool district.* There was no dearth of ancient industries in Yorkshire. Wool from the sheep reared on the moors was woven in the dales. Metallic

London Docks. The port is the basis of all London's activity and the busiest in England.

ores in the mountains supplied lead, baryta and fluorspar. But the Industrial Revolution proper was based on the exploitation of coal in the west and iron in the east. Gradually the coal centre shifted eastwards to the foot of the Lincoln Edge. It is by far the richest of the English coalfields, and has yielded a tonnage almost equal to that of all the deposits in France put together. Coal is taken to southern England by rail and exported to other countries via the North Sea ports.

The ancient woollen industries which were dispersed along the line of soft water springs were rejuvenated by the introduction of the steam-powered loom in 1822. Yorkshire supplies 86 per cent of England's woollen yarn and does as much as 90 per cent of her wool-combing. Other supplements to the textile industry proper were the manufacture of textile machinery, and the development of banking and finance houses and the wholesale wool markets — although some raw wool is still supplied through London. One could almost say that the area's textile

Asterton and the Stiperstones, as seen from the Long Mynd, Shropshire. On average only 11 to 15 per cent of the heavily industrialised Midlands is cultivated, but Shropshire, a lush green county of rolling landscapes, has 45 per cent under crops.

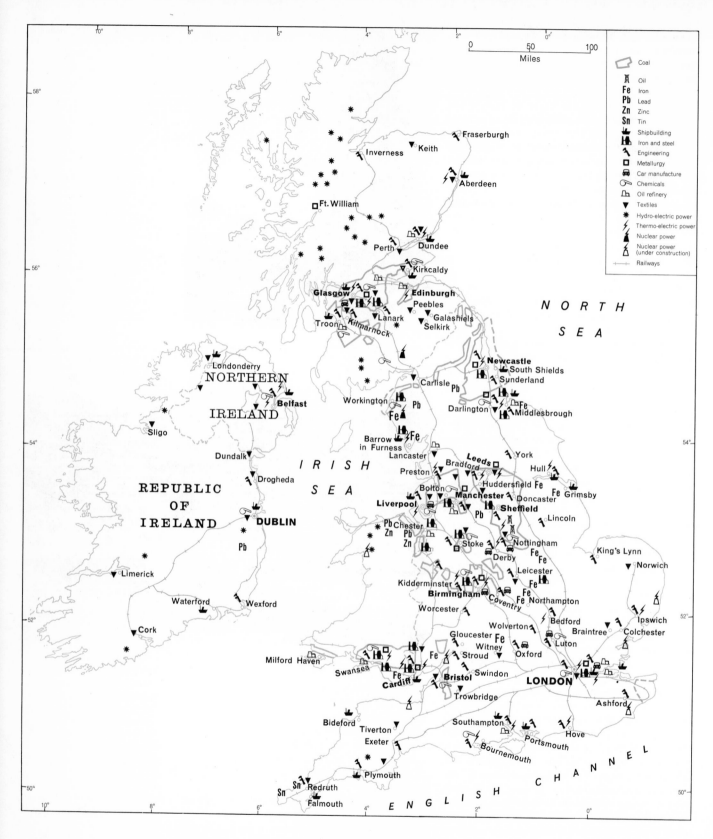

The main concentration of Britain's industry is still in the areas where nineteenth-century industrialisation began: in the Midlands, Lancashire and Cheshire where there is easy access to coal and other raw materials. The one exception in this pattern is London, which is England's leading industrial centre with a wide variety of manufactures requiring few raw materials. Since the 1942–5 War both Government policy and national organisations have aimed at minimising further industrial development in already congested areas and offering incentives to development where local labour needs are greatest.

industry is one vast oval conurbation, 25 miles long and more than 12 miles wide, containing more than 40 towns and nearly two million inhabitants. Most of the towns have their own speciality. Bradford, for instance, is the chief centre of wool-combing and the manufacture of worsteds. Leeds is engaged chiefly in the manufacture of ready-made clothing; it also has introduced mechanical engineering and the manufacture of steam and diesel locomotives. These two cities have the biggest volume of trade. Rayon manufacture is being developed and competing to some extent with natural fibres.

*The steel industry: Sheffield.* From the end of the Middle Ages onwards, metallurgy and cutlery manufacture in south Yorkshire were encouraged by local iron deposits, forests, numerous swift-flowing streams and the presence of a sandstone especially suitable for the whetting of steel. The blast furnaces have long been extinguished but the steelworks retain their importance. Sheffield is a town of contrasts. It has highly concentrated factories employing the very latest techniques, such as the manufacture of stainless steel with new alloys, and yet still retains traces of the old ways of working. Grinding, for example, is still carried out by craftsmen. Sheffield's fame is based mainly on its production of cutlery and special steels, and is due to the inherited skill of generations of workers. More than half the country's output of alloy steel is produced here.

*New metallurgical districts.* The iron ore deposits in the Cleveland Hills in north-east Yorkshire and north Lincolnshire brought to life new blast furnaces, followed by the introduction of industry and the growth of the old towns. Expanding metallurgical and other industries have doubled the population of Doncaster, the ancient Roman camp of Danum, in a very short time. The region had two other big Roman cities, Lincoln (Lindum) and York (Eboracum). The former now contains engineering works; York, the most densely populated town in the north of England during the Middle Ages, remains commercial rather than industrial.

*Fishing and commercial ports.* The whole of the region's North Sea coastline is constantly threatened by the sea. Nearly thirty coastal settlements have disappeared since Roman times. Several fishing ports situated opposite the rich North Sea banks have increased considerably in size since the opening of rail routes connecting them with London. The most important are Hull and Grimsby. With the gradual silting up of the rivers and increases in tonnage the up-river commercial ports have decreased in importance. The coal export traffic is shared between Goole, Grimsby and Hull or, more correctly, Kingston-upon-Hull. At one time a whaling port, Hull's trade has increased and the port has become the fourth in England for imports and the fifth for exports.

LANCASHIRE AND CHESHIRE: THE COTTON COUNTRY. On the other side of the Pennine upland, Lancastria is divided into the counties of Lancashire and Cheshire. The factory towns extend into the narrow valleys of the Pennines, while the countryside offers a contrast between barren, deserted moors and fertile plain. For more than two centuries the area's industry has concentrated on one textile: cotton. The westward boundary of the region is a coastline of crowded summer

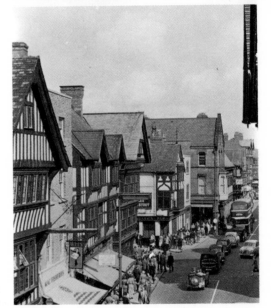

The industrial landscape that is Lancashire, home of cotton and the vast, smoky conurbations sprawling outwards from Manchester.

Once the Roman station of Deva, Chester is the only city in England with its walls still complete. The half-timbered houses give the city a picturesque character.

Blackpool, one of industrial Lancashire's most popular holiday resorts. Its numerous entertainments, its long sandy beaches and its accessibility draw thousands of people away from urban drabness at fine summer weekends.

An oil refinery outside Manchester. With the declining prosperity of the cotton industry, Lancashire's main source of revenue since the beginning of the nineteenth century, new industries have been introduced in an effort to employ one of the densest urban populations in the world. These industries in turn make new demands on fuel supplies.

Cotton spinning at Tulketh Mill, Preston, Lancashire. Lancashire's once prosperous cotton industry has seen a recession in trade in postwar years, but it is still the principal cotton county, with Manchester as its centre.

resorts (Blackpool, Southport, Morecambe); nearby is what was once the busiest fishing port on England's west coast, Fleetwood.

There are many features which distinguish Lancashire from its neighbour and rival, Yorkshire. Lying to the west, it is better watered. The soils derived from glacial deposits yield some of the best arable and grass land in Britain. Farmers concentrate on potatoes and animal fodder crops rather than on wheat. But the principal activity is rearing pigs and the best milch cows and veal calves in England.

Criss-crossed with faults, and plunging too sharply beneath the plain, Lancashire's coal seams are shallow. Although the county still exports certain grades of coal to Ireland, it has to import it from Yorkshire and Northumberland for its own principal industries.

Like Yorkshire, it was once a woollen district. The almost total substitution of cotton for wool was the direct result of the absence of organised corporations at Manchester in the eighteenth century. This left industrialists with a free hand at the very moment when the demand for cotton was spreading. In the nineteenth century, Lancashire became the principal cotton centre in the world. Most factories and many towns specialise in a single stage of cotton manufacture, such as spinning, weaving or dyeing.

Well situated for safe trading when England was at war with the continent and for easy connections with the English Plain, Liverpool became the second port in England; it now serves the metal industry as well as the textile trade, supplying both Lancashire and Yorkshire, and importing more wool than Hull. However, in 1894, Manchester, nearly 21 miles away, opened a ship canal from coast to city which has transformed it into the third port in Britain. But docking facilities, commercial organisations, and a vast cotton futures market still ensure for Liverpool cotton imports twice as large as Manchester's, and yarn exports eight times larger.

Manchester nevertheless remains the brain behind the whole industry. Spinning and bleaching are concentrated in the neighbouring towns of Oldham, Bolton, Bury and Rochdale. Weaving is almost wholly centred farther north, in the Ribble basin; there are some spinning mills, mostly downstream (Preston, for example), while Accrington specialises in printing. The chemical industry, fed by the saline outcrops of the Triassic strata, provides dyes for cotton cloth and supplies the needs of manufacturing centres of all kinds. The engineering industry, born in Salford and Oldham to satisfy the demand for textile machinery, now makes a wide range of products. Preston is one of the major engineering centres.

The cotton industry today is not as prosperous as once it was. Production is a fraction of its 1913 level. Other textiles have been introduced in an attempt to halt the decline, and today more than one-sixth of the yarn production is made up of rayon or cotton-rayon mixtures. New industries have been introduced: aluminium and glass, oil refining, and gas engines. In spite of this it is still proving difficult to employ the whole of the region's manpower.

The two county towns are situated at the two extremities of Lancastria: Lancaster in the north, on the Lune, and Chester in the south, on the Dee. Both were ancient Roman strongholds and are almost untouched by modern industry, rich in old buildings and scenic beauty. Manchester is the principal city. Its administrative and trading centre fills to overflowing the old municipal boundaries, and its urban extension has had to surround Salford to accommodate its 2 million inhabitants.

THE MIDLANDS. In the south the Pennine upland dips beneath the Midlands which separate it from Wales. The Midlands is the centre of a natural drainage system and its waters escape to the Mersey, Humber and Severn. The region was formerly crossed by Roman roads whose place is taken today by canals, main roads and railroads. Pasturage and animal husbandry find more favour with the farmers than crop-growing. Livestock for meat and milk are reared close to the main lines of communication. If reared solely for their meat, they are raised in the most luxuriant pastures farthest from the towns. The Leicester basin contains the highest density of cattle in England: 130 per square mile. While on average only 11-15 per cent of the area is ploughed, Shropshire has 45 per cent of its surface under cultivation, and the Vale of Evesham 62 per cent. The latter is noted for its abundance of fruit and vegetables.

Industry in the Midlands follows the old traditions, making use of the produce of local stock-farming, leather and wool, to which it has added mineral resources.

There are three coalfields adjoining each other. In the west is the south Staffordshire coalfield (the 'Black Country'), once very active but now almost exhausted. The Leicestershire and Warwickshire coalfields, however, have a combined annual output of nearly 9 million tons. A fourth Midland coalfield, the north Staffordshire field, produces about 10 million tons annually.

Iron ores, which are worked in the Jurassic rocks east of Leicester and Northampton more than compensate for the exhaustion of the Black Country's coal deposits, with a production of 15 million tons annually.

Four large industrial and urban regions can be distinguished:

The Potteries in the north-west use as their raw material clays of the coal measure rocks of the North Staffordshire coalfield. A large number of factories manufacture all kinds of terracotta, earthenware and porcelain goods. In 1907 the six main towns were fused into one vast city, Stoke-on-Trent (265,000 inhabitants in the county borough), which also processes rubber.

The Black Country, without adequate supplies of iron or coal, has lost most of its blast furnaces. But since the beginning of the century a wide variety of new products has been introduced, from heavy engineering to ironmongery, and Birmingham has been nicknamed 'the toyshop of the world'. Extremely varied manufactures explain the flourishing state of a conurbation of 1,700,000 inhabitants.

Several centres have grown up in the south-east Midlands between Charwood Forest and the foot of the limestone escarpment, near the fields of coal and iron ore. Coventry, although it suffered one of the heaviest bombardments of the Second World War, has resumed its rôle as the capital of cars, trucks and tractors. It also produces turbines and equipment for

Industrial giants in the north of England.

A view of the potteries in Staffordshire. Associated with such famous names as Wedgwood and Minton, 95 per cent of all output comes from this area.

Streets in Birmingham. England's second largest city, typifying the monotony of working-class districts, particularly in industrial provincial towns. Aware of the need to create a new environment for its inhabitants, Birmingham, like many of its smaller Midland neighbours, has pursued a policy of replanning its town centre and developing its suburbs that is both vigorous and forward-looking.

jet aircraft. Leicester has become a centre for knitted goods and for leather shoes, while still remaining an important market town. Northampton shares the same activities and is also a blast furnace centre.

To the north-east, a series of towns situated along the line where plain meets mountain indicates proximity to Yorkshire. Derby contains the main rail workshops for British Railways' Midland Region. Car manufacture is another important industry. Nottingham developed in the Middle Ages as a fort, a stronghold and — because of the charcoal from the neighbouring forests — a centre of ironworks. An important hosiery and lace-making centre, it has also flourishing tobacco and bicycle factories and a large pharmaceutical industry. In the manufacture of hosiery it competes with its neighbour, Leicester.

## THE ENGLISH AND WELSH MOUNTAINS

Even though the mountains are nowhere very high, northern and western England offer a vastly different landscape from the flat or gently rolling south-east. Arable land and forests are left behind and population densities are low.

The mountains, hills and plateaus are divided by two depressions into three systems: the Bristol Channel separates Cornwall from Wales, and the Midlands separates the Pennine Chain from Wales. There is continual contrast between industrial districts and large expanses of territory without a single industry. In the mountain areas men have become used to thinking independently, and it is by no means surprising that the Trade Union movement developed first in the west. Rural life plays an appreciable part in Cornwall and Wales, where proof of its strength lies in the long retention of the Cornish and Welsh tongues.

CORNWALL. In south-west England a peninsula composed of Devon and Cornwall and a fragment of Somerset protrudes into the sea between the English and the Bristol Channels. Four groups of high points, corresponding to four outcrops of hard rocks, are separated by broad corridors of soft rocks: Ex-

Steelworkers in the 'Black Country', south Staffordshire, centre of heavy industry. Once Britain's principal iron and steel district, many of its blast furnaces closed when local iron and steel resources declined sharply at the beginning of the century. They were gradually replaced by new industries of every kind: heavy, mechanical and electrical engineering, synthetic textiles, clothing and ironmongery. Variety has been the secret of success supporting a conurbation of almost two million people.

moor along the Bristol Channel, and its extension the Quantock Hills (1,708 feet); Dartmoor (2,039 feet); Bodmin Moor (1,375 feet); and Saint Austell (1,015 feet), the three last being composed of granite. Their appearance is that of a series of plateaus at varying heights, yet they are high enough to bring rainfall of more than 30 inches to the whole peninsula. They form a strange, deserted world of heaths and moors on which neighbouring communities have grazing rights.

Permanent settlements exist only below 1,000 feet and are dispersed into a multitude of hamlets and isolated farms. Most of these are smallholdings, and more than half have an area of less than 20 acres. Land on the uplands is divided by a patchwork of dry-walling. Animal husbandry continues to increase at the expense of crops. The beasts often spend day and night out of doors all the year round; oats and barley are grown to feed them.

The mild winters have encouraged certain sheltered coastal sectors to specialise in early new potatoes and cauliflowers, while fruit is grown on the banks of the Tamar, and flowers in the Scilly Isles.

The ancient rocks contain a profusion of metalliferous veins which in ancient times made Cornwall a noted mining district. Centuries ago tin was extracted (the Scilly Isles were part of the *Cassiterides* where the Phoenicians came for supplies of metal); in the Middle Ages and after, copper and — more recently — tungsten were worked on a large scale. Today Cornwall is better known for its kaolin or china clay, granite and slate. Well suited for fishing and tourism, the peninsula has a rocky coast frequently escarped and indented by gulfs and branching rias along its whole length. But the fishing industry lacks the capital necessary for modernisation, and the vast numbers of summer visitors are inducing the fishermen to turn from their nets in summer to the more profitable ventures of running pleasure cruises. In the winter seasonal unemployment is widespread.

The area has no big towns. Exeter, the administrative and commercial centre, has 80,000 inhabitants. Plymouth alone is truly industrial, mainly because of its advanced position as a naval base and commercial capital of the peninsula.

WALES: PENINSULAR AND MOUNTAINOUS. The Welsh peninsula, lying between the Bristol Channel, St George's Channel and the Irish Sea, differs considerably from England in its mountainous nature and its rôle as a place of refuge.

Heights frequently reach 1,200 feet, several ranges exceed 2,800 feet, and some isolated peaks top 3,000 feet. Eastwards the Welsh beds dip beneath the English Plain but occasionally emerge again as wooded, dome-shaped hills amid more recent sediments. The Wrekin, the Malvern Hills, the Forest of Dean, and even the Mendip Hills east of the Bristol Channel are examples of such hills. Annual rainfall, which exceeds 40 inches throughout most of Wales, reaches about 200 inches on Snowdon. The duration of sunshine is short; the permanent humidity modifies the cold, however, and on the top of Snowdon the mean temperature does not fall below –1°C. (30°F.). Consequently snow is infrequent: 5 days a year on the coasts, 40 on the highest peaks.

A slight drop in the temperature during the Ice Age

Lands End, at the furthermost point of Cornwall, in southwest England. Metalliferous veins in Cornwall's rocks made it an important source of tin early in history: the Phoenicians came here for supplies. In the Middle Ages copper was worked; today quarries have taken pride of place from the mines, and kaolin, clay, granite and slate are worked.

was enough to cover the whole country with thick ice-caps. Nearly all the valleys are glacial, with their upper ends forming corries. The ancient moraine-dammed lakes have been transformed into peat-bogs. Tongues of the early ice penetrated and deepened even the smallest cols, so that there are no insuperable barriers to lines of communication.

The mountains facing the English plain have often served as a place of refuge. Wales has preserved its own distinctive civilisation longer than Cornwall or the Pennine region. Nearly one-quarter of all Welshmen speak Welsh habitually. Mostly smallholders, they practise stock-farming in preference to agriculture. The sheep are left to graze on the interminable upland moors, coming down to the farms only once a year for dipping and shearing. Only below the 1,000-foot contour line does pasturage give way to grassland of enclosed fields.

In a number of places there are signs of coal-mining amid the fields, and agglomerations of factories produce a landscape more like that of England.

Brixham Harbour, South Devon. A picturesque fishing port and popular holiday resort, Brixham is a typical Devon coastal town. Inland, the region is no less attractive: gentle hills are capped with woods; in the valleys, pastureland is interspersed with crops.

Snowdon, the skeleton of an ancient volcano uncovered by erosion. Lying in the centre of a mountainous area in North Wales, Snowdon's 3,560-foot summit is the highest in England and Wales.

A ram sale at Capel Curig. Sheep-breeding is economically important in Wales. In the north the highest districts specialise in breeding and the valleys in fattening; in Central Wales transhumance is practised.

The ruins of Tintern Abbey, Monmouthshire, a thirteenth-century Cistercian monastery.

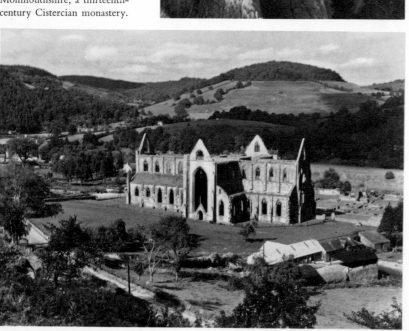

*North Wales.* Two of the highest peaks (Snowdon 3,560 feet and Cader Idris 2,927 feet) are in north Wales. On the coast, long depressions have wormed their way in between the massifs. Some of them (Conway, Clwyd) are covered with the sediments and have become plains used for stock-farming and crops, others (Dee, Tremadoc) are still rocky defiles. The highest chain of mountains protrudes into the seas in the form of the Lleyn peninsula. The Menai Straits separate Anglesey from the mainland.

The North is the most typically Welsh region. Welsh is used for teaching at University College, Bangor, one of the four colleges of the University of Wales. Specialisation between the sheep-breeding districts on the highest land and the fattening districts in the valleys below has done little to modify the upland pastoral way of life.

The north-eastern coalfield was one of the early homes of the metallurgical and chemical industries. But now the field is nearing exhaustion and the industrial towns are of minor importance. The port of Holyhead has offered the most convenient boat service to Ireland.

*Central Wales: fruit-growing and pasturage.* Central Wales is lower lying than North Wales though its relief is more distorted, is less wind-swept, and has higher-class crops including orchards and hop fields which carry the Midland tradition over the border. Iron deposits, now exhausted, have established a series of towns built along the line where the mountains meet the plain in Shropshire. Mineral springs explain the existence of a few spas (for example, Llandrindod Wells). Peat covers broad valleys. The seasonal movement of sheep (transhumance) holds sway again. For many years this was organised by such abbeys as Strata Florida, whose ruins are one of the seats of Welsh tradition. At Aberystwyth, on the sea, is a college of the University of Wales and the National Library, and a centre of applied agricultural research.

*South Wales: industry against economic crisis.* The south comprises two mountain chains separated by a cultivated depression. The northern chain of barren red sandstone rises in a crest culminating in the Brecon Beacons (2,906 feet). The southern chain is intersected by the two large bays of Swansea and Carmarthen, forming three comparatively low peninsulas: Pembroke, Gower and Glamorgan. The land is more fertile here than elsewhere: wheat is still grown and sugar-beet has been successfully introduced. Strata of coal and iron in numerous beds, easily reached, enabled this region to flourish prodigiously at the very beginning of the industrial revolution, when the basis of its iron and steel industry was established.

But the Welsh coalfield has seen its best days. Iron was exhausted first and most of the ore for what is still Britain's most important steel-working region is imported. Now coal is threatened in turn. Extraction has fallen from 56 to 23 million tons and the coalfield suffers from unemployment. In an effort to create employment, in 1936, for the first time in Great Britain, the State intervened to direct the establishment and location of new industries. A big drive was made in the metal industry. But the main development has been the formation of 'trading estates' to encourage new industries by reducing the cost of equipping factories and by streamlining operations. The list is

NETHERLANDS: Amsterdam docks.   Winter of the IJsselmeer.   Transporting milk by boat at Giethoor

remarkable for its variety: coking plant, new metals (such as magnesium), light engineering, paper and packaging mills, and the production of rubber, fats and wireless sets.

They have not proved enough to keep the whole population from unemployment and migration. Merthyr Tydfil, which once had the highest population, has fallen from 83,000 inhabitants (1939) to 59,000 (1961). Rhondda once had 170,000 inhabitants; now it has less than 100,000.

The ports have suffered less. To the east, Newport is an important ore-importing centre. Llanelly, to the west, has copper and tin works. In the centre, Port Talbot has grown up side by side with the old town of Neath.

Two large centres dispute the commercial crown: Swansea and Cardiff. To the west of the Glamorgan peninsula, Swansea has a name which recalls its Scandinavian origin — 'Isle of Sweyn' (a Viking chief). Apart from its extremely important and long established tinplate industry, it now possesses copper, zinc and nickel works. Even so, it has been unable to stay a slight fall in its population. Cardiff owed its prosperity to the export of iron and later of coal; it exports very little coal today, but remains a steel centre and factory town, a minor fishing port and, more especially, the main commercial centre in Wales. It also has claims to being her intellectual capital, containing one of the University colleges and the National Museum of Wales.

*The Pennine upland: moors and lakes.* The Pennine upland stretches from the Midlands in the south to the Scottish border in the north: a broad Hercynian fold shaped into an immense plateau around the 2,000- and 900-foot contours. The loftiest peaks are not very much higher than the upland plateaus. The whole range is markedly asymmetrical. It dominates the coastal plain of the Irish Sea with abrupt slopes whereas its eastern flanks descend towards the North Sea.

Underground water courses have carved out a strange world of caves and grottoes in the limestone escarpments. Throughout the region, glaciation has over-eroded the valleys to such an extent that in two places at least it has opened up easy lines of cross-communication, the Tyne Gap in the north and the Aire Gap in the south. It has shaped the Cumberland valleys into basins that are occupied by lakes. Over most of the region the rainfall exceeds 40 inches, and snow lies on the ground for more than forty days. Strong winds blow across the broad treeless plateaus, and dense mists form on the hilltops.

Much of the south is covered by uninhabited moors and peat-bogs. Farther north the soil is less acid and supports a few flocks of sheep; cattle are becoming rare on the pasture land.

*Northumberland and Durham: coal and shipbuilding.* In the east the ancient Northumbria, now split into several counties including Northumberland, has the second largest coalfield in England. A wide variety of types of coal and the ease with which deposits in the narrow valleys were reached made this district rich. Annual production is 40 million tons a year.

Inland, the least productive region is situated around Durham, a small ancient stronghold and a town rich in religious associations. Built on a spur, its picturesque old castle is now occupied by the University.

Factories are located on the coast along three estuaries. The Tyne is tidal for fifteen miles and can be used by ships drawing nearly 30 feet. Where the valley narrows, on a spur ten miles from the sea, a castle (Newcastle) was built by the Normans on a site on the north bank (Pons Elii) which had already been occupied by the Romans. By weight, coal represents all but one-twentieth of its exports but only one-half in value, for, in addition to the shipbuilding industry, countless engineering works have been set up. At Gateshead, safety glass, steel goods and porcelain are made. In the estuary, South Shields and the fishing port of Tynemouth complete this vast conurbation.

Farther south, on the Wear estuary, Sunderland imports pit props and builds ships. The first Railway line in the world ran from Stockton to Darlington. A second impetus followed the discovery of the Thomas process which made it possible to use the ore from the Cleveland iron beds close by. The proximity of strata of rock salt in the local Jurassic beds has

A steel works in Ebbw Vale, South Wales. The area has had a long history of economic depression. In 1936 Government intervention directed the establishment of new industries. Now, although still insufficient to absorb the whole of the working population, new developments include a thriving iron and steel centre, light engineering, paper and packaging mills, copper, zinc and nickel works, and rubber and electronic equipment factories.

Another industry recently introduced into South Wales: synthetic fibre manufacture. Here, a batch of nylon yarn is wheeled into a setting cabinet as part of the stabilising process.

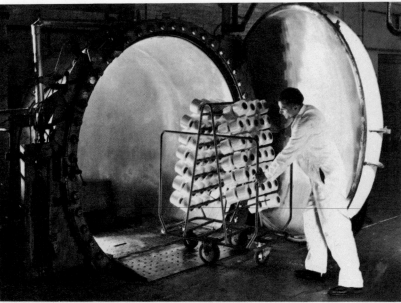

Tarn Hows, Lancashire.
Glaciation has over-eroded the
valleys of the Lake District,
shaping them into lake-filled
basins. Mountain heights are
modest (Scafell, the highest,
is 3,210 feet) but some of the
most delightful scenery in
England is found here.

The heavy organic chemicals
division of the giant
Imperial Chemical Industries
in Co. Durham.
The proximity of rock-salt strata
in the local Jurassic beds
has encouraged the growth
of a vast chemical industry.

Calder Hall, the world's first
full-scale nuclear power
station, was opened in 1956
in Cumberland.

encouraged the growth of the chemical industry at
Billingham and Wilton (near Middlesborough).
*Cumberland: an area of exhausted mineral resources.* In
the past a hand-weaving industry which made wool
cloth for sale in America flourished here, but it was
ruined by the War of Independence. The output of
coal is declining. There is very little iron left today,
but metallurgy and shipbuilding continue. Carlisle, a
rail junction on the borders of England and Scotland,
has a few textile industries, while further south, near
the coast, the first atomic energy station was built at
Calder Hall. On the whole Cumberland's fame today
rests mainly on the delightful scenery of the Lake
District, so popular with tourists.

## SCOTLAND

Scotland covers an area approximately equal to half
that of England and Wales combined. She has some
English-looking physical features, such as high plateaus
covered with moors and cultivated and industrial
lowlands, but the Highlands contain the highest peaks
in the British Isles (Ben Nevis, 4,406 feet). The areas
of plain are discontinuous; the Scottish Lowlands
extend from sea to sea, isolated by the Cheviots.
Unprotected by the barrier of Ireland, she is open to
oceanic winds from the Atlantic and has a higher rainfall than England — at least in the mountains — and
more snow because she is at once farther north, higher
and more oceanic. On the other hand she is farther
from Europe, the source of early invasions. The
Roman Emperor Antoninus strove in vain to push the
Wall, which was his defence against the mountain
clans, as far as the Lowlands. After the break-up of
the Roman Empire, the Scots, who had fixed their
frontier along the ridge of, or at the foot of, the
Cheviot Hills, resisted English encroachment for centuries before union was effected in 1707. Scotland
still preserves many of her own institutions, her own
administrative service, and her own legal code. The
original language, Gaelic, has been slow to disappear;
the Scots are clan-conscious and remain deeply
attached to everything evoking their earlier independence.

THE SOUTHERN UPLANDS: TWEED COUNTRY. The
Southern Uplands, which are best known for Tweeds-
dale, are not very high (Merrick, 2,764 feet), although
the landscape is harsh and often desolate. Horned,
black-faced sheep graze on the moors of the flattened
peaks.

The valleys fall into two groups. In the west, as
dales, they form a series of parallel north-west south-
east corridors which are followed by the lines of
communication between England and Scotland. The
dales spread out into small peninsular and coastal
plains which are less humid and fairly agricultural,
such as the Rhinns of Galloway and the Machers of
Wigtown. Despite the flourishing state of stock and
dairy farming, the population continues to fall and
the district has lost the individuality which ensured
its semi-independence up to the fifteenth century.

Eastwards the valleys are concentrated in the basin
of the Tweed, the centre of the industry which produces cloth of the same name. Here the Cheviot
breed of sheep (white faces and no horns) are reared

on farms often smaller than the mountain holdings (an average of about 200 acres against 5,000). Each farm employs from three to five labourers who take their employment on a yearly contract. Sheep-farmers specialise in judicious cross-breeding aimed at producing specific qualities of wool. Industry, far from the coalfields, has survived by concentrating on high quality goods. The region's woollen cloth is sold all over the world; so is the knitwear manufactured at Hawick.

Towards the North Sea coastline there is the Merse, a country of small glacial hills, or drumlins, with a north-east south-west grain. Here crops of oats and barley for brewing complement stock-farming, and the density of population is considerably higher. The small border town of Berwick-on-Tweed was lost by Scotland to England in 1649.

THE LOWLANDS. The Lowlands form one of the richest, most varied, most industrial and most urbanised regions in Great Britain.

The name 'Lowlands' does not mean that the region is plain: the relief is broken up, with hills following the line of geographical folding, lines of glacial deposits, and impressive volcanic hills from which long tongues of lava have run down. The volcanoes look as if they had become extinct only yesterday, yet they are the remnants of activity in the Primary era, 800 million years ago. Smothered with sediments, they were exhumed much later by selective erosion which was defeated by their basalt rocks and trachyte lava. The whole region is depressed in relation to the Southern Uplands and the Highlands, whose almost rectilinear faults form a rigid boundary to the Lowlands. Because of this subsidence, the sea has made broad inroads: to the east, the Firths of Forth and Tay separated by the Fife peninsula, and to the west, the Firth of Clyde. But ancient volcanic hills and moraines conceal a deep, varied structure dividing the coalfields into four basins: two to the west, in Ayrshire and from Glasgow to Stirling, and two in the east, in Fife and Midlothian, east of Edinburgh.

*Large fields and small meadows.* Consisting of a low-lying corridor in which rainfall decreases from west to east and virtually without snow, the Lowlands utilise all the lower ground for large fields and small meadows. Only volcanic outcrops and a few isolated massifs such as the Ochils in the north or the Pentland Hills in the south are abandoned to moorland and pasturage. However, high latitude, frequent fogs, and the short summer make growing certain crops a risky speculation. Wheat is grown on the driest soil, but the main cereal crop is oats. Wartime needs gave a vigorous impetus to crop-growing and, whereas the reverse was generally true in 1939, arable land far exceeds grassland in eleven counties even at the present time.

The two types of climate are reflected in the agronomy. The west remains faithful to stock-farming, mainly for dairy produce. Permanent and temporary grassland covers 60 to 70 per cent of its surface. Co-operative dairies collect milk and sell it. Potatoes are an important crop around Girvan. Land not used for cattle is covered with orchards, hot-houses for tomatoes, and strawberry fields for the jam factories of Carluke.

In the east arable land is predominant: the plains and hills of the Lothians around Edinburgh, the Fife

Loch Scarnadale, in Lorne, Argyll. In the background are Beinn Chapull and Carn Dearg.

A harvest scene at Inverbervie, Kincardineshire, on the east coast of Scotland. This huge acreage of oats was cut with a reaper and stooked by hand — an unusual achievement in an age of combine harvesting.

Glasgow Docks. Glasgow, built on the River Clyde, is the fifth port and the third city in Great Britain: it imports foodstuffs, iron, pig-iron, and oil, and exports manufactured products. The metallurgical and engineering industries, employing half the city's workers, are devoted mainly to shipbuilding.

peninsula, the Carse o' Gowrie stretching along the coast between Dundee and Perth, and the straths at the foot of the Highlands supply a rich variety of produce. Wheat alone covers up to 16 per cent of the arable land, and oats from 30 to 50 per cent. The Second World War encouraged cultivation of special types of potatoes along the eastern coast. Around the Tay estuary, raspberry and strawberry fields supply Dundee's jam factories (they also make marmalade). Sugar-beet has also been introduced and there is a refinery at Cupar. Stock-farming is practised only as an ancillary to crop growing.

*Glasgow: from tobacco to metallurgy.* The west has more active factories, ports and traffic than the east.

In the past there was no shortage of old handicraft industries (mainly wool and leather) but the trastorm-ation of Glasgow dates from the Act of Union of 1707. The sudden acquisition of the right to trade with English colonies and the advantages of geographical position which shortened transatlantic crossings were exploited to the full, and Glasgow became an important centre for the tobacco trade. There is a good deal of literal truth in the words 'The Clyde made Glasgow, but Glasgow made the Clyde'. The maximum draught of the river was increased from $12\frac{1}{2}$ feet in 1820 to 18 feet in 1851; today it is 36 feet 8 inches. The rich tobacco princes were followed by cotton kings, and later by iron and steel barons. The metal and engineering industries, employing half the workers in Glasgow, are devoted mainly to shipbuilding; they also produce boilers, locomotives, and machinery of all kinds. Other industries are wool and weaving, and chemical manufactures (dyes and explosives).

Nevertheless Glasgow's future may not be completely assured. The output of the Ayrshire and Lanarkshire coalfields has declined: the mines are too small; many have had to close, and thousands of miners have been transferred to the east Lowlands. Iron has to be imported and there is a preference for buying it in the form of pig-iron, so that the blast furnaces are closing down.

Glasgow has had serious unemployment problems:

the result of clinging too closely to old industrial methods. Poverty is more obvious there than in any other town in Great Britain. For all that, Glasgow remains the fifth port and the third town in Britain. Imports consist of foodstuffs, iron pig-ore and oil; exports, of manufactured products. Its rôle as the point of departure for transatlantic passengers has to some extent been taken over by Prestwick airport, about 30 miles south of the port.

Glasgow was first built on the slopes of the right bank of the Clyde; its suburbs now overspill into several neighbouring towns (Paisley, Dumbarton, Greenock) which reach as far as the sea to the west and the nearest Highland lakes in the north.

*The nodal point of the Lowlands.* A second group of industrial towns cluster round the upper end of the Forth estuary. This is the most central point in Scotland. It also contains the battlefields of Falkirk and Bannockburn and the fortress of Stirling perched on its volcanic rock.

Although Stirling was an important junction when rail communications were first introduced, its fortune has declined since the opening of the gigantic viaducts over the Forth and the Tay farther downstream. The commercial centres have shifted towards Edinburgh and Glasgow. But industry is making great strides; the country is dotted with pit-heads and factories have been set up in all the small towns. There are foundries at Alloa in the north and at Falkirk in the south. The port of Grangemouth, on the Forth, was built to serve them; it also handles imported oil in a vast refinery, and processes the by-products in large factories manufacturing dyestuffs and plastics.

*Edinburgh: a majestic capital.* A little farther east, on the south bank of the Forth, is a series of volcanic necks parallel with the sea and separated one from another by small valleys running in the same direction. Edinburgh was built on these necks in the Middle Ages, a small market town with a castle and a few monasteries. First chosen as the royal residence in the fifteenth century, it has been a capital ever since, even after the dissolution of the Scottish government. It is a banking, insurance and trade headquarters. Its uni-

Coal-mining, formerly mainly concentrated in the west around Glasgow, is being increasingly developed in the east around the Firth of Forth, where a more dispersed industrial region is being established, with more varied modern industries. Here, a conveyor is being positioned in Wellesley Colliery.

Edinburgh, the capital of Scotland, has all the attributes of a capital city except ministries and a parliament.
As the main business centre, it is a banking, insurance and trade headquarters.
It is also a cultural and intellectual centre, with a flourishing university.

versity has a teaching staff of 700, and more than 7,500 students. At one time Edinburgh's industry boasted only a few large flour mills, paper mills and printing works, but the defect was soon remedied. The coal of Midlothian and of East Lothian is being increasingly worked (4 million tons). Its port, Leith, is the second biggest exporter of coal in Scotland and, together with the two small neighbouring ports of Granton and Newhaven, an important fishing centre. Factories of all kinds have sprung up in its suburbs, especially since the Second World War. But Edinburgh owes its unique character to its architecture. It is not a very large town: its population does not reach the half-million mark. But it is admirably adapted to its site, being built entirely of stone, in contrast to the more usual brick of so many of Britain's towns. Princes Street, the main thoroughfare, stretches on a rise for more than a mile and is bordered by shops on one side and on the other by parks and gardens set in a ravine. The ravine also allows the railway lines to reach the very heart of the city without unsightly signs of mechanisation. To the north, wide roads lead to the ports. To the south, the suburbs are built on the hill slopes and are interspersed with large parks. Fine civil and religious buildings, and the special quality of the light, endow the whole city with a majestic dignity that makes it one of the finest towns in Europe.

*Dundee and Aberdeen: jute and fishing.* Perth, at the head of the Tay estuary, was the Scottish capital for a short time. Dundee, on the north bank of the estuary, is a seaport and industrial centre. It first grew as a whaling port, then concentrated gradually on local handmade textiles. In the nineteenth century it specialised in the manufacture of jute from British-ruled India. It has been hard hit by Indian competition and has suffered heavy unemployment, although an attempt has been made to adapt the town to the new situation by switching some of its manufactures to linoleum, electric cables and shipbuilding, and by developing the traditional industry of jam and marmalade making.

A whole group of small and medium-sized towns in the neighbouring Fife peninsula, conveniently connected with Dundee by the enormous Tay bridge, produce 7 million tons of coal. St Andrews is the seat of the oldest Scottish university, and its students still wear their traditional red gowns.

The Lowlands extend towards the north-east in a series of plains which separate the Highlands from the North Sea. Intensive drainage and stone clearing have made it possible to farm the indifferent soil of this district. Here the climate is harsher, with more than thirty days of snow a year. The crops best suited to it are oats and turnips, but the main activities are raising beef cattle and fat lambs almost entirely for the London market.

The ports specialise in deep-sea fishing and the main trade is concentrated at Aberdeen. Originally a centre for the export of wool and furs to the Hanseatic towns of Germany, Aberdeen expanded as a direct result of the prosperity of its woollen and paper mills which used wood from Scandinavia. It remains first and foremost a fishing port, although far from the big inland consumer centres, but has lost some of its markets in Russia, Poland and the Baltic states.

THE HIGHLANDS. The Highlands comprise the whole of the north-west of Scotland. The deep and narrow valley of Glen More separates two masses of high crystalline rock. It represents the scar left by a very ancient structural fracture which split the western from the eastern mass. It contains a series of lakes (including the famous Loch Ness) and is traversed by the Caledonian Canal, whose eight locks enable ships to reach its highest point.

The Grampians in the east and the north-western Highlands consist of plateaus worn down by erosion, dotted with volcanic outflows, cut into deep cradle-shaped valleys (the glens) and often filled with ribbon-like lakes or lochs. These features are the work of the ancient glaciers which also carved long estuaries branching out from lesser rivers. The coast has a long fringe of long peninsulas and sheer columnar islands where the waves have carved strange features at sea level, such as Fingal's Cave. The peaks are never very high but sometimes dominate the valleys with precipitous slopes. Ben Nevis, the highest (4,406 feet), is a granite mass. More often the heights resemble vast plateaus of roughly the same altitude, about 3,000 feet. Heavy rainfall, duration of snow-cover, and violent winds are more troublesome than cold (which is insufficient to freeze Loch Ness). Centuries of over-cutting have destroyed the forests. The inhabitants live mainly by sheep-farming. Population is low, with 20 people to the square mile. Vast regions, absolutely deserted, are privately owned game reserves.

Pasture land and game preserves end abruptly a short distance from the sea or the principal rivers, where they are bounded by a continuous wall of stone known as the head dyke. Beyond it the narrow coastal plain is overpopulated. Every inhabitant farms a small croft of a few acres on which he grows oats and vegetables in a primitive fashion (soot from his own home is often the only fertilizer used), and raises a few sheep or makes short fishing trips with poor catches. For many years wool was home-spun and home-woven. Modern industry is almost unknown. However, since World War II watercourses have been systematically harnessed for the production of

Glaciated landscape in Glen Torridon on the north-west coast of Scotland.

Freshly caught fish being packed
on the quayside at Aberdeen,
at the mouth of the Dee,
on the North Sea.
Aberdeen is the chief fishing port
of Scotland, and almost every
one of its inhabitants is in
some way connected with the
fishing industry.

An early stage in the
manufacture of one of Scotland's
most celebrated exports —
its whisky. There are three
production stages: mashing, or
preparation of the liquor or
wort from grain and malt;
fermentation of the wort to
produce the wash; and separation
of the spirit by distillation.

Laggan Dam, Inverness,
Scotland. Although hydro-
electric development has been
successful in Scotland, it will
supply only a small proportion —
3 per cent at most — of Britain's
electricity production, which
remains essentially thermal.

electricity, which provides power for a large aluminium factory at Fort William, at the foot of Ben
Nevis.

THE SCOTTISH ISLANDS. Scotland possesses three archipelagos: the Hebrides, the Orkneys, and the Shetland
Islands. The Orkneys, in the north, are an extension
of the coastal plains and hills of east Scotland. They
are tablelands of Old Red Sandstone, falling away
into the sea in remarkable cliffs. The population of
about 60 to the square mile cultivates about half the
island's surface. Experiments are being made to generate electricity by hydro-electric power. Scapa Flow,
on the main island, is used as a naval base.

The Shetlands, on the other hand, lost in the ocean
60 miles farther north, resemble the Highlands, if
not in height (900 feet) at least in their schistose and
gneissose soil. Fiords divide them into long peninsulas
and their scanty crops cover only one acre in thirteen.
One-third of the inhabitants live by fishing.

To the west, the Hebrides have preserved an archaic
social structure. Drawing lots for fields and fishing
grounds is still practised in places. Seaweed, now harvested mechanically, supplies the chemical industry.
The main source of income is from the sale of tweeds,
spun in the mills at Stornaway but woven at home.
The island's houses in some places are no more than
black cottages with thatched roofs held down by
rope. The local people cling to their uncompromising
land but are sometimes forced to admit defeat: the
whole population of St Kilda left in 1930 after a
thousand years of continuous occupation.

THE SCOTTISH PROBLEM. The basic problem is to
strike a balance between the threat of over-population
in the industrial districts and coastal crofts, and the
lack of men and resources over whole counties in the
Highlands. The development of sheep-farming is undesirable because existing farmers and weavers already
find it difficult enough to find a market for their products. A decision to utilise water power was opposed
by coal-owners and salmon fishers. Millions of pounds
have been invested in new factories covering more
than 500 acres. The reforestation of waste land has
begun and it is hoped to use the timber in the new
industries.

New activities often originate from abroad. American capital is making its way into Scotland. Scotsmen
who emigrate are often replaced by Irishmen or
Englishmen. Inevitable centralisation based on London
is constantly drawing more head offices away from
Edinburgh. It is easy to understand why the reaction
of some Scotsmen is to demand a return to comparative independence and the establishment of a separate
parliament. But it is doubtful whether current international patterns favour the subdivision of economic
units. Perhaps the Scottish problem is rather an integral part of Great Britain's problems.

## THE ISLE OF MAN

The Isle of Man (227 square miles) is a fragment of
Ireland. Its mountains (Snaefell, 2,034 feet, South Bar-
rule, 1,585 feet) dominate uplands surrounded by low
plateaus or plains. Mountain vegetation is scant:
heather, gorse (burnt every year) and coarse grass.
Local reforestation schemes have been successful and

the plains have excellent deep soil derived from glacial deposits. The climate is remarkably mild for its latitude.

Manx, a form of Gaelic, has practically disappeared today. Place names, the agrarian structure, and various local traditions also have strong affinities with Ireland. The island is proud of its Scandinavian heritage which includes the parliament, or Tynwald, one of the oldest in the world. The Isle of Man does not form part of the United Kingdom; the Queen is 'lord' of Man and appoints a governor.

The main crops are potatoes (harvested in June), oats and fodder crops, a small amount of barley for brewing and some hot-house tomatoes. The principal resource is tourism.

## THE CHANNEL ISLANDS

The fortunes of medieval history gave the Channel Islands (geographically and climatically a fragment of Armorica rather than Great Britain) to the English crown. They have none the less preserved their autonomous status, and their Assemblies are the sole arbiters of their laws. The lieutenant-governors who represent the Queen on Jersey and Guernsey have only very limited powers.

The whole archipelago is rich in archaic custom. For example, there is the Dame and her court at Sark, where cars are banned, and there are the vestiges of collective crops on open fields at Alderney. The islands live by market-gardening and tourism. The island cattle enjoy a considerable reputation both in Britain and overseas.

St Helier airport (Jersey) is, after London, the busiest in the British Isles. The influx of money from visitors compensates for the adverse balance of trade. It encourages over-population (1,300 inhabitants to the square mile) and the hypertrophy of the towns (St Peter Port and St Helier).

English is gradually reducing French to a dialect, although in Jersey French is still the official language. The way of life is making the islands thoroughly English in character.

BRITAIN'S PROBLEMS. A quick glance at the position which Great Britain holds in the world immediately reveals paradoxes and apparent contradictions. It is a leading member of the European Free Trade Association. It ranks as one of the great powers, with the biggest volume of external trade in 1938 and the third biggest in 1963. Its colonies and former empires are linked in the Commonwealth, the most extensive and highly populated confederation in the world. Its merchant navy is the second in the world and was for many years the first.

A shadow is cast over this impressive list of facts by its persistent adverse trading balance, the fall of cotton from the list of its major industries, and the ruin of the export trade in coal.

There are further apparent contradictions between its admirable adaptation to the discipline and effort needed in wartime, and its relatively slow adaptation to post-war conditions.

Agriculturally, much of Great Britain remains virtually unused, devoted to moors, game reserves, and excessive pasturage. After 1914 the public authorities tried to counter this by settling ex-servicemen in the country, allocating them smallholdings, regulating the price of agricultural produce, and introducing new crops such as sugar-beet. Really systematic development was first undertaken during the Second World War. Whereas in 1914 England produced only one-quarter of its annual consumption of food, in 1964 it produced approximately one-half. Nevertheless, it has to import about fifteen hundred million pounds worth of foodstuffs (wheat, butter, meat, vegetable oils, etc.), an expenditure which seriously affects its balance of trade.

*Shortage of raw materials.* English sheep meet less than one-tenth of the demand for wool; the shortage has to be made good by purchases from Australia, Argentina and South Africa. Iron ore, despite the providential occurrence of low grade in the East Midlands, has to be imported from Spain, Sweden and Algeria. Copper, tin and lead mines are exhausted. It no longer extracts bauxite and is forced to buy timber and rubber.

*Production costs.* For a long time excessive production costs were imposed on British goods by the high level of wages, the high standard of living — housing, clothes and entertainment being more important than food — and above all by toleration of, and indeed obstinate adherence to, obsolescent organisation. Many of these weaknesses have now been overcome. Today selling prices are comparable with Germany's and often less than half those of France, but during the years of high prices many customers left England for other markets.

*Sources of energy.* Coal, especially steam coal, was for long a cheap source of power and a product for export all over the world. In 1860 Great Britain met two-thirds of world coal consumption. The exhaustion of the seams, war damage, and the high production costs of out-of-date mines have considerably reduced the exportable quota. Following nationalisation, a fifteen-year plan will at least make it possible for production to keep step with consumption. Successful hydro-electric development in Scotland will supply only a small part of electricity production, which remains essentially thermal. Great Britain therefore has to rely on imported liquid fuel; to reduce the resulting expense it is buying crude oil and refining it. With a refining capacity that has multiplied thirtyfold in fifteen years (1938-53) and has increased again since, it is able to sell petroleum products and recover a part of the cost of its purchase.

*The Commonwealth.* For many years Britain thought her colonies and dominions inexhaustible suppliers of raw materials and insatiable purchasers of manufactured goods. But political independence and the desire for economic autonomy went hand in hand, and in many places Great Britain has retained a place in the trade of its overseas territories only by agreeing to limitations of its own commercial independence. The amount of trade of former colonies with Britain diminishes while Britain's trade with them increases. The commercial importance to the Commonwealth to Britain is one of the factors to be considered in the current question of Britain's admission to the European Economic Community.

THE SOLID BASES OF PROSPERITY. *The Merchant Navy.* The importance of British shipping dates back to Cromwell's Navigation Act, which allowed foreign ships to unload only their own countries' products in England. From then on all colonial and transatlantic trade was the monopoly of British vessels. The Merchant Navy has exceeded its 1938 tonnage, though it has not recaptured the first place, now held by the United States. Favoured by a government lavish with subsidies and reparations for wartime losses, its flag still prevails on every sea. It carries cargoes between foreign countries and consequently earns a considerable amount of foreign currency. It created an entrepôt and redistribution trade now on the decline. It stimulated the growth of the largest insurance system in the world: freight, brokerage and maritime insurance bring more than 750 million pounds' worth of foreign exchange into Great Britain every year.

*Banks and co-operatives.* The deposit and investment of capital remains of primary importance. Although Britain had to sell about 45 per cent of its foreign share-holdings, especially in America, to finance the Second World War, it still has investments abroad worth more than £8,000 million (21,500 million dollars).

No other non-communist country in Europe has so many members of consumer co-operatives (almost one person per family). There are few countries in which the difference between cost price and retail price is so small, with the result that in comparison with the Continent, the same amount of money purchases a larger quantity of goods and consequently offers a safer market for the goods produced.

PAST AND PRESENT. *Reorganisation.* Geography and political economy alone are not enough when it comes to understanding and assessing Britain's achievements. Psychological factors must also be borne in mind. In the 'thirties' the late André Siegfried gave a brilliant description of some aspects of the British psychology which appear to the foreigner to have made the country vulnerable to crises. He placed particular emphasis on the intellectual apathy which prevented the man in the street from considering serious problems, on the dual drug of the cinema and spectator sports (taken in much greater doses than in other countries), and on the remnants of Victorian pride which blamed crises on 'others' rather than on defects that are peculiar to the British system.

Conversely, certain other qualities have often helped the British to combat crises with particular success. These are an unostentatious tenacity, common sense which refuses to subordinate economic policy to ideological squabbles, and a marked consciousness of the higher interests of the nation.

Britain owes the reorganisation of its economy to this flexibility. Agriculture, as we have seen, is closely controlled by the State; in cases where it seemed necessary, nationalisation has put the State in control of industry.

Thus the 117 rail companies were first reduced to four companies (1923) and then became a nationalised government organisation (1947), just as London Transport and the inland waterways are. In 1930 a law was passed closing down 1,000 coal mines working at a loss, and in 1946 the whole industry was nationalised. In shipbuilding, 201 old-fashioned yards out of a total 684 were reorganised. In the textile industry, scores of old spinning mills were scrapped and the number of spindles reduced. These measures, which marked a setback statistically, resulted in increased productivity, lower selling prices, and better sales opportunities. Moreover, no single rigid system has been imposed. Britain has not given up capitalism or liberalism; the big companies and trusts continue to function and prosper.

Some of the traditional industries (particularly coal and cotton) are shrinking. On the other hand, industries which were once unknown or few in number are making great strides: aluminium, rayon and artificial fibres (800 per cent), plastics, isotopes. Also flourishing are industries manufacturing consumer goods: chemicals; automobiles, which have had vast new markets created by the gradual replacement of trams and trains in densely populated countries; electrical and allied apparatus such as radios and, more recently, television (more than 1·6 million sets a year are sold); the building and allied trades, stimulated by the enormous war damage, by the construction of new satellite towns and trading estates; clothing and shoes.

*Commercial insecurity.* Yet in spite of all this almost revolutionary progress there are still problems to be solved. There is an adverse balance of trade. The search for new markets abroad is not always crowned with success. Nevertheless, since 1964 deterrent tariffs imposed on imports and inducements offered to exporters have combined to reduce the deficit. The Merchant Navy, banking, insurance, the cinema, and even the tourist trade are supplementary sources of revenue.

*The population problem.* During the post-war years the demand for labour has been at a high level and the peak figure of unemployment, reached early in 1963, was still less than 4 per cent of the working population. Although immigration is now restricted, large numbers of immigrants have been absorbed from Commonwealth countries: 290,000 from 1960 to 1962, two-thirds from the West Indies, many from Pakistan. Thanks to the comprehensive National Health Service, the nation's health has improved, and annual births exceed deaths by almost 300,000.

In the nineteenth century emigration acted as a safety-valve to the pressure of overpopulation and unemployment. In this century about 100,000 to 150,000 have emigrated annually, chiefly to Australia, New Zealand, Canada and the United States. There is thus still a considerable excess of emigrants over immigrants, and emigration may still be regarded as a safety-valve — though much less effective than in the past. Great Britain also has extensive areas of uncultivated land which might absorb thousands of workers if reforestation schemes or stock-raising were to be introduced on a wide scale.

Great Britain has for too long been living in the reflected glory of her early supremacy in commerce and industry and this, perhaps more than any other single factor, has contributed to the difficulties she has encountered in adapting her economy and way of life to the realities of the twentieth century. There are signs, however, of genuine efforts to recognise the economic weaknesses and to do battle with and overcome these problems.

Great Britain, if no longer a premier world power in economic and financial terms, is still a great nation.

# IRELAND

Ireland is an island of 31,842 square miles situated to the west of Great Britain. It is divided into the independent republic of Ireland (Eire, 26,600 square miles) and Northern Ireland (5,242 square miles) which is part of the United Kingdom. The Republic includes the old provinces of Leinster in the east, Munster in the south, Connaught in the west, and three of the counties of the province of Ulster. Northern Ireland consists of the other six counties of Ulster.

*The most maritime climate in Europe.* Ireland is the most westerly part of Europe, excluding Iceland, and is exposed directly to the winds and rains from the west. Over most of the country it rains for at least 200 days a year, and even during the driest month it still rains, on average, every other day. During fine weather the atmosphere is clear and the western ocean a deep tone of blue. The maritime influence results in an extremely mild climate, and snow at sea level is rare. Some southern plants flourish in certain western parts.

*Primary rocks, glacial drift and bog.* The solid geology of Ireland consists of a great variety of Primary rocks, including limestones, schists, sandstones and granites. The most recent deposits occur in the north-east of the island; they are the Triassic marls, Secondary limestones and Tertiary basalts. Central Ireland is a plain floored with limestone, extending 120 miles from east to west and 100 miles from north to south. Its height seldom exceeds 300 feet; in places solution of the limestone has resulted in disappearing streams, and temporary lakes, locally known as 'turloughs'.

The mountain blocks, separated by broad valleys, form an intermittent low rim round the plain and are extraordinarily diverse: there is the high granite mass of the Wicklow mountains, the 'Appalachian-type' parallel ridges and valleys of Munster, the limestone plateaus of the Burren district in County Clare, the quartzite peaks of the north-west peninsulas, the basaltic plateaus of Antrim in north-east Ulster, and the schistose block of the Sperrin mountains in central Ulster. The mountain masses also show evidence of Quaternary glaciation — corries or cirques, and U-shaped valleys. The highest point of the island is Carrantuohill (3,414 feet) in the dissected range of the Macgillcuddy's Reeks which overlooks the lake of Killarney in the south-west.

Almost the whole island has been covered by a mantle of drift left by the Quaternary ice sheets. The weathering of the drift has given a fertile soil. In the south the earlier drift has been eroded and levelled off, but in the north the later drift has kept its original forms. Irish has provided two words, now universally used, which describe the relief forms of certain glacial deposits — 'esker' and 'drumlin'. Eskers are irregular ridges, sometimes winding and frequently several miles long. Drumlins (literally 'little backs') are the oval-shaped hills scattered over almost all the northern lowlands. These recent and relatively undisturbed relief features have interfered with the drainage and produced innumerable shallow lakes. The Shannon in parts resembles a lake rather than a river.

Many ancient lake basins are today filled with peat-bogs, which cover nearly 5,900 square miles. There are no bogs on the eastern plains in Leinster and Munster; in the lowlands of the Shannon and its tributaries, however, there are wide bog areas, separated by eskers. In the north-east, the lowlands between the drumlins are often boggy, and in the west, peat-bogs envelop mountains and plains alike.

*The invasions of Ireland.* The first agricultural settlers built innumerable megalithic monuments which can still be seen. Most of these people came from Britain and Iberia, which undoubtedly explains certain southern characteristics of the Irish. At a later date, invaders came from Gaul and Britain; some of them introduced Gaelic, the national tongue of Ireland at the beginning of historic times. In the days of their independence the Gaelic people remained grouped in tribes, leading an essentially pastoral life, and cultivating a distinctive taste for poetry and music. Modern Ireland has preserved part of this heritage. The Vikings built Dublin, Limerick, Cork, Waterford and Wexford. The Anglo-French built other towns and began methodical agricultural settlement in some of the bog-free lowlands.

A ghillie's cottage. Small whitewashed dwellings such as this, with lean-to outhouses and thatched barns, are typical of habitation in rural Ireland.

In the sixteenth and seventeenth centuries the English finally conquered Ireland. Wars caused much devastation, and the country suffered particularly from the 'plantation system' whereby a large proportion of land was confiscated and given to the English or Scottish 'planters'.

'Landlordism' left the Irish as mere peasants. At the beginning of the seventeenth century the 'plantation of Ulster' drove the Irish population from several areas and installed in their place British farm workers of Protestant faith.

*Depopulation and independence.* In 1841, the population of eight million subsisted almost entirely on potatoes. The potato blight of 1845-6 caused a terrible famine (one million people died) which was followed by the eviction of thousands of farmers by the great landlords. These two scourges released such a flood of emigration that the population declined continuously until 1931. The descendants of the emigrants form a considerable part of the population in many English speaking lands. An agrarian revolt finally compelled the British Government to institute a system of land transfer to the farmers. Nationalist activities received new impetus; finally Ireland proclaimed 'Home Rule', or self-government. This reform was unacceptable to the Ulster Protestants. The Great War then intervened and it was suspended. The Dublin riots of Easter 1916 stirred national sentiment, and in 1919–20 the whole of Ireland except the Protestant parts of Ulster ceased to recognise the British Government. After a hard struggle a treaty was signed, acknowledging the Irish Free State with the status of a dominion and full jurisdiction over the twenty-six counties. In 1937 the state adopted an independent constitution, and the Republic of Ireland was proclaimed in 1948.

Ninety-four per cent of the Republic's population is Roman Catholic. Northern Ireland returns members to the Parliament at Westminster, which is responsible for questions of defence, foreign affairs, trade, and the postal services. For domestic affairs the province has a Parliament which sits at Stormont near Belfast. Fifty-four per cent of Ulster's population is Protestant. In both countries the currency is the English pound sterling, but special coins are minted and notes printed for the Republic. English is the only official language of Northern Ireland, while English and Gaelic are both official languages of the Republic.

*Enclosures and pasture.* The basic territorial division of Ireland is the 'townland' (366 acres on average) which has no administrative function but constitutes the foundation of Irish country life. Farms may be grouped in small villages, one or two to a townland. Sometimes the arable or pasture land of these villages is still in 'rundales', that is in small scattered strips in the open fields. Two centuries ago, the big landlords declared war on the villages and the rundales, enclosing them and dividing them into long parallel strips, giving one to each farm. In the Republic, the Ministry for Lands is continuing this policy of enclosure but has retained the villages.

Grass is Ireland's chief crop, for the mild humid climate suits it admirably. Some of the grasslands have not been ploughed for more than a century and still show traces of the ridge and furrow made at the time of the famine or even during the continental blockade of the Napoleonic Wars. The less fertile lands are ploughed from time to time, and potatoes and oats grown on them. After two or three years' cropping, grass is sown and the land is given over to pasture again for a period of 4–8 years. This is typical 'ley' farming. Sheep, and even cattle, are grazed in the mountain districts, but the old practice of transhumance (booleying) has disappeared. The peat-bog provides free or cheap fuel in a country that has very few coal deposits.

The dockyards of Belfast, the principal city of Northern Ireland, are the third most important in the United Kingdom, after the Clyde and Tyne estuaries.

Peat cutting near Sneem, Co. Kerry. Peat provides the cheap or free fuel used throughout Ireland, and is a valuable resource in a country almost totally deforested and with few coal deposits.

## NORTHERN IRELAND (ULSTER)

Northern Ireland contains some lowlands, divided by highland masses. The eastern lowlands are populated mainly by the descendants of Anglican and Presbyterian planters; the old Irish Catholic population has tended to keep together in the western basins, especially in the glens of the Sperrin mountains and in the mountains of Antrim.

*Rural life.* Most of the farms are very small. One of the distinctive features of the countryside is the white-washed house with its neatly trimmed hedge, 'Protestant hedges' as they are often called. The normal Irish ley-farming system has been improved upon here for several centuries by the cultivation of flax, usually grown in seven-year rotation with other crops, but well suited to small-scale production. The mechanisation of agriculture is quite advanced. Farming is tending more towards the production of fresh milk and towards specialised crops such as seed potatoes, soft fruit and, particularly, grass seed — all grown for export.

*Towns and industries.* The linen industry was developed by the Huguenots after the repeal of the Edict of Nantes, and is the chief industry of the region. However, much of the flax has to be imported, chiefly from Belgium. Linen goods and yarn worth about £15 million (40 million dollars) are exported annually from Northern Ireland. The textile and clothing industries combined give employment to about 74,000 people.

The dockyards of Belfast, built in the nineteenth century, are the third most important in the United Kingdom. Because these two specialised industries are subject to serious fluctuations, the government has encouraged the introduction of new industries — aircraft construction, electrical engineering, and the manufacture of optical instruments and leather.

Unemployment nevertheless remains a serious problem and the Government offers special inducements to old firms to expand and to new firms to establish new factories in Northern Ireland. By 1962 this policy had provided employment for an additional 45,000 workers.

Situated on the estuary of the Foyle, the old settlement of Derry became Londonderry when it was given to the guilds of the City of London. It is a typical 'plantation' town with its central market place or diamond, its Anglican cathedral and its city walls. It is also an industrial town and has a university college.

Belfast, which has long been the industrial and commercial capital, became the political capital in 1920. Its university is especially notable for its faculties of geography and drama. The sees of the Catholic and Anglican Primates of Ireland have remained at Armagh, although Belfast could claim to be the Presbyterian centre of Ireland. To provide the city with a modern harbour the silted estuary of the Lagan has been dredged. The city centre, with its large public offices, is Victorian in character. The extensive working class suburbs are monotonous but respectable. The county borough of Belfast contains 413,900 inhabitants.

The population of Northern Ireland declined after the famine until 1891, but since then has steadily increased. At present it is about 1,435,000.

## THE REPUBLIC OF IRELAND (EIRE)

*Country life: a pastoral economy.* In the western counties many ancient customs, the Gaelic language and the oldest folklore have been retained. These districts are always overpopulated, and the farms are often very small. Small plots of potatoes are cultivated with spades, in a manner similar to that of the mountain peoples of the Andes. Small quantities of oats and hay are also grown, and some cattle and sheep are raised on the mountains. The villages and rows of long narrow farms form islands amid the brown and black peat-bogs. In the region of Rosses and in Connemara (part of Western Galway) comparatively poor ground is cultivated. The thatched crofts are being replaced more and more by whitewashed houses roofed with slate. Farms in the centre of the island have been allocated to ease overpopulation, further enclosure has been effected by the Ministry for Lands, subsidies have been granted towards the building of houses and the construction of glasshouses for tomato growing, roads have been opened across the bogs, and generous unemployment benefits and bounties have been paid to Gaelic-speaking families.

In the southern counties overpopulation is less of a problem, and dairy farming is quite well organised. In the northern counties, temporary emigration to Great Britain allows the people who remain to scrape

A useful export: Guiness from the Dublin brewery, which has the largest fermenting vessel in the world.

a living. Connemara, lying between these two areas, is the poorest and most primitive part of Ireland.

From west of Munster to the frontier of Northern Ireland there is a belt where the farms are slightly larger, averaging 30 to 50 acres. In Munster and the northern parts of the provinces of Connaught and Leinster, the sale of milk to the co-operative dairy forms the basis of the economy. In the greater part of Connaught, stock-rearing is the main activity. These areas remain exceptionally backward in certain respects. The small villages lie some distance from the roads, on the slopes of a drumlin or near a lake. Long, embanked bridle paths (boreens) lead to the isolated farms. One of the less fertile regions, the Ox Mountains, has been improved by the recent introduction of potatoes; sugar-beet is now grown in Connaught and Munster and since 1960 an accelerated freeze drying plant in Co. Cork has helped market gardeners.

The largest and richest farms, 250 acres and over, are found to the east of the Central Plain in the counties of Meath, Dublin and Kildare. These are

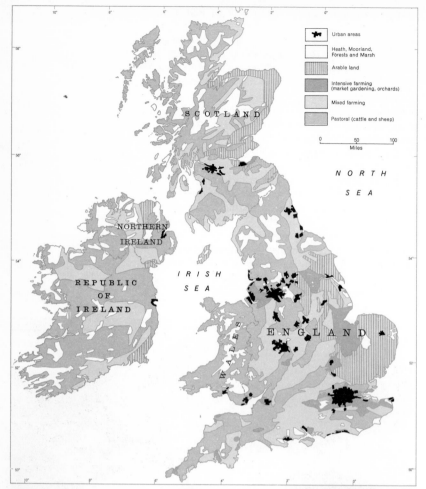

Urban areas

Heath, Moorland,
Forests and Marsh

Arable land

Intensive farming
(market gardening, orchards)

Mixed farming

Pastoral (cattle and sheep)

0   50   100
Miles

SCOTLAND

NORTHERN
IRELAND

REPUBLIC
OF
IRELAND

NORTH
SEA

IRISH
SEA

ENGLAND

WALES

Agriculture is one of the largest and most important of Britain's industries, giving employment to more than a million people, producing one half of the nation's food and using almost 80 per cent of the total land area. In the United Kingdom as a whole there are 30·9 million acres under crops and grass. Although most farms produce a variety of products, one particular type tends to prevail in many areas, imparting a local characteristic. For example, arable crops are found mainly in East Anglia, Kent, Lincolnshire and the East Riding of Yorkshire; vegetable growing is strongly characteristic of Lincolnshire, Cambridge and the Thames alluvial area. Wheat, barley and oats are the principal grain crops.

O'Connell Street, one of the main commercial streets of Dublin, the capital of the Irish Republic. The liveliness of Dublin may be explained by its function as a historical political and intellectual capital; it is also Ireland's largest port.

fatstock farms, buying store beasts in the markets of the west and exporting them as fat cattle to England or the Continent. The great estates of parkland surrounding old family residences give these parts of Ireland a similarity to the pastoral lowlands of the English Midlands.

County Kildare is well known for its racehorse stud farms. This prosperous countryside has offered little decline in population, though it is sparsely inhabited. Where the land is not naturally very fertile, the pastures need to be ploughed and resown, but the old pastoral tradition looks askance on ploughing. Of the two chief Irish political parties, one favours a 'natural' economy founded on grass and the fattening and export of cattle; the other fears that this policy will end only by jeopardising the independence of Ireland. The second group recommends an 'arable' policy — return to the plough.

*Town life and industry.* The Government has made considerable efforts to industrialise the country, particularly since 1932. The nationalised electricity authority has built hydro-electric stations and peat-fired generating stations.

The old industries of brewing, whiskey distilling and bacon curing remain important, but the various new industries introduced have not checked the slow decline of the small towns of the West and the Central Plain, built by the great landowners of the eighteenth century and now serving as country markets. The medium-sized towns are all growing. Cork (78,000 pop.) is a large regional market: it has a busy port with an excellent roadstead in Cobh, the port of call for transatlantic ships. The most important industries are textiles, butter-making, bacon curing, brewing, whiskey distilling and automobile assembly. The city also has a university college, which includes an important school for dairy farming and a well-known faculty of medicine.

The urban life of the Republic is centred in Dublin (535,000 pop.) which is the historical, political and intellectual capital of the country; there are two universities and a number of learned societies. It is the main port with a passenger outport at Dun Laoghaire, and a fishing port at Howth. It is linked by air with the chief cities of Great Britain, and with Amsterdam and Paris. It is becoming increasingly important for its industrial activity.

The Dublin region is the only part of the Republic where population is clearly increasing. Recently the increase has almost offset losses in other areas, and the total population of the Republic (now 2,818,000) has been decreasing only slightly.

In most of the counties the population is declining slowly because of emigration, which averages about 24,000 per year. There is a surplus of births; one of the great problems is to employ the increase population locally and to reduce the flow of emigration. Present industrialisation is still inadequate to achieve this end. The balance of trade has shown a deficit since the Second World War. Invisible exports, which make up the balance, include interest payments on capital invested in Great Britain, and money payments by emigrants and tourist earnings. Nevertheless, a determined attempt has been made to try to solve the agricultural problem and to raise the standard of living in the western counties.

# BELGIUM, THE NETHERLANDS AND LUXEMBOURG

Belgium and the Netherlands cannot be completely separated from one another: the vicissitudes of history have given good reasons for an alliance. Here were two small nations, divided, yet often with similar or identical interests, and belonging to a single geographical unit. These tendencies have now taken practical shape in an economic association, with Luxembourg as the third partner — namely, Benelux. All three are members of the European Economic Community.

No natural boundary separates the two countries. The same low, swampy coastal plain and stretches of infertile sand, the same plateaus covered with a fertile loam known as *limon* are to be found on both sides of their common frontier. The Belgian rivers, the Scheldt and the Meuse, have their outlets in the Netherlands, and Belgium's only communication by water with Germany is through the Dutch Lower Rhine. Yet there are differences. In the Netherlands the sea penetrates inland in several places, but Belgium has only the head of the Scheldt estuary, while the Netherlands controls its outlet. Southern Belgium is more continental; it is connected through the Ardennes with the low mountains of Central Europe; southern Luxembourg is linked with Lorraine, and thence with the Paris basin.

All three countries are situated at a crossroads of traffic and trade routes. The long sea coast brings within reach sources of raw materials and provides access to all overseas markets. Great Britain lies across a narrow sea that is the busiest in the world. The plain gives access to the Rhinelands, to the Paris basin, and to the south of France: the valleys of the Meuse and Rhine penetrate the Ardennes barrier.

In the Middle Ages, Bruges, a Hanseatic town, was the centre of the maritime trade of western Europe, and roads from Flanders to the Rhineland and to the fairs of Champagne were always busy. Antwerp took over Bruges' role in the sixteenth century, and later Amsterdam. At present the ports on the combined delta of the Scheldt, Meuse and Rhine control the most densely populated and industrialised hinterland of Europe.

Latin and German civilisations fused harmoniously to make the Netherlands and Belgium cultural centres which at that time had no equal outside Italy. Its central position also made Belgium the classic type of buffer state and the constant battlefield of the Continent.

## HISTORICAL DEVELOPMENT

The total area of the Benelux countries is 26,268 square miles: the Netherlands 13,514 square miles, Belgium 11,755 square miles and Luxembourg 999 square miles. The coastline is 264 miles long. The frontiers have been decided by conquest and treaty; hence the peculiarities of outline. Within the Roman Empire and the Frankish kingdom, present-day Netherlands and Belgium formed only marginal

provinces. Charles the Great, by virtue of his conquests, gave them the central position which they maintain today. With the break-up of the Carolingian Empire at the Treaty of Verdun in 843, Flanders, integrated with France, became increasingly self-governing; Lotharingia, which had been attached to Germany after 925, was exhausted by internal struggles and in time broke up to form the Duchies of Brabant, Limburg and Luxembourg, the Counties of Hainaut, Namur, Holland and Zeeland, and the religious principalities of Liège and Utrecht. Soon they formed a single unit, the lowlands near the sea, or Netherlands. Political unity was only achieved by the dynastic marriages of the house of Burgundy. By 1467 at the death of Philip the Good, Burgundy and Franche-Comté, Flanders, Artoise, Hainaut, Holland, Zeeland, Friesland, Namur, Brabant, Limburg and Luxembourg had all been united.

The marriage of Mary of Burgundy to Maximilian of Austria made the southern Low Countries into little more than an appendage of the distant Hapsburg empire, a status which was to persist for more than three centuries. Charles V completed the work of

The economic union between Belgium, Netherlands and Luxembourg was a logical, though long-argued, measure for territories that shared similar interests and lacked natural frontiers to separate them. With the long sea coast (264 miles) attracting prosperous shipping trade, the ports of the combined delta of the Scheldt, Meuse and Rhine today control the most densely populated and industrialised hinterland in Europe.

The Netherlands port of Rotterdam, chief port of the world, with New York taking second place.

Marram grass is planted along the Belgian coast to prevent sand from the dunes encroaching upon fertile agricultural land.

unification and fixed the international status of the Seventeen States. The Pragmatic Sanction of 1540 stipulated that, united with Franche-Comté and Burgundy, they should 'be bound together for ever' under the same monarch. Unfortunately, at the zenith of its prosperity, this splendid state was divided by religious wars and rebellion against Spanish rule. The Union of Utrecht, made up of the Protestant provinces, formed the beginning of the republic of the seven United Provinces whose independence was recognised in 1648 by the Treaty of Munster. This treaty had serious consequences for the southern Low Countries (i.e. Belgium), which had remained Spanish: it allowed the United Provinces to annex the Zeeland part of Flanders, northern Brabant and part of Limburg, and closed the Scheldt to sea navigation, thus crippling the port of Antwerp.

Soon the wealthy and powerful Protestant sea power in the north had nothing in common with the impoverished Catholic southern provinces. Sheltered behind the great rivers and protected by Belgium, it had little difficulty in preserving its frontiers. On the other hand, Belgium lost to France: Artois, part of Luxembourg, western coastal Flanders, Gallican Flanders, Cambrai and Western Hainaut.

The Congress of Vienna (1815) created a Kingdom of the Netherlands, uniting the North and South under the crown of William I of Orange-Nassau. By the same treaty, Luxembourg was elevated to a Grand Duchy and became part of the German Confederation. The eastern boundaries were also modified.

The reunion of the Netherlands and Belgium was a great economic success; yet too many factors divided the two peoples, and the Belgian revolt of 1830 restored the partition. Belgium became an independent kingdom under Leopold I, but was obliged to cede the eastern part of Limburg, including Maastricht; from Luxembourg she recovered only western Walloon. Fortunately, the freedom of navigation of the lower Scheldt, restored by the French in 1793, was retained. With the dissolution of the German Confederation, the Grand Duchy of Luxembourg was recognised in 1867 as an independent and neutral

state, whilst remaining within the German Customs Union (Zollverein). In 1920, the Treaty of Versailles allowed Belgium to recover part of the territory ceded to Prussia in 1814. Luxembourg, having left the Zollverein, concluded an economic union with Belgium in 1921 which removed all customs barriers between them.

Today, Belgium and the Netherlands are kingdoms, and Luxembourg a Grand Duchy. In the three states the legislative power is exercised jointly by the sovereign and the parliament (in Belgium, the House of Representatives and the Senate, in the Netherlands, the States General, consisting of the First and Second Chambers, and in Luxembourg, the Chamber of Deputies).

Belgium is divided into nine provinces, the Netherlands into eleven, and Luxembourg into twelve cantons. Their respective capitals are Brussels, Amsterdam and Luxembourg. The Dutch Court sits at The Hague, which is also the meeting place of the States General.

## THE PHYSICAL OUTLINE

South-eastern Benelux is part of the Hercynian zone of Central Europe; it is a region of resistant, folded Primary rocks, eroded to form low mountains. Northern Belgium and the Netherlands form a region of subsidence where great thicknesses of more recent and less resistant sediments have accumulated. Lying between the two zones are the low plateaus, undulating and rocky south of the Sambre and Meuse, monotonous and covered with *limon* in the north. In the extreme south are parts of the Triassic and Jurassic arc of the Paris basin.

*Plateaus of hard rocks.* The Belgian Ardennes, like the Oesling of Luxembourg, is primarily a steep, forested region. The plateaus reach a height of 1,300 to 2,000 feet; they culminate in the peaty massif of Hautes-Fagnes, but are deeply cut into by the incised meanders of the tributaries of the Meuse and Rhine. The weathering of the sandstones and schists produces a cold, damp soil. The climate is harsh and wet, and snow often lies for long periods. This region contrasts with Belgian Lorraine and Luxembourg's Gutland in the south, where the soils are often marly and more fertile, and the winters milder. Here one finds the extension of the Lorraine escarpments, notably the iron-rich Côte de Moselle.

To the north of the Ardennes the land descends rapidly. At first there is a narrow limestone plateau undermined with caves and riddled with swallow-holes which absorb the surface water. Then comes the schist depression of Fagne and Famenne; in the Condroz region the hills rise again (800 and 1,150 feet) and the sandstone ridges separated by limestone valleys run from east to west. The deep trough of the Sambre and Meuse, running north-east to south-west, is incised in the coal measures. To the west, the trough is continued by the broad valley of the Haine in Hainaut; in the east it is continued in the picturesque valley of the Vesdre.

*Limon plateaus and sandy plains.* Towards the north, the hard rocks disappear under more recent formations. Between the Meuse and the Vesdre the relief is surprisingly varied in the chalk and clay plateau of Herve (800 to 1,150 feet). On the other side of the Dutch frontier the average height of the land is 300 to 650 feet, and the surface is without marked features. Towards the west the land opens out across the whole of Belgium, and the *limon* or loam almost completely covers a permeable subsoil. Towards the north beds of clay occur between layers of sand, and surface drainage is increased. Hesbaye and Hageland are covered with hills, and between the Dendre and the Scheldt there lies an area of undulating hill and vale.

To the west of the Scheldt, hills are less common and gentler, and beyond the Lys, bordering the southern edge of the Yser basin, they give way to the Plain of Flanders with its sandy-loam soil in the south and its pure sand in the north. The same monotonous relief is seen in the sandy stretches of the Campine and Dutch Brabant. It is only in the east that there is a plateau, 80 to 100 feet in height, with sides that are steep and eroded, exposing the gravels laid down by the Meuse in Quaternary times. Farther north the coarse alluvial gravels of the Meuse mix with those of the Rhine to form the underlying base of the Netherlands. In the south-east the subsoil conceals rich coalfields. In the lower parts of the Meuse and Rhine the sands soon give way to recent alluvium which forms one vast, damp plain.

North of the great rivers, the widespread fluvioglacial sands and the boulder clays are evidence of Quaternary glaciers that descended from Scandinavia. Following the old north-to-south routes, the glaciers produced many push-moraines in Overijssel, Gelderland, in the area between the Rhine and the Meuse to the south-east of Nijmegen, and especially between the Kromme Rijn-Vecht and the IJssel. Here, the curving sandy hills of Utrecht and Veluwe form the boundary of the huge amphitheatre of the Gelderland valley. In Drente, the boulder clays of ground moraine are overlain with sand and, as a result, undulate only slightly.

*An unstable coastline.* The coastal plain is formed entirely of the accumulation of recent marine sediments. Towards the end of the Quaternary era the glaciers retreated; then followed submergence of the plain and the formation of an offshore bar, surmounted by sand dunes between Cape Blanc-Nez and the island of Wieringen. The shallow lagoon thus formed slowly silted up. The return of the sea in the fourth century overthrew the first line of dunes, but the coastline immediately began to re-form, and a new chain of dunes emerged on another coastal bar, attached this time to the island of Texel. In the shelter of this bar, deposition of alluvium was renewed whilst the sea channels which had seriously eroded the peatbeds were finally silted up. In Holland the peat is level throughout and silting up of the hollows no longer occurs; in Friesland and Groningen, flooding in the Middle Ages halted completion of the silting process.

*A maritime climate.* The whole region has a moderate climate, with prevailing westerly winds, though it is somewhat harsher in the Ardennes and in the extreme north. January has an average temperature of 1·5°C. (35°F.), July of 18–19°C. (64–66°F.). There is no shortage of rainfall: the total amounts to 25–30 inches, with rather heavier concentrations in the Ardennes region.

*The conquest of the land.* In the Ardennes, successive generations have tried to convert the forest into arable land, but with only partial success. In the *limon* zone Neolithic people had already opened up large clearings, and from Gallic-Roman times onwards open landscapes were doubtless a familiar sight. As for the sandy and peaty plains, it seems that they were never more than sparsely wooded, so that the combined efforts of foresters and grazing sheep transformed them into cultivated land or barren waste. In short, from Lorraine to Drente only hard work with axe and hoe could turn the land into a truly agricultural country.

*The struggle against the sea.* In parts the dunes give effective protection from the sea, but if it were not for the dykes bordering the estuaries and the Wadden Sea, the entire lowland would be flooded at every high tide. It is also necessary to ensure the escape of water from the interior: rainfall, percolating ground water, and rivers which the rising tides turn into lakes. Moreover, the land is constantly subsiding — since 1880 a rise of about one inch every ten years in the average level of the sea has been recorded.

It has been estimated that during historic times nearly 2,300 square miles of the Netherlands have been swallowed up by the sea and that only two-thirds of this land has been reclaimed. The Zuider Zee dates only from the thirteenth century, when the sea gradually invaded Lake Flevo. In February 1953, a high tide accompanied by a violet and persistent storm forced the waves over the dykes where the unprotected inner slopes were worn down and destroyed. The flooding, serious enough on the Belgian coast and in the lands along the Scheldt, was catastrophic in the provinces of Zeeland and South Holland. Flood waters ruined 5·7 per cent of the arable land of Holland; 3,700 houses were destroyed, and 1,794 people perished. Since then still more careful watch has been kept to guard against possible danger, and no similar disasters have occurred in recent years.

From the twelfth century onwards more and more foreshores were reclaimed by means of embankments,

The 19-mile Afsluitsdik that was
the first stage in the ambitious
project to separate the Zuider Zee
from the Wadden Sea and then
to drain it and reclaim the
land beneath.

Aerial view of Wieringermeer,
in the Netherlands. The whole
area once lay beneath the shallow
but dangerous Zuider Zee; 
construction of the Afsluitsdik
(seen above) allowed reclamation
of 50,000 acres for cultivation of
corn, sugar-beet, flax and
fodder crops. When the whole
drainage plan for the Zuider Zee
is complete, dykes, artificial
drainage and a controllable
water table will have wrested
550,000 acres from the sea.

and before long the coastal plain was an irregular
collection of dyked sections (polders) crossed by
drainage ditches. It was not until the twelfth and
thirteenth centuries that dykes began to be built
around the Zuider Zee and along the banks of the
main watercourses, including the Zaan, Amstel and
Rotte. Barrages or dams were built at their mouths
and near them were founded the towns of Zaandam,
Amsterdam and Rotterdam. By the end of the following century, small areas or polders had been isolated
by dykes. But the combined effect of a further rise in
sea level and subsidence of the dried peat soon made
artificial drainage necessary, and since the fifteenth
century the Dutch countryside has been dotted with
windmills.

Meanwhile larges expanses of water persisted,
floored with fertile clay. In the seventeenth century,
the wealthy citizens of Amsterdam drained the lakes
north of the IJssel, including Beemster and Schermer;
these were enclosed by a dyke and drainage canal lined
with windmills. With the arrival of the technical
innovations of the nineteenth century, especially the
application of the steam pump, a start could be made
in reclaiming the huge flooded bogs stretching
between Amsterdam and Rotterdam.

Finally came the attempt to conquer the Zuider Zee,
a shallow sea but liable to fierce storms which
threatened to flood the low-lying land bordering it.
After 1932 the dyke linking Holland and Friesland
changed this huge bay into a freshwater lake, now
known as IJsselmeer. The smallest of the five projected
polders, the 50,000-acre Wieringermeer polder, was
the first under cultivation. The 120,000-acre North-
East polder has been dry since 1942, and its development is well advanced. The embankment of the
Flevoland East polder (125,000 acres) has begun, and
by the time the other two are completed, the Netherlands will have gained 550,000 acres, or nearly 7 per
cent of its present land area.

The threat of the great rivers must also be countered.
Nowhere is more care necessary than along the lower
Meuse and Rhine, whose waters are normally above
the level of the lands they cross. The enlarged winter
floodwater channels, covered with grass and willow,
are likewise bordered by high strong dykes.

## THE RURAL LANDSCAPE

In Belgium there is a southern region, with
clustered settlement and open or unfenced fields, and a
contrasting northern region with dispersed settlement
and enclosed fields. This, however, is only a broad
division, and there are many variants.

*The high wooded plateau of the south.* In the Ardennes
and in Oesling, forests and fields share the land
perceptibly. Grassland is increasingly replacing the
poor crops of rye, oats, potatoes and fodder. The
broad and squat stone farmhouses combine living-
quarters, stable and barn under the same huge slate
roof. In general the farms are grouped in villages and
hamlets around which the open field system prevails,
bound to old farming customs, which dictated the
same rotation for all the small plots in the same 'field'
and prohibiting fencing in order to allow communal
flocks access to the fallow land and stubblefields.

In Belgian Lorraine and Gutland the forests emphasise the brows of the hills, extending more widely on the sandy soils. Groups of unenclosed fields in strips spread to the plateau; pasture land and orchards bordered with hedges cover the valley floors. The Moselle valley, rich with vineyards, has an air of the South about it.

*The undulating plateaus of Condroz and Herve.* The depression of Famenne shows a succession of woodland, arable land and pasture. However, in the Condroz, where the subsoil and relief features are more varied, forest is found only on the rocky soils. The better soils, those of the limestone depressions floored with *limon* (loam), produce wheat, oats and fodder. Permanent pasture land is increasing. The farmstead is imposing, with its huge structure of bluish limestone or yellow sandstone, and its large slate roof whose turret rises above a massive porch. It may be isolated in the middle of large fields, but more often it is found with several other smaller farms standing in the centre of a village.

In the Pays de Herve, pasture and orchards long ago replaced arable land. Each small plot is surrounded by a hawthorn hedge. The farms, whose chief production is butter and cheese, are scattered or grouped in hamlets.

*Open landscapes of the limon area.* Across the Dutch frontier and westwards, even before reaching the Meuse, the green countryside is transformed by the appearance of the *limon*. In southern Dutch Limburg and in Hesbaye wheat, barley, oats, sugar-beet and fodder crops are extensively grown. There is little pasture but numerous cattle are stall-fed. There are neither woods, hedges, fences nor dwellings in this bare and uniform countryside, but there are numerous villages which are surrounded by broad belts of hedged orchard.

West of the Gette-Dyle interfluve, the landscape changes in Brabant and Hainaut: settlements are more dispersed, woods occur among the fields, and pasture increases in importance. The scene alters again towards the northern boundaries of the *limon* plateau. Hesbaye has attractive half-timbered farmhouses, grouped in villages along the waterways. Hageland, with its wooded hill-tops, gives a foretaste of the Campine with its poor crops. Finally, to the north of Brussels, and as far as the area round Alost, Antwerp and Louvain, market-gardening is gradually replacing the cultivation of cereals.

*The varied landscape of Flanders.* The Flemish landscape is anything but uniform. In the hilly regions between the Scheldt and the Dendre the countryside remains open, with strip-like fields. To the west of the Scheldt there are no more stripfields; the plots are as broad as they are long and surrounded by hedges and rows of poplars. Everywhere, between the large villages and the small towns, there are farms, small elongated houses and *hofsteden*, with three separate buildings arranged round an open courtyard. The *limon* soils of the south produce wheat, oats and industrial crops, especially flax; the sandy lands of the north yield only rye, potatoes and fodder (grown partly as a catch crop).

North of the Scheldt, from Eeklo to Antwerp, dispersed settlements are replaced by concentrations of one-street villages. In the east the long narrow strips are bounded by hedges or copses; in the west, in the region of Waas, the small square plots are grouped together into long, narrow fields by hedges and rows of trees.

*The sandy plains.* In the sandy regions of the Belgian Campine, northern Brabant and northern Dutch Limburg, pine forest replaces heathland. Crops are poor; rye, oats, potatoes and fodder are grown. Meadowland, formerly confined to the alluvial plains, has increased. In spite of the recent growth of dispersed settlement, the original village and hamlet groupings can be distinguished, and the long open fields, the *akkers* that were once collectively farmed. The agricultural areas have been extended and heathland has been reclaimed piecemeal in many parts. Around the old centres, hamlets have grown up haphazardly amid irregular fields surrounded by hedges, strips of brushwood and sometimes earth-banks planted with bushes and oaks.

To the north of the broad alluvial zone of the Meuse and the Rhine in Drente, the three territorial elements of the old agricultural economy are found again: the heath, today often covered with pinewoods, then the moist pastures divided by earth banks, and finally the arable land, or *essen*, in long, narrow, unfenced strips on the dry hummocks. The houses are distributed without system; here and there they are found in a circle round a cultivated hillock. The old Saxon-type farmhouse is still found. But the open spaces between the villages are now filled with new farms, although the old customs of the countryside are slow to die, because the *marken*, or peasant societies, made sure that inherited land should pass to a single descendant and that the common heathland should be kept intact.

In Overijssel and in Gelderland, the *marken* have had less influence. Small peasants have established themselves in fenced fields, or *kampen*, virtually punched out of the heathland. In Salland and Graafschap, the settlements have, from the beginning, been split up into numerous very small hamlets set amid hedged fields.

In the extreme north of the sandy regions in Zevenwouden, in the south Westerkwartier and in Oldambt, there are one-street villages similar to those in the Waas region, with narrow plots stretching back behind the houses given over to pasture.

Finally, in the high bogs of eastern Drente and Groningen the houses are arranged in tightly packed rows on each side of the canals, and the narrow fields stretch out between the draining ditches. These 'bog colonies', the first of which dates from the eighteenth century, produce large quantities of rye, oats and potatoes.

*The coastal plain.* On the oldest polders of Flanders and Zeeland settlement is closely linked with the old filled-up channels which are slightly raised above the general level of the land. The farms lie amid large fields yielding good crops; in Flanders these farms are mostly isolated, and in Zeeland grouped into villages. In Zeeland, Flanders and along the banks of the Meuse and Rhine estuaries the houses are often built along the dykes.

In Holland, along the old Rhine, the Lek, the Gouwe, and the Dutch IJssel, settlements have existed on high ground since the twelfth century; later villages were built along the dykes. In Western

Friesland, the villages have also formed long roads, although not necessarily confined to the dykes and the edges of the polders. These boggy regions are essentially pastoral. In contrast, the large drained areas of Wieringermeer, Beemster and Haarlemmermeer grow corn, sugar-beet, flax and fodder crops on their clay soils. Finally, at the foot of the inner slope of the Dutch dunes, is the region of early vegetables and flowers, often grown under glass. This region is well-known for its tulips.

In Friesland and Groningen, settlement was once confined to the *terpen,* or artificial mounds, on which houses were constructed as a protection against flood. Once dyke building had ensured reasonable security, the farms of the *terpen* were often dispersed, and the old village was reduced to a mere religious and administrative centre, or disappeared altogether. The west of Friesland is now entirely pastoral. Eastwards from the edges of the Lauwerszee, crops play a more important part, and great quantities of corn, oats, barley and sugar-beet are produced.

On the alluvial plain of the Meuse and the Rhine, gradual changes in the land level influence settlement. The cultivated fields spread over the slightly rising ground and the old filled-up river channels. The marshy bottoms are left as meadows and only the ridges are inhabited.

A LARGELY URBAN POPULATION. Few of the towns in Belgium and the Netherlands have ancient foundations. In the Roman period, Tongres, Tournai, Arlon, Maastricht, Utrecht and Nijmegen were of some importance, but the fall of the Empire reduced them to rural settlements. After the tenth century, when the merchants set up wharves, warehouses and markets beside fortified towns, ecclesiastical palaces or abbeys, the cities of the Meuse region began to develop. These were followed by the Rhenish centres and finally the Flemish towns with those of Brabant and of Hainaut. The cloth industry, in particular, increased the power and wealth of the towns which soon became city-states, defended by fortified walls.

In Holland, urban development was slower. Many towns owe their origin to the construction of dams across the rivers during the twelfth and thirteenth centuries: the necessity of trans-shipping goods from the lower reaches of the rivers which served as sea-ports to the upper reaches serving the interior determined the position of towns like Amsterdam, Rotterdam and Edam. Overseas trade also encouraged the growth of ports, especially Dordrecht on the Merwede; industry enriched towns like Leyden, Delft and Haarlem, but only in the sixteenth and the seventeenth centuries did they receive a real impetus with the increase in fishing and overseas trade.

In the extreme north, urban life is more recent in origin; apart from Groningen, the Frisian towns are growing very slowly. It was not until the beginning of the twentieth century that industry brought them new vigour.

*Urban settlement in Belgium and Luxembourg.* In Belgium, the numerous cities contain about 50 per cent of the population. However, urban life never flourished where navigable waterways and highroads were lacking, as in the Campine, Hesbaye, and south of the Sambre-Meuse valley. Moreover, there are only four large cities: Brussels, the capital, with over a million inhabitants; Antwerp, with a quarter of a million; Ghent and Liège, with just over 150,000 each. Four other towns have populations between 50,000 and 100,000: Malines, Ostend, Bruges and Deurne with their suburbs. Charleroi, the centre of an industrial region of about 375,000 inhabitants, could also be added.

Brussels, with about one million inhabitants, has all the appearance of a great cosmopolitan city. Its central position gave it political significance and spared it the decline which affected its rival, Louvain, at the times of the Dukes of Brabant. The 'low' town has kept its maze of medieval streets around the famous *Grand' Place* and gothic Hôtel de Ville. The 'high' town with its palace and its ministries and banks is the administrative and business area.

To the east of Brussels, along the old highroad from Flanders to the Rhineland, are Louvain, well known for its ancient buildings and its university, Tirlemont, Saint-Trond, Tongres and Maastricht. To the north

The village of Esch in the Grand Duchy of Luxembourg on the banks of the River Sure, which marks part of the frontier between Luxembourg and Germany.

Amsterdam, the largest and busiest city in the Netherlands, owes its distinctive character and charm to its semi-circular canals (*grachten*) linked by transverse ones.
A national rather than an international port, it imports twice as many goods as it exports.

is Antwerp, with its fine historic houses overshadowed by the slender spire of the Cathedral of Notre-Dame. It owes everything to its port, and has now absorbed the neighbouring parishes and increased its population to over 700,000.

In the Campine, only Lierre, Turnhout and Herentals are really worthy of being called towns; but industry has led to the growth of a number of large garden-cities, particularly round Genk.

Ghent, at the confluence of the Scheldt and the Lys, whose branches divide the old parts of the town, was revived by the introduction of cotton spinning and weaving at the beginning of the nineteenth century.

Industry, especially the textile industry, has invigorated other old towns like Grammont, Ninove, Alost and Termond on the Dendre, and Courtrai and Menin on the Lys. It has led to the growth of centres such as Saint-Nicolas, Lokeren, Eeklo, Renaix and Roulers. The once powerful medieval cities of the coastal plain are today only shadows of their former selves: ancient Bruges, the 'Venice of the North', Ypres, Furnes and Nieuport. All activity now is concentrated in the seaside resorts of Ostend, Blankenberge and Knokke, especially during the holiday season.

The old towns in Hainaut and south Brabant have never been as prosperous as those of Flanders. Only Tournai, on the Scheldt, clustered round its large cathedral, and Mons standing on a hill in the middle of a marshy plain, are exceptions. Mons is ideally situated in the large conurbation based on the Walloon coalfields, where one-seventh of the Belgian population is concentrated.

Namur, at the huge confluence of the Meuse and the Sambre, and Huy — both attractively situated at the foot of a citadel — escaped the encroachment of large-scale industry. Liège is enriched by its wonderful ecclesiastical palace and numerous old churches.

The conurbation of the coalfield has extended upstream as far as Seraing, and downstream as far as Herstal; it has climbed the valley sides and spread out on to the plateau. At present some 500,000 people are concentrated here.

In the Vesdre valley, Verviers is the most important of a series of towns which depend upon wool manufacture. In the regions lying south of the Sambre, Meuse and Vesdre, there are only small towns which have grown up in the shelter of a fortified castle or an abbey, flourishing in varying degrees due to their administrative importance, their markets, or their tourist industry.

It is the same with the small towns of the Grand Duchy. The only important town is Luxembourg, with its suburbs spread out on the edges of a dissected plateau falling steeply into the deep gorges of the Alzette and Petrusse. Towards the southern limits of the country, at the foot of the Côte de Moselle, are industrial towns comprising one-third of the population of Luxembourg. This area is, in fact, part of the huge industrial region which includes Athus in Belgium, and Longwy and Villerupt in north-eastern France.

*Urban settlements in the Netherlands.* The towns have increased considerably in size since the First World War, particularly in recent years. At present there are thirty-four towns of more than 50,000 inhabitants which alone make up 44 per cent of the population. The most important are in the west, forming an urban girdle round the polders of South Holland. Here are to be found three towns with more than half a million inhabitants (Amsterdam, Rotterdam and The Hague), three of more than 150,000 (Utrecht, Haarlem and Hilversum), and six of more than 50,000.

As in Belgium the contrast between the old town centres and the modern extensions is marked; there is the central maze of canals bordered by old gabled houses, and the outlying modern suburbs, often imaginatively planned and laid out. Amsterdam, with its 870,000 inhabitants, owes its distinctive character to its *grachten* (semicircular canals linked by transverse ones) and to its quays, many of them shaded and bordered by high, narrow brick houses with triangular pediments. All the activity of Rotterdam (population 730,000) is based on its port, which is formed by the New Maas (Nieuwe Maas), and immense modern docks. The old town was totally destroyed by fire after bombing in 1940; it has now been largely reconstructed. The Hague is the residential and administrative centre divided by broad avenues round the *Binnenhof* where most of the government offices are housed, yet it has still preserved a small town atmosphere. Following a revival in industry, Haarlem, a beautiful city at the junction of the dunes and the polders, has extended far beyond its circular canals. Leyden has remained pre-eminently a university city. Utrecht has also benefited from modern economic development, but has kept its prestige as an ancient political, religious and intellectual stronghold.

Outside these large urban centres there are still many old towns, especially along the rivers; most of them are attractive, sleepy market towns. The same somnolence has affected the villages of Zeeland, of which only Middleburg and the port of Flushing retain some importance. The coast is dotted with holiday resorts and fishing ports.

In the north-east of the country there are few towns of real importance. Parishes are often well populated because they cover large areas of land, and contain a

The intricate facades of the Quai aux Herbes in Ghent, Belgium. Ghent is now the chief cotton manufacturing town, and a port with considerable import traffic.

large number of purely rural settlements. Groningen is the commercial, industrial and intellectual centre of the north, and is linked by water to the port of Delfzijl. In Twente, a group of modern towns has prospered with the development of the local cotton industry.

Between the IJssel and the Vecht are some very old towns; large residential centres have also sprung up in this attractive region, such as Apeldoorn, Hilversum and Bussum (a neighbour of the ancient small town of Naarden which remains secure behind its strong city walls). Father south, the old Rhenish towns of Arnhem and Nijmegen, both seriously damaged in the Second World War, owe their growth to industry.

In North Brabant, Hertogenbosch with its magnificent St. John's cathedral has not grown as rapidly as the series of industrial towns extending from Bergen-op-Zoom to Helmonde. In Limburg, very old centres are strung out along the Meuse: Venlo, Roermond and, most important, Maastricht.

Finally, coal-mining is responsible for the expansion of Sittard, Heerlen and Kerkrade.

*Language and religion.* The Netherlands has no linguistic problem: Dutch is spoken everywhere, though the tendency is to use the Frisian tongue in Friesland. The Grand Duchy of Luxembourg has two official languages: French and German. Belgium is a bilingual and even trilingual country: Dutch or Flemish is spoken to the north of the so-called linguistic frontier, French to the south of this boundary, and German near the eastern frontier. A large proportion of the citizens of Brussels form a French-speaking enclave in the Flemish-speaking area. South of the linguistic frontier, the true local dialects are Walloon, Rouchi (a variation of the Picardy dialect), and Gaumais (similar to the Lorraine dialect). Dutch comprises a large number of dialects which can be related to the languages of the three main ethnic groups that took part in the settlement of the Netherlands and northern Belgium: Frisian, Saxon, and above all Frankish.

The Dutch-speaking Belgians (usually but wrongly called Flemings) are more numerous: 42 per cent of the Belgian population speaks only Dutch, 34 per cent French, and less than 1 per cent German; 23 per cent speaks both chief national languages.

In Belgium and Luxembourg the great majority of the population is Roman Catholic, although the law recognises and assists other religions — Anglican, Protestant and Jewish. The Netherlands, however, is divided over the religious issue. About 36 per cent of the population is Protestant, and some 42 per cent of it is Roman Catholic.

POPULATION PROBLEMS. In 1964 the Netherlands had a population of 12,042,000, Belgium of 9,328,000, and Luxembourg 324,000. Thus Benelux has a total population of over 21·5 million, giving the high density figure of 822 to the square mile.

Within each country there are marked local variations: the sparse population of the rocky plateaus of South Belgium is in strong contrast with the masses in the industrial belt of Hainaut and the Sambre-Meuse valley. In the metallurgical district in the south of Luxembourg, density is comparable to that of the industrial region of Wallonia. Nearly one-half of the population of the Netherlands is confined to the

area between the sea and the towns of Amsterdam, Utrecht and Dordrecht.

In Belgium the population has doubled in the last century, due primarily to the excess of births over deaths, and to some extent to an influx of foreign workers, especially Italians. The countryside has remained populated because many of the agricultural labourers and smallholders who have been drawn into the factories travel to and from their own villages. In the Grand Duchy, the rural population declined, and it was not until after the development of the iron industry that there was an increase in the total population.

In the Netherlands the recent rise in population has even threatened to disrupt the economic and social balance. The rate of growth is about 1·4 per cent, against 0·5 per cent in Belgium. The increase springs entirely from a very high birth rate coupled with one of the lowest death rates in the world. In order to find work for the continually increasing numbers, the Netherlands has speeded up its land reclamation projects, including drainage of the Zuider Zee, and has introduced new industries. The population has been further swelled by immigrants from Indonesia and Surinam. Part of the pressure of population has found an outlet in emigration, especially to Canada and Australia.

THE AGRICULTURAL ECONOMY. In few countries is there such intensity of economic activity as in Benelux. Belgium concentrates on coal-mining, heavy metallurgical industries and textiles, Luxembourg on iron manufacture, and the Netherlands on agriculture, shipping and commerce. These are, however, generalisations, for both Belgium and Luxembourg have a prosperous agriculture, the port of Antwerp is a rival of Rotterdam, and Dutch industry is rapidly expanding.

*In Belgium.* Agricultural land occupies three-fifths of the total area, though for a century it has hardly increased. The forest area has steadily expanded and at present covers about one-fifth of the country. Four-fifths of the farms are small — less than 25 acres — and tenancy predominates.

Belgium's agriculture has changed since the corn crisis of the years 1880–90; pasture land has continued to increase. The traditional food crops have been replaced by fodder cultivation, and sometimes by intensive market-gardening. Ploughed land covers 48 per cent of arable land (32 per cent for cereals). Belgium still has to import three-quarters of its wheat requirements, but oats are still grown and barley is replacing rye.

Sugar-beet is grown on the fertile soil of the coastal plain and the *limon* region. The districts surrounding Brussels and Malines form a specialised market-gardening area, whilst around Hoeilaart, south-east of Brussels, table grapes and peaches are grown in 30,000 hothouses.

Grassland occupies approximately 53 per cent of the total agricultural land. Cattle are increasing rapidly, especially beef cattle. The rearing of the famous Belgian horses has suffered severely from the effects of the mechanisation of farming.

*In Luxembourg.* Excluding the industrial region in the south, Luxembourg has remained agricultural, and forest covers more than a third of it. The Luxembourg peasant, usually the owner of his lands, remains attached to his traditional crops: oats and rye in Oesling, corn and fodder and fruit in Gutland, and grapes on the valley slopes of the Moselle.

*In the Netherlands.* Agriculture accounts directly or indirectly for about 35 per cent of the exports. The country has done its utmost to increase the productive areas, but the most remarkable feature of Dutch agriculture is its technical efficiency. There is a predominance of small-scale farms of less than 25 acres. The farmers are usually owners of their land.

Wheat is most important on the marine clays, and rye on the sandy soils, whilst oats are grown everywhere. As in Belgium, the country has to import three-quarters of its grain needs. Potatoes are grown everywhere but especially in the bog colonies of Groningen. The country is also a large producer of dried vegetables. Finally, the good clay lands of the coastal plain also produce sugar-beet and flax. But the Netherlands fame lies in its horticulture; it is most specialised in the zone where dunes and polders meet, between the mouths of the great rivers in the south, as far as Alkmaar in the north. In the extensive glasshouses of Westland early vegetables and table grapes are grown; in those of Aalsmeer flowers are grown for cutting. In the open fields, vegetables are grown over large areas, and the area devoted to bulb-growing comprises almost 22,000 acres.

Cattle rearing has been particularly successful. The rich pastures produce fine animals, especially in the provinces of Holland and Friesland; half the cattle are milch cows. The animals are reared for dairy produce (butter in Friesland and in the sandy areas, and cheese in Holland) which forms a large proportion of Dutch exports.

FISHING. Sea fishing is not very important in Belgium. However, the fleet of large trawlers is well equipped and operates off the shores of Britain, Iceland and Spain, in contrast to the Dutch fleet which confines itself largely to the North Sea.

In the Netherlands, the sea fisheries provide a livelihood for some 10,000 fishermen. The sea-going fleet catches mainly herrings. Offshore fishing, with catches of anchovies and mussels, is divided among a large number of little ports on the estuaries of Zeeland, and on the shores of the Wadden Sea. The Zuider Zee, now transformed into a freshwater lake, yields only eels; some of its fishing ports still send part of their fleet to the North Sea, but other ports have successfully attracted new industries.

INDUSTRY AND COMMUNICATIONS. *Belgian industry.* Industry is the basis of the Belgian economy, employing almost half of the working population. Mainly imported raw materials are used: minerals, textiles, potash, oil and rubber. A proportion of good coal for the metallurgical industry has to be imported. On the other hand, Belgium sells between 35 and 40 per cent of its products abroad: partly finished goods, bulky and heavy goods, cement, chemical products, fertilizers, glass, cables and textiles. The engineering works produce locomotives, machines and spare parts, but Belgium has to import precision instruments, electrical goods and motor vehicles.

Industry is mainly concentrated in the coal-mining and metallurgical basin of the Haine-Sambre-Meuse, in the region of Verviers, in the west of Hainaut along the Senne-Rupel-Scheldt axis, in Flanders, and in the Campine.

Annual coal production has recently fallen from 30 to 21 million metric tons. The Walloon coalfield, still a big producer, is on the way to exhaustion; the thick, regular coal measures of the eastern Campine are increasingly productive.

Heavy industry is concentrated near the Walloon coalfields and along the great navigable waterways. Belgium annually imports about 12 million tons of iron ore from France, Luxembourg and Sweden to feed some fifty blast furnaces along the Charleroi-Brussels canal, in the Centre Basin, in Belgian Lorraine and throughout the regions of Charleroi and Liège. The steel works and rolling mills process approximately 7 million tons of pig iron. The biggest mechanical engineering works are in the Centre Basin and the Charleroi and Liège districts. In addition, there are the shipyards, the most important of which are located at Hoboken, near Antwerp.

Shrimp fishing at Ostend, Belgium. Although sea fishing is not the country's most important industry, the fleet of large Belgian trawlers is well equipped, and operates off the shores of Britain, Iceland and Spain. Ostend and Zeebruggen are the two main fishing ports.

Tulip fields near Edam, in the province of Holland. This region is also famous for its cheeses. The town of Edam itself, once flourishing, has declined in importance, depending today on a modest local and tourist trade.

Belgium is one of the world's principal producers of zinc. Copper ore, tin ore, cobalt and radium are refined at Hoboken and in the Campine. Large quantities of cement are exported from the cement works around Tournai, Mons and north of Liège. Glass manufacture has remained important in the Charleroi area, but the white sand in the Campine has attracted it to that region. Glass-making is also carried on in Hainaut and along the lower Sambre, and the famous works of Val-Saint-Lambert, near Liège, continues to export fine glasswear.

Factories on the Walloon coalfield, in the Campine, and along the navigable waterways between Brussels and Antwerp produce chemical products and artificial fertilizers. The textile industry is carried on in Flanders and in the region of Verviers, and has also increased in importance in Hainaut and Brabant. Wool, flax, jute and rayon are spun and woven, and Ghent is the chief of many cotton manufacturing towns. Verviers specialises in the preparation, spinning and weaving of wool. Also noteworthy are the huge brickworks on the banks of the Rupel and those of the northern Campine, the potteries of Hainaut, and the limestone, marble and sandstone quarries of Hainaut and Condroz.

*Industry in Luxembourg.* Apart from a few tanneries, potteries and spinning mills, industrial activity is confined to the mining of iron ore and to iron smelting on a considerable scale. The Côte de Moselle produces about 7 million tons of iron ore annually and the steelworks 4 million tons of steel. The iron industry of Luxembourg suffers from three main disadvantages: no home-produced coke, no waterways, and a negligible home market.

*Industry in the Netherlands.* There is not such a long industrial tradition here as in Belgium but nevertheless today there are two and a half times as many workers employed in factories as there are on the land. Several factors have contributed to this development. A large proportion of the country's agricultural products and imported raw materials are processed, and industry has had to feed a steadily increasing population. Furthermore, since the beginning of the century coal-mining in southern Limburg has stimulated industrial enterprise.

The concentration of industry is greatest near the ports, but spreads through southern Limburg, Twente and northern Brabant. There is little heavy industry.

Agricultural products are usually processed in small co-operative factories; butter and cheese in Friesland and northern Holland, starch from potatoes in Groningen, and sugar from the clay polder-lands. Imported goods are processed as well; there are cane sugar refineries, factories for preparing rice, cocoa, and chocolate at Amsterdam and Zaandam, vegetable oil refineries, margarine and soap factories, as well as distilleries in Rotterdam and its neighbouring towns.

Many shipbuilding yards are concentrated near the great ports; Amsterdam, Rotterdam and especially Flushing build large ocean-going vessels. Mechanical engineering is primarily directed towards the home market, and the same is true of the blast furnaces, steel works and rolling mills of Velsen near IJmuiden. The tin refinery at Arnhem, using ore from Indonesia, produces almost entirely for export. The famous Philips factories at Eindhoven occupy a special place. The original small factory for making incandescent lamps has developed into a huge establishment producing a range of electrical equipment.

The textile industry is less developed here than in Belgium and is designed particularly to provide employment in the poorer, somewhat overpopulated districts: North Brabant and Twente.

Other types of industrial activity include petroleum refining near Rotterdam, the manufacture of footwear, rayon, artificial fertilizers, cardboard and paper. Extraction industries produce salt, clay, peat, petroleum and, most important of all, coal.

Of the three Netherlands coal basins, those of east Gelderland and Peel appear to be uneconomic. The south Limburg coalfield provides part of the country's needs and a surplus for export too. The giant Maurits mine, the largest in Europe, produces 56 per cent of the total production; it also has important coking plant and factories for nitrate products.

*Communications in Belgium and Luxembourg.* The

A Belgian stevedore from Antwerp. The port is essential to industrial activity, for Belgium imports most of its raw materials and exports almost half of its products.

The industrial region of Charleroi, in Belgium. Industry is the basis of Belgian economy, employing one half of the population.
Primarily a steel and coal power, and one of the world's principal producers of zinc, Belgium also exports copper ore, tin ore, radium, cobalt, cement and textiles. Shipbuilding is an important industry too.

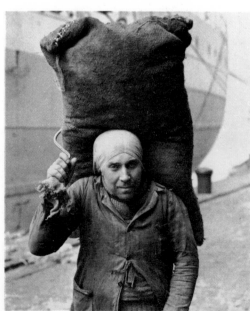

A refinery processing imported crude oil at Antwerp. The port is essential to Belgian industry. It is excellently situated: it is the port nearest to the heavily industrialised areas of western Europe (northern France, the Saar, Westphalia) with which it has good rail and waterway communications.

Belgian road network is well developed but through motorways are still few and incomplete. The rail network with 2,900 miles is dense, and the whole country is a focal point for the great international lines of western Europe. It is also at the crossroads of international air routes. In addition, regular helicopter services link Brussels with other Belgian towns, and with Paris, Lille, Rotterdam, Cologne and Bonn.

The network of navigable waterways is extensive, though only one-third as dense as that of the Netherlands. Most Belgian canals have been in existence for over a hundred years. Communications by water between the Meuse and Scheldt basins was achieved only by means of several extensive and complicated engineering feats, like the huge cuttings of the Albert Canal west of Maastricht. Sea-going ships are able to reach Ghent, Bruges, and even Brussels through the deeper canals. Heavy industry is well served by the system of rivers and canals which link it to the port of Antwerp. The canals give access to France, the Netherlands and, through that country, to Germany, The water traffic is colossal: 26 million tons of national and 38 million tons of international goods, with 3 million tons of goods in transit.

Luxembourg is almost without navigable waterways, except for the Moselle, which is accessible to small ships for part of the year. The railroads are of much greater importance to the iron industry.

*The Belgian ports.* The port of Antwerp is essential to the industrial activity of Belgium. It is excellently situated: it is the nearest port to the densely populated industrial sections of western Europe, northern France, Switzerland, the Saar, Luxembourg and the Westphalian region of the Rhine; and it is connected with these areas by good navigable waterways and a close network of railroads. These advantages, to-

gether with excellent outfitting facilities, have helped it to meet competition from Rotterdam and Hamburg with success. The navigation of the lower Scheldt is not without inconveniences: sandbanks, strong tides and an exit controlled by the Netherlands. Antwerp has 27 docks with a total area of 1,000 acres.

It has few advantages as a passenger port and devotes itself almost exclusively to goods. Every year 23 million tons are unloaded, and 15 million loaded. Antwerp handles large quantities of packaged goods which require much and varied equipment, as well as numerous and specialised dock workers. Transit trade accounts for a large part of the tonnage, and this illustrates the port's international importance; along with Ghent, it handles one-quarter of the overseas trade of the Rhine area.

*Communications in the Netherlands.* Water transport was once the chief means of communication, and the broad waterways were a serious obstacle to land communication. Today the country has a fine network of roads with enormous steel bridges at many points. Railroads, too, have been developed: in 1860 there were only 236 miles of track, at a time when Belgium already had 1,056 miles. Now there is a total length of 2,000 miles. Air transport has increased; from Schiphol airport the large transport aircraft of K.L.M. operate the world routes.

The transport of goods by water greatly exceeds transport by rail: 155 million tons against 28 million tons. Several factors encourage this: the numerous navigable rivers, the relief of the land (almost sea level), and the absence of watersheds between the river basins. The total length of navigable waterways is about 4,660 miles; relative to area this is the greatest density to be found anywhere in the world.

Improved by artificial channels, the estuaries in Zeeland and in Holland give the ports easy access to the sea.

The great inland waterways branch off directly from the sea channels. All are linked by important navigable channels, such as the new Amsterdam-Utrecht-Rhine canal. Rhine navigation is extended by the IJssel. Groningen is connected with Delfzijl, from where the way is open towards the sea, and towards the Ruhr by the River Ems and the Dortmund-Ems canal.

*The Dutch ports.* The seaports are more important in the Netherlands than in Belgium. Rotterdam handles nearly 80 per cent of Netherlands trade. Since the growth of the Rhine-Westphalian industry over the last 100 years, with its satellite ports and the Hook of Holland it has formed one of the great dock areas of the world. The New Waterway, an artificial channel only 19 miles long, gives excellent connections with the sea; it forms an extension to the Nieuwe Maas on which are situated extensive docks totalling 1,160 acres. Rotterdam's position is particularly advantageous in relation to Western Germany; it continues to attract Rhine trade, and handles half the tonnage passing along the river to the German frontier. About 24,000 ships with a tonnage of 104 millions now enter the port annually. The outgoing tonnage, however, is little more than one-third of the goods discharged. This is because enormous quantities of cereals, petroleum, minerals, and other raw materials are imported from overseas, while from the industrial regions of the Netherlands and Germany much smaller quantities of raw materials and manufactured goods are received for export.

Transit business plays a considerable part in Rotterdam's trade. As fewer than half the ships can be certain of a return freight, many have to take on more cargo in England or even at Antwerp. Because of this, Rotterdam is particularly sensitive to economic fluctuations in other countries.

The Netherlands has an important merchant navy of some 700 ships with a total gross tonnage of 4·7 million tons. (Belgium has only 91 ships with a total tonnage of 625,000 tons.) Many shipping companies have their head offices in Rotterdam, and it is also the terminus for large passenger liners sailing regularly for America and the Far East.

Amsterdam is a very different type of port: it is a great entrepôt for colonial products, and a North Sea port because of the North Sea Canal link. It imports more goods than it exports, mainly tropical products which are distributed to the hinterland after processing in Amsterdam's own factories. It is also the port for numerous shipping lines, in particular passenger services.

Flushing, in Zeeland, although accessible to the largest ships, has not developed as might have been expected because of competition from the nearby Belgian port of Antwerp.

BENELUX AND INTERNATIONAL TRADE RELATIONS. The overseas trade of Belgium, Luxembourg and the Netherlands is now entirely dominated by the agreements made between the three countries forming the economic unit of Benelux. These agreements, signed in London in 1944, stipulated that the three countries should have a common tariff for goods imported from other countries, and that they should remove all customs duties on goods of the member countries. But at the end of the Second World War there was a significant difference between Belgium, with its industrial plant almost unscathed by war, and the Netherlands, destroyed and impoverished. Dutch imports were limited to the raw materials essential for the industries producing exports. Prices and wages were kept at the lowest possible level. Pre-union agreements of 1944 came into force in 1948, and the full union agreement of 1958 has been applied since November 1960.

The balance has now been largely redressed. Both the Belgian-Luxembourg union and the Netherlands import large quantities of foodstuffs and raw materials for their industries, paying for them with manufactured goods sold abroad. Exports do not match imports in total value, but the deficit is mainly offset by the income from large capital investments abroad, from allowance made for the cost of transport of the imports, and from income earned by merchant shipping.

Together the three countries of Benelux lie fourth in world commerce, after the United States, Western Germany and United Kingdom. Western Germany, The Netherlands, France and the United States are the chief sources of imports for the Belgian-Luxembourg union. The Netherlands is the most important customer, then Western Germany, France, the United States, and Great Britain. The Congo still supplies Belgium with a variety of goods which have stimulated industry: diamonds, raw copper, tin ore, gold, vegetable oils, coffee, copal, cotton and rubber. The economic effect of Congo independence since 1960 has been a regression of exports, while imports of raw materials from the Congo have remained almost unchanged.

During the period following the Second World War, the Netherlands showed a tendency to return to the pre-war trading pattern. Western Germany therefore again became the chief customer, followed by the Belgian-Luxembourg economic union, Great Britain, France, the United States and Sweden. The Netherlands buys most of its goods from Western Germany, then from the Belgian-Luxembourg union, America, Great Britain and France, in that order of importance.

At international level, Benelux is potentially a great power, with 20 million people and control of the common delta of the Scheldt, Meuse and Rhine. The three countries belong to the European Coal and Steel Community, producing one-fifth of the total steel output. They are also all members of the European Economic Community.

It is only natural that such co-operation should present problems. Competition occurs in certain industries, notably in textiles and agriculture. Prices and wages in the Netherlands are always kept at a slightly lower level, which presents difficulties for many Belgian industries. Rivalry between the ports of Rotterdam and Antwerp is another source of contention.

The aims of the three partners of Benelux are the same as those of the European Economic Community; as a result, a further individual development of Benelux is not to be expected.

# FRANCE

## OUTLINE AND POSITION

France is the terminal point of Western Europe, facing the Atlantic Ocean to the west, the Mediterranean Sea to the south, and the partially enclosed seas of the north, the English Channel and the North Sea.

The Mediterranean brings France into contact with one of the most curious seas in the world, a sheet of water extending in a general east-west direction, whilst most of its basins face in a north-south direction. Around it lie the highest moutains of Europe; the Alps, Pyrenees, Sierra Nevada, Atlas, Rhodopes, and Apennines. Its climatic characteristics include mild temperatures, clear atmosphere, strong winds, drought in the hot season, and light rain occurring mainly in the unproductive cool season.

Such conditions produce a vegetation that is drought-resistant and shows little seasonal change. In southern France the Mediterranean climate extends farther north than elsewhere; olive trees are found at Nyons, evergreen oak as far as Lyons, and lavender up to and including the Pelvoux massif. The reason for this is that elsewhere the sea is enclosed by high land; the only wide gaps are found in France. The Rhine valley gives access to northern Europe by routes that climb little above 1,000 feet, through the Belfort gap and the Burgundian Gate; the corridor from Languedoc is even lower (360 feet high at Naurouze) and leads towards the Atlantic. So, as well as having a window on the Mediterranean, France possesses the best approaches to it.

Almost four thousand years ago, true civilisations had already appeared on these shores. France derived the benefit of the first towns and ports, fine buildings, highways, Roman roads and, thus, many of those elements which helped shape her language, literature and philosophy.

In the north, the English Channel and the North Sea are enclosed seas formed above the continental shelf and barely exceeding 100 fathoms deep; they are recent, unstable extensions of the North Atlantic Ocean. They allow the mild Atlantic waters to reach French shores and have helped the development of the mild, damp climate which makes north-west Europe an unusually warm gulf. Such climatic conditions particularly favour the growth of vegetation. The area is one of green pasture and woodland; its flat fields and meadows are relieved by countless trees, primarily oak, beech, elm and hornbeam.

Since the Middle Ages these seas have attracted trade and encouraged the growth of European ports. Nowhere else in the world is there such a concentration: Rotterdam (Netherlands), Antwerp (Belgium), Dunkirk, Calais, Boulogne, Le Havre, Rouen, Cherbourg (France), London, Dover and Southampton (Great Britain). The northern seas have had a predominantly economic influence on France, whereas the Mediterranean has been of more cultural importance. On the coastal lowland of the North Sea and English Channel there are nearly 100 million inhabitants earning their livelihood variously, in farming, industry, and mining. Such activities have in turn fostered financial development.

The Atlantic for a long time played a minor part; it was undefined and without known shores. The ports here (Nantes, La Rochelle, Bayonne, and even Lorient) did not develop until modern times when their prosperity was sudden and rapid.

*Three seas: variety of coasts.* The 2,000 miles of coastline provide a great variety of scenery. There are the sandy beaches and cliffs of the Channel and North Sea, the deep groove-like rias in the ancient rocks of Brittany, the resistant headlands which project boldly into the sea from Cotentin to the estuary of the Loire, the great bay of Mont-Saint-Michel which is still invaded by the regular flood of the high tides, and the huge stretches along the shores of Vendée and Charente, no longer submerged at high tide but silted up and reclaimed. Ridges of dunes extend south from the Gironde, breached fortunately at the Basin of Arcachon. In the south there is more sand and lagoons, and fixed or shifting alluvial stretches protecting

France's coast looks out on to three seas: the Mediterranean, the Atlantic and the English Channel. At Etretat, on the Channel coast, the Caux plain, flat and wide, ends abruptly in chalk cliffs. Population density along this coastline is high.

The château at Chambord, the biggest on the Loire.

The Mer de Glace, near Chamonix, in the French Alps, is a glacier 3½ miles long, formed by the junction of three others, the Glacier de Géant, the Glacier du Talèfre and the Glacier de Leschaux. Glaciers are formed when the rate of precipitation is greater than the rate of melting of the snow.

Fishing is a traditional Breton occupation.

The forests of les Landes, the largest French forest. Pines were planted during the nineteenth century between the Gironde and the Adour, on the huge stretches of infertile soil. Though they were intended only to fix the dunes and to produce some return from this region, once considered useless, the exploitation of the resin and timber has brought real prosperity. Unfortunately, numerous hazards, such as repeated fires and invasions by crickets, have seriously jeopardised exploitation of the pinewoods and even their future.

the shores of Languedoc and the Rhône delta. The mountains reach to the sea on both the Atlantic and Mediterranean coasts — on the Basque and Catalan shores of the Pyrenees, and on the shores of the Maures, the Esterel and the Maritime Alps.

The islands of Bréhat, Batz and Sien are little above sea level. Ushant is the highest in the west (100-160 feet); Belle-Ile and Yeu, and the northern part of Noirmoutier belong to the Breton islands. Southern Noimoutier, Ré, Oléron, Aix and Madame are seaward extensions of the flat outlines of Aunis and Saintonge. Like the Mediterranean islands of Hyères, all are close to the continental shores. Corsica, the most easterly island, is over 100 miles from the mainland, a remnant of a submerged land mass.

*The continental links.* The broadest of France's continental links is in the north-east towards Belgium, following the line of the rivers Oise, Sambre and Meuse, where the Cambrésis-Vermandois divide is scarcely noticeable. It is a traditional invasion route and the scene of many historic battles.

The second link, which is narrower, lies between the Vosges and the Jura. It corresponds to the curious gap at Belfort, called the Burgundian or Alsatian Gate, and links the two great north-south valleys of the Rhine and Rhône, at a point where they are little more than 60 miles from the sources of the Danube.

The third continental link, the southern one to the Iberian peninsular, does not offer such easy communications.

A land frontier, even of high mountains, has never completely checked movement. The Alps offer proof of this: there was a Cisalpine Gaul even in ancient Piedmont; French is still spoken in the upper valleys on the Italian side; and even the old Italian dynasty was the House of Savoy. France itself has been influenced by numerous continental factors.

*Climate and vegetation.* There is no specifically French climate. Sometimes the rain-bearing winds of Atlantic depressions sweep across France, and sometimes the continental anticyclone which extends towards the Iberian peninsula, or the Mediterranean winds bring the dry influences of the Sahara. In addition there are pockets of purely local climate, especially in the mountainous regions.

Considerable climatic changes occurred during later geological times, and the effects are still visible in the landscape. The forest cover of France is quite recent and has spread since the last Ice Age. These advances of vegetation occupied different sites according to local conditions, hence the amazing variety of French woodland vegetation. The south-west and west are more suited to the oak; the Paris Basin and the interior plateaus favour beech; while on the high peaks are the resinous trees: the fir and spruce. The Mediterranean region has kept its evergreen oak (holm oak) and cork oak, with a dense aromatic undergrowth that merges into *garrigue* or *maquis* (scrub). There are exceptions; in the Alps, there is a zone between the dry woodlands of the south and the damp forests of the north that is given over to the larch, which covers the region of Briançon and Haut Champsaur.

*The agricultural landscape and natural regions.* The main change in natural vegetation are primarily manmade. He began marking out his fields almost as the post-glacial reforestation was taking place. Fields were occasionally cultivated on burnt-out woodland and forest which provided the earliest form of fertilizer. The forest also provided secondary resources: hazelnuts, raspberries, bilberries, strawberries, mushrooms, There was also wood for fuel and building, branches for litters, pasturage for cattle. Thus, a forest with clearings has often formed the basis for agricultural colonisation.

The many variations of landscape have in large measure been fashioned by the different ways in which trees and forests have been treated in different areas. Sometimes man has penetrated the woodland on his own, opening up his fields by felling the trees. When this was so, the population was usually dispersed; as a result the country is dotted with crofts and small farms of the kind known as *métairies*.

This was the common practice in the lands of the west, but these areas (Brittany and Vendée) are today the least wooded in France. Trees flourish in relatively narrow strips round the fields or the estates, as enclosure. Elm and hornbeam have prevailed over beech, but oak and ash remain in large numbers, the former providing timber for the carpenter, the latter wood for the wheelwright. Also, these trees took on a distinctive appearance; outside the high forest the branches spread out, only to be lopped off by the farmers, leaving a kind of bushy stump. Treated in this way, the wooded borders offered the same advantages as the coppice of fully grown trees; the bole was used for woodwork; branches for fuel.

A totally different method was followed in the east: for example, in Burgundy and Lorraine. Here the people settled in groups, felling a broad clearing around the common dwelling site and gradually pushing back the forest. Each feature of the countryside had a definite place; the houses were grouped into a village; the surrounding fields were divided into narrow strips but without enclosures. The forest was cut back to a point where it still covers quite large areas. This is the landscape called *champagne* or *campagne*.

In many areas fields have made way for trees. In the Mediterranean zone the olive occupies the place of honour, and more recently orange and lemon trees have been introduced. In Dauphineé, there are walnut trees; the whole of the Garonne basin favours fruit-growing. In the Cévennes, lower Limousin and Corsica there are entire woods of sweet chestnuts. The regions of the lower Loire and Anjou also have fields dotted with trees, including walnuts and pears; but Normandy is the supreme fruit-growing region.

Different methods of managing the land have produced different types of countryside: a zone of stock-rearing by the side of a rich pasture region, wheat lands next to rye, the *pays* of the vine next to the *pays* of apples, the *pays* of olive not far from that of the chestnut; slowly they formed themselves into complementary regional groups.

In this fashion provinces were shaped, more often by history than geography. These small units evolved earlier than the vast natural and geographical regions which came into being as a result of synthesis and research; Burgundy, Lorraine and Flanders were terms used long before the discovery of a Massif Central, a Rhône corridor, or a Paris Basin.

POPULATION AND SETTLEMENT. We have seen that France is a terminus of the continent, but not an isolated one; it is an isthmus serving as a bridge or a thoroughfare, which brought a continuous influx of new settlers. It is almost impossible to attempt an anthropological classification—so varied were the peoples in the Frenchman's ancestry.

Settlement dates back to the first stages of early Palaeolithic man, when the whole of northern Europe was uninhabited, as was most of the Mediterranean region. France, with its great river basins, was among the most settled parts of Europe at the dawn of Quaternary times. When the last glacial invasion occurred, man suffered great hardship and was threatened with extinction. He had to seek refuge in caves and concern himself with clothing and heating. but this difficult period encouraged technical progress.

There followed an era when cold, steppe conditions prevailed and France became a great stretch of grassland overrun by large herds of hairy cattle or bison. Some of the limestone caves became the homes of hunters of bison, reindeer, and mammoths, and drawings of animals have been discovered in the caves of Périgord and the foothills of the Pyrenees.

The Quaternary era was followed by a mild, humid climate when the forest actually took possession of the land. The mammoth disappeared among among the swamps of Siberia, probably not very long ago; bison are still found in some of the most remote parts of Russia and Lithuania, while reindeer are confined to Lapland. The hunters of the reindeer followed them, and their place was taken by other peoples from the south.

During this great migration the first cultivators appeared; they established themselves in the forest and the centuries-old struggle between woodland and pasture land began. The era of Neolithic cultivation appears to have been a period of peace and prosperity when, judging by the extent of the clearings, the population must have increased very rapidly. It has been estimated that the population of France was about five million at the end of the Neolithic period but that in Palaeolithic times it never exceeded one hundred thousand.

A landscape of Provence, the most important fruit and vegetable region of France, with a total of 650,000 tons a year, of which over half comes from the irrigated plains of the lower Durance. On the unirrigated land, grapes and fruit are grown, and higher up are the terraced slopes dotted with remote villages, while around Sisteron and Laragne, apple and pear orchards clothe the remote Provencal hillsides.

The Iron Age, which followed the Neolithic, was marked by warlike invasions, mostly from the east, and the people were obliged to seek protection in *castella* built on the hilltops. This put an end to peaceful and prosperous agriculture. Then came the Roman conquest, followed by the long *Pax Romana* which saw a rapid decline in production, prevented any increase in population and merely paved the way for new invasions.

*Early development.* The scattered fragments of France were gathered around a new nucleus centred on the Seine, which administered the Ile-de-France, a fairly small territory. Consolidation was difficult. Until halfway through the Middle Ages, France looked on to the Mediterranean across the marshy coast of Languedoc; the Rhône formed the frontier, and groups of people who spoke the *langue d'oc* were settled on the Mediterranean shores. After the arrival in Provence of Charles of Anjou, brother of Louis IX, the Alps united volutarily — Dauphiné, Savoy and Nice; and the frontiers were advanced even farther into the French-speaking valleys of Aosta, Susa and Pinerolo.

The provinces of the north and east, those nearest to the Paris nucleus, were bitterly disputed. There were attempts to include additional territories: Lorraine, Burgundy, the Low Countries and Spanish Franche-Comté. Today the European Coal and Steel Community is perhaps as much an indication of this difficult frontier as it is the beginning of a European economic organisation.

The people of the countryside were the first to be aware of belonging to a territorial community, the first to pay the costs of public administration. Many towns, as *bonnes villes du Roi,* were given privileges and often a special right or charter. But the Breton or Basque fishermen took advantage of the common right of the sea to free themselves from all submission; there were many forest dwellers who regarded the woodland as their traditional inheritance, and mountain people who lived in their remote cantons and refused to acknowledge the existence of any central authority.

*The mixed races.* The true assimilation of the peoples was brought about by natural rather than legal processes. The country has always been traversed by people continually on the move. Certain products have been particularly instrumental in bringing people together; for example, the vine and wheat at harvest time. There are, too, irregular local needs for extra labour; for example, tree felling and charcoal burning can only be done when the sap has stopped rising.

To this mingling of population within the national framework can be added a continuous and important influx of foreigners: Italian bricklayers, Spanish and Majorcan traders in fruit and early vegetables. France has also been a haven for refugees and political exiles from numerous countries. These foreigners have seldom formed separate colonies; generally speaking, they have quickly been assimilated. The only serious problems concern the Italian and Polish communities in the Lorraine mining area and the North Africans, particularly the Algerians.

*Demography and density.* The constantly changing population has maintained a slow but regular increase in density. The birthrate declined perceptibly in the second half of the nineteenth century, and during the twentieth to the alarming point where births no longer equalled annual deaths. Since the Second World War, however, there has been an appreciable increase in the birthrate. Nevertheless, France has been outpaced by some of her neighbours — Great Britain, Germany and, to a lesser degree, Italy.

*Houses.* France is one of the most built-up nations in the world. Furthermore, it is estimated that nearly half the present-day buildings are at least one hundred years old.

Today, the west and north still retain a preference for the self-contained house; even the industrial towns of the north have built semi-detached houses with yards and sometimes gardens. However, the towns of the east have a well-established preference for blocks of flats. Paris seems to have wavered between the two alternatives, but apartment buildings have become increasingly popular.

In contrast, the individualism of the west separates each dwelling from the next by an alley (to prevent fire) and a narrow ditch or drain.

PARIS. Assisted by the erosion of the former Seine, the streams and rivers have removed all the alluvium which once formed a monotonous landscape, and the Ile-de-France has won back its variety. Three stretches of limestone opening fanwise join up in Paris itself: the coarse limestone from very old quarries that was used for many of the buildings of Paris, the limestone and millstone grit of Brie, and the limestone of Beauce. Between the limestone regions are three layers of sand whose outcrops afford Paris more than 250,000 acres of forests. These even penetrate into the city itself: the Tuileries and the Champs-Elysées are the sites of old forests which advanced as spurs. The loess-covered plateaus are suitable for growing cereals; small, well-exposed slopes, heating quickly in the sun, encourage the cultivation of vines and fig trees.

Paris was not always the capital of France; at first, as Lutetia, it was a small and relatively unimportant town in Gaul. The Romans had established their centres along the Mediterranean, and as movement occurred along the great European axis of the Rhine-Rhône valley, Trèves became capital. The emperor Julian settled at Lutetia with the purpose of finding peace in pleasant surroundings; it was not until the beginning of the eleventh century that the king settled in Paris in his small castle. The city's fortunes have fluctuated but it has remained France's capital for a thousand years.

Since the eighteenth century, highways have radiated from Paris. One natural highway from the south-west to the north-east follows the line of the Oise, Sambre and Meuse towards the Rhine and Westphalia. A second intersects this diagonally, joining the English Channel with the Mediterranean by means of the Seine and the Rhône. Paris therefore found itself at the meeting point of a number of vital strategic and commercial crossroads, and has often played a part in the country's defence. The buildings and plan of the city are reminders of military function: the Arc de Triomphe, the Avenue de la Grande Armée, the Invalides, and the Grand Boulevards have all replaced earlier fortifications.

The nucleus of the old city is the Ile de la Cité, a secure position for the seat of royal and ecclesiastical power; the inhabitants used it as a retrateat in times of invasion. The island has remained the official and religious centre, with the University on the left bank of the Seine and the main centre of commerce on the the right. In the nineteenth century Haussmann's planning gave the city spacious squares from which radiate wide avenues crossed by broad, straight thoroughfares.

Paris was once a small bridge town, making use of the Ile de la Cité to facilitate the crossing of the earliest highways, the route from south to north, now the Rue Saint-Martin and Rune Saint-Jacques. It has become an inland port, the meeting point of canals and waterways from all over the country. Paris was neither a natural nor an inevitable capital city. But at certain critical junctures it exerted a unifying influence for France, and for Europe it has been a disseminator of ideas. 'In every inhabitant of the world', said Michelet, 'there is a little of Paris.'

THE TOWNS OF FRANCE. Before the days of Rome, ancient Gaul had no true cities. First came Greek and then Latin colonies, such as Massilia, the future Marseilles. Once the conception of town life had been introduced by these Mediterranean colonists, urban development spread throughout Gaul. Towns took the form of a unit with a geometrical plan, and identical styles of building and undivided houses. By the end of the Middle Ages France had almost too many towns. Some, built during the insecure feudal era, proved superfluous and even disappeared with the return of peace. The sixteenth and seventeenth centuries saw fewer new foundations than earlier centuries. There were some residential towns, like Versailles; some were new ports facing the New World in the west (Le Havre), and certain fortified places on the frontiers (Rocroi).

In the nineteenth century revolutions in industry and transport resulted in a fresh growth of a new, dense type of town. There were colliery towns and factory towns. The railroads brought the growth of a number of typical settlements connected with important junctions, and ports appeared to provide the new navigational requirements of deep water and speed.

A new wave of urban development has more recently resulted from the organisation of leisure and the tourist trade: there are more than 350 resorts scattered along the 2,000 miles of French coast; there are the towns in the mountains, and the winter sports resorts in the Alps and in the Pyrenees; there are long-established spas and new springs; finally there are the religious towns, above all, Lourdes, which has the second busiest rail station in France.

Today the urban population of France is 54 per cent of the total; the Paris conurbation alone has more than five million inhabitants, more than one-tenth of the total.

*Their siting.* A town is a concentration of people, a centre of work and wealth; it is an obvious target for attack and must be protected. Concentration affords shelter and refuge, and it is natural that towns should flourish in times of insecurity.

Concern for self-protection prompted the choice of sites that were easy to defend. Many towns started

Paris is situated at the centre of a strong communications network and thus enjoys many advantages. The Seine, too, has played an important part in the city's commercial development.

Fishing in the Seine from the Quai d'Anjou. This is a popular Parisian pastime on a Sunday afternoon.

Church of St. Ouen, Rouen; its magnificent gothic style is one of the glories of the historic city on the Seine.

Marseilles, the chief port of France and her gateway to trade with the Levant and the Far East, competes directly with Genoa, which is advantageously linked with the Rhine by the Simplon and St. Gotthard rail routes.

on insular sites, for example Lille (once spelt 'l'Isle'), Beauvais, and Paris. Others arose in the centre of swamps and remain surrounded by marsh.

Considerations of trade have also played an important part. Some towns preferred a place where several regions met. Areas of marginal exchange are important in France, because the country has many regions with specialised activity and production.

Urban concentration is a centre of wealth, but wealth is of value only if it circulates. It was often the function of towns to promote circulation, and here communications played a part. Such towns tended to grow up at points where the highways encountered difficulties. The chief obstacle to road communications is water, with its threat of swamps and floods. In early times tracks over plateaus and along ridges were preferred. In Aquitaine, for example, the *camis de la serre* is almost always older than the *camis de la rivière*. The easiest crossing places gave rise to ford towns like Limoges, and bridge towns like Amiens. When it was possible to develop communications along the rivers the town was sited, usually where there was a change in the flow of the water, a transverse valley, or a break in gradient.

*Major towns.* Lyons, which should have become France's capital, was the great link between the Kindom and the Empire at a time when the Rhône formed the frontier, and, more importantly, between the Mediterranean and the West. This undoubtedly avoided a division of the European continent and the formation of a 'Minor' part paralleling the situation in Asia. Europe has not developed a 'Europe Minor' because its Mediterranean region was firmly linked to its northern part by the remarkable Rhône-Rhine

corridor controlled by Lyons. The town has throughout its history been more concerned with European than with purely French affairs.

Marseilles is the chief continental gateway of the Mediterranean. It benefited at an early date from being the first safe inlet beyond the endless swamps of the Languedoc coast. Aix, which has remained the capital of Provence, is quiet and peaceful, a university town and a parliamentary and administrative centre.

For a long while Rouen, well situated on the Seine, existed quite independently of Paris, cut off by frontiers and fortified castles. It was steam shipping that showed the real value of the Seine and made Rouen the port of Paris.

Lille, at the southern edge of the Flanders swamps, was the most southerly point reached by ships carrying the products of the industrial towns of Flanders: Bruges, Ghent and Antwerp. This was the 'Isle de Flandres', where the change was made from waterways to roadways.

Not far away are Dunkirk, Calais and Boulogne; three ports on an inhospitable shore but near the busiest strait in the world. Dunkirk is primarily industrial, and has become the third largest port for the import of goods; Calais is the leading passenger port and the railhead of many European expresses; Boulogne is a fishing centre and a transatlantic port.

Several French towns have recently undertaken the heavy task of restoration and planning; two world wars have tested them sorely. The danger of severe congestion of population in the towns has been appreciated and modern transport methods provide services to the countryside. It is not clear whether France has reached the limit of her urban expansion.

## FRENCH AGRICULTURE

Farming and fisheries occupy over 20 per cent of the working population; this is one of the highest proportions in Western Europe. Yet the density of agricultural workers is low. Another significant fact is the relatively restricted area of agricultural land (excluding woodland): 83 million acres or 61 per cent of the national territory.

*Smaller acreage: more wheat.* In spite of a decline of about 10 per cent since pre-war days, arable land still forms the greater part of the cultivated area. Almost half of this arable land is sown with cereals, and nearly half of the total cereal land is devoted to wheat.

Wheat remains a vital part of the economy. Total production reaches about 10 million tons annually; previously the peak of 10 million tons had been exceeded only in 1907, and then with an acreage half as large again. The increase seems to be largely due to the spread of more productive and disease-resistant varieties of corn. There has also been increased use of artificial fertilizers. All the areas with high yields (more than 16 cwt. per acre) are situated north of a line from La Rochelle to Geneva; fifteen departments from Eure to the Ardennes and from Pas-de-Calais to Yonne form a continuous area which produces nearly half of France's corn, giving over 20 cwt. per acre. However, Brittany and the Armorican border

Mechanisation and improved methods have brought an annual increase of 4 per cent in production figures. Wheat remains a vital part of the economy and the cultivation of maize has been increased. Rice is grown in the Camargue. Fruit and vegetables account for 11 per cent of agricultural revenue, but viticulture still suffers from the ravages of phylloxera.

Forests

Arable land

Mixed farming

Pastoral (cattle and sheep)

Intensive farming (market gardening, orchards, vineyards)

A fifth of France's workers are employed in agriculture or fisheries. This is one of the highest proportions in Europe, yet the density of agricultural workers is lower than anywhere else in Europe except Great Britain.

Cavaillon, in Provence, is famed for its melons — and for early spinach, tomatoes, peas, aubergines and artichokes.

The introduction of rice cultivation now allows some use to be made of the marshy region of the Camargue, in southern France. The workers in the ricefields are mostly Spanish and Italian.

areas now form a second important wheat-growing area. The general rise in the standard of living has naturally resulted in a decline in the consumption of bread, and France now has an exportable surplus of wheat which could eventually reach two million tons a year.

As for maize, the introduction of American hybrid varieties has brought a revolution in its cultivation; production has already resulted in a heavy reduction in imports. No other cereal provides such a high yield per acre; in Béarn the yield is 81 cwt. per acre.

Finally, rice cultivation in the Camargue provides the whole of the country's home consumption needs.

In balanced mixed farming, at least one field is reserved for 'cleaning crops' (usually roots or tubers). These are excellent for preceding cereals; maize, however, is both cereal and cleaning crop. Of the old textile crops, only flax remains; it is important in the agriculture of the Caux region and the Flemish plain.

*Fruit-growing and market-gardening.* Vegetables are grown in alluvial valleys with a maritime climate, the drained marshes of the Atlantic coast, and the irrigated plains of the Mediterranean Midi. There are numerous apple-growing areas, situated on sunny slopes which also suit the vine; Mediterranean areas are favoured by the early growth and quality of both crops. The large urban centres of northern France have also stimulated the development of surrounding zones of market-gardening and fruit-growing.

The golden belt of Armorica specialises in early vegetables: potatoes, artichokes, green peas and cauliflowers. The Loire valley and its neighbouring areas justify the description 'Garden of France' and produce equal quantities of fruit and vegetables: salad crops, French beans, cauliflowers, pippin apples and asparagus. In the Aquitaine Basin traditional crops still predominate: the plums of Agen, the Chasselas grapes of Moissac, the peas and beans of Villeneuve-sur-Lot, and the tomatoes of Marmande.

In the last ten years or so there has been an important extension of fruit-growing in the Rhône valley; peaches, apricots and cherries are the chief products.

Provence is the most important fruit and vegetable region, with a total of 650,000 tons a year, of which over half comes from the irrigated plains of the lower Durance. Melons, spinach, tomatoes, peas, aubergines, and artichokes often give two crops a year. On the unirrigated land, grapes are grown at Thor; higher upstream there are tomatoes, asparagus and potatoes. Still higher, apple and pear orchards now form small fertile islands in the solitudes of Haute Provence.

Towards the Cote d'Azur, the productive areas are split up into oases of a few hundred or at most a few thousand acres; and in Corsica there are the market-garden crops of Ajaccio and the artichokes of Bastia.

Finally, there are the valleys of Rousillon, where a Spanish type of climate produces the first of the early crops: winter lettuce, tomatoes and artichokes, and apricots.

Although France produces a vast variety of fruit and vegetables, these do not play as extensive a part in French economy as might be expected. In spite of the establishment of refrigerated fruit stations, old-fashioned marketing methods still prevail.

NORTH-WEST ENGLAND: Crummock Water (in middle distance) and Buttermere, now separated by an alluvial fan, once formed a single la

*The crisis of 'vins ordinaires'.* The permanent crisis of viticulture raises one of the most serious problems of French agriculture. Between 1871 and 1875, before phylloxera had attacked the vineyards, vines provided about 160 million bushels (worth at least 15 per cent of agricultural income at that time). Today the vineyard area has been reduced by more than a third, though in some recent years the crop has still reached nearly 140 million bushels; its value is about 8 per cent of agricultural income.

The well-known wine localities, Bordeaux, Burgundy, Champagne, Alsace, Beaujolais, Arbois, concentrating on quality production, now have an expanding market with good export opportunities.

The reverse is true of wines for current consumption, which in metropolitan France often show a surplus of about 18 per cent of the average crop. This is the result of three factors: competition from Algeria, reduced consumption, and a decline in quality that has come with larger yields.

Huge irrigation programmes are projected in some Mediterranean departments to allow grapes to be replaced by intensive mixed farming. The future of French viticulture will only be assured by transferring production to the hills where soils are drier and yields smaller but better.

*The growth of stock-rearing.* An increase in livestock has had two important effects on agriculture: provision of good organic fertilization of the soil and better prospects for the mountainous regions which were unsuitable for arable farming.

Technical progress is everywhere tending to reduce the number of breeds by the adoption of distinct and well-bred types instead of persisting with the innumerable crossbreeds which existed before the war. Increased selectivity in cattle breeding has been accelerated by the number of artificial insemination centres established since 1948. Artificial insemination is also being practised in sheep farming. Although French meat production may allow important exports in the future, dairy products are still handicapped by high production costs, insufficient modern equipment, and a poorly organised market.

Poultry farming has made marked progress since 1950; it is carried on in the traditional areas of Bresse, Gâtinais and Gascony, and on innumerable small, modern farms.

*Changes in French agriculture.* French agriculture is in the process of complete transformation, and production is now increasing at the rate of 4 per cent a year.

Increased mechanisation is the most spectacular aspect of general modernisation; equally important are education in modern techniques, the equipping of agricultural industries, and the foundation of a rational marketing organisation. In particular, the traditional inadequacy of agricultural teaching is being remedied by the increase in technical courses and the establishment of winter schools; experimental farms and study centres have spread modern methods of selection and fertilization into remote regions.

*Conversion of French forests.* The forested area of France covers over 28 million acres, and has increased under the auspices of the National Forestry Foundation, which finances reforestation of wasteland and planting of coppices with pines. On the other hand, fire has destroyed more than a million acres in the Landes. At the present time, the largest and most productive wooded areas are the limestone plateaus of the east—the Vosges, Jura, Morvan, and the Alps.

The composition of French woodland is badly balanced. It includes too many broad-leaved hardwoods at a time when the trend towards the chemical rather than the mechanical use of wood favours coniferous softwoods. What is more, annual production includes up to 530 million cubic feet of firewood, but the modern demand for wood-fuel is declining. A conversion to pines and other softwoods is essential especially in the forested areas of the Paris Basin, where the slump in the sales of wood-fuel is serious.

*Undeveloped sea resources.* With 2,000 miles of coastline, France is one of Europe's most favourably situated countries for sea fishing. Yet the quantity of fish landed is just over 520,000 tons; consumption is low and consequently production is relatively undeveloped. The fishing fleet is smaller than before the war, though the value of the catch has risen.

France's wines need no introduction: they are world famed. The value of the crop is about 8 per cent of agricultural income. Yet the permanent crisis of viticulture since phylloxera attacked the vines at the end of the last century is one of the most serious problems of French agriculture.

NCE: Landscape between Gap and Digne, Basses Alpes.     Grape harvesting in Burgundy.

The chalk plateau east of Rouen: covered with limon, it yields rich crops of corn and sown grasses.

Landscape near Roquefort in the Massif Central. Artificial lakes created by hydro-electric projects have given the Massif Central an added tourist attraction.

Since 1946 the coalfield of Lorraine has been expanding, in sharp contrast to the rest of the French coal industry. The Lorraine reserves exceed 5,000 million tons, and annual production is higher than that of Germany's Ruhr.

Two-thirds of the fish handled by the trade is sold as fresh fish, the main types being herring, sardines (very irregular production), tunny (production could be doubled), mackerel and whiting. Cod provides one-eighth of the tonnage landed; one-third is exported to Brazil, Portugal and elsewhere. The crustacean catch cannot be increased because the grounds are already over-fished; but shell-fish culture is expanding, even under the primitive methods often used.

Amalgamation with the canning industry is obviously necessary to reduce the costs of production, and probably two-thirds of the existing canneries should be closed. The three indispensable conditions for the expansion of sea fishing are modernisation, more refrigeration, and reorganisation of distribution systems. THE PROBLEM OF POWER. When coal was the only source of industrial power, France was considered an impoverished country, incapable of rivalling the other great economic powers. But during the first half of the twentieth century there was a second industrial revolution as important as the first. In the face of competition from new sources of energy (hydro-electric power, petroleum, natural gas), coal has suffered a fairly rapid decline. Now nuclear power is adding to the competition.

In France, where technical progress is less advanced and where the national resources of petroleum are still small, coal constitutes nearly 70 per cent of the power used; production leaves a considerable deficiency to be made up by expensive American imports.

*Regional coal problems.* Once the most important, the Nord and Pas-de-Calais coalfield is declining with the increase of low-grade coal and because structural conditions are often adverse. To overcome the difficulties, large central electrical generating stations have been built which can use the low-grade coal, and attempts are being made to attract other industries to the mining areas.

In contrast, Lorraine has been expanding since 1946. Reserves here are much greater, exceeding 5,000 million tons, or four centuries' supply used at the present rate. Processes have been evolved to produce coke for the nearby blast-furnaces, and gas for piping to Paris by the East grid; at the same time by-products are recovered which provide raw materials for the chemical industry.

The problems facing the French coal industry reflect to a large extent the situation in many parts of continental Western Europe and in Britain, where the peak of production was reached as early as 1913. The prospect of oil from the Sahara and the increase in the use of gas and electricity, has necessitated a radical rethinking of the position of coal in the second half of the twentieth century. Production is being streamlined, and only those mines which show a satisfactory profit will continue to be worked.

*Development of hydro-electric power.* The first competitor of coal was hydro-electric power. In 1882 Aristide Bergès installed the first head of water (1,640 feet) to produce electricity at Lancey, near Grenoble. However, electrical equipment did not begin to develop until 1897 with the introduction of the alternator and transformer. In the Pyrenees, in 1910, the power station at Orlu supplied the first electricity at 55,000 volts and allowed power to be transmitted more than 60 miles. In the same area, in

1921, the Compagnie du Midi started the first large-scale railroad electrification.

In the Alps and the Pyrenees the heads of water are often very high with an uncontrolled flow; in the Massif Central, on the other hand, because of its relief and geographical position, dams have been built to store and control the flow. The first of these large dams was built at Eguzon on the Creuse. Then the Tarn (Le Pinet) was tackled, the Dordogne (Marèges) and lastly the Truyère.

After 1947, an unprecedented programme of hydro-electric installation was undertaken within the framework of the Monnet plan, and by 1963 production was 88,200 million kWh (43,400 m. hydro-electric).

The French hydro-electric power potential has recently been estimated; if the small falls which are only just beginning to profit from technical progress are included, it is something like 100 thousand million kWh a year. This is the highest in Europe except in Scandinavia. Almost half of this potential is south of the line La Rochelle-Strasbourg, while most French industry is north of it. This situation involves heavy costs for distant transmission, and raises the cost of the power; it is one of the factors favouring industrial expansion towards the south.

The most northerly hydro-electric power reserve is the river Rhine between Basle and Strasbourg. In the Massif Central the most recent schemes are the 'water staircase' on the Dordogne, the Aigle, Chastang and Couesque dams, and the diversion of the upper Loire to the Rhône. In the Rhône basin, the areas with the biggest potential are the Jura, the Arve and the rivers of Haute-Savoie, the Isère valley, the Rhône itself, and the Durance.

The wealth of power in south-east France will no doubt be modified by the building of the first tidal generator at Rance (640 million kWh). But the utilisation of tidal power will be expensive, and the scheme may be abandoned if nuclear power stations are able to provide western France with cheaper power.

*Discoveries of petroleum and natural gas.* National production of petroleum was once virtually non-existent. But the estuaries of the Atlantic and the mouth of the Rhône corridor were very suitable sites for importing crude oil and distributing refined products. The refineries, now extended and modernised, and the adjoining petroleum-chemical factories, have become huge works employing about 50,000 people.

Until 1950 French consumption was entirely dependent on overseas imports, apart from the insignificant oilfield at Péchelbronn. A programme of systematic research was undertaken and in 1950 petroleum was found at Lacq, near Orthez. Another, more important field was discovered near the edge of the Etang de Parentis in the Landes. A survey is proceeding in all areas of potential oil-bearing sedimentary rocks, and extraction has begun in the Paris Basin.

French resources of natural gas were limited to the small field of Saint-Marcet (Haute-Garonne) discovered in 1942, which produces only 8,750 million cubic feet because of the limited reserves.

In 1954 there was the even more important discovery of a deposit of sulphurous gas below the oilfield at Lacq, most probably greater than 10 billion (million million) cubic feet.

*Nuclear power.* Uranium, the raw material used in nuclear power production, is found in crystalline rocks. France is very well provided with these, and uranium deposits are already being worked in Limousin, the Madeleine hills, the Morvan, and the Vendée. The first atomic power stations have been built on the banks of the Rhône at Marcoule, and at the confluence of the Loire and Vienne, and at Cadarache. The transport of the raw material does not influence the cost of production, for a pound of uranium will produce as much electricity as 500 tons of coal.

## THE BASIC INDUSTRIES

Basic industries are those which supply the processing industries with raw material or with semi-finished goods for further manufacture. They have a common characteristic: their locations are determined by mineral resources or availability of power. They

Operations to exploit the oil at Lacq revealed an even richer natural resource: an extensive deposit of sulphurous gas. Production is already considerable and it is estimated that within a few years French production should equal that of Italy.

A petro-chemical plant at Berre, strategically placed to take advantage of the crude oil imported to feed the refinery at the mouth of the Rhône corridor.

can be divided into three main groups: iron and steel, non-ferrous metals, and heavy chemicals.

*Restoration of the iron industry.* Before 1890 France did not seem to have great potential as a steel producer. The iron industry was dispersed, it used low-grade ores, and it was still dominated by the traditional iron masters.

Once the Thomas process had been perfected the *minette* ores of Lorraine became usable.

The iron-bearing deposits of Lorraine are found in the Jurassic rocks; mining concessions stretch from north to south for about 60 miles, from the Belgian-Luxembourg frontier to south of Nancy. The mines are mainly concentrated in the area of Briey, which has the largest reserves of calcareous iron ore (self-fluxing); siliceous iron ore is less desirable because lime has to be added on smelting.

The *minette* ore has a low iron content. This characteristic, although economically undesirable, has favoured local development of the industry: it is more advantageous to erect the blast-furnaces on the iron field and to bring the coal to it.

Lorraine which mines about 60 million tons of iron ore annually seems about to be exhausted. The ore field in the west offers important reserves and the position of Lorraine, long favoured by its mineral deposits and the proximity of Moselle coke, has declined with a recession in certain outlets.

The 100 French blast-furnaces produce more than 14 million tons of pig-iron, four-fifths of which is converted into steel. Founded near the coalfield, the mills of the north make crude steel and some semi-finished goods, sheet metal in particular. Denain has a continuous hot strip mill, and at Montmaire (Oise), there is a cold rolling mill. The other iron centres of the north are Valenciennes-Anzin and the Sambre valley and, above all, the new 'combine' at Dunkirk.

Two other groups of works are of interest. The first makes pig-iron, and this is supplied especially to foundries for further processing; it includes, besides six works in Lorraine, individual works on the coast or near local deposits. The second group manufactures steel in electric furnaces which are often constructed in mountainous areas rich in hydro-electric power.

In spite of a determined attempt at modernisation and expansion, the industry remains appreciably smaller than that of its competitors, Britain and Germany. Although production capacity has increased, expansion is held in check by the state of the markets.

*The leading European producer of aluminium.* Metropolitan France is poor in non-ferrous minerals. The sole exception, fortunately an important one, is bauxite, the aluminium ore. Bauxite is a red clay containing 50 to 70 per cent aluminium. First it is calcined to give alumina (1 ton of lignite and 174 lb. of soda required for 1 ton of alumina). In the second stage, the production of aluminium needs per ton of metal: 2 tons of alumina, 1,100 lb. of carbon for the electrode, and 18,000 to 20,000 kWh. So the cost of the metal depends primarily on the cost of the electricity; electrolytic works are nearly always built in the main hydro-electricity producing area.

Aluminium is subject to a continually increasing demand. France has kept her place as the principal European producer, due to wealth of hydro-electric power and rich supplies of bauxite. Concentrated in the Midi, the bauxite fields have more than doubled pre-war output. The alumina works are situated near Marseilles, for using Provençal lignite. The most important and modern works is at Saint-Jean-de-Maurienne. Subsequent extensions, however, may take place in Africa, where hydro-electric power can be produced more cheaply.

*Building materials.* Only one mineral product has been used in building up to now: asbestos. Since 1949 the development of the Corsican deposit of Canari has provided one-third of internal consumption. The post-war resumption of building also encouraged a marked expansion of quarry products.

*France in the chemical age.* The great rise of plastics, chlorine products and fertilizers has created a demand for a wide range of raw materials and has brought rapid growth in the chemical industry. Chemical fertilizers have benefited from the recent expansion of agriculture. The production of synthetic nitrate is centred mainly on the north-east coalfield and at Toulouse. Superphosphates are obtained from the phosphates of North Africa and the pyrites of the Lyons region which give sulphuric acid, or from basic slag, a by-product of the iron industry.

The Alsatian potash mines, modernised since 1945, have more than tripled their output. The deposit is situated north-west of Mulhouse, where model towns for the workers have been built in the forest itself.

Most of the sodium chloride comes from the great deposit in Lorraine; Franche-Comté also has important saline deposits; and finally there is the salt from the Mediterranean and Atlantic, which provides one-third of total requirements. From salt, limestone and carbon, sodium products are obtained — caustic soda and carbonate of soda; production is concentrated in Lorraine and in the Jura.

From salt, too, chlorine can be obtained by electrolysis; this basic product is perhaps the most important in modern chemistry. And it is from chlorine that polyvinyl chloride is obtained, nowadays the most commonly required plastic. The production centres of chlorine, now a key industry, are in the Alps, or near the salt deposits. At Saint-Auban (Basses-Alpes) it is produced with calcium carbide, an electro-chemical product giving acetylene and rising out of the manufacture of vinyl resins.

Electro-chemistry also provides silicon carbide, artificial corundum, phosphorus and its derivatives, electrodes, etc. With electro-metallurgy it forms the the group of electrical industries linked to hydro-electric power which has brought economic growth to the Pyrenean and Alpine valleys.

Yet coal remains the basis of a fully expanding organic chemistry. Concentrated in the northern coalfield and the Lyons area, with an extension into Lorraine, it produces in particular methanol, and in the field of plastics, nylon and polystyrene.

Petroleum chemical industries around the refineries (Etang de Berre and Seine Maritime), now manufacturing detergents, will soon produce synthetic rubber and will also find a vast outlet in plastics.

Mention should be made of synthetic textiles, usually obtained from cellulose, or, more recently,

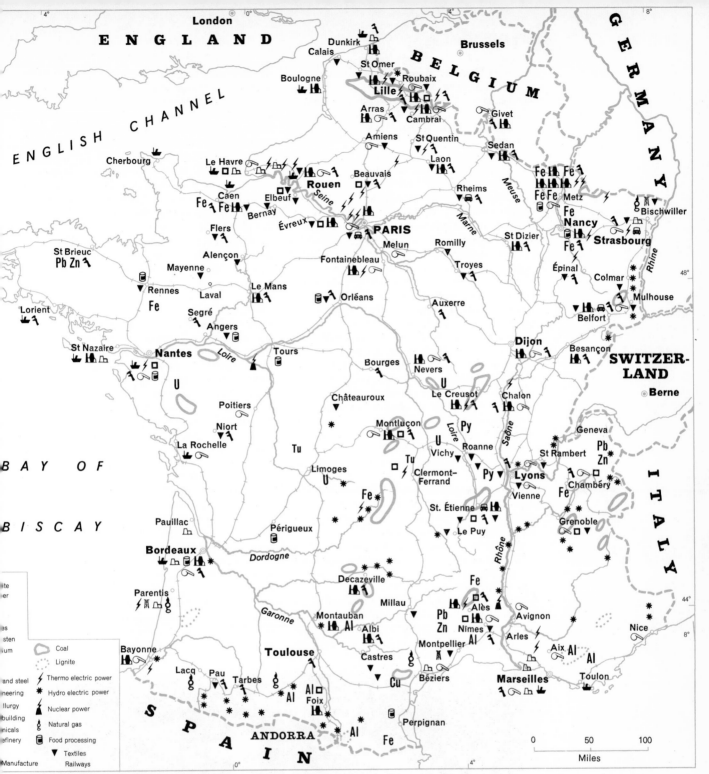

from castor oil, and of pharmaceutical products; both are particularly concentrated in the Lyons region.

Closely linked with chemicals is the glass industry, a large coal consumer and particularly concentrated in the north-east and Saint-Etienne areas.

*Paper and pulp.* France still remains dependent on Scandinavian imports for wood pulp, the raw material for some artificial textiles and plastics. An attempt has been made to develop national resources, and factories have been extended; they are situated in particular in the valleys of the Seine, the north-east, the Alps, the Landes and the Vosges.

SECONDARY OR PROCESSING INDUSTRIES. The processing industries, employing more than 4 million workers, are fairly well dispersed apart from an excessive concentration around Paris; they have as a common characteristic almost complete geographical freedom. Technical progress and social development cause important differences in rate of growth. The engineering, electrical, plastics, and certain food industries, and the manufacture of chemical derivatives, are developing faster than others. The old-established textiles, the leather industry and mechanical wood-working are all gradually declining.

*Problems of the textile industry.* This industry, which ushered in the nineteenth-century Industrial Revolution, still creates serious employment problems in the old exporting countries, such as France and England, for today their markets are restricted by the industrialisation of the underdeveloped countries, their former

In proportion to area, metropolitan France is one of the richest countries in the world for iron-ore. But it is one of the poorest in non-ferrous metals, except for bauxite. The basic industries employ one worker for every eight in the processing industries. The present trend is towards decline in the old-established textile, leather and wood-working industries and towards rapid expansion in mechanical and electrical engineering, and in the chemical industries.

customers. Yet 1963 brought an improvement in trade. The chief textile area is the north-east. Roubaix is a leading wool centre of the world; the centres of Lille and Tourcoing specialise in cotton, and Armentières in linen, with the traditional retting in the waters of the Lys.

At the other extremity of France is the region of Castres, now the second wool centre because of the proximity of Mazamet, an important region for the production of wool from sheepskins. The following isolated centres are also important: Vienne, Cours (Rhône), Sedan and Elbeuf.

In the cotton industry, the Vosges region has become most important. It has a valley-type industry, highly dispersed and often producing its own power hydraulically. The area often suffers from partial unemployment, and attempts are now being made to attract alternative industries. The situation is not much brighter in Normandy.

The silk industry lies around Lyons, which is also the centre for synthetic fibres; the two industries closely overlap. The silk mills of the Ardèche and Dauphiné also carry out nylon processing.

*Leather industries.* Leather is meeting strong competition from plastics for most of its traditional uses except footwear. Tanning, tawing and furriery are widespread and rarely form the chief occupation of a region. Glove-making, however, is distinctly localised; so is shoe manufacture, and some areas are suffering a crisis.

*Expansion of the mechanical and electrical industries.* This huge sector of metal-working now employs more than 1,370,000 people, and there is hardly a part of France where it is not represented.

Some of the manufactures are directly connected with the building trade. Agricultural equipment is another expanding section, at least for tractors and power-driven cultivators.

Most of the mechanical engineering labour force is is employed in the manufacture of transport equipment. There are four branches: railroad equipment, aircraft, commercial and domestic vehicles, and cycles

(including motor-cycles). The chief coach and carriage builders are in the north. Aircraft construction is almost completely nationalised, and the State is almost the only customer. Mass production of automobiles is almost six times the pre-war figure and, as concentration has reduced the number of firms, this comes almost wholly from a few concerns. Although production is mainly in the Paris area, there is a tendency to decentralisation: Renault is expanding at Le Mans and now near Rouen; Citroen has works at Rennes and Strasbourg; Peugeot has expanded at Sochaux (Doubs). In contrast, cycle and motor-cycle manufacture is almost entirely provincial. Since 1950, the industry has undergone a complete change in which the bicycle has lost ground to the auto-cycle and the scooter, though their production is now failing too.

Electrical engineering has more than doubled its pre-war output. The two main centres are the Paris area and the Alpine regions. In the Pyrenees, Tarbes and Bazet manufacture electro-technical porcelain. A policy of decentralisation has made Rheims one of the leading centres of domestic appliances, manufacturing vacuum cleaners, washing machines and refrigerators. The industry also includes the manufacture of all types of cutlery in the traditional areas of Nogent-en-Bassigny and Thiers. Watchmaking and precision engineering are localised, as at Besançon in the Doubs valley, Haute-Savoie, etc. These two branches of the industry have benefited from the demand for instruments in the aircraft and car industries.

*Towards the dispersion of industry.* The increased applications of electrical equipment, telecommunications and road transport control the future development of the processing industries. They also explain how industries which require little heavy transport may very often be divided into average to small-sized units, provided that these units are specialised and able to undertake mass production.

Today two tendencies may be observed: one towards financial integration, with or without merging companies; the other towards specialisation and

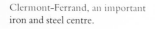

Clermont-Ferrand, an important iron and steel centre.

regional dispersal of the manufacturing units. One can foresee an expansion of industrial activity throughout France, an expansion which is vital for the well-being of agriculture.

TRANSPORT AND TRAVEL. The first apparent general trend is that the internal transport of goods by rail or water has increased little if at all, while expansion of private car travel has checked the growth of public passenger transport. In contrast, air transport has encouraged a rapid growth in foreign travel, and transport of goods by sea has continued to increase.

*Decline of tonnage at the ports.* The statistical increase in tonnage loaded and unloaded at French ports is due entirely to petroleum products; other types of trade have sharply declined.

With the end of imports from Britain and with the competition from oil bunkering, the coal trade has suffered a serious collapse in all ports. Trade in other products has declined appreciably, particularly imports: oils, sulphur and pyrites, cereals and wines and liqueurs.

The present prosperity of the ports varies considerably according to whether they specialise in passenger traffic or goods, and whether or not they include refineries. The passenger ports are suffering more and more from the competition, while a certain degree of concentration has benefited Calais, Le Havre and Marseilles.

On the other hand, the ports serving the great refineries handle 84 per cent of all imports today instead of 76 per cent as in 1958. First comes Marseilles, with its subsidiaries; second is Le Havre; third is Dunkirk, which is expanding; fourth is Rouen, declining in post-war years; fifth, Nantes with subsidiaries; sixth, Bordeaux; and last, Sete.

Shipbuilding is the main activity of some ports. The merchant navy of France had a gross tonnage of 2,280,000 in 1947. Partly as a result of generous State assistance it now has a tonnage of well over 5 million.

*Air communications.* The expansion of air transport is astonishing. In common with many countries, the growth of air services, not least the domestic traffic, has been a notable feature of the past decades.

Of the three or four large civil airports in metropolitan France, by far the most important are Orly and le Bourget; then come Marseilles-Marignane and Nice–le-Var, which are linked to Paris by internal routes.

*Railroads.* The greater proportion of goods and passenger traffic is carried by rail. Rail transport was revolutionised as early as 1920, when the replacement of steam traction by electric traction began. Diesel traction was introduced later.

The rail network was first conceived under Louis Philippe as a political measure intended to secure relations between the capital and the Prefectures. In 1937 all existing companies merged to form the Société Nationale des Chemins de Fer (51 per cent State shareholding). Total length today is 24,000 miles. Rail density is thus appreciably less than in Germany or England but a revolutionary technique employing industrial current of 25,000 volts has reduced the cost of fixed equipment by half and allowed the speeding up of the electrification and equipping of lines carrying moderate traffic.

*Navigable waterways.* Inland water transport, mainly for building materials, coal and petroleum, is almost entirely north of a Paris-to-Basle line. All things considered, the only new waterway that is really profitable is the Alsace canal, which by means of locks combined with hydro-electric power stations allows Rhine navigation to reach Basle. In the interests of efficiency, 2,600 miles of small waterways with negligible traffic could well be abandoned.

*Roads.* Road transport shows increasing activity and is still unrivalled for the carriage of most types of goods over short and medium distances. There is an excellent road network consisting of 50,000 miles of main highway, 170,000 miles of secondary road, and 260,000 miles of by-road (now usually surfaced). Only a few motorways have been constructed and length for length the cost has been three times as high as double-track rail line, which can handle a greater volume of traffic.

The revival of the roads has been more marked because of the continued increase of the important tourist trade. Today the tourist takes prosperity to the most remote areas. Development here has been aided by the improvement or construction of roads giving access to the most beautiful parts of the French countryside; the southern part of the Central Massif, the infertile Alps, and central Brittany today enjoy a noticeable degree of prosperity; and Corsica is on the way to becoming a second Côte d'Azur.

OUTLOOK FOR THE FUTURE. France possesses unexpected assets. Its agriculture has many natural advantages not found elsewhere in Europe; it possesses the most varied hydro-electric installations, which have allowed it to exploit unusual conditions. Its shores provide the opportunity to develop tidal power and extensive deposits of natural gas and petroleum are being exploited. Raw material for nuclear power are more abundant here than anywhere else in Europe. There is a traditionally high regard for the individual, and social changes continue to improve the laws and rights of citizens. Resolute in purpose and bold in vision, France is still essentially a pioneer land.

Lyons, at the confluence of the Saône and Rhône, is an important silk centre and has a prosperous synthetic fibres industry.

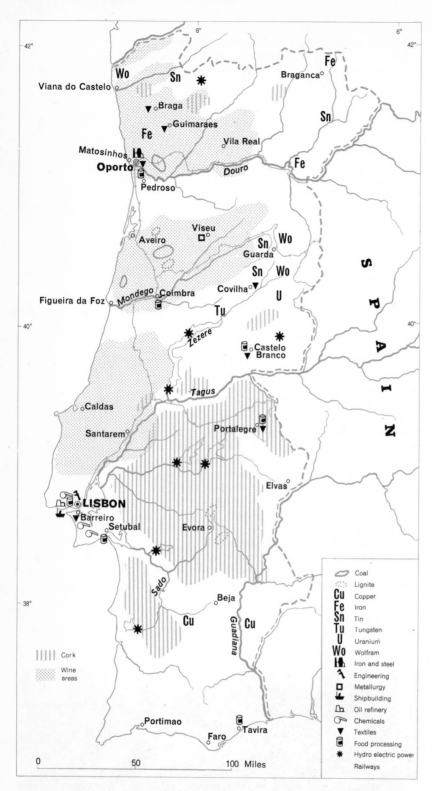

| | Coal |
| | Lignite |
| Cu | Copper |
| Fe | Iron |
| Sn | Tin |
| Tu | Tungsten |
| U | Uranium |
| Wo | Wolfram |
| | Iron and steel |
| | Engineering |
| | Metallurgy |
| | Shipbuilding |
| | Oil refinery |
| | Chemicals |
| | Textiles |
| | Food processing |
| * | Hydro electric power |
| | Railways |

Cork

Wine areas

0    50    100 Miles

Portugal is a small state with a population too large for its resources, for although it has preserved roughly the frontiers it had in the thirteenth century, it remained untouched by the agrarian and industrial revolutions that changed the face of north-west Europe.

# PORTUGAL

Portugal has preserved approximately the same frontiers since the thirteenth century. The original nucleus of this political structure was a small principality whose Christian population, driven back by the Moslems, afterwards set out along the coast to reconquer the south. Its language had developed from the original Romanic language and was distinct from the Castilian tongue.

The Portuguese and Castilian peoples share certain traits of character and temperament; but the Portuguese are more easy-going, more melancholy, and more tolerant of weakness.

Portugal preceded Spain in pioneering the great voyages of discovery at the dawn of the Renaissance. After a century of great commercial activity Portugal, by then part of Spain, shared its decline during the seventeenth century. It remained on the fringe of the great agrarian and industrial revolution in north-west Europe. Hence its present position as a small state with too large a population and too low a standard of living.

*Physical differences.* To understand the conditions of the peasant and the fisherman, reference must be made to the difference in the physical features of northern Portugal (Minho) and southern Portugal (Alentejo), and then to the direction of the Reconquest, which took place from north to south, from an area with a high population.

The north is mountainous. Parts of the plateaus have been raised to 6,500 feet (the Serra da Estrela), and towards the coast the land is broken up into numerous ridges, blocks, and wide-mouthed valleys like that of the Minho. Cultivated land is scarce; it is more extensive on the plateaus, but here severe winter conditions limit the possibilities of cultivation. The only large area of lowland, the coastal triangle with the lagoon of Aveiro at its centre, is covered with sand and planted with the maritime pine. The whole of northern Portugal has the advantage of abundant rainfall and a short summer drought.

In contrast, southern Portugal is composed of huge plateaus between 300 feet and 1,000 feet high, where the winters are very mild. However, the summer drought lasts from May to October, prohibiting continuous cultivation of everything except trees. The north-west, with mild winters and abundant rainfall, has a relief that is too rugged to provide extensive areas of soil. Agriculture on the high plateaus of the north-east is limited by the severity of the winter and by the summer drought; drought is also the chief obstacle to cultivation in the low plateau lands of the south. In the intermediate zone, especially the Tagus lowland, there are large areas of cultivable soils and the climate is relatively humid. Here the mildness of the winter allows two consecutive harvests.

*The over-populated north.* The north-west supports the densest population. In Minho, the rural density of population exceeds 500 per square mile though barely half the land is cultivable. Intensive mixed farming is carried on, but the methods are old-fashioned and there is a lack of capital. Tiny fields are surrounded by fruit trees or by climbing vines which yield a wine that is light and sharp. During the winter, grass, carefully irrigated from small springs or wells dug in the sand, yields four or five cuttings. In spring, the meadow lands are sown with maize, the staple food.

On the high eastern plateaus of Trás-os-Montes or Beira Alta, rye alternates with fallow; potatoes, introduced relatively recently, can be grown only in the damp lowlands.

In contrast, the narrow incised valleys experience a dry, scorching summer, especially where the rock is schistose. Viticulture here has required enormous effort; the steep slopes have been fashioned into a gigantic staircase of terraces which are covered with soil carried there in baskets. Wine is made at Oporto (Porto).

In the north-west numerous small workshops are devoted to the manufacture of cloth or metal goods fashioned mainly by craftsmen. Industry does not provide sufficient opportunities for this overpopulated countryside, and emigration is a necessity.

The surplus population also moves naturally to the plains and low plateaus of central and southern Portugal.

*Settlement of the southern plateaus.* The land here is divided into huge estates, employing either tenant farmers who rent an area of land, generally for a year, or agricultural workers hired by the day. The land grows wheat, oats, or lies fallow in regular succession. The oats feed big flocks of sheep. Portugal is the world's leading producer of cork. Agricultural activities are not enough to ensure regular employment for the skilled and semi-skilled workers of the villages, who compete with migrants from the north.

Conditions improve where the rocks of the peneplain are less sandy, or where they are covered with sediments of chalky marl. On the right bank of the Tagus the country's largest olive groves are found. The soil is suitable for wheat, and the low part of the plain is partially converted to rice plantations. But the land is not yet being put to its full use. There are too many pastures in the Sado and especially in the Tagus valley which should be drained or irrigated instead of

Vineyards in the Douro valley. Intensive cultivation of the vine is Portugal's biggest agricultural asset.

A peasant family in the
province of Estremadura.
The general standard of living
is low, for Portugal is heavily
overpopulated and has
insufficient industry as lack of
capital has restricted expenditure
on industrial equipment.

The grape harvest borne to the
presses in traditional procession.

Fishermen at Cascais, near
Lisbon. About forty-five
thousand Portuguese earn their
living from the sea.
Fish is a staple item of diet, and
the canning of sardines and tunny
a flourishing export trade.

given over to bull raising. The rivers are still adequate
even in summer, and this is the only part of Portugal
where planning and improved equipment might lead
to an important increase in agricultural production.

In the south, Algarve's limestone hills and tiny
coastal plains, where snow and frost are unknown,
are devoted to intensive mixed farming based on
Kabylo-Arab methods of agriculture. Almonds, figs,
carobs or locust beans and early vegetables are grown.
*The role of the sea.* About forty-five thousand Portuguese earn their living by fishing; fish is a more
important item of food than meat. Sardine canning at
Matosinhos and tunny at Portimao is a flourishing
export industry. Mechanisation of the fleet is still
incomplete and its methods are outdated. The fisherman lives like a peasant; he is part of a caste, isolated
from the rest of the population.

The large urban centres are all ports. Oporto
(746,000 pop.), a medieval city, had very early trade
relations with Flanders. Wines, fishing boats and
textiles are produced, dispersed in small workshops.

Lisbon, on the edge of an inland sea formed by the
broadening of the Tagus estuary, has grown since the
Moslem period; its national and international pre-
eminence dates from the centuries when it became
the capital of a colonial empire and an entrepôt for
rare merchandise from the Indies. Today, it has a
population of 1,335,000, over 15 per cent of the total.
It is an international port of call for sea and air
passengers, and receives the bulk of the country's
foreign and colonial imports. It is also the chief
industrial centre of Portugal, with shipyards, chemical
works, jute mills, and soap and candle factories.
*Overpopulation and industrialisation.* Portugal is undoubtedly overpopulated in relation to its existing
resources. As the country's coal resources are poor and
its iron resources difficult to mine, the advisability of
establishing heavy industry is doubtful. Since 1927
the Government has been chiefly concerned with
the development of light industry. A fine network of
communications has been built; with the construction
of great hydro-electric power stations on the northern
rivers the production of electricity has doubled in the
last ten years. Cotton spinning and weaving and
production in the chemical industry have increased.
However, in total value and in value per head of
population, the figures do not bear comparison with
those countries with a higher standard of living.
Industrial equipment has been restricted through lack
of capital, a reluctance to borrow from abroad, and
concern to maintain the value of the escudo, which
remains very steady.

# THE
# PORTUGUESE ISLANDS
# OF THE ATLANTIC

In the fifteenth century the Portuguese occupied
the uninhabited islands of the Azores, Madeira and
Cape Verde, on the route of the great voyages of
discovery. These islands have played an important

The Avenue de Liberdade, Lisbon's main street. The capital of Portugal was once the capital of a colonial empire too; now, although an international port of call and an industrial centre, it cannot compare with west Europe's other great cities.

rôle as ports of call and in spreading plantation cultivation in America. They are inhabited by peasants of Portuguese origin who brought with them characteristics of rural Portugal. They are part of a group of islands of volcanic origin, some of which are very old and have been worn down by erosion; eruptions have occurred in historic times. Farming on the mountain side is very difficult, and variations in latitude and in the distances from the coast of Africa cause important climatic differences.

The Azores (888 square miles), situated in mid-ocean in latitude 40°N., experience humid conditions throughout the year. The chief areas of specialised cultivation are confined to the lowland — pineapples under glass, chicory, tea and sugar-beet. Cultivated meadows higher up provide food for the fine breed of Dutch dairy cattle. The chief islands are Sao Miguel, Terceira (where the capital, Angra do Heroismo, is situated), and Pico.

Madeira (302 square miles) is situated in latitude 33°N. and nearer to the African continent. Its typically

Mediterranean climate commends it particularly to tourists. Rainfall is confined to the winter months and almost all the fields have to be irrigated. In the fifteenth century, the first large plantations of sugar-cane were started; today, banana plantations are replacing them almost everywhere. A special wine, produced with great care, is still exported. A dense population of peasants exists on corn, yams and sweet potatoes; everywhere, stock-raising is closely associated with agriculture.

The Cape Verde Islands extend over an area of 1,557 square miles; their chief island is Sao Tiago, which contains Praia, the capital. They form a tropical archipelago with a short rainy season in summer. The cultivation of maize is restricted by shortage of water and backward methods. The only important export is castor oil.

The importance of these islands as ports of call on the routes to South America and South Africa is declining. Even Funchal, the capital of Madeira, has seen a decrease in trade.

Terraced fields in the hills, behind Funchal, in Madeira, a Portuguese possession in the Atlantic, off Morocco. Madeira was the first place to have large sugar-cane plantations, started there in the fifteenth century; today banana plantations have largely replaced them.

# CENTRAL EUROPE

# THE ALPS

The Alps occupy a vast area of Europe between southern Germany and northern Italy; 780 miles measured along the outer limits from the Col de Tende to Vienna; 165 miles from the Karawanken Alps north of Ljubljana to the most eastern spur of the Wienerwald. With an area of 64,000 square miles, they form a barrier between two civilisations: that of the Po valley and the northern Adriatic, and that of the North Sea and the Baltic Sea.

They have been settled since earliest times, and are surrounded by a foreland, often fertile, which fosters a semi-mountainous type of existence complementary to mountain life proper. Their waters, swollen by melting snow and ice, feed the Dutch Rhine and the Rumanian Danube, helping to form the Rhône and the Po.

*Asymmetry of the Alps.* Originating in a geosyncline of various strata, the Alps usually slope towards the outside of the curved line of folding. Symmetry is prominent in the western region, where the Piedmont Alps are less than a fifth as high as those in nearby France, and between Monte Rosa, Lake Maggiore and Lake Thun. East of Lake Como it is less evident, because on the borders of the Po lowlands the Alps are raised into many folds. This arrangement of the mountain range has facilitated military attacks in the direction of Turin and the Ticino; it has also resulted in drainage being developed more on the outside than the inside slope. Finally, it is at least partly responsible for the exceptionally high rainfall in the Ticino area, and the strength and extent of the föhn winds.

*The highest mountain range in Europe.* Between Annecy, Chillon, Thun and Lucerne on one side, and Lanzo, Ivrea, Biella and Varese on the other, the width of the Alps is reduced to between 78 and 85 miles, reaching a height of 14,022 feet on the Finsteraarhorn, 15,200 feet on Monte Rosa, and 15,781 feet on Mont Blanc.

Between Montélimar and Saluzzo, however, and between Vienna and the outskirts of Ljubljana, where the width of the mountains is more than 125 and 160 miles respectively, there are no peaks over 13,000 feet. The eastern Alps only just exceed 8,000 feet in the Karawanken.

The supple folding of the Alps included longitudinal folds. In this way the high mountain masses of Argentera, Pelvoux, Mont Blanc, Bernese Oberland, Ambin and Tauern are contrasted with the valleys of Lanzo-Susa (near Mont Cenis) and the Brenner.

The Alps are composed of flexible rocks that tend to yield into troughs aligned along the axis of the range, presenting long zones of homogeneous formations, often very liable to erosion.

*Longitudinal valleys.* There is an almost continuous route of 250 miles from the approaches of the southern French Alps to Grisons. In the same way the Rienza valley, the Gail and the Drava open a direct route between the southern end of the Brenner Pass and Maribor in the Hungarian Basin. The trough of the River Inn extends diagonally from the gay countryside of Lake Como to the misty plateau of Bavaria. These longitudinal valleys are linked to outer limits of the Alps by transverse valleys, the most remarkable of which are probably those of Grenoble, the Rhine above Lake Constance, and particularly that of the Upper Rhône between Martigny and Lake Geneva. The dominant direction of the Alps and of the parallel valleys is roughly south-west to north-east; the valleys thus have one sunny, fully exposed slope which is suitable for the vine, and a shaded side rich with orchards, woods and meadows.

*Mixed mountain climates.* The Alps would appear to promise a fairly uniform climate, because the range of latitude between Thun and Vienna is little more than 100 miles. However, although there is little difference between the precipitation and vegetation of Chablais and Salzkammergut, the reverse is true of the Styrian and Carinthian Alps, and the opposite end of the range. In the former, continental influences from Hungary penetrate deeply into the area; precipitation is sometimes reduced to less than 40 inches, and the deciduous trees, pine copses and

The Alps, a barrier 780 miles long and 165 miles wide, reach across Switzerland, France, Italy, Germany and Austria. Their melting snows feed some of Europe's biggest rivers: the Rhine, the Danube, the Rhône and the Po.

The traditional alpine economy
is agricultural.
Where once most of the work
was manual, today agricultural
machinery is being introduced
to minimise labour and to
increase yields.

The remote valley of Herens,
in the Swiss Valais.
Few areas owe a greater portion
of their economy to tourist
trade than the Alps.
A favourable climate and
breathtakingly beautiful
scenery attracts tourists in
summer and winter.

fields of maize offer a prospect that is more picturesque
than the Tyrol landscape. The opposite slope is
typified to the east of the Val d'Oasta by heavy
precipitation brought by the Adriatic winds. The blue
sky, the mixed crops on the lower slopes and the
terraces of vines are strongly reminiscent of the
Mediterranean landscape.

Where the Franco-Italian Alps begin to follow a
north-south direction they naturally provide more
contrasts. The Mediterranean depressions let loose
northerly winds, the *bise* and the *mistral,* while the
*marin* and the *levant* bring rain from the south and
east. The southern French Alps suffer the drought of a
Mediterranean summer and there is a deficiency of
summer rainfall in the interior.

In the southern Alps, the difference between
opposite slopes is just as marked. Except to the west of
Mont Genèvre the minimum rainfall is in winter, not
summer as it is to the north of the river Maira. The
vegetation cover is always richer on the more exposed
slopes. In the most central parts of the Alps there are
small areas of relative drought.

*The Alpine types.* The French Alps, in the south, are
larger and lower than those in the north, simpler in
structure, but less accessible. Only the valley of the
Durance resembles the great longitudinal corridors
which are such a dominant feature of the central
section of the Alps between the southern French Alps
and a line joining Lakes Como and Constance.

The central section includes, besides the northern
French Alps, the greater part of the Swiss Alps, less
the area to the east of Grisons. This is the most spectacular region. The Swiss Alps feed 534 square miles of
ice. The construction of this central section differs
completely on the two sides of the River Arve. In the
'Grandes Alpes', the high limestone Alps are linked
to the central blocks, and the piling up of over-folds
or nappes has raised Monte Rosa over 3,000 feet
higher than the Levanna of Maurienne.

The western Dolomites and the Austrian Alps are
broader and lower (Marmolada is 10,965 feet), and
complicated by faulting and volcanic extrusion. In
the western Dolomites, to the east of Cima d'Asta
and the porphyritic platform of Bolzano-Cavalese, a
series of folds is aligned with impressive slopes. In the
extreme east the dense woodland and soft outlines of
the Wiernerwald set off the rugged ridges and eroded
limestone of Rax and the Schneeberg. The Alps of the
Mur sweep towards the Hungarian plain with the
rigid barrier of the Karawanken.

*The gateway of the Alps.* Some great passes have played
vital rôles throughout European history. The Col de
Tende (6,143 feet) became part of Savoy, with the
Comté de Nice, at the end of the fourteenth century,
and until the French Revolution was the chief
trans-alpine pass for wheeled transport. The Brenner
Pass served as the axis of the Tyrol. Savoy, or rather
the State of Savoy-Piedmont, founded its fortunes on
the exploitation of several great Alpine passes
including the Mont Cenis (6,834 feet) and, until
expelled by the Swiss in the sixteenth century, the
Great Saint Bernard (8,110 feet). The early Confederation of the Swiss cantons was bound together in the
thirteenth century by the necessity of developing,
exploiting and defending the route leading to the
Saint Gotthard Pass (6,926 feet). Turin, Venice,

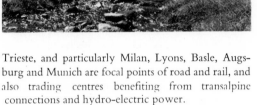

The source of the river Rhône: the Rhône glacier at the head of the Rhône valley.

The Matterhorn (14,701 feet), one of the peaks of the Pennine Alps.

Trieste, and particularly Milan, Lyons, Basle, Augsburg and Munich are focal points of road and rail, and also trading centres benefiting from transalpine connections and hydro-electric power.

*The traditional economy.* The salt in the Triassic rocks has played and often still plays an important part in Alpine economy. With certain metals, such as lead and copper, it encouraged early settlement, and has given rise to trade since prehistoric times. Iron, coal and lignite are located at La Maure, Aime in Tarentaise, La Thuile in the Val d'Aosta, and Gonzen in Switzerland, with several deposits in Styria and Carinthia; however, the present industrial centres are merely the survivors of a once more widespread Alpine iron industry.

Food production is surest and most successful in the heart of the Central Alps, with its warm spring climate, long periods of sunshine, and efficient irrigation. It is a countryside of patchwork fields, orchards, vineyards, forests and meadows on the lower slopes, and broad Alpine pasture above.

*A vital agricultural economy.* The population of the mountain region is steadily decreasing, especially in the Southern Alps; this will not necessarily lead to the decline of agricultural economy. In the southern Pre-Alps new methods of farming are being introduced, based on the use of artificial fertilizers and agricultural machinery; the lean sheep have been replaced by fat lambs and milch-cows; lavender and fruit have been introduced, and the vine, olive and wheat continue to hold their own. In Tarentaise the high mountain pastures are used for grazing combined herds of several hundred cattle, selected for the production of Gruyère cheese.

The pastoral system of the French Alps is also changing rapidly. Land-rover type vehicles, motor-mowers and weed-killers are in more general use in the area.

*Hydro-Electric power.* There is an important mining industry in the Alpine region, with a considerable production of lime and cement; leather-work and textile manufacture are also widely practised. Primarily, however, the Alps are a valuable source of hydro-electric power, and within the mountain region there are several large electro-metallurgical factories.

*The tourist industry.* The Alps offer magnificent scenery, unrivalled mountain peaks, ski-slopes, and an invigorating climate to the tourists who pour in almost all the year round. It has been estimated that 10 per cent of the adult population of Haute-Savoie owe their living directly to the tourist trade. The Swiss Alps alone receive an annual average of more than one and a half million 'home' tourists and three million foreigners. In the Austrian Alps, the corresponding figures are 3,900,000 and 4,900,000.

# SWITZERLAND

The Alps are the cradle of the early Confederation of the 'Waldstätten'. They helped to ensure the preservation of independence: of all the present Alpine states, Switzerland is the only one which reaches the bordering plains on both sides of the range. Occupying nearly 16,000 square miles, it has a population of 5,660,000.

*A country of diversity.* Regional divisions as different in relief and climate as in language, religion and ways of life, are found side by side within a small area. Northern Switzerland, with its thundery summer climate, long winter snow cover, and mists over the peat-bogs, is related to central Europe. In the extreme south-west, the country falls within the sphere of influence of the Gulf of Genoa with its atmospheric depressions, and of the *bise* with its heavy autumnal showers; the slopes of Tessin (Ticino) are in the Adriatic part of the Alpine region.

Switzerland sheds its annual precipitation through streams and rivers of very unequal catchments: the Rhine, the Rhône, the Po, the Inn, and the Adige. The Rhine is the major outlet because of the spread of its branches and the Aar. However, the Rhône basin, fashioned by a huge glacier to which western Switzerland owes some of its distinctive features, is an important source of power.

Switzerland has three languages, even four, since a

popular vote made Romansch a national language. The Rhaeto-Romansch area suffered the intrusion of Italian and German during the Middle Ages. Language is often linked with religion. The people of Bivio speak German, Romansch and Italian; the Romansch are Protestant, the Italians are Roman Catholic. Linguistic limits, however, do not coincide with the boundaries of the cantons, any more than with the political frontiers.

The religious variations are related to the historical conditions under which the Reformation spread, the differences of interpretation, and the religious rivalry that followed. Because of its relief and its historical and economic development, Switzerland lends itself to division into special groups; and within the Federation each canton retains its individual framework, with its own institutions, authorities, local customs and its own extensive powers in education and religion.

*Communications.* The Great Saint Bernard Pass, much used in Roman times, and the Saint Gotthard made accessible by the early cantons, are situated in the narrowest and loftiest sections of the Alpine range. In the Grisons, the Julier, Splügen, Septimer and Maloja passes have been used since ancient times. The Saint Gotthard is the shortest route from Milan to the industrial and densely populated lowlands of the Rhine. Other trans-alpine routes neglected the old historic passes and emulated the Saint Gotthard — this route runs via Berne, Lötschberg, Brig and the Simplon.

*The division of Switzerland.* There is a western Switzerland, a central Switzerland and an eastern Switzerland; or rather, there are the longitudinal strips of the Alps, the Plateau and the Jura. However, two of the largest cantons, Bern and Vaud, are closely associated with all three regions, and the term Middle Lands is more apt than Plateau.

The Alps cover nearly two-thirds of the country and tower over the other zones. They occupy 42 per cent of the canton of Bern, but only 22 per cent of Vaud; this accentuates the differences between French-speaking Vaud and Bern, both of which belong to the even greater geographical unit of western Switzerland.

Geneva, the most international city in Switzerland, with part of its population consisting of United Nations staff, and an influence that extends far beyond the borders of Switzerland. The country's long history of neutrality makes Geneva an ideal meeting place of nations. The town stands on two hills divided by the Rhône where it leaves Lake Geneva, the largest lake in the Alps.

## WESTERN SWITZERLAND

Western Switzerland consists of the Geneva, Vaud, Valais, Fribourg, part of Neuchâtel and Bern cantons, plus the southern part of the canton of Solothurn (Soleure). This area of 7,000 square miles includes the linguistic and cultural unit of French-speaking Switzerland. From Lake Geneva (Léman) to Lake Constance, there are flat stretches of land, broad horizons, slow and placid rivers, and extensive interlinking lakes. There are numerous areas with moderate rainfall and rich alluvial soil; wine, wheat, tobacco and sugar-beet are important products. Seventy per cent of Switzerland's vineyards are in western Switzerland.

From the thirteenth to fifteenth centuries the territory of the House of Savoy extended to the gates of Sion and north as far as Morat. The State of Bern in its turn established itself firmly on the highway along the sub-Jurassic trough; in 1475 it gained access to the Rhône route by annexing the Aigle region. Then came the occupation of Vaud until 1798, and finally a part of the Jura in 1815.

*The fringes of Lake Geneva.* Geneva is one of the smallest Swiss cantons, with a population density of more than 2,300 to the square-mile. The old town, with its cathedral of Saint-Pierre, grew up on a spur of alluvium from the old confluence of the Arve and the Rhône. The parks encircling the Palais des Nations provide a green belt which includes the peaceful slopes of Saconnex and Pregny. Industry is now more varied than in the days when watchmaking flourished in the small workshops of the *cabinottiers.* By 1961, the metal industries (turbines, motors, parts for electric traction) employed almost four times as many workers as watchmaking.

The sunny vineyards of Vaud are among the finest in western Switzerland. East of Lausanne the vineyard of Lavaux extends for nine miles and covers 2,224 acres. A good quality white wine is produced from chasselas grapes.

Lausanne, an ancient cathedral city, has become a residential and tourist centre, and an industrial town. Its industries are dispersed among many workshops and small factories (woodwork, paper, printing equipment and measuring instruments), and have not affected the city's distinguished appearance.

*Development of the lake valley.* To the north of Morges, the sub-Jurassic valley widens. In this swampy valley, drainage is satisfactory under the 'Waters of the Jura' improvement scheme, and the plains of the Orbe, lower Broye and Bernese Seeland are intensively and scientifically farmed, producing cereals, sugar-beet, tobacco and vegetables. At the very foot of the Jura is Lake Neuchâtel, 25 miles long, with its deepest point about 500 feet below the level of the plain. In Neuchâtel, the castle ruins and the old Collegiate Church dominate the lake.

Biel (Bienne), at the mouth of the Suze, has become a watchmaking town, as well as a centre for mechanical industries (car assembly, cycle, precision machinery, repair works for the Federal Railways), paper manufacturing and woodwork. Solothurn (Soleure), in German-speaking Switzerland, was an old Roman town; today it is surrounded by factories.

*The Middle Lands.* The Broye, the Saane (Sarine), and

PORTUGAL: The harbour at Lisbon.    Harvesting in southern Portuga

the Aar all carve a course into that part of the Middle Lands which most resembles a plateau. Agriculture consists mainly of cleaning crops and mixed fodder. Milk production is important. On all sides are the scattered Bernese farms, with their curved ornamental fronts, their balconies and broad windows. This is a great cheese-producing region. The industries of the Bernese plateau and valleys include food products— chocolate, powdered milk, beer and preserved foods; in Bern and the surrounding area they embrace metal-working, engineering, paper manufacture, clothing and printing. The Federal capital with its well-preserved historic centre contrasts vividly with the modern spacious suburbs on the plateau.

*The Jura.* The Jura belong almost entirely to western and French-speaking Switzerland. Towards the north the mountains are lower, and there are changes in landscape, economy, and even language. The cool, damp, heavily forested Jura are given over to dairy cattle rather than crops. The watchmaking industry is active here.

The Val de Travers is the first of many valleys devoted entirely to watchmaking. In 1752, there were fewer than 500 watchmakers in the mountains of Neuchâtel; in 1941, the canton had 12,000 engaged in watchmaking and jewellery (15,000 by 1962.).

Several gaps in the barrier of the Jura link Basle with the Middle Lands. This relative ease of communication accounts for the spread of the German language in the extreme north of the area. In 1840, the valleys of the Birse and the Dunnern accounted for half the blast-furnaces of Switzerland; there are now foundries and engineering workshops.

In the open countryside of the plateau of Ajoie (Porrentruy), cereals are quite extensively grown, and the plateaus of Franches-Montagnes are used for beef cattle and horses.

*The Pre-Alps and central Alps.* In western Switzerland, in front of the central Alps, are spread the Pre-Alpine ranges of Chablais, Vaud, Fribourg and Bern. In the Saane region the medieval town of Gruyères is surrounded by farms and chalets situated in the middle of forest clearings, evidence of the pastoral activity of a region famous for its rich cheese.

Above the Tine, the valley of the Saane runs almost west to east, forming a series of gorges and open valleys. From Saanen, Bernese Gessenay corresponds to the upper north-south section of the Saane. The language and landscape are typical of the Simmental. Deep valleys lead towards the high Alps, whose steep slopes of grey limestone and glaciers contrast with the gentler outlines of the much lower mountains of flysch. The wooden houses are generously proportioned, with overhanging eaves, tiers of windows, painted decoration and German inscriptions.

In the central Alps, the extensive canton of Valais is distinguished by the depth and uniformity of the Rhône trough. Valais is the most clearly defined longitudinal valley of the whole Alps, with its double rank of peaks over 13,000 feet high and 330 square miles of glaciers (almost twice as much as in the French Alps). Deeply cut into the mountain mass, the trough has a sparse rainfall, so that the clarity of the atmosphere and the colouring of the great slopes is almost southern. Valais, with Vaud, is the chief producer of Swiss wine: 4,686 thousand gallons, almost all white wine. The lowland produces apples and pears, apricots, tomatoes, asparagus and strawberries. The aluminium factories, the chemical industries, the work in progress on the huge reservoir dams, and the construction of miles of tunnel occupy an ever-growing labour force. Valais has something of the air of a new land, and its population has doubled in a century. However, it still remains a collection of dissimilar regions.

*The Bernese Oberland.* The Alpine basin of the Aar, or the Bernese Oberland, is particularly noted for its glacial mountains in the region of Grindelwald and Lauterbrunnen. The Susten, a very modern road, links Wassen to Innertkirchen, and the track and

SWITZERLAND:
The Eiger Glacier on Mönch, in the Alps.

Switzerland has an area of nearly 16,000 square miles and a population of 5,660,000. Note the importance of agriculture in the Middle Lands, especially in the central and southern parts and in central Valais. Eastern Switzerland is devoted to forests and pasture.

| | |
|---|---|
| Agricultural areas | |
| Natural grasslands and fields | |
| Natural grasslands | |
| Forest and alpine region | |
| Rocks and glaciers | |
| Principal forests | |

A watchmaker superintending the nickel-plating of watches. Watchmaking is concentrated mainly in the Jura region. The Swiss economy is directed towards specialisation, and Swiss products enjoy a reputation for reliability and quality.

Tiefencastel, a typical Alpine village in the Graubünden.

The hay harvest in central Switzerland, high above the Lake of Aegeri. Huge bundles of hay have to be carried up slopes too steep for machinery; harvest time requires the help of the whole family.

tunnel of Lötschberg link the Aar to the Simplon. From Interlaken the railroads carry tourists to the foot of the Jungfrau, or even hoist them up the Jungfraujoch at 11,342 feet. The district of Interlaken which includes, with Grindelwald and Lauterbrunnen, the whole of Lake Brienz and the eastern end of Thun, is fairly densely populated, and more people are employed in trade, catering and transport than in agriculture. The district of Oberhasle, thinly populated and little visited by tourists, is an important source of power.

## CENTRAL SWITZERLAND

Central Switzerland is well served by communications. It was not without reason that the Romans selected the site of Windisch (Vindonissa) near Brugg, and the Hapsburgs that of the castle which perpetuates their name. At the end of the fourteenth century, seven of the eight cantons of the Federation were situated here.

*The region of Lake Lucerne.* On the alluvial lowland which extends upstream from the lake is Altdorf, immortalised in the legend of William Tell, At Brunnen the lake takes a right-angle turn and the mountain is divided into isolated blocks by valleys and sparkling lakes.

The tourist industry has made the reputation of Lucerne. From the top of the wooded Gütsch the view embraces the bay with its tower, the Wassertor, the bridges of the Reuss, the fortifications of the old city, and the new town. Below the town there are metal works, rayon and nylon factories, and mechanical engineering workshops.

*The industrial Middle Lands.* Lucerne, Basle and Winterthur form an industrial triangle. Industry originated with the work of the early craftsmen of the surrounding regions. The linen industry came to Appenzell and Thurgau, cotton to St. Gallen and the Oberland of Zürich, ironwork to the northern Jura, Fricktal and Schaffhausen. Many towns of the Middle Lands have put their capital into silk industries, or cotton, or printing. The development after 1836 of the rocksalt deposits of Schweizerhalle, Rheinfelden and Zurzach helped the chemical industry.

In the cantons of Bern and Solothurn, there has been a fair amount of success in developing industries devoted to the processing of local raw materials: linen weaving and bleaching, pottery at Langenthal, footwear at Schönenwerd, braid for hats, and lime and cement at Aarau and Olten. Metallurgy and mechanical engineering are close to the Jura. The Basle district has a very important chemical industry, and also pharmaceutical production and heavy ironworks. At Dornach and Pratteln there are silk and cement industries.

The eastern zone of the industrial triangle is particularly noted for engineering and a variety of equipment. Zürich is Switzerland's leading city.

*On the road to the Saint Gotthard.* Above Lake Lucerne, the Reuss valley reintroduces fine Alpine scenery. Urseren is a high valley reached by three passes, the Furka, the Oberalp and the Saint Gotthard, and here pastoral life remains well established.

*Tessin (Ticino).* The canton of Tessin is divided into two unequal parts by Monte Ceneri: in the north is

Sopra Ceneri, with Locarno and Lake Maggiore, in the south Sotto Ceneri with Lake Lugano. In Sopra Ceneri the valleys are deeply incised into a thick and relatively homogeneous mountain layer with continuous slopes. In Sotto Ceneri the relief is divided into sections; broad corridors and small mountains contrast with abrupt slopes. The main activities are tourist trade and commerce.

In this extremely rough countryside, where cultivation is made difficult by the steep slopes, and where the valleys are subject to flooding and swamping, there has always been every incentive to emigrate. Part of this population loss has been compensated for by immigration of foreigners and Swiss from other cantons. Tessin's problem, therefore, is how to preserve its ethnic and cultural personality. More people are employed in catering than in most other local Tessin industries (tobacco, clothing and building); only metallurgy provides work for more people.

### EASTERN SWITZERLAND

This area includes the cantons of Schaffhausen, Thurgau, St Gallen, Appenzell and the Grisons; the greater part is Alpine. The Middle Lands consist here of the limestone plateaus and well-wooded upland of Schaffhausen, and the hills of Thurgau.

*The canton of Schaffhausen.* The Rhine falls separate the navigable stretch of Lake Constance-Schaffhausen from the downstream section. Schaffhausen owes its past prosperity to compulsory trans-shipment as much as to its rapids and their motive power. The region concentrates on woollen products and metal-working with aluminium at Neuhausen.

*Valleys and orchards of Thurgau.* On the other side of the Rhine lies Thurgau, a land of east-west valleys between hills formed partly of material deposited by the old Rhine glacier. It is less wooded than the canton of Schaffhausen, with lush meadows and orchards of apples and pears. The cotton industry of St. Gallen has spread through the whole southern part of the region. Embroidery has in many places given way to knitwear, hosiery, or the manufacture of voile and muslin. The engineering industry today employs more of the remaining manpower than the textile and clothing industry.

*The textile region.* South of the gentle landscape of Thurgau, the Middle Lands become both higher and steeper. Valleys are incised into conglomerate rocks and the region passes imperceptibly into the Pre-Alpine zone where farms are isolated or huddled together in an open countryside devoted entirely to pasture. The canton of St. Gallen overcame the decline of certain textiles by developing metal and engineering industries and the manufacture of equipment for silos, flour-milling, brewing, cables and artificial silk.

*From the Rhine valley to valleys of the Grisons.* Since the embankment and straightening of the Rhine and the systematic drainage of the lowland the Rhine valley has become fertile agricultural land. It gives access to the principality of Liechtenstein and Austria. The Grisons League in the sixteenth and seventeenth centuries engaged in politics with France, Tuscany and Venice and with Spain, ruler of Milan. Grisons is a huge canton, a replica in miniature of Switzerland itself, with its federal organisation, and its distinctive politics. Its German name is Graubünden.

Once Chur controlled a circle of routes. Today, the main rail routes skirt the north of the canton. Nor has it developed in proportion to the country as a whole. The people speak more German than Rhaeto-Romansch. The landscape remains distinctive, with countless north-south valleys (whose slopes are subjected to avalanches), rich vegetation checked by the lower rainfall in the east, and a Dolomite character in its mountains sheltering whitewashed and painted houses.

The snowy winters, hard but sunny, have made the Grisons the leading health centre and the region of

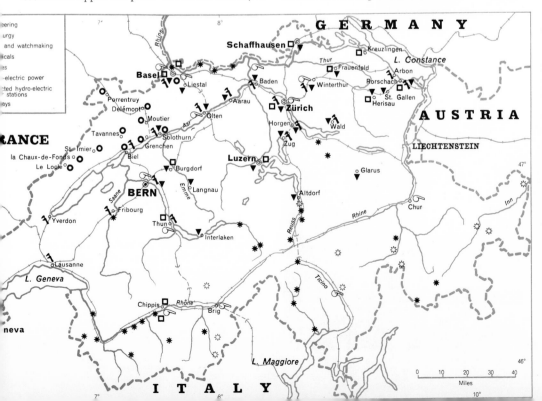

A mountain state crossed by important international routes, Switzerland concentrates on the type of production best suited to her topography and her skilled labour. The economy is very deliberately directed towards specialisation and continued research into methods of improving traditional specialities such as watches and precision instruments. Note the industrial triangle of Middle Lands (Lucerne, Basle, Winterthur) and the concentrated activity in the Jura; note, too, the lack of industry in Ticino and the extreme east. Valais is the leading power-producing area.

Traditional methods, with individual processing and treatment during several months in special cellars, account for the excellence of Swiss cheeses.

Grimsel Lake and the Spitallamm Dam, with a hydraulic power station at its foot. This part of the Bernese Oberland is an important source of power, for it contains the torrential waters of the Unteraar and the Oberaar.

Tiny, attractive Liechtenstein is tucked away on the right bank of the broad valley of the Rhine, between Switzerland and Austria. It is Alpine in character and shares the tourist trade common to the Alps.

winter sports: Saint Moritz, Davos, Arosa, Pontresina. The canton has remained agricultural, with 12 per cent of the inhabitants living off the land and Alpine pastures; the same proportion is engaged in industry. Electricity production is important.

*Switzerland's prosperity.* Everything proclaims prosperity: the towns with their carefully kept properties, building sites bristling with cranes and scaffolding, and the volume of traffic on roads and railroads. This stems partly from internal factors, from the Swiss virtues of orderliness, hard work, attention to detail and community spirit. Switzerland, a land of refuge in the centre of an agitated Europe, owed some of her past industrial prosperity to Huguenot immigrants and her policy of neutrality enabled her to escape the drain of two world wars on population and national purse. The Swiss franc, although devalued, has maintained its purchasing-power. Finally, the country has been a refuge for capital as well as for people, and this has helped the expansion of Swiss economy.

Swiss economy is very deliberately directed towards specialisation, to continued research into higher yields and quality of traditional specialities, to watching fluctuating demands or future potentials in the international market. An abundance of available capital is used for foreign investment and loan; interest yields from such sources improve the country's world position and help to secure the necessary supply of raw materials and food. With exported goods exceeding 9,000 million frances (2,900 million for machinery, appliances and instruments, 1,300 million for watches, 1,600 million for pharmaceutical products, dyes and basic chemicals, nearly 500 million for cotton, embroidery and cheese, and a tourist industry whose gross revenue was estimated at 1,000 million) Switzerland, within its small and mountainous territorial limits, is an important economic power.

# LIECHTENSTEIN

This tiny pleasant country of 62 square miles and a population of 19,000 (mainly Catholic and German-speaking) is tucked away in the broad, transverse Alpine valley of the Rhine, on the right bank of the river.

Liechtenstein originated at the Roman Rhaetia; Vaduz is its capital. It was established as a principality in 1719 for the benefit of the House of Liechtenstein, then residing in Lower Austria. A member of the Holy Roman Empire, and then of the German Confederation until 1886, Liechtenstein formed a customs union with Austria from 1852 to the end of the First World War. After the war, it concluded a currency, postal and customs union with Switzerland, which also became responsible for its diplomatic representation abroad.

Liechtenstein is made up of two regions of unequal size. The Unterland, the smaller, includes the flood plain of the Rhine, and the alluvial fans from the Schellenberg ridge. The Oberland, which includes the eastern slope of the Rhine valley, is Alpine in character and has become a tourist region.

Agriculture, including market-gardening and viticulture, once the mainstay of the economy, is now centred on the edge of these two regions, in an area influenced by the warmth of the föhn (a warm, dry wind).

Industry has developed rapidly since 1945 and now occupies 57 per cent of the population. The manufactures, often related to neighbouring Swiss and Austrian industries, include precision instruments and textiles.

# AUSTRIA

The Austrian Republic is, geographically and politically, rather like Switzerland; both are Alpine and both have federal governments. The Alps occupy 71 per cent of Austria's 32,000 square miles compared with 62 per cent in Switzerland. Thus Austria is a more integral part of the Alps. This fact has important consequences. Austria controls only a very small part of the Alpine foreland, and lies on the fringe area of the economic current which unites the lowlands of the Po and the Rhine through the centre of Switzerland. The Brenner route is the main artery of the eastern Alps. However, the political and population centre is far to the east of this axis; the triangle of Linz-Vienna-Graz contains four-fifths of Austrian industry and two-thirds of the population.

## WESTERN AUSTRIA

*Vorarlberg, Rhine province of Austria.* This province is situated 'before' the Arlberg Pass, and incorporates a small part of the Rhine foreland, the Rhine valley, the large village of Lustenau surrounded by orchards and market-gardens, and the textile centre of Dornbirn. Feldkirch and its castle lie in an area of glacial ridges at the end of the transverse valley section of the Ill through the Pre-Alps, the gateway to the Federal Republic from the west. With the forest of Bregenz, the Ill basin includes most of the Alpine Vorarlberg and can be divided, apart from the Grand Walsertal, into two main valleys: Montafon and Klostertal.

Very remote, like Walsertal, the Montafon region has produced a steady flow of emigrants from the mountains. After the Union, Germany constructed a reservoir dam in the valley to form Lake Silvretta.

The power station at Rodund produces almost 300 million kWh.

Eastwards, bare, harsh Klostertal provides a direct route which is, with difficulty, followed by the railroad. The Arlberg line has the steepest gradient of any of the main Alpine routes and was intended to weld the Rhine Province of Austria to the rest of the country, and to encourage communications between Switzerland and Western Europe and the old Austro-Hungarian Empire. In Vorarlberg snow is abundant, and Walsertal accommodates at least 350,000 foreigners each winter.

*Tyrol, the accessible region.* Since the inclusion of its southern part in Italy, Tyrol and East Tyrol have been separated, and in this volume East Tyrol will be considered with eastern Austria. It grew up as a State on the crest of the Alps, controlling the Brenner Pass: completely Alpine, it stretches from west to east along the Inn, which bends in the opposite direction at each end, at Landeck and Kufstein. To the south of the Inn is the junction with the Sill valley, or Wipptal, which leads up to the Brenner; this is framed on both sides by the glaciated valleys of Ötztal and Zillertal. To the north of the Inn the calcareous and schistose Alps, including the Karwendel (9,013 feet), rise in a steep, defensive wall. Fortunately there are several breaches opened up by former glaciers, so the Tyrol is easily linked to the Bavarian foreland, and to the province of Salzburg by the glaciated passes of Saint Johann and Kitzbühel.

The Inn valley forms a very good natural region. It is over 80 miles long and is part of the longitudinal valley which starts in Klostertal and extends eastwards along the Salzach and the Enns. The warm, dry föhn wind and the sunny aspect of the northern slopes help to make it a warm, sheltered valley, although the winters are severe. The upper Inntal adheres to a three-course rotation of rye, barley and potatoes; Landeck produces electro-chemicals and numerous textile workshops make *loden* (thick local woollen cloth), cotton and ribbon. The broad alluvial lowland of the lower Inntal is the region of the 'pounds', a system whereby the fields are put to

The Tauern hydro-electric scheme in the province of Salzburg. In the foreground is the Margaritzen Reservoir with the Möll Dam on the left and the Margaritzen Dam on the right. They form part of a network of dams serving several power stations. Increasing quantities of electricity are 'exported' to Germany and Italy.

Agriculture is the chief occupation in the Alpine foreland along the Danube, and in the Styrian foreland to the east and south-east of Vienna (Burgenland and the Graz district), as well as in the Mur valley and Carinthia (Klagenfurt). These agricultural districts cover little more than twenty per cent of the total area of Austria, but the intensity with which they are cultivated varies greatly: in the Burgenland district the soil benefits from volcanic outcrops and supports a very high rural population. Climate, as well as relief, has determined the concentration of agriculture, for these districts are on the fringes of the Hungarian Plain.

grass for a number of years. Around Innsbruck the important industries are engineering, metal-work and optics; at Wörgl and Kufstein, pharmaceutical products, timber and cement. The copper, silver and salt industries were once responsible for the wealth of the Tyrol. Electric power is one of the foundations of the region's economy today; more than 1,000 million kWh are available.

Finally, tourist trade is important in the Tyrol in summer and winter alike. Innsbruck, a popular centre, controls the Brenner and the Arlberg passes. The alluvial fan of the Sill has pushed the Inn against the valley side at Hötting, and thus determined the site of the bridge to which the town owes its name. It is a ski-ing resort, a tourist base, a commercial and residential town, and a university centre.

*The province of Salzburg.* Before the construction of the Tauern tunnel and the opening of the Gross Glockner tourist road, the ecclesiastical State of Salzburg controlled the longitudinal Alpine valleys. The province is shaped like an inverted T, the horizontal line of the T formed by the Salzach and the upper Enns, with part of the upper Mur, and the vertical line consisting of a strip of territory between the German re-entrant of Berchtesgaden and the Salzkammergut in Upper Austria.

The high limestone Alps of Salzburg, with those of neighbouring Salzkammergut, belong to a particularly rugged section of the mountains. The snow-line here is about 9,000 feet; the limestone conceals wonderful caves splendid with ice cascades, such as those at Dachstein, and especially the Eisriesenwelt, 'the Ice Giants' World' of the Tennen mountains. The wild beauty of these mountains is enhanced on the northern slopes by the pleasant lake of St. Wolfgang and the deep and forbidding-looking Lake Hallstatt at the foot of the Dachstein.

The longitudinal valley of the Salzach is not so varied in shape or colouration. From Krimml to

St. Johann, the Pinzgau or valley of the upper Salzach stretches for about 50 miles. The railroad now runs through Pinzgau, formerly one of the most isolated parts of Austria, linking Salzburg and Innsbruck via Zell and Kitzbühel with its schistose highland. Smoke from its aluminium factories draws attention to Lend some distance away; the steep, ice-covered High Tauern are very suitable for hydro-electric development and Salzburg is a big producer of power for the Federal German Republic (1,300 million kWh).

This is one of the most popular tourist areas. The castle looks down on Salzburg, a handsome town of over 100,000 inhabitants, enhanced with squares and buildings in the baroque style; and every year music-lovers gather for a festival devoted mainly to the works of Mozart.

### EASTERN AUSTRIA

East of Salzburg Austria extends nearly 190 miles from north to south, and also 190 miles from east to west. With East Tyrol, Upper and Lower Austria, the federal area of Vienna, Burgenland, Styria and Carinthia, this part of Austria covers 24,450 square miles out of a total of 32,000 square miles, and includes 87 per cent of the population of the Republic.

*The eastern Alps.* In eastern Austria the Alps widen out and lose height. The Styrian mountain mass of Totes Gebirge barely exceeds 8,200 feet. The well-named Nieder Tauern is nowhere higher than 9,500 feet. And unlike the rest of the Alps, the southern slope is broader than the northern slope which has only a small share of Alpine wealth and population.

Whilst the economy of Salzkammergut is dependent of the development of salt-mining and cattle-rearing, plus the income from the tourist industry, the transverse valley of the Enns concentrates in particular on metallurgy. The combined resources of iron ore and wood encouraged the development of the iron

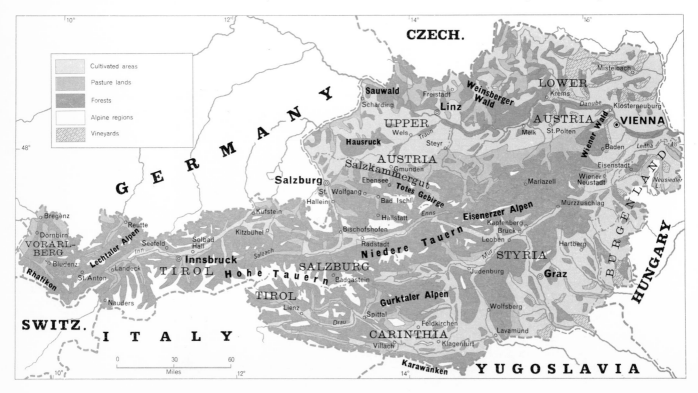

industry in this region of Steyr, from which Styria derives its name. The Enns provides some of the electric power of Upper Austria, on the northern Alpine slopes, producing nearly 700 million kWh per annum.

On the southern side of the Alps, East Tyrol is fairly isolated. The lands of the Drava begin here—a series of east-to-west valleys, including the Drava itself, bordered by the magnificent ridges of the Austrian Dolomites south of Lienz. The valleys are quite low (about 1,700 feet at Spittal, on the Drava) and the area has an almost southern appearance along the lakes of Millstatt and Wörth, which are very popular in the summer.

Southern Carinthia lies at the foot of the high wall of the Karawanken separating Austria from Yugoslavia. The railroad to Ljubljana and Gorizia overcomes the obstacle with a five-mile tunnel. Industrial activity is represented by mining and by lead and zinc processing.

In the north-south valleys of Görtschitz, Lavant and the middle Mur, and in the south-west north-east trough of the upper Mur and the Mürz, local resources of timber, iron ore and lignite have been developed.

Such industrial development gives a high density of population to the valleys on the south side of the eastern Alps. From Semmering with its frontage of large hotels to Bruck, the valley floor of the Mürz is under grass. Fields and barns increase in number towards Mürzzuschlag; there is a succession of villages of roughcast houses, where timber is seen only in roof shingles and occasional hay lofts. The slopes are covered with mixed broad-leaved and coniferous forest. At night the activity in the streets of Graz resembles that of a Mediterranean town. A market town, communications centre and second city of Austria, it is also an industrial area with factories for automobiles, shoes, paper and engineering.

*The Bohemian Massif.* Part of the south side of the Bohemian Massif is shared between the provinces of Upper and Lower Austria. The Weinviertel, the region of fertile hills east of Krems, concentrates on intensive wheat production, viticulture, and raising stall-fed cattle, encouraged by the proximity of the Vienna market.

*The Alpine foreland.* The Hausruck (2,625 feet), an old alluvial fan of the Salzach and Traun, recalls on a smaller scale the Swiss Napf. In this rural area industry is gaining ground. The lowlands of fluvio-glacial gravel between the Traun and the Enns have been cut up into terraces and used for arable farming. Orchards surround the villages. Linen is manufactured at Lambach, glass at Wels, and there are paper works along the Traun. Between Durnstein, on the Danube, and the approaches to Vienna the countryside has a prosperous look. The vineyards and plum orchards are replaced by open fields with strips where maize and cultivated grass are grown in rotation on the arable land. Apple and walnut trees are everywhere. In the broad valley of St. Pölten, parallel to the Wachau, the villages are close together, and the large farmhouses with their closed yards are surrounded by small houses.

VIENNA AND THE VALLEY OF THE DANUBE. *The unity of the northern fringe.* The stately Danube is not

Of the working population, 23 per cent are engaged on the land. Austria's is an agricultural economy that almost satisfies home demands: food imports are only 20 per cent of the total.

Salzburg, a handsome town of 100,000 inhabitants overlooked by the castle.

entirely free from disadvantages. Between Linz and Vienna it cuts into the spurs of the Bohemian Massif, and its speed is between 7 and 10 feet per second. Linz, with Urfahr on the opposite bank, controls the confluence of the Traun with the Danube as well as the crossing leading, via Freistadt, to Budejovice in Czechoslovakia. Linz is also an important industrial centre, with blast-furnaces, steelworks, coke ovens and a thermal power station.

The descent of the Danube by boat is of most interest below the confluence of the Enns. Leaving Pöchlarn, the feudal ruins conjure up thoughts of the legend of the Nibelungen. In Wachau the Danube valley is like the gorge section of the Rhine. The wooded slopes are crowned by medieval ruins, with terraced vines at Spitz and Dürnstein.

The Danube is a rich source of potential power. The plant at Ybbs-Persenbeug provides more than one million kWh, and has been jointly constructed by Austria and Germany; a further twelve stations are planned.

*The eastern lowlands of Austria.* A series of rivers descending the Graz Alps to the south-east have dissected the Styrian foreland into hills, and their sands and clays form part of the infilling of the Hungarian Basin. The prosperity of this region is based on maize, orchards, poultry, cattle and horses. In the region of Eisenstadt, to the west of the Neusiedler lake, the vine is exceptionally important.

The Vienna Basin is bordered by a fault-line and a thermal line running from Mödling and Baden as far as Burgenland. To the south of Vienna and along the mountain slopes the plain is edged with gentle and highly cultivated hills. The metallurgical industry is important at Wiener Neustadt, and other industries include engineering and tyre manufacture. To the north of the Danube, the alluvial lands of the Marchfeld form the granary of Lower Austria. In the north of the plain, an oilfield, Zistersdorf, extends from the neighbourhood of Vienna to Breclav in Czechoslovakia.

*Vienna.* Vienna (Wien) owes its name to the modest River Wien. The Wienerwald is notable for its numerous valleys and dense forest cover, preserved in the past by the landed gentry. Thus the capital has at its gates a huge natural park, invaded every weekend by crowds of its citizens. In Vienna itself the Danube is divided into three branches: the Canal, the boundary of old Vienna on the north side; the Old Danube, suitable for aquatic sports; and the Danube proper, straightened after 1868 and confined between the high banks of its larger bed. The famous Ring was constructed in the second half of the nineteenth century on the site of the fortifications and glacis which surrounded the 'Innere Stadt' and was dominated by the bold spire of St. Stephen's Cathedral. With its public buildings and gardens bordering the Hofburg, the Opera House and its avenues, the airy and peaceful Ring contrasts markedly with the early eighteenth-century suburbs found between the Ring and the Gürtel, encircling avenue on the site of the old defensive wall. These suburbs include the very busy districts of the West Station and the Mariahilferstrasse. There are varied industries: engineering (automobiles), textiles (linen, hemp and jute), factories for footwear, glass and petroleum. In spite of economic crises, civil war, the fighting at the end of the Second World War which damaged it severely, and a long military occupation, the noble bearing of this great city augurs well for the future of the Austrian State.

THE FUTURE OF AUSTRIA. *A sound economic basis.* The economy of Austria rests on solid foundations. After 1918 it had to cope with the inevitable difficulties of becoming a neighbour to the successor States which were now its rivals. This situation was aggravated by the misfortune of having to support a capital too large for the rest of the country, which was almost entirely

Hay-making figures largely in the agricultural routine throughout Austria. Farm equipment increased after the war with help from Marshall Aid.

Alpine in character. Complete readjustment was necessary, and this was interrupted by the Anschluss. The Second World War and the Occupation weighted the scales still further against it.

Austria is more capable than Switzerland of feeding itself. Of the working population 23 per cent (against 12 per cent in Switzerland) are engaged in agriculture. With a total population 30 per cent greater than that of Switzerland, Austria produces slightly less milk and almost the same amount of wine; on the other hand, it harvests twice as much wheat, four times as many potatoes, even more barley, oats and maize, and about eight times as much sugar-beet. Agricultural equipment increased considerably after the Union and after the abolition of customs barriers between Austria and Germany; more recently, in the post-war years, it was helped by Marshall Aid.

Austria produces six million tons of lignite annually, two-thirds of which come from Styria. This is insufficient for home needs and some coal has to be imported from Germany and Poland. It also has important petroleum resources and an annual hydro-electric production of 10,640 million kWh, with a potential vastly greater. Raw materials include iron ore, magnesite and several non-ferrous metals, Forest production is almost three times as important as in Switzerland.

The heavy iron and steel industry of Styria has not developed many secondary industries, and a large proportion of its products are exported; these include pig-iron, crude steel, refractory bricks and slabs of magnesite, paper, fertilizers and electricity. This type of economy has its origin in history: Austrian industry was intended to supply the requirements of the old Austro-Hungarian Empire, and then the Third Reich.

Unlike Switzerland, Austria lacks a solid financial foundation. With the Anschluss, three-quarters of the firms became German property; then petroleum was considered as coming under reparations and was put under Russian control until the signing of the peace treaty. American help was necessary after the Second World War.

*A future of promise.* Financial stability was achieved as a result of measures which included nationalisation of all electricity undertakings producing for distribution, certain banks, transport companies and mines. The three-year investment plan introduced in 1950, which was partly financed by funds from the Marshall Plan, also helped to stabilise finances. Austria has had to find work for several hundreds of thousands of refugees and displaced persons. New industries have been started, notably the glass industry; factories have opened using the newly acquired manpower. Increasing quantities of electricity are exported to Germany and Italy, for power produced in western Austria exceeds local requirements and is available for export. Finally, the tourist industry is one of Austria's most important resources and covers an important part of the trade deficit.

Because of its position in Europe, Austria can prosper only in an atmosphere of good will with its neighbours. It remains a transit country for movements from north to south. Any improvement in East-West relationships could only be to its economic and political advantage and must therefore be fostered.

Chemicals are an important industry in Linz. This ammonium sulphate plant produces 180,000 tons annually.

Panorama of Vienna, the capital of Austria, showing the Danube and, in the distance, the forest of the Wienerwald. In Vienna, the Danube is divided into three branches: the Canal, the boundary of old Vienna on the north side; the Old Danube; and the Danube proper. Today a frontier town, Vienna's old buildings recall a more glamorous past.

# GERMANY

Germany occupies a northward-sloping region of Central Europe. With the exception of the Bavarian plateau, the whole country drains towards the North Atlantic and its gulfs. It is the most exclusively European of all the great national units.

During the tenth, eleventh and twelfth centuries, the Holy Roman Empire, as it was from 962 to 1806, waged a struggle of varying fortunes, and ended by reconquering beyond the Elbe the Germanic people's original homeland, which had been abandoned to the Slavs when the Germanic tribes pushed westwards. From the thirteenth to the fifteenth centuries, the Germans penetrated still farther eastwards and carried their arms beyond the Vistula.

The German 'Push towards the East' *(Drang nach Osten)*, which during the eighteenth and nineteenth centuries assumed largely the shape of an economic and technical domination, had before its ebb in the twentieth century determined that Germany's future should be very different from that of the maritime nations by the ocean.

*Achievement of Unity (1871).* Germany has always had shifting frontiers except in the essential regions of the Rhineland and the Hercynian massifs which formed its cradle. In addition, the country was continually subdivided in an ever-changing mosaic of units of different degrees of political importance. These small States, although they enjoyed various political constitutions (kingdoms, principalities, ecclesiastical fiefs, free towns, Hansa cities, Länder), have always been held together by a succession of links — leagues, confederations, empires.

The concept of one unified nation, *das Deutschland,* was gaining ground as early as the end of the eighteenth century; between 1802 and 1806 Napoleon reduced the number of sovereign German States from about 300 to 39, thus meeting some nationalist aspirations. The Germanic Confederation of 1915 was the first effective step towards unity. From 1828 to 1854, the Customs Union *(Zollverein)* obliterated most of the economic frontiers within Germany. A final internal conflict took place in 1866 between victorious Prussia and the southern German States, but with the alliance of 1870–71 German unity became an accomplished fact in the form of the Second German Empire.

After defeat in the First World War, Germany was thrown once more into a period of confusion. The so-called 'Weimar' Federal Republic (1918–33) preceded the era of the Third Reich during which the nation was first swept up in a whirl of triumphant expansion and then cast down into the abyss of defeat. Now, under the regime of the Bonn Federal Republic, West Germany has effected an almost incredible revival.

During the last half-century Germany has undergone several changes in area and population; in 1946, at the end of the Second World War, it contained 137,063 square miles and 66 million inhabitants. By 1961 the population had risen to 73 million.

*Dissection in 1945.* Although the territorial modifications brought about by the Second World War (and by the 'Cold War') have not been recognised or

Foundries and copper works along the lower Rhine at Duisburg-Hochfeld.

The Zugspitze (9,720 feet), the highest peak in Germany, on the boundary of Bavaria and Austria.

confirmed by international treaty, Germany was divided into the British zone in the north-west, the American in the centre, the French in the south-west, and the Russian in the east. The Prussian provinces beyond the Oder and the Neisse have been detached from Germany, their populations have been displaced and the regions annexed to Poland or the U.S.S.R. (39,758 square miles to Poland, and 4,246 square miles to Russia). What remained of Germany was split into two States in 1949, the frontiers determined by the arbitrary boundaries of the military occupation zones; they are linked together by a common past, a single nationality, and a firm hope of reunification, but divided by the most diametrically opposed economic and social policies. The German Federal Republic (the *Bund*) in the west is a federal state basing its fundamental policy on liberal capitalist ideas and practices, while the German Democratic Republic (*Deutsche demokratische Republik*) in the east is a centralised, State-controlled unit developing along communist lines.

LANDSCAPE AND REGIONS. *Four major natural regions.* Germany is a central European transition zone in which continental and maritime climates are almost evenly balanced. The July average temperature is 16°C. (60·5°F.) on the coastal plain, while on the southern plateaus the average is 17°C. (61·5°F.) and exceeds 19°C. (66°F.) in the mild Rhine valley. In January, the Rhine and Moselle valleys, Westphalia and the Frisian area are the only regions with temperatures mostly above freezing point.

In Schleswig-Holstein and on the Great Plain, cool winds and a misty atmosphere lend the landscape a rather greyish 'western' colour all the year round. Rainfall is fairly regular at all seasons; autumns are mild and long, springs chilly and late; on the Baltic slope and in Brandenburg the weather is drier.

Over the hills and up the deep valleys of the Rhine or the Weser summer rain is heavy on the heights, and both warmth and cold are more marked because the low-lying areas sheltered from the westerly winds are relatively dry. After a fine autumn, the brilliant winter sun — except when masked by the frosty Danube fogs — shines uninterrupted for hours over the snowy expanses.

Four great natural regions (of unequal area) make up the land of Germany today: the narrow fringe of the Bavarian Alps; the Subalpine plateau of Bavaria and Swabia, south of the Danube; the most ancient massifs (Hercynian massifs) north of the Danube and the basins they enclose; and the western extremity of the broad, low, alluvial glacial plain of northern Europe, lying between the Hercynian massifs and the North Sea and the Baltic.

*Alpine fringe and Bavarian plateau.* In the extreme south and stretching for some 160 miles (drained throughout by the Danube), the Bavarian Alps are an Alpine fringe made up of short 'links', intersected by grassy corridors, with three deeper indentations: the Allgäu, the upper valley of the Iller; the Garmisch basin on the Amper, and the Berchtesgaden basin.

The Bavarian plateau is a fairly uniform glacis, or slope, pierced by rivers that fan out on its surface. Here the moraines of the most ancient Alpine glaciation have left a jumble of low hills whose rounded surfaces are covered with grassland. Wide clearings surrounding the villages cut into the mantle of huge spruce forests. Generally speaking, this region is rather poor. Farther north, as far as the Danube, where the plain was not subjected to glaciation, the landscape is drier and more rolling, and its dales more densely populated.

The river Lech is an ethnological and natural barrier between Bavaria and Swabia. Bavaria has something eastern European about it, with its monotonous landscape, its Danubian, essentially peasant and only partly modernised character; Swabia, more varied in appearance and more attractive, is definitely Western and very unlike the Rhineland. Upstream, in a rolling country of recent moraines and morasse, the attractive Allgäu Pre-Alps are covered with rich meadows and dairy-farms. Westwards, beyond the Iller, the Upper Swabian plateau in Württemburg spreads out in open fields, and peat-bogs. In the south lies a jumble of grassy 'molehills', with clumps of firs, and a sprinkling of high-perched farms. The northern shores of

The Black Forest, or Schwarzwald, clothes Germany's highest summits outside the Alpine region. Cultivated and cheerful on the Baden side, its immense, solid forest stretches silent to the north-east.

A view of Oberwese on the Rhine. Here summer rain is heavy on higher ground; the low-lying areas are relatively dry. Vines clothe the terraced valley. Germany's vineyards are the most northerly in Europe and demand great care to protect them from frost damage.

Lake Constance enjoy a mild climate and are dotted with gardens and villas set among orchards and even vineyards.

*Ancient massifs.* The ancient massifs of the Hercynian zone present the most typical of German landscapes — gently rounded, well-wooded hills stretching away to the horizon. In the vales neat fields and villages are surrounded by orchards. Here, the Rhine runs between the Vosges in France and the Black Forest in Germany.

The Black Forest, or Schwarzwald, raises its loftiest bare granite summits in the south (about 4,900 feet), the highest points in Germany except the Alps. It is scored by steep, narrow valleys with many glacial terraces. On the Baden side are very small fields, cheerful farms and terraced villages; on the Württemberg slopes, an immense, silent mass of fir forests.

In the neighbourhood of Karlsruhe, on the right bank of the Rhine, the mountains give way for about 30 miles to an attractive and fertile region: the Kraichgau. Before reaching Heidelberg the ground rises to enclose the sinuous course of the Neckar and its outlet on to the plain. The great beech forest makes its appearance as the Odenwald; it is a lonely region but a sportsman's paradise.

Opposite Karlsruhe, on the left bank, is another sandstone plateau of the same height, covered with pines and beeches — the Haardt. Still further west and abutting on Lorraine, is the Saar, a district of rolling pasture and hills that rise to the foothills of the Hansrück.

*The Rhine.* The Rhine traverses 540 miles of German territory, through four natural well-defined regions. First there is the narrow passage through which the great torrent pours to border or cross Swiss territory as far as Basle, harnessed en route for hydroelectric power at the roaring Schauffhausen Falls. Beyond Basle is the upper and mid-Rhine basin, where the waters flow less turbulently as far as Bingen. Beyond Bingen is the 'Heroic Gorge' where the deep, swirling waters have cut their way for about 62 miles through the schist massif. For the final 95 miles of its course the Rhine, majestic and calm, flows slowly over an immense plain to its estuary in Holland. Navigation is possible all the year round, except for a few days of fog or ice-jams each winter.

*The wealth of the middle Rhine basin.* The splendid alluvial plain of the Rhine's middle course is enclosed and sheltered, warm and with clear skies, though liable to winter frosts. This plain is the heart and the crossroads of northern Europe and from this point the river is navigable. The built-up areas are prosperous, urbanised townships set in the dry, narrow and attractive Breisgau to the south and in the damper plain of central Baden (Karlsruhe) with its crops of maize and colza, walnut-trees and chestnut woods. The *Bergstrasse* is noted for its plums, cherries, almonds and peaches. The Palatine plain is well wooded but its main feature is a slope of loess and of wheat fields rising to meet a long line of low hills, the *Weinstrasse*, which are covered with vines that come right down to the river bank farther north.

Finally, the Rheingau terraces from Wiesbaden to Rüdesheim (on the right bank) look across the river to the fertile market-gardens of the Mainz area, while on the Rheingau slopes the famous grapes that yield the golden Rhine wines ripen.

*The compact block of the schist massif.* The Rhine schist massif is a fourfold block of monotonous, wild and barren plateaus, containing some of the most isolated parts of Germany. On the right hand the Taunus raised it beech-covered summits, 2,885 feet above the Rhenish Hesse towns. Opposite, the Hunsrück is still more harsh and foresaken, rising to a high, grassy plateau (2,585 feet). Beyond the course of the Moselle. the Eifel, a wind-swept moorland with rocky roads winding among copses and scrub, pushes upward to a height of 2,490 feet. It was formerly a military area and played a considerable part in the frontier strategy.

On the other side of the Rhine is the Westerwald, more inviting, less monotonous and more populated, with great herds of cattle on its basalt plateaus and extensive beech-covered schists.

*The busy Rhine gorge.* Through the rocky Rhine Narrows, below the old castles and walled vineyards, winds and twists a heavy volume of river-traffic.

Downstream the Rhine broadens out at Koblenz, where it is joined by the Moselle and the Lahn. The Moselle reflects in its lazy loops steeply sloping vineyards, flourishing orchards and quiet but cheerful old villages.

At Bonn the Rhine flows into the Cologne basin which retains some trace of a mild southern climate even as far north as Düsseldorf. A fertile agricultural region lies round Düren and Krefeld. In the Cleves area stock-breeding and dairy-farming occupy most of the plain. On the right bank, three rivers (the Wupper, the Ruhr and the Lippe) serve to mark the gradations of the great coalfield as it descends to the Westphalian plain.

*Swabian-Franconian basin and Bohemian borderland.* The Swabian-Franconian basin is situated in the heart of the Hercynian area and forms a crescent. The Neckar, Württemberg's principal river, rises between the Black Forest and the Swabian Jura, or Swabian Alb. Open and cultivated areas contrasting with the dark forests of the sandstone massifs extend from west of Stuttgart to north of Würzburg. This is the granary of the region, but on the slopes of the Neckar, the Rems and the Main there are also numerous vineyards.

Lower Swabia is divided into attractive little districts by a tangle of valleys. Neighbouring Franconia has the same substratum but a harsher climate, poorer soil, lower and less diversified hills, and a less gracious landscape.

The Swabian Alb comes to an abrupt end at the flat, fertile and circular basin of the Riess. Beyond, the Franconian Jura raises a wide semicircle round the gloomy, sandy countryside and pine forests of Nuremburg.

The upper Main, near Bayreuth, and the Naab of the Upper Palatinate, run through a transition region entirely covered with the most deserted and wildest of all the German fir forests. Rainfall is heavy, and the population, whose life is hard, is concentrated in the long fissure of the Regen that runs through the middle of the area.

The bright, mild valley of the middle Main, through which the river meanders in lazy loops, is set with vines and plum orchards. Two dead volcanoes covered with peat-bogs and rain- and snow-soaked meadows surround the verdant basin of Fulda. This area is one of the poorest in Germany, from which emigration was once among the heaviest. Between the Vogelsberg and the Taunus, the fertile, well-tilled depression of the Wetterau is the easiest natural line of communication between south and north Germany and this is the reason for Frankfurt's prosperity.

To the north of Kassel, the curved ridges of the Weser, crowned by beech forests, descend gradually through a countryside of ancient little towns. To the east of the broken Weser ridges, two tall Primary massifs rise as horsts, or elevated blocks, and surround the sedimentary basin of Thuringia. First comes the Harz with the legendary granite promontory of the Brocken enveloped in cloud and fog. Fir forests and peat-bogs cover over one-half of the Harz plateau, while on its broad slopes lies a belt of industrial towns. To the south juts the slender spur of the Thruinger-wald, a wooded barrier, but very highly industrialised.

To the south-west lies the Saxon Erzgebirge, a crystalline massif (2,855 feet) on the Bohemian frontier and the first of the Hercynian secondary ranges to be cleared, cultivated and worked. It is an over-populated region; towns, villages, workshops and factories stretch up to the round, blunt summits. THE NORTHERN PLAIN. From Dresden, the Leipzig-Halle depression and the outlet of the Thuringian basin to the Weser heights beyond Hanover lies a region without charm but one of the most fertile in Germany, long established and densely populated. Northwards there is a region of moors, with pink or red heather and juniper bushes covering immense areas of the middle course of the Elbe. The heath is being replanted with pines in a number of places.

*Brandenburg and Mecklenburg.* To the east, and in the middle of Brandenburg, the soil is sandy or peaty, and at times marshy. Here and there are stretches of gently rolling, fairly fertile land that is well cultivated and populated. But for the most part the landscape is one of vast pine forests and is rather monotonous.

Farther north, beyond another forest zone, the middle of the Mecklenburg plateau (655 feet) presents innumerable sheets of water, where the extremities of the frontal moraines lie. Some of them are of considerable extent, surrounded by woods of beech and pine.

*The Geest. The Marschen. Schleswig-Holstein.* To the west of the Elbe and Lüneberg Heath is the melancholy countryside of the Geest, once glaciated and subsequently eroded. Sterile peat-bogs extend interminably, flecked here and there with the waters of reed-ringed meres. The bogs are worked for fuel, but more and more they are being drained, cut into squares, covered with small farms, and cultivated as in neighbouring Holland.

Between Geest and the sea-silts of the Watten there are a number of fertile polders along the coast and the estuaries. They were protected by dykes as early as the eleventh century and are known as the *Marschen*. The string of high dunes of the Frisian Islands from Borkum to Sylt forms a protective screen and cuts off the Watten and the Marschen from the North Sea.

West of the middle course of the Elbe stretches the vast Lüneburg Heath, a region of moors and juniper bushes covering 2,315 square miles of the Northern Plain.

An oil worker at Heide, northern Germany. Although the main industrial resource is coal, Germany has considerable oil reserves, near Celle on the Netherlands frontier and south of Hamburg.

The castle at Würzburg, built in the eighteenth century. Würzburg itself, once the capital of Lower Franconia, is also a university town and an industrial centre.

Lastly, Schleswig-Holstein has portions of each of these eastern and western landscapes on both sides of its isthmus.

POPULATION AND HABITAT. The German people, who since 1945 have been squeezed between the Oder and the Ardennes, do not today include any ethnological minority except for a small number of Danes and the 60,000 Wends or Slavs of Lusatia.

As a people, the Germans are hard-working and tenacious, serious and eager to learn, filled with ideas of grandeur and expansion; at the same time they are conventional, respectful of social and official position, and of rather solemn disposition. They like orderliness and are ready to accept orders and to submit to what seems in the general or national interest. Enjoying the most modern equipment and employing the most advanced techniques in a highly traditional setting, they are, generally speaking, of bourgeois behaviour — and with post-war prosperity many workers are now able to enjoy middle-class living standards.

The German population still shows signs of the division between the old great Germanic groups, divisions which were perpetuated in the duchies of the early Middle Ages and which perhaps to this day are the real internal frontiers rather than the political borders of the Länder and districts. There are differences of character, for instance, between the Westphalians, who are energetic, uncommunicative and undemonstrative, and the slightly Latinised Lower Rhinelanders, who tend to be vivacious and enterprising.

Differences of origin are reflected in the houses, in tastes and, particularly, in dialects. Though the High German of Hanover has become the official language, 'Middle' German is spoken from Saxony to the middle Rhine (between Speyer and Düsseldorf), and Low German in the north.

*The village.* The earliest form of German habitat we can discover is the village agglomeration, with houses set haphazardly in the middle of a piece of land divided equally among the inhabitants. Such villages are almost the general rule throughout western Germany up to the Elbe and the Saale. Names ending in *-ingen, -ing, -heim* and *-dorf* indicate the oldest of such villages. Other, more recent villages — the *Wald,* or *Marschhufendörfer* (twelfth or thirteenth centuries) — strung out along a single street, mark forest-clearings in the Black Forest, the Odenwald, the Spessart, Saxony and the Frisian marshes. Beyond the Elbe are the *Strassendörfer,* winding along the sides of roads; the *Angerdörfer* set in an oblong common round the church, the pond and a few trees; the *Rundlinge,* formerly fortified and more or less of Slav origin, rounded and enclosing a central square.

*Types of house.* The typical German dwelling is a house with a visible wooden framework that is painted or more often blackened, and walls of whitewashed brick or cob. Each storey has a row of small, close-set, shuttered windows. There is no balcony. The high, pointed roof (perhaps with eaves in the front) has tall dormers and cowled chimneys, and is covered with Flemish-type tiles or, in the south, with fish-scale shingles. There are, of course, local variations on the basic type. Stone houses are found only in parts of Swabia and Franconia and from Frankfurt to Cologne and Trier in the schist massif, where they are roofed and faced with slates.

Farms with open yards and separate outbuildings are common, especially on the Lüneberg Heath. The Franconian type, with enclosed yards, closed gateway and blocks of buildings forming three sides of a square (dwelling, barn and stalls), is the commonest all over central Germany. The single house that shelters men and beasts under the same roof assumes a variety of forms. To the east of the Lech, in Bavaria, there are wooden chalets with several storeys, balconies, and low roofs that project far beyond the walls.

*Spacious towns.* In the towns, the characteristic picture of Old Germany is of a market-place surrounded by houses with four or five projecting storeys (or, in the north, with Flemish gables of brick), a fountain and a sixteenth or seventeenth century *Rathaus* (town hall). Watchtowers, turrets, lanterns and belfries are numerous: the tall green copper spires of the northern towns, onion-bulb belfries and pepper-pot roofs.

A number of German towns have Roman foundations; many were important in Carolingian times; in the eleventh century yet others sprang up as market-places or settlements round castles or monasteries. Many towns were founded during the recolonisation of the east. The industrial towns date from the nineteenth century.

The German towns soon won their liberties. In particular, the Hanseatic cities in the north and the Imperial cities in the south supplied an enterprising class of patricians and a body of skilled and experienced craftsmen who laid the foundation for modern Germany's commerce and industry. The towns of today have developed extraordinarily during the last century, but no one can claim to be the sole arbiter of taste and fashion or the inevitable leader in the political sphere.

*The importance of religion.* It was during the struggle between Emperors and Popes and, later, during Luther's Reformation that a certain awareness of the existence of the German 'Community' came into being. The seventeenth-century religious wars broke up this 'Community' into little principalities with different religions. Today the area of contact between the dominating Catholicism of the south and the Protestantism of the north is the Rhine, and the two Churches are among the clearest links between the two Germanies at the present time.

In West Germany (since the division between East and West) the figures for Protestants (51 per cent) and Catholics (44 per cent) almost balance. However, in East Germany the Lutherans form 81 per cent of the population and, in consequence, the Protestants in West Germany are particularly anxious to see Germany reunified. In the Federal Republic there are now about 25,000 Jews against 280,000 in 1930.

In the economic sphere in southern and western Germany, Protestantism is especially associated with industrialisation and modernisation. Factory owners have tended to inhabit the Lutheran towns and villages, while the Catholic towns have been mostly agricultural and residential centres. Modern economic life has, however, blurred this pattern: in the Ruhr, for example, are both Protestants and Catholics.

## THE GERMAN FEDERAL REPUBLIC (WEST GERMANY)

The territory of the *Bund,* the German Federal Republic, covers 95,683 square miles. It has become the country's main axis, so that the Federal Republic's 'Atlantic' character has been markedly accentuated.

At present, with a population of 55 million (578 to the square mile), West Germany swarms with people. In North Rhine–Westphalia there are 1,080 inhabitants squeezed into each square mile.

The *Bund* also has the largest population of any Western European country. In matters of population it may indeed be compared with a Great Britain without the support of a Commonwealth or the supplies from overseas territories. The Rhine basin occupies almost one-half of West Germany's total area but the area's relative importance is still greater from historical, demographic and economic points of view. All due allowances being made, the new Germany has increased its resemblances with German Switzerland and Holland: the same federalist spirit, the same religious composition, and the same economic structure to ensure that output, markets, business and trade assume more importance than politics.

ORGANISATION AND PROBLEMS. *The ten-State Federal Republic.* The German Federal Republic (*Bundesrepublik Deutschland*) is governed according to the Fundamental Law of May 8, 1949, by a Chancellor (*Bundeskanzler*) who is chosen by the Diet (*Bundestag*) and assisted by nineteen federal ministers appointed by the Federal President (*Bundespräsident*), himself elected for five years by the Federal Diet and the Federal Council (*Bundesrat*) combined. The Chancellor is responsible to the *Bundestag*, whose members are elected for a term of four years by general election. The *Bundesrat* is composed of forty-two members appointed by the local governments of the ten States making up the Federation.

Bonn was chosen as provisional capital in 1949. This university and residential town was chosen in preference to Frankfurt (larger, more central and traditionally more important) because it is nearer to Cologne and the Ruhr, and with the intention of stressing the temporary character of the makeshift federal capital.

The ten federated States (Länder) are as follows: Schleswig-Holstein, Hamburg, Bremen, Lower Saxony, North Rhine-Westphalia, Hesse, Rhineland-Palatinate, Baden-Württemberg, Bavaria and the Saar.

Schleswig-Holstein (capital: Kiel), to the northeast, is an essentially agricultural land, today overcrowded with refugees. From 1459 to 1863 the region consisted of two Danish duchies. In 1863 Schleswig and Holstein were annexed by Prussia; in 1920 four districts in Schleswig were returned to Denmark.

Hamburg, first an ancient Hanseatic city and then, from 1474, an Imperial Free Town, was the main heir of the Hansa after its disappearance; it remains the richest and most important town in West Germany. Bremen, a point of departure in the Middle Ages for a stream of missionaries who set off to evangelise northern Europe, has had a history which mirrors that of Hamburg.

Lower Saxony (Niedersachsen) is, except for

a collection of industrial towns in the south, a predominantly agricultural State, although the soil is not very fertile. The capital is Hanover.

The State of North Rhine-Westphalia (Nordrhein-Westfalen) comprises the *Ruhrgebiet* and contains over a quarter of the Bund's population and two-thirds of its industry. This is Germany's 'Empire State', formed from the north of the Rhine Province, assigned to Prussia in 1815, and Westphalia (also Prussian from 1815). The capital is Düsseldorf.

Hesse (Hessen), on the crossroads from north to south, includes the old State of Electoral Hesse, part of Nassau, the old Free City of Frankfurt and that part of the Grand Duchy of Hesse that lay across the Rhine. There is a strong contrast between the rich slopes of the banks of the Main and Rhine in the south and the relative poverty of the Weser's slopes to the north. The capital is Wiesbaden.

The Rhineland-Palatinate (Rheinland-Pfalz), inconveniently grouped on the left bank of the Rhine, is made up of bits and pieces of territory from former Prussia, Bavaria and Hesse. The capital is Mainz.

Baden-Württemberg is composed of three Länder: North Baden-Württemberg, Württemberg-Hohenzollern and South Baden. The capital is Stuttgart.

Bavaria (Bayern) was, even in the eighteenth century, the largest of all the south German States, and largely Catholic by religion. It extends right up to the gates of Frankfurt, though the Bavarians' unswerving individualism looks rather to the Danube and the Inn than northwards. Bavaria has remained exceptionally rural. The capital is Munich.

The Saar (Saarland), for forty years the international see-saw of France and Germany, was returned to the latter in October 1955 and was constituted the tenth *Land*. About two-thirds of the population is made up of workmen, miners and small landowners, who depend for their foodstuffs (except beef and potatoes) on imports from neighbouring regions. The capital is Saarbrücken.

*Social and financial problems.* The population has increased by 36·8 per cent (14,800,000 persons) since 1939, due in great measure to the influx of people expelled from the east, of the refugees from the Communist zone of East Germany, and of Germans who have returned from abroad.

The destruction of the towns brought a temporary rise in the rural population, but today the towns have surpassed their pre-war population figures.

The population actively engaged in work is 64 per cent of men, 33 per cent of women. Self-employment continues to fall, but the numbers of those with private incomes, or living on pensions and retired pay, continues to increase, as does the number of employees and civil servants. Unemployment is practically non-existent; in 1965 nearly one million foreign workers were employed and skilled and trained workers can get jobs anywhere in a country where there is a shortage of such men.

During the period 1948–56 there was a movement towards economic concentration by selling cartels and *Konzerne*. Traces of a 'paternalistic' attitude among employers (dating back as far as 1880) exist alongside social lesgislation. Workmen and employees of all sorts are concerned with the efficient running of the enterprise they serve and of which they are generally proud. The workers' reasonable claims were at first confined to a participation in management. But in 1952 the *Deutsche Gewerkschaftsbund* (which comprises over six million trades-unionists) was able to secure the enactment of a law establishing joint management.

*Cultural activities in the Länder.* Cultural activities are still entirely in the hands of the individual *Länder*. There are 32,000 public elementary schools divided almost evenly between the 'Christian community' schools, and the schools that are wholly Catholic or Protestant, and 9,000 technical schools. The nineteen universities (in addition to the six in East Germany) enjoy a considerable degree of autonomy. There are also four new universities and nine technical high schools of university status.

The libraries and museums are heavily subsidised and, in addition, scientific research is strongly supported by the industrialists. Academies, institutes and large special schools of national importance are

Hamburg seen from across the Binnenalster lake.
Heavily damaged during the Second World War, it has been largely rebuilt, and the port entirely reconstructed.
The Hamburg shipyards are now the third largest in the world, and the city is prosperous once again.

scattered all over the country. Some 22,000 books are issued every year (Stuttgart and Munich are the main publishing centres). There are 600 daily newspapers in Germany, nine of which have circulations over 200,000, and 600 important magazines.

*Preservation of historic monuments.* Constant care is devoted to the upkeep and restoration of historic monuments: the Romanesque churches of the Ottonian era (A.D. 936–1002), the castles that top the hills of south and west, the great cathedrals of the Rhinelands, the Cistercian monasteries, the fifteenth-century late Gothic monuments, the seventeenth-century patrician dwellings in the northern cities and, above all the unique and highly original collection of abbatial churches and basilicas in eighteenth-century baroque and rococo styles found in Swabia. Franconia and Bavaria. To these must be added the palaces, more or less modelled on Versailles, built in the same golden age in the prosperous towns where the princes and bishops lived.

The Germans are much attracted to folklore and there are few towns of any importance where there is not a *Heimatmuseum* or a *Landesmuseum*, and traditional local festivals have lost nothing of their earlier brilliance. There is an ever-increasing stream of *Post-war refugees.* Since 1949, some 320,000 Germans have emigrated. Against this, thirty-five times as many Germans have entered West Germany, from the former Prussian provinces occupied by Russia and Poland or from various countries in central Europe where they had been settled for centuries, or from the Democratic Republic (East Germany). It is estimated that, in all, some 17 million Germans have been obliged to leave the homes where their ancestors lived for centuries. The number of immigrants has risen since 1949 with the arrival of refugees who, despite the establishment in 1952 of a forbidden and strictly guarded strip three miles wide, running along the frontier between West and East Germany, managed to leave the East German zone through Berlin and by air at the rate of 15,000 to 20,000 a month until it was sealed off in 1961.

A special ministry was set up to deal with the immigrants, and a second migration — to the Ruhr, etc. — was organised. New industrial concerns were set up; big businesses moved their plant from East to West, or redeployed their workmen into factories already existing. Assimilation within the new surroundings has made good progress.

*Housing problems.* In 1945, 400 million cubic metres of rubble and 17,000 million bricks which had been retrieved and utilised in random fashion cluttered up the German towns. Of the housing blocks, 42 per cent were uninhabitable, and about one-half of this number irreparably destroyed. Since then millions of new dwellings have been built and four-fifths of the urban areas have been reconstructed. All the same, this considerable achievement has not yet been sufficient to end overcrowding.

AGRICULTURAL AND MARITIME ACTIVITY. *Agriculture and food supply.* Agriculture takes second place in Germany, where political and economic priority is given to industry and commerce as a means of providing a national income.

In 1945, with 75 per cent of the population, West Germany contained only 45 per cent of the arable

The Karlsplatz, Munich, capital of Bavaria. In the centre is the Karstor, relic of the medieval town walls, and in the background the tower of the Frauenkirche.

land and livestock, 40 per cent of the potato fields, and 32 per cent of the sugar-beet crop. Moreover, German agriculture has had to face a population pressure of 880 inhabitants to the square mile of arable land.

The commonest item of diet is the potato. In parts of the south flour is more often employed in the form of noodles than as bread. More meat is being eaten but less butter, vegetables and sugar. The tendency is for the consumption of milk, cheese, eggs, and especially margarine, to rise, together with that of citrus and other fruits.

*Mechanisation and principal grain crops.* Mechanisation is highly developed. About 108 lbs. of chemical fertilizer are used per acre. Farmers trained in technical schools represent 15 to 20 per cent of the whole, and co-operatives of all kinds have a membership of one-half of those engaged on the land.

Rye is still the main grain crop and is grown mostly in the cold lands of the Geest in Lower Saxony and in that part of Franconia lying round Nuremberg. Half the wheat is grown in the Baden plain, the Württemberg and Würzburg *Gaue*, and the Straubing plain; the other half comes from Rhenish Hesse and the Cologne-Düren basin. Barley does best in the Alzey area, Franconia and Swabia. Oats come mostly from the Frisian region. Holstein and Westerwald. Potatoes are cultivated everywhere. The area under sugar-beet has doubled since 1938, in the region of the lower Rhine and especially in the Hanoverian *Börde*. Market-gardening flourishes near the large towns; asparagus is grown at Mainz and Schwetzingen and *sauerkraut* cabbage to the south of the city of Stuttgart.

*Stock-breeding. Fruits and vines. Fisheries.* The area of tillable land is 54,750 square miles. Hay fields are rarely enclosed. Cattle are still used to draw long farm-carts here and there, especially in Bavaria, Upper Swabia, near the North Sea and the Dutch frontier. Pig-rearing increases, sheep are decreasing, and there is more and more poultry.

Carefully tended orchards dot the slopes of all the Rhineland valleys as far as Cologne.

Apple-juice rather than cider is the national drink,

together with beer; consumption of table fruit continues to rise. Tall rows of hops stretch from the Upper Rhine and the Neckar to Lake Constance, but nine-tenths comes from middle Franconia and the Bavarian Hallertau. Tobacco is grown on the Baden plain.

The German vineyards, the most northerly of Europe, demand great care because of the danger from frost. They occupy, roughly, parts of the regions that were Romanised in ancient times, spread over the slopes of the Rhine banks, and on terraces through the Rhine Gorge as far as Honnef. Vineyards twist along the winding banks of the Moselle, the Ahr, the Neckar and the Main. The yield varies from 2,260 to 520 gallons an acre and produces only wines of high quality.

Members of the nobility still own some large estates (reduced to some extent by agrarian reform) but these are mostly made up of forest land. Most farms are from 15 to 50 acres, the average being 19 acres, though one-third of all holdings are of under 5 acres.

The fishing industry is organised on very modern lines and the annual catch is enought to furnish every inhabitant of Germany with 26·5 lbs. of fish.

*Forest.* Trees and woods occupy an essential place in German culture. Covering 17 million acres, even today, woods reach right into the suburbs of the largest cities. The typical German forest is composed of beech among fir-trees regularly planted.

INDUSTRIAL DEVELOPMENT. *The origins.* Well before the fifteenth century wool, flax and silk were woven in today's Ruhr area, and elsewhere in Westphalia and Saxony. By the eighteenth century the peasants of Thuringia, Saxony and Württemberg had managed to eke out a living from their inferior soil by the

Agriculture takes second place in Germany, where political and economic priority is given to industry and commerce. West Germany, with 75 per cent of the population, has only 45 per cent of the arable land and livestock. Mechanisation in the Federal Republic is highly developed. Rye is still the principal grain crop. In the Democratic Republic urban workers represent 40 per cent of the population and agricultural workers 17 per cent; there is more arable land than pasture and stockbreeding is still inadequate. Agrarian reform in the East has brought rapid extension of socialisation since 1960.

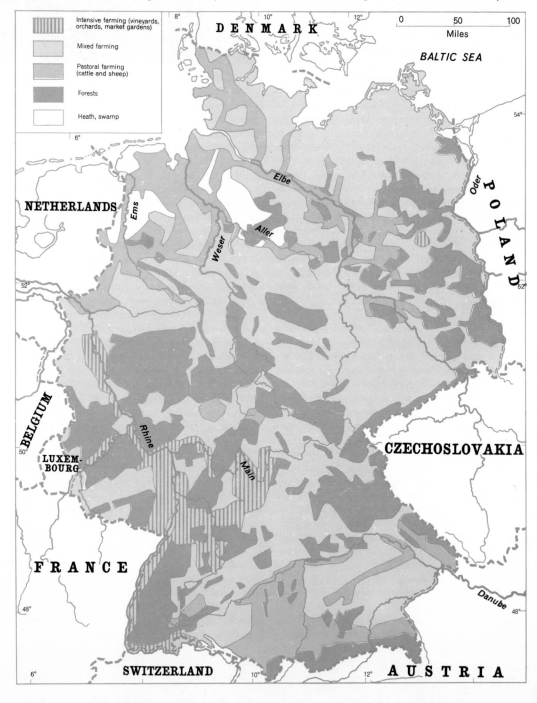

Intensive farming (vineyards, orchards, market gardens)

Mixed farming

Pastoral farming (cattle and sheep)

Forests

Heath, swamp

products of their handicraft. The French Huguenots brought with them their manufacturing methods, but it was only from about 1850 that the working of the coalfields allowed Germany to develop her industrial plan on a huge scale. Later on, under the leadership of Krupps, came the first of the *Konzerne*, which included in one holding company and under a single management a whole group of enterprises needed in the manufacture of a product and in its delivery to the consumer.

Industry's dominating position in German economy before the Second World War was strengthened during the country's post-war recovery period. There was a general and complete transformation (carried out with the aid of the Marshall Plan), and the currency reform brought with it a broad-minded, liberal policy and, after 1949, heavy investment.

*Coal, oil, metals, electric power.* German industry still depends on coal. After the war four of the country's main coalfields fell to the lot of Western Germany. The first, and one of the very highest class, is the great Ruhr basin, with ascertained reserves of 64,000 million tons and probably another 55,000 million tons to be added to that. Lying one above the other are 124 seams of all sorts of coal, easily worked by shafts which have been used for a long time and have an average depth of 2,450 feet.

The Saar basin extends under forested land over an area of 467 square miles. The parallel seams of lean coal at Ottweiler in the north-east, and the cannel and soft coal elsewhere contain about 10,000 million tons of reserves, and produce 18 million tons of coal annually.

The Aachen coalfield, whose seams are more dislocated, is a continuation of the Franco-Belgian fields. The very extensive lignite deposits to the south-west of Cologne are being increasingly worked.

There are oil-wells in production near Celle in Hanover and on the Dutch Frisian frontier and it is proposed to drill another field south of Hamburg. Natural gas and potash are also exploited. The excellent iron deposits of Siegen and the Dill are now approaching exhaustion and the deposits in Hanover

are of rather poor quality. The metallurgical industry's needs have to be met by imports, but German steel production is now greater than that of Great Britain.

In view of Germany's economic potential, the production of electric power is of great importance. Large dams for hydro-electric projects have been constructed to help meet growing needs, and hydro-electricity, oil and, to a small extent, nuclear power are now competing with coal.

*The Ruhr. Germany's industrial capital.* The Ruhr is the unquestioned industrial capital of continental Europe. Its growth was favoured by the presence of iron and coal. The first blast furnace (at Mülheim) was set up in 1849, and the first pit-shaft sunk in the north of the Ruhr in 1850. The importance of the Ruhr in German industry's employees and capital, 50 to 60 centred there today is about 40 per cent of West German industry's employees and capital, 50 to 60 per cent of its industrial production, 80 per cent of its heavy metallurgy, 40 per cent of the rail freight traffic, and 48 per cent of the tramway lines. Over 7 million inhabitants live in a concentrated nucleus within 3,200 square miles.

Going from south to north, three zones can be distinguished according to variations in the depth of the seams and differences in operational life to date. The first zone has remained relatively rural in character, dotted with little groups of houses and small workshops. Düsseldorf is the administrative, social, financial and commercial capital.

This southern zone specialises in the manufacture and production of all sorts of finished goods — metallurgy, chemicals, plastics, all the Ruhr textiles, hardware and tools.

The second zone stretches for thirty-eight miles along the ridge between the rivers Ruhr and Emscher with an average breadth of about thirteen miles, from Mörs and Duisburg to Dortmund. Here, in the great coalfield is the real heart of the Ruhr. This is the realm of raw materials and heavy industry, with four-fifths of the coalmines, and three-quarters of the output of steel, pig-iron, metallurgical products, sheet-metal, tubing and wagons. To this must be

Vineyards are found along the Rhine. the Neckar, the Moselle, the Ahr and the Main, but never on the plain. The total area devoted to viticulture is approximately 143,000 acres.

An intensively cultivated valley under the system of strip-farming. Neat orchards dot the slopes while the fields alternate with crops of grain, sugar-beet, vegetables and hay for the livestock.

The Bayer dyestuffs works
at Leverkusen, on a bend of the
Rhine below Cologne. Bayer
was one of the powerful
*Konzerne,* the big monopolistic
combines of German industry,
which, though to some extent
broken up since 1952, still exist in
the form of limited companies
with tens or hundreds of thousands
of shareholders.

Ruhr miners from the *Schlägel
und Eisen* (Hammer and Anvil)
mine in the heart of the
Ruhr district.
This is the industrial capital of
continental Europe and an area
of intense productivity.
Out of a total of 440,000 miners
in the whole of West Germany
345,000 live in the Ruhr region.

Completing a four-ton cylinder
for a reciprocating compressor
for use in the mines.
Mining machinery is widely used
in the Ruhr, as coal production
mounts and old equipment
is unable to stand the strain.

added sheet-glass, basic chemical products, synthetic
petrol, and so on.

Farther north lies the third zone of the coalfield,
yielding cannel coal. New towns with new steelworks, coke ovens, chemical products and synthetic
rubber factories have sprung up.

Between them fourteen *Konzerne* produced 55 per
cent of the coal and turned out 75 per cent of the steel.
The names of Hibernia, Harpener, Haniel, Hoesch,
Kloeckner, Stinnes, Mannesmann, Thyssen and Krupp
remain inseparable from the mammoth works of
Essen, Hamborn, Oberhausen, the Demag at Duisburg, the Rheinische Stahlwerke and so on.
*Secondary industrial areas.* From the great nerve centre
of the Ruhr there run two main lines of secondary
industrial concentrations to which the Ruhr sends
power-producing coal, gas and electricity.

The first of these lines stretches out to the north
and east, over the plains of Westphalia and Hanover.
The Detmold area turns out furniture. Equally busy
are the industrial centres of Hanover and Brunswick,
the blast-furnaces of Salzgitter-Watendtedt and the
Wolfsburg factories on the Mittelland-kanal where
80,000 workmen turn out 5,000 Volkswagens a day.

Another and more important string of factory-
cities runs down to the south-east of the great Rhine
artery — interrupted by the gorge of the schist
massif. Cologne produces machines, cables, chemicals,
aluminium, rubber. The Neuwied basin has works for
transforming the surrounding tuff into refractory
earth or fireclay. Metallurgy and tanning, optical
works and camera manufacture flourish in the valley
of the Lahn. Frankfurt is the seat of many industries:
machines and presses, rubber and wagons (Mainz),
dyes and chemical products, automobiles, jewellery
and leather. Mannheim produces agricultural implements, mirrors, jute, leather, Ludwigshafen chemical
products and Heidelberg chemicals.

Following the Neckar, fifty miles upstream lies
the Bund's second most important industrial area:
the Baden-Württemberg region. The economic
structure here is quite different from that farther north
and is founded on the high quality of the labour
force. The workmen-peasants are often heirs of a
centuries-old tradition of handicrafts; some of the
enterprises, of medium size, are still run on patriarchal
lines. Each little town has its own speciality; in the
centre of the Alb, for instance, is an area that turns
out precision tools, and surgical and musical instruments; the speciality of the Black Forest is clocks,
of Pforzheim, jewellery and of Stuttgart, automobiles
and optics.

On the Saar coalfield and at Neunkirchen there is
a large-scale iron and steel industry, started in 1759
but developed under the Röchling and Stumm
dynasties after 1880. The Aachen-Düren complex
(textiles, metals, paper) the industries of the neighbouring Walloon parts of Belgium. The textile, china
and glass production in Upper Franconia reflects that
of neighbouring Saxony and Bohemia.

There are large towns where industry is concentrated in the centre itself and in the immediate
suburbs, including Bremen — automobiles, shipyards, jute, linoleum; Hamburg — shipyards, electro-
technical products, non-ferrous metals, petroleum
refineries, oilworks, chemical products, rubber; and

Munich, the most intellectual and least industrialised of German capitals — automobiles, furniture and beer. COMMUNICATIONS AND TRANSPORT. *Railroads and Autobahnen.* The German railroads have a total length of about 24,000 miles, of which 20,000 miles belong to the State. Electrification has been completed or is in progress on most main lines. The volume of traffic is enormous. No station handles more international express trains than Cologne, while at Frankfurt, the headquarters of the whole network, two main lines converge — Scandinavia-Hamburg-Basle and Holland-Cologne-Munich-Austria-Italy.

There are 2,500 miles of special motor-roads (*Autobahnen*), by-passing built-up areas. The main arteries run from Berlin to the Ruhr and Cologne along the track of the old medieval Hellweg, and from Hamburg to the Swiss frontier.

*The Rhine, the main river of Europe.* The system of natural navigable waterways comprises the four rivers flowing from south to north — the Elbe, the Weser, the Ems, and the Rhine with its two affluents, the Main and the Neckar — and the Danube downstream from Regensburg (Ratisbon). The system of fluvial waterways is linked by seven main canals in the northern plain. These carry about 125 million tons.

From Basle to the Dutch frontier, the Rhine (and to a lesser degree, its tributaries) accounts for more than three-quarters of this traffic. Great tugs, long strings of barges (most of them about 1,350 tons but some of them as much as 3,000 tons), motor-boats and passenger steamers maintain a steady service.

A third of Germany's exports by sea and half her imports (ore, oil) are carried on the Rhine, Rotterdam being her great export terminus. The main cargoes

Since 1949 Germany has been uneasily divided into the territory of the German Federal Republic, which adheres to the Western bloc, and the territory of the German Democratic Republic, which adheres to the Russian Bloc. The four major coalfields, the Ruhr, Saar, Aachen and Westphalian basins, fall within the Federal Republic.
The phenomenal prosperity of the Ruhr is based on the twin presence of iron and coal; there is a second major industrial region in Baden-Württemberg.
The Democratic Republic, in contrast, has little coal or iron but rich lignite deposits and important salt and uranium resources.
Its industrial output comes from state-run factories.

Volkswagen assembly lines.
The factory at Wolfsburg in
Lower Saxony employs 80,000
people and produces 5,000
passenger cars a day — one
every 12 seconds.

The *Esso Nürnberg* in dock at
Hamburg. In 1945, half
Hamburg's ruins lay in ruins;
the port was entirely reconstructed
and restored, and now ships
of 205 different lines
call there.

are coal and lignite, taken on from the Wesseling
wharves near Cologne; these are directed principally
to the twin ports of Mannheim and Ludwigshafen
upstream, the storage centres for the whole of
southern Germany.

*The revival of the ports.* Although Germany has had its
seaboard reduced to a narrow frontage on the North
Sea and to the Baltic shores of Schleswig-Holstein, it
has retained its two largest ports: Bremen and
Hamburg.

In 1945, the days of Hamburg's prosperity seemed
past. Since 1953 the port has been entirely reconstructed and now consists of twenty-five huge docks
fanning out on to the Elbe. Two-thirds of the traffic
is represented by imports; British, American and
Asian raw materials head the list, consisting mainly of
oil, coffee, wheat, wool and jute. Hamburg has also
won back its Austrian customers and, despite political
barriers, many of those in Berlin, East Germany,
Czechoslovakia and Hungary. The port of Bremen
is also engaged in shipbuilding and voluminous
cotton and wheat imports; it is the largest cotton market in continental Europe and also the principal
passenger port.

*The rapid recovery of commerce.* Large trade fairs, each
with from 3,000 to 4,000 exhibitors, attract huge
crowds of visitors every year to the principal business
towns and railroad junctions of inland Germany —
Frankfurt, Hanover and Cologne, etc. Foreign
trade, which is the primary source of German
economic stability, increases annually — especially
with the Far East, South America and Africa. This
development is directly related to attractive pricing,
quick deliveries according to contract, and adaptability to customers' tastes and needs.

West Germany is among the principal customers
and suppliers of France, Switzerland, Benelux, Italy,
Sweden, Austria, Turkey, Denmark, Spain, Iran and
Brazil. Except in the case of her relatively undeveloped agriculture, the progress of Germany's economy
has been uninterrupted since 1948 and shows a yearly
increase of between 10 and 20 per cent.

## THE GERMAN DEMOCRATIC REPUBLIC
## (EAST GERMANY)

The German Democratic Republic, or *Deutsche
Demokratische Republik,* was founded on 7 October
1949 in the Soviet occupation zone. It has found
difficulty in achieving stability, and has been recognised neither by the Federal Republic (where East
Germany is always called the 'Soviet Zone' or
'Central Germany') nor by the Western Allies who
use the term 'East Germany'. It is cut off, too, from the
former German eastern provinces which used to
supply it, separated from Berlin which (officially) is
an 'external enclave', and isolated from the two great
sources of industrial power — Silesia and the Ruhr.

*The fourteen districts.* The D.D.R. — whose capital is
the east sector of Berlin, has an area of 41,380 square
miles and a population (including that of East Berlin)
of 17,300,000 (398 per square mile). It includes
Mecklenburg, part of western Pomerania, Brandenburg as far as the Oder, Saxe-Anhalt (once Prussian

Saxony and the Duchy of Anhalt), Saxony proper (i.e. the former kingdom of Saxony) and Thuringia; the last was formerly a jumble of eight small principalities forming the heart of Old Germany, the cradle of German culture, the land of Luther's Wartburg and Goethe's Weimar, and ceded by the Americans to the Russian zone in July 1945.

These five *Länder* were dissolved in 1952 to effect a greater degree of centralisation, and their place was taken by fourteen districts. Rostock controls the whole Baltic acrea; Schwerin and Neubrandenburg divide the agricultural plain of Mecklenburg; Potsdam and Frankfurt-on-the-Oder lie respectively west and east of Berlin. Kottbus is the capital of unproductive Lower Austria (Lausitz). Magdeburg dominates both the middle reaches of the Elbe and the Harz. Halle is the centre of the lower basin of the Saale. Gera, Suhl and Erfurt divide Thuringia. Leipzig, Karl-Marx Stadt (formerly Chemnitz) and Dresden divide Saxony. These districts are subdivided into 217 'circles'. The basin of the Elbe is almost more important to East Germany than the Rhine basin to West Germany. Only the Baltic slopes of Mecklenburg, a corner of Brandenburg, and what remains of Pomerania and Silesia lie outside the basin. The East German population is most densely concentrated in the south, on the middle stretches of the Elbe and on its principal tributary, the Saale, distribution being related to centres of industry.

POPULATION AND AGRICULTURAL PROBLEMS. *Stable population.* Since 1939 the population has increased only very slightly, despite the influx of 4,300,000 persons expelled from former German provinces farther east or from Czechoslovakia. An excess of births over deaths has so far failed to compensate for the exodus to the West of tradesmen, industrialists, peasants, doctors and civil servants. Migration from West to East has been much less marked. The present population includes more workmen (46 per cent) than peasants (17 per cent).

*More arable land than pasture.* Forests cover 27·4 per cent of the land — beech woods on the Mecklenburg plateaus, immense forests of pines mingled with birches in the Mark of Brandenburg and in Lower Lusatia, and firs on three mountain massifs. Cereals and root-crops cover three-quarters of the cultivable area. The *Börde*, in the neighbourhood of Magdeburg, the Saale basin, the Saxony 'piedmont', the marly regions of Mecklenburg, and the Ukermark are the granaries of wheat, barley and forage crops. Much of Mecklenburg consists of highly productive sugar-beet fields, numerous also in the Magdeburg region. Potatoes, especially in the north and in Saxony, are abundant, but the real national cereal is rye. Hops are grown at Stendal and especially at Naumberg. The apple and plum orchards of Saxony and Thuringia rival each other but towards the north the fruit trees thin out. But the area given over to pasture is insufficient and the quantity of livestock bred still inadequate.

*Far-reaching agrarian reforms.* In the industrialised areas of the south very small holdings have always prevailed. In Lusatia and Saxe-Anhalt holdings were of medium size. But Mecklenburg was the traditional land of the Junker's large estates, which sometimes covered 35,000 to 50,000 acres. Throughout the country all estates of more than 250 acres (100 hectares) have now been split up, and most of the land has been made over to farm labourers or refugees in the form of small lots of 12 to 50 acres. What remained of the large estates was made over to the 'State Lands', the 'Nationalised Properties'. The socialisation of agriculture has accelerated since 1960.

INDUSTRIES AND MINERAL RESOURCES. *Industry and nationalisation.* In an area stretching from the Werra to the Neisse and between the Thuringerwald and the Erzgebirge, there flourished what was probably the oldest established community of craftsmen in Europe. The Erzgebirge silver mines, long since exhausted, provided the foundations of the mining industry from the Middle Ages onwards. The mines encouraged local crafts and industry, but the regional industries never coalesced into the colossal combines and trusts common in West Germany.

Between 1945 and 1958 these East German industries were hard hit by dismantling, the heavy tribute on output levied by the Russian occupation authorities and, after that, the transfer of the main enterprises to Soviet companies. These, however, were handed back in 1954. Since then, industrial output has been restored.

*Importance of lignite and uranium.* East Germany has little or no iron and coal. However, at the end of the nineteenth century lignite deposits were discovered in Tertiary formations underlying the Great Plain, and this lignite today makes East Germany the 'brown coal' country *par excellence*. Lignite, especially when used to produce electric power, has contributed — together with the great dams on the upper Saale — to the intense industrial electrification of the middle Elbe basin. East Germany has copper mines and foundries, but, above all, the largest potash deposits in Europe and an abundance of salt. Finally, several thousand men are employed in the precious uranium mines in the Erzgebirge and at Wernigerode in the Harz.

*Light engineering and heavy metallurgy.* There was, in East Germany, a grave shortage of iron and steel production, and of metallurgical and heavy engineering plant. Great efforts have now been made to make the country self-sufficient, mainly through the creation of two powerful iron and steel *Kombinats*. One near Magdeburg uses lignite coal in special blast furnaces. The other, among the Oder pine forests near Fürstenburg, is the model iron and steel city of Eisenhüttenstadt, created from nothing in 1950, whose six blast furnaces use Russian or Swedish ore and Polish coal. There are other new plants, mainly around Berlin. Flourishing manufacturing activities include musical instruments, toys, glass, china furniture, paper (two-thirds of the total German production), optical instruments, spectacles, gloves and shoes. Leipzig is the main fur market of continental Europe. The presence of mineral elements in the soil has helped in the development of this important chemical industry.

Finally, Saxony, with its many towns, is the great textile centre of Germany. The cotton zone is in the valleys of the central Erzgebirge, touching the plain. The woollens area (the largest in Germany) is lower in the plain, stretching from the Gera and the Greiz dyeworks to the industrial areas of Lusatia.

The port of Stralsund, East Germany.

COMMUNICATIONS AND TRANSPORT. *Railroutes, roads and canals.* There are in East Germany about 10,000 miles of railroad, and 2,200 coach and bus lines, a large proportion of them concentrated in the vital regions of the Elbe, the south and the south-west. Long-distance road transport accounts for only 5 per cent of the freight hauled, and private cars are uncommon. Six *Autobahnen* radiate from Berlin for a total distance of 885 miles. Inland water transport on the Elbe and on the axis of the Rhine-Oder canals carries only 4 per cent of the freight transported. The most important cargoes are lignite, ores and beets.

Since 1950 the docks at Rostock and those of its outer harbour have been increased and shipyards have been rapidly developed at Wismar and Stralsund.

Leipzig, which has kept its reputation as a great publishing centre and headquarters of the printing trades, is also a commercial city and, despite separation from the West, its annual fair is the most celebrated in Europe. Four-fifths of the foreign trade of East Germany is with countries to the east — from Poland to China — and also with the Arab and Scandinavian countries. The U.S.S.R. is the main supplier of raw materials and foodstuffs.

CULTURAL AND SOCIAL LIFE. Primary and secondary schools have been standardised and secularised. The teaching of Russian as the first foreign language is obligatory. The *Freie Deutsche Jugend,* 'Free German Youth', to which many young people of both sexes belong, supplements the political education given at school. Special faculties set up in 1949 provide preparatory training for the numerous technical schools, the universities of Berlin, Rostock, Griefswald, Halle, Leipzig and Jena, and schools for advanced studies. Scientific research institutions are heavily subsidised, but cultural life, the restoration of

View over Leipzig. The city has a proud history as a cultural centre and continues to be cosmopolitan in spite of the political problems that divide Germany.

damaged buildings and monuments, the reorganisation of museums, and the protection of folklore are not neglected.

There are tourist resorts and spas on the Baltic coast, in the Hartz, Thuringia and the 'Saxon Switzerland' which have been nationalised and transformed into low-priced holiday resorts for workers of all kinds.

East Germany's standard of living is lower than that of West Germany and her cost of living a third higher. Reconstruction has been hampered by difficulties in obtaining raw materials.

## BERLIN

In the thirteenth century Berlin was an island township of fishermen set amid the forests, swamps and lakes of Brandenburg. In the fifteenth century the Electors of Brandenburg chose it as their capital. The city developed as the capital of Prussia, largely owing to the influx of Huguenot refugees. In 1871, it was raised to the position of an imperial capital. The great industries and trade of Berlin were, in 1939, second only to those of the Ruhr.

In 1945 Berlin lay in ruins, detached from a dead Prussia and indeed from Germany as a whole, occupied by the representatives of four world powers, having lost its political importance and its enormous industrial potential. Three-quarters of the plant, chiefly in the metallurgical and electro-technical industries, was dismantled by the Russians. Some 500,000 of the inhabitants had fled the city. In addition, it was divided into two: East Berlin and West Berlin, destined to live together in uneasy juxtaposition under two antagonistic administrations and with two currencies.

East Berlin (155 square miles), with 1,055,000 inhabitants, is the seat of its government, although not officially a part of the German Democratic Republic. It includes Unter den Linden, the district of government offices, the business sectors, the museums, the Humboldt University and the eastern suburbs. Most of the rebuilding has been done on the main arteries such as the Karl-Marx-Allee. However, since 1946, in the Lichtenberg, Schöneweide, and Köpenick districts, and along the Spree and its canals, industries including machinery, electrical equipment, cables and the graphic arts have been reorganised, and production has been stepped up to twenty times its former capacity.

West Berlin (185 square miles and 2,204,000 inhabitants) is a *Land,* albeit 'in abeyance', of the Federal Republic, participating in its public finances and providing twenty-six representatives (as 'consultants'). Along the main axis of this part of Berlin are several open, airy districts which in the nineteenth century were still suburbs. The most important is Charlottenburg, whose Kurfürstendamm is a highway of luxury shops. West Berlin also includes the sector of industrial plant in the north and on both sides of the Teltow Canal as well as the Tempelhof airfield, and the residential suburbs that give on to Havel lakes and woods and extend towards the southwest as far as Potsdam. The intellectual and artistic activities have recovered much of their old brilliance. The new university attracts more undergraduates each year, though not all come from West Germany. Industrial activity has revived. Once again the electro-technical precision machinery and clothing industries account for 50 per cent of the total turnover in West Berlin.

GERMANS ABROAD. Although Germany possessed an overseas empire only for a short time, her nationals emigrated continuously from the Middle Ages on, and despite enforced repatriations there are still numerous German settlements abroad. In Europe there are the remains of 'Saxon' colonies in Transylvania and 'Swabian' colonies in the Banat and Batchka, established in the eighteenth century. There are today 18 million people of German descent in the United States, 1 million in Brazil and 400,000 in Canada, 60,000 to 70,000 in Australia, and 12,000 in South-West Africa.

The Kurfürstendamm, with the Kaiser-Wilhelm Gedächtniskirche in the background. This is the liveliest street in West Berlin, with luxury shops, theatres and cinemas.
It is considerably farther west than the commercial centre of pre-war Berlin, which now lies within the eastern sector of the city.

# CZECHOSLOVAKIA

Halfway between the North Sea and the Mediterranean and some 220 miles from the nearest seashore, the plateau of Bohemia rises between two great lines of communication, the north German plain and the Danube valley. Since the ninth century, Bohemia, Moravia and Silesia have been linked politically, although until 1918 they came within the sphere of influence of Vienna and the alien Hapsburg dynasty. Immediately after the First World War, Slovakia, farther east, was joined to the Czech lands.

These regions together make up Czechoslovakia, a state born of the peace treaties concluded after the 1914–18 war.

The western zone (Bohemia, Moravia and Silesia), belongs to the Hercynian formations. Here landscapes and ways of life are characteristic of western and central Europe. The eastern zone, consisting of the Moravian-Slovakian confines and of Slovakia itself, belongs to the Carpathian-Danubian complex on the threshold of eastern Europe. Between the two zones runs a corridor of great physical and social importance, the valley of the Morava, the link between the Germano-Polish plain and the Danube valley.

## THE CZECH LANDS

*Bohemia.* Bohemia is, essentially, a peneplain which has the appearance of being a rather large assymetrical basin.

To the north-west the 'Ore Mountains' (Erzgebirge, or Krusne Hory) mark the German frontier from the Cheb passage to that of the Elbe (Labe in Czech) known as the 'Gate of Lusatia'. The Ore Mountains extend eastward as the Stredohori (Mittelgebirge), a massif of extinct volcanoes cut through by the Labe (Elbe) before it enters Germany. The mountains of Lusatia (Luzicke Hory), the Riesen-

gebirge (Krkonose), the Orlicke Hory and the Jeseniky then form a series of continuous ranges between the countries of Bohemia and northern Moravia.

In western Bohemia and all along the Bavarian frontier, the Cesky Les (Bohemian Forest), a range varying in altitude from 2,250 to 3,300 feet, forms a screen against winds from the Atlantic. It is flanked on the south by the Sumava, the southern part of the Bohemian plateau, where the Vltava (a tributary of the Labe) has its source. Furthermore, to the north of the Sumava there stretches a region covered with rather infertile Tertiary sediments—that of the Trebon and Ceske Budejovice meres.

Continuing down the course of the Vltava, we reach a point where the valley widens into a plain on which Prague (Praha) is built. To the west, beyond the Kladno coalfield, is the Plzen (Pilsen) basin into which flow four rivers and which has favoured the growth of a large industrial city. To the north-east or Prague, the Labe plain, or Polabi, is an area of Cretaceous sediments covered with loess, and drained by the upper courses of the Elbe.

Finally, to the east, the Bohemian-Moravian ridges form a sort of thick fold with rather irregular relief, a transition area between the plateaus of Bohemia and Moravia.

*Moravia-Silesia, an international corridor.* The main axis of Moravia is formed by the course of the river Morava, a north-bank tributary of the Danube linking Poland with the Danube valley. The plain of Moravia is bounded on the west by the Bohemian-Moravian ridges and on the east by the range of the White Carpathians (Bile Karpaty), which is easily crossed by the Vlara Pass (935 feet) leading into the valley of the Vah, tributary of the Danube. Like Bohemia, Moravia has two basins worth noting: that of Olomouc (or the plain of the Hana) and that of Brno (Brünn). Between the two basins and to the north of Brno, the principal town of Moravia,

Winter in the Carpathians. The extremity of the Carpathian arc — which reaches as far as the Black Sea — forms the backbone of Slovakia.

stretches the region of the Moravian *causses*, whose karst-like grottoes attract numerous tourists. Moravia is basically an agricultural land but has become highly industrialised under the influence of the rich Silesian coalfields.

*Slovakia, the gate of eastern Europe.* Slovakia is the most mountainous part of Czechoslovakia, and the extremity of the Carpathian arc forms its backbone. The mountain chains, which enclose fertile, sheltered valleys, are exposed to southern influences.

The core of the Slovakian Carpathians is composed of two ranges, the High and the Low Tatry, between which extends a tectonic depression containing a string of basins. Gerlachovsky Stit reaches 8,737 feet. The High Tatry were heavily eroded by glacial action, of which there are many traces. A number of health resorts lie clustered about the southern slopes. To the south of the High Tatry lie the Low Tatry, much wilder and more thickly wooded but not so lofty. To the south-west are the Little Carpathians, the White Carpathians, the Javorniky chain, and the Beskids on the right bank, and on the left bank the Inovec chain and the Great and Small Fatra.

In central Slovakia is the Slovenske Rudohorie ('metalliferous mountains' — a significant name) a mountain mass made up of extinct volcanoes.

The Slovakian plains are in general, fertile basins, the most extensive of which is formed by the widening of the Vah, Nitra and Hron lower valleys.

CLIMATE. Czechoslovakia lies in the centre of Europe, wholly in the northern temperate zone. The climate is varied but generally speaking temperate, the result of a balance between oceanic influences and continental influences.

The January isotherms are —1°C. (30°F.) for Bohemia, —2°C. (29°F.) for Moravia, —3°C. (27°F.) for eastern Slovakia. The July isotherms of 18°C. (64°F.) and 19°C. (66°F.) follow more or less the line of the Bohemian peripheral mountain ranges, but the interior of the country is warmer (20°C., 68°F.).

Both Moravia and Slovakia have July isotherms of 21°C. (69·5°F.).

Though the rainfall is abundant, especially in the western mountains, the average annual figure drops in most of the basins to about 20 inches, and sometimes less.

Moravia has a clear atmosphere, a rainfall that favours development of intensive agriculture, rather more severe winters and slightly hotter and drier summers than those of western Europe. The Slovakian climate is characterised by warmer and drier summers and harsher winters.

POPULATION. Czechoslovakia, which in 1938 had a population of 14,638,000, had only 13,970,000 in 1963. The drop followed the expulsion of the Sudeten Germans, and of the Magyars from Slovakia, and, by the Treaty of Moscow, the transfer to the U.S.S.R.

Wenceslas Square, Prague, with the National Museum in the background. This is part of the Nové Mesto (New Town); the more picturesque and historically interesting parts of the city are to be found in the Old Town.

Post-war economic plans have attempted to co-ordinate Czech and Slovak agriculture. The largest crop is wheat, which covers one-third of all cultivated land. Then come rye and barley. There is also a large potato crop and sugar-beet production is almost back to its pre-war level.

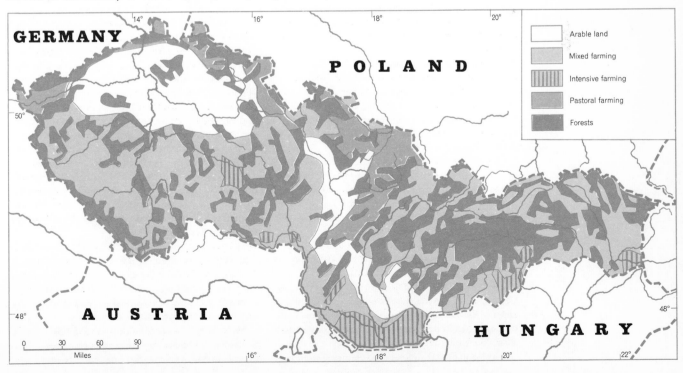

GERMANY

POLAND

AUSTRIA

HUNGARY

Arable land

Mixed farming

Intensive farming

Pastoral farming

Forests

0   30   60   90
Miles

Agricultural planning to increase yields operates on a large scale and includes instruction in new methods and theories. This group is studying methods of stockbreeding.

of Subcarpathian Ruthenia in 1945, and largely thanks to the excellent social welfare services developed, the population has again begun to increase. The death rate is lower and the infant mortality rate is the lowest in the world.

*A Slav country.* Czechoslovakia is now a country with a population almost entirely Slav.

The Czechs and Slovaks belong to the western branch of the Slav ethno-linguistic community. The Czech language is written in Roman characters although related to Old Slavonic and Russian. Czech used to be spoken almost only in the country districts and did not become a literary language until the early part of the nineteenth century. About the middle of the last century Slovakian emerged from one of the main dialects current in Slovakia. All Czechs can understand it without having studied it. The sense of belonging to the Slav linguistic community helped to awaken Czech and Slovak nationalistic feelings during the years of subjection more than any other single factor.

*Westernised Slavs.* Notwithstanding their Slav origin, the Czechs and Slovaks have also been exposed to non-Slav influences — the Czechs because they lived side by side with Germans for centuries and the Slovaks because of their close connection with Hungarians. Bohemian civilisation owes much to Austria, Bavaria and Saxony.

Throughout their history the Czechs have, in times of crisis, found spiritual leaders whose fame has often spread beyond their own frontiers; men like Jan Hus, Comenius, Palacky, Havlicek, Masaryk or Benes, who were always supported by the Slav majority, responding to the rallying cry of liberty and independence. Long years of subjection taught the Czechs the value of solidarity for the eventual attainment of national and cultural independence.

The Slovaks, separated for many centuries from the Czechs, are in general more impulsive, more artistic and more intuitive than their western relations. They, too, have had leaders fired with ideas of Slav nationalism, like Kollar and Safarik.

Czech and Slovak differences of temperament have

occasionally given rise to feelings of mutual suspicion; two different languages and religious disagreement have also provided fuel for the fire.

A CHANGING ECONOMY. During the second half of the nineteenth century and the beginning of the twentieth Bohemia, Moravia and Silesia (then part of the Austro-Hungarian monarchy) were provinces whose abundant coal, fertile soils, dense populations, craftsmen and traditional family enterprises put at their disposal an immense home market for their finished products.

The Czech lands had taken full advantage of the nineteenth-century industrial revolution; Slovakia, however, was less favoured with power potential, and the population was dominated by a Hungarian landed aristocracy and was not accustomed to handicrafts in conjunction with large-scale industry. It remained an underdeveloped country, dependent largely on its agriculture.

When, in October 1918, the Czech lands and Slovakia united to form the first Czechoslovak republic, the new state was immediately faced with the loss of many of its former markets. Between the two World Wars everything was done to make the country an exporter of manufactured goods and an importer of raw materials. Consequently, when the world crisis of the early Thirties hit eastern and east-central Europe, the new state suffered. The leaders of the Third Reich proceeded to take advantage of the uncertain political situation, the result being the signing of the Munich agreement (September 1938), the occupation of Prague (March 1939), and the dismembering of the Czechoslovak State.

After the Second World War Czechoslovakia began to build up a society based on socialist principles and had then to reorganise its industry.

The object of the Two Year Plan (1947–48) was to restore an economy ruined by war and occupation. The essential features of the scheme were the nationalisation of industry, banks and foreign trade, an economic change-over in the frontier zones evacuated by Germans and Hungarians and an agrarian reform which limited private holdings to 125 acres, the excess going to landless farm workers. Then followed the first Five Year Plan (1949–53), which although completed in four years, did not yield the expected results. Its main aim was to eliminate the differences between Czech and Slovakian economies. Stress was laid on the development of power supply, and the supply of machinery for the consumer goods industries and collectivised agricultural enterprises. The second Five Year Plan (1956–60) concentrated on capital goods production. In this period industrial production increased. The third Five Year Plan (1961–65) aimed to preserve the increase. It was suspended in 1963 and was replaced by a subsequent seven-year plan (1964–70).

*Development of power supply.* Czechoslovakia has been especially favoured by nature with sources of power. The country has huge reserves of solid fuel, to some extent compensating for the lack of petroleum. Power is produced from thermal sources and from hydro-electric stations, particularly in Slovakia.

Most of the coalfields and lignite deposits are in Bohemia and Silesia; the most important coalfield is the Moravska Ostrava-Karvina with reserves that are estimated at over 20,000 million tons. These deposits belong to the most extensive coalfield in eastern Europe, the Silesian basin, which is as important to the East as the Ruhr is to the West. The largest coalfields in Bohemia are those of Kladno-Rakovnik and Plzen-Radnice; the former, being nearer to Prague, supplies the capital's great industrial plants. The Plzen-Radnice collieries contributed greatly to the growth of the engineering plant at Plzen (formerly the Skoda Works). In Moravia, the Rosice-Oslavany basin supplies the fuel for the factories of Brno.

In the Ohre (Eger) valley of Bohemia, at the foot of the Krusner Hory, there are exceptionally extensive lignite deposits which are easily worked by open-cast methods. The famous pitchblende (uranium ore) deposit at Jachymov in northern Bohemia could also contribute significantly towards Czechoslovakia's resources in power and a nuclear power station is being built. As it is, the Czechoslovaks have already increased their power resources by adding to their already numerous thermo-electric stations or by constructing more hydro-electric stations. The hydro-electric stations already supply 15 per cent of the current used; among the largest are those of Slapy on the Vltava and Orava in Silesia. However, prospects seem brightest in Slovakia, where eleven dams have been built in the Vah valley alone. Plans are being drawn up for the electrification of the Hron and Hornad valleys.

*Central Europe's industrial leader.* The Czech lands and Slovakia have long been considered particularly rich in metallic ores. During the Middle Ages the Kutna Hora mines of argentiferous lead allowed the Bohemians to mint money and put the thaler (ancestor of the dollar) on the international market. During the time of the First Republic a mint was established at Kremnica in Slovakia, using the gold and silver extracted from the nearby mines of Kremnica and Banska Stiavnica.

Much more important to the present-day Czech economy are the iron ore deposits between Kladno and Plzen (Bohemia) and in the Slovakian 'Ore Mountains'. The existence of manganese deposits relatively close to the Silesian power-producing area lend these central Slovakian mines considerable importance. At present Silesia is still the principal centre of the heavy metallurgical industry. Under the Five Year Plan a huge iron, steel and multi-metal *kombinat* was erected at Kosice, a regional capital in Slovakia, to treat both ferrous and non-ferrous ores from the Ore Mountains.

Before the war, machinery manufacture utilising materials furnished by the heavy metal industry was established at Plzen (Skoda Works) and turned out large quantities of armaments, locomotives, factory equipment and machine-tools. This has grown since nationalisation. Similarly, Prague, Brno and the surrounding country (Blansko), and Prostejov still have works turning out specialised machinery, and branches of industry have now been extended to almost all parts of the country and particularly to Slovakia. Lastly, Czechoslovakia still has a high reputation for its precision instruments, which are exported to other Eastern European countries.

The chemical industry is also expanding. Among the more important chemical plants are the synthetic petrol works at Most, which treats lignite, and the works in the Labe valley where the manufacture of fertilizers, acids, pharmaceutical and photographic products is concentrated near Usti. In Moravia the former Bata factories at Gottwaldov treat rubber, and at Bratislava there are synthetic fibre factories. Finally, the graphite of southern Bohemia provides raw material for two thriving pencil factories of international repute.

*A brake on light industry.* Among the different branches of what is called 'light' industry — that is, manufacturing consumer goods — those depending on

Czechoslovakia is a state with rich coal, lignite and metallic ore deposits. An organised industrial pattern introduced after 1945 aimed at restoring the war-ruined economy. The series of economic plans included nationalisation of industry, banks and foreign trade, the elimination of traditional differences between Czech and Slovakian economies, the development of industries supplying capital goods, and the direction of labour.

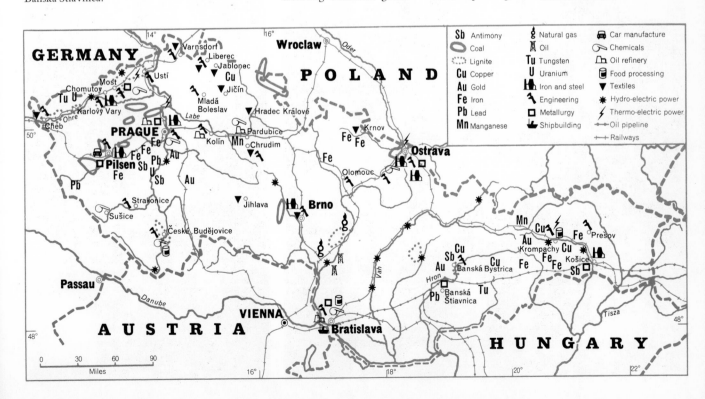

agriculture are of special importance. The industrial utilisation of wood has been encouraged, and two *kombinats* have now been established for the treatment of ligneous by-products. Paper is manufactured mostly in mills situated in north-western Slovakia and in northern Moravia, where Zabreh boasts òne of the largest papermills of central Europe. Cabinet-making has developed immensely in connection with the State's housing policy.

The manufacture of glass and artificial jewellery has long been encouraged by the abundance of fine sand in the Labe valley as well as by the existence of large numbers of skilled glass workers on the southern slopes of the Krushe Hory and the Krkonose. These products were exported all over the world as 'Jablonec ware'. The departure of the Sudeten Germans dealt a hard blow to this industry, which has now been largely reconverted owing to the lack of skilled workmen and technicians, and also to the dwindling foreign markets for artificial and costume jewellery. There is, however, no noticeable falling-off in the output of window-glass, glass vessels, laboratory glassware, and bottles.

The ceramics industry has had to face similar problems. It has for long been located near the north-western Bohemian kaolin deposits — in the region of Karlovy Vary (Karlsbad). Changed circumstances have modified the nature of ceramic production. Although luxury ware is still the speciality of Karlovy Vary, there has been a great development in the production of china for technical uses and of household crockery.

The old-established textile industry has suffered more than any other from the new economic policies. The U.S.S.R. has partially replaced non-European sources of raw materials. The mills in northern Bohemia, which no longer had the necessary technicians, have been shut down or transferred elsewhere. Gottwaldov (in Moravia) and a number of places in southern Bohemia, on the other hand, have been developed as textile centres, and the industry is showing signs of rapid growth in Slovakia

Boot and shoe manufacture is linked with the textile and chemical industries. The works of Bata, the great industrialist, at Zlin (now Gottwaldov) are nationalised; the Plan called for a total national production of over 76 million pairs of boots and shoes during the year 1960.

Gloves, famous for their high quality before the Second World War, were manufactured in the Sudeten mountain regions and in Prague; luxury-type gloves are now made in smaller quantities.

Food-products manufactured from home-grown raw materials have not entirely maintained their former reputation. Production of refined sugar and beer are both running above pre-war levels.

*The new agricultural economy.* Broadly speaking, Czech agriculture, being closely connected with industry, is intensive; Slovak agriculture is in many regions extensive. Agricultural planning since the war has attempted to remove this disparity. By a decree published in June 1945 confiscated estates were distributed in this order of priority: to wage-earning agricultural labourers (at the rate of nearly 20 acres of

Blast furnaces at Kladno in Bohemia. The coalfield of Kladno-Raknovik is very near Prague and serves its heavy industries.

A view of Baroque Prague.

arable land per family); to small landowners (who received about 30 acres each); to large peasant families (from 25 to 38 acres); to workmen, civil servants and craftsmen (about an acre and a quarter); and finally to communes and public associations. This decree also encouraged the resettlement of the frontier regions. After the 1948 *coup d'etat*, a less comprehensive redistribution swept away all that remained of large estates in the Czech lands and in Slovakia. To prevent too great a drop in output by a further extreme subdivision of land, in 1949, agricultural machinery stations, agricultural production co-operatives and State-owned model farms were set up.

Though some private farmers remain, most of Czechoslovakia's agricultural production now comes from co-operative farms, where the profits are shared out monthly on the basis of work performed, and to a lesser extent from State farms, where the workers are paid wages. Co-operative farms now have considerable autonomy; they can work out their own short-term plans and working systems and most now own the bulk of their machinery, calling on the machine and tractor stations only for specialised heavy machinery and for repairs and maintenance.

The largest crop is wheat, the main cereal grown in the plains and valleys; then comes rye which grows on poorer soil and especially on the Czech-Moravian hills. After rye comes barley, formerly grown in Bohemia and Moravia but now spreading to Slovakia. There is a large potato crop. Hops are grown with much care in Bohemia and exported. Beet for sugar or for distilling is now up to roughly the figures of the immediate pre-war years. Flocks and herds are not increasing rapidly.

*Rural dwellings.* The profound transformation wrought in agricultural economy has not yet had any very decisive effect on the traditional appearance of rural dwellings and villages. Most of the Bohemian and Moravian villages are still made up of enclosed farms. In the German-type mountain villages of the frontier wooden houses are common; in the villages on the plains and plateaus and in the valleys, the dwellings are of plaster-covered brick. In the Slovakian mountains the commonest type is the small house with rough-cast walls and a wooden framework at the base. In the Tatry the houses are made entirely of wood, while in eastern Slovakia *pisé* dwellings are the most usual. In many parts, however, and especially in Slovakia, two-storeyed houses and 'community' buildings are under construction.

*The main urban centres.* The most obvious visible results of planning are in the towns. Czechoslovakia has five towns of more than 100,000 inhabitants — Prague (Praha) with nearly a million, Brno, Ostrava, Bratislava, and Plzen — which have long been regional capitals and industrial centres. Prague is undoubtedly one of the most beautiful towns in central Europe and rich in historical monuments and relics of the past. The capital of Czechoslovakia, it is situated on the Vltava at a point where the valley widens out, surrounded by hills that afford good defensive positions.

The old medieval city, where the Town Hall is situated, has remained the principal business district. The new city (Nové Mesto), with streets at right angles and two immense squares, was laid out under the Luxembourg dynasty of Bohemian kings in the fourteenth century. There are magnificent specimens of seventeenth-century Italo-Spanish baroque art in certain parts of the town. Like most Western European towns, Prague expanded in the nineteenth and twentieth centuries, adding industrial districts and residential areas. Between the two World Wars, Greater Prague grew rather haphazardly because of the difficulties involved in absorbing the built-up areas annexed immediately after 1918. The new regime has established more systematic plans.

*International communications.* Czechoslovakia is a land of international transit. The Calais-Paris-Nuremburg-Plzen-Prague line links Czechoslovakia with Western Europe. The line to Decin and Dresden leads to East Germany. The Prague-Ostrava-Warsaw railroad (a very important line with a branch at Ostrava leading to the Soviet border) communicates with Poland. The line from Brno to Bucharest links Czechoslovakia with Hungary and Rumania. In addition to these lines there are important ones linking it to Austria and, through Upper Austria, to Italy. A good deal of work has been done in recent years to extend the rail system in Slovakia. There is a road system (about 44,000 miles) which is much more extensive in the Czech lands than in Slovakia; the roads (often with macadamised or concrete surfaces) are excellent.

Water communications are much less satisfactory. Only below Melnik can the Labe be used for river traffic, being navigable from that point to Hamburg. The main river ports are Usti and Labem and Decin. In the east the Danube is of increasing importance since the ports of Bratislava and Komarno now handle heavy freight from the U.S.S.R.

An impressive post-war project — the construction of a navigable canal between the Odra (Oder) and the Danube — will allow the Morava to be regulated. Both Poland and Silesia would gain much by facilities for transporting heavy freight directly down to the Danube, and Czechoslovakia would be able to make more use of the Polish port of Stettin (Szczecin) at the mouth of the Odra, where she has been ceded an extra-territorial area.

*New trends in trade.* Before the war, the principal supplier and customer of Czechoslovakia was Germany (24 per cent by volume of all the foreign trade); then — far behind — came Great Britain (4·5 per cent) and France (4 per cent). Thirty per cent of Czechoslovak foreign trade was with countries outside Europe. Now, and more especially since 1948, the U.S.S.R. is Czechoslovakia's principal customer and main supplier.

Poland, too, has become one of the biggest customers and suppliers, with Rumania, Bulgaria, East Germany and China.

Czechoslovakia is also supplying finished products and industrial equipment to the underdeveloped countries of the Near and Middle East and to South America. Czechoslovak industry is immensely diversified, but present policy advocates some rationalisation — which will no doubt come about naturally in view of the increasing volume of trade with many countries of West Europe and the Mediterranean, for which Czechoslovakia is geographically placed.

# HUNGARY

In contrast to Poland, a resuscitated state, and to Czechoslovakia and Yugoslavia, both recently created states, Hungary is the rump of a former and much larger country. In 1914 — as part of the Austro-Hungarian Empire — Hungary had an area of 125,500 square miles and a population of 21 million, of whom only 54 per cent spoke the Magyar language. By the Treaty of Trianon the country was reduced to about 35,900 square miles and a population of 8 million. The Second World War occasioned fleeting territorial readjustments in Hungary's favour — southern Slovakia fell to her under the Munich agreements, Subcarpathian Russia (Ruthenia) when the independent State of Slovakia was constituted in 1939, and northern Transylvania and the Banat of Temesvar (Timisoara) were regained in 1940 and 1941. However, since Hungary's fortunes were bound up with those of the Axis powers, the country was in 1945 once more reduced to its 1919 boundaries — with the exception of a few frontier rectifications. The present boundaries enclose a relatively dense population of over 10 million; about 90 per cent of the inhabitants are of Hungarian origin and speak the Magyar language. Germans form the largest alien group (about 200,000). There is a scattering of Yugoslavs in the south-east, and a Slovak minority (about 10,000) is found mainly in the north. The Rumanian minority also numbers about 10,000.

Hungarians settled abroad are fairly numerous (most of them left before the First World War) and may total more than four million. There are Hungarian colonies in Austria (Vienna and the Burgenland) in Subcarpathian Russia (where they live in the townships), in Slovakia (691,000 according to the official figures), in Rumania from 1½ to 2 million in Transylvania and the Banat), and about 500,000 in Yugoslavia. More than 1,500,000 Hungarians live in the United States; Cleveland has the second largest Hungarian population of any city in the world.

Hungary is a small country, full of life and, in contrast to Yugoslavia and Rumania, geographically homogeneous, composed of the plains and valleys of the Pannonian basin's northern region. From the end of the ninth century, the region was occupied by a people of Finno-Ugrian origin.

*Hungary's two axes.* The Danube (Duna) and the mountain ridges stretching from Lake Balaton to the Carpathians form the two axes of the Hungarian State. Hungarian economy gravitates toward the Danube, on whose banks are sited large towns, including the capital itself. It is by this great river that Hungary, now without ports or coasts, maintains contact with its northern and southern neighbours. During the nineteenth century Hungarian capital developed navigation on the Danube and the Sava rivers, and also built the railroad from Budapest to Fiume (Rijeka). The waters of the Danube, slowed down in the Pannonian plain, flood and fertilize a valley several miles wide and feed the canals and irrigation channels on the plain.

The Danube is a natural frontier between western and eastern Hungary. To the west extend regions of higher altitude and more varied relief, where the population is more dense and where life in the countryside is in many respects like that in Austria or southern Germany. To the east, however, stretch monotonous plains with a drier climate and a sparser population — a foretaste of eastern Europe, the world of the steppes.

The Danube has not always been the main artery

Stud Vernier horses grazing in Hosszuhát Farm of the Animal Husbandry Institute, County Hajdu.

of the Magyar lands. In the sixteenth century Hungary was occupied by the Turks sweeping on towards Vienna. During the ages of invasion, the real frontier was not the Danube but the mountain backbone cut through by the river swirling through picturesque gorges. These mountains — or rather hills, for they do not exceed about 3,000 feet in height — present a most varied relief: rounded summits covered with oak and beech forests, arid limestone plateaus on which flocks of sheep graze, hills cut out of the mass of clay and sand deposits laid down by the Pannonian Sea, and volcanic hills to the east of the Danube, where the fertile soil is most favourable for market-gardens and vineyards. Deep valleys cut into the mountains and isolate both massifs and ridges, which lie in a general south-west to north-east direction. There is the asymmetrical Bakony (2,200 feet) which dominates the Balaton trough, the Vertes (2,070 feet), and the Pilis (2,480 feet) whose southern section is cut through by the Danube. There are also precursors of the more lofty Carpathians, such as Mounts Hegyalja, Bükk (3,150 feet) and Matra (3,400 feet). The heights are mantled with fir forests, and thermal springs follow the fault-lines. In the basins there are extensive deposits of lignite, bauxite and various ores. This was the region where the first Hungarian industries were established, and it is still one of the areas which holds out most promise for modern Hungary.

*The north-west: Raba and Kisalföld.* In the north-west, where it borders on Czechoslovakia and Austria, Hungary has a very mixed population. There are groups of Slovaks, Germans and Croats, and the high density of the population can be ascribed to the excellent soil and to the fact that this region, protected by the Bakony, served as a refuge area when the Pannonian plain was occupied by the Turks. All the soil is tilled, and the climate favours

cereal crops. Extremes of temperature are less marked and rainfall is heavier than in the southern plains. The covering of deciduous forest was cleared in Roman times, so that there is a landscape of varied crops, of *bocage,* and of open fields — very much like the countryside in Moravia or Lower Austria. There is still marshy ground at the bottom of the Danube and Raba valleys, but the dry terraces and hills of the Kisalföld (the 'Little Plain') have lent themselves to the establishment of large villages. The yield of wheat and oats is decidedly higher than in other parts of Hungary, and a prosperous agriculture (run on modern lines with a rotation of cereals, sugar-beet, hops and forage plants) is combined with the breeding of livestock. Industry, concentrating on heavy engineering, textiles, foodstuff and furniture manufacture, also flourishes in and around Györ.

*Fields and steppes. Alföld and Puszta.* The landscape changes to the south and east of the mountain backbone. The climate becomes drier, trees are scarcer, the villages more widely spaced, and population density lower. These are areas which have frequently been devastated and depopulated, a no-man's-land during the sixteenth and seventeenth centuries, a bone of contention between Hapsburg and Turk. The region was resettled as the wave of Islam rolled back at the beginning of the eighteenth century — after the conclusion of the Treaty of Karlowitz in 1699. The development of the Pannonian South was encouraged by a number of factors: proximity to Vienna, the rise of a middle-class trading community in Budapest, and the dense population to the north of Bakony and in the German lands. But until quite recently both settlement and economic progress were directed by men from the north. The feudal magnates and the Hungarian and Austrian landed proprietors attracted Serbians, Hungarians and Germans who built villages, repopulated the

Esztergom, ancient capital of Hungary, situated on the Danube above Budapest and facing Czechoslovakia across the river. Esztergom is the seat of the Primate of Hungary, and the town is dominated by the nineteenth-century cathedral (seen in the foreground).

LAND : Fourteenth-century Niedzica Castle, overlooking the Dunajec gorges, in the Beskids.

valleys, drained the marshes and tilled the steppe. Consequently, there are two types of country characteristic of the Danubian plains — Alföld or 'field' (i.e. cultivated plain) and the Puszta, the wild steppes, traditionally discouraging to permanent settlement, where the earth was too dry or too wet, and where huge flocks of sheep found pasture. This is the region of the old, traditional, picturesque Hungary, the Hungary of shepherds, poets and artists, 'the country of gypsies, fine horses, good wines, colourful costumes and beautiful women'. It is hard to distinguish any clearly defined natural regions in this vast expanse of plains. To the west of the Danube the ground is still fairly rolling. The Mecsek hills rise, isolated, out of the plain to more than 2,000 feet. Round the town of Pecs there are mines and industries. In the fertile low hills and broad, marshy valleys stretching between the Mecsek hills and Lake Balaton on one side, and the Drava River on the other, there is a predominantly intensive system of cultivation. However, because of the great heat of

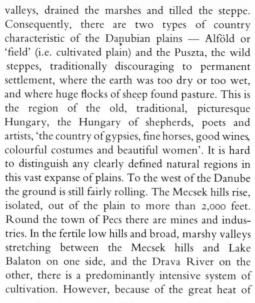

The population of Hungary is almost wholly peasant but settlement and social structure are slowly changing in character, and 40 per cent of the population is now urban.

summer, maize is the principal cereal crop. The shores of Lake Balaton have always attracted settlers and the average population there is more than 350 to the square mile. The steep northern slopes are covered with vineyards, while market-gardens are more common on the south side where the small homes of the fishermen, interspersed with spas and holiday resorts, are scattered haphazardly along the shores of the lake.

To the east of the Danube is the Nagyaföld, the Great Hungarian Plain, a loess plateau which occupies more than half the total area of Hungary. It is an area of irregular low rainfall with an annual average of barely 16 inches steadily decreasing from west to east, where the rivers have meandering courses, spreading sheets of alluvial soil and eating into the edges of the plateau. The main river, the Tisza, whose valley is narrower and less humid than that of the Danube, divides the Plain into two distinctly separate areas.

Over the past century increasingly organised efforts have been made to improve this vast area, and in particular the most barren parts, known as the Puszta, which for centuries were given over entirely to hunting and fishing and which were subject to floods. Large areas of the Puszta consisted of sand dunes stretching in parallel rows, pin-pointed with stagnant pools. Expanses of salt covered the valley floors to the east of the Tisza, left as a white crust on the earth's surface after evaporation of the winter floods and making cultivation impossible. In many places the loess soil was potentially fertile but was in practice left useless.

Today almost every part of the Puszta has been improved to a greater or lesser degree. Owing to the irregular rainfall there were few trees to bind the drifting sands, but acacia plantations and vineyards established in the nineteenth century are now a familiar part of the landscape. An equally familiar improvement on the old system is the network of irrigation channels and the natural or man-made dykes which surround many of the villages, perched on little hills rising above the former marshes, or spread out in a semicircular pattern following the course of an abandoned meander of the river. Most of these irrigation and drainage channels were built in the past two decades and consolidated earlier large-scale regulation of the Danube and the Tisza and drainage of marshy and swampy areas. Scientific soil improvement has also brought great benefits and yields per acre have consequently improved.

A few areas of the old-style Puszta remain as an exception — and a tourist curiosity; but even in the most barren areas, such as the Hortobagy Puszta, near Debrecen, irrigation makes some farming possible. Fish breeding is carried on and livestock breeding has in recent years become intensive rather than extensive.

The most successful development has occurred west of the Tisza, which is also the area where efforts were first started. In the eighteenth century, after the end of Turkish rule, the peasants who had taken shelter in the market towns swarmed out on to the depopulated plain, built their *tanya,* a small farmstead or hut, and started cultivating the soil, which had lain fallow for generations. It was a difficult life, for often the soil had degenerated into drifting sands, and even today these *tanyas* bear the mark of the pioneer farmstead. Though they are still small and isolated, great efforts have been made to improve health and education facilities, and the government has set up *tanya* centres as nuclei of modern community settlements.

The most spectacular change in farming methods, however, is in the fields, which now produce vegetables and fruit, in particular 2 million apricot trees around Kecskemét. Farther north wheat, maize and sugar-beet are grown.

The towns of Szeged, Szolnok and Debrecen, the economic centres of eastern Hungary, were for long little more than market-towns, though Debrecen had a famous university. Now they have developing industries, and their growth is being encouraged, as is that of other provincial towns, in an effort to counteract excessive centralisation on Budapest. Szeged has grown in commercial importance, Szolnok has paper, chemical and iron works, while Debrecen has pharmaceutical, engineering and ball-bearing works.

## HUNGARIAN ECONOMY

*Agrarian reform.* Hungarian agrarian economy was in pre-war days marked, more than that of any other part of central Europe, by the overwhelming preponderance of great estates worked by thousands of peasant-servants. The Esterhazy family, for instance, owned more than 320,000 acres, which included 164 villages. Estates of more than 1,200 acres covered a third of the cultivated land surface. of 285 to 1,200 acres occupied 13 per cent, while small owners farmed barely one-fifth of the cultivable land. More than a quarter of the peasant families owned no land at all. Hungary was the 'land of three million beggars'.

The huge estates, half of whose acreage was composed of forests and pasture and was preserved for hunting and shooting, remained intact. Of all the states in the Danubian area Hungary was the least affected by the agrarian reforms which followed on the First World War. In the period between the two wars only a few of the large estates were actually broken up.

Then, in March 1945, the law prescribing the expropriation and division of all properties over 144 acres was strictly enforced; the changes effected by this second agrarian reform appear more far-reaching in Hungary than in any other country of central or eastern Europe. More than a third of the country's area (about 7½ million acres in all) was redistributed. A million agricultural labourers received tiny holdings of about 5 to 7½ acres. The estates of German and Hungarian magnates added to the acreage available for distribution to landless or very poor peasants. Yet some of the *latifundia,* or large estates, have been spared. Forests and model farms (more than 16 per cent of the total area) are directly administered by the State. The disadvantages of running a vast number of tiny holdings have been to some extent offset by the formation of various types of production and labour co-operatives. Their numbers have increased greatly since 1952, and nearly 4,000 co-operatives with 1,500,000 members cultivate 80 per cent of the arable land.

*Agricultural problems.* The trend towards State-run and collectivised agriculture stopped after 1953. The marked drop in agricultural output can be explained by the division of the arable land into far too many tiny units; by the opposition of the middle-class group of peasants; by the considerable losses sustained by Hungarian agriculture in the war (half the live-stock, a third of the machines, and a tenth of the buildings); by the preference accorded to heavy industry during the first Three Year Plan; by the succession of droughts after the war; and by political difficulties. Little of the arable land is untilled. The acreage under grain crops is smaller than before the war: the wheat and maize harvest is still insufficient. Unprofitable co-operatives have been disbanded, and lower taxes are now imposed on

A farmyard in Hungary. Agriculture remains Hungary's largest single industry, though the proportion of imported foodstuffs, in particular maize, has increased. Agriculture provides one-third of the national income.

Post-war agrarian reform
redistributed more than a
third of the country's area
among the million agricultural
labourers. A drop in output
was in part the result of this
subdivision into too many tiny
holdings and this led to
increased collectivisation.
The acreage under grain
is over 60 per cent, but is
still less than before 1939.
Recent changes have encouraged
industrial crops; especially
sugar-beet and fruit and vegetables
for export.

private property. Small landowners have received a
good deal of State aid in the form of seed, fertilizers,
livestock, and machines. The Government will also
grant them credit and gives them technical instruction.
It is hard to say whether the new agrarian legislation
has had immediate and favourable effects. A fresh
wave of rapid collectivisation contributed to the
1956 uprising and although the trend continued
afterwards it was with less haste and more discretion.
All the same, by 1962 agriculture was almost wholly
socialised in some form or other. More than 60 per
cent of the cultivated land is still under grain crops.
Only in the north-west is there more wheat than
maize, but rye is still the main crop on the sandy
soil of Nyirseg or Kiskun. In large-scale farming,
whether by the State of the collectives, 'white cereals'
are substituted for the traditional maize. The yield

reaches 12 cwt. per acre for wheat, and 19 cwt. for
maize. Recent changes have aimed at developing
industrial crops. The sugar-beet area is increasing.
There was an ambitious plan to plant about 320,000
acres with sub-tropical crops on the irrigated lands
of the Tisza valley and on those of its tributaries as well
as in the Hortobagy, but this plain failed, and was
abandoned in the mid-1950s. It was succeeded by
more successful efforts to encourage fruit and
vegetable growing and viticulture, as well as intensive
stock-breeding.

Such crops may permanently change the traditional
face of the Puszta, where the problems presented by
poor soil, dry climate and human negligence are
comparable to those encountered on the Russian
steppes. Good results have already been obtained by
planting screens of trees, by reforestation, by combat-

A new residential district at
Dunaujvaros, a centre of
heavy industry.
The town is entirely a creation
of the post-war years.

ing soil erosion, and by tilling some of the migration lands hitherto reserved for flocks and herds. Such measures were to have been rapidly undertaken by a concentration of the old *tanyas* and by the establishment of huge, modern, rural population units and highly mechanised collective centres. But these plans have encountered resistance.

*Conditions of industrial development.* Hungarian industry is hampered by economic and technical backwardness, a consequence of age-long economic and political subordination, and by the loss of much of its former territory. Before 1914 the government of Vienna did everything to hamper development in all branches of Hungarian industry (especially metallurgy and textiles) which might compete with those of Austria. The leading Hungarian port, Rijeka, had poor connections with Budapest, and navigation on the Danube was mostly under Austrian control. After the First World War Hungary had close connections with Germany, which invested capital, delivered manufactured goods in exchange for agricultural produce, and controlled Hungarian commerce and

industry. It is true that in 1938 a fifth of the population was employed in industry, but nearly two-thirds of this labour force was concentrated in Budapest and its suburbs. German pillage and war damage still further weakened the industrial potential. By 1945 the Hungarian population was starving and its currency worthless.

However, the prospects for a restoration of Hungarian industry and for its future development were very far from unfavourable. The coal and lignite are of poor quality (except the Mecsek coal), the deposits are scattered, and communication between them is not good. Vertesalja-Esztergom, Dorog, Tatabanya, Tokod, Salgotarjan, Komlo and Ajka are the principal mining centres and are all in the mountains. Nevertheless output, which was not more than 10 million tons before the war, reached 12 million tons in 1950 and has since risen to 30 million tons; most of this, however, consists of lignite or brown coal.

Hungary is one of the richest European countries in petroleum. The Lispe field, to the north of the

Raw materials arriving at the Danube Steelworks in Dunaujvaros, south of Budapest. Hungarian industry, negligible in 1945, now accounts for two-thirds of the national income, and prospects for its future development are good.

Hungary's economic and technical backwardness was a consequence of long economic and political subjection. However, much progress has been made already. Petroleum deposits are among the richest in Europe and bauxite deposits the second richest. There are also extensive reserves of natural gas. The main manufacturing industries are found on the north-west plains and in the Alföld. Further development can be expected only when the need for agricultural machinery can be satisfied, for only mechanisation can free the rural labour force in the scattered villages.

Drava, in 1963 produced 1·8 million tons and is linked by pipeline to Budapest. Extensive reserves of natural gas have been prospected to the east of the Tisza.

As there are no high mountains, Hungary cannot count on hydro-electric power, and lignite is used to supply the thermo-electric stations in the north-west. Dams on the Tisza and the Danube have increased power resources but imports of both oil and electricity from the U.S.S.R. through Comecon are still needed.

Metallic ores are not abundant, with the sole exception of bauxite. The extraction of this important ore was intensified by the Germans during the war (north and north-west of Balaton and south of Pecs) and has put Hungary second only to France among European bauxite producers (excluding the U.S.S.R.).

The nationalisation policy has been carried out more slowly in Hungary than in other eastern European countries. In 1945 the coal mines were expropriated, then, in 1946, the electric plants. Heavy industry and enterprises employing more than 100 persons were not taken over until 1948. Businesses with more than 10 employees were nationalised in December 1949. Economic planning has been adopted since the war: the first Three Year Plan (1947–49) which was to effect the reconstruction of the country, the first Five Year Plan (1950–54), whose object was to increase output by modernising equipment. The rapid application of these Plans (according to official figures, production has more than quintupled since 1938) has greatly changed the location of the industrial zones. Towns that have hitherto always been agricultural have become industrialised. *Kombinats* spring up near sources of power or lines of communication.

However, the years of the first Five Year Plan were marked by too sudden a spurt in the development of heavy industry. In July 1953 a revised Plan was put into operation — very largely because a serious food shortage afflicted the towns during 1951 and 1952.

The new measures were aimed at reducing investments in the large industrial centres and in engineering and at developing manufactures and the output of consumer goods. The revolution of 1956 disrupted the country's economic life. Recovery was complete by 1958. Attempts have since been made to raise urban living standards and at the same time to encourage the production of high quality goods, even luxury goods. The later Plan (1961–65) aimed to raise industrial production by more than 80 per cent over 1958 figures and agricultural production by 30 per cent over the same year.

*New industrial geography.* The heavy industry *kombinats* are located on the lignite deposits stretching from Lake Balaton to the Slovakian frontier. These plants use the iron ore from the north-east basin divided between Hungary and Slovakia, Czech and Polish coke brought in through Bratislava, current from the thermo-electric stations, and bauxite from north and north-east of Lake Balaton. Although the 'vertical' structure of State enterprises is fairly far advanced, each industrial centre of any size tends to specialise: Thus Miskolc is a mining town with foundries, cement and engineering works; briquettes and cement are produced at Tatabanya; Ajka and Almasfüzitö treat bauxite at different stages, and Urkut processes manganese. Two isolated industrial centres are fast developing: engineering at Pecs (near the Mecsek coalfield and bauxite deposits) and steelworks at Dunaujvaros (on the Danube upstream from Budapest). The Dunaujvaros plant has been established at a point where advantage can be taken of river transport. The first works there were opened in 1951 and the town — which now already has 40,000 inhabitants is destined to become the main centre of Hungarian industry. A great chemical combine has been opened on the upper Tisza.

The main manufacturing industries (especially for agriculture) are grouped on the north-western plains (chiefly spinning and weaving) and in the Alföld

The Danube divides Budapest into two cities: the old historic Buda on the left and the modern business centre of Pest on the right.
With a population of over 1,800,000, Budapest has more than one-sixth of the total population of Hungary.

(principally flour-mills, tobacco, canning, starch factories and refineries). But the industries of these 'peasant towns' can develop only when the output of agricultural machinery is sufficient to supply the needs of State or collective farms; only the mechanisation of agriculture will free the rural labour force that is still scattered among the traditional-style villages now becoming industrialised.

## BUDAPEST

The oldest town in Hungary remains the most important. Budapest, like Vienna, is the large capital of a small state, and its population (about 1,850,000) is more than a sixth of that of the whole country. The town has, of course, owed its good fortune to its geographical position. The old districts, perched on Buda hill, overlook the alluvial plain of the Danube, a river that is navigable and easy to cross. Budapest is a river town, a town commanding many lines of communication. Its historical rôle as the focal point of a large and unified state has been considerable. Built in the thirteenth century, Buda citadel was later a Turkish stronghold and then a headquarters of Hapsburg domination. It was also the seat of government, the place of residence of the Magyar aristocracy and the foreign bourgeoisie.

The town's growth was closely conditioned by the reconquest, settlement and cultivation of the south-eastern territories and by the development of traffic between Vienna and Budapest. From the end of the eighteenth century the population of Budapest grew rapidly; there were 35,000 inhabitants in 1780, 178,000 by 1850, 850,000 in 1900, and 1,585,000 in 1940.

The present-day pattern of the different sections of the city still shows their traditional character. Buda remains a historical town of palaces, churches, mansions, parks and thermal establishments. Across the Danube (about 440 yards wide) lie the streets of Pest, regularly laid out, strung along the banks of the river and spreading into the plain beyond. Surrounding the whole is a belt of workers' districts which bear witness to the industrialisation of the latter part of the nineteenth century, encouraged — more than in any other part of the country — by the investment of Austrian, German, British and French capital.

Buda was bombed during the Second World War. The bridges and river port were destroyed and much reconstruction and rebuilding had to be done. The town-planning programme aims at transforming Buda into an area of parks and museums; at improving communications between Pest and the outskirts; at laying out a 'Greater Budapest' reaching 15 miles from north to south and 19 miles from west to east; at dispersing some of the great concentration of factories to provincial towns and improving the suburbs; and finally at enlarging the port at Csepel island.

HUNGARY'S FUTURE. Hungary's future depends, without doubt, on the industrialisation of the south-west, on the transformation of the steppe-lands, and on increased output. Since the tragic events of October 1956, Hungary has been linked more closely than ever with the policy of the Soviet Union and the other Warsaw Pact signatories. Two-thirds of her foreign trade is with the eastern States, which take her raw materials and agricultural produce and increasingly manufactured goods. But since 1957 a new, liberal trend has been a feature of economic, social and cultural life.

Hungary's resumption of commercial relations with Western countries and Yugoslavia, the growth of trade relations all over the world and her participation in the world's major trade fairs are encouraging — especially as Hungary, like Czechoslovakia and Poland, is well placed for playing the rôle of intermediary with the West.

# POLAND

The Second World War inflicted incalculable damage and loss of life upon Poland, bringing with it social and political changes. Moreoever, the country was transformed by a 185-mile translation from east to west, under the Potsdam Agreement between the U.S.S.R., the U.S.A. and Great Britain (2nd August, 1945), and the Treaty of Moscow between the U.S.S.R. and Poland (17th August, 1945).

## THE LANDSCAPE

*The new frontiers.* The treaty of Moscow settled the controversy about Poland's eastern boundaries. With the exception of two small concessions to Poland, the new frontier follows approximately the Curzon Line (suggested by Lord Curzon at the Paris Peace Conference of 1920). The first concession is in the region of Krilow, between the Bug and the Volokia: the second comprises the Bialowieza, Niemirov, and Bialystok area.

The amount of Polish territory lost to the east of the new frontiers is about 66,200 square miles, which in 1938 held a population of 11,750,000. According to the Potsdam Agreement, the new Polish-German frontier was to run from the north-eastern corner of the Bohemian quadrilateral, following the line of the western Nysa (Neisse), then that of the Odra (Oder) as far as Gartz, and then to the north, leaving Szczecin (Stettin) and Swinoujscie (Swinemünde) as Polish territory.

This agreement has not been officially recognised but is recognised *de facto* by the U.S.A., Great Britain and France, pending final delimitation in the signing of a peace treaty with Germany. It was agreed that the territories in question should be handed over to Polish administration, and the section of the Potsdam Agreement laying down that the German population in Poland including that of the Western Territories were to be evacuated to Germany was recognised both *de facto* and *de jure*. Poland's pre-war frontiers were extended westwards by the addition of Dolny Slask (Lower Silesia) and part of Gorny Slask (Upper Silesia), Ziemia Lubuska (East Brandenburg), and the greater part of Pomorze. In 1948, a decree was issued declaring these territories to be an integral part of Poland. The regained area covers about 40,000 square miles which had a population of 8,463,000 inhabitants in 1938. Most place names have been restored to their Polish original.

*An immense plain.* Poland today consists mostly of an immense plain where surface and soil are largely a legacy of the great Quaternary glaciers. In the south is an area of hills and high plains stretching from the San to the Nysa, and a mountainous fringe which is of a very different character on each side of the low hills at the Gate of Moravia. To the east are the Carpathians and the Tatra massif, and to the west the Sudeten mountains.

From Pomorze to Mazury (formerly East Prussia) and from Ziemia Lubuska as far as the Bug stretches the vast plain left by ground moraines and subglacial drift. Elsewhere, and especially in the north of the plain, the old terminal moraines form isolated hills, often in parallel lines and generally preceded by a glacial slope formed by the action of streams in spreading the moraine sands. In other areas there are numerous hills, all in a line and pointing in the same direction. These are the drumlins, long branching ridges.

The clay soils of the ground-moraine or subglacial drift are not infertile, but impermeable and rather mixed. The terminal moraines and their dispersal zones, on the other hand, are much poorer, with a predominance of sands, heaped up as dunes in some places and spreading out as extensive moorland in others.

The long coastline of this plain is made up of light glacial material which tends to silt up. In consequence the shore is low and not very inviting. Gdynia is an artificial port and an outport has had to be constructed for Szczecin at Swinoujscie.

The most distinctive feature of the Polish plain is the very wide corridor formed by the middle and lower course of the Vistula, which describes countless meanders and is bordered by broad terraces.

Northwards, in the morraine ridges near the Baltic, the Vistula plain is narrower and more deeply embanked, but in the Warsaw region it spreads out to a width of 19 to 25 miles and forms the rich heartland of Poland.

*Southern hills and mountains.* The hills and high plains of the south form a belt 150 miles long. The main feature of the relief in Silesia and in Little Poland is a number of rather high plateaus, often dry and covered with glacial deposits, particularly with loess, which makes them very fertile.

This belt of high land is not continuous. The Upper Silesian depression separates the Silesian plains from the plateaus of Little Poland. Farther east, the broad valley of the Upper Vistula has a rich soil of glacial muds and silts.

The southern and mountainous frontiers of Poland are divided into two groups of unequal size: to the south-east part of the Carpathians, and to the south-west the Sudeten mountains.

The northern face of the Tatras — a small portion of the Carpathian 'central massif' has been left to Poland by a bend in the Polono-Slovak frontier to the south of Nowy Targ. It is an Alpine region with steep high mountains, deep-cut glaciated valleys, and huge forests.

Farther north, the much lower Beskid ridges run from west to east. The hills are often of soft rocks and take the form of rounded eminences separated by wide valleys containing lazily meandering rivers.

To the west of the Moravian Gate is the new frontier with Bohemia, an ancient massif whose summits (between 3,000 and 5,000 feet) are formed by tabular plateaus cut by a number of sunk basins well linked by valleys with deep gorges.

*Soils and climates.* The glaciation which extended over the Polish plain as far as the southern plateaus and the northern part of the Sandomierz basin resulted in much of the area being rather poor agricultural land. It is a region of grey, powdery soil more or less podzolised, of sandy or stony soil, or of spongy soil: land which cannot be expected to yield good crops without extensive drainage and improvements. Still, there are in Poland some regions of excellent soil: on the alluvial plains, on the beds of former lakes, and on drained marshes. Then there are the southern Silesian plains and their extension east as far as the Lublin plateau. A long belt of loess and chernozem (black earth) runs along the foot of the Carpathians, reaching its greatest width north of Cracow (Krakow). In this area lies more than half the agricultural potential of Poland.

The climate restricts crops to those of temperate lands with a continental climate. Although the winters are cold (in January at Warsaw about —2·9°C. (27°F.), the summers are warm (in July at Warsaw about 18°C. (65°F.) and allow of good harvests, especially if summer rains are abundant. The fertile soils are suitable for sugar-beet and wheat, while the north and centre of the plain, cooler in summer, are better suited for certain poorer grain crops, for stock-breeding, and for forests.

### PROFIT AND LOSS ACCOUNT

*Population.* The Second World War was immensely destructive, the amount of damage having been estimated at more than 50 thousand million U.S. dollars (38 per cent of the entire national wealth). Many towns were completely destroyed. The greater part of Warsaw on the left bank of the Vistula was heavily damaged, in parts almost razed to the ground.

More than six million Poles were killed: 123,000 soldiers in combat, 521,000 civilians, and 5,384,000 in concentration camps. Thus Poland lost almost 22 per cent of her population.

In the 'regained territories of the West', there remained 3½ million Germans, yet the Poles there numbered not more than 1 million. During 1945–48, under the terms of the Potsdam Agreement, the Polish government carried out the wholesale transfer of these Germans into the Soviet and British zones of occupation in Germany. These measures had two consequences. First, Poland suffered a serious drop in population, and the new Poland lacked labour at a time when it was urgently needed for the reconstruction of the country. Second, population was distributed evenly. After the expulsion of the German population, the 'regained territories of the West' had less than half their 1938 population. On the other hand, many country districts of 'old' Poland were overpopulated: holdings of about 2½ to 3½ acres of tilled land were common.

The government took a number of measures to increase the population. Two million Poles were brought in from eastern territories ceded to the U.S.S.R. and efforts were made — with varying degrees of success — to attract back to their homeland Poles living abroad, in France, in Germany, in Danubian Europe, and in the Balkans. The results were on the whole satisfactory for, counting the repatriations and the rapid population increase, the total population was about 30 million in 1960 and is increasing all the time.

*Material losses. New resources.* In the east, Poland lost the greater part of the north Carpathian oilfield and all its former deposits of potash. It is now deprived of excellent lands in Podolia and Volhynia (annexed to the Ukraine) and of the flax-growing districts of Brest (Brest-Litovsk) and Vilnius (Vilna). Furthermore, the areas ceded to the U.S.S.R. comprised 17 per cent of the Polish forests.

Losses of territory have also been abundantly compensated for by four kinds of gain. Poland was formerly squeezed in between Pomerania and East Prussia and had but one port at her disposal — Gdynia. Now the Polish seaboard extends for over 300 miles

The shipyards at Szczecin (Stettin). Before the war, Poland had only one port, Gdynia; the Polish seaboard now extends for over 300 miles along the Baltic shores.

along the Baltic shores and there are two new Polish ports, Gdansk (Danzig) and Szczecin — Swinoujscie. Moreover, in addition to the Vistula, the Poles now have a second great navigable river, the Odra (Oder), linked by canal with the Upper Silesian coalfield.

The second gain is in new agricultural resources far superior to those lost in the east — pasture lands and potato-fields in Pomerania and Brandenburg and the rich loess soils of Silesia.

The third gain — and the most valuable — is the Silesian coalfield which with the lignite deposits to the east of the Nysa provides the bulk of the new Poland's solid fuel.

Finally, the fourth gain: Germany, in order to relieve congested and vulnerable areas in the west, established in Silesia a great number of new factories and installed much industrial equipment. These are a very important Polish asset.

*Poland as a great coal power.* Coal, and abundant deposits of lignite, have put Poland in sixth position as a world solid fuel power. The bulk of the supply is in the Upper Silesian basin, now entirely within the Polish frontier, with the exception of the Czech Moravska-Ostrava area. It must, of course, be borne in mind that the relative backwardness of Poland's economy is explained by the fact that throughout the whole of the nineteenth century it was divided by occupying powers who were interested only in exploiting it.

The advantages offered by the Upper Silesian basin are considerable. The reserves are larger even than those of the Ruhr, the seams are thick, and working is facilitated by the average depth of the deposit. Finally, and this is a particularly important advantage. the Upper Silesia field yields all types of industrial coal. Today it furnishes about nine-tenths of the country's production.

Poland has other coalfields too: the annexation of Lower Silesia secured the collieries in the Walbrzych area of the Sudeten mountains. In addition to coal there is Tertiary lignite in the western part of the Polish plain. Even peat is used in eastern Poland and is employed at electric power stations.

*Shortage of subsoil resources.* Poland has kept only a small field of crude oil in the Jaslo, Krosno, Ustrsyki Dolne area. Natural gas too, is tapped in the Jaslo and Krosno districts as well as in the south of the Silesian basin, and a pipeline takes the gas to Warsaw.

Most of the iron ore comes from the Czestochowa region, but new deposits have been found at Leczyca in central Poland, where the reserves are estimated at 300 million tons.

Only one non-ferrous metal occurs in quantity — zinc, which is mined at Bytom in Upper Silesia, and in small workings at Olkusz and Chrzanow. Other non-ferrous metals are found only in insignificant amounts — lead in Silesia from mines near Bytom which formerly allowed the Poles to export very large quantities; and copper in Silesia, near Boleslawiec, as well as in the neighbourhood of Kielce and in the Sudeten mountains. There is nickel at Klodzko, chromium at Swidnica, arsenic at Klodzko and Jelenia Gora, and uranium at Jelenia Gora.

Salt is extracted from the rock-salt mines at the foot of the Carpathians and also in the Kujawy and Bydgoszcz area, south of the Lower Vistula. The Poles are endeavouring to make up their loss of potash by working a deposit of potash salt in the Kujawy area. In the Tarnobrzeg region, to the south of Little Poland, sulphur has been discovered and production has increased greatly of late. Phosphate deposits, too, have been discovered recently in the voivodships of Lublin and Kielce, in the neighbourhood of Krasnik, Radom and Sieradz.

NEW TRENDS IN POLISH ECONOMY. Very soon after the war, from 1945 onwards in fact, first the Polish National Liberation Committee and then the Warsaw government were controlled by the Polish Workers' Party. From 1948 onwards the government was entirely in the hands of the Polish United Workers' Party. It is, then, not surprising that the government revolutionised the economic and social structure of the country and followed Soviet example in nationalising industry and commerce and effecting agrarian reform.

*Agrarian reforms.* The social structure of the country

Winter in the Tatras Mountains of Poland. The northern face of the Tatras forms a small portion of the Carpathian central massif.
It is an alpine region, with steep, high mountains, deep-cut glaciated valleys, and huge forests.

Warsaw's rebuilt Market Square, which was completely destroyed during the war.
Reconstruction work was based on photographs, engravings and paintings of pre-war Warsaw.

created a very numerous peasant class, poor and in debt, and a handful of big landowners with huge fortunes in estates.

The reform began with the decree of 6th September 1944 and was later supplemented by the decree of 6th September 1946 covering the 'regained territories of the West'. German properties were at this point expropriated without compensation. Large Polish-owned estates were partially expropriated, this time with compensation. In the old Polish lands, properties of more than 130 acres and in the 'regained territories' over about 260 acres were nationalised; Church lands were excluded from this reform. The State redistributed land thus acquired. The purchase terms were very liberal, with low prices and long repayment periods. The sums thus received by the State were made over to a 'Rural Fund' whose object was to provide agricultural equipment.

State agricultural enterprises were started, whose evolution recalls that of the *sovkhozes* (State farms) in the U.S.S.R. These State enterprises (set up on lands that were in part fallow and in part confiscated from the big landlords) were divided into three groups. First were those producing seeds for sowing; then those specialising in cereals and industrial crops; and thirdly those devoted to stock-breeding.

The same tendency towards collectivisation and nationalisation has been strengthened since 1949 by establishing 'State machine centres', the Polish version of the U.S.S.R. machine and tractor centres. But the most important event was the introduction of production co-operatives in 1949, an attempt at collectivisation of the *kolkhoz* type. However, these have made very slow headway.

*Agricultural progress and difficulties.* Natural conditions explain the development of farming of the continental temperate type, of forestry and of stock-breeding.

The two crops that provide the basis of the nation's food are potatoes and rye. Wheat and oats fall a long way behind, followed by barley. Maize is a very unimportant crop. In addition to the main crops there is a recent small-scale development of industrial crops, flax and hemp, hops and some oil-producing crops (colza and linseed). Poland is also rich in forests.

Stock-breeding is practised on a comparatively small scale. There is also the fishing industry: sea fishing in the Baltic, the North Sea and subpolar areas; lake fishing in northern Poland.

The relatively small amounts of certain products compel Poland to depend upon imports. There is not enough home-grown wheat to satisfy demand and the number of cattle is also insufficient.

Technically, Polish agriculture is very backward indeed. The amount of fertilizers employed per acre has, it is true, increased enormously since the war, but quantities are still too small. Mechanisation is still poorly developed. The reason for the general situation is to be sought, probably, in the subdivision of Polish farms under agrarian reforms.

Attempts have been made to step up production of the four main cereal crops and of potatoes, to increase the number of cattle by developing forage-plant culture and to establish advice centres for the stock-breeders. Agronomical research has been pushed forward vigorously. For instance *kenaf* (gumbo hemp)

and *kanatnik* (flax dodder) are being developed to yield superior quality fibres. Virginia tobacco is in the initial stages of development in the west of Poland. Castor-oil plants are being grown experimentally Attempts to acclimatise cotton are being made in the south. Still more out-of-the-way plants, such as *koksaghiz* and the Abyssinian cabbage, are being tried out, and even rice has been grown. Progress is being made in training agricultural technicians and the Polish State has adopted a system for encouraging the peasants to grow new crops.

*Nationalisation.* Nationalisation was not only a politico-social reaction against industrial capitalism in general, but a nationalist reaction against foreign capitalism. The State had to take over a number of works whose owners had disappeared during the war. It was also authorised to confiscate German enterprises, and did so in 1945. The Polish State had become inevitably the largest employer of industrial labour in the country. In the new Poland industry was too concentrated in a few places, while the overpopulated country districts of the centre and south were far away from the industrial development areas.

Add to this political pressure, and we have the explanation for the nationalisation law of 1946, relating to commerce and industry. Within a year, 70 per cent of Polish industry and commerce was entirely controlled by the State. This percentage has risen a good deal since and the pattern of industry and commerce is modelled on that of the U.S.S.R., comprising only a small, nominally free handicraft sector, existing side by side with large and medium-sized industries that are completely State-controlled.

*Planning and new economy.* The Three Year Plan (covering the period from 1947–49) was first and foremost a programme of economic reconstruction. Then came the Six Year Plan (for the period 1950–55), which was much more like the Soviet plans — especially in the place accorded to industrial development. By 1950 the task was not one of reconstruction but of ending the chronic pre-war inferiority of Polish industry, and the main aim of the Polish Six Year Plan was wide-scale industrialisation of the

Sugar-beet harvesting on a farm in Sroda Slaska, south-west Poland. Although Polish agriculture is technically backward, the fertile soils of Poland are suitable for sugar-beet, and the harvests are good.

country. The rôle of agriculture was to ensure the necessary food supply.

This rapid industrial development presents two main features: the marked growth of basic industries (power, iron and steel) and a new and better-balanced distribution of enterprises within the present-day territory of Poland. Two new groups of equipment industries have been introduced — engineering (machine-tools and motor-cars) and chemical industries (especially those producing nitrogenous fertilizers and superphosphates).

The Plan called for a more balanced distribution of industry; as a result, Warsaw is becoming a great metallurgical and textile centre, and the eastern districts, Bialystok and Lublin, have numerous new factories.

For implementing the agricultural programme, four lines of approach have been adopted: first, mechanisation (facilitated by the development of the new tractor works); second, electrification of many rural centres; third, the large-scale use of fertilizers (made possible by the growth of the chemical industries); and lastly, the development of production co-operatives 'on the basis of free participation', which according to the Plan 'represent superior types of farming'.

The general improvement of Polish agriculture (increases in harvest yields and in stock-breeding produce) constituted the most immediate aim and the most urgent problem from 1953 onwards. The obligatory deliveries in kind made to the State were maintained at their former level or decreased; some were abolished altogether. In the production co-operatives the principle was solemnly laid down that 'the peasants must have a material interest in increasing the productivity of the co-operatives'.

Industry had to be organised in order to improve agricultural output and, to this end, production first of farm machinery and then of chemical fertilizers had to be stepped up. A very real improvement was effected in the domain of consumer goods (textiles, wirelesss sets, bicycles, etc.) which had previously been badly neglected.

The Six Year Plan (1950–55) was followed by two Five Year Plans (1956–60 and 1961–65).

*Industrialisation.* To what extent have the main economic aims of the Plans been carried out? The two sources of power for industry have been considerably developed. However, Poland today is faced with technical difficulties caused by disparity between the output of coal (which is nevertheless great) and the rapid progress of industry.

Production of electricity increases rapidly but hydro-electricity still awaits large-scale development. But the main standby is still coal. Most of the electric power has been generated from Silesian coal, but both lignite and peat are also used.

Iron and steel manufacture is an old Polish industry which before the war was concentrated mostly in the Silesian basin. The increase in production in only a few years is the result of three different kinds of enterprise. First, existing plants have been rebuilt, enlarged or modernised, and their output much increased. Secondly, a number of new plants have been erected. Thirdly, the large V. I. Lenin works began production in 1951 and have been working to capacity since 1954 (at Nowa-Huta near Krakow). A third works, more important because it produces high-grade steel, has also been set up at Bielany-Mlociny near Warsaw.

We have already noted the aim to increase production of such consumer goods as textiles, which in fact occupy a high place among traditional Polish manufactures. In only fifteen years cottons showed an increase of 17 per cent, woollens 177 per cent, and silks 290 per cent.

The production of cotton goods is still necessarily concentrated round Lodz (three-quarters of the output), while a secondary group of cotton-mills exists in the Sudetes and at Wroclaw. The woollen factories are more dispersed — at Lodz, Bielsko-Biala, Zielona Gora and Bialystok. Poland also produces millions of yards of silk goods, while hemp and flax manufactures are still more important, especially at Wroclaw and at new factories in the north-east of the country, where the raw material are grown. In addition to these traditional manufacturers, Poland now

Krakow, former capital of Poland, on the left bank of the Vistula.

has works for spinning and weaving synthetic fibres.

Another old-established industry is food production — mostly sugar-refineries, breweries, and canneries — Poland has become the world's fifth producer of beet-sugar. The refineries are naturally sited in the fertile regions of the west where the beets are grown — Lower Silesia, the Poznan district, and the middle Vistula plain, especially the Kujawy area.

Cement, glass and china works existed long before the war and have continued to prosper. The cement industry is particularly flourishing.

*New industries.* The creation of machine and machine-tool industries was considered essential for the new Poland. She must produce her own machines for the industrialistion and agricultural mechanisation programme, and must endeavour to export to underdeveloped countries such as the Danubian lands and China. So almost from scratch a machine-tool industry developed whose 1959 putput was 36,250 tons.

The motor-car and tractor industry is also a new one. Manufacture of trucks and lorries has increased. The largest automobile plant in Poland — at Lublin — even has furnaces and a foundry. The agricultural machinery industry has also made great strides.

Existing shipyards were enlarged and modernised. Not only is their output much greater than before the war, but they can now build ships of considerable tonnage. The reconstruction of the Wroclaw railway-carriage works brought considerable progress in the manufacture of rolling-stock.

Pre-1937, the electro-technical industry was represented by an output of some objects of common use. Heavy electro-technical material was imported Now turbines and all sorts of material for electrical equipment are manufactured in Poland.

Another striking new feature is the appearance and development of a chemical industry which looks like becoming Poland's second most important industry after metallurgy. The creation of a special Ministry of Chemical Industry in December 1950 was proof of official determination to fill a gap in the national economy. Poland's coal, lignite, sulphur, rock salt, gypsum and anhydrite are chemical raw materials of first-rate importance. The output of artificial fibres and plastics is rising steadily.

Before the war the territories making up present-day Poland produced only zinc and lead, but now a copper metallurgy (including production of electrolytic copper) has been created with works at Boleslaw near Olkusz, at Chrzanow and Skawina. Likewise, an aluminium industry has been created from scratch and is supplied with bauxite, which is imported from Hungary.

Another new industry is that of wood and wood products. There are factories turning out plywood, furniture and veneers. The output of paper has doubled. Poland now has a viscose plant and cellulose works.

*Redistribution of industrial areas.* The old distribution of industry in Poland presented two features: the first was its concentration into four regions — Upper

Poland enjoys two features indispensable in a great modern economy — coal and favourable agricultural conditions. Most of the coal and lignite supplies come from the Upper Silesia basin, which has reserves even larger than those of the Ruhr. There has been a marked development of the metallurgical industries in the post-war years, for in order to carry out industrialisation and agricultural reforms machines must be produced. Vehicles and tractors, electro-technical equipment and both light and heavy chemical products are also increasing in importance. There has been an attempt to create new industrial areas to redress the old lack of balance.

Silesia, the Lodz district, the Warsaw area and the 'central industrial region' which was being organised in 1939. The second feature was the specialisation of industrial centres in one given type of industry, for example Lodz in textiles, Upper Silesia in metallurgy.

This geographical lack of balance had grave consequences for the country's economy. Many regions had too large a rural population with a low standard of living. On the other hand, it was desirable that industries should be transferred to the source of raw material supply or to main centres of consumption.

Therefore new industrial areas were created. The Wroclaw region and those bordering on the Sudeten moutains became areas of large-scale and diversified production. Industrialisation is spreading to Opole in the south-east and, in the west, in the Sudeten mountains. In the centre and east of Poland new industrial areas have appeared on the rural plains. The industrial region of Lublin is also expanding, not only with new plant treating agricultural products for the foodstuffs industry, but also with the large-scale automobile and other machine industries. In north-east Poland, Bialystok has become the centre of a small industrial zone. Again, two industrial areas are growing up near the Baltic, Gdansk-Gdynia and Szczecin — with shipyards and even iron and steel works. Between these two areas in the Notec basin, new industrial enterprises founded on wood processing are growing up.

*Communications and transport.* Distribution of goods within the country and foreign trade depend almost entirely on the railways, but these are most unsatisfactorily planned.

Again, the waterways play much too small a part in transport — they take only about 1·5 per cent of the freight that goes by rail. The lower reaches of the Odra, the Gliwice canal, part of the Notec and the Bydkoski canal are the only waterways that can take vessels of more than 400 tons. This situation hampers the development of the country, and a programme of improvement has been drawn up according to which a whole circuit of navigable waterways would be constructed, consisting of the Odra-Warta-Notec Canal, the Gliwice-Vistula Canal and the Oldra-Vistula network, to link up the most important of the industrial centres all over the country. This circuit would have two outlets to the sea, through the lower reaches of the Odra and Vistula.

*Changes in foreign trade.* Two factors have contributed to the increase in the volume of Polish trade. First, the recent economic changes have released large exportable surpluses of coal and industrial products; on the other hand, they have created new demands for imported foodstuffs because of the crisis in agriculture, and for ores, industrial raw materials and equipment needed in the expansion of Polish industries.

Secondly, Poland today enjoys commercial facilities far better than those before the war, since in addition to the port of Gdynia there are now the two ports of Szczecin and Gdansk.

Gdynia is especially a port for ocean shipping and passenger lines, but also handles various sorts of freight. Gdansk is more a port for European coastal shipping and specialises in cargoes of coal and in bulk goods.

Other considerations have directed Polish trade towards the U.S.S.R. The 'Battle Act' and the refusal by the Import-Export Bank to extend credits to Poland led the Poles to turn to the U.S.S.R. for the industrial equipment material necessary for the reconstruction plan and then for the industrialisation plan.

Polish trade has assumed the proportions of that of a great modern state. While it still remains a great European coal exporter, it also exports electrical products, zinc, glass, china, wood and wooden articles. The significant new feature is the appearance of Polish goods in the great import markets for metallurgical products, machines and machine-tools, wagons and locomotives.

Imports, too, have changed in character. Poland still buys foodstuffs and certain industrial equipment, but the two essential changes are the rapid increase in the import of raw materials (related to industrial development) and an increase in the purchase of consumer goods.

The U.S.S.R. has become Poland's chief commercial partner. However, commercial relations have been developed with Czechoslovakia, Rumania, Hungary, Bulgaria, and East Germany. Trade with China began in 1950 and was developed by an agreement in January 1951 and by later trade treaties. Poland is trying also to increase her commerce with other countries, Great Britain, France, the Scandinavian countries, Argentina, India, Pakistan, Egypt and the U.S.A. among them.

# RUMANIA

The word 'Rumania' did not appear on the political map of Europe until the end of the nineteenth century. It constitutes a geographical entity that is original and attractive, adjoining the vast and monotonous Russian steppes, and the winding, wooded mountain ranges of the over-partitioned Balkan peninsula. Rumania is a small Latin state surrounded by Slavs and set on the shifting frontiers of Orthodoxy, Catholicism, Protestantism and even Islam; it was in former times torn between the Russian, Turkish and Austro-Hungarian empires. A crossroad of rival routes and influences, it is a fruitful and attractive land, an open glacis of wide plains surrounding a mountain fastness.

*An outline of Rumanian history.* Dacia, conquered by the Emperor Trajan, was the core of what was later to become Rumania. Its heartland was Transylvania, but it spread out beyond the mountains and was well protected on the east by a succession of palisaded ramparts. During a hundred and fifty years of Roman occupation, Dacia adopted the Latin language and civilisation.

In A.D. 270 the Emperor Aurelian withdrew his legions to the south of the Danube, and for seven centuries Dacia was the victim of innumerable invaders and rival foreign princes. The Magyars (who arrived in Pannonia in the ninth century and then penetrated Transylvania) and the German settlers (whom the Hungarians invited) fixed a political frontier on the Carpathians. Old Dacia, henceforth cut in two, developed under the dual influence of the West and of the Byzantine East, the latter being superseded later by the Moslem East. The memory of

Dacian-Rumanian unity survived, and under Michael the Brave (1593–1601) it was almost reconstituted. Then the Danubian and Carpathian lands fell into the hands of the Turks and were subjected to the most ruinous oppression, while the princes' courts maintained a brilliant Neo-Greek culture. The weakness of the Ottoman Empire encouraged the greed of Austria and Russia, and there followed annexations, new colonisations, and policies of assimilation.

Among the Rumanians, who were reduced to a condition of near slavery, there appeared symptoms of a national awakening as early as the seventeenth century. But not until 1856 was the independence of Wallachia and Moldavia recognised. The two provinces quickly chose a single ruler (Alexander Cuza) and then a king (Charles of Hohenzollern). In 1878 the Rumanians exchanged the Dobrogea for the southern part of Bessarabia. However, after their costly participation in the First World War, they recovered almost all the Dacian heartland.

With twenty years of zealous effort, the Rumanians endeavoured to make up for time lost under the foreign yoke. Then the country was involved in the Second World War — first against the U.S.S.R. and then against Nazi Germany. The result was invasions, Russian occupation, widespread ruin, thousands of dead and, lastly, a harsh peace treaty in which the country was reduced to 91,671 square miles with some 16 million inhabitants. When Rumania became a People's Republic, the Constitution was modelled on that of the U.S.S.R.

*Ties with the past.* Old traditions among a mainly peasant population deeply attached to the soil of their ancestors have been the major factor in ensuring the survival of the Rumanian people.

The language remains very close to Latin despite a number of foreign elements. There are customs which undoubtedly pre-date the Romanisation of Dacia. The national folk art is remarkable for harmony, delicacy of colouring and decorative motifs that are mainly geometric and floral.

Archaeological remains attract the visitor's notice less than the Transylvanian castles perched on rocky spurs, and the Carpathian churches and monasteries whose Byzantine and Oriental art is touched with Western influences.

*From mountain to plain.* During the nineteenth century the peasants were still 'going down' into the Wallachian or Pannonian steppes. The marked ethnical and religious unity of the Rumanians appears to be closely related to the mountain refuge where the purest and oldest of their peoples are found. From the eleventh to the nineteenth centuries and with economic, fiscal, military or political aims, a number of foreign settlers were planted on this Rumanian foundation. These settlements, however, did not modify the numerical predominance of the compactly established Rumanian people. In 1960, 86 per cent of the country's 18 million inhabitants were Rumanian. After 1919, among the non-Rumanians only the Hungarians, the Germans and the Jews presented problems for the new and enlarged Rumanian State.

*Land ownership.* Large estates were formed between the sixteenth and the eighteenth centuries and the landowners jealously maintained their privileges; it was not until 1864 that serfdom was abolished, and then a very modest measure of agrarian reform showed that some of the more liberal-minded boyars (privileged classes) were concerned with improving the peasants' lot. But the laws enacted between 1866 and 1908 (after the peasant uprising in 1907) did not produce very satisfactory results. Despite great practical and legal difficulties, abuses and errors, $14\frac{1}{2}$ million acres were distributed among nearly $1\frac{1}{2}$ million families by 1921; by 1935, 612,000 men with justified claims were still clamouring for land; the peasants' holdings (too small in any case to support large families) had been further diminished by subdivision among several heirs, and there was, in addition, the serious problem of rural debts. A law was enacted authorising sale of land up to a maximum of about 125 acres with the result that a period of excessive subdivision was followed by a certain amount of reconstitution into larger units.

Modern architecture in Republic Square, Bucharest.

Since 1945 the agrarian problem has taken on a different look. In March 1945, almost 3 million acres and their livestock were taken without compensation from 143,219 owners. Two-fifths of this land was to be distributed to the State, the rest to 796,129 peasants. Collective farms of the Soviet *kolkhoz* type increased from 56 to 2,045 during the five-year period from 1949–54. Collectivisation of the land met with so much resistance that the process had to be slowed down — no doubt only for a time. The obstacles have not yet been all overcome; in 1954 only 22 per cent of the arable land had been socialised and in 1955 only 26·5 per cent. In 1963 there were 4,870 collective farms with 77 per cent of the arable land. State farms toal 637. In all, socialised land accounts for 92·8 per cent of the arable land.

*Post-war problems.* The treaties of 1919 left Rumania doubled in size and population. It was still suffering from the effects of the war against Germany, from the Russian defection, and from the harsh Treaty of Bucharest. Some of the most pressing problems were those relating to the assimilation of provinces which differed from each other in geographical, ethnical, social, economic, administrative, religious and cultural conditions. When the Second World War broke out Rumania was suffering from many growing pains. Isolated on the edge of a seething Europe, it had to try to preserve a balance between two Powers each intent upon reducing it to the status of a satellite. Then, after 1945, the country had to adapt itself to the new political, social, cultural and economic conditions imposed upon it.

## RUMANIA, A CARPATHIAN LAND

The country owes its origin to the Carpathians and has been able to survive only because of them. This curved range, pushed towards the east, the north-east and the south-east during the ultimate phases of the Alpine uplift, includes the Eastern Carpathians (Transylvanian Alps to the south and Moldavian Carpathians to the north) and the Western Carpathians.

The Carpathians have been aptly described as a

Intent anglers on the banks of the Floreasca Lake, outside Bucharest.

citadel, and Transylvania as a geographical and historical keep. The Carpathians are cut through by the rivers or traversed by easily negotiable passes. At the foot, the Subcarpathian counterscarp conceals a maze of small basins and corridors. Beyond this stretches the glacis, sometimes flat, sometimes rolling, wooded in part and elsewhere bare; there are huge plains bounded by moats — three in the north (Siret, Prut and formerly the Dniester) and two in the south (the Danube and the Black Sea).

*The Transylvanian keep.* This is a sunken basin in the heart of the Carpathians, a plateau of about 1,300 to 2,600 feet divided into winding ridges. Two transversal cuts and a ring of wide valleys determine the site of the string of towns—the 'Seven Fortified Towns'. The mineral wealth of Transylvania attracted settlers in very ancient times. Except in the south-east, the Rumanian inhabitants predominate. The considerable reserves of methane gas will soon accentuate still more sharply the present industrial pre-eminence of Transylvania in the national economy of the country as a whole.

*The Carpathian ramparts.* The transition from the hills of the keep to the Carpathian ramparts is abrupt. The mountains all rise over 3,000 feet. The highest peaks are Rodna (7,560 feet) in the north, Retezat (8,076 feet) in the south, and Vladeasa (5,922 feet) in the west. Needles and sharp peaks are uncommon. In the crystalline rock regions, even at heights over 6,000 feet the flattened summits are remarkable. The only exceptions are steep-walled limestone outcrops, and the wooded cones of ancient volcanoes.

There are many local peculiarities and differences. From north-west to south-east the Moldavian Carpathians form a range of stumpy, wooded massifs, seventy-five miles broad, their narrow crests dominated by escarpments. These are as follows.

To the west, on one of the most marked seismic rifts in Rumania, an almost uninterrupted succession of volcanic massifs, covered with forests but little inhabited.

In the middle, a string of little basins linked by high passes, natural clearings and crossroads, where native Rumanians live together with Slav, Magyar and German aliens.

In the east, little ridges covering the flysch zone of a well-watered region. Valleys with swift rivers lead to passes in use for centuries, some of which are crossed by rail routes today.

From east to west, from the Bucegi to the Danube cutting, the southern Carpathians are loftier, more massive, more enclosed, despite the deep troughs of the Olt, the Jiu and the Danube. The whole makes up a vast domain of woodlands and pastures, but one where through communications are difficult.

Different again are the Pannonian Carpathians. These are composed of isolated massifs separated by great gulfs of plains and containing interior basins. These mountains are easily penetrated. The wooded or grassy *causses* are more extensive here than elsewhere, and intense volcanic action has left impressive traces in the topography and in the mineral deposits (auriferous quadrilateral near Zlatna; iron in the Banat and Poiana Rusca). The mineral resources have given rise to small industrial centres, isolated in a rustic countryside where archaic modes of life persist.

CRETE: Irrigation by water pumps. RUMANIA: A primitive water whe

*The Subcarpathian Podgoria.* The outer foothills between the wooded mountains and the fertile plains have offered the most attractive living conditions. The first political units *(knezats)* developed here, and the earliest princely capitals. The lowlands, cleared long ago, are now covered with tilled fields, vineyards, orchards, chestnut and walnut groves; this is the Podgoria. The plain's prosperity is closely linked with the roads, the railway, the salt-mines, the oil-wells and cultivation.

The Podgoria widens out from the Moldava river to the Prahova, ends at the curve of the Carpathians, and then reappears in the west from Cimpulung to Tirgu-Jiu.

The Pannonian Carpathians sometimes cease abruptly above the plain (Siria), and sometimes sweep out into great amphitheatres (Taut), with wooded or cultivated terraces. Here rocky islands project upwards at some distance from the mountains; there tongues of flat country worm their way right into the heart of the massifs, often cut by picturesque little gorges. Elsewhere, wide slopes, cool and wooded, drop down into the old, badly drained region of the plains. There is a striking contrast between the Rumanian villages of twisting, narrow streets, the geometric plan of the 'colonies', and the innumerable isolated farms, or *salase,* in the mists of the Pannonian 'lake'.

*The glacis of peripheral plains.* In the west, Rumania has only a narrow strip of rich and densely populated plain. To the east of the Carpathians, the glacis is more extensive and of more varied appearance. Farther north-west the plain reaches a width of about 95 miles but is infinitely monotonous.

These are fertile lands, with extremes of climate, seasonally burning hot or freezing cold under the lash of the east wind. There are few villages. From the Carpathians to the Prut there extends a low plateau cut up into strips by a series of rivers flowing into the Danube. In the north the soil is a rich loess with *côtes* or vine-covered slopes and orchards; in the south there are steppe-like plains. But the plateau strips of Moldavia and Bessarabia are such excellent trade-routes that they are still objects of envy, explaining the mosaic of peoples inhabiting the Rumanian borderlands.

*A belt of rivers.* All the eastern plains lead to wide river corridors — those of the Prut, the Siret and the Danube. For about 940 miles from Suceava to Bazias a continuous line of navigable waterways form the frontier. The valleys are broad and uniformly wide, with flat bottoms and slight gradients.

The Danube offers all these characteristics on a larger scale. When the waters are low, huge areas of meadow, reed-brake and willow are exposed. By damming the estuaries of the tributary valleys an accumulation of alluvial material has formed an immense and curious delta of lagoons of fresh water or, where it faces the sea, of salt water.

*The maritime Dobrogea.* The advantages of the peninsula between the sea and the Danube are those of a bridge leading from the Moldavian steppes to the Balkans and those of a seaport that is almost always open. This redoubt is joined to the south by a low plateau dropping to a minimum of about 390 feet. This plateau exhibits similar features throughout; sometimes flat, sometimes undulating, but always bare and monotonous. On its edge are sunken valleys ending in rather shallow lagoons. Recent settlements have been made in this region of mixed and scattered population where traces of the Turk have remained very obvious. The coast has few natural harbours and consists of crumbling cliffs and salt lagoons. The port of Constanta is largely an artificial one and handles Rumanian oil and wheat exports.

## RUMANIAN ECONOMY

A short time ago a visitor to Rumania would never have suspected a rich country. Yet Rumania has an appreciable number of economic potentialities. The problem is to develop them. Unfortunately, statistics are not yet as complete and precise as would be desirable.

*Uneven population distribution.* The population had risen by 1963 to 18·8 million, and it is steadily increasing. There is now a fall in the birthrate, offset in part by a drop in the mortality rate.

There is a marked contrast between the thickly settled hill country and the sparsely populated plains and mountains. Between the two wars attempts were made to relieve the congestion by forming settlements in the more sparsely peopled areas, but Rumanian peasants have their roots deep in the soil, and will not leave their native homes unless forced to do so.

In industry the present-day technical assistance furnished by the U.S.S.R. helps to fill the gap that has long existed; trade and banking were largely in the hands of Jewish concerns. The R.P.R. is speeding up the training of its own skilled workmen. But in agriculture, progress has been slower. The great problem is to lead the peasants to new methods and ideas without violently upsetting their way of life and, above all, without interfering with traditions and the ownership of their land, for they cling tenaciously to their property.

*Villages, houses and towns.* The strength of the old traditions is strikingly shown in differences between

A landscape in the Transylvanian Alps. The mineral wealth of this part of Rumania attracted early settlement.

the old villages and the products of a more highly evolved social organisation or a directing authority.

To the first type belong the villages or hamlets in the Padureni or Poiana Rusca or in the Motzi of the Bihor, with brown wooden houses covered with high thatched or shingled roofs. These are rustically picturesque but uncomfortable. The most characteristic Rumanian settlement is the 'dissociated' village half-hidden in an oasis of greenery. The houses are scattered in gardens and orchards; the dwellings are separated from each other and strung haphazardly along winding alleys or river banks that serve as highway, laundry and duck-pond. Wood is used in the forest regions, *pisé* (rammed clay or earth) on the plains. The dwellings are built on a foundation of compressed earth or of stone, or they may be set above a ground floor of storerooms. They almost always have a balcony that affords shelter against rain, snow or sun, and extra sleeping accommodation on summer nights.

The second type of rural settlement is more like that of western Europe: a village without any definite plan spreading outwards from a small central square, or taking the form of a large encampment with a geometric ground plan and broad streets intersecting at right-angles. These are the settlements of the Swabian, Saxon, Magyar or Rumanian rural or military colonies.

Rumania has 176 towns, but with the exception of Bucharest, only nine have populations exceeding 100,000. Most of these towns are market centres or situated on highways. Generally the green open spaces of the residential districts are pleasant and the densely populated *mahallas*, more rural than urban, are picturesque; indeed clean streets, magnificent parks and modern apartment houses are reported of today's *mahallas*. The old fortified towns of Transylvania have kept their ancient German traits. Constanta suggests the East rather than the West. There is still a Turkish minaret and formerly there was a bazaar. None of the towns resembles the industrial cities of western Europe, for rural influence is felt everywhere.

*Climate and soil fertility*. Rumania's brown soil of forest origin bordered by a broad belt of chernozem (black earth) make a superb agricultural domain.

But the country is more exposed to harsh weather from the east than to soft Atlantic rain-clouds; it has a continental type of climate described as 'Danubian'. The winters are freezing cold and the summers are scorching hot, with prevailing dry north-east winds and drought on the plains. The snow lies long and the rivers freeze—including the Danube and sometimes the inshore waters of the Black Sea. The graphs of the harvest show extraordinary spurts of abundant crops (bringing low prices) and years of scarcity (followed by high prices); both are damaging to the country's economy. Irrigation is indispensable for production of cereals, forage plants, sugar-beet and even rice and cotton. The R.P.R., following Russian

Forests, pasture land and prairies are grouped inside the mountainous framework of the eastern and western Carpathians; the extension of the maize-growing steppe region from the east predominates. Industry is highly dispersed.

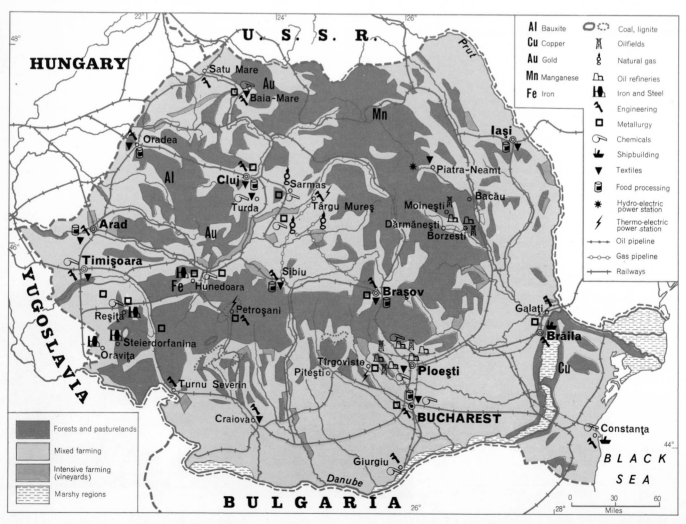

example, has planned to modify local climatic conditions by planting belts of trees to protect arable land; just as urgent are measures for soil conservation.

*A land of farmers.* Despite the capricious climate, Rumanian agriculture (on soil that is especially suited to grain crops, fruits, vines and pasture lands) is still the foundation of the country's economy. The R.P.R. is now aiming at two long-envisaged objectives: an increase in cultivated land (by draining and irrigation) and, above all, higher yields, for current figures seem low compared with those of Western agriculture for corresponding crops.

Maize is still the cereal best suited to most of the farming regions, and it forms the basis of the peasants' diet. During recent years wheat production has sometimes exceeded that of maize; rye, oats and barley are grown on a much smaller scale than either. Buckwheat, sorghum and industrial crops occupy the acreage lost by oats and barley. Despite progress made, sugar and vegetable oils are particularly lacking. Wine and fruits are exported but could find a better market at home.

Mechanisation (much advocated today) and the ravages of war have combined to reduce the numbers of all livestock. To increase the herds and improve the rather poor quality of the livestock, the area under forage must be increased and the pastures improved.

For years special government organisations have been taking measures to effect changes. It must be admitted that progress has been slow, that enthusiasm for first one crop and then another has induced alternation of hope and disappointment. An added retarding factor is the peasants' reluctance to take advantage of the benefits of co-operation.

At least, the country has at its disposal sufficient foodstuff resources, even though they are not very varied. The frugality of the peasants might surprise foreigners but, except in one or two very isolated mountain regions, real scarcity is unusual. However, a starting-point for famine was the drought of 1945-46, aggravated by reduced acreage under maize, resistance of the peasants to the new agrarian system, and reparations in kind made as part of the war indemnity. The bad times lasted until 1954, when two abundant grain harvests made it possible to abolish rationing.

Rumania possesses, too, splendid and vast forest regions which are almost virgin in places. These provide an additional source of income for the peasants, and furnish almost all the domestic fuel, building material, and wood for carpentry. Timber is also an important export item. But the forests have been mistakenly sacrificed to extend the area of pasture lands and to satisfy the U.S.S.R.'s demands for war indemnity. The R.P.R. is wisely planning to conduct large-scale reforestation.

*Lack of industrial raw materials.* Except for its power resources, Rumania has no appreciable quantities of basic industrial materials. The ores needed in modern heavy industry are widely distributed in deposits of small extent, difficult and expensive to reach, of complex composition, and of doubtful value.

*Oil and natural gas.* The very name Rumania traditionally suggests abundance of oil. Natural gas resources, though less often mentioned, are even greater than those of oil and may well take its place one day.

Although deposits had been known from the fifteenth century, petroleum did not become a source of national wealth until 1857. After the First World War (when the wells were seized by Germany and capital was needed to repair the damage) foreign participation in the oil industry increased and by 1938 predominated. Thereafter, measures taken to limit and even eliminate non-Rumanian capital explain, at least in part, the drop in output from 1936 to 1939. By employing technical methods now used by oil specialists everywhere, the Rumano-Soviet 'Sovrompetrol' has been able to increase output considerably beyond pre-war totals. Although it is difficult to estimate the amount of the reserves, there is little doubt that they are sizable. An annual production of 10 to 13 million is nevertheless a heavy drain. To date oil has been found only in the curved belt of the Eastern Carpathians, and although output of the various wells has varied, the general area of operation has not changed much and is still confined to three zones in Muntenia and to the Moldavian group. Most of the prospecting is now taking place in the second group, but the Muntenia wells are still the most productive.

Natural gas reserves are found in Transylvania, in the form of methane, cheap and almost pure, and in the oil regions of the 'Old Kingdom'.

These sources of power supplement a meagre coal and hydro-electric production. The only coalfields (in the Banat and in Transylvania) give fuel of poor quality.

Hydro-electric production is limited to numerous small stations utilising the power of low waterfalls and supplying local current, either urban or industrial. The production in 1938 was little more than 1,000 million kWh. A ten-year electrification plan (1951-60) aimed to raise the production fivefold by treating as a single project the schemes for irrigation and for the Danube-Black Sea canal on the one hand, and those for producing hydro-electric power on the other. In 1950 installed power was 740,000 kW; in 1963 it was 2,356,000 kW.

A new block of flats in Bucharest, with a street-level supermarket. Before modernisation Bucharest was a picturesque, colourful city with a densely populated *mahalla* or working-class district.

*Heavy industry.* Rumania today has increased need of sources of power since, following the example of the U.S.S.R., the R.P.R. is today advocating industrialisation and especially the development of heavy industry. Industrial equipment of pre-war Rumania did not even satisfy its then moderate needs. Producing only for the home market, the factories developed slowly; lack of capital, raw materials and skilled labour hindered any great development; industry was scattered near sources of hydro-electric current and lines of communication, so that it was sited in isolated clusters and never attained a concentrated grouping of the Western type.

In 1948 all industrial and processing enterprises were nationalised. Today the R.P.R. is concentrating on heavy industry, to the extent of sacrificing temporarily its output of consumer goods. The marked progress is due in part to imports of Russian iron and coke which reach Orsova up the Danube. The supply of power has greatly increased, and with a bigger steel output it has been possible to develop machine manufacture, the electro-technical industry, chemical and pharmaceutical products, and the wood and textile industries. But the craftsmen's output has not yet been supplemented by the concentration and modernisation of new factories, and consumer goods do not yet meet demand.

*Inadequate communications.* In 1939 poor conditions of roads and railways brought many complaints. The only two metalled roads were those crossing the country from side to side. According to statistics, Rumania now has 6,500 miles of single track, 380 miles of double-track railway, and 7,400 miles of national roads. The main railway lines follow the relief of the land closely and describe two concentric rings, one around Transylvania and the other on the outside of the Carpathians. The subsidiary lines are in urgent need of improvement and of considerable extension to link them with other lines. The war wrought havoc on tracks and rolling-stock alike.

Waterways are confined to the Danube, the Prut (now a frontier) and the Siret. There only a few barges on the Bega and the Mures, and timber-rafts on the Olt, Bistrita, Tosza and Siret. Everywhere frost and silt are serious handicaps to navigation.

*Lack of capital and foreign investments.* Until 1945 attempts to develop the resources of the country, and equip it industrially, repeatedly came up against the problem of investments. The weakness of Rumanian finances was that the savings of a population with modest resources and a low standard of living were insufficient to provide loans to the government, and foreign capital had to be called on. Two ruinous wars militated against a balanced budget for many years. The Second War brought heavy loss of life, equipment and stocks of all sorts, and a tremendous burden of war debt to the U.S.S.R. Inflation and its effect on prices raised the face value of the banknotes in circulation, and was followed by two very harsh devaluations (1947 and 1952) and the linking of the Rumanian *leu* with the Soviet *rouble*.

Just as foreign capital had in former days allowed the recovery of the country, the U.S.S.R. provided economic support on a large scale after 1945. Joint Russo-Rumanian companies are reminiscent of holding companies in capitalist societies. Each party holds 50 per cent of the shares and the profits are divided equally. Rumania has supplied resources and labour, the U.S.S.R. part of the property annexed from former enemies (Germany, France, Belgium, Holland, Switzerland) and the gear and equipment. The real management is in the hands of Russian technicians.

It is, however, in Rumanian trade that Russian control is most clearly visible: the U.S.S.R. and the 'Popular Democracies' supply 80 per cent of Rumania's imports. Agreements concluded in 1954–55 with ten countries related only to small quantities of goods (mostly wood and oil), but they served as a starting-point for further developments in the 1960's.

So, as we have seen, Rumania does not lack resources, and their exploitation, long hampered and delayed, is being accelerated. Although it is still difficult to assess the general position, it is clear that there is a complete break with the past. In the social and economic life of Rumania a new spirit is being created, although some of the features are those which for centuries have been so attractive and have gained so many friends for the Rumanian people.

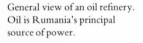

General view of an oil refinery. Oil is Rumania's principal source of power.

# BULGARIA

Bulgaria (42,796 square miles) lies in the east of the Balkan peninsula, bounded to the north by the lower reaches of the Danube and to the east by the black Sea. It borders on Rumania in the north, Turkey to the south-east, Greece to the south and Yugoslavia to the west.

During the ninth, tenth and eleventh centuries Bulgaria was the most flourishing state in the Balkans, but later on, because of rivalry with Byzantium, the country suffered many afflictions. It recovered a precarious independence under the Asen dynasty in the thirteenth century but was finally conquered by the Turks at the end of the fourteenth; in 1878 it regained partial independence. Since then the country has undergone a number of territorial changes.

Bulgaria lies on one of the main crossroads of eastern Europe and its strategic position makes it very vulnerable. In ancient times the country was crossed by the Silk Route and until 1961 was traversed by the rail service known as the 'Simplon-Orient-Express', linking western Europe with the Near East.

## THE LANDSCAPE

*A central range surrounded by plains.* The main physical feature of Bulgaria is the ancient Stara Planina (Balkan) range which cuts through the middle of the country from west to east for about 375 miles. Over part of this distance, the Stara Planina is accompanied by a parallel range, the Sredna Gora (Anti-Balkan). Between the two chains lies a depression formed by a line of basins. In the south-west corner of the country rises the imposing Rhodope massif, forming a mountain mass whose highest point rises to 9,600 feet.

The remaining third of Bulgaria consists of plains, the largest of which lies between the northern slopes of the Stara Planina and the Danube and is part of the Danubian plain linked directly with central Europe. To the south of the Stara Planina, the rivers on the Aegean slope — the Maritsa, Mesta and Struma — flow through the wide valleys, which, eastwards, broaden out into the huge coastal plain of the Black Sea. A number of basins are scattered between the Stara Planina and the Rhodope.

Bulgaria is cut off from the influence of Atlantic winds but in the north is exposed to that of north and north-east winds, icy in winter, hot and dry in summer. However, south of the Stara Planina on the plains under the influence of the Aegean and Black Seas, the climate is more variable and much milder.

*Turco-Tatar influence.* In the seventh century Bulgars, of Turco-Tatar stock, subjugated the Slav population which for two centuries had lived at the mouths of the Danube in what is today Bulgaria. The newcomers were soon assimilated by the more numerous Slavs and the present-day Bulgarians would appear to be a Slavised people speaking a language that is akin to Russian but still more closely related to Old Slavonic. It is written in Cyrillic characters.

In 1964 there were 8,177,000 inhabitants; estimates show that 85 per cent are 'Slavs' and Orthodox by religion. There is still a Turkish minority. The Tziganes, or gipsies, once more numerous, make up only 1.2 per cent of the population. Some Rumanians, mostly migratory shepherds, are still found in parts of the north-east. The Jewish population (which settled here from Spain in the sixteenth century) is 6,000; heavy emigration to Israel has reduced the numbers from a fairly recent total of 50,000. New economic trends tend to increase the urban population (18.8 per cent of the whole in 1887 and 40.8 per cent by 1964).

*Rural dwellings and towns.* Living conditions in the rural areas have remained primitive. In the mountains the typical peasant dwelling of a single-roomed wooden hut is being replaced by solid houses. On the plains the houses are little more comfortable; thatched cottages tend to prevail in the outskirts, their places being taken in the urban centre by many-storeyed blocks with a shop on the ground floor. Sanitary conditions have improved since 1947 following the introduction of a free public health system.

There are few large towns in Bulgaria although

The Rhodope Mountains, an imposing massif in south-west Bulgaria rising to 9,600 feet at its highest point.

Lake Atanasovo, near Lake
Burgas, by the Black Sea.

Sofia, capital of Bulgaria,
with Mount Vitosa in the
background. The mosque in the
foreground was built when Sofia
was part of the Ottoman Empire.

Turnovo, once capital of Bulgaria.
Situated on the Danubian plain,
on a deeply embanked meander of
the River Jantra, it is one of the
most picturesque towns in
the Balkans.

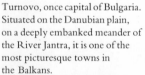

there are many big market-villages. Sofia, the capital, which in 1963 had a population of 731,000, dates from Roman times. The city lies in a fertile basin, about 1,800 feet above sea level and at the foot of the Vitosa, part of the Rhodope massif. Sofia is also the most important political, administrative, economic and cultural centre. Plovdiv (formerly Philippopolis) on the Maritsa river and, like Sofia, on the Calais-Instanbul railroad route, is a tobacco town linked by rail with Burgas, a military and commercial port on the Black Sea. Varna (formerly Stalin) is also a maritime base. Turnovo (a previous capital), situated on the Danubian plain, on deeply embanked meander of the River Jantra, is one of the most picturesque towns in the Balkans. Mention must be made of two urban centres which are being rapidly transformed; the 'socialist' towns of Dimitrovo (formerly Pernik), a mining centre, and Dimitrovgrad on the Maritsa, the headquarters of the chemical industry.

THE NEW BULGARIAN ECONOMY. Since the end of the Second World War Bulgaria has been a 'People's Democracy' whose political and economic systems closely resemble those of the U.S.S.R. The Bulgarian leaders have adopted an industrial and agricultural planning policy which stresses the importance of developing industry and increasing the output of goods for the country's equipment. Industry accounted for 15 per cent of the national income in 1939, for 51 per cent in 1963, and is still increasing steadily.

*A land of grain fields and orchards.* Cereals are grown in the inland basins and on the plains, especially those of the Danube and the Dobruja, and also in the basins at the foot of the Stara Planina and in that of the Maritsa. Fifty per cent of the land under grain crops is devoted to wheat. Rye is grown on the hillier ground, especially in the lower areas of the Rhodope. Maize does well in the western part of the Danubian plain, in the Dobruja, and at the foot of the Stara Planina's southern slopes. Rice is cultivated mostly in the Maritsa basin. The acreage of industrial crops shows the greatest tendency to increase. The tobacco of the Rhodope and the Maritsa and Mesta basins is of high quality, and represents 12 per cent in value of Bulgarian exports. However, the most characteristically Bulgarian culture is that of rose-bushes in the celebrated Vale of Roses, at the foot of the Stara Planina. The roses now cover some 16,000 acres; but cultivation has not increased rapidly, since on the international market synthetic perfumes are ousting the Bulgarian attar of roses, which is costly and an export of great value.

In the sheltered basins, orchards abound. Kyustendil apples and Bulgarian plums are celebrated all over eastern Europe. Vines grow mostly in the south, and the grapes, are exported in large quantities. Vegetables, especially tomatoes, are also exported.

Bulgarian livestock has not yet recovered from the losses incurred during the two World Wars (717 head of cattle per thousand inhabitants in 1900, 182 head in 1964) but milk yield has trebled, Pigs have greatly increased since 1945, and, at 10 million, the number of sheep is considerable. Mulberry trees grown on the southern plains encouraged silkworm breeding and set Bulgaria fourth among European raw silk producers.

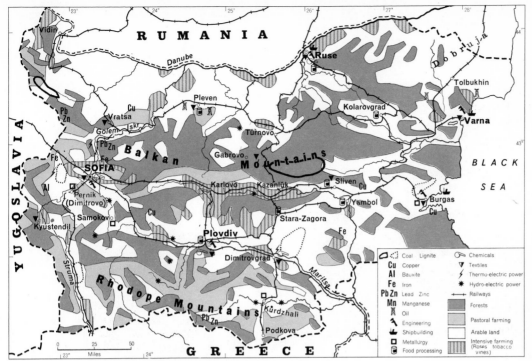

Much progress has been made in industrialisation but Bulgaria still derives half its income from agriculture. The spread of irrigation and fertilizers has brought progress here too. The plains and basins are favourable for grain crops (wheat and rye), and in the mountains an extensive type of stockbreeding is practised. Tobacco products represent 12 per cent in value of national exports, while raw silk production is the fourth largest in Europe.

*The advance towards industrialisation.* After the Two Year Plan of 1947-9, which encompassed the reduction of the private sector of industry from 83.6 to 5 per cent, subsequent Plans aimed to increase the country's power resources and to create an industry producing essential equipment without the aid of foreign capital (before the war it had been heavily dependent on German finance and machines). In the 1958-62 period industrial output rose by 60 per cent, it is claimed.

Bulgaria is not rich in good quality coal, but there is abundant lignite. The Dimitrovo field, not far from Sofia, and that of the Black Sea coast are the most important. Oil, discovered in 1951, is produced at Pleven and north of Varna and is refined at Burgas. Natural gas is found at Vratsa. In addition to the old thermo-electric stations a large new one, the Maritsa-East, was opened in 1961, and some hydro-electric stations have been built, mostly in the Rhodope.

Dimitrovo, on the lignite deposits, has become quite a large producer of heavy metallurgical goods; machine-shops have been set up all over the country, and the pre-war output of machines has increased tenfold. A chemical industry is being developed at Dimitrovgrad and concentrates on fertilizers.

Output of consumer goods, particularly textiles, discouraged under the early Plans, is to be quintupled during 1960-1980. Plovdiv is an important centre.

*New trade relations.* Before the war there were few railroads to Bulgaria. Since 1945 existing lines have been improved and new ones laid. The total length of line is now about 2,700 miles, the main route being that of the old Simplon-Orient-Express, part of the famous route from Calais to Instanbul and running through Sofia and Plovdiv. Of the 53,000 miles of highways needed, under one third exists. Still, 1,250 miles of new roads have been constructed since 1945.

The Danube provides communications with Austria, Czechoslovakia, Hungary, Rumania and the U.S.S.R. Sea traffic is considerable, especially since Bulgarian foreign trade is more and more with the U.S.S.R. There are various airlines linking the principal Bulgarian towns with the capitals of the other People's Republics and with Moscow.

The U.S.S.R., which once had very little trade or contact with Bulgaria, has now become the main customer and supplier. After the U.S.S.R. come the other People's Republics, with Czechoslovakia in third place. Trade relations with the West are restricted.

Construction of a power station at Sofia-East, near the capital.

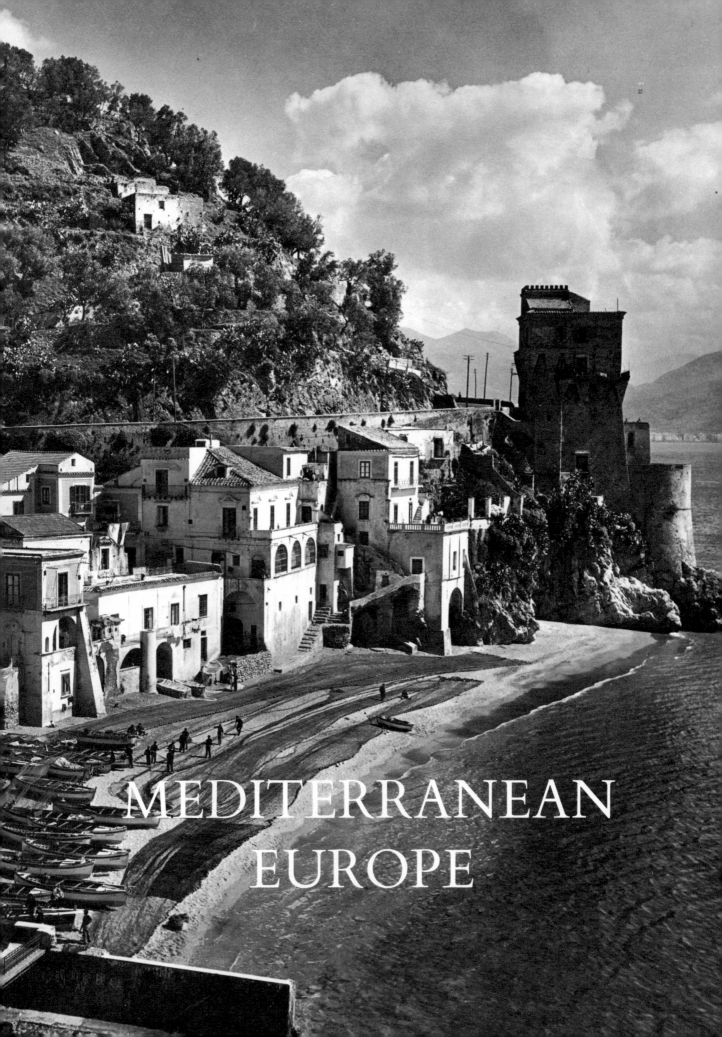

# MEDITERRANEAN
# EUROPE

# YUGOSLAVIA

Yugoslavia, together with Bulgaria, forms the 'Land of the Southern Slavs'. It has no linguistic unity. Several closely related languages are spoken — Serbo-Croat, Slovenian and Macedonian — but each differs from the other and each is subdivided into a number of dialects. Nor is there any religious unity. In Slovenia and Croatia there are some groups of Protestants; Roman Catholics form the majority of the population in Croatia; and most of the inhabitants of Serbia and Macedonia are Orthodox. Certain districts of Bosnia, Herzegovina and Macedonia have a Moslem majority. In addition, the various parts of Yugoslavia have no common history, for before 1914 they were divided between Austria-Hungary, Turkey, Italy and Serbia. Islamic, Byzantine, Germanic and Roman civilisations have all left a deep imprint on this part of the Balkans. Finally, there is no geographical unity. From the Danube to the Adriatic, from the Alps to the Rhodope, there is a succession of varied landscapes. The lands to the north of the Sava belong to central Europe; to the south the Balkan world begins, a meeting-place of peoples of different races, and an age-old battlefield.

Nevertheless, the present Yugoslav state is both stable and assured of a continued existence. The country survived the Second World War and under the Agreement of February 1947 increased its territory by annexing from Italy about 2,850 square miles with a population of some 500,000 Slavs. The strength of Yugoslavia springs from its national unity. The creation of a Slav state in the south of Austria-Hungary and the liberation of oppressed peoples was the aim of the Illyrian movement in the nineteenth century. Called the 'Kingdom of the Serbs, Croats and Slovenes' immediately after the First World War, it became the 'Kingdom of Yugoslavia' in 1929. After the 1939-45 war and the Constitution of January 1946, it became a socialist Federal Republic composed of six republics: Serbia (that is Serbia proper plus the territories of Kosovo-Metohija and the Vojvodina), Croatia, Slovenia, Bosnia-Herzegovina, Macedonia and Montenegro (Crna Gora). Each of these units enjoys a large measure of administration and financial autonomy (especially since the decentralisation policy of 1950), has its own legislative assembly, and is governed by its own council of ministers. The language in use in the army is Serbo-Croat, but official documents and enrolments are drawn up in two languages in districts where there are ethnic minorities, and these (750,000 Albanians, 500,000 Hungarians, 250,000 Turks, 117,000 Czechs and Slovaks, 62,000 Rumanians, 57,000 Bulgarians and 33,000 Italians) enjoy the benefit of special statutes. Most of the German population was expelled by 1945; some 60,000 remain.

Its very diversity makes the Yugoslav state a harmonious geographical unit. The country comprises two regions of complementary cultures and economics, between which a constant exchange of products, ideas and men has been maintained. The two regions are the mountain nucleus and the surrounding plains. The contrast between the central redoubt and its glacis is emphasised on relief maps, and is marked by the nature of agricultural and industrial activities, by communications and by the distribution of population. In the centre are high plateaus and mountain ranges with a harsh climate (even near the Adriatic), regions of forests and grasslands penetrated by the Pannonian valleys, so that access to the coast is not easy. There are regions hostile to occupation, peopled by Aromani or Wallachs (speaking a Latin language and formerly shepherds), or by Serbs from Old Serbia who took refuge in the mountain regions during the Turkish invasions.

The periphery is made up of plains or valleys threaded with the great, ancient highways of commerce. These are conveniently linked by the passages afforded by the Postojna gap, the corridor of the Morava, and that of the Vardar. It is here that rich agricultural land abounds and here that towns and industries flourish. The population is mixed; Slavs intermingle with peoples of central or Mediterranean Europe. Montenegro, Raska and Stari Vlah have been regions with distinctive cultures based on pastoral occupations and on the family communal unit. In our times the surplus of the mountain population has spilled over on to the plains. Albanians, Serbs and Bosnians have flooded the peripheral areas, especially the Vojvodina and Slavonia, where the Austrians established military Marches, a strategic cordon surrounding the central redoubt on the west and north to contain the forward thrust of Islam.

The contrast between the 'hive-lands' and the 'colonisation lands' is marked. Now that the resources of the mountains are being developed and there is increased activity in the mining areas, labour from the plains has been attracted once more towards the central areas. It is just this demographic and ethnic osmosis, this life of economic symbiosis, that has forged the unity of Yugoslav civilisation as it is today.

Despite regional differences, there is no longer fundamental opposition between the various population groups. But only geographical description can bring out the great natural contrasts. When we have examined the nature of the central mountainous zone (and it is one most unfriendly to man), we shall deal at some length with the economic rôle of the peripheral regions — the corridors of the Morava and Vardar, the Danubian plains, Slovenia and the Adriatic coast.

THE CENTRAL REDOUBT. The traditional epithet for this redoubt is 'Dinaric', although the term is usually reserved for the ranges overhanging the Adriatic coast. From Trieste to Albania there stretches a huge mountain mass which covers more than half of Yugoslavia. Some edges of this mass are steep — for the great subsidence of the Adriatic caused a rift in the Dinaric structure and induced the uplift of a coastal barrier. Others are indistinct: the line of contact between the Alpine and Dinaric ranges in the Postojna area, the gently sloping terraces that join the last crystalline massif of the north to the Tertiary hills of Pannonia, and the eastern border, where recent tectonic disturbances have interrupted the continuity of the ranges, offering a foretaste of the architectonic style of Greece and Macedonia.

Yugoslavia's relief is jumbled and broken. On the whole the formations are folded in a north-west to south-east direction, widening and rising towards the south-east. But it is difficult to distinguish, classify and compare the different formations with the naked eye. The terraced high plateaus, the *planina,* are curiously horizontal and stretch as far as eye can see, with only a few stumps of hard rock that have resisted the slow process of peneplanation jutting up here and there. In some places the plateaus have been rejuvenated by Tertiary movements which provoked — as in the Durmitor — a rapid sinking of canyons (the Piva and Tara are the most beautiful in Europe) or the subsidence of extensive basins.

Penetration of the massif is not easy: the valleys, narrow and very deep, rarely run longitudinally; they isolate rather than link the mountain blocks and basins.

The harshness of the mountain climate accentuates the impression of isolation, and the asymmetry of the whole complex, the rarity of through corridors, and altitude have all combined to restrict the zone of Mediterranean vegetation. Above about 1,600 feet it freezes for three months of the year. The slopes are covered with grass and trees. Wheat grows only below 3,500 feet, and maize below 3,000 feet. Resinous trees have disappeared from the heavily eroded coastal slopes—a consequence of the disastrous deforestation practised by Venice and the Dalmation cities, or of the strain imposed on Montenegro's pastoral resources at times of danger from the Turk. 'Many flocks, little forest' runs an old proverb. It is reflected in the small centres of pastoral life that have grown up in clearings conveniently situated for the migrating flocks of sheep and herds of cattle. The high valleys were for long isolated and constituted autonomous units in which ancient legal institutions and customs were maintained. It is only within quite recent years that pastoral farming has seen a rapid decline. The mountains are now deserted or are becoming industrialised, though there may still be seen a number of old features. The relief of the land, the historical and social evolution, and the degree of economic backwardness have produced perceptible differences between one region and another.

*The Dinaric karst.* The karst lands are something apart, turning Yugoslavia into a museum of strange limestone formations. Over a wide area geological conditions conspire to add to the dryness that results from water seepage: the strata are more than 4,900 feet thick, the limestone is particularly pure and hard, and there are no interposed strata. It is only through faults that the clays or sandstones outcrop to produce extremely strange landscapes. There are tall, jagged crests, asymmetrical peaks, and isolated domes gashed by dry ravines; wide areas are deeply scored and perforated with *dolinas,* or closed hollows; *lapies* as sharp as a knife's edge are everywhere. The two greatest obstacles to settlement are lack of water and discontinuity of the soil. The smallest spring attracts a house or a village. During the summer the cisterns are mostly dry, and in high mountain regions huge masses of ice are covered with straw and kept to provide water for this period. In Montenegro, for instance, the traveller will more often be offered milk to drink than water. The arable land is leached red earth, or softer and fairly impermeable dolomitic sands, which occur in very small sheets.

Dwellings, then, are isolated. Each farm lies near cultivable land. But in a country without valleys, communications are difficult—tracks over the rugged rock are the links between the villages. The oases, the

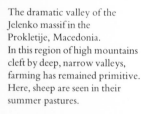

The dramatic valley of the Jelenko massif in the Prokletije, Macedonia. In this region of high mountains cleft by deep, narrow valleys, farming has remained primitive. Here, sheep are seen in their summer pastures.

inhabited spots more than 3,500 feet up, are covered
with moraines, depressions hollowed out in the mass
of impermeable rock, and *poljes* (closed-in depressions
traversed by a short stream which tumbles into a
bottomless pit, or *ponor,* at the foot of the slope).
These basins all offer the same advantage to the
peasant: deep soil, easy communications, abundance
of water—even too much water, for most of these
areas are partially flooded or marshy for several
months of the year. Nevertheless, the alluvial soil
of the bottom is cultivated, and round them are
big market-villages on the roads linking the Adriatic
with Pannonia.

This classical karst landscape is moderated or
accentuated according to the nature of the limestone,
the altitude, the historical development of each
region, and, of course, the present-day economic
transformation.

*Green Bosnia, golden Bosnia.* North of a line running
from Bihać to Foča, the relief changes in character.
Outcrops of impermeable rocks are indicated by a
countryside of verdant plateaus and isolated hillocks
or ridges criss-crossed with an extraordinary network
of tiny valleys. Despite a progressive drop in altitude
in the direction of the Sava, the climate is still harsh
(–4°F. in January at about 1,600 feet) and typically
continental, although rainfall is abundant. This is
also a region of forests amd pasture lands, but little
grain is grown. The main source of prosperity will
probably long remain stock-breeding, though in this
part of Bosnia there are other resources. A treasury
of mineral wealth lies in the ancient geological
formations. The region has been variously described
as damp Bosnia, green Bosnia, and also as golden
Bosnia.

It was the Turks who developed the mines, so
it was not surprising that the imprint of Islam is much
more marked here than in the karst. It is in 'impermeable' Bosnia that the *komsiluk* (patronymic hamlets)
are scattered along the valley terraces, overlooking
the streams — these are typical dwelling-places
of the Islamised Slav shepherds. The houses of the
ancient *begs* are no longer distinguishable from the
huts of the Christian population, the *rayah.* However,
the architecture is still oriental and white minarets
rise from the villages. In the valleys, at the crossroads, in the middle of the basins, are the large villages
whose streets wind between the shops of the *čarsija,*
the domain of the leather-workers, potters and
coppersmiths. These towns have developed as markets,
commercial centres, fairs. The influence of the East
is today diminishing. The harems are closed. Veils
are forbidden. The big estates have been carved up.
And with the collapse of the middle-classes, handicrafts have declined. New districts have been built
on to the towns. The cemeteries and the mosques,
a few of the old traditions, and a curious outlook
on life all bear witness to the once flourishing and
colourful Eastern civilisation.

Contrasting with the spacious valleys are the
backward mountain areas. To the west, the Krajina
(the Turkish counterpart of the Austrian Marches)
is an advance post of Islam; the people, still shy
and retiring, are 95 per cent Moslem. The Una,
the Sana and the Vrbas attract all the economic
activities of the region. The upper basins are the

Kamnisko Sedlo, near Ljubljana,
in the Alps of Slovenia.

domain of extensive stock-breeding, while agriculture of the Pannonian type is spreading upstream.
Where the rivers reach the plain, large urban centres,
such as Banja Luka, are found. The vital area of
Bosnia is, however, the valley of the Bosna and the
Sarajevo basin, containing a string of towns and
factories which are of great importance as centres of
economic activity for a large region. The only great
highways to cross the Dinaric mass meet at Sarajevo,
originally a Turkish capital and a military base, and
and now prospering from the industrial development
of the Bosna valley.

*Pastoral mountains: Stari Vlah and Raska.* To the east
of the Drina appear signs of another type of geological formation. Between the Upper Drina, Kosovo
and the western Morava, there rises a massif with
few valleys and covered with oak and beech forests,
where the cores of ancient volcanic rocks project.
This was once the domain of shepherds (Wallachs
and Serbs), and then a Turkish stronghold commanding the roads from the Adriatic to Serbia, Bosnia
and Macedonia. The armies of the sultans used the
valleys and passes of what, at the end of the nineteenth century, was to be the famous *sanjak* of Novi
Pazar (or Novi Bazar), a buffer-state between Serbia
and Montenegro administered by Austria-Hungary.

The south-west is in complete contrast to the
north-east: the basins of the Drina and its tributaries

have Moslem populations; a few karst-like *poljes* recall those of Montenegro, while the upper valleys incised in the schist formations are Alpine in appearance. On the other hand, the massifs overlooking the Ibar and the western Morava are made of crystalline cores; there are fewer rivers and streams, the valleys are shallower, the general appearance is wilder, and the mountains still serve as refuge areas.

The early Serbian population cleared very small areas of pasture land, which were centres of a high culture, reflected in the great Orthodox monasteries Today these mountains are deserted. The exhaustion of the Ibar mines, the losses of livestock and the dissolution of the religious communities have combined to induce an exodus of the population. The shepherds have bought land in the valleys of the periphery; the highest villages are inhabited only for short periods at a time; flocks and herds are becoming rare, and during the past half-century the cultivation of maize in the valley bottoms has brought about an agrarian and social revolution. The mountain people have emigrated to the basins and hills of the Morava and the Vardar; Stari Vlah and Raska are transition areas.

## THE MORAVA-VARDAR TROUGH

Because of their mountainous character, the rel-tively backward state of their economy, and Moslem influence, these regions are those most like the Dinaric redoubt. But they are primarily areas of communications important to Europe as a whole, linking the Mediterranean and central Europe, and West and East. The Niš fair used to attract merchants from Vienna, Leipzig, Trieste and Constantinople. From Belgrade to Sofia or to Salonica roads and railroads cross the fairly low ridges, linking basins and valleys. The Crusaders took advantage of the Morava-Vardar corridor, which was a route for invasion as well as for the Serbian state's southward expansion. The region is still a meeting place of nations — Greeks, Turks, Bulgarians, Rumanians, Albanians, Serbs — a country of contacts between north and south where different climatic influences and civilisations mingle. The resultant opposed elements are to be seen in the agrarian system, in the kind of crops grown, in the layout of the villages and in the style of the houses.

*Plains and mountains in Macedonia.* South of the Morava, climate and landscape afford a foretaste of the Aegean world; even so, it freezes for twenty days a year at Skopje, the peaks are more than 6,500 feet high, and the Vardar has to flow through very narrow gorges before reaching the coast. West-wards transhumance is still practised, from the valleys of the Tetovo, Debar and Bitola (Monastir) to the heights of the Stara Planina and the Prokletije, former domain of the Aromani and Tzintzars. After the Serbs left these regions in the eighteenth and nine-teenth centuries, they were settled by Albanians who practised a rural economy of very primitive type. The settlers in the cleared or drained areas of the Kosovo or in the Polog and Bitola basin spread the cultivation of maize and vines, but on the whole time stands still and the countryside has changed

little for hundreds of years. However, the region's rôle as a highway is affirmed by the former prosperity of lake-side towns such as Ohrid, by the traditional *pecalba* (itinerant hawking), and by the constant intermingling of populations neither very numerous nor really permanent.

The economy is of a more varied character to the east of the Vardar, and here recent development has been more rapid. Mediterranean features can be distinguished in the farming. There are ricefields on the irrigated lands of the Strumica and the Bre-galnica. When the rice is harvested in September millet is sown on the same ground. Sheep graze on the sides of the basins. Speculative crops, such as mul-berries, poppies and tobacco, have brought some slight prosperity to the Vardar peasants despite the irregularity in yield. Population is, then, very dense on the Greek and Bulgarian frontiers. The moun-tain framework is, however, being gradually deserted. Skopje, devastated by an earthquake in the summer of 1963, owes its continued importance to its strategic position on the Salonica railroute and the road that links it to the Morava.

*Northern Serbia: Šumadija, Morava, Timok.* North of the Morava-Vardar corridor, the basins are deeper and wider, the surrounding massifs are pierced by broad high-walled valleys, and the summers are wetter. Pannonian farming systems have moved on up the Morava, the Timok and the Nišava. Wheat and maize cover the hill-terraces while the alluvial fans and gentler slopes bear vineyards, orchards and market-gardens. The thick, deciduous forests on the upper slopes were cleared only at the end of the nineteenth century. The Šumadija, to the west, recalls only by its name (*šuma* means 'forest') the oak and beech woods that once covered the crystalline bed-rock and the terraces as far as the gates of Belgrade. Southern Serbs, living in innumerable scattered hamlets, have given new life to a definite type of economy based on maize, pig-breeding and the sale of plums for making spirits. This is a region of a rather well-to-do though somewhat rough rural middle-class, whose land was the centre and arsenal of the Serbian revolt against the Turks.

The steppe-like climate and the working of the mines have played a bigger part than systematic deforestation in stripping the Carpathian extension south of the Iron Gates. In the Timok valley (an area that yields good crops only if the land is irrigated) large villages huddle at the bottom of the slopes, half-hidden in the oases of greenery. The development of this area of rich soil has been hampered by the old organisation of the *Krajina* (the frontier region) and, despite the rise in the output of the Bor mines, by its belated peopling.

## THE DANUBIAN GRANARY

To the north of the Sava and the Danube lies Pannonia. Roman settlers cultivating the loess plains, and legionaries keeping guard on the imperial frontier were more numerous here than in any other part of present-day Yugoslavia except Dalmatia. Pannonia, long famous for its cereals, supplies 60 per cent of Yugoslavia's agricultural output, and population density is in some areas more than 260 to the square mile. The large, prosperous villages stand amid fields of wheat and maize. The people of Syrmia and the Banat are cheerful and hospitable. In spite of wars and droughts, the peasants are still rich and though quite modern in their outlook (and inclined to take risks), they have not forsaken their ancestral traditions. It was not so long ago, for example, that marriageable girls wore their dowries as breastplates of gold coins and medals.

This prosperity is due to soil and climate. The loess and Quaternary alluvium are impermeable, fertile and continuous, and lie several yards thick over the rocky substratum. Stone is so scarce that the houses are built of *pisé* or brick. Clouds of penetrating dust rise from the ground in summer; in winter the earth changes to thick mud which, by December, is overlaid with snow. However, the harsh, typically continental climate — like that of the Hungarian *puszta* — is everywhere favourable to grain crops. Torrid though rainy summers and brilliant autumnal skies are excellent for maize and even for such subtropical crops as mulberries, rice and cotton.

Pannonia has been rich even since Roman times, though the long period of prosperity was broken by the Turkish invasions, which ravaged the plains to such an extent that resettlement did not take place until rather late. After the Treaty of Karlovci (Karlowitz) in 1699, Pannonia was peopled mostly by Serbs, though there were some Germans (Swabians), Hungarians and even some French (three villages in the Vojvodina, Saint-Hubert, Charleville and Seultour, were founded in 1771 by families from Lorraine). Instead of scattered farms large villages sprang up — strung out along one street or forming a compact cluster. These villages were re-sited by the Austrian army in the Marches zone — street-villages along the highways, fortified *palanke* on the Danube's banks. The Austrian administration insisted, too, on triennial rotation of crops, forest rights and common pasture — in fact, an agrarian regime modelled on that of the West. But this regime lasted only a few decades. In the regions not under military control, real-estate capitalism developed round the towns, which are more like overgrown villages. From the eighteenth century on, Hungarian magnates, Austrian nobles, Croatian bishops and Serbian horse-dealers grew speculative crops, annexed the common lands, improved the soil, drained the marshes, cleared the forests and invested their profits in rural industry. Here, then, is the explanation of a type of agriculture relatively rich for central Europe and marked by a regular increase in yield and a preponderance of cereals, industrial or market-garden crops. Such are the elements of unity.

*The Vojvodina.* To the east of the Danube, in the Vojvodina, wheat is king. The region is flat and monotonous and has certain steppe-like features of climate. There are no trees, and wood for fuel is very expensive in a land where there is no coal. Wheat covers more than 60 per cent of the area under main crops on the loess soils of the Baranja, the Banat, the Bačka and the Titel; only acacias grow in the dune belt of Peščara. Valleys like that of the Tisa (Tizsa) were the first areas to be occupied

during resettlement in the eighteenth century. The large villages are laid out chess-board fashion. Grain trade on the Danube led to the growth of large towns. After the 1919 agrarian reform hamlets were established on the sites of places destroyed long before. Water is scarce, and wells have to be dug to a depth of several dozen yards. On the big State farms as well as on the small properties, crop rotation of the modern type is practised, and sugar beet is increasingly grown. Hops, forage plants, oil-producing plants and maize are the main crops on the small farms. The towns have a character that is all their own: just over half of Subotica's 100,000 inhabitants are agricultural workers, and the proportion is even higher in Senta. The town centres are essentially agricultural, occupied by farms, while shops and factories string out along the roads that radiate from it. Only Novi Sad has taken on a more conventional look.

*Slavonia and Croatia.* To the west of the Danube, the land surface and the type of agriculture are more varied. Slavonia's characteristic feature is a number of curious forest patches that cover the remains of collapsed crystalline massifs enclosed in the deposits of the Pannonian sea, which is dissected by a network of small streams. These are the Prigorje (that is, lands at the foot of and around the mountains), whose economy is typical of all vine-growing hillsides. Strips of vineyard or orchards once owned by the bourgeois of the plain fan out along the slopes. At the upper end of each holding is a shed containing a wine-press and a storehouse for wine (*klet*). But here, as everywhere else, the vineyards producing high-quality wine have suffered crises, and maize fields have partly replaced them, although in recent years increasingly large quantities of table grapes have been produced. The hollows of the plains and the bottoms of the Sava and Drava valleys present two different landscapes.

Bordering the rivers is the *lug,* an amphibious zone of meandering streams, inhabited by frogs, beavers and storks, a game and fishing preserve, a no-man's land in the nineteenth century, the inviolate fringe of the Austrian Marches. Some of the plains have now been drained by the State or by the co-operatives, and experimental rice crops are being tried. The large villages, which in former times benefited from the traffic on the Sava, stand on abandoned meanders or the steep banks of the streams. In the drier areas are magnificent oak forests whose wood has been exported throughout Europe since the eighteenth century. Still the haunts of herds of wild pigs, the forest was ruined between the two World Wars by ill-advised deforestation by Yugoslav and French firms.

The second landscape shows remarkably well-defined continuous terraces with dry, well-cleared terrains. Contrasting with conditions in the Vojvodina, maize is the main crop here. Only a few areas specialise in speculative crops — hops grown by Czechs round Daruvar, sugar-beet in the Podravina (Drava plain), forage plants and chicory near Bjelovar, market-gardening around Zagreb. Croatian Zagorje (the land 'behind the mountains') is over-populated and remains faithful to the old type of general mixed farming.

The towns resemble villages strung along high-

Macedonian peasants, who form one of the many distinctive ethnic groups of Yugoslavia. This variety means that three related languages, Serbo-Croat, Slovenian and Macedonian are in use, together with a number of dialects, and four religions are practised, Orthodox, Roman Catholic, Protestant and Moslem.

the flocks and herds, and for some years past the high pastures and summer chalets have been given over to tourists, while the cattle, fed with forage from the artificial pastures, are kept in stalls in the hamlets perched on the moraines and fluvio-glacial terraces. More milk and butter (supplied to Gorica and Ljubljana) is now produced than cheese. The Slovenian mountain people, like the Tyroleans and the Swiss, have adapted themselves to changing economic conditions, and have taken advantage of developments in industry and tourism, and work to cater for the towns and plains.

The vital artery is the Sava trough. The villages —of German pattern—are strung round the edge of the Ljubljana basin. The marshy and wooded bottoms were drained and cleared in the Middle Ages, and it is possible that the numerous peasant population then practised some system of crop rotation; now hayfields are taking over at the expense of cereals, flax and hops. The men travel daily to the textile factories of Kranj and the metallurgical works of Jesenice. There is a distinct migration towards Ljubljana that is becoming more marked. Ljubljana is a former provincial capital, Austrian in appearance, with numerous baroque buildings. It was once the capital of the Illyrian provinces of Napoleon's empire. The approaches to Maribor and Celje are marked by prosperous villages with tall white churches, dotting attractive hollows or lining the river courses. Rye and maize, hops and apple trees cover the fields, while planned forestry and wool-weaving form the basis of a very varied economy.

## THE ADRIATIC COAST

Yugoslavia is also a maritime state with a Mediterranean coastline of well over 400 miles. The Croats are traditionally the nation's seamen, and Croatian songs tell of fishermen's adventures and of the exploits of the *Uscocchi,* who were doughty pirates. The Adriatic ports have had most of the emigration traffic; most of the foreign trade goes through Rijeka (Fiume). For the southern Slav world, then, this seaboard is of special importance. Here, in the Primorje, contrasting with inland regions of cold, mist and mud, are lands of stone and sun, of wine and fruits, of salt and fish. This coast has also a place apart in the Mediterranean world, for it is indeed one of the strangest in Europe. Post-glacial encroachment raised the sea level by over 300 feet and partly drowned a relief of limestone anticlines and synclines packed with softer, impermeable deposits. The anticlines constitute the island heights whose narrow ridges rise like marine monsters from the waves. The depressions deepened into channels (*kanali*). This invasion by the sea is so recent that erosion has hardly had time to modify the shape of the shore, whose outlines are moulded on the forms of the ancient relief. Communications are easy and constantly maintained. When Dalmatia was swept by invasions the inhabitants sought refuge on the islands, which enjoy a milder climate than the mainland. The coast facing the open sea is sheltered from the *bora* (a cold wind heavy with salt blowing from the

ways or the valley terraces. Each farm, at right angles to the road, has a long strip of field that stretches as far as the woodlands. Such towns were command-posts in the Marches (e.g. Varazdin), bridge towns or frontier towns on the Drava (such as Djurdjevacs), contact towns between the Prigorje and the plain (Krizevci), twin towns on the Sava (the two Brods), or navigation termini (Sisak).

## THE SLOVENIAN ALPS

Yugoslav territory includes only the most southerly spurs of the southern Pre-Alps — the Karawanken and Julian Alps — whose peaks are little higher than the Dinaric mountains. The abundance of mineral ores attracted settlers to this region even in Roman times. Pastoral life (developed during the Slav occupation) still predominates in the upper valley of the Soca (Isonzo) and in the Triglav massif, but the valleys are shallow and do not offer room for a true mountain life. Only a few inhabitants follow

Mostar, former capital of Herzegovina. Its Old Bridge was built in the sixteenth century by a Turkish architect on the site of a Roman bridge spanning the River Neretva with a single 90-foot arch. In the distance chalk plateaus rise harsh and bare.

continent), and offers areas very suitable for settlement. However, while some of the islands are over-populated (Prvic has 500 inhabitants to the square mile), others, such as Kornat, have been inhabited only for a few decades. In the times of droughts, flocks and herds are shipped across from the mainland to feed on the short grass of the uninhabited islands. The *kanali* facilitate coastal shipping and fishing. All communication used to be by sea, but now there is a good road along the coast from Rijeka to Dubrovnik. Reefs, however, present a danger to navigation and legend has it that the boat says to the fishermen, 'Save me from the land and I'll save you from the sea'.

The climate is distinctive. It can be as cold as in the interior, and the port of Senj, for instance, presents a strange winter spectacle of boats covered with ice, unable to put to sea because of the *bora*. The winter months are cold and dry; the summer is burning hot under prevailing *jugo*, sirocco or south wind. Except in autumn, drought — the curse of the limestone islands — is always a danger, and often water has to be distributed by tanker.

The agriculture of the islands cannot, then, be considered typically Mediterranean. Grain crops are not important, and less wheat is grown than maize. It is only south of Split that olive trees are numerous, and then they yield fruit only every other year. The decrease in acreage under vines is the result of phylloxera and a slump in the market. Irrigation is possible only in the hollows. Forestry was again the main pursuit of the inhabitants, but the Venetians ravaged the coasts, and attempts made to reforest the Karst have not been very successful. The sheep were decimated during the war. Though the Adriatic is not rich in fauna, individual fishing, practised at night and by the light of acetylene lamps, is still moderately rewarding and offers a supplementary means of livelihood to some of the people. As a consequence the population congregates more and more in the large ports—Roman towns that were once constantly menaced by waves of Slav invaders,

A market scene at Zadar, on the Dalmatian coast.

towns that are now industrial or commercial centres, such as Rijeka, Zadar (Zara), Sibenik and Split.

There are distinct variations in coastline. To the north, Istria, whose sparsely populated continental areas ('White' Istria) are cold, has plains and a coast ('Grey and Red Istria') where a different climate prevails. Here population is more numerous, originally settled by Slavs living on *stancia* (large estates) whose Italian owners resided in the towns. The Kvarner — with large islands and indented coastline — is an industrial area that also attracts tourists. Rijeka is its capital. In the central section of the coast, the fall in coastal relief has caused a widening of the plains in the Ravni Kotari. But the coast is dotted with silted-up ports, such as Nin, and the people abandon little used harbours such as Zadar and Sibenik and migrate to the islands or south to the mainland. The extent of the Split hinterland (and that in western Bosnia, the *poljes* of Knin, Sinj or Imotski), the abundance of livestock and wine in the large islands (for example Brač, Hvar and Korčula), combined with the mild climate are all favourable factors for human settlement. Split is no longer a town confined within the ruins of Diocletian's palace; houses have spread beyond the walls and the tentacles of a great industrial port reach round the shores of the Kastel bay.

Farther south, the sea deepens and the eroded coast, no longer protected by the islands, is buffeted by the high waves. The mountain crests overlooking the shores rise up into a brilliant sky. The *bora* no longer blows so fiercely. Fig and olive flourish in the warm basins of the Konavlje and the Zupa of Dubrovnik. Oranges and lemons ripen on the shores of the Kotor Bay (the Bocche di Cattaro), and many of the features recall the shores of Greece. At Cavtat (Civitas) the temple of Aesculapius has been restored. On all sides are relics of Ragusa's ancient splendour. This former republic, now Dubrovnik, attracts tourists from all over the world. Not only has the town preserved intact many vestiges of its glorious past, but present-day economy has benefited much by the drainage of the delta of the Neretva, the coastal plains and Lake Shkodër (Scutari). With the development of Montenegrin mines and industries, traffic in the southern ports is increasing — the region is, in fact, one of the republics of the Yugoslav Federation with a very promising future.

## YUGOSLAV ECONOMY

*Climate and agriculture.* Nearly 60 per cent of the Yugoslav population still live in the country. In addition, some large 'towns' are peopled by peasants. And, if we exclude Slovenia (which is more urbanised) the peasant population constitutes more than 65 per cent of the whole, and reaches 75 per cent in the Kosovo-Metodhija region. The problems, then, which must preoccupy government and people, are rural problems, for they determine the economy of the country. They relate, first of all, to the inadequacy and irregularity of the grain harvest. One factor, a climatic one — drought — seems insurmountable; the other difficulties have been inherited from former regimes or from applying earlier agrarian reforms without adequate preparation.

The great disadvantage of the continental or Mediterranean climate is the irregular rainfall. Summer droughts have occurred annually since 1945. The example of 1952 is illuminating and characteristic. After an excessively mild autumn and winter, March frosts caused considerable damage, while drought together with high temperatures (maximum 111°F.), prevailed over the whole region from Slavonia to Macedonia. In Serbia the rainfall was only 30 per cent of what was needed, and a hot dry wind burned up what remained of the harvest. Compared with the yields of an average year, the figures were 55 per cent for wheat, 32 per cent for maize, and 23 per cent for sugar-beet. On the whole harvests were only half those of normal years. Lack of forage forced the peasants to kill off their livestock, and the mountain areas had to supply foodstuffs to the plains, for it is in the richest regions that spring and summer droughts have their most disastrous consequences. In Yugoslavia, moreover, these misfortunes have even more serious results than would normally be found in other countries, for such a combination of unfavourable natural factors revealed the defects of an agrarian system still based entirely on small family farms which were quite unable to cope with such crises. In 1961 droughts seriously compromised the results of the plan.

*Vicissitudes of the agrarian system.* Yugoslavia is one of the European countries where the legal and economic results of a feudal-type regime were longest maintained. In the Austrian dominions the peasants were freed in 1848, but not until 1919 in the regions controlled by the Turks. The peasants were never owners of their land, their livestock or even their harvests. Under Turkish rule there prevailed a system of re-forming large farming estates by which the *rayah* (non-Moslem subjects) were reduced to the condition of serfs. In the areas colonised by the Venetians, the Slav peasantry near the towns was bound by share-cropping contracts to the urban nobility, and as commerce declined so did agriculture. In the military Marches, the soldier-peasant was in fact provided with tiny holdings, but he had neither time nor the means to farm them. Where feudalism of the German or Magyar type prevailed, either very small concessions were made out of the big estates or the peasants had to work as serfs on the *latifundia*. In Serbia the laws promulgated during Miloš's reign resulted in increased numbers of smallholdings between 1804 and 1890. Either because the peasants, under the burden of financial obligations, desired it or because the governing classes wanted it for military reasons, the ancient patriarchal communities were maintained, often under tutelage, with elders, or *starješine,* appointed by the government or by the land owners. There was no place for development of that class of small owner-farmers which in other countries constituted a factor of stability and even prosperity.

Thus it was that sudden liberation, without any guarantees, coming at different dates, provoked a widespread crisis in the nation's agricultural life. Large properties were retained by the nobility, and the partition of estates in Slovenia and Croatia met with insurmountable difficulties. The dissolution of the patriarchal communities (a consequence of the abolition of feudal obligations) resulted in an exodus of population, the end of joint land ownership, rapid diminution in the size of properties recently acquired, unwarranted subdivision of land, the decay of pastoral activities and heavy debts on the farms.

The subdivision of the land was accentuated by the effects of the two agrarian reforms. The first —from 1920 to 1939—was not completely carried out, though the *latifundia* in Slavonia were broken up; the new owners were not sufficiently backed by a government that was miserly with credits, and they received only land in poor condition, which they were unable to farm properly without capital and equipment.

The second agrarian reform, promulgated by the law of August 1945, decreed the expropriation of 740,000 acres in the Vojvodina alone—and 3,700,000 acres throughout Yugoslavia. Some 316,000 families received parcels of land, but the disadvantages of tiny holdings became only the more evident. By

Macedonian folk-dancing.

1950, 95 per cent of the rural population lived on farms that were too small. The aim of recent reform has been to reconstitute large farms in the form of co-operatives of various types, ranging from simple buying and selling associations to fully fledged *kolkhozes*. A proportion of the expropriated lands is managed by the State, and their part in the country's economy is already an important one, although only a very small proportion (5 per cent) of the peasant population is employed on them. The co-operatives and the State farms comprise respectively 13 per cent and 29 per cent of the cultivated land, and produce more than a quarter of the total yield of 'white' cereals, artificial forage and industrial crops, whereas maize growing is principally confined to private farms, most of which are very small. Properties of more than about 75 acres are uncommon. Sixty per cent of the tilled land is in the hands of

peasants with holdings of less than 12½ acres each. The State sector is by far the best provided with agricultural machinery—on average one reaper per 385 acres of arable land against one per 395 acres of co-operative land, and one per 740 acres of privately owned land. The figures for tractors are one per 1,420 acres, one per 1,265 acres and one per 11,300 acres respectively. By any standards this disparity is spectacular.

*Improvements.* Many obstacles of a material or psychological nature have hampered the application of the new policy. Some co-operatives were dissolved in 1953 and, at the same time, a new agrarian law limited the size of rural properties to a maximum of about 25 acres. The State domains do not as yet have the necessary personnel, material or credits. The average agricultural output is no higher than before the war, and flocks and herds have been brought up to their prewar figures only with great difficulty. However, the crop switch-over (begun after the partition of the family communities) has been continued. Maize, which gives a high yield and is most cultivated where the population is densest, has taken the place of the old traditional crops, buckwheat, rye and millet. Stock-breeding is improving, even in the south, thanks to wise stock selection and progress in establishing hygienic conditions.

Market-gardens have taken the place of the uprooted vineyards. In the Vojvodina more and more sugar-beet is being grown. Potatoes are not as yet very common but are being increasingly favoured in Slovenia and Croatia. Increased acreage of oil-producing and fibre plants has given fairly good results.

Attempts to increase the cultivated areas and to increase the yields are being made by large-scale improvement measures. The forests of Yugoslavia are rich in fine timber trees and are, therefore, too precious to be sacrificed to extensive clearing. But the marshy lands in the Lika and Herzegovina *poljes* have been drained. *Podzol* and *vriština* soils, a sort of leached red earth, have been dressed with lime. The marshes of Macedonia, the Sava (Jelas and Lonja), the Vojvodina, the Istrian plains, and the lands around Lake Shkodër (where malaria is still rampant) are becoming progressively healthier, while new crops are being grown on the fertile soils: rice, cotton (49,000 acres), vegetables and fruits that are sent to the large canning factories. The irrigation of the Banat, undertaken in conjunction with the construction of the Danube-Tisa-Danube canal, will offset some of the dangers from drought and provide 1,235,000 acres of arable land. The Popovo Polje and the Macedonian basins could easily become the Tennessees of Yugoslavia.

Finally, developments of the last few years have led more and more to centralizing production and to the formation of huge highly specialised farms, furnished with modern farming equipment. In 1961, there were 800 State domains (half of them in the Vojvodina) covering 700,000 acres, and 230 co-operatives. Smallholdings have received large subsidies, but many problems still remain: reconstruction of larger farming units, supplies of seed and fertilizers, electrification of rural areas. Now, more than ever, Yugoslav agriculture requires support from industry.

## PROGRESS IN INDUSTRY
## AND URBANISATION

*Economic backwardness.* Yugoslav industry is in its early stages, and the general situation is still not favourable. This can be ascribed, in the main, to the economic and technical backwardness of the Balkan countries. The heritage of former regimes lies heavy on economic life. The Turks encouraged nothing but handicrafts. The Austro–Hungarian government showed an interest in the food industries. The output of the mines, worked with the help of foreign capital before 1939, was exported, and equipment industries and manufacturers were sited in the north and north-west, that is, near the Austrian and Hungarian frontiers. Yugoslav industry is handicapped by old-fashioned equipment, and output is at once too small and too expensive. Almost everywhere the craftsman's tradition has been preserved. High-quality metallurgical and textile products have to be imported.

The general economic backwardness is shown, too, by the unsatisfactory state of communications. The rail system is inadequate and the average speed (including stops) is low (about 18 m.p.h. on the best runs). The mining areas and the Adriatic ports are badly served. Freight charges are high and the volume of main-line traffic is not great. It is only in the north that there are good roads, but the number of vehicles in use is still much too small. The Belgrade-Zagreb motorway has been extended to Ljubljana and to the Greek frontier. The Dalmation motorway has now been completed. However, attention must be drawn to the economic importance of the railroads built since 1945 in Bosnia (from Samac to Sarajevo and from Bihać to Split) and Montenegro (from Nikšić to Titograd).

Population statistics present a more satisfactory picture. Despite war losses (estimated at 1,700,000 dead), the total population (with an average density of more than 185 to the square mile) continues to increase. In only five years, from 1948 to 1953, the total rose from 15,772,000 to 17 million and today is well over 18 million. The birth rate exceeds 22 per thousand. The death rate has continued to fall and is now about 9 per thousand; the infant mortality rate on the other hand is one of the highest in the world.

Also the distribution of population is rapidly changing, and the number of town-dwellers continues to rise. Indeed, after the war, the peasants flocked to the towns. The young people take jobs in the factories, which thus absorb part of the surplus population in the poorer parts of the land. But this sudden social transformation raises problems that are not easy to solve. How, for instance, can skilled workmen and competent technicians be trained in a very short space of time?

The distribution of sources of power does not seem to favour the development of large industrial centres. Coal furnishes four-fifths of the energy used, but the coalfields are scattered (the largest of them yields 400,000 tons annually), so that difficulties of communication are increased and exploitation is less concentrated than it might be. The Rasa coal from Istria is of fine quality, but nine-tenths of Yugoslav

solid fuel production consists of lignite and brown coal which cannot be used for coking, and coal has to be imported. Great hopes are set on oil but output does not meet one-quarter of the demand. No doubt hydro-electric power, which already furnishes 42 per cent of the total current produced, will be the great resource of the future. Large modern stations like that of Jablanica, on the Neretva, have recently begun operation. Dam-building in Slovenia, Croatia and Macedonia is progressing rather more quickly.

Yugoslavia is rich in ores, whose working has always been profitable, and export or local processing provide an important source of State revenue. Iron

been a general increase in output and expansion of the metallurgical industry. Yugoslavia now has at its disposal a greater quantity of coal, steel and cast-iron than before the war. The Jesenice, Sisak and Zenica blast-furnaces have been re-equipped. The problem of coke supply has been solved, in part, by the erection of the Lukavac works in Bosnia, where experiments are being made with new processes. Non-ferrous ores are being treated near the mines (as in the case of Bor) or near the hydro-electric dams by 'colour' metallurgy. Aluminium works are confined to Slovenia and Dalmatia. Strong efforts have been made to increase the output of machi-

One of the principal streets of Belgrade, capital of Yugoslavia. In 1830 the city had only 30,000 inhabitants; today, with its suburbs, it has more than 500,000.

is found mostly in Bosnia, copper in eastern Serbia, bauxite in Istria, Dalmatia and Montenegro. Lead, antimony, chromium, molybdenum and wolfram deposits are of considerable size. The Idrija mercury mine—which before the war belonged to Italy—is among the largest in Europe. In non-ferrous metal production Yugoslavia occupies an enviable place in the world.

*The industrialisation trend.* Positive results have been obtained from the application of a drastic industrialisation programme. Nationalisation has been extended to include small enterprises. The targets of the first Five Year Plan turned out to be too ambitious, and external difficulties have prevented the full accomplishment of the programme laid down. The aims of the second Plan (1957-61), although of the same kind (that is, concentrating on development of heavy industry and economic expansion in the more backward areas), were more modest. The aim of the last Plan (1961-65) was economic growth at the annual rate of 14 per cent.

The essential features of recent developments have

nery and agricultural, electrical and rail equipment. Some oriental countries are already buying machines and vehicles in Yugoslavia. On the other hand, the lack of skilled workmen and high-quality raw materials leaves the textile and chemical industries in a precarious condition. The spinning and weaving mills are hampered by old-fashioned equipment and suffer from irregular and indifferent supplies. Half the country's leather, 60 per cent of the woollens, and 90 per cent of the cottons are imported.

Yugoslav industry is changing and concentrating fairly rapidly. The old, traditional centres are expanding—in Slovenia, the Dalmatian ports, the Serbian and Bosnian mining towns, the headquarters of agricultural industry on the Pannonian plain, and the capitals of the federal republics. New achievements and really successful economic ventures have in some cases increased the importance of these places: for example, the 'Litostroj' works turning out electrical equipment in the suburbs of Ljubljana, and the 'Jugovinil' enterprise producing plastic goods near Split. What strikes the traveller from western Europe most

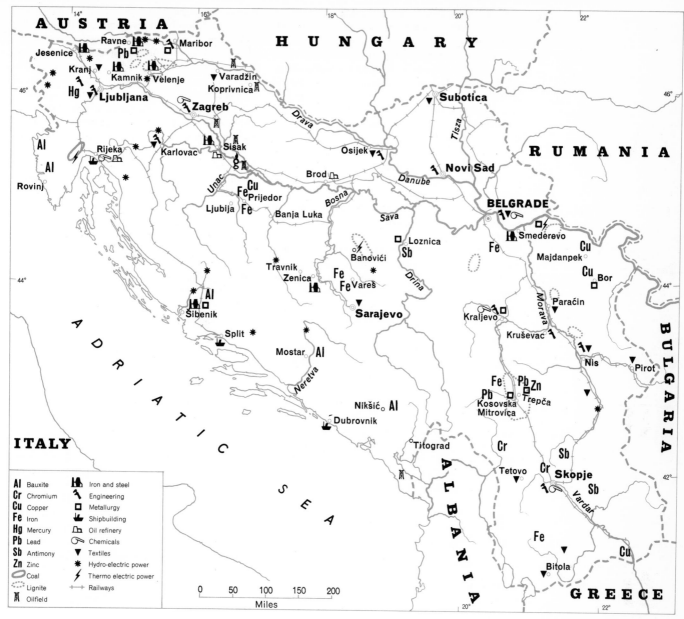

| | |
|---|---|
| **Al** Bauxite | **⛏** Iron and steel |
| **Cr** Chromium | **⚒** Engineering |
| **Cu** Copper | **◻** Metallurgy |
| **Fe** Iron | **🏭** Shipbuilding |
| **Hg** Mercury | **⚗** Oil refinery |
| **Pb** Lead | **⚙** Chemicals |
| **Sb** Antimony | **▼** Textiles |
| **Zn** Zinc | **✳** Hydro-electric power |
| Coal | **⚡** Thermo electric power |
| Lignite | Railways |
| Oilfield | |

0  50  100  150  200
Miles

forcibly is the immense progress made in the backward regions of Macedonia and, still more, in those of Bosnia and Montenegro. The population of northern Bosnia clings to the coalfields and the valley bottoms, where some factories employ more than 2,000 workmen. Almost half the rural population has migrated to big industrial centres like Banja Luka, Doboj, Zenica and Tuzla, and round the edge of the Pannonian basin a new economic area is growing up.

A comparable development has taken place in Montenegro. Shepherds and peasants are leaving the mountains for the coast in large numbers (in the Zeta valley at Nikšić and at Titograd). Despite heavy losses in the war, the population in the five main towns of Yugoslavia's smallest republic has continued to increase, and between 1948 and 1953 rose by 40 per cent.

*Rapid growth of the towns.* It is in the capitals that the rapid growth of population is most marked. The towns show clearly, in architecture, layout, social structure and activities, the influence of those civilisations that have dominated them. The old Moslem townships are those which have changed least, but they, too, have lost some of their craftsmen. The Dalmatian and Istrian cities, which lay halfasleep within their walls, have been partially awakened by tourists and increasing traffic in the ports. Pula and Zadar are slowly recovering from the exodus of the Italians; not so Rijeka and Split. The towns making the most remarkable progress are those on the plains or in the valleys, former fortresses or places of residence of the Austrian, Serbian or Magyar middle-classes (with the exception of the Banat towns); the populations of Maribor, Novi Sad, Niš, Subotica, Osijek and Ljubljana are mostly made up of workmen. Everywhere, the expansion of State commerce and the nationalised industries has attracted inhabitants from the surrounding countryside into the towns. Mushroom towns — temporary or permanent — are constantly springing up near the dams, the mines and the big metallurgical plants.

Zagreb and Belgrade are far and away the largest towns and have all the appearance of metropolitan

Yugoslav industry suffers from the technical backwardness that is general in the Balkan countries. Handicapped by old-fashioned equipment, output is small and expensive. The rail system serving the mines and ports is inadequate. Yugoslavia is rich in ores and the essential feature of recent development has been general expansion in the metallurgical industry.

cities. Zagreb has grown along the banks of the Sava and at the foot of the Medvednica (a massif over 3,000 feet high); it lies on the crossroads between the Adriatic, Hungary and Austria, and is linked with Slovenia and Croatia. The geographical position and the site of Belgrade are much more favourable for the development of a great city, for it lies on one of the great European cross-roads. Highways from the south (Salonica, Sofia, Istanbul) along the Morava, the Vardar and the Strumica, roads from the east (Iron Gates, Bucharest and Black Sea), roads from the west (Slavonia and Slovenia) and roads from the north cross at the meeting point of the Sava and Drava rivers, where the waters are dominated by the terraces of the 330-foot high Kalamegdan, the site of a fortress since Celtic times. Yet fortune tended to favour Zagreb, at least until the end of the nineteenth century. It has always been an important market for Venetian, Austrian and Hungarian goods, with an active and prosperous population which has directed the town's expansion along hills overlooking the river (and thus out of the way of floods) and, later, along a highway parallel to the Sava, the Ilica. Zagreb has nonetheless preserved the calm, rather baroque appearance of an Austrian provincial town, for it was never occupied by the Turks, nor even seriously threatened by them.

In contrast, it was the varied fortunes of Austro-Turkish warfare that hindered the growth of Belgrade, whose cobbled streets, balconied houses, and picturesque craftsmen's shops still give an oriental impression. The fortress, today surrounded by a park, was several times the stake in bloody battles, and the old wooden town itself was often attacked by fire. It was only after 1804, particularly after 1919, that the unique situation of the town influenced its development and it became first the capital of Serbia and then of Yugoslavia. In 1830 Belgrade had only 30,000 inhabitants. Today, with its suburbs, it has well over 600,000 inhabitants—against Zagreb's 430,000. New factories have sprung up to the south-west, at Rakovica and Zeleznik. On the other side of the Sava and the Danube, the satellite towns of Zemun and Pančevo have always been large markets for Pannonian produce; now they are becoming important industrial and commercial centres.

The development of the Belgrade conurbation has been somewhat held up since the Second World War by the rather unsuccessful attempt made to create the new town of Novi Beograd on the alluvial plain nearby.

The expansion of Zagreb and Belgrade is proof of the new Yugoslavia's economic and political renaissance. However, rapid urbanisation presents new problems. Increased agricultural output is necessary and the almost insoluble problem of housing is especially acute. Industrialisation thus has very grave limitations. If increased demands are to be met, agriculture must be modernised; but it cannot be modernised unless industry can supply machines and fertilizers. As Yugoslav industrial output is too low to bring this balance, recourse must be had to foreign sources of supply. Since, too, foreign exchange can be obtained only by exports of agricultural produce (the tradditional pre-

war exports), great care must be taken that over-industrialisation does not compromise the future of agriculture. This is one of the vicious circles of Yugoslav economy. And the problem becomes still more complicated in years of poor grain harvests. In 1952, 900,000 tons of wheat had to be imported, 200,000 tons in 1954, and an average of over 1,000,000 tons annually from 1955 to 1958. The Five Year Plan for 1961-65 aimed for an average annual increase in industrial production of 11 per cent and in agriculture of 7·2 per cent.

YUGOSLAVIA AND THE WORLD. *A Balkan, Mediterranean and Danubian State.* During the last hundred years, increased population has sparked off a movement of emigration. From 1870 to 1940 hundreds of thousands of peasants (probably more than half a million) were driven abroad by destitution and the slump in agricultural prices. There were Serbs from the Šumadija, Slovenes from the coast, Croats from the Lika and the Zagorje, Montenegrins and Dalmatians from the islands. Until 1914 all headed for America, then, after the First World War, for Germany, Belgium and France. Yugoslavs can be found in fairly compact groups in the Great Lakes region, in the north-east United States, in the Mississippi delta and in the Canadian woodlands. Some have established themselves and founded families in Brazil and Australia. Others have returned to Yugoslavia after making their fortunes abroad—these are the 'Americans' who have built villas on the coast, constructed roads and modernised villages. Many, again, have remained permanently overseas and have been assimilated in the New World. Their children no longer learn their mother-tongue, though the emigrants still remember relatives who have stayed at home; postal-orders and packets from all over the world pour into Yugoslavia, and some islands, like Vis or Krk, live at least in part on supplies sent through Rijeka. Abroad, the Yugoslavs retain their old customs and found folklore clubs (as at Pittsburgh and Cleveland). The economic and political influence of these groups of emigrants has been considerable.

Yugoslav foreign trade is expanding, although on the whole the balance is unfavourable. Half the traffic of the Danube is in the hands of Yugoslav companies. The merchant fleet, wiped out during the war, has been rebuilt. Ocean-going freighters and coastal vessels carry most of the exports, which are transported by sea rather than rail or road. There are five shipyards and they are working to capacity. Even the fighting fleet has been considerably increased. Rijeka, well situated at the head of a sheltered roadstead, is linked with Sušak, and is in closer touch with an industrial and forested hinterland than are the other Adriatic ports. Since 1946 Rijeka has been reconstructed and industrialised and is in the process of becoming a great Mediterranean port—the successful rival of Trieste. Traffic is now much greater than that of the other Yugoslav ports, Split, Šibenik and Dubrovnik-Gruž. Commercial aviation, too, is expanding; international lines are already in operation.

The pattern of Yugoslav foreign trade is subject to all the sudden fluctuations which may be produced by the political situation, and changes in currents of trade were made as many as four times in twenty years (1940-60). Yugoslavia imports cereals, coal, cotton and machinery from the West; she exports wood, maize, fruit, tobacco and ores to Great Britain and France. But new trends are already visible: there is exchange of maize and ores for Austrian and Swiss textiles, electrical and optical appliances; of agricultural produce for West German coke and machinery. Textiles, cement and even some equipment are exported to countries still more backward than Yugoslavia itself—to the Near and Middle East (mainly to Turkey), Egypt, India, Pakistan, Ethiopia and Burma.

Then the tourist industry must not be overlooked, for there are few European countries as rich in varied natural beauty—high Alpine or Dinaric mountains, Adriatic beaches, Montenegrin canyons, and grottoes in the Karst. The mineral and hot springs of Serbia and Slovenia have been famous since Roman times. Yugoslav art treasures and folk lore are rich and rare—the Macedonian and Bosnian mosques, the Orthodox monasteries of Metohija and Serbia, the Romanesque churches and Renaissance palaces of Dalmatia. There were few tourists before the war. The figure is now rising rapidly, and by 1963 had reached over 1½ million. There are still relatively few foreign residents, but their numbers are increasing (1,200,000 in 1962). Swiss, Germans and Austrians are gradually taking possession of the coast again and are replacing the Czechs and Hungarians. The French run short-stay cruises, while Americans of Yugoslav origin flock to the coast.

Since relations between Italy and Yugoslavia have improved, Italian tourists are now found in Istria and Dalmatia. But internal communications and roads and standards of comfort are in need of considerable improvement. And, from this point of view, there is much still to be done. However, new winter-sports resorts have been set up in Slovenia. The new coast road already reaches from Rijeka to Dubrovnik and the southern islands are organising themselves to receive winter visitors, while camping is popular with the younger people.

This then is the place of Yugoslavia in international politics: she is a Danubian Power, the most important of the Balkan lands, with a strong position in the Mediterranean. Despite traditional economic difficulties (related to geographical and historical factors), and because of the vitality and patriotism of her people, Yugoslavia may come to play a part in world politics. She remains a socialist state. Her experience of decentralisation through the establishment of communes and industrial undertakings has brought prestige in the countries with which she is linked. Still, the country is set between two blocs. The internal regime is inspired by Marxist principles, and foreign policy tends towards a prudent neutralism.

Steering her way between threats and promises, Yugoslavia seeks to follow a middle course—no doubt that which is most advantageous for her. Adversity has strengthened national unity, but this question remains: will Yugoslavia be able to effect and secure at one and the same time the revival and independence of her economy?

A view of Dubrovnik, an Adriatic town that attracts tourists from all over the world. Dubrovnik has not only preserved many vestiges of its splendid past (it was formerly the republic of Ragusa), but it has also a flourishing economy.

# ALBANIA

Albania is one of the wildest and most mountainous countries in Europe, a little bigger than Sicily and a little smaller than Belgium, with a sea coast of something over 150 miles. The average density of population is only about 163 per square mile. Up to 1947 Albania was the only European country without railroutes. Thirty five years ago the capital, Tirana (Tiranë), had only about 20,000 inhabitants. Agriculture is primitive and industry is hardly developed at all. Both conditions stem from the nature of the country and from its history.

*Wild mountains.* Two-thirds of Albania's area lies at a height of over 3,000 feet, and the country is closed in on the land side by a barrier of tall massifs over 6,000 feet, and in places reaching over 8,000 feet. Geological structure and morphology are complex and varied. To the north, the limestones of the Prokletia (Prokletije), or 'Accursed Mountains', are tilted as in Montenegro (Crna Gora). The sharp crests, the glacial cirques, the deep valleys littered with moraines, give them an Alpine look. Above the Yugoslav plains of the Kosovo and the Metohija rise tall massifs, cut by the middle course of the Drin. Karst-like platforms alternate with more jagged ridges in the ancient formations of the Korab, the Dejes, the Lopes, and the Merdita. To the south-east and south, as well as in the centre, the Dinaric folds, full of crystalline nuclei, are lower. Some basins have subsided; others, as in Macedonia, are still occupied by lakes. The intensely folded coastal ranges overlook a rocky shore running from north-west to south-east beyond the Gulf of Vlonë (Valona). The network of rivers is of little help in penetrating this mass of mountains. The Black Drin, flowing from Lake Ohrit (Ohrid), runs through impressive gorges spanned by flimsy wooden bridges and joins up a number of marshy basins. The rivers of the Mediterranean basin do not reach as far as the Yugoslav frontier, and the upper valleys are simply narrow gashes in the rocks. Only the Korçë and Ohrit basins, the valley of the White Drin coming from the Metohija, present a few gaps. Through them the *Via Egnatia* ran in ancient times, taking the trading caravans from Italy into Macedonia. Caravanserais, or *han,* are still dotted along the line of these ancient roads.

The mountains, then, have remained wild. Patriarchal families, grouped together in clans (*stirpes* or *fis*) preserve their old traditions there. Ancient customs (fidelity to the sworn word and the vendetta, for example) flourished until recently, and even the present Albanian government has had to recognise the tribal regime. Moreover, the massifs and the high valleys are divided into a number of units with closed economies. Activity is confined to handicrafts and stock-breeding. The heights are covered with grass and are favoured by a wet climate (rainfall about 160 inches a year) and cool summers (average for July about 63°F.). Since the Second World War there have been fewer migrating flocks and herds, but pastoral life generally has altered little. The mountains, too, offer an asylum. In addition to the shepherd's hut, the commonest type of dwelling is the stone *kula,* a sort of square tower with thick, high walls and very few windows: in fact, a fortress within which chiefs, women and outlaws can gather together. In the south, on the other hand, a feudal regime has replaced the clan system and here, as in Macedonia, the *cifliks* or large farming units can be seen.

*Unhealthy plains.* Plains make up only one-seventh of the total area of the country. They stretch along the sides of the rivers and form a belt of about 6 to 18 miles wide along the seashore. Landwards, Albania is protected by its mountain barrier but it is open to the Adriatic. Here, more than in any other region round the Mediterranean shores, the lowlands are marshy. The torrents dashing from the heights scatter a rather coarse alluvial soil, winding about on the alluvial fans, capturing each other's water and silting up the coastal bays already half shut in by headlands of Miocene sands and clays. The climate, which is mild in winter, becomes very hot in summer and unhealthily humid. The coast is infested with malaria and, before the war, more than half the local population was infected. Drainage of the marshes is not very effective and a plain like that of the Myzegeja is flooded during the winter months. Crops do well only in the driest areas—in the Arzen valley, for instance—or after drainage has been undertaken. There is no site on the coast where a large port could develop. Only the Vlonë Gulf, protected by the Island of Sazan, offers fair anchorage, but the hinterland is poor.

*A hilly and populated fringe.* Where mountain and plain meet population is thickest. This is a region of drier hillside terraces, of fertile alluvial fans, and hills cut out of the Tertiary deposits. In this area there are more than 150 inhabitants to the square mile. At the entrances to the narrow valleys are the large market-towns — Shkodër (Scutari), Tirana, Elbasan and Berat. Here, as far as temperature is concerned, the climate is still Mediterranean. Rain is heavier in the autumn than in the spring. It is only in the south that the summer is really dry, and here more rain falls in March and April than elsewhere. On the slopes, bush and scrub mingle with forests of oak, pine and chestnut. In the valleys and hollows cereals are grown (more maize than wheat). These areas are dotted with fruit-trees: apricots, peaches and figs in the centre, citrus fruits in the south. Olives are the most widely cultivated fruit-tree, though they are fewer in the south and on the coast than in the north and the interior. The shores of Lake Shkodër form a region apart; the fishermen, like those of Ohrit, use flat-bottomed boats known as *lundras.* The fields of the peasants are well irrigated and their life is a relatively easy one. This hilly country still forms the economic centre of the Albanian state, for in it is concentrated most of the agriculture and industry on which Albania's development depends.

*Political and economic structure.* Albania is, according to its Constitution of March 1946 (the republic was proclaimed in January 1944), a 'People's Democracy'. It is, in fact, the only one giving on to the Mediterranean, and the 'advance post of the Communist Bloc'. Linguistically and ethnically Albania is a united country. A language of Asiatic origin, Albanian has annexed a number of Slav, Greek, Turkish and Latin elements and is divided into two dialects, Tosk in the south and Gheg in the north. Non-Albanian minorities are not numerous—only 4 per cent are Slavs and Greeks, and nearly 70 per cent of the population is Moslem. The Bektashis form independent communities. Albanians are scattered all over the world. According to a recent Yugoslav census, there are 750,000 in Macedonia, Kosovo, Metohija and Montenegro. Hundreds of thousands live in Greece, Italy, Sicily, and, above all, the United States.

This state of things can be explained by Albania's history. It is a country whose people have always opposed the Turks with a fierce resistance, yet it is a modern state that achieved independence only by the Treaty of London in 1913. The reign of the German Prince William of Wied—imposed upon the country by the Great Powers—did not last long. Between the two World Wars, Albania, whose southern regions were coveted by the Greeks, became an Italian colony. Capitalists from Milan, Rome and Naples invested in a number of industrial and agricultural enterprises on the Albanian plains. 300,000 Italians occupied the country and the famous 'Good Friday attack' in 1939 was the death-knell of Albanian independence. After the Italo-Greek war, the German occupation of Albania cost the country about 2·5 per cent of its population, 37 per cent of its buildings,

and 50 per cent of its livestock. Since the end of the Second World War, quarrels between Yugoslavia and Albania—quarrels in which ideological, ethnical and economic considerations are curiously mixed—have hindered the application of development plans, the Two Year Plans (1947-48 and 1949-50) as well as the third Five Year Year Plan (1961-65) designed to raise the value of industrial output to around half Albania's total production. The result of her quarrels is that Albania has remained isolated with nothing but her own resources. After the war the country had to ask for help from the U.S.S.R. and after the breach with the U.S.S.R. in 1961, from far distant China. The present condition of the Albanian economy presents many problems, all very far from being solved.

*Agrarian reform.* Legislation in August 1945 prescribed the expropriation of large estates which, before the war, comprised rather more than 52 per cent of the arable land. Some 500,000 to 460,000 acres were divided among the poor families in the mountains or landless peasants at the rate of about 12 acres to each family of six members. Contrary to the pattern in other 'People's Democracies', co-operatives have not developed much and comprise only a relatively small area (6 per cent) of the land under grain crops. On the other hand, flocks and herds of more than 400 beasts have been taken over by the State, which now possesses 100,000 head of cattle, sheep and other animals. Due to the important

A market at Shkodër (formerly Scutari), a large market-town at the entrance to a narrow valley, and on the shores of Lake Shkodër.

place held by stock-breeding and by Mediterranean or small shrub crops, the agrarian reform has not yet had much effect on agricultural output. Furthermore, only 18 per cent of the land is cultivated. Large-scale engineering works have been undertaken to drain the marshes round Lakes Maliq and Shkodër (Scutari) and on the plain between the rivers Semeni and Shkumbeni. Maize is the commonest cereal but emphasis is increasingly placed on wheat. The yields do not, however, satisfy home demands, and wheat has to be imported from abroad. The Italians extended the area of sugar-beet cultivation, and production should increase tenfold. A modern sugar refinery has been set up at Korçë. But the real hope for agriculture lies in the improvement and development of industrial crops. Cotton and rice should do well in the marshy plains. More potatoes are being grown. Tobacco — a traditional crop — has become, as in Turkey, a large-scale export item. Several million olive trees have been planted, while presses and refineries are being set up for processing the oil. Stock-breeding (the principal product of which is the *kackaval* cheese) suffers from the lack of hygiene and routine, and from prejudice. Pig-breeding, despite a 41 per cent Moslem population, has developed rapidly in post-war years. Cattle are far less numerous than sheep and goats; horses are few.

*Industrialisation begins.* In addition to the food industries, Albanian mines may bring future prosperity to the country. Though lignites of the Tirana and Tepelenë basins are poor, the bitumen mine at Selenica — already exploited by the Italians — is one of the best in the world. The Pukë hematite and copper, and the Kukës, Krumë and Pogradec chromium (several hundred thousand tons of ore) are exported. The petroleum deposits were formerly worked by British, French and Italian companies. During the war output was a million tons, but production seems now to be sagging.

Exploitation of subsoil riches and the construction of plant come up against a number of difficulties: lack of skilled labour, lack of technicians (now supplied by China), poor quality material and, above all, lack of communications. The first railroad line (about 27 miles long) from Durrës (Durazzo) to Peqin (the first section of the Durrës-Elbasan line) was opened in November 1947. The second section (20 miles) was opened to traffic in December 1950, while the Durrës-Tirana line (24 miles) became operative in 1948. Three short sections to link industrial centres to the capital were opened by 1962. Albania also has over 2,000 miles of roads, but the mountains are still virtually inaccessible.

It is still too early to judge what has been achieved in Albania. The development of this backward country has certainly been speeded up by the legal measures taken to emancipate Albanian women, who were formerly little better than slaves; by improving public health and medical services; by the spread of education (made obligatory for all in 1952) and by the foundation of agronomical and technical schools. The future of Albania, a country surrounded and isolated by states rather hostile to her, is bound up with that of the other Balkan States. Much depends on the outcome of the conflict between Soviet and Chinese ideologies.

# GREECE

It is only since 1830 that Greece has existed as an independent state; before then 'Greece' was a rather vague geographical expression. Today Greece means as much the 'Hellenism' of the past as the formal territorial limits of the country.

## THE LANDSCAPE AND REGIONS OF GREECE

*The influence of physical geography.* The physical character of the Greek lands has played an all-important rôle in the life of the Greeks and is reflected in the present-day economy.

The country (51,168 square miles) consists mainly of regions of indented coastlines and island-dotted seas. It borders on Albania, Yugoslavia, Bulgaria and Turkey, so that northern Greece is linked with the Balkan world and bears the mark of Balkan influence. The north is the only part of present-day Greece that lay on the borders of the ancient Greek world or beyond its limits. Farther south is a domain that is Mediterranean. The western slopes are rather abrupt, the eastern slopes gentle and open toward the sea.

Northern Greece has a more spacious landscape, more massive mountains and more extensive plains than the rest of the country. Northwards from the Aegean Sea, Thrace and Macedonia contain the prolongation of the Rhodope massif. Between the plateaus and residual buttes (rising almost to 6,500 feet) there are plains, where the rivers slow down and during the rainy season waters are stagnant or form lakes. The coast is flat and little indented, except for the Khalkidike peninsula which thrusts its three 'prongs' seawards; at the end of the most northerly prong stands Mount Athos, which for centuries has sheltered a monastic community. Two islands, Thasos and Samothrace (Samothraki) occupy the Sea of Thrace. Safe anchorages and natural harbours are rare. Kavalla, a town which owes its importance to the tobacco trade, has grown up around an isolated rock where moorings are good. The Vardar valley (ancient Axios), cutting through a broad belt of sediments, opens a highway into the interior — towards Yugoslavia — and ends at the head of the Gulf of Salonica (Thermai) in a huge alluvial plain. This is a crossroads where the ancient *Via Egnatia* ran from the Adriatic to the Sea of Thrace. Salonica (Thessaloniki), a busy port, has grown up in this area.

Thessaly is a land of plains surrounded by mountains, where the wet seasons alternate with periods so dry that the earth takes on the appearance of a desiccated, dusty steppe. The waters, drained by the Pinios, make their way through a narrow corridor cut in the limestones of Olympus, where great trees intermingle with shrubs, bushes and climbing and twining plants, offering a strong contrast in summer with the burning plains. This is the Vale of Tempe extolled by the poets.

The climate is harsh, the winter cold, the autumn rainfall more abundant than is typical in Mediterranean lands. The summers are usually dry and, in spite of storms, the heat is stifling inland. However, Pelion's flanks leading down to the Gulf of Volos enjoy a Mediterranean climate.

The western regions, western Macedonia and Epirus contain mountain ranges parallel to the coast which drop precipitously to the sea; the highest is the Pindus (8,445 feet). They have a plentiful rainfall and are covered, especially in the north, by fine forests. Their topographical features prevent penetration by Mediterranean influences. There are valleys or small basins, often occupied by picturesque lakes, such as those of Kastoria and Ioannina. In the south, Acarnania and Aetolia have the same mountainous aspect as north-western Greece, but the Gulf of Amvrakia, the valley of the Achelous and the Agrinion basins are more open to the sea breezes.

Offshore, the Ionian islands, which resemble the mainland opposite in relief, were never occupied by the Turks and have, in contrast to the mainland, fruitful and well-tended fields as well as a very dense population.

Central Greece and the Peloponnese (Morea) are the heart of the classical Greek scene. Sea and land mingle, and mountain masses seem to spread in all directions. There is a great variety of rock, though limestones and marble predominate. Small plains dot coastal areas and, less often, the mountains. To the south of the valley of the Sperchius, the tallest mountains (Oeta, Parnassus) rise well above 6,500 feet with patches of pine and fir forests. At their feet stretch the Locris, Phocis and Boeotia basins, exposed to cold winds in winter but very hot in summer. To the south-east the most markedly Mediterranean promontory of Attica thrusts out into the sea.

The 'Isle of Pelops' or Peloponnese is joined to the mainland by the narrow isthmus of Corinth. On the northern shores mountains rise abruptly in the region of Achaia to surround the basins of Arcadia and then spread out to form the peninsula of Messene, the long, rocky ridge of the Taygetus which stretches as far as Cape Matapan and the mass of the Parnon.

A smaller branch breaks off towards the east in Argolis. In the north and east are the plains of Corinth and Argos, to the south the valley of the Eurotas, the Messene (warm enough for bananas to ripen), and in the west, the far-reaching landscape of Elis.

Climate varies according to exposure, distance from the sea and altitude. The regions giving on to the west are dampest and greenest. The inland basins, with more extreme temperatures, are less suited to Mediterranean crops. Arcadia, whose basins lie at altitudes of 2,000 to 2,600 feet, has patches of oak forest and some of the valleys are very verdant. The eastern areas are drier. In summer long hours of sunshine on the limestone landscape give everything an air of desiccation, accentuated by the irregular rainfall and the permeable soil. The run-off waters accumulate in the hollows, from which they issue through chasms in the permeable rocks — the *katavothra*; if the subterranean passages become blocked a lake may form, like Stymphalus. Lake Pheneus is now dry. In Boeotia, extensive construction work has secured the drainage and cultivation of Lake Copais.

*The Greek islands.* The islands are the peaks of mountain ridges that once linked the Balkan peninsula to Asia Minor and were partially submerged by the subsidence of the Aegean Sea. The Sporades, in the north, are an extension of the Othrys range and reach Mitilini (Lesbos) and Chios. Euboea and Attica seem to crumble away in the Cyclades that lead to Ikaria and Samos. Strung along the wide arc of a circle are Kithira, the great island of Crete, Karpathos and Rhodes, stepping-stones to the indented peninsulas of south-western Asia Minor. To the north of Crete, between the submarine platforms supporting these groups of islands, run deep troughs—more than 9,500 feet deep.

The influence of the sea is all-powerful among these islands, but they present varied faces. Mitilini, Chios,

The fishing port of Tourkolimano, near Athens.

Rhodes, and Crete especially, have well cultivated, fertile plains, still fresh-looking in, say, Mitilini but almost African in Crete. The most typical island aspect is that of the Cyclades, where trees are scarce and the inhabitants build terraces to retain the soil. Regular northerly winds keep the summer temperatures lower than on the mainland, but rain is not abundant and from June onwards the whole countryside is baked tawny by the sun.

Over all Greece there are certain common features: the mountains, covering 80 per cent of the country's area; an impression of dryness in the long hours of intense summer sunlight; the irregularity of the rainfall; the rarity of running waters. Such conditions do not favour abundant vegetation; the few detailed accounts left by classical writers suggest that the Greek climate has not changed greatly. The country's geological history is quite recent, and the Aegean region has retained a marked instability, proved by frequent earthquakes and the existence of volcanoes.

FROM PAST TO PRESENT. *The past.* From the beginning of the third millennium B.C. brilliant civilisations flourished around the Mediterranean, civilisations whose focal point was Crete. The Hellenes came down in several waves from the north — the Achaeans about the twentieth century B.C. and the Dorians about the twelfth century B.C. These diverse elements formed the Greek people. By the eighth century B.C. Greeks were settled in the whole Aegean region, in the south of the Balkan peninsula, on the coasts of Asia Minor, and as far away as Cyprus. The eighth, seventh and sixth centuries B.C. saw a vigorous movement of expansion and colonisation, to the shores of the Black Sea, in North Africa (Cyrenaica), in southern Italy, in Sicily, and as far afield as Gaul and Spain. The centre of Hellenism was still the narrow belt that stretches from Thermopylae to Sparta, yet this restricted area created a civilisation at once highly original and profoundly human.

In the fourth century B.C. Hellenism — as a consequence of Alexander's conquests — spread over the East. Later, after the Roman conquest of Greece, Hellenic influence was felt in Italy and the provinces of the Caesars' Empire. When that Empire crumbled under barbarian blows, Byzantium, or Constantinople (now Istanbul), became the New Rome and guardian of classical tradition. Greece itself was an obscure province, overwhelmed by Slav invaders in the seventh and eighth centuries A.D., attacked by Moslems and Normans, and conquered by the Crusaders in the year 1204.

After the fall of Constantinople in 1453 and the Turkish conquest, Greece, cut off from the rest of the world, was reduced to one of the most miserable lands in Europe. The great trade routes ceased to make use of Greek ports, and the small units dropped back into a wretched, circumscribed, rural way of life. The population decreased and the Turks endeavoured to colonise Greece with Albania.

*The rebirth of the Greek people.* However, rich and busy Greek communities grew up elsewhere: in south Russia, in Rumania, at Constantinople. In Greece itself patriotic feeling never died, emerging in the struggles of 1821-9. The Treaty of Adrianople and the London Protocol of 1829-30 created an independent kingdom of the Peloponnese, central Greece and the Cyclades. Thereafter, Greece annexed the Ionian Islands, the Arta and Thessaly regions from Turkey and Crete. Southern Epirus, Macedonia and Thrace as far as the Mesta were added after the 1912-13 Balkan Wars.

After the First World War, Greece received eastern Thrace and the administration of the Smyrna region. At the Lausanne Treaty of 1923 the Greeks had to renounce Asia Minor, eastern Thrace, and the islands of Imbros and Tenedos. Exchanges of minority populations resulted in the return of 1,222,000 Greeks from Turkey, while 450,000 Turks and 93,000 Bulgars left Greece. The Anatolian coast where Greek civilisation had flourished for so long was lost, and the influx of refugees produced economic problems.

The events of the Second World War, the Italo-German occupation and then the civil war between Communists and non-Communists (which went on until 1949) caused immense damage. But hard work backed by generous help, first from Great Britain and then from the United States, allowed Greece (now

The Acropolis looks like the fortress it once was.
In the centre of the rock are the ruins of the Parthenon, in the foreground the Propylaea, and to the left the Erechtheum.

embracing the Dodecanese) to enter a new phase of national progress.

*Greek vitality.* Whatever the vicissitudes endured in the past, the Greeks are remarkably homogeneous. Foreign elements have been assimilated. The only minority groups are non-Orthodox Greeks—less than six per cent of the population. The religion is that of the Orthodox Church. Modern Greek is ancient Greek transformed by a long evolution.

Since 1830 the population has increased rapidly with annexations of new territory, the influx of refugees from Turkey, and a marked excess of births over deaths. Sanitary conditions have been improved. The draining of marshy areas and the destruction of mosquitoes by American teams have abolished the malaria scourge. Today the total population of Greece exceeds eight million.

Although the current of emigration is not as strong as it was at the beginning of the century, it is still flowing. The largest colonies abroad are now to be found in the United States, in France, around the Rio de la Plata (Argentina), in Egypt, in Ethiopia, along the Red Sea and in Madagascar. On the whole the Greeks are slow to give up their own customs and become assimilated. In two regions they have defended their ethnical character and demanded annexation to Greece; one is northern Epirus (joined to Albania), the other Cyprus, until 1960 a British colony, where Greeks form approximately 80 per cent of the population.

*County and Town.* For a long time the population was mainly rural; there are few isolated dwellings because of the scarcity of springs and because the country was for long unsafe. On the islands the whitewashed houses are covered with flat or domed roofs and huddle together. Furniture consists of very low tables and chairs, and sometimes there are fine collections of brass and copper utensils, embroidered linen and ancient pottery. On the mainland the stone dwellings with four-slope roofs are not built as close together as those of the islands. In northern Greece there are houses with outside woodwork and sash-windows as in the Turkish lands.

The urban population has risen considerably with the influx of refugees and the trends after the Second World War. The areas showing the biggest increase are those around Athens, the Piraeus, and their suburbs which, together, now have a population of about 1,400,000. Thessaloniki has about 220,000. Patras, Volos, Kavalla, Iraklion (formerly Candia, in Crete), are all seaports with factories.

Political struggles can be explained by economic difficulties and foreign interference or influence. The monarchical regime lasted from 1832, except for the period from 1924 to 1935 during which the dominant influence was that of the great democratic leader Venizelos, until the coup d'état of 1967. The regions of 'Old Greece' are firmly attached to monarchical tradition but republican tendencies are more pronounced in the large towns and in the north.

### GREEK ECONOMY

*General conditions.* Greece is a country where there is striking contrast between traditional forms of life unchanged since classical times and quite up-to-date resources. There are, for instance, regions served neither by road nor by railroad but with radio and air services. Greek economy, medieval until 1830, has since developed continuously despite unfavourable conditions. However, it is impossible to present a clear picture of economic development — or even one of the present economy, for it is in the throes of a complete transformation.

*Agriculture.* For several centuries Greek economy was based on the produce of a poor, dry soil, relatively small in area. At best it was unhealthy or cut up into large estates unsuitable for intensive farming. The peasant tilled with an archaic hoe-like plough a soil he could never manure; he planted wheat, barley and a little maize, and every other year left his land fallow. Other traditional crops were vines and olives. Sheep and goats were kept on fallow land, and as season followed season great flocks migrated from place to place. All transport was by donkey or mule. This archaic agricultural life still survives in the mountains

The volcanic island of Santorin, in the Cyclades group. Whitewashed houses, flat-roofed, huddle together on the steep slopes.

A Greek boatman. The coastal population of Greece depends less on the sea than might be imagined, and the inhabitants of many of the islands are mainly farmers. However, a new fishing fleet has been built — the old one was almost entirely destroyed during the war — and attempts have been made to increase home demand for sea-food.

The vine is a traditional crop and efforts have been made to improve the quality, for agricultural produce accounts for more than 60 per cent of the country's exports.

A tree tapped for resin, on the island of Aegina.
Resinated wine, *retsina*, is commonly drunk throughout Greece.

Factories at Eleusis, on the Bay of Salamis.
An increasing population and the limited potential of agriculture make industry's future rôle vital. Greece has neither coal nor oil, but varied mineral resources have been revealed by prospecting (bauxite, chromium, copper, iron, nickel, lead and zinc) and the industrial output index has shown a marked rise since 1938.

and on the smaller islands. Grain threshing and grape pressing is done on the spot, and windmills grind the flour. Wool is spun and woven or knitted as a domestic industry.

But wherever possible efforts have been made to improve agricultural productivity. Cultivated land, which in 1920 formed not more than 20 per cent of the country's total area, is now estimated at 30 per cent, and this is being further increased by tilling plains and valleys that were once marshy or exposed to flooding, and also by irrigating areas that were too dry. Other arable land has been gained by clearing the belts that served as tracks for migrating flocks and herds, and by adopting crop rotation and fertilizers instead of allowing fields to lie fallow. The farmer's lot has been improved by the establishment of co-operatives, insurance schemes and credit facilities. The production of wheat now leaves a surplus for export.

Crops fully suited to the physical conditions are being sown. Leguminous plants, potatoes, maize, and rice have been developed; output of fresh and dried fruits (which can be exported) and of industrial crops such as cotton has risen, and sugar-beet cultivation has been introduced. Efforts have been made to improve quality rather than increase quantity of the main export crops (grapes and tobacco).

Progress in stock-breeding is not so marked. The increased acreage of arable land has reduced that available for grazing and hampers transhumance in the northern plains. However, the compensation lies in an increase in the area under forage plants. The number of domestic animals is just about what it was in 1938, and the amount of fresh meat available barely meets increasing demand.

In 1938 less than a fifth of the country's surface was tree-covered; trees are abundant only in central Greece, Euboea, Thessaly and the mountains of the west and north. Today, efforts are being made to safeguard the trees and to increase their coverage as well as to improve forestry methods. Even so, Greece produces barely half the wood she needs to satisfy her home demands.

The fisheries, too, satisfy only part of the home demand, and the coastal population lives less from the sea than might be imagined. The fishing fleet, almost entirely destroyed during the war, has now been rebuilt, and attempts have been made to increase the amount of sea-food eaten.

*The industrialisation of Greece.* The rôle of industry is vital in view of the limited possibilities of agricultural output and rise in population. Greece has neither coal nor oil. Her only sources of power are lignite deposits and the water of mountain streams and rivers. Nevertheless, careful prospecting of the subsoil has revealed the existence of mineral wealth that is greater and more varied than had been suspected: bauxite, barytes, chromium, copper, emery, iron, magnesite, manganese, nickel (produced in only one other European country — Finland), lead and zinc.

War reduced productivity by more than 50 per cent. The whole programme of industrial restoration depends on the production of electric current, and some dams and hydro-electric stations have already been constructed; others are planned. The thermo-electric stations use Greek lignite, and a very large station is situated at Ptolemais, near the Yugoslav frontier.

There are industries processing Greek products: foodstuff factories (flour, noodles, canned goods, edible oil, alcohol and its derivatives, beer); cigarette factories; textile mills using Greek cotton, wool (mostly imported), silk (introduced by the 1923 refugees) and, quite recently, man-made fibres. Carpets are made and building materials are produced. Another plant recently installed treats ores (so far exported as raw material) and turns out aluminium, magnesium and ferro-nickel. New chemical works have been built for the production of nitrogen (fertilizers) and soda. Petroleum refineries are being erected. The industrial output index shows a very marked upward trend since 1938.

*Transport difficulties.* The size and the number of the mountains and the isolation of some regions restrict transport in many areas to donkey- or mule-back. On many of the islands there are no wheeled vehicles. The Second World War destroyed almost all the roads, railroads and bridges, as well as most of the rolling-stock, automobiles, merchant marine (three-quarters) and port and harbour installations.

The rail network has now been rebuilt, but the mountainous nature of the country forbids extensive mileage. All parts of the Greek mainland can now be reached by highways carrying regular coach services. Regular services of coastal vessels run between the islands and most of the ports and the Piraeus, which at some hours of the day is more like a crowded and lively rail terminus than a busy commercial port. The most modern means of communication — air transport — already has fairly well developed links with the major capitals of the world.

In volume and weight goods transported by sea occupy first place. The Greeks, in fact, tend to invest their money in commercial enterprises and shipping rather than in industry. Ports have been built or improved.

*Import and export balance.* Greece has to buy extensively abroad, and attempts to raise domestic industrial output — and thus reduce imports — result in initial price increases in basic materials. Even today agricultural produce accounts for more than 60 per cent of the exports. Imports include cereals, flour, legiminous plants, sugar and meat. Tobacco is still the main export and represents, on average, 50 per cent of the total exports value; then, in order, come raisins, currants, olives and other fruits.

Among raw materials imported are petroleum and coal, then metals, basic products for the chemical industry, wool, hides and building materials. Products not manufactured at home must be bought too: fertilizers and chemical products, machines, automobiles, electrical equipment and paper.

As a result, the foreign trade balance must show a deficit. Commercial treaties aim at obtaining what the country needs in exchange for what it can give, and in conclusion of such agreements political considerations may be a determining factor. This explains why before 1939 Germany held first place in Greek foreign trade, whereas from 1948 to 1950 it was the United States. Normally the greatest volume of foreign trade is with countries of eastern and central Europe, Turkey, and Yugoslavia, Austria and Germany, then with Great Britain and finally the United States. When the war ended, foreign aid had to be sought.

The imbalance between exports and imports is to some extent made up by remittances from Greeks abroad, by the earnings of the merchant navy, and by money brought into the country by tourists, for Greece is, of course, the ideal land for the tourist. Nevertheless constant improvements must be made to hotels, roads and means of transport.

*Present progress.* The Greeks have had to face very grave economic problems. Work is zealously going on to carry out a plan whose first results seem encouraging. But progress demands more and more capital expenditure on equipment, and finding financial support for improvement plans sets a crucial problem, for investment of this kind depends on the confidence felt in the enterprises and on political stability. Efforts made since 1949 have given Greece a developing modern economy.

Delphi landscape.
The mountainous nature of the land and the isolation of some regions restrict communication; in many areas the donkey and the mule are the only forms of transport.

Shepherd boy and his flocks,
near Boghaz, Cyprus.

Maltese terrace cultivation.
Agriculture does not flourish
on the island: the ground is stony
and the surface soil thin.
Crops consist of a few vegetables,
citrus fruits, some cereals,
and vines.

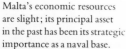

Malta's economic resources
are slight; its principal asset
in the past has been its strategic
importance as a naval base.

# CYPRUS

Of the Mediterranean islands, Cyprus is the most easterly and the third largest; geologically it belongs to Asia Minor. Two mountain ranges run parallel with the Taurus: to the north a narrow limestone ridge 3,135 feet high; to the south a more massive ridge (highest point Mount Troödos, 6,403 feet) composed of diabase and serpentine rocks. The capital, Nicosia, has developed in an oasis on the very dry central plain. The island as a whole enjoys a warm Mediterranean climate, while forests cover nearly one-fifth of the surface. In ancient times it was rich in metals—especially in copper. However, copper mining has long since been abandoned, and the island's resources are almost wholly agricultural — cereals, vetches, a little cotton and tobacco, and large quantities of carobs, olives, citrus fruits and wine. Trade is not on an extensive scale, and the ports—Limassol, Larnaka and Famagusta — are neither populous nor busy.

Set at the intersection of sea routes between Egypt and Asia Minor, between Syria and the world of the Aegean, Cyprus was subjected to the influence of widely varied civilisations. It lived through a brilliant Bronze Age; then in the first millennium B.C. it was divided between Greek and Phoenician cities. Later, the island was held in turn by all the great oriental empires of antiquity and the Middle Ages. In 1878 the Turks ceded it to Great Britain who annexed it in 1914, making it a Crown Colony in 1925.

The population (about 585,000) is divided linguistically into two antagonistic communities: 82 per cent are Greek- and 18 per cent Turkish-speaking. Britain was assailed by the claims of the Turkish minority and exposed to the hostility of the Greek population which demanded union with Greece. Following the London Agreement (1959), Cyprus became a republic in 1960, and a Commonwealth member in 1961. In 1964 a U.N. peace-keeping mission was called in.

# MALTA

Malta is a small archipelago (63 miles from Sicily) made up of three islands: Malta, the main one, with the port of Valletta, and two smaller islands, Gozo and Comino. The combined area is 122 square miles and the population is about 330,000; this gives a high density — 2,667 inhabitants to the square mile.

Malta's economic resources are slight; the ground is stony and the surface soil thin. Rainfall is sufficient but is not well captured, and the islands lack both springs and trees. The land is subdivided among a great number of owners; crops are just a few vegetables (including potatoes), citrus fruits, some cereals, and vines.

A few manufacturing and processing industries have been set up — breweries, textile-mills, workshops producing pipes and stockings, and a few small-scale handicrafts. There are few exports, and imports represent 90 per cent of the total trade. Labour is over-plentiful and was only partially absorbed by the British dockyard, now a civil ship-repairing firm.

Only emigration can raise the standard of living in such overpopulated islands.

*A traffic junction.* The Maltese islands are the remains of subsided Mediterranean mountains. Their habitation in very remote times is proved by the discovery of human fossils, ancient temples and rock-paintings. Malta was a regular halting-place on the way from the Tripolitanian desert to Sicily.

The Archipelago was inhabited successively by Phoenicians, Carthaginians, Romans and Moslems, and from the eleventh century onwards, under the rule of Angevin and Aragonese dynasties, the population was increased by Norman, Sicilian and Spanish settlers, not counting a few Greeks and Jews. Physically, the Maltese resemble Arabs, but this is due more to a Sicilian and Spanish influx from the twelfth to the seventeenth centuries than to the Moslem domination from A.D. 870 to A.D. 1090. The language, of Phoenician origin, is now composed of roots that are Arabic by etymology and by intonation. The educated Maltese speaks three languages (Maltese, English and Italian) while some speak French too. There is a university and numerous schools.

Under the Angevin and Aragonese dynasties and under the rule of the Knights of Malta, Roman Catholicism gained a strong hold. The influence of the clergy is still decisive and the parishes are also adminstrative and electoral units.

*The Knights of Malta.* From 1530 to 1798 Malta was governed by the Knights of the Order of St John of Jerusalem, who continued the rôle as paladins of Christendom which they had played for five centuries on land and sea against the infidel. The Order was founded in Palestine at the time of the First Crusade. In 1523 it received Malta from the Emperor Charles V, with the mission of containing the Turkish forces and of clearing the southern Mediterranean of pirates.

The island prospered under its rule, since most of the Western sovereigns made presents to the Order. The Knights were great builders, and the hospital at Vittoriosa was the most famous in Europe. Despite a number of demolitions, many monuments of their munificence still remain.

*Present-day Malta.* Bonaparte seized Malta in 1798 but had to relinquish it after his defeat at the Battle of the Nile. The British then occupied the island; Malta became a Crown Colony which enjoyed self-government from 1947, that is, autonomy in all home affairs, though the British were responsible for defence and diplomatic representation. In 1964 Malta attained complete independence within the Commonwealth. Until 1974 Britain will maintain its naval base in Malta, and in return will provide capital aid for development.

For centuries Malta's strategic importance was considerable; its many deep-water inlets could accommodate two or three fleets, and its soft, chalky rock (it can be cut with a hatchet or even with a knife) provides underground storehouses, caverns and cellars.

The value of the British naval base is no longer what it was, for it is a particularly easy target for air attack, and in time of war it would prove a heavy liability, since the overpopulated island would first have to be fed before effective use could be made of it for the transit of armed forces. Nevertheless, its great port installations are still important strategically.

# ITALY

Italy is sharply distinguished from the other two Mediterranean peninsulas — first by its narrowness, which allows the sea air to influence it and make it damper and greener, and then by its geographical position. It is a kind of bridge between Europe and Africa, a midriff, as it were, between West and East; throughout the ages it has been a meeting-place. Again, Italy's abundant population and high degree of technical skill had a much greater influence on the country's politics and economy than the populations of Spain or the Balkans had on theirs.

## TWO ITALIES

*The rampart of the Alps.* Physically there are two Italies: northern or continental Italy, and southern or peninsular Italy. The 700-mile rampart of the Alps determines the geography of northern Italy.

The Alps are a 'recent' range, that is, one whose rocks were folded in the second half of the Tertiary Era. This explains the sharpness of the eroded outlines. There are three almost equal sections: to the west the Piedmont Alps, in the middle the Lombard Alps, and in the east the Venetian Alps.

The Piedmont Alps extend from the Cadibone Pass to the Simplon. They resemble cliff edges rather than mountain slopes and in some places as little as 15 miles separate plain from 9,000-foot peaks. The vast expanses of black schist are often pierced by crystalline massifs 13,000 feet high; such are the Grand Paradis, the Monte Rosa, and the immense barrier of Mont Blanc. To the north, planing by ancient glaciers has widened the valleys a good deal more.

Beyond the Simplon, and stretching as far as the Passo di Resia, lie the Lombard Alps. They are wider than the Piedmonts, more varied in aspect, and easier of access. They owe their special character to the harmonious development of three geological zones: in the north a continuation of the Piedmont lustrous schists; then a crystalline axial zone; and finally, in

Amalfi, a small fishing port in the Gulf of Salerno, and perhaps the most popular resort on the Sorrento peninsula.

the south, the limestone Pre-Alps or Bergamasques. A feature of the utmost importance for communications is that the massifs are generally separated by longtitudinal furrows.

Since the Lombard range is greater in mass than the Piedmont Alps, precipitation too is heavier and glaciers bigger. During the Quaternary Era, conditions were similar, and widened such passes as the Splügen, the Stelvio and the Tonale. Again, glacial action in the past has made the valleys suitable for hydro-electric stations. Glaciers produced the magnificent lakes of the Alpine foothills — Maggiore, Lugano, Como, Iseo, Garda — fashioned from above by tongues of ice and dammed below by terminal moraines.

Peace treaties after the 1939-45 war confirmed the cession of the Julian Alps to Yugoslavia, and the Italian portion of the Venetian Alps now ends at the Tarvis Pass. The Venetian Alps show some resemblance to the Lombard Alps. They have similar longitudinal furrows. But they are on the whole lower: the Tyrolean massifs barely exceed 11,000 feet, and the Carnic Alps, 8,000 feet. The celebrated Brenner Pass is only 4,693 feet above sea level. In consequence there are few glaciers. Intersecting transverse fractures produce an extraordinary maze of valleys. The accessible character of the mountain is all the more useful since due north of Verona the Alps are twice as broad as the plain of the Po itself.

Excessive widening of the calcareous zone explains the 'bulge' of the Venetian Alps and has influenced the formation of karst: the plateaus are dry and pitted with funnels, and the rivers are often subterranean. In the Dolomites, the properties of magnesian, a particular sort of limestone, have produced rock formations like the walls of ruined buildings, and panoramas of unusual colours.

*The Po plain.* The Po plain is a deep geological trough which before the end of the Tertiary Era was a huge gulf of the Adriatic. Gradually the Gulf was filled in with debris brought down from the mountains. Here, as in every piedmont plain, debris nearest the mountain barrier is coarsest, while fine alluvial soil covers the middle of the plain. In places these deposits have built high banks and raised the river's bed.

In the northern half of the plain, right up against the Alps, lies a belt of moraines forming high hills, generally arranged arc-wise, which dam up the sub-alpine lakes. The semicircle around Lake Garda is the most perfectly formed of these accumulations. In many cases the waters have managed to break through the barrage, so that the moraine takes the shape of a broken horseshoe.

The surface of the zone of high terraces of broken stone is covered with a hard crust, so coarse that water percolates all the same.

Then comes the zone of low terraces of finer materials and furrowed with streams rising in springs along the line of contact between the high and low terraces. This row of springs, of the greatest utility, yields from 90 to 270 gallons of water per second per mile of its length.

The flood-plain of the Po on the whole narrow, broadens out in the Polesine downstream. The Po and its affluents carry a considerable amount of alluvium. When the water is exceptionally high in the streams, the dykes and banks burst, and the countryside is flooded. On the right bank of the Po the line of springs is narrower and there is no belt of morainic hills.

Luckily, the monotony of this landscape is broken by a few hills from 1,250 to 1,900 feet high which, in remote ages, were islands in the sea gulf that formerly occupied the Po plain.

It is a huge plain and a splendid one — 'the most fertile plain in the world', said Napoleon; but only engineering skill and sustained effort has allowed man to get the most out of a soil that is sometimes too dry and sometimes too wet.

The sea-frontage of the plain is low and marshy. The mud and sand deposited in the Adriatic by the rivers are pushed south by the inshore current and extend as long coastal strips (*lidos*) enclosing lagoons, some of which still communicate with the sea and are 'alive' — such is the lagoon of Venice and its celebrated lido.

*Erratic action of climate and sea.* The climate of northern Italy is temperate, continental and sub-Mediterranean. Like central Europe, northern Italy is exposed to polar air in winter, and in summer is swept by warm air from the Atlantic. But it is separated from the ocean by more than 350 miles of land, screened by the Alps, isolated from the Mediterranean by another mountain barrier, and the influence of the Adriatic is slight.

Northern Italy therefore presents distinctly continental features: surprising differences between summer and winter temperatures, and regular seasons. Even so, the climate is sub-Mediterranean, since the heaviest rainfall is in spring and autumn. In the Po valley the seasons generally follow this pattern: little rain in winter, which is misty and very cold with frequent frosts; the spring is warm but very wet; the summer heat is stifling, with a sultry atmosphere and frequent storms; in October the heavy rains fall. This is a trying climate but excellent for maize, rice, mulberries and sugar-beet.

South of the Po's cold mists, the climate is more agreeable; vines and sometimes olive trees make their appearance. The best-known example of this climate (Insubrian) is that of the great lakes, where Mediterranean plants flourish, and of the Borromean Islands. The climate on the Adriatic is less equable and the shores are often swept by gusts of the *bora* (a cold north-east wind).

In the Alps, the higher the altitude, the greater the precipitation and the lower the temperature. In the eastern Alps, which are exposed to humidity from the Adriatic and so have a heavy rainfall, there are extensive forests of coconut oak and beech at heights of 7,550 feet.

The Po is the largest river in Italy, yet it is hardly navigable at all and has been always more of a barrier than a link. Its seasonal variations are interesting. In January comes the first low water, for the rainfall is slight; then in May comes the first spate from the Alpine tributaries swollen by melting snows. In July-August there is a second period of low water (caused by evaporation). Lastly, in November, comes the full flood produced by abundant autumn rains. The Po regime is, then, dependent upon snow and rain, and this imparts a central European physiognomy.

*The Apennine jigsaw.* The Apennines are the backbone of the peninsula. Occupying what is now the Tyrrhenian Sea there was formerly a land mass of crystalline rocks, called Tyrrhenis. During the Tertiary Era, folded mountain ranges were grouped round it; it then sank beneath the waves, and portions of the mountain framework were left above the surface. The Apennines and the large islands are all that is left of this great geological drama.

The Apennines as a whole are a very young chain, and as erosion has not yet weathered the surfaces, their landscape presents plenty of plateaus and gorges but few peaks and few sharp needles. The frequency of earthquakes proves that folding is not yet finished. 'Folding' is misleading in this context, for the rocks here have been fractured more often than folded. Consequently numerous hollows or basins are formed which, a few millennia ago, were still lakes. Another special feature is a 'Pre-Apennine' chain that is often volcanic; there are the extinct volcanoes of Tuscany and Latium and the active ones such as Vesuvius, Stromboli and Etna. Violent storms produce dangerous landslides which may efface roads and shift villages and split the ground into widening gullies, swallowing fields and pastures.

The Apennines present an astonishing variety of landscapes. In the north is the very narrow screen of the Ligurian Apennines, dropping sharply down into the Gulf of Genoa and forming a precipitous face which the road cannot always follow. The Apennines of Tuscany and Emilia, although not very high, are of a much more complicated structure. The white marble walls of the Apuan Alps are the only different formations; their subterranean extension contains the Cortemaggiore oilfield.

In the central Apennines the presence of limestone rocks produces a sequence of various forms. First, the Apennines of Umbria, the Marches with karst plateaus and the first of the sunk basins. Then, in the Abruzzi, they broaden into a massive fortress-like feature. Progressively, as the green hollows of Aquila, Sulmona and Avezzano spread out, the arid high plateaus expand, the limestone blocks become higher, and in the complex of the Gran Sasso d'Italia the scenery takes on an Alpine character. In the southern Apennines, limestone still occupies an outstanding place in the landscape, but in the Neopolitan Apennines and in Luciana it is cut up into squarish *blocs* by argillo-schistose corridors. Finally, in the far south, lie the Calabrian Apennines, an unexpected granite 'toe' sticking out of a limestone 'boot'.

*A few good plains.* The useful low-lying areas, flattened against the flanks of the Apennines, are more often hills and little plateaus than true plains. These good lands are situated (except those in Apulia) on the Tyrrhenian side of the Apennine arc, overshadowed by the volcanic heights of the Pre-Apennines and filled with fertile alluvial soil.

The typical Tuscan landscape — illustrated in the paintings of the Florentine and Sienese Primitives — is made up, principally, of argillo-schistose hills whose outlines are soft and gentle. Farther south, extinct volcanoes follow one another in quick succession and contribute much to the region's fertility. The Roman Campagna yields wonderful harvests, the gardens on the Alban Hills have been famed since classical times, and still more fruitful are the Neapolitan plains.

Unfortunately, a rise in sea level during prehistoric times has made the shores alluvial, malarial and uninviting; the Tuscan Maremma and the mouths of the Volturno and the Sele are still marshland where wild boar and buffalo roam freely.

Marshes are less common on the Adriatic slope of the peninsula, but the lowlands are not as hospitable to man. Aquila is a flat tableland, fertile only when irrigated.

*The Mediterranean islands.* Italy possesses the two largest Mediterranean islands — Sicily and Sardinia. The richer and more famous is Sicily. The ancients called it *Trinacria,* 'Island of the Three Points'. In the north are the Sicilian Apennines, a mountain chain less than 7,000 feet high, and an extension of the Calabrian heights. On the Tyrrhenian side this range drops down steeply into the sea. A few small irrigable recesses break up the arid stretch of mountains. On the southern side the land slopes gently towards

The three peaks of Lavaredo (9,850 feet) in the Dolomites. The Dolomites owe their jagged outline to the composition of their rocks.

Africa in a slanting plane from which erosion has cut hills, whitish ravines and a jumble of plateaus. To the east is the damp plain of Catania, above which rises the majestic, snow-capped cone of Etna (10,741 feet). The soil of the plain, which is of volcanic origin, is most productive.

Sardinia is rocky and wild, but tabular formations predominate and altitudes are not great. There are the high, granite plateaus of the Barbagia, the volcanic caps of the Logoduro, the coal- and mineral-bearing masses of the Iglesiente.

The other islands are all rocky, small and wild. Elba is an ancient weathered mass. Ischia is an extinct but still warm volcano. Capri is white and craggy. Stromboli and Vulcano still throw out their flaming bombs into the sea.

*Contrasting climate.* Peninsular and insular Italy is set entirely in the Mediterranean zone, also termed 'sub-tropical': in winter Italy receives the warm, damp Atlantic air, while in summer it is swept by dry, hot Saharan air. However, because of its shape, it feels the moderating influence of the warm Mediterranean.

Let us take an example: Rome. Here the winters are cool, the skies often overcast; rain is intermittent, snow unusual. There are a few very fine days when the icy north wind blows. In spring the temperature rises rapidly and rainfall is more abundant, with a south wind both damp and hot. Then summer bursts forth suddenly; three months of skies that are gloriously and implacably blue. It is hot. There is no rain save an occasional storm. The soil cracks and splits. In October the temperature drops and deluges of rain show that Atlantic air prevails again. It is interesting to note that in any given year Rome has half as much rain again as London.

The climate excludes all plants which cannot support cold as well as heat, drought as well as wet. Non-deciduous trees and exotic but well acclimatised plants make up landscapes of serene and intense beauty.

On the eastern slopes, behind the screen of the Apennines, we find this climate again, but drier and with colder winters. It is excellent for wheat-growing but most unfavourable for citrus fruits.

Inland, distance from the sea and altitude produce mountain climates of astonishing severity. Autumns are warm, and the winds violent; in winter there are furious snowstorms. A few forests, such as those of the National Park in the Abruzzi and of the Sila in Calabria, are justly famous. Wolves are common.

To the south of Naples the climate is warmer. Winter temperatures are over 10°C. (50°F.). There is only one rainy season, occurring during the cold weather. The torrid summer lasts four months and gives the country the appearance of a steppe. It was in Sicily, scorched by the African sirocco, that an Athenian expeditionary force perished of thirst in 413 B.C. Dwarf palm-trees grow everywhere and bananas ripen in well-watered Calabrian gardens.

The combination of very dry summers and great heat results in very shallow rivers in summer. But, as their gradient is steep, all the streams fill up rapidly as soon as a storm breaks, causing floods. In peninsular Italy and the islands, then, streams can be used for irrigation and generating electric current, but there is no hope of making them navigable.

*Who are the Italians?* It may be argued justifiably that Italian national unity dates only from 1861 and is still young. To understand this, and a number of other aspects of Italy's human geography besides, we must turn to the past.

The men who lived on Capri and at Monte Circeo hundreds of thousands of years ago disappeared long before our era, and the first event of any geographical importance was the great migration of the Neolithic Mediterranean peoples, who settled on the plains in about 5000 B.C.

About the same time the first wave of Italic peoples swept the peninsula. They were a warlike pastoral people from central Europe speaking Indo-European languages. The second Italic wave, about the year 1000 B.C., was contemporary with the Dorian influx into Greece. The invading tribes also spoke Indo-European languages; they pushed their predecessors southwards, for the newcomers had the advantage of wrought-iron weapons. The Mediterranean inhabitants left the plains to the invaders and fled to the Apennines. Sardinia, however, was off the line of advance and the people were left in peace to build their fortified towers, or *nuraghi*, as they had done in the Bronze Age. It is thought that no Indo-European invasion reached the island before the Roman conquest.

Later invasions affected the fringes: Illyrians settled in Venetia and Apulia; in the eighth and seventh centuries B.C. the Etruscans colonised Tuscany. An oriental people, probably from Asia Minor, the Etruscans wrote a language which we can read but not understand; they knew how to construct arches and how to cast iron, and they could produce reasonable portraits. At the same period, emigrant Greeks founded wealthy cities farther south — Naples, Cumae, Agrigentum, Sybaris. The Carthaginians gained a foothold in Sicily and then on the Sardinian coasts. In the fifth century B.C., the north, which had so far been spared, was overrun by the Gauls.

Rome was originally a settlement of coarse peasants, but as its site commanded the last easy crossing of the Tiber before the sea, the population assimilated the oriental heritage of the Etruscan and Greek traditions. The Romans succeeded in conquering first Latium,

Sardinia is rocky and wild, and life on the island is simple. Prosperity may increase if recent attempts to promote a tourist trade succeed.

then Italy, then the whole of the Mediterranean. By the first century B.C. the name *Italia* was applied to the whole peninsula. By the third century A.D. the name designated the territory we now call Italy. The *Pax Romana* was everywhere imposed upon the peoples; riches poured into Italy with soldiers from all nations, new ideas and influences of every sort. Italy became the first officially Christian country with Rome as its centre.

Then Rome succumbed, and in the fifth century Italy became once more a prey to invaders: Vandals, Visigoths, Huns, Arabs and Hungarians swept through her cities and over the countryside. For five hundred years trade was paralysed; the coastal plains were deserted and abandoned to malaria. There were a few attempts at political organisation, but neither Theodoric's Ostrogoths nor the Byzantines, nor the Lombards, nor the Franks, nor even the Papacy succeeded in reconstructing a coherent State in Italy. During the Middle Ages, for instance, the essential political units were the cities, strongly fortified, overpopulated and teeming with craftsmen. In the thirteenth and fourteenth centuries 'tyrants' and warlords — the *condottieri* — seized power: the Este family ruled Ferrara, the Orsinis Rome, the Viscontis Milan. In the fifteenth century the cities became the capitals of powerful principalities. Florence of the Medicis — the rival of Siena — dominated much of Tuscany. Political subdivisions multiplied and were constantly changing right into the nineteenth century. Among the various patches that made up this harlequin costume was the Pontifical State.

Italy has had the sad distinction of being the European country to suffer most invasions in the course of her history. The eighth- and ninth-century invaders were the Carolingian Franks. In the tenth century Italy was annexed to the Holy Roman Empire, and German hegemony began. In the eleventh century, the Normans succeeded the Moslems as masters of Sicily. After the Normans followed the Hohenstaufen Germans, then the Angevin French, and after them the Aragonese. In the sixteenth century there was the French and then the Spanish occupation. The eight-eenth century was that of Hapsburg domination, broken for a time by the French but resumed when the Austrians returned in 1815, remaining until the middle of the nineteenth century.

Oppressive police measures, bad administration, confiscation of works of art, were some of the results of foreign invasion. The influence on Italian culture and civilisation was profound: how can we understand Sicily without taking into account the Moslems, or Verona without considering the Austrians, or Ragusa if we ignore Spanish rule?

*The importance of the sea.* Italy in the past was a country of seamen. As early as the eleventh century, Amalfi was a powerful republic. Venice concluded advantageous agreements with Constantinople. Genoa traded with Morocco, and Pisa with Tunisia. Competition was fierce between these cities. Through her ports not only merchandise came to Italy but ideas, skills, artistic themes. But later, after Columbus, the Ocean routes drained away European trade, and the Mediterranean ports sank slowly into decay.

Sea-borne trade brought activity in other parts of Italy. Craftsmen worked for export, and Florentine cloth, Venetian glass and Faenza ceramics were justly renowned. This commercial activity quickly made the Italians skilled in the handling of money. Their adaptable book-keeping methods and their contacts with their agents abroad ('the Lombards') made them the founders of modern banking and maritime insurance. If Italian civilisation from the fourteenth century to the eighteenth was brilliant, it owed much to the liberal patronage of such great and wealthy families as the Medicis, the Borgias and others. Behind Dante and Machiavelli, Raphael and Michelangelo, we find the figures of intelligent and highly prosperous men of affairs.

*Final unity.* In 1815 Austria had carved Italy into small provinces and imposed on each one a reactionary government. When they were at last freed from foreign control, the Italians united under the leadership of the House of Savoy in Piedmont. In 1860 Piedmont annexed the Kingdom of the Two Sicilies. The Kingdom of Italy was officially proclaimed in

Genoa, the major port for imports. Its ships feed the busy industrial regions of northern Italy with raw materials.

Mount Vesuvius, though not the largest, is the most famous of the Italian volcanoes, with a core rising 3,850 feet above the Bay of Naples. The first recorded eruption, in A.D. 79, destroyed Pompeii. Later eruptions, though violent, have been less devastating.

A square in Trento, in Alto Adige. During the course of its history, Trento has been ruled by Ostrogoths, Lombards, by medieval Italy and Germany, by Austria, and by Italy once more. German is therefore as frequently spoken as Italian, as in all the province of Alto Adige.

Acerenza, in the province of Potenza. High-perched towns are as diverse in Italy as they are picturesque.
A troubled early history made easily defended sites particularly necessary.

1861. After yet another war Italy absorbed Venetia (1866); the troublesome problem of Rome, which obviously had to be capital of the new State, was solved by force of arms in 1870. Unity was achieved.

Difficulties confronted the new state — backwardness in agriculture, lack of industrial plant, shocking poverty of the southern peasantry. The government was handicapped by quarrels between North and South, by the politicians' excessive individualism, the arrogance of the great landowners, the inertia of the illiterate masses and the hostility of the Church. Nevertheless, by the beginning of the twentieth century a good deal of progress had been made. The rail network had been linked up with these in foreign countries. Hydro-electric stations were increasing in number. Universal suffrage had been established in 1921. At the same time the number of inhabitants to the square mile had risen to more than 250: this constitutes Italy's eternal problem of over-population.

After the First World War, matters came to a head; social disturbances became more and more numerous. The alarmed business classes turned to Mussolini who, by drastic measures, re-established order and set up a totalitarian regime in 1921. Mussolini's Italy sought for political reasons to be self-sufficient and did manage to produce more wheat and electric current. Substitute materials such as hemp and artificial silk were increasingly used. Unfortunately, side by side with this fairly effective economic policy, Mussolini engaged in an absurd demographic policy: he gave excessive support to an increase in the birthrate and at the same time forbade emigration. In 1946, ruined by the war, Italy chose to become a democratic and parliamentary republic. Six years afterwards the country had resumed its place in international affairs.

*People and language.* Three main ethnic types can be distinguished in Italy. First there is the Mediterranean: dark, lively, rather short, narrow-headed — the traditional 'Italian' type. Then comes the Alpine: chestnut-shaded hair, broad-headed, medium height, general appearance rather heavy. Lastly there is the Dinaric type, with dark hair, a head both broad and high, tall of stature. Generally speaking, the Mediterraneans occupy the peninsula and islands, the Alpines northern Italy, and the Dinarics Venetia. But on more detailed study we find many regional variations.

Although we know very little about the origin of these physical types, there is reason to believe that the Mediterraneans represent the Neolithic natives who were pushed down into the peninsula; the Alpines, the Terramare and Villanovan invaders; and the Dinarics, the immigrants from Illyria. We should expect that certain features would have been attenuated, or accentuated, by local infiltrations. But nowhere has it been possible to show, conclusively, the existence of such influences.

Like Spanish and French, Italian is derived from Latin and is thus of Indo-European origin. Since Latin was spoken by peoples used to several different languages, it did not evolve everywhere in the same fashion — so there are vigorous dialects: northern, Tuscan, and central-southern. There is a standard Italian taught in schools and local dialect: the 'divine tongue of Dante', time-honoured by centuries of literature, is of Tuscan origin but has lost its Tuscan accent.

Along the frontiers the national language gives way to fringes of foreign speech: French in Piedmont and Val d'Aosta, German in the upper Tyrol, and Slovene near Yugoslavia. Elsewhere there are a few scattered patches of language recalling former settlements: thus Catalan is still spoken at Alghero in Sardinia, and Byzantine Greek in the extreme south of Apulia and Calabria.

In such conditions of extreme social and physical diversity it is difficult to describe the average Italian: there is no 'type' common to the whole of Italy. The Milanese, for instance, are often cold, precise realists; the Florentines are considered reserved, and the Romans good humoured and impetuous. The Sicilians and the Sardinians are often quick to take offence. It could be said that the Italians are generally individualists, yet gregarious; generous and imaginative, they understand intuitively rather than by thorough reasoning — which at times makes for superficiality. They are at once shrewd and sentimental, and their firm religious sentiment is usually fused with emotionalism.

In the north, between the more or less free-thinking wealthy businessmen and the discontented proletariat, there is an intermediate social group on the whole faithful to the Church. In southern Italy there is a conservative paternalistic landed aristocracy, with a wretched and often illiterate mass; there is no middle-class.

*Settlement of the towns.* Her troubled history predestined Italy to be a land of towns. The number of large cities is not disproportionately high. But the number of small towns is immense: more than a hundred have from 30,000 to 100,000 inhabitants; in the south especially, where insecure conditions lasted long, urban centres are the most numerous. It is often difficult to distinguish between a town and an overgrown village. Nicastro, in Calabria, has 25,000 inhabitants, but farm produce is still brought into the town in carts.

Towns that grew up on lines of communication are numerous: they may lie at the foot of a pass, such as Susa, or at the entrance to a valley, like Verona they may be bridge-towns, such as Piacenza; citadels, such as Alessandria. There are also two kinds of town peculiar to Italy. First, in the north, there are the settlements situated along the lines of springs, such as Turin and Milan, Second, in the south, there is the group of towns whose inhabitants cultivate, at great risk to themselves, the fertile lower slopes of Vesuvius and Etna. Because the subsoil is so poor, there are very few towns near the mines. Carbonia, on the Sardinian coalfield, is quite a recent and artificial creation. Generally, the industrial towns have an historical rather than economic origin.

Because of long-lasting insecurity, the Italians have always chosen easily defended sites. There are on the plains, it is true, towns that were Roman colonies, towns that have existed from ancient times, but on the whole, and especially in the peninsula, both pre-Roman and medieval settlements were on heights. In the Apennines the site may be any rocky eminence, but in the regions bordering on the mountains steep-sided hills were the favourite choice: Siena and Perugia are typical examples. Sometimes, as at Orvieto, the site is a volcanic table with precipitous sides. In Lucania, whose valleys were infested with malaria, the hill crests were chosen. On the coasts, advantage was taken of easily defended peninsulas by building across their necks, as at Syracuse. In modern times many of the high-perched towns have moved gradually down into the plain where there are roads and railroads, so an upper town, massive and silent, looks down on a busy lower town. A typical example of this is Bergamo. Often, also, on the shores of Liguria or the Marches, towns long perched on the heights decided in the nineteenth century to build 'marinas' by the shore. Carrara, for instance, now has a twin in Marina di Carrara.

The high-perched towns are as diverse as they are picturesque. Generally the streets coil round the foot of the castle and unfold down the hillside as at Assisi and Urbino. But when the site was a long hill or a spur, as at Aquila or Benevento, the ground-plan was rather like a fern-leaf pattern. On the plains, some towns are composed of concentric streets round an old piazza as at Bologna. But, in general, the flat ground permitted a strictly geometrical layout. The most curious plan is that of a star: star crossroads as at Bitonto in Apulia, star fortresses as at Guastalla and Palmanova on the Po plain. The commonest plan is that of a chessboard, a sign of systematic town-planning, whether a product of Roman colonisation, as at Turin, or of later settlement, as at Vittoria. At Lucca and Piacenza, the chessboard is surrounded by protecting ramparts. Venice, with its winding canals, presents an altogether special case. Certain towns with rectilinear street-plans have been reconstructed in modern times after disastrous earthquakes, and are characteristic of the south of Italy: Avezzano and Messina. Very often a chessboard of new roads cuts into the capricious, narrow streets of an old town; nowhere is the contrast so striking as at Bari.

ROME, THE ETERNAL CITY. Rome has a special place among Italian cities. It has about 2,300,000 inhabitants and is the seventh city in Europe. Its past, its position

Built on the mud banks of the Veneto, Venice, the queen of the Adriatic, is a city of bridges and canals which wind through the heart of the city. Gondolas have been a common form of transport since the end of the eleventh century.

Bologna, capital of Emilia, showing the radial plan of the old city. At the centre are two medieval towers, leaning to one side as a result of subsidence.

at the heart of Italy, at the centre of a network of splendid roads, on a famed site, all combine to make it 'The City' *par excellence*.

However, the factors which usually govern a city's fortunes do not appear to be very favourable to Rome. It has no hinterland; Latium produces nothing for export, nothing to be processed or manufactured except travertine building stone. Rome has no outlet, the Tiber is not navigable, and the Campagna, which only fifty years ago was still malaria ridden, is only just now beginning to be cultivated. The Roman springs are hot, and water must be brought at great expense from the mountains. There is no labour force: the Campagna has only about 50 inhabitants to the square mile. The city, with its famous hills, is unsuited for modern traffic.

Fundamentally Rome is a creation of history, and three factors have been of prime importance in its past. First, it would not have become a great metropolis had it not succeeded in conquering the Mediterranean by force of arms. Egyptian wheat, Tunisian oil and Syrian iron supported a city of a million inhabitants. Thanks to slaves and to booty, Rome was able to live magnificently, to erect splendid buildings, to build fine roads and aqueducts, and to construct drains.

The second factor was the permanence of the Papacy. Had the Popes not resided at Rome, the city — deprived of its political power, reduced to its own resources and assailed by brigands — would scarcely have survived the Middle Ages. When the Popes left Rome in the fourteenth century, the population fell to 17,000.

The third factor was the restoration of Rome to its position as the capital of Italy when, in 1870, the House of Savoy was obliged to conform to tradition

and come to reside in Rome. For prestige reasons, Mussolini's government forced the population up to over a million.

As a result, this huge city has no economic rôle. Its primary function, as the capital of the Italian Republic, is administrative and political. There is also a double set of diplomatic representatives: those accredited to the President of the Republic and those accredited to the Holy See. In addition, Rome is the headquarters of some international organisations such as the F.A.O. (Food and Agriculture Organisation). A map showing the radiating spokes of the rail network demonstrates graphically the centralisation at the seat of government.

Then Rome is the capital of Catholic Christendom, since over 520 million Catholics are joined by spiritual ties to the Sovereign Pontiff. In the 1950 Holy Year nearly two million pilgrims visited Rome. Roman ruins, churches, palaces and museums offer archaeological attraction for many other visitors besides pilgrims. Although Rome has the largest university and the greatest number of newspapers in the country, it is not the intellectual capital; Florence and Naples rank before it. From an economic point of view it is a city of many consumers and few producers. As a result, there are few industrial suburbs.

Since the war, the situation has changed a little. Rome's outskirts are beginning to be built up and industrialised: there are factories manufacturing pharmaceutical products, oil refineries, rubber factories, tile-works and film-studios. Market-gardens are pushing out into the Campagna. Rome has become the second largest banking centre in Italy. This is no isolated phenomenon: the economy of the peninsula as a whole is undergoing a complete though not rapid transformation of character.

A panorama of Rome from the
roof of St Peter's
Its past, its position as the capital
of Catholic Christendom,
and its situation at the centre of a
network of excellent roads
give it a special
political significance.

## RURAL LIFE

Ever since Virgil's time, Italy's main resource has
been agriculture, and to this day it occupies about
30 per cent of the labour force. However, there are
too many workers on the land and as a consequence
increased mechanisation is purposely delayed for fear
of creating unemployment.

There is a strong contrast in the types of land
ownership: on one hand a mass of tiny holdings
quite useless for feeding a family, and on the other,
land concentrated in a few large estates generally
farmed by share-croppers.

*Northern Italian peasants.* In the Alps the physical conditions are such that men have had to adapt themselves
to them in more or less the same way in whichever
country the conditions exist. Only the southern fringe
presents some original features.

The country is open and the climate, on the whole,
good in the Po valley, but the soil itself only fair.
'Elementary' farming gives only indifferent results:
flocks and herds scattered over great expanses of
heather moors, the poorer cereals such as rye and millet, some vegetables, some fruits. The vine flourishes,
however, on well exposed hills.

But the face of rural Italy has been determined by
the historical conditions of land ownership. It is impossible to separate the agrarian from the social structure.

The Romans divided the land into little parcels
farmed by free settlers and share-croppers. During the
early Middle Ages, the farmers were in some cases
reduced to the condition of serfs. About the thirteenth
century the movement for the emancipation of the
communes entailed also the freeing of the serfs; from
that time onwards the development of the countryside
was linked with that of the towns, for townspeople

who had made money and bought land possessed
the means and the will to improve farming methods
and conditions. In the nineteenth century the industrialisation and consequent wealth of the north Italian
towns was important for Italian agriculture.

Farming methods were directly influenced by this
social development. If he has a long contract or lease,
a farmer has a personal interest in increased yield and,
also, he feels he has the time to plant trees. Hence the
prevalence of multi-course farming, in which the
same field is planted with alternate rows of herbaceous
plants and shrubs. The wet climate has favoured this.
The method of farming, together with the division
of the land into smallholdings and the abundance of
water, has made for the scattering of dwellings.

The monasteries and the towns exercised much
influence upon agricultural methods and skills. In
Lombardy the technique of crop rotation was perfected, and in the thirteenth century the monks
applied the *marcite* method, which consisted of
warming the meadows by flooding them during
winter with the tepid waters from the springs. In
Lombardy, as early as the twelfth century, land was
irrigated by tapping the waters of Alpine streams
where they reach the plain. Today the Cavour Canal
is the largest of these irrigation canals, and about a
third of the agricultural land in Lombardy and in
Piedmont is irrigated.

On the low plains and the delta, the problem was to
drain off the surplus water. The Venetians were so
occupied with maritime ventures that drainage was
only undertaken tardily; the major undertakings date
from Mussolini's time. By means of canals and
drainage pumps, nearly 2½ million acres were converted into dry land — especially around Ferrara. Such
large-scale hydraulic undertakings can be carried on

only by powerful concerns: hence large estates have a firm grip of the region, and the men who till the land are mostly labourers.

Thanks to the full use of water-control methods, the original multi-course farming has been supplemented with wheat, maize and potatoes, temperate zone fruit trees such as mulberries, as well as tomatoes and forage plants. Industrial crops, or those lately introduced, such as tobacco, sugar-beet, and especially rice and hemp, are grown in special areas.

Thanks to the fields of clover and lucerne, many cattle and other beasts are raised in the north. Manure from the cattle stalls is of course most valuable for the soil, and gives the north a great advantage over Mediterranean Italy. The Po plain agriculture has also benefited much from capital supplied by industry, and is quite up-to-date. Certain figures for yields on the Po plain are remarkable. The north Italian rice-fields, for instance, have a higher yield than those of the Far East.

Although, from the physical point of view, north Italy stops at the Apennines, sun-drenched Liguria is part of northern Italy, and northern-type multi-course farming and scattered dwellings can be found in Tuscany and the Marches. This seems to be due to the combined influence of the medieval middle class and impermeable soils.

*Backwardness of southern agriculture.* Mediterranean Italy, both peninsular and insular, offers in its agriculture a sharp contrast with northern Italy.

The really apalling number of unfavourable factors are due, in part, to physical conditions. In the peninsula flat fields are uncommon; it has been estimated that in the whole of Mediterranean Italy (Tuscany and Latium excepted), more than half the arable land is inaccessible to tractors. The soil is not good, and for one area of light, fertile, volcanic earth, there may be ten of earth that is stony, or too shallow, or devoid of humus. More rain falls than in other Mediterranean countries, but the dryness of the summer kills many plants; the sudden, violent showers loosen and wash away the topsoil, cover the fields with mud, and flood the low-lying areas. Plants that can grow without any help from irrigation are almost all shrubs or bushes — gnarled olives, almond and fig trees, vines and carob trees. Yet wheat (of Mediterranean origin), barley, lentils and maize also thrive.

Insular and peninsular Italy also had the misfortune to be invaded, long ago, by peoples who were stronger and more highly developed than the native population. Now unless special techniques are employed, the soil of the Mediterranean countries can be cultivated only on a large scale. Thus new conquerors repeatedly carved out *latifundia* (huge domains), on which they set the enslaved population to work. As slaves of the Carthaginians, of the Greeks, of the Romans, as serfs or very short-term share-croppers under Normans, Angevins and Spaniards, the peasant did not plant or build. Hence the great estates and open fields, which lasted right into the nineteenth century; to this day feudal ideas have not completely died out despite the efforts of land reform laws to redistribute agricultural land.

But we must take into account the smaller properties which certainly existed near Rome and also to the north of Naples; the voluntary breaking-up of *latifundia*, as at Trapani; reclamation work, as in northern Sardinia; and also the diversity of contracts and leases, which varied from very short ones, as in the Tavoliere, to very long ones granting perpetual rights, as at Bari. A great variety of ethnical and technical influences have been important: irrigation works undertaken by the Moslems in Sicily; the Norman fiscal system in Apulia and the influence of towns such as Naples, Palermo, Bari and Rome.

Physical factors are extremely complex: in the summer, the rivers have no water and the mountainous, broken nature of the relief makes any effective canal system impossible. The limestone massifs store up the spring rains, while the karst underground waters burst out in the most unexpected places. However, locally it is often possible to divert springs into channels, as is done in the hollows of the Abruzzi. Again, sheets of water lying deep down can be tapped by wells, and there are the wells worked by little blindfold donkeys on the island of Ischia, in the Bari countryside

Agriculture in the Po plain has benefited from capital supplied by industry, and certain production figures are high. The northern ricefields, for example, have a higher yield than those of the Far East.

Orange trees in Sicily, with Mount Etna, an active volcano, in the background. Where there is water to mitigate the parching effect of the summer sun, citrus fruits flourish.

or in the Palermo *huerta* (irrigated, intensively culti-vated land). In such areas, water reduces the deadliness of the sun, and the local crops include citrus fruits, all sorts of other fruit trees, various vegetables, and even tropical crops such as cotton, sugar-cane and bananas. Differences of climate due to natural screens and shelters also exist. Thus in some regions, while the windward slope is almost useless for the farmer, the sheltered slope, the so-called *riviera,* is mild and useful.

Since there are no high pastures or well-watered meadows, flocks and herds have to wander about. Great cattle with splendid horns can be seen moving about in the Tuscan Maremma; black buffaloes wallow in the mud of the Campagna, and horses gallop wild in Apulia. Everywhere on fallow ground and on the scrubby wastelands and heaths useless for cultivation one may see flocks of sheep and herds of goats. The best way to take advantage of the moun-tains is to drive the sheep up on to the high grounds in summer. Sheep from the Abruzzi still go up to the high plateaus in summer and down to the pastures of Apulia and Latium in winter. A highly evocative sight is that of flocks shut in for the night behind net enclosures, just as they were two thousand years ago, right at the gates of Rome, and watched over by white dogs with iron collars.

One of the consequences of extensive (as opposed to intensive) stock-breeding is deforestation; in south Italy the forests have now become rare. But brush-wood abounds, and from it the peasants get cork in Sardinia, acorns and mushrooms in Calabria, chestnuts in Tuscany, and, above all, fuel.

There is in addition the harvest of the sea. Many of the communes are on the coast, and it is the ex-ception for the high-perched villages on the hills not to have a *marina* and a few dozen sailing boats so that, in addition to the produce of the soil, the

Italy's main resource is agriculture, which gives employment to 42 per cent of the labour force. But in a country where unemployment figures are already high mechanisation has formerly been deliberately delayed in order to avoid exacerbating the problem. Types of land ownership are strongly contrasted, with a mass of tiny holdings on the one hand and large estates farmed by share-croppers on the other. Production shows a disproportion between the richness of crop resources and the poverty of livestock resources. Fruit growing accounts for 12 per cent of Italy's exports and is becoming increasingly commercialised. Wheat, maize, rice and vegetables are the other principal crops. Italy is the world's second largest exporter of wine and olive oil.

Intensive farming (orchards, olive groves, vineyards)

Rice

Mixed farming (crops and livestock)

Arable farming

Pastoral farming

Forests

Alpine regions

inhabitants can count on some crawfish, anchovies, a few swordfish and cuttle-fish.

On some wet plains, rural living conditions have been revolutionised by drainage and irrigation. The achievement of the Fascist regime must be considered noteworthy, since in eighteen years about 2½ million acres of land were made fit for cultivation. The social effects were, unfortunately, non-existent: of the 35,600 acres making up the bed of the former Lake Fucino, 21,250 acres were let on lease to farmers, but each one had to live off less than 7½ acres of land. The overall picture is not a very bright one; the average wheat yield is 10 cwt. to the acre. But whereas for instance, one can find areas in the Abruzzi where the crops are cut with sickles and the wheat threshed under the hoofs of mules, there are places in Apulia where farming is mechanised and the wheat yield is 20 cwt. to the acre.

*Regional agriculture.* In the countryside of north Italy there are more different ways of life than the physical conditions would lead one to expect.

In the high valleys of the Alps the country people's subsistence is based on a traditional combination of poor farming and stock-breeding, the latter on Alpine pastures in summer, and in winter in stalls. The Pre-Alpine pastoral type of life in the Carnic Pre-Alps and in the Lessini depends almost entirely on milch cows. Pre-Alpine forestry is limited to lumbering — as in the Carnic Alps and the Dolomites. The only original type of livelihood is that called 'Insubrian', practised on the foothills of the mountains. There, from one end of the region to the other, chestnut trees, maize and fruit trees on terraces, together with stock-raising of all sorts, ensures the prosperity of a very dense population.

On the Po plain, different ways of life follow belts running roughly parallel with the river. First, at the foot of the Alps and coinciding with the high stony terrace, runs a long strip of irrigated land bearing a variety of crops: wheat, mulberries, maize. Emilia, on the other side of the Po and bordering the Apennines, has a similar agricultural landscape, but there the main rotation of crop is wheat, and stock-breeding is widely practised. This is the region of Parmesan cheese.

Between these two zones of mixed crops, almost parallel to the river, is a long belt of highly specialised farming and of large estates worked by labourers, the *braccianti*. In the western part of this belt the rice-crop is the most important, and at the time of trans-planting, the ricefields are covered with crowds of women (taken on temporarily), the so-called *mondine*. In the middle of this belt is Lower Lombardy, a region primarily of forage crops and cattle-breeding on a large scale; about a quarter of Italy's milk production comes from here, and also Gorgonzola cheese. Lastly, in the eastern part of this belt are the polders of the Po delta, where sugar-beet, hemp and wheat are grown. But here, too, the condition of the agricultural labourers presents a very grave social problem; poverty is prevalent.

The fruit-growing areas are more varied in character. So as to escape fogs and mists, the orchards are generally planted on the edge of the Po plain and border the Insubrian chestnut groves. Vineyards predominate everywhere. On the cultivated terraces of Liguria, which are kept watered by pressure-pumps,

there are olives as well as flowers and early vegetables.

The cultivation of peninsular and insular Italy seems to be a jumble of different agrarian systems. The least evolved are the *latifundia*. In the Maremma of Tuscany and Latium 53 per cent of the useful land consists of properties of more than 1,200 acres. The fields have no trees, and are covered with wheat or beans which are cultivated extensively. The agricultural labourers live in large, often wretched, villages. These *latifundia* must not be confused with the fields (also open) of the Sardinian Campidano or of the small basins in the Abruzzi, where the land is divided into smallholdings and community customs still flourish.

There is some specialised fruit-growing. We may mention too the fig-tree plantations of Cilento (in Salerno) and the vineyards of Salento (in Lecce province). The holdings are small and the houses scattered among the trees in the vineyards of Marsala, the olive-groves of Bari, and the orange-gardens of Sorrento.

The most intensive and the best developed multi-course farming is in Tuscany, for the historical and geographical reasons already mentioned. In the well-watered depressions there are artificial meadows which favour stock-breeding. On the hills around the scattered farms is an astonishing mixture of cereals, vegetables, fruit trees and vines (Chianti wine). The elegant silhouettes of cypresses stand out against the silvery green of the olive-trees. Everywhere is evidence of care and love of the soil — and of social resentment against the large estates and share-cropping. This type of agriculture is found also in the Marches and as far south as the Adriatic shores of the Abruzzi.

In the centre and south of the country, the peasants grow not only the old combination of crops — wheat grapes, olives — but also make some profits from small-scale stock-breeding and a primitive sort of exploitation of the coppices. The houses are generally grouped together, holdings are rather small, and the land is worked either by the owners themselves or by share-croppers. In parts of the south it is difficult for agricultural workers to find work throughout the year.

On the Neapolitan plain, intensive mixed farming is possible in the damp climate; gardens at every altitude, full of wheat, vegetables and fruits, indicate exceptional prosperity. But here also the holdings are too small, and the common lot is hard. Mixed farming exists also in the famous *huerta* of Palermo and in the large irrigated depressions of the Abruzzi.

The last type of agricultural landscape is that of the 'improved' lands where the estates are held by capitalists and worked by share-croppers. The fields have neither hedges nor trees; the dwellings are disposed in various ways: scattered on the Pontine Plain or Marshes, or grouped together in large villages on the edges of the Sele Plain. Agriculture is in general intensive, the main crops being wheat, tobacco, market-garden produce and forage plants. In addition, milch cows are kept.

*Five types of peasant dwelling.* One quarter of Italy's population—the peasants—live in isolated dwellings. The most primitive is the cave. In those regions where the rock is soft, as in the province of Matera or in Viterbo, caves with a front extension are common.

Another primitive type of dwelling is the straw hut, or *pagliare*, found in marshy or wooded areas.

The simplest type of house — in one block, with everything under a single roof and at ground level — is comparatively rare in modern Italy. The most picturesque examples of such dwellings are the *trulli* of Apulia. The *trullo* is simply a cone of dry-course stone, whitewashed outside and of elegant appearance.

Much commoner, especially in the centre and south, is the simple multi-storey structure where the family lives on the upper floors. This type of building demands more advanced construction techniques. The familiar example of such houses is the Alpine chalet. Whether of stone and wood, or stone only, the chalet always has a deep, overhanging roof, a hay-loft, and a wooden balcony. The balcony serves for drying as well as for communication within the chalet itself. The traditional Abruzzi house has a plain façade and an ordinary roof. In Molise, rural houses have outside staircases and loggias with heavy stone columns. The most complex type is found in Umbria: outside staircase, loggia with pillars, and square tower used either as a pigeon-loft or a drying-room. The Tuscan house is simpler, although it often has a pigeon-loft and an arcaded loggia; its overhanging roof and its squat and heavy appearance suggest some connection with the architecture of ancient Etruria. The white houses of Capri and Amalfi, half-hidden in green gardens, have low cupolas that recall the Arab lands. On Ischia and at Trapani, the houses are the simple cubes of North African type.

Houses with enclosed courtyards whose life and movement is jealously hidden do not add so gay a note to the countryside, but are marks of greater prosperity. In Lombardy, for instance, the *corte*, with its cattle-sheds and its dairy, conveys an impression of solid economic power. The plan is probably derived from that of the Roman house.

The house with an open courtyard is probably the most uncommon in Italy, perhaps due to a long tradition of insecurity and the reluctance to change later what had become a traditional style.

There are two recent points which should be mentioned in an account of Italian rural dwellings. The first concerns provinces subject to earthquakes (for example Sicily, Calabria, the Abruzzi): here rebuilding of edifices that have suffered damage must, by law, be low and without vaults — a prudent measure, but not a very attractive one. On the other hand, in areas where agrarian reform is taking place, new rural dwellings still conform to purely architectural traditions.

*The economics of Italian agriculture.* Italian agricultural production, like that of the other Mediterranean lands, shows a striking disproportion between the wealth of crop resources and the poverty of animal resources.

First comes wheat, which nevertheless fails to meet the home demand. Next comes maize, covering only one-quarter of the area devoted to wheat. But the continued demand for white flour is such that it exceeds the demand for maize each year. In the third place is rice; more is grown in Italy than anywhere else in Europe and it is sufficient to meet the home demand.

The harvest of vegetables for drying is heavy, and fresh vegetables are being grown on an increasingly large scale; of these the commonest are undoubtedly tomatoes.

Fruit is still more important than cereal crops, and accounts for 6 per cent of Italy's exports. Specialisation in fruit-growing is increasing and is becoming steadily more commercialised. Italy keeps its place as the world's second greatest exporter of wine. The olive oil output is also the second in the world and is (like that of wine) in excess of home requirements. Citrus fruits occupy first place among Italian agricultural exports. Other fruits are also abundant but, with the exception of figs and apricots, of mediocre quality.

The combined profits from industrial crops and lumbering amount to less than a third of those from fruit-growing. The output of timber is rather small and the proportion of wood used for fuel is much too high. The forests are often worked in an unsystematic fashion. There is very little flax, a little cotton and some sugar-beet. However, the tobacco crop, which increases yearly, is the largest in Europe, and the hemp crop is still the largest in the world.

Livestock and its products are, on the other hand, quite definitely insufficient. As elsewhere, the proportion of the smaller livestock has diminished during the last fifty years, and that of pigs and cattle has increased. Most of the milk goes into the making of cheese, and Italy is, in fact, the third largest producer of cheese in the world. The cheeses exported are of high quality. The fisheries too, yield less than might be expected. The Mediterranean is poor in plankton and as a result not rich in fish. Furthermore, except in the Adriatic, the offshore waters are too deep for trawling, and the fishermen's equipment is often still amateurish.

*Food imports and exports.* Foodstuffs amount to 15 per cent in value of the total exports. The main customer is West Germany. Tinned tomatoes are sent especially to the United States and Great Britain. Wines and spirits go mostly to Switzerland, while Italian cheeses are bought all over the world.

Foodstuffs make up only 16 per cent of total imports. The most important of these is wheat, mostly from

Tuna fishing in Sardinia. The sea contributes less to Italian economy than might be expected in a country so markedly peninsular. But the Mediterranean is poor in plankton and, therefore, in fish. The offshore waters of the Adriatic are too deep for trawling and equipment is still amateurish and out-of-date.

North America. Then, almost as important as the wheat, comes livestock from Yugoslavia, meat from Argentina and Denmark, fish from Scandinavia and Portugal, together with milk, butter, eggs and cheese — all needed to make up for the insufficiency of Italian animal products. The third place is occupied by tropical products, among them coffee. Imported foodstuffs are on the whole more expensive than those exported — hence the unfavourable trade balance as far as foodstuffs are concerned.

## INDUSTRIAL PROBLEMS

The fine quality of Milanese silks and cotton goods, the excellent design and workmanship of Italian automobiles, and the first-class construction of Italian ships are known throughout the world. And yet Italy has virtually no coal, no oil and none of the raw materials indispensable to modern industry.

*Lack of raw materials.* Italy has quite large quantities of antimony and pyrites. It is also the world's biggest producer and exporter of mercury. Much boric acid is recovered from deposits laid down by natural jets of steam, and in the Alps there are talc and asbestos. At Iglesiente in the south-west of Sardinia barytes and argentiferous lead are found and, more important still, the finest European deposits of zinc and cadmium. Sicily is the second largest producer of sulphur in the world. There is sea-salt on all the coasts. Everywhere is an abundance of building materials: marble in the Alps at Carrara, alabaster at Volterra, travertine at Tivoli, pozzolana in the volcanic areas.

But the really basic metals such as iron and aluminium (or aluminum), are almost entirely lacking — and this constitutes one of the basic problems of the Italian economy. Elba and a few small workings elsewhere supply a little iron; bauxite has been worked at Monte Gargano, but the quantities extracted fall far short of home needs.

Italy is, then, in the position of having to import twice as much mineral raw material as is extracted from Italian soil. The situation is a little better for raw materials of vegetable or animal origin. Italian

agriculture is in a position to supply a flourishing foodstuffs industry, while tobacco, hemp and raw silk are sometimes plentiful enough to allow some export. The result of all this is that to purchase raw materials other than food Italy spends three times as much as the sale of comparable materials brings in. Industry is therefore heavily handicapped. And in all fields, even those of road construction and the building of hydro-electric dams, shortage of raw materials is felt.

*Inadequacy of coal deposits.* The geological structure of Italy precludes the existence of extensive coalfields. The Hercynian formations are buried miles deep under layers of limestone and clay. When there is an outcrop, as at Thuile in the Alps and at Carbonia in Sardinia, it is very small, and the total output of Italian coal is less than one-hundredth that of Germany. Attempts are made locally to use lignite extracted from the sites of former lakes in Tuscany, Umbria and the Abruzzi.

Luckily those geological formations which are unfavourable for the presence of coal are often favourable for that of the liquid hydrocarbons. Mainland oil deposits are small and uneconomical to work. The Cortemaggiore deposit, recently discovered in the Po plain yields little, and the small field at Alanno (Abruzzi) has been abandoned. The best field is that of Ragusa in Sicily, one of Europe's largest (1964: 2,595,000 metric tons). However, methane gas was discovered during the search for petroleum and at present the borings drilled in the Piacenza-Cremona region yield annually 3,000,000,000 cubic metres of excellent gas that is conveyed as far as Turin and Venice over a network with more than 1,850 miles of pipeline. This abundant supply of natural gas is a factor that will be of great importance in Italy's economic future.

For many years past Italian engineers have sought to compensate for the serious lack of power by utilising hydro-electric energy. Naturally enough, the first attempts were made in the Alpine regions. Since the Second World War more work has been done in the central region of the Apennines and in Sardinia. One of the advantages of the hydro-electric stations in peninsular Italy is that output is at the maximum in

An aerial view of the extensive Fiat works on the outskirts of Turin, at the foot of the Piedmont Alps. The manufacture of automobiles is a vital industry; home and export sales are high.

winter, the season when that of north Italy declines. To this must be added the substantial amount of geothermic electricity generated by the *soffioni*, or natural steam-jets, at Larderello in Tuscany.

A great deal of fuel must be imported for the production of power, as well as to furnish raw materials to industry. Through purchase of some 10,000,000 tons of coal from America and Europe, and an equal quantity of oil from Arabia and Iraq, demands are almost met. But such purchases cost twice as much as the revenue provided by the export of agricultural produce.

*Difficult communications.* Everywhere, except in the Po plain, land transport is hampered by mountains and ravines. Engineering work to improve communications is therefore costly and traffic consequently rather slow. In the northern Apennines, for instance, six out of seven of the rail routes that cross the range run through tunnels, and the tunnel between Florence and Bologna is about $11\frac{1}{2}$ miles long. The engineering feats accomplished in the construction of roads cut into the flanks of mountains are often quite remarkable. Road-building in southern Italy (where there is always a danger of landslides) is also noteworthy.

Far too much of the rail track is still single and although electric traction is very highly developed many steam-engines are still in service. While the trains carry a considerable number of passengers, freight is rather limited; this is curious in a country with few waterways, but it shows that Italian industry manages to operate with a minimum of bulky materials. Furthermore, road haulage competes strongly with rail.

The road network has had to adapt itself to the same natural obstacles as the railroads, and also varies widely in quality: there is a great deal of difference between the main highways and the country roads. While layout and alignment are excellent, materials used for surfacing are very poor. The number of private cars on the roads is not great; except in the north, there are relatively few vehicles. In 1964 the following totals were reached: cars, 4,674,000; buses, 24,000; lorries, 606,000; motor cycles, light vans etc., 4,639,000.

The country is ideal for interior air communications, but, though Italian air traffic is completely modern, the air routes within the country are as yet relatively little used. On the other hand, owing to its position, Italy is a port of call of first importance for international air traffic, especially between western Europe and the Near East.

As we have seen, the Italian maritime tradition is a very old one, and to this advantage must be added that of conveying overseas thousands of emigrants, and of keeping Sicily and Sardinia linked with the mainland. At the present time, the Italian merchant navy is the sixth in the world. The cargoes carried by ocean-going ships are mostly imports. The main port of entry for freight is Genoa, then comes Venice, and after it Naples. The principal passenger port is Naples on the west coast.

*Abundance of labour.* Italy, like Japan, is literally condemned to industrialisation in order to provide work for a superabundant labour force: seven million workers is a heavy burden for a country that has no raw materials. This figure is, moreover, bound to

Marble quarrying at Carrara. Widespread new construction throughout Italy is well served by an abundance of building materials; marble in the Alps and at Carrara, alabaster at Volterra, travertine at Tivoli, and pozzolana in the volcanic areas.

The 'Rasiom' refinery in Augusta, Sicily. The island has the best of Italy's oilfields, most of which are small and uneconomical to work. Demand has to be met with imports from Arabia and Iraq. Rich reserves of natural gas play an important part in the industrial economy.

increase, not only with the natural rise in population, but also with the ever-growing attraction that the industrial towns have for the peasantry. A mobile mass of unskilled labourers that moves from field to factory and back again according to the demand for labour is a considerable disadvantage. If employers were to pursue a policy of getting the maximum output there would be even more unemployment; but both the trade unions and the Government have, in effect, forbidden any laying-off. So the factories are often run with staffs that are not only too big but even, in part, useless. If the system can be justified from the social point of view, from the economic one it is disastrous, for it raises the cost-price of all goods considerably, and this is already adversely effected by the very high price of raw materials. Further, this system holds up the modernisation of equipment, plant and techniques; it is a curious brake on progress in the country where Branca invented the steam turbine, Volta the electric battery, Dal Negro the electric motor, and Marconi the radio.

Larderello, a thermo-electric plant in Tuscany.
Power is generated by *soffioni* or natural steam jets.

The Viadotto di Corso Francia, Rome. New highways to carry fast traffic are an impressive feature of Italian communications.

Whereas throughout western Europe industry has gradually replaced small craftsmen, in Italy factories have not squeezed out the small workshops. More than a million people find a livelihood as glass-blowers (Venice), straw plaiters (Tuscany), wool-weavers (Apulia), or coppersmiths (Abruzzi). As their overhead expenses are very light, these craftsmen can turn out products that are extraordinarily cheap. But real industry is not very concentrated. There are a few large factories, but small and medium-sized enterprises are the most numerous. This is another cause of the low output and high prices of manufactured products.

Money to back development is not easily obtained at a reasonable rate of interest. Low personal incomes (due in part to the poor rates of pay), together with the high cost of living, mean that the average Italian, frugal though he is, can put no money aside.

However, since the war the Government has been a big purchaser of industrial products, and because a policy of large-scale investment has been followed, a great deal of capital has been injected (rather artificially) into the economic blood-stream. Also, although big industry does not yet dominate the scene, the internal financial structure is very concentrated. Such combines as Fiat (automobiles), Montecatini (chemical products), Pirelli (rubber), Marzotto (textiles) and Edison (electricity) display all the features of modern capitalism.

There are plenty of people in Italy inspired with a will to progress. We may ask, however, whether much progress can be achieved with such a formidable handicap of overpopulation.

*Concentration of industry in the north.* There is, perhaps, no other country in Europe where industry is so strictly localised as in Italy. The north, with 44 per cent of the population, has 65 per cent of the industrial workers and receives 71 per cent of the investments made in industry. Here capital is available and communications with western Europe easier than in the south.

'North' means those regions north of the line of the Po. The area that has been industrialised longest is that bordering the Alps. Among the favourable factors were, first, the supply of wool from Alpine sheep, then, later on, local silk production, and the existence of electric current from the Alps. All the way from Piedmont to Venetia runs a string of busy factories. Biella turns out three-fifths of the Italian woollens and Como is a great centre of the silk trade. There are shoe, cement and paper factories and there are also metallurgical works that supply finished products. Railroad rolling-stock comes from Pinerolo, typewriters from Ivrea. Varese produces automobiles, Brescia arms, Schio turbines. In the Alps Val d'Aosta has blast-furnaces, and special steels are made at Bolzano.

Not far off is Milan. This Lombard city was the terminus of the medieval routes used for trade with the Germanic countries, and the Milanese wove silk and manufactured arms. Today, Milan is the economic capital of Italy. It is the centre of a whole constellation of workshops and industrial plant stretching from the Alps right down to the Po. Lombardy produces almost three-quarters of Italy's cotton goods; jute and artificial silk come from Vercelli; and almost everywhere, especially on the low terraces, foodstuff industries have grown up. In fact, the province of Milan, less than 1 per cent of the area of Italy, possesses 14 per cent of the country's industrial works.

Turin developed its industry very late (under Cavour), and, unlike Milan, does not possess a great range of industries. Artificial silk, food products and clothing are turned out, but the main industry is the manufacture of automobiles: Fiat produces 85 per cent of the Italian motor vehicles.

The supply of raw materials to the industries of the Po valley naturally enough presents a problem. The most obvious port of entry is Venice, but this is some 220 miles from Turin. Hence a considerable percentage of the materials imported at Venice, especially coal, oil and minerals, goes for initial processing to its industrial annexe, Porto Marghera. With current from the Alps, aluminium, carbides and special steels are also produced at Porto Marghera. Trieste is still farther off and although its oil refineries, important shipyards and canning factories form an integral part of the Italian industrial complex, as a commercial port it serves almost exclusively that part of Europe watered by the Danube.

Despite the barrier of the Apennines, Genoa is a much more convenient port of entry. As in all large ports, a proportion of the raw materials is treated locally; there is now a line of factories running along nearly eight miles of the coast: coke ovens, steelworks, shipyards, chemical factories, and so forth.

The towns of Emilia from Piacenza to Forli have flourishing foodstuff factories and engineering works, but could develop still further with utilisation of the methane gas supply.

*Inadequacy of peninsular industry.* Peninsular Italy has isolated and apparently unlinked industrial centres.

In central Italy some of these have been inherited from the past, such as the forges in those parts of Tuscany where there are metals, the woollen industry at Prato, the Fabriano papermills, and even the Leghorn shipyards. Of recent origin are the Pisa Leghorn and Rosignano chemical industries, the Piombino heavy metallurgy, the Terni electro-metallurgy and engineering works. Still more modern are the electro-chemical works at Bussi (in the heart of the Abruzzi) and the Rome pharmaceutical industries.

Paradoxically, it is in southern Italy, at Naples, that we find the largest single concentration of industry in the peninsula. All the shores of the famous bay are disfigured by blackened industrial plant: shipyards, canning factories, chemical works, oil refineries, spinning-mills and blast-furnaces. It is in part due to its industry that the Naples region is, from the economic point of view, fourth in Italy. In the rest of southern Italy, there are only a few chemical plants at Crotona, some foodstuff factories, some cement works, a few shipyards. These together employ only 23 per cent of the total working population.

To explain this exaggerated lack of balance between northern and southern Italy, we must once more turn to history. In the nineteenth century, before Italy was unified, there were in the peninsular part of the country numerous long-established industrial centres which were still very active. Among these were Tuscany, and especially Naples, which had the first Italian railroad, the first system of gas-lighting, and the first arsenal. Then came unification: effected by the

The 400-feet-high Pirelli building in Milan, symbolic of northern Italy's prosperity. Ten lifts and an automatic post system ensure rapid inter-office communication.

An alley in Naples. Between north and south there is an exaggerated lack of balance. The average income in the south is half that in the north: Although Naples has the largest single concentration of industry in the peninsula, its poverty is notorious.

Piedmontese, it naturally benefited the north, which was rapidly industrialised, while the sprouts of industrial activity in the south were entirely neglected by the Government. In industry, then, the 'Southern Question' has existed for a century.

Since he can find no work in an agriculture that is anyway very poor, the southern Italian lives in conditions of continual hardship: his average income is less than half that of the northern Italian. In order to mitigate this poverty, the population ought to be drawn off into factories. But, as we have seen, the south has almost no industry at all: only 6 per cent of Italian industrial and commercial investments for 37 per cent of the population. The situation is extremely serious.

*The deficit in industrial exports.* Given the general conditions of production, it is easy to understand why industrialists hesitate to manufacture objects which demand a great deal of material and little labour. The

processing industries (foodstuffs, textiles, clothing, chemical products and, above all, machines) provide 54 per cent of industrial revenue. Two-thirds of the exports consist of processed goods. Textiles and clothing are most important: silks and woollen goods, excellent cottons and a great quantity of man-made fibres. The main customers for these are the Near East, India, Pakistan and South Africa, and these exports bring in four times more than is spent on corresponding imports.

Engineering production exceeds that of the textile industry in value. The most important producers are electric motors exported to France, textile machinery to the United States and Brazil, and precision machinery, especially typewriters and calculating machines. The automobile industry is handicapped by excessively high cost-prices. Motor vehicles are exported to central Europe and North Africa but, all told, the profits are small, for Italy imports almost as many vehicles as

There is, perhaps, nowhere in Europe where localisation of industry is so pronounced as in Italy. The north, with 44 per cent of the population, has 65 per cent of the industrial workers and absorbs 71 per cent of all industrial investment. Factors favouring the north have been the supply of wool from Alpine sheep, local silk production, electric power generated in the Alps, and a favourable political history after unification. Peninsular Italy on the other hand is overpopulated and has only a few isolated industrial centres.

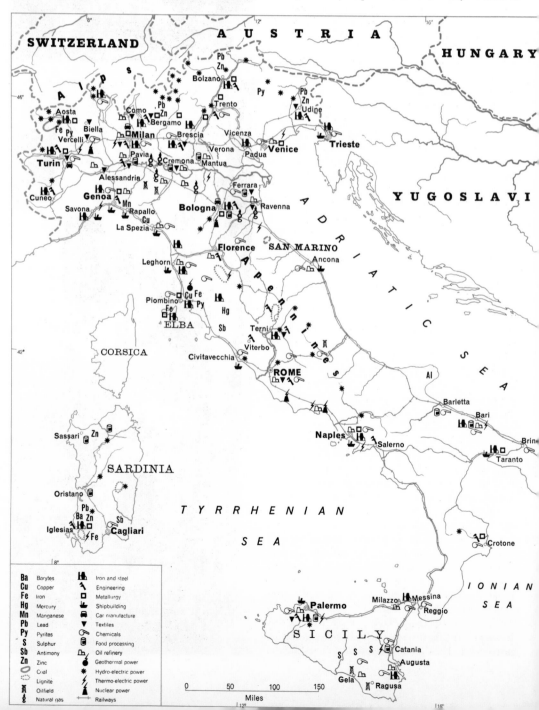

she exports. The chemical industry, however, is in a better position: sulphuric acid, nitrogenous fertilizers, medicaments and copper sulphate are produced in quantity.

Nevertheless, despite great efforts, the commercial balance of Italian industry is unfavourable: the deficit is six times greater than that of food products.

Additional revenue is sought in the tourist industry. About eight million foreigners annually visit famous beauty-spots and museum cities, spending from 150,000 to 200,000 million lire every year; this sum covers more than a quarter of the Italian foreign trade deficit.

THE RESULTS OF OVERPOPULATION. Italy is therefore not such a poor country as it is sometimes supposed, although beneath every problem lies that of over-population: the annual rise in population is about 400,000, and during the first half of this century the increase was 44 per cent. At present there are about 51 million Italians in Italy. The average density of population is 425 to the square mile, and while the mountains are thinly populated, 28 provinces have a population density of over 500 to the square mile. One worker out of every ten is unemployed — the highest figure anywhere in Europe. And to buy a pound of bread the average Italians must do twice as much work as, say, a Swiss. The standard of living in Italy is inevitably influenced and thus the rôle of the Italian as a consumer. Since foodstuffs absorb two-thirds of his income, an Italian can rarely afford to buy books, furniture or manufactured goods.

Emigration, mainly to the United States, was for long a safety-valve for excessive population pressure. In about half a century, 15 million Italians (principally from the south) left their country. For a time, the Fascists thought that they had found a better solution in colonisation. The present Italian Republic has resumed the emigration policy, but on a moderate scale and directed mainly to Argentina. Far-reaching reforms in the social and economic structure have also been undertaken. Since the first agrarian reforms in 1950, a considerable area has been divided among 114,000 new smallholders, while the Tuscan Marem-

ma, the Sila and the Tavoliere are almost unrecognisably changed. The 'Fund for the South' has also invested 550,000 million lire in making extensive improvements in agriculture, industry and amenities for tourists. Throughout Italy the vigorous efforts put into reconstruction and an evident determination to make progress are impressive.

Taormina, on the island of Sicily. The ruins of ancient Greece and Rome are strong tourist attractions bringing additional revenue to economically underdeveloped areas.

The Colosseum, completed in 80 B.C. The largest of the Roman amphitheatres, it held 100,000 spectators.

# THE VATICAN CITY

The Vatican City, the last remaining relic of the former Papal State, has been a sovereign state since 1929 and lies in the west of the city of Rome. The official language is Italian. With its quiet little streets, its magnificent museums, its old-fashioned customs and its Swiss Guards in their sixteenth-century uniforms, it is a unique type of state. It is without economic resources, bar those provided by the sale of postage stamps, and with an area of about one-fifth of a square mile and a population of no more than a thousand persons it is the smallest state in the world.

It is also one of the most powerful, since it is the personal property of the reigning Pope, Head of the Catholic, Apostolic and Roman Church, and is thus the spiritual capital of about 520,000,000 Christians. Buildings, such as St Peter's administrative offices, polyglot printing presses, the broadcasting station, the Academy of Science, the newspaper *Osservatore Romano,* are on the scale befitting the Vatican City's rôle in world affairs rather than its physical size.

The principality of Monaco.

San Marino and its castle.

# SAN MARINO

San Marino is one of the smallest sovereign states in the world (area 38 square miles and population 14,000). Founded, so it is claimed, in the fourth century A.D., it is the oldest republic in Europe.

Completely surrounded by Italian territory, it is situated on the foothills of the Apennines, where the provinces of Romagna and the Marches meet, about six miles from the sea. The capital, San Marino (2,500 inhabitants), rises proudly on Monte Titano. The dwellings are scattered, and agriculture is of the characteristic Romagna type. Wheat, livestock and vines afford a profitable livelihood to the inhabitants. Tourists bring in an appreciable revenue. About 5,000 to 6,000 San Marinesi live abroad.

# THE PRINCIPALITY OF MONACO

The Principality of Monaco is an independent state covering an area of 370 acres, bounded to the west and north by France and to the south and east by the Mediterranean Sea.

According to the constitution of 1962, the government is conducted by a Minister of State aided by a council under the supreme authority of the sovereign. The legislature consists of the Prince and the National Council of eighteen members, elected every five years by the vote of all adult citizens of the principality. The Communal Council (of sixteen members elected for four years, also by general suffrage) debates the business of the commune. The conventions which governed Monaco's relations with France were terminated by the latter in 1962, but were replaced by new conventions the following year.

The reigning Prince is the thirty-third member of the Grimaldi family to rule over the principality.

Monaco enjoys a Mediterranean climate that is particularly mild in winter, and has been a busy tourist centre since the middle of the nineteenth century, when the city of Monte Carlo, with its casino and hotels, was created.

The Prince's palace (begun in 1215) stands on the rock of Monaco-Ville, where there are also various public offices and the Oceanographic Museum (opened in 1910) built by Prince Albert I, founder of the science of modern oceanography. The principality also has a Museum of Prehistoric Anthropology and a National Fine Arts Museum.

During the past few years the principality has made much progress in industry and commerce. At the present time there is a number of textile, mechanical, printing, chemical and pharmaceutrical plants, as well as factories turning out foodstuffs, and a number of crafts such as ceramic and glass manufacture flourish.

The financial resources of the principality come mostly from taxes on turnover and on civil registration, which account for 60 per cent of the total revenue. A further 20 per cent is provided by the customs (there is a Franco-Monegasque agreement on customs union) and the profits from the postal, telegraph and telephone services. The duty on tobacco amounts to 4.5 per cent of the total, and payments from the gambling monopoly in Monte Carlo Casino total 2 per cent to 5 per cent.

The population of the principality increases steadily: it was 15,543 in 1903 and 22,297 in 1961. The density of population is therefore astonishingly high at 52,500 to the square mile.

Monegasque nationals number about 3,000. There is no land tax or income tax, and no estate duty is payable on estates descending in direct line. Foreigners domiciled in Monaco enjoy the same tax exemptions as Monegasque citizens, although French nationals must have resided in the principality for five years before they can claim this privilege.

The official currency is the French franc, but the Prince of Monaco, in accordance with his sovereign rights, issues coins of low denomination by agreement with the French Government.

# ANDORRA

The interest of Andorra is not to be measured by its area (191 square miles) or the number of its inhabitants (about 10,300). The outlook and the activities of the Andorrans depend upon the survival of medieval institutions. Andorra is enclosed within a 70-mile circle of mountains. Isolation and poverty are its outstanding characteristics, but they have been a guarantee of independence.

The country's history goes back to the agreement concluded in 1278 which put an end to the rival claims of the Counts of Foix and the Bishops of La Seo de Urgel. It was recognised that the claimants had equal rights, and Andorra is thus a co-principality of two absolute and hereditary monarchs (Count and Bishop), who enjoy unbounded rights over their subjects; they have divided their authority so that one of them exercises secular and the other ecclesiastical dominion. The rights of the Counts of Foix passed by

inheritance to King Henri IV of France, and from him to all succeeding heads of the French State, but since the power of the French State far exceeds that of the Bishops of La Seo de Urgel, the latter have tended to rely for support on the Spanish government, although it has no rights at all in Andorra. Rivalry between French and Spanish influence has thus arisen.

During the Spanish Civil War and the Second World War, Andorra was an asylum between France and Spain, a listening-post and an escape route. During the post-war period, it took advantage of the fact that there was a free market in Spain for certain articles but not in France — and vice versa — and imported all sorts of merchandise in great quantities, since objects supposed to be 'Andorran' are free of import duty into both France and Spain. So, from 1947 onwards, tourists arrived in car-loads to purchase supplies. Since 1950, when the Spaniards opened their frontiers again, and when there was no longer the same scarcity of goods, fewer tourists have made their way to Andorra although there has been a renewal of 'shopping' interest since 1959. The far-seeing Andorrans then began to invest their large profits in sound enterprises, especially in hotel construction, since the tourist trade could provide a good source of revenue.

Andorrans are passionately attached to a regime that assures them so many advantages, but our high-geared civilisation no longer permits them to avoid the problems of our time by a policy of isolation. A moral and geographical drama tears Andorra between traditional and modern ways of living.

The small state of Andorra is enclosed within a 70-mile circle of mountains. Isolation is one of its principal features.

# SPAIN

Spain occupies the most westerly position of the European continent and the most southerly. The whole country slopes towards the west so that three-quarters of the rivers empty into the Atlantic. One result has been that the Spaniards have been lured to the Ocean and to discover the American continent, to which they are still linked by strong migratory movements. The sea, in the form of *rias* and estuaries, stretches inland. Thus Spain is the homeland of hardy seamen whose basic activity is fishing and whose main food-stuff is sea food.

*A land of West and East.* Since the ocean was for long centuries unsailed and mysterious, the Spaniards, of necessity, looked toward the Mediterranean. However, to the Mediterranean peoples Spain was a far-off peninsula at the limits of the known world. This remoteness preserved her autonomy. All the migrations and all the movements of peoples who have influenced Europe ended in Spain, which is as Celti-cised as France or Great Britain, as Romanised as Italy, and was for centuries colonised by Germanic invaders.

On the other hand, Spain is separated from Africa by a strait that is only just over eight miles wide. Since prehistoric times Africans have been able to reach the peninsula, and many of the inhabitants of ancient Spain, especially the Iberians, were closely related to the peoples of the Maghreb, particularly the Berbers. These influences were accentuated by the Moorish incursions into ancient Baetica and, in the eighth century A.D., by the Moslem invasion.

Spain's mineral wealth always attracted travellers and covetous adventurers. The Spanish shores were visited by Cretans, Phoenicians, Greeks, Carthaginians and, later on, Byzantines — who brought a leaven of oriental civilisation together with their commerce. Thus Spain is also an oriental land; it welcomed Jews, known later as Sephardic, and here Islam reached its most brilliant development.

*Unity, diversity, contrasts.* There are two Spains: 'damp Spain' (Oceanic) and 'dry Spain' (Mediterranean). 'Dry Spain' covers three-quarters of the peninsula, and there irrigation is practised and Mediterranean modes of life flourish. Thus, Spain inclines towards the East as far as climate and ways of life are concerned. Mediterranean influence, moreover, seems to be greater today because of the recent development of irrigation over huge areas, which has transformed the economy. However, Spain will continue to preserve its individuality: the Pyrenean chain remains a formidable barrier over which there are roads, but only recent ones.

The Spanish coasts are not greatly indented. Quite close offshore the sea is very deep, and the peninsula rises above it in one mighty mass. It may be concluded from this that Spain's structure is the result of fractures. The numerous volcanic manifestations to be noted along the Mediterranean shores are evidence used to support this theory. In this connection, also, it is relevant to mention the numerous earthquakes which are sometimes appallingly destructive (Lisbon, 1755; Andalusia, 1884).

Thus the peninsula is composed of bits and pieces, clearly and rigidly defined. The Spanish Meseta, which makes up most of central Spain, is surrounded by ramparts of mountains (Sierra Morena, the sub-Baetic folds, the Iberian Mountains), and has gathered around it peripheral depressions which have become sedimentary basins (the Ebro, Guadalquivir, Valencia and Portugese regions), whose horizons are in turn bounded by high mountain ranges (Pyrenees, Baetic chain, Balearics). So any study of Spain should be undertaken on a regional principle, since a central Spain (comprising the two Castiles, Estremadura and Aragon), a northern Spain (from Navarre to Galicia), Andalusia, and an eastern Spain can be distinguished.

## CENTRAL SPAIN

Central Spain appears 'internal', that is directed inwards, as compared with the other regions, which are 'peripheral' and directed towards the outer world. Central Spain consists of the lands of the geographical Meseta: the two Castiles, Estremadura and Leon. The region is large: 84,740 square miles with more than 8 million inhabitants — about a third of the population in half the area of Spain. To this block must be added Aragon (18,380 square miles), with more than a million inhabitants, for with the Castilians the Aragonese were the principal architects of Spanish political unity.

*The Meseta and the surrounding sierras.* Plateaus and high plains predominate. The landscapes are bounded by flat horizons; one must travel for hundreds of miles until the end of these vast plains is reached; then, from afar, appear long narrow mountain ranges stretched out like a long cord: hence the name *cordillera*. The *cordilleras* surround the central plateau: the central *cordillera* between Old and new Castile; the Toledo Mountains and the Sierra de Guadalupe between New Castile and Estremadura; the complex of the Iberian Mountains between the Castiles and Aragon.

The Meseta is a block of Palaeozoic or Pre-Primary

Racking sherry in a *bodega,* or wine cellar, at Jerez de la Frontera, the sherry centre of Spain. Sherry is an important export with large markets.

rocks which become increasingly ancient towards the west. The whole of this 'Hesperic' massif was worn down and its levelling accomplished by the end of the Primary Era. Later movements have affected the massif only to the extent of fracturing it and making it uneven, especially in the east, without modifying the general landscape.

The present-day relief results, above all, from the deposit of immense horizontal sheets of sedimentary strata on the levelled Hesperic massif, which produced tables (paramos) ending in ledges: hence the term Meseta used to designate the centre of Spain. The absence of water means that there are few clefts and rifts.

The Mancha is an almost perfect limestone plain, a 'Tertiary landscape' that has been preserved and has fossilised the folds of the substratum. In the centre of Old Castile, dissection by the River Duero and its tributaries has led to the formation of little separate *mesas,* which are dazzling white buttes. On these level surfaces the rivers have smooth profiles, and they meander through quite wide valleys with pebbly terraces into which the platform of the *paramos* falls abruptly. Here and there the valleys may widen out into plains of reddish clay. In Leon the limestone gives way to the lower strata of marls from which the peasants dig subterranean cellars and where they find the tawny, earthy substance that serves as *adobe* to make walls for the houses. These structural reliefs are so flat that the waters do not always drain off well. There are even lagoon areas from which quantities of salt are recovered.

In the west of the Castiles and in Estremadura, the superficial deposits are thinner and the ancient siliceous bedrock is exposed in places. But, as it is weathered down, the landscape still presents the form of a plateau.

In the western and southern regions of the Hesperic massif, the Meseta appears to have been uplifted from the eastern side which produced the recognisably volcanic relief in the Campo de Calatrava. Likewise, a fold seems to have formed near the Portuguese frontier, and is responsible for the sharp bends in the Guadiana and Duero rivers as well as for the high walls enclosing them as they flow towards the steep drop to Portugal. All the watercourses (with the exception of those of Aragon) flow westward, and scoop out ever deeper beds as they go, carving from the Hispanic bedrock vast rocky and deserted gorges such as those of the Tagus near Toledo.

Above the level of the peneplain run the ranges of *sierras* composed of hard rocks: the Central Cordillera (Sierras de Guadarrama and de Gredos extended eastward by the Sierra de Gata); the Toledo Mountains; the Estremadura *sierras* — 'Hispanids' rejuvenated by vertical movements. Other movements have pushed against the Hesperic massif a number of folded ranges (generally of limestone), such as the Iberian and Cantabrian mountains.

The plateaus and plains of central Spain reach a high altitude everywhere — on an average about 2,600 feet in Old Castile, and in New Castile 1,900 feet. The Meseta does not sink appreciably anywhere except in Estremadura (820 to 1,300 feet). Aragon is lower (Saragossa lies about 650 feet above sea level) but is more enclosed. Hence the effect on climate.

*Violent climate: Mediterranean flora.* The Castilian climate is continental and harsh. The winters are long and cold. Valladolid in Old Castile has 30 days of frost a year, and although the mean temperatures rise in New Castile and in Estremadura, the absolute minimum for Madrid is −5°C. (23°F.). On the other hand, the summers are very hot and the temperature shoots up suddenly. In the southern half of the Meseta the heat becomes intolerable, with such maxima as 44°C. (111°F.) at Ciudad Real, 47°C. (117°F.) at Badajoz, and 47.8°C. (118°F.) at Ruidera. The summer in Estremadura is as stifling as in the Guadalquivir valley, and even higher up it is not much cooler. In Aragon, at Saragossa, the thermometer varies between −6.1°C. (21°F.) and 44.1°C. (111°F.). The daily variations may exceed 20°C. (36°F.), especially in the spring, when the rapid increase in temperature from February to April is often interrupted by sudden bursts of cold weather which are particularly harmful to the crops. Generally speaking, rainfall is scanty. In the summer the water lost by evaporation may be twenty-six times greater in volume than precipitation. As a result, the Castilian sky is marvellously clear.

Leon, Old Castile and the Pyrenean part of Aragon have what may be called 'European' rivers, able to feed a whole expanding network of irrigation channels. But in New Castile the rivers are bordered with strips of verdure arranged in a series of oases.

The flora is definitely Mediterranean, which is surprising when we reflect that the Meseta slopes toward the Atlantic. However, the uplift of the eastern edge is a geologically recent phenomenon. Formerly Spain's surface sloped towards the east and thus, in ancient times, the penetration of Mediterranean flora was facilitated. It remains in the centre as a sort of relic, preserved from Atlantic influences by the aridity and continental character of the climate and by mountain walls which shelter it from humid winds blowing in from the sea.

As late as the seventeenth century Velasquez portrayed figures against a background of woodlands rich in game, quite near Madrid. Not all these woods have disappeared, but the forests of central Spain have survived only in patches. Change of climate has been offered as an explanation for their disappearance, but to feed their foundries and to extend the arable areas the Spaniards have decimated the forests.

In former days, it was necessary to provide vast grazing grounds for the flocks, and the natural growth of trees was protected. But at the beginning of the nineteenth century the *Mesta* (association of stockbreeders) was dissolved after a long and fierce struggle with the peasants and farmers. Then followed a mad scramble to clear the land, which gave a few short seasons of good harvests and then became severely impoverished. It was this time especially that central Spain took on its barren appearance. Towards the end of the nineteenth century the State began systematic reforestation. Two million acres have been reforested since 1940.

*Old and new activities.* The dry, open lands of Castile have been pre-eminently areas of grain crops since Neolithic times. Before the specialisation in olive trees and in vines the Mancha was also a land of cereals, and so, to some extent, it still remains. Estremadura, in contrast, is mainly a land of flocks and herds which in summer are driven up to the cooler mountains of the north or of Soria. Until a few generations ago this transhumance was supervised by the *Mesta*. Don Quixote, we may remember, attacked the *Mesta's* sheep, taking them for an army of infidels. The very fine wool of these merino sheep built up an industry which was the glory and the fortune of Castile. Although a number of textile factories still operate, the woollen industry is declining, and the numbers of sheep decreasing, for the reduction in grazing ground area has added considerably to the difficulty of feeding the flocks.

Central Spain is self-supporting. Cereals, wool, the wood of the sierras, and the cattle that feed there, the pigs in the oak forests, the olive oil, the vines, beets and market-gardens in the irrigated valleys, as well as the industries that utilise the raw materials, afford an excellent example of man's adaption to his surroundings.

However, the population of the centre compared

The rich and elaborately decorated cathedral at Burgos, in Old Castile, built in the thirteenth and the fourteenth centuries. It contains the tomb of the national hero, Roderigo Diaz de Bivar, the 'Cid' who won fame fighting against the Moors.

with that of the provinces grouped around it is small. There are, indeed, regions that become depopulated as a result of the discovery of the 'Indies'. The towns are rather small and provincial. However, the astounding growth of the capital, the large manufacturing enterprises utilising surplus electricity generated by the big barrages and dams, the hundreds of thousands of acres which will be irrigated in Estremadura and New Castile, the opening of new rail lines and the very large-scale trade in primary agricultural produce (oil, wine, sugar, flour) all prove that Spain's central economy is sprouting new branches of activity, sturdy and productive of wealth.

Castile created Spain, often by the sword, and here everything recalls the Reconquest. Castile was a vigorous and expanding state, ruling, until the early part of the nineteenth century, a great colonial empire. Castile is also traversed by the *Calzada*, the Way of Santiago, most popular of all medieval pilgrimages and all along is strung a line of Romanesque and Gothic chapels which are to be found even in the humblest hamlets. Nearly all of Spain's history can be traced in the art of central Spain. The centre is the essential Spain, the region that is without doubt the most typically Spanish.

OLD CASTILE. *The 'shell' of Old Castile.* The heart of central Spain lies in Old Castile and in Leon, two distinct historical entities geographically forming one region, sometimes called the 'Shell of the Duero'. It corresponds to the whole hydrographic network of the river and is an immense bowl bordered on all sides by mountains which form its walls. In this mountainous wall there are only two large breaches the Agreda passage and the wide passage of Burgos between the Iberian and Cantabrian mountains which has been a thoroughfare for ideas and influences as much as one for merchandise.

Castile seems steeped in a simple, age-old rural way of life. The towns are both markets and historic cities: Burgos, a strategic and military stronghold, Leon, in a strategic position at the foot of the Austrian Pajares pass, Salamanca, the most ancient university town in Spain, adorned with colleges, places and cathedrals of all architectural styles from Romanesque to Baroque; Medina del Campo, whose very name shows how closely it is linked with its countryside, a town whose celebrated fairs were held below the castle of La Mota; and lastly Valladolid, the most industrialised, the most lively, and the most populous city, a military centre and a university town which bears witness to Spain's great riches in the sixteenth century.

With the increase in the value of agricultural land and the modernisation of agriculture, the population in some places has increased by 80 per cent during the last few decades. The same thing has happened in the Mancha and in Estremadura.

*The Central Cordillera.* The massive range of the Central Cordillera, with its snow-capped summits, bounds the horizon of Old Castile to the south. The range is preceded by broad, rocky plateaus where stock-breeding and dairy farming flourish. The clear, sweet waters of the *sierras* are gathered into great artificial lakes which irrigate extensive regions in both of the Castiles.

Eastwards, the Sierra de Guadarrama is broken only

by the valley of the Lozoya; the passes are few and high. To the north and the south the cool rocky plateaus provide land where cattle are bred and city families escape the intense summer heat. To the south-east of the *sierra* is the Escorial plateau (about 3,000 feet). To the west and the north-west is the plateau of Avila, crowned with the city of Saint Teresa, and to the east is Segovia with its Gothic palaces, its cathedral and its baroque Alcazar on a spur of rock.

Farther to the west, the Sierra de Gredos rises higher (Almanzor, 8,500 feet), is wilder and more exclusively to granite formation. Here considerable erosion has carved out striking features.

Still farther on, beyond the great structural clefts of the passes of Tornavacas and Bejar, come the Sierras de Bejar, de Francia and de Gata, cold and partially snow-covered. Their soil is almost barren, though they hide in the dreary southern slopes valleys of impressive grandeur. To the north there is some industry on a small scale.

ESTREMADURA. *The two Estremaduras: Caceres and Badajoz.* To the north, in the Estremadura of Caceres, the granite bedrock is weathered down to a peneplain and for immense areas appears bare. The soil is poor and shallow: some cereals are grown, but the land affords only scanty pasture. Human life is concentrated on the little *sierras*. The inhabitants are obliged to eke out resources by practising various minor handicrafts or by seasonal emigration. Many of the American *conquistadores* were natives of the province, and returned to embellish their home towns.

To the south, in the Estremadura of Badajoz, the granite of the ancient bedrock has been heavily weathered or is covered with alluvial deposits laid down by the Guadiana river or by former lakes. Only in the Serena is the ancient rock exposed, and then it forms pastureland. Generally, the soils are rather rich. The climate, although very hot in summer, is milder and more oceanic than in the north. The region is a rich granary, chosen by the Romans as the site of their Lusitanian capital, *Emerita Augusta*, now Merida. The Moslems moved the capital to Badajoz, for long a bone of contention between the Spaniards and the Portuguese, and now, thanks to the frontier trade, a thriving place. Great irrigation works are beginning to open up for cultivation a huge area of hitherto barren lands. However, the unequal distribution of property is proving a serious obstacle to economic progress.

To the east, Estremadura is isolated from New Castile by rather low *sierras*. To the south, there are mines, including mercury deposits at Almaden. In the north, the monastery-museum of Guadalupe, perched on a lonely height and heavily perfumed with citrus, is set amid *sierras* that roll away to join the mountains of Toledo farther east.

NEW CASTILE. *Madrid.* New Castile has a wholly Castilian air because, after the Reconquest, it was peopled with Castilians, and because its level landscapes are just like those of Old Castile. In the south, in the Mancha, these features are most strongly marked. A limestone table, it facilitates rapid, easy communications. But its flatness hinders drainage: the waters stagnate, and the cracked and fissured rocks often absorb them. During the eighteenth century specialised agriculture transformed the arable land —

particularly in the south where the oil and wine trades thrive. The north and east remain faithful to cereals, but Don Quixote's windmills have all but disappeared. A special crop is saffron, whose mauve flowers with red pistils brighten the primitive villages of the Mancha in the autumn months. The inhabitants have remained very close to the soil, and often lead a troglodyte life in the caves. In the east, much has been done to make the most of the soil by reforestation with pine trees.

Northwards, the Mancha platform ends at the depression of the Tagus river.

Toledo offers an outline of Spanish history. The Visigoths, successors of the Romans, had their capital here. Islam lingered long in the city, and the Toledan translators' schools transmitted to Christendom both classical and oriental science and learning. Here the Gothic arts of the north mingle with the Moorish life of the south. As a result the town lives on tourist trade.

The modern Spanish capital is a little farther north

Loading cork bark in the south of Spain.

The Tower of Madrid building and Gran Via, Madrid.

where until the end of the Middle Ages, there was only an overgrown village. It was a stroke of genius on Philip II's part to choose Madrid as his capital city, for thanks to its central, strategic position it not only commands the various provinces of Spain, but also exercises on them a unifying influence. Its rôle is essentially thus administrative, political, intellectual and scientific. During Spain's Golden Age Madrid was the most important city in Europe, and under Philip IV had more than 100,000 inhabitants. The population at the 1960 census was 2,260,000. During the last few decades, and particularly since the end of the Second World War, a number of industrial plants have been erected in Madrid, and current from new dams will permit extension of this industrialisation. The conurbation maintains a fairly high standard of living; and a 'Madrid region' with various activities and resources has grown up and extends from the Tagus to the *sierra*.

To the north-east of Madrid lie those areas of New Castile that have best retained their ancient appearance, and form, so to speak, the 'Marches' leading to Aragon. The rivers have been dammed, a sign that economic transformation is at hand. The Alcarria touches on the Serrania de Cuenca, an immense, almost uninhabited limestone plateau whose only activity is timber-felling in the pinewoods. The logs must still be floated down the Jucar and the Cabriel, tortuous streams flowing deep down in deserted canyons. The capital, Cuenca, is unpretentious but picturesque, perched on a spur between two ravines above which the houses hang precipitously.

ARAGON. *Saragossa*. The Aragonese Reconquest was undertaken independently of that of Castile, and Aragonese customs, laws and general development have been peculiar to the region, which kept its Moriscos for longer than any other part of Spain. The inhabitants, the *Baturros,* have the reputation of being obstinate and hard-headed. The climate, harsh and severe at all seasons, lends life and manners a touch of austerity more marked even than in Castile.

Aragon contains a huge, low-lying Tertiary basin whose sediments are deposited in an ancient depression lying between the Pyrenees and the ancient bedrock (the Meseta). The waters of the basin join to become one river, the Ebro. The climate is continental and dry.

The Pyrenean axis never proved an obstacle to communication; pilgrims headed for Compostela poured through the passes during the Middle Ages and commercial relations were maintained between the French south-west and Aragon, explaining mutual influences.

Aragon, anyhow, belongs to Central Spain. The various regions have comparable types of agriculture: sheep and cereals on the steppes, enclosing oases in the valleys. Road and rail communications pass through the Agreda and Jalon corridors. Constant interchange has made for a resemblance between Aragonese and Castilian ideas and sentiments.

Aragon, moreover, encroaches on the Meseta with the high plateaus of Teruel and Albarracin, separated by the long corridor of Daroca Caminreal. This is a very cold region, sparsely wooded and grazed by sheep. The towns are colourful but small and the sturdily built houses seem to huddle together to seek shelter from the cold. It is an unattractive region adjoining the wooded Maestrazgo and the snow-capped Sierra de Javalambre (6,625 feet), which cuts off Aragon from the Mediterranean. Without the Utrillas coal mines this central part of Aragon would have little importance today — the figure of 41 inhabitants to the square mile for the province of Teruel is the lowest in all Spain.

From this high plateau the land slopes down towards the north-west to the Tierra Baja of Alcañiz. Near the springs large villages have grown up, and the warmer climate permits the cultivation of extensive olive-groves and vineyards on the marls of the Ebro basin. Farther west the great valley of the Jolan cuts obliquely across the Iberian folds and, passing through Calatayud, affords a line of communication between Madrid and Saragossa.

The central part of the Ebro basin is the real heart of Aragon, for not only is the land there lower and warmer but it is also watered by large rivers — the Ebro fed by Cantabrian rains, and its tributaries swollen by melting Pyrenean snows. The valleys of these streams are of rich alluvial soil which is further invigorated by irrigation canals. This region yields valuable crops: olives, sugar-beet, cotton for processing in local mills, early fruits and vegetables for export and for home consumption, mainly in the large urban area of Saragossa.

Saragossa itself (326,000 inhabitants) is in all senses the Aragonese capital. It is a religious and academic metropolis, a regional, administrative, military and economic capital, the centre of a web of communications, a city that as a result of war has recently become industrialised.

The least complicated and most typical features of the Spanish Pyrenees can be seen in Aragon. First there is the zone of the Aragonese *sierras,* pierced by rivers whose ravines have been dammed to form lakes. It is followed by a depressed zone of Tertiary marls, and badlands with an exceptionally dry climate. There are industries at Sabiñanigo.

Next comes the very thick southern layer of secondary limestones of the axial zone of the range. From

Panorama of Toledo, in New Castile. The Tagus has dug a gorge through the granite of Toledo, and describes a wide curve which encloses the rocky hill on which the city stands, providing the perfect site for a fortified town. Toledo is of ancient origin and here the Gothic arts of the north mingle with Moorish influences from the south

Anso to La Noguera deep, parallel valleys, sometimes with impassable canyons, cut into it. This region contains some magnificent gorges (Ordesa) and the most splendid Pyrenean peaks (the limestone massif of Mont-Perdu-Gavarnie). This is a region of timber, mines, hydro-electric power stations and, above all, of tourist resorts. There is only one railroad but three roads. Depending upon this region is the Val d'Aran, the upper valley of the Garonne in France; it has always been part of Aragon and its contacts have always been with Aragon — through the Viella Pass. Geographically French, historically Spanish, it is a symbol of the strong links forged between the population on the Aragonese and the French slopes of the Pyrenees.

## NORTHERN SPAIN

On the Pyrenean passes, the blue skies of the Meseta give way to fogs and rain which, all along the Atlantic and the Bay of Biscay, give an unusual appearance to a fairly wide belt of green countryside stretching from Navarre and the Bosque country to Galicia. This is the *Norte,* northern Spain.

*Mountains, seas and westerly winds.* For a Spaniard the term *Norte* has just as definite a meaning as has the 'South' for Americans. The landscapes owe their appearance to the mountains, the sea and the westerly winds. The mountains form an almost uninterrupted *cordillera* rarely below 3,000 feet and very often twice that altitude. The range is often snow-capped, and it rises like a great wall from a narrow shore, so that there is only occasionally a narrow ribbon of land between beaches and mountains. These ranges look out on to a sea which is the richest of all those that wash the Spanish shores; often wild and savage, it has produced such wonderful mariners as the Basques and Cantabrians, who have throughout history formed the backbone of the famed Castilian Navy. It is also a fairly warm sea. Mists and clouds float up from it almost constantly and fall as rain on the mountain slopes. *Galernas* (gales) and *sirimiri* (thin rain) are frequent.

As a result, there is verdure everywhere: deciduous oak trees which, in Vizcaya, are the emblem of the Basque people; sweet-smelling hay; lush, grassy meadows and after-grass; sturdy maize, typical of the country and well adapted to it, and lastly, cider-apples. Forests are still extensive and in the Asturias still the home of bears. The heaths are either russet with ferns or overgrown with furze and gorse which are burned down from time to time.

The country being barred and isolated by mountain walls, curious phenomena have survived — such ethnic groups as the Basques and, farther west, the Celts, found almost pure in Galicia and in the Asturias. Shepherds live in huts or cabins, using tools that have not changed much since Neolithic times. Other archaic peculiarities may be attributed to the surroundings and the climate. Thus, so that the harvest does not rot, it is stacked into the *horreos,* granaries on piles; there is also the habit of wearing clogs with three high strips of wood under them, and the *caroza* or straw raincoat of the Galician shepherds — possibly a Celtic legacy.

*Influences on climate.* Everything in the *Norte* recalls the Atlantic peninsulas or western Europe; but it is a southern land (lat. 42° to 43°30′), and very close to those Mediterranean influences which find their way along the Ebro valley and penetrate the Aragonese Pyrenees; these support olive-trees in southern Navarre, and are felt in the Basque country and in the Montaña where the great south-facing limestone slabs are covered with dark ilex. The equable winter climate, where frost is unknown, allows orange-trees to be grown out of doors in the Asturias, and also eucalyptus. The climate, damp and hot in summer, is ideal for hay and maize.

Since the eighteenth century the lands of the *Norte,* for long neglected and wild, have undergone a development that began with the American trade and continued with the development of heavy industry during the nineteenth century. In the last few decades it has become the most important industrial area of the whole peninsula. The centre and the north are together bringing about the transfer of Spain's basic activities to the Bay of Biscay.

NAVARRE. *A marked individuality.* Navarre is made up of three very distinct regions. In the centre, the broad basin of Pamplona contains the capital of Navarre, a city whose old walls have given way to modern town-planning and a real industrial suburb. The Pamplona basin separates northern from southern parts of Navarre.

To the north lies Pyrenean Navarre — damp, cold, well-wooded — which has remained Basque in language, customs, dwellings and economy. In the east, the region is difficult of access and covered with fine, dense forests whose timber has since the eighteenth century been floated away down the rivers and streams. Westward, beyond Roncevalles with its historical highway, are Hercynian massifs, dense, well wooded and almost uninhabited.

Southern Navarre is Mediterranean, bright and attractive. To the south lie the sunny plains leading to the banks of the Ebro, an area of rich harvests, a sea of cereals, vines and even olive trees. It is furrowed by well-watered valleys with irrigated strips of alluvial soil which produce sugar-beet, early vegetables and fruits.

Navarre was for long a wholly independent kingdom and its people are still fiercely attached to their ancient rights. The country constantly looked toward France rather than Castile and Aragon, and a number of bonds linking Navarre to the Pyrenean and Atlantic worlds were thus forged, making it essentially a northern land.

THE RIOJA AND THE LANDS OF THE UPPER EBRO. *Diversified and prosperous.* 'Upper Ebro' lands form a region intermediate between central and northern Spain. It begins to the east with an area that is both Castilian and *norteño* — the Rioja, whose climate is tempered with western influences and which, practically speaking, has no low winter temperatures. The Rioja is a rich agricultural land with a variety of crops. In the east is an area of ancient human settlement and of very varied crops, mainly early vegetables and choice fruits for export and for canning. To the west, the Ebro flows deep down between pebbly terraces in a land of vineyards. It is diversified and prosperous agriculture. The chief town is Logroño.

Spain occupies the most westerly and the most southerly position in the continent of Europe. Cultivation of early fruit and vegetables has been a natural development and Spain is the Mediterranean's principal citrus fruit producer. But further increase in production can only be achieved by extending the irrigated areas. The weakness in the present system is the irregularity of exports in bad years. Rice, which can be grown on land that loses salt quickly, is now well on the way to becoming the staple cereal and harvests are good. There is, however, a tendency for the rural population to desert the land for the new urban areas. This presents fresh social and economic problems in the form of a large unskilled proletariat.

Upstream the Ebro gorges at the Conchas de Haro forming the gateway to a rather poor, isolated area. On its meandering course, the river passes from one depression to another, linking a series of small units. Miranda is an important rail junction and also a centre where some fairly large factories for foodstuffs (sugar, flour) and chemicals (cellulose) have been developed.

THE BASQUE COUNTRY. To the north of these Ebro lands lie the Basque provinces, or Vascongadas. Some of the curious Basque characteristics have become fashionable today: the houses with great roofs, built around a single ground-floor room, open to allow carts and farm implements to be brought in, but sheltered from the weather, so that the harvest can be threshed in it; the game of *pelota*; the berets made popular by the Carlists. Basque manners, customs and language (Euskara) are unique; their survival is curious, as the Basque country is the main highway between Spain and the rest of Europe.

*Alava, Guipuzcoa and Vizcaya.* There are two Basque countries. The upper Basque country is Alava, a depression stretching from east to west and constituting an excellent corridor for the main roads and railroads of the peninsula. The edge of this Alava basin is marked by pale, harsh, rigid limestone heights, often snow-covered. The Alava's soil is very rich and bears a variety of crops. The capital, Victoria, is a road and rail junction and has become industrialised. Thanks to the old iron mines at Araya, Victoria manufactures

ploughs and agricultural implements that are sold all over Spain.

Down the many twisting roads and the long downward gradients of the electrified railroads we reach the lower country — Guipuzcoa and Vizcaya. Guipuzcoa is more open to the sea than Vizcaya, and damper and greener, for in Vizcaya a vegetation of almost southern character makes a rather surprising appearance. For long the agriculture of this lower country languished, but after the discovery of America the introduction of maize brought revolutionary changes.

The sea has always been a source of revenue for the Basques. Nearly all the Spanish shipping companies have their head offices in Bilbao, and most of the merchant sailors are Basques. Bilbao, in the estuary of the Nervion, is the first port of Spain, and San Sebastian is the peninsula's principal summer resort.

Industry has now become the main resource of the lower country. In the past an abundant supply of wood and power encouraged the establishment of furniture factories. Today these are somewhat overshadowed by the big papermills, and the real source of wealth is in mines and in metallurgy. Iron ore was once exported to Britain, but later was smelted at the local Spanish blast-furnaces set up on the banks of the Nervion about the middle of the last century. From then on Bilbao became a city of iron. Vizcaya is the most densely populated of all Spanish provinces.

Guipuzcoa has also turned to metallurgy, because

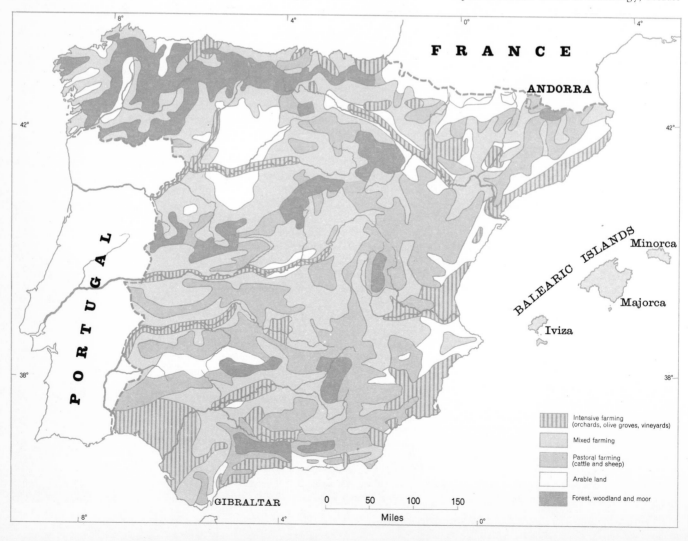

Intensive farming
(orchards, olive groves, vineyards)

Mixed farming

Pastoral farming
(cattle and sheep)

Arable land

Forest, woodland and moor

FRANCE

ANDORRA

PORTUGAL

BALEARIC ISLANDS

Minorca

Majorca

Iviza

GIBRALTAR

0      50      100      150

Miles

of the abundant supply of hydro-electric power, and to electro-chemistry. On all sides factories producing ceramics, plastics and various synthetic products are being built, and as a result traffic through its port, Pasajes, is increasing.

THE MONTAÑA OF SANTANDER. *Milk and meat; industry and tourism.* The Santander region has a feature peculiar to itself — the Montaña. It owes its name to the fact that, although it lies lower than the high plains of the Meseta, it seems more mountainous. The Montaña is Castilian, historically and administatively. Santander is the port through which wheat and flour are exported from Castile. The Montaña is Castilian, too, in its climate, which is distinctly less wet than that of Vizcaya and that of the Asturias, due to a northerly advance of the Meseta's influence. The landscape is clear and attractive, the little hills and the vales are carefully cultivated and yield a variety of crops, and are dotted with patches of eucalyptus woods. It is one of the most ancient areas of human settlement in Spain. As in the Asturias, prehistoric caves are numerous. The Paleolithic cave paintings of Altamira were the first to be discovered. In the country districts, where nearly every inch of the soil is cultivated, dwellings are scattered. Their overhanging roofs are rather exposed balconies are an indication of a fairly dry climate. It rains enough, however, for cattle and sheep rearing to bring prosperity to the Montaña.

So some compensation has been found for the decline of shipping, for the *rias* are silting up and fishing has become less profitable. At Hinojedo, the Besaya *ria* has to be kept dredged so that ships can come up and take on industrial products of Torrelavega, for a Belgian enterprise is working the lead and zinc of nearby Reocin. Pyrites are also treated, and have given rise to a chemical industry and production of cellulose and man-made fibres. These products are exported in increasing quantities through the port of Santander, which is also a fashionable resort.

THE ASTURIAS. *A developing industrial area.* The Asturias have preserved a very pronounced and remarkable individuality, cut off from the Meseta by the Cantabrian chain. The coast, too, is precipitous and pierced by grottoes. The cliffs are very high and inaccessible; the coastal villages are therefore few in number, and those which do exist are reached by steps cut into the rock. Had the lower courses of the rivers not been drowned into *rias,* there would be neither beaches nor ports; however, Aviles has become the port of a great national iron and steel combine that should soon produce 3 million tons of steel.

The climate is equable and gentle. Frosts never occur, so that palm trees, orange trees, and, of course, early vegetables and fruits grow out of doors. The soil is particularly well suited for maize growing. Stock-breeding has attracted a good deal of speculative capital, and co-operative dairies are numerous. Still, life is hard for the rural population, which is compelled to emigrate.

However, the future holds out other prospects. From 1900 to 1950 the population of the Asturias increased by more than a third, attracted by the increasing importance of Asturian industry. In the area south of Oviedo lie the most extensive and richest coalfields in Spain. Asturian coal has led to the formation of a great metallurgical industry, the second in Spain after that of Vizcaya. The discovery of new iron deposits and the opening of new coal mines have given rise to a project for a coal 'Institute' at Oviedo, and for an iron and steel combine at Aviles able to turn out over 600,000 tons of steel a year.

In order to house its 127,000 inhabitants, Oviedo has erected huge housing blocks in the green countryside. An airfield has been laid out so that communications may be speeded up between the Asturias and the rest of Spain.

GALICIA. *A land's end.* Galicia, too, is beginning to evolve rapidly, although throughout its history it has been isolated and remote.

Lying in the far west of Spain, its remoteness has enabled it to preserve languages and dialects that are not Spanish, its own costume and folklore, carts with solid, creaking wheels, a low cost of living, and a marked local patriotism.

Galicia received its language from Portugal and

The discovery of new iron deposits and the opening of new coal mines have inspired the foundation of an iron and steel combine at Aviles producing over 600,000 tons of steel a year.

Peasant farmers bringing firewood down from the hills, near Ribadeo, in northern Spain.

shared it again with Portugal after the Reconquest. They have many social and agrarian customs in common. There was a time when Galicia's wealth in tin attracted the attention of the ancients, and navigators bound for the 'Cassiterides' touched Galician shores. Galicia was strongly marked by Roman influence. Compostela became the most famous place of pilgrimage in medieval Christendom and the goal of a migration that was as much economic as social and spiritual.

From the eighteenth century, when Galicia was allowed to trade with the Indies, the provinces yielded to the irresistible attraction of the sea. The country abounds in harbours and fishing ports: so many, indeed, that the Galician catch is the largest in Spain, while Galician canned fish is known all over the world. There are commercial ports and ports of call such as Corunna and Vigo, and naval bases such as El Ferrol.

The coast, however, is harsh and wave-beaten. Bad weather is common and the fishermen are poor. The peasants are no better off than the fishermen. The rural population is high, but although it is extraordinarily hard-working, the land is subdivided into holdings too small to be profitably cultivated. During the nineteenth century, the ease of sea communications favoured a strong current of emigration across the Atlantic, directed partly to Spanish colonies such as Cuba, and partly to the Latin-American republics. However, since 1914 conditions in Spain and in the Americas have made it much more difficult to emigrate than it was before that date. The result is that the population of Galicia has risen by nearly a million in the last fifty years and it is now grossly overpopulated.

The remedy for this unsatisfactory situation has been recognised: colonisation within Spain itself. The inland areas are, in their natural condition, very poor. But there are huge areas which are not utilised in any way; some very extensive reforestation has been undertaken, and Galicia is now covered with pinewoods. During the last few years, industry has rapidly developed. Dairy and meat production have increased correspondingly.

Cotton pickers at work near Cordova.

## ANDALUSIA

Andalusian economy and population occupies quite an important place among the great units making up Spain. Although the eighth Andalusian provinces amount in area only to 17.26 per cent of Spain's total area, population (5,893,396 at the 1960 census) is 20 per cent of the whole. And Andalusia is rich. The province of Jaen has the highest income in the country after that of Valencia, and is derived very largely from olive oil and its products.

*Utility and individuality.* There are great advantages in Andalusia's geographical position. Washed by two great seas and juxtaposed between two continents whose lines of communication it commands, it has always formed a link between Europe and Africa, and between West and East. Later on, through Andalusian monopoly of American trade, the province became a meeting place and a mart shared by the Old World and the New.

Tarifa (36°N.) is the most southerly point of the European mainland. Frosts are unknown, as is the stifling heat of the tropics. The summers are very hot, even 'African' in the Guadalquivir depression, but, generally speaking, the sun invigorates without desiccating; the climate favours an extraordinary variety of plant life. In addition to the citrus fruits of the Mediterranean shore, subtropical crops flourish: sugarcane, bananas, cherimoyers. Inland, owing to the altitude, it is rather cold in winter (40 days of frost at Armilla airfield near Granada), but also brilliantly fine. Yet the violence of the winds, of the autumn squalls from the Mediterranean and of the Atlantic rain storms must not be underestimated.

Provided that it gets water, the soil is remarkably fertile, and the alluvium of the rivers and deltas, and the black earth around Cadiz, is rich. Stock-breeding is an additional source of wealth in the Andalusian plain. Many sheep graze in the mountains and the pastures of the plains. Acorns in the oak-woods feed a great number of pigs; Malaga and Granada goats are excellent, and the horses of the Guadalquivir studfarms are famous. Fighting bulls are bred, and at Ronda the rules for the *corrida* were drawn up. The mineral wealth of the ancient kingdom of Tartessus was the Eldorado of the ancient world, and Andalusian copper, lead, iron and mercury are still an essential part of the province's riches.

*An ancient seat of civilisation.* The province of Andalusia is one of the most ancient seats of civilisation in western Europe. Remains of Neanderthal Man have been found in caves at Gibralter. Greek mariners knew the rich realm of Tartessus (already highly civilised), for whose trade they had to contend first with the Phoenicians and then with the Carthaginians. The two centuries during which Andalusia was subject to Byzantine influence served to accentuate certain oriental features. It had been completely absorbed into the Roman Empire and the native language had yielded to a form of Latin. A number of monuments were so solidly constructed that they still stand: the bridge at Cordova (Cordoba) and the Almunecar acqueduct, and the ruins of such splendid cities as Italica remain.

The Emperors Trajan and Hadrian came from Baetica, as did Seneca. Christianity was preached in

Andalusia and practised from very early times.

In spite of this, from the eighth century A.D. onwards, no other part of Spain received a deeper Moslem imprint. *Al Andalus* was the most brilliant centre
of medieval Moslem civilisation; together with a
flowering of art and thought went agricultural prosperity and active seaborne trade. The impetus was
checked by the Christian Reconquest of the Guadalquivir basin, but Moslem Spanish civilisation lasted
for a further two and a half centuries in mountainous
Granada.

In 1492 the Catholic monarchs conquered the realm
of Boabdil. The Moriscos' fierce revolt in 1568 was
followed by a terrible repression. The Moriscos were
deported, their places taken by immigrant Castilians
and Andalusia was 'Castilianised'. Estates were
granted to the conquerors, and this was partly
the cause of Andalusia's agrarian problems. Grain-
crops and olives were grown and, as time went on,
increased with the need to provide food for the early
settlers in the Americas, since the discovery of the
New World was primarily an Andalusian enterprise.
Commerce with the Indies, monopolised by Seville,
transformed and enriched Andalusia which, except for
the Meseta, was the first of the great Spanish regions
to develop. Riches stimulated artistic development:
the finest buildings date from the sixteenth century,
while the seventeenth was the golden age of Andalusian painting.

The eighteenth century was a period of stabilisation.
The population increased, more land was cultivated
and new industries sprang up. Increasingly, cereals
gave way to olives. The vineyards of Jerez and Malaga
developed. During the nineteenth century lead, copper, coal and iron mining became important. Metallurgical works were built. The nineteenth century
was the most prosperous period in the history of
the Andalusian economy.

But, from 1900, the effects of phylloxera on the
vines and the drop in the output of the mines brought
a general decline. Today deep-sea fishing and an
increased demand for certain agricultural produce
(sugar, oil, cotton) have restored a degree of prosperity that is tending to increase. Under a policy of
systematic irrigation, the development of virgin
lands, and the establishment of electric power stations,
Andalusia is once more becoming a rich land.

REGIONAL ANDALUSIA. In the south, isolated by a continuous barrier of high mountains, lies Mediterranean
Andalusia. To the east, on the high plains, is the
steppe-land of Andalusia. Contrasting with it, in the
west, are the Guadalquivir depression between the
Sierra Morena and the Sub-Baetic range, Cadiz looking towards the Atlantic and Gibraltar, and the Intra-
Baetic trough leading to Granada.

*The Guadalquivir.* This is made up for the most part
of an ancient Tertiary arm of the sea between two
ranges of mountains. To the north the Sierra Morena
forms the edge of the Meseta. After charcoal burning
and winter pasturage for Castilian sheep, mining
offers most of the employment.

To the south the folded limestone Sub-Baetic ranges
(6,905 feet in the Magina) rise blue against the horizon
of Mediterranean haze. Plentiful springs support cereal
crops, olive trees and, indirectly, a fairly dense
population can be supported in the marly basins.

In the Andalusian plain
stock-breeding is an additional
source of wealth. Sheep
graze in the mountains
and on the plains; horses are bred
on the famous stud-farms of
Guadalquivir and fighting bulls
are reared for their part
in the *corrida* or bull-fight.

The Patio de los Arrayanes,
the Alhambra, Granada's splendid
relic of the Moslem civilisation
that flourished in medieval Spain.

The Sierra Nevada, near
Granada. In the Alpujarras, the
southward-looking high
valleys of the Sierra Nevada, the
climate is so mild that the
slopes are terraced, irrigated
and cultivated.

The central plain, through which the 'Great River' flows, lies low and is therefore hot and hazy. In ancient times the *Betis* (Guadalquivir), like the Rhône, flowed into a lake, the *Lacus Ligustinus,* which was long ago filled in by the delta's alluvial soil and now forms the Marismas which have been brought under cultivation quite recently. The soil, which in natural conditions is dry, is being transformed by new irrigation works. Already there is a visible increase in the area of olive-groves and even wheatfields. This rich Baetica is, however, inhabited by poor Andalusians. The system of large estates is unfavourable to the peasants. who are simply day labourers.

The two major cities of the plain are Cordova and Seville. Cordova was for long embalmed in its Roman and Moslem past and oppressed by its hot climate. At last it is expanding into new industrial districts. Seville, round, compressed, white and a maze of streets whose twists and turns afford some shelter from the heat, is becoming increasingly industrialised, and the port could well be extended.

Westward, a rather low plain has been made more habitable by the planting of vineyards and of eucalyptus. Here the sea has broadened the river estuaries; hence such fine ports as Huelva on the Odiel and Ayamonte on the Guadiana. The virgin soils are gradually being brought under cultivation by settlers in new villages, who work on a co-operative plan. The area's Jerez vineyards are one of Spain's most famous and important enterprises.

*Cadiz and the Strait of Gibraltar.* This region, which has a more Atlantic character, has abundant rains, mists and winds favouring a vegetation typical of treeless moors, though the countryside is dotted with dwarf palms. Only the mountains, more sheltered, support trees, mainly fine cork-oaks which are stripped for their bark. The port of Cadiz (Cadir), founded by Phoenicians and later ruined by English privateers, lived through its golden age in the eighteenth and nineteenth centuries when trade with the American colonies and the Philippines was active. In quite recent years a free port has been established at Cadiz, and it is hoped that it will become a base for Spanish and American communications by both sea and air.

Its position on the Strait of Gibraltar, which is no more a barrier than a river, has given the Cadiz area a world-wide importance. Algeciras, Ceuta and Tangier control the north-south traffic, but Gibraltar keeps watch over east-west movements. The historic rock, a spur of Jurassic limestone, rises from the Mediterranean an impressive, steep and faulted wall (1,396 feet), joined to the mainland by a sandy spit of land. Since the Treaty of Utrecht (1713) Gibraltar has been a British colony. It has been employed as a formidable fortress and the defence works have been constantly strengthened. In an age of submarines and aircraft, however, although still an important commercial port of call, it is no longer the 'key' that locks the Mediterranean.

*Mediterranean Andalusia.* From Gibraltar to Cape de Gata, along the warm shores of the Mediterranean, stretches another and distinctive Andalusia. It is isolated by an almost uninterrupted barrier of high mountains: to the north, Spain's highest range, the Sierra Nevada (Mulhacen, 11,420 feet and Veleta,

11,155 feet); to the west, the lower and much wetter Serrania of Ronda (6,271 feet). There are few passages through this lofty and deserted mountain barrier, and they are difficult. Though isolated on the land side, Andalusia benefits from its position on the inland sea. The province has always enjoyed easy maritime communications with the rest of the world. Almeria and Malaga are important fishing and trading ports.

Mediterranean Andalusia enjoys an almost ideal and sheltered climate. Sugar-cane, bananas and cherimoyers are grown. In the sheltered valleys citrus and early fruits flourish. In the mountains, especially in the south-facing high valleys of the Sierra Nevada, the slopes are cut into terraces which are irrigated and cultivated. The region is self-supporting. The population is quite large, and the economy varied, well established and prosperous. Social conditions are more satisfactory than by the Guadalquivir, and there are many small landowners.

*The intra-Baetic trough.* An elongated and more or less continuous structural depression drives its way between the northern mountain barrier of Mediterranean Andalusia and the Sub-Baetic ranges.

Granada, the region's capital, owes its importance to its communications with regions beyond the mountains. It was once the seat of a Court, its craftsmen produced articles of luxury, and the town possessed the most magnificent of Moslem palaces. Today the old Moslem town slumbers on its conical hills of red alluvium, while below is the Christian city, throbbing with modern industrial life.

East of Granada stretches the driest region of Spain, where annual rainfall registers less than eight inches in places. Hence it is a region of 'badlands'. High altitude (almost everywhere more than 3,000 feet) produces extremes of temperatures. Most of the landscape is steppe-like, and only the valley of the Almanzora, which lies lower and is irrigated, produces some citrus fruits and has some vineyards. The whole area is sparsely populated.

There are few towns, and those which do exist are small and set on the edge of shrunken *vegas* (upland irrigated areas); Baza and Guadix are two such towns, the last with troglodytic dwellings cut from the soft rock.

*Individual character of Andalusia.* Many traditions have been preserved: dances to the sound of clicking castanets and stamping heels, local costume (spotted dresses and tall combs for the women and widebrimmed sombreros, tight-fitting jackets and leather breeches for the men), religious festivals even more elaborate than elsewhere in Spain, and finally the bullfights, for there is hardly an Andalusian who is not an *aficionado.*

*Two metropolitan provinces, extensions of Andalusia: The Canary Islands.* Before they conquered America and left their mark on it, the Andalusians settled in the Canary Islands and in Africa.

The Canaries are an archipelago of seven islands: Lanzarote, Fuerteventura, Gran Canaria, Tenerife, Gomera, La Palma and Hierro, with a combined total area of 2,804 square miles.

The islands are mountainous and scored with ravines. The mountains are almost exclusively of volcanic origin. Eruptions in historic times have left

outlines that are almost intact: cones, *calderas,* shattered craters, and lava streams. There are mysterious phenomena such as the 'Mountain of Fire' on Lanzarote, which has been burning ever since the eighteenth century and which it is now proposed to use as a source of energy. It is probable that the island's orogenesis is an extension of the Atlas Mountains. The Canaries are thus African, and a submarine ledge links them with the African shore 57 miles away. Saharan influence is noticeable in the eastern Canaries, where locusts are a plague and camels are used as beasts of burden; the trade-winds bring very dry weather.

The original islanders were also African: the Guanches were Berbers. At the beginning of the fifteenth century, the islands were annexed by Castile and peopled with Andalusians, so that the Canaries became, to all intents and purposes, an integral part of Andalusia.

The Canaries lie some distance out in the Atlantic, and the mildness and the oceanic equability of a temperature varying between 17°C. (62°F.) and 21°C. (70°F.) permit the cultivation of wheat and barley on the heights and vines on the volcanic soil, and also of more delicate crops in the sheltered valleys: bananas, citrus fruits, tomatoes, early potatoes, and tobacco. The Oratava valley is a paradise, and higher up are forests of Canary pines. The fish catch in the 'cold current' is good. Las Palmas and Santa Cruz are international ports and fuel oil is produced by the Santa Cruz refineries. Although the archipelago is fairly prosperous, the islands have a relatively small population — about 890,000.

## EASTERN SPAIN

The difference between central Spain and the surrounding provinces is more marked in the east than elsewhere. Yet there exists no equivalent of the Cantabrian range or of the Sierra Morena separating the two. Although the coastal plains of the Spanish Levant are bounded in the west by a line of fairly close mountains (which in the Sierra de Javalambre exceed 6,500 feet in height), the edge of the Castilian high plateau of the Mancha, which hangs like a balcony over Valencia, acts as a link rather than a barrier. Both road and rail communications to the plateau are fairly easy.

Can we say, then, that climate gives eastern Spain its highly individual character? The Mediterranean influence is very marked, but this affects most of central Spain too; the climatic rhythm, subdesert in summer and rainy only in the cool season, is the same. What is most lacking is water: the region between Cartagena and Almeria has the lowest annual rainfall in Europe (7½ inches). For the Moslems Murcia was a serene, azure realm and nowhere is the atmosphere so limpid, with soft winds and blue sky. *Huertas and irrigation.* Eastern Spain is above all the land of early vegetables and fruits. The plains bear the significant name of *huertas,* derived from the Latin *hortus,* garden. The export of oranges (790,000 tons out of a national total of 880,000 tons comes from the eastern provinces) was for long a favourable factor in the Spanish trade balance.

A typical Andalusian village set among olive-groves common throughout the region.

A landscape on Tenerife, one of the islands in the Canaries archipelago. The islands are mountainous. and almost wholly of volcanic origin and their orogenesis is possibly an extension of the Atlas Mountains.

The Rock of Gibraltar, from the air. Gibraltar is a ridge of Jurassic limestone, and its 1,400-foot vaulted wall rises vertical at the eight-mile strait between Spain and Morocco. The Rock controls traffic between Mediterranean and Atlantic.

NDORRA: Mountain landscape in the small independent state in the Pyrenees.   SPAIN: Harvesting the orange crop near Valencia.
A modern iron and steel works, an example of Spain's early steps towards industrialisation.

The vegetation has adapted itself to the climate and takes a summer rest. In these conditions there can be no profitable agriculture without irrigation. This is regulated by a complicated, delicate and perfected system which owes something to the Romans, since the aqueducts and canals constructed in the days of Roman Spain are still used. In their present form, regulations relating to the utilisation of the waters date back to the medieval Reconquest. Where the watercourses are sufficiently fed by rains and still contain water, as in Catalonia and in Valencia, the river waters are tapped by irrigation canals. and it is unusual for any limit to be imposed on the amount of water utilised. Farther south, in Alicante and Murcia, where rain is much scarcer, dam-reservoirs have been constructed from which water for irrigation can be distributed as needed.

Water, however, remains a rare and precious commodity. The door-to-door water-seller is a common sight. At Lorca water left over after irrigation is sold by auction. Every Thursday in the porch of Valencia Cathedral, there is a meeting of the 'Water Tribunal' which passes sentence in cases of breach of the water-distribution code.

However, the specialisation which has been the main factor in making agriculture more prosperous did not begin until rapid transport made possible the export of such delicate produce as fruits and early vegetables. Before that time, the poverty of the Mediterranean areas of Spain was even more acute than that of the interior.

*The attraction of other lands.* Civilisation came to these lands from the Mediterranean in Ancient times and oriental influences were felt in the Middle Ages. For a time the Byzantines were the lords of the southern part of the Spanish Levant; Islam, too, has left its mark on manners, customs and place-names. Subject to such influences, the narrow coastal plains, peopled by Iberians and lying at the foot of the huge central plateau, turned their back on the higher lands.

The Reconquest in the Levant began in the eastern Pyrenees and was independently conducted from the Carolingian *Marca Hispanica,* now Catalonia. There

eastern Latin evolved into Catalan. Murcia, on the other hand, was reconquered by Castilians, and its dialect is not Catalan.

With the exception of Murcia, the eastern provinces were part of the Kingdom of Aragon, whose focal point was not Saragossa but Valencia. The Crown of Aragon derived its strength from its overseas trade. For a time the administrative headquarters were transferred to the Balearics to protect and further this Mediterranean trade; so arose the kingdom of Majorca (1260-1343), which became a true thalassocracy.

At the beginning of the sixteenth century came decline. The discovery of America switched the focus of world communications to the Atlantic. The Mediterranean was infested by Barbary pirates, aided by Moriscos who had remained in Spain. Commerce on a large scale was attracted away from the Inland Sea. It was not until 1869, when the Suez Canal was opened, that extensive trading was resumed on the Levant shores. The population then increased rapidly so that by the twentieth century Catalonia and the Spanish Levant had assumed a leading place in Spanish economy and politics.

Dependence on the fluctuating fortunes of the Mediterranean has been responsible for the cultural and social isolation of these regions.

THE LEVANTS. The Spanish Levant stretches from the Ebro to the neighbourhood of Almeria, a distance of over 300 miles. General conditions are comparable everywhere: a coastal position; steep mountains with wild torrents whose deposits and sediments have helped to form narrow coastal plains; a dry climate whose mildness, when aided by irrigation, permits an uninterrupted succession of all sorts of crops, mostly intended for export. Hence the seaborne traffic, the industries, and dense population of the plains, in marked contrast to the almost deserted mountains. Valencia is the province with the highest per capita income.

*The three Levants.* There are three Levants: that of Murcia, that of Alicante and that of Valencia.

In the south, the Murcian Levant is a province of Castilian speech. The mountains of the coast are completely bare and impoverished, rich only in mines. Those of the interior enclose fairly large populated basins. Between these two mountain zones runs a long corridor which the River Segura reaches a little before Murcia. This is one continuous *huerta* where early fruits and vegetables grow, from oranges to pimentos. Lemon-growing is a speciality. This corridor is also a route for road and rail communications, and is dotted with towns (Lorca, Orihuela). Murcia itself, despite its 220,000 inhabitants, is an overgrown village. By contrast, Cartagena, on the coast, with fewer inhabitants than Murcia, is more urban. Petroleum products come by sea and are refined at Escombreras, where one of the most modern thermic power stations in Spain has recently been set up.

The Alicante Levant is dustier and drier, since it has no large river to water it. A succession of limestone ridges borders a number of narrow, parallel valleys. The mountain folding terminates magnificently at the great capes of San Antonio and La Nao and in huge cliffs, often dropping sheer to the sea. The sheltered climate and the sunshine favour numerous orchards,

Valencia, the third largest city in Spain. It was once the centre of a prosperous silk industry. Today, new districts have sprung up to serve its recently developed industries.

the olives and figs, and the vines from which wines and raisins are made. Alicante, sheltered by Santa Barbara rock and well exposed to the sun, has a climate so uniformly mild — winter mean, 11.1°C. (52°F.) — that it has become a winter resort, while the port, which is particularly safe, continues to grow.

The Valencian Levant is Valencia's rich plain, bordered to the west by a semicircle of arid and sparsely peopled mountains. Rice cultivation, introduced in about the thirteenth century, was once a means of purifying and improving the soil. It is now carried out on a large scale, so that the province of Valencia alone provides half the total rice crop of Spain.

On either side of the rice-growing area the soil has been longer established and is rich enough to support other crops: around Valencia early fruits and vegetables and, as far as Benicasim and Gandia, oranges.

The province of Valencia has a population of 1,424,000; the average is 324 persons to the square mile, but in some places in the low-lying lands the figure exceeds 1,000, which is comparable with that of Asiatic deltas or the valley of the Nile.

Valencia, with 522,000 inhabitants, is the third largest city of Spain. It has narrow, zigzagging streets of Moorish quarters, and a few fine buildings bear witness to the early prosperity of the town's trade and of the silk industry. Extensive new districts have sprung up to serve the industries depending upon Aragonese iron brought to the blast-furnaces of Sagunto, the shipyards and new buildings, the chemical industry necessary to agriculture, and the construction of new railroads to Madrid, Aragon and Santander. A town-planning scheme has been drawn up that already looks more than thirty years ahead of the year 2000!

CATALONIA. Catalonia is composed of the four provinces of Lerida, Tarragona, Barcelona and Gerona. It has just under 3,250,000 inhabitants, of whom 1,446,000 live in Barcelona itself. Most of the area has poor soil, but for more than a century the rest of Spain was one great market for the industrial products of Catalonia; today there is both home and foreign competition.

The region has no geographical unity, since it has spread out beyond its natural framework, from the Pyrenees to the sea, and in the Middle Ages part of the Ebro basin was 'Catalanised'. Today it extends over two mountain chains forming a V: the Pyrenees, which run from west to east, and the Catalan Coast Range bordering on the Mediterranean coastline and running south-west to north-east. These chains enclose the plains of 'inland Catalonia', and meet at the sunken basin of the Ampurdan which is blocked by the Olot volcanoes.

*Features of the Catalan country.* There is a Catalan country physically as well as linguistically. In eastern Spain, it is distinguished from the Levant by a cooler climate and by vegetation that is thicker and of a darker green. From the summit of the Tibidabo, above Barcelona, the view is one of wave after wave of hills black with forest. Northward the picturesque Costa Brava offers the surprising vista of trees growing right down to the water's edge in the creeks. Montseny (5,560 feet) is the southern limit of beech and fir trees.

Barcelona's average annual rainfall is about 23 inches; sea mists linger long in the mornings. But this humidity does not extend to the Lerida region in New Catalonia. which shares the dryness of the Ebro valley and was a steppe before its nineteenth-century transformation by irrigation.

The plentiful rainfall and the generally low altitude would favour Catalan farming if only the soil were richer. But inland stretch huge areas of pudding-stone and conglomerates such as those that make up the dramatic serrations of the crests of the Montserrat, 'the saw-edge mountain', bearing mothing but sparse trees. The good soils of Catalonia are confined to the irrigated areas of the Ebro basin and the coastal plains.

The Catalans have retained a certain number of customs which are peculiar to them. Corduroy clothes and sandals bound on by long laces are still common. The national dance, the grave *sardana,* is not an expression of joy but of ritual tension: it is, so to speak, a manifestation of the sacred, almost mystical sentiment the Catalans feel for their country.

Llafranch, Gerona.
The climate and picturesque Mediterranean coastline of the three Levants have made Spain one of France's closest contenders for tourist trade.

The wealth of Catalonia varies a great deal from one region to another. Four natural regions can be distinguished: the Pyrenees, Inland Catalonia, the Catalan Coast Range, and Ampurdan.

*Catalan Pyrenees and Inland Catalonia.* The Catalan Pyrenees, in their western and well-defined sector, that of the Nogueras, have been 'Catalanised' only recently. In the centre the Concha de Tremp is a well-cultivated synclinal depression where two large artificial lakes furnish water for irrigation and hydro-electric current. Farther north lies the axial zone, here very broad and made up of ancient rocks on which are perched miserable villages whose poverty is extreme. Farther east along the Segre, the Cerdaña, a sunken area, forms a gap with a belt of low rainfall, and here are the sunny skies and fruit trees of Puigcerda. The real Catalan Pyrenees are little more than thin folds of ancient rocks. In the Alberes the chain narrows still farther and dips down as low as 950 feet at the Perthus, the lowest of all the Pyrenean passes, and one that has been used since very ancient times. Then the mountain chain rises again to a height of nearly 4,000 feet before being lost in the Mediterranean at Cape Creus and at Cadaques.

Inland Catalonia spreads out in a triangle between the Pyrenees, the Ebro and the Catalan Coast Range. The land suffers much from drought, but a great irrigation scheme carried out in the nineteenth century transformed it into a rich area bearing a variety of crops. The valley of the Segre now has a plentiful vegetation downstream from Balaguer and even the interior of the country is thickly planted with olive trees yielding a high quality oil. Rice is now grown on soils that were once salt. Lerida, an ancient Iberian outpost, looks down from its hilltop crowned by a huge Romanesque-Gothic cathedral on this new landscape of agricultural activity.

*Catalan Coast Range and Ampurdan.* The Catalan Coast Range forms, from the Ebro to Ampurdan, a narrow and complex mountainous region. The interior *sierras* reach a height of 5,500 feet at Montseny. The coastal *sierras* are lower, rarely reaching more than 2,000 feet, and are wooded with pine and cork-oak. This is the *garrotxa* or 'maquis'. Where this range borders directly on the sea it forms what is known as the Costa Brava (Wild Coast), now the haunt of summer visitors and artists. A narrow fringe of little coastal plains is devoted to the growing of delicate plants, including carnations, and is part of a zone which from Barcelona to Blanes bears the name *Costa de Levante* or *Maresma*.

A longitudinal depression runs between the coastal and the inland *sierras*. It begins at Gerona, whose monuments of many different epochs indicate its former importance.

The most important areas in the Catalan Coast Range are the passages cut by the rivers. The Ebro cuts through to the south, and at Tortosa turns towards the sea and irrigates fine terraced *vegas*. Beyond Amposta, the Ebro spreads out into an enormous delta whose long spits shelter lagoons. This fertile delta has been transformed virtually into an immense rice-field.

Farther to the east, entirely cultivated and covered with almond and hazelnut trees, is the Campo de Tarragona. There once stood Terraco, the capital of Roman *Hispania's* largest province. The medieval cathedral is magnificent. Today Tarragona is a commercial city whose volume of trade is still small, but the port has been gradually improved and its trade should benefit. Still farther west and towards the interior there are busy cotton spinning and weaving mills.

In the extreme east is an area folded and fractured with recent Quaternary volcanoes, a depressed region linking inland Catalonia with the sea. Communications have only just been established and are not yet very reliable. That portion which remains of the original depression forms the Ampurdan basin, a subsidence area which has been filled in. The Ter has formed a delta now covered with rice-fields. But, on the whole, the Ampurdan gives the impression of a region whose agricultural possibilities have not yet been fully exploited.

*Barcelona.* Barcino began as a small Roman town. The medieval town remained small and the slow expansion of the city of the Counts of Barcelona reflects the sluggish development of Catalonia as a whole. The modern town grew up during the second half of the nineteenth century and the beginning of the twentieth. As we have seen, the opening of the Suez Canal as well as the increasing utilisation of electric power explain the development of the Catalan cotton industry and the sudden prosperity of the whole region. Trade and traffic during the 1914 war induced still further expansion. Barcelona's great boom years were from 1910 to 1930, when the city doubled in population and had more inhabitants than Madrid (952,000). But wars, blockades and restrictions have had their effect. Madrid's population is now double Barcelona's.

THE BALEARIC ISLANDS. The Balearics were reconquered by Aragon and have Catalan-speaking inhabitants, but for centuries the islands have been integrated into the Spanish political system and more especially into that of eastern Spain. Despite natural and historical links, however, the atmosphere of the islands is not very Spanish. The sea lends them a certain softness of climate unknown in Spain itself. The climate is equable, too (mean temperatures at Palma: winter, 10.9°C. (51.5°F.); spring, 15.1°C. (59°F.); summer, 23.7°C. (74.5°F.); autumn, 18.9°C. (66°F.). The blue skies are intensely clear.

The sea, which during the Middle Ages made the Balearics important, still links the islands with shores that are not Spanish. Majorcan ships discharge their cargoes of oranges at Marseilles, and in Algiers the gardeners come from Port-Mahon (Minorca).

Many of the islands' special features stem from the sea. There are important salt-marshes, especially at Formentera. Seaweed is added to the local wine and gives it a taste of violets. Smuggling is also fairly profitable. The Balearics have had a strategic importance in Mediterranean politics: the Carthaginians had a naval base at Ibiza, where there is an immense Punic cemetery; the Kingdom of Majorca was a thalassocracy. At the head of its long *cala,* or creek, the old fortress of Mahon in Minorca surveys the sea-routes of the western Mediterranean.

Again the people present a number of characteristics which may well be due to their island isolation. Everywhere, but especially in Minorca, there are megalithic buildings which suggest that in prehistoric times the islands were closely linked to the others in the Mediterranean.

The economy of the islands is typically Mediterranean. Once more we meet the three-fold crops: olives, cereals (mainly wheat and some barley, rice and maize) and vines. As soon as there was demand in the nineteenth century from Europeans in Algeria for fruit and vegetables (then unobtainable in North Africa), the Balearic islanders planted orchards and cultivated market-gardens. Shipping fresh and dried fruits has become a fairly important business: almonds, figs, lemons, oranges and, more recently, grapefruit and apricots are sold to wide markets.

The manual dexterity of the islanders was in olden days displayed in the famed workrooms of the Majorcan cartographers, who prepared the accurate Qortolano charts and the so called 'Catalan' atlas of Charles V. In more recent times, the skilful and industrious islanders have been employed in footwear factories where very high-class products are turned out. Tourist souvenirs are also made.

Since the islands are some distance from each other, each has retained its own personality. Palma, the capital of Majorca, is the only town of any size in the whole archipelago. The other urban centres are very small, whether in Majorca, on Ibiza (the township bears the same name as the island), or in Minorca (Ciudadela, Mahon). The tendency towards urban concentrations is marked. Formentera, an exception, has no town at all.

THE DEVELOPMENT OF SPAIN'S RESOURCES. *Marked population increase.* Spain's population increased slowly during the nineteenth century. During the twentieth century, however, the rate of increase has accelerated — 25,878,000 inhabitants in 1940; 31,077,000 in 1963 The increase has been mostly urban. The rural communities have to struggle against all sorts of difficulties, and the tendency has been for the country people to desert the land. But in the large urban areas the rural newcomers form a pool of unskilled workmen, making up a proletariat that is subjected to great hardships and presenting the country with still more economic and social problems.

*Extension of irrigated areas.* As the twentieth century progressed Spain had to deal with two increasingly pressing problems. First, the cost of imports had to be balanced by the sale of exports. Advantage was taken of the climate to develop the cultivation of early vegetables and fruit; Spain is, in fact, the main producer of citrus fruits in the Mediterranean region and the world's largest producer and exporter of olive oil. But almost all the export crops demand a great deal of water; therefore any increase in production must be preceded by extending irrigated areas.

Secondly, the cultivated areas had to be extended so that too much dependence would not have to be placed on agricultural exports, which might be heavily reduced in bad years or by events abroad. However, since all the areas which could be cultivated without irrigation were already fullly utilised, it was

Spain has deposits of copper and aluminium and of several rare metals including mercury, tin, manganese, wolfram and zinc. Increased application of electro-techniques has produced a sound ferro-alloy industry and a rapidly developing engineering industry. Progress made in the chemical industry has brought a decline in the traditional textile manufactures, now facing strong competition from synthetic fibres. Above all, Spain's problem is to raise foreign capital to back further industrial expansion.

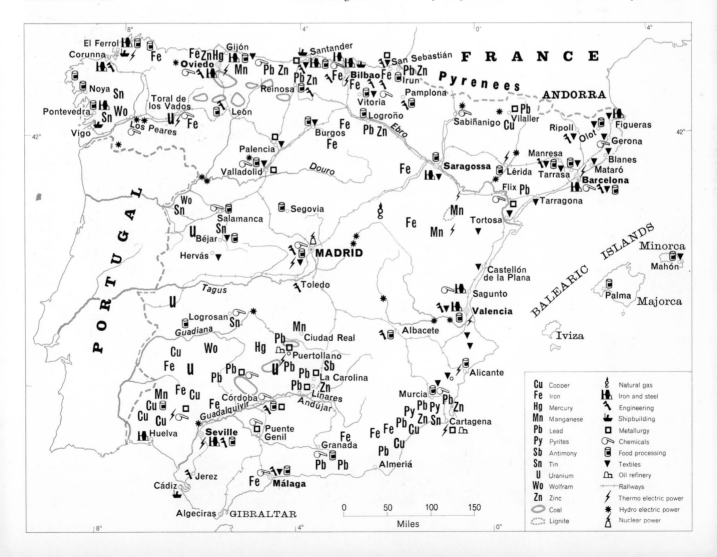

decided to bring water to some of the waste-lands. On such soils, which gradually lose their salt, rice is grown, and it is tending now to become the staple cereal in Spain, for the harvests are remarkably good.

Even before 1914 plans had been drawn up for dividing the peninsula into hydrographic units. At the beginning of the century there were only 13 dam-lakes with a total capacity of 98,000,000 cubic metres; in 1963 the capacity was 22,985,000,000 cubic metres. At the present time, 27 per cent of the arable land in the Valencia region is irrigated. On the Meseta, vast irrigation schemes, starting with the damming of the upper Tagus, the Duero and the Esla, will transform the traditional agriculture into an economy with intensive production. In the south-east, where the dryness of the climate is such that irrigation can hardly be increased, much is expected from cactus plantations, which will provide fodder and forage as well as help to loosen the hard crust of the soil. Here esparto grass is grown and utilised in the manufacture of paper.

Spain is, therefore, carrying out what may be called home colonisation. The *Instituto Nacional de Coloni-zación* has set up 201 new villages since 1940. By 1963 741,000 acres had been transformed into irrigated lands; a further million acres were otherwise improved: salt lagoons were reclaimed and deltas or marshland became rice-fields. The greater part of this acreage came from the break-up of big estates, most of them in the southern half of the country. The *Instituto* is now planning further irrigated lands involving more than 2 million acres, as well as better drainage in the marshes (2,336,600 acres). The annual target for irrigation is an area of 133,380 acres.

Pastureland in Spain is also being modernised. The improvement in the quality of agricultural produce can be judged by the continuous growth of the food-stuffs industries, and to these must be added sea-food products, for fisheries form the second of Spain's national resources and the catch is the sixth largest in the world.

*Industrialisation.* Electrical potential has quadrupled during the last forty years. The current is, for the most part, generated by water-power, and in view

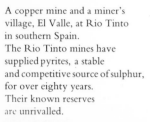

A copper mine and a miner's village, El Valle, at Rio Tinto in southern Spain.
The Rio Tinto mines have supplied pyrites, a stable and competitive source of sulphur, for over eighty years.
Their known reserves are unrivalled.

of the ever-present menace of drought, dependence on hydro-electric source is an obvious disadvantage. Therefore the erection of thermal plants burning waste products or coal has begun in Galicia, Leon and Aragon. A thermal power-station has been added to the oil refinery at Escombreras. From 1935 to 1955 the current produced at these thermo-electric stations increased more than tenfold. But the most spectacular development has been in hydro-electric power. The principal stations are on the Meseta, and include the new dams of the upper Tagus, on which the industrialisation of the Madrid region depends, and especially the great dams on the Duero and its tributaries, which have made the province of Zamora the best supplied with electricity. Production in 1963 was 25,200 million kWh and that planned for 1967 was 40,000 million kWh (against 13,750 million in 1956). This figure brought Spain's electric energy up to the level of other western European countries.

After much drilling, oil has been discovered in Spain, in the Paramo de la Lora, in Burgos province. Also, a little methane gas is found at Gastiain in Navarre. There is active coal-mining in Leon and the Asturias, but the output is insufficient and some coal must be imported. At Andújar uranium deposits have been discovered. An atomic pile has been set up near Madrid.

With increased sources of energy, Spain has been able to turn its attention to the better exploitation of the soil and the subsoil mineral riches for which the country was renowned in the ancient world. These were exported in their crude state until recently, but now the establishment of a number of processing industries is beginning to turn Spain into a manufacturing country.

Cement output has been stepped up so that demand can now be met entirely by home production. The metallurgical industries (steel, iron) have been developed and now employ electric furnaces rather than blast-furnaces.

There are deposits of rare metals in Spain: mercury, tin, manganese, wolfram and zinc. Thanks to the use of electricity, these metals have enabled Spain to take a high place in the ferro-alloy industry. Electricity is also used in treating copper ores, in which Spain is so rich, while aluminium is produced in plant at Alicante and Sabiñánigo in the Pyrenees. The metallurgical output is most useful to the engineering industries, which are now rapidly developing (domestic, agricultural and industrial machines, machine-tools).

The textile industry was once the glory of Spain, but the traditional textile manufactures are in decline. The weaving of natural silk is confined to the province of Murcia. The quality of the fabrics turned out is high, but the quantity is small. The same is true of woollens. The quantity of cotton produced has also decreased, for the mills are handicapped by having to import raw cotton; the Spaniards have attempted to grow their own cotton but the quality of the fabrics is only average. The synthetic textile industry is thriving to a marked degree.

This situation reflects the remarkable progress made in the chemical-industrial field: cellulose, soda, boron, sulphuric acid (of which Spain is one of the world's largest producers), plastics and dyestuffs. A rubber industry has also been opened, chiefly turning out tyres.

However, the problem of capital rouses anxiety. Capital must be sought abroad, and foreign investors demand certain economic and political privileges, which would put Spain once more into a position of dependence. By the Hispano-American agreements of 1953 the Spanish government accorded mainly military facilities in return for financial aid, comparable with those the U.S.A. enjoys in other countries of Western Europe. But the increase in industrial output itself has produced a greater deficit in the foreign trade balance, because it has entailed the import of greater quantities of raw materials and equipment. Invisible imports from tourists have largely contributed towards righting the balance.

*Inadequate communications.* Much still remains to be done before Spain is in a position to develop fully all its potentialities and latent energies. The basic weakness of the economy, and one which needs correction as soon as possible, is the country's poor communications.

Although Spain is one of the few countries, at least in Europe, where railway construction is going on, there are not yet nearly enough lines. There is, too, a great number of lines waiting to be electrified. Rail communications are unsatisfactory, first because Spain is the hilliest country in Europe — and haulage is therefore expensive and slow — and secondly because the radial plan of the network with lines running from the centre to the periphery is ill suited for linking up the important exporting areas of the country.

So it comes about that much of Spain's internal trade is conducted by sea. Spanish coastal shipping carries a considerable tonnage of freight; the figures for 1964 were 37 million tons through the ports — about the same tonnage as is hauled on land. The fact is that Spain is a maritime nation. In the eighteenth century the Spaniards had the finest mercantile marine of the day. But the scarcity of coal greatly hampered the development of steam, and the tonnage subsequently declined. Legislation effected to encourage the revival of merchant shipping has been highly successful. In any case, for a country in whose economy fishing plays such an important part, the re-creation of the merchant fleet is a necessity. But at the present time, hindered by slow deliveries and the high cost of shipbuilding, Spain has not yet a merchant navy as large as she needs.

On the other hand, Spanish internal airlines are much utilised for regional travel because of their convenience and because of the great saving of time.

There is a reasonable mileage of roads and since 1950 surfaces have been regularly remade and improved. Since 1953, with American support, an enormous amount of work has been done on the Madrid-Cadiz highway, which is now an arterial route as good as can be found anywhere. It is through roads rather than through the less flexible railroads that Spain is endeavouring to solve the crucial problem of communications.

In almost all departments of social and economic life, Spain today displays changes that have shaken her out of the old ways which for centuries ensured her stable, if modest, strength.

# FROM THE MEDITERRANEAN TO OCEANIA

The next section of this volume deals with the Mediterranean basin. Shielded from the influence of the Atlantic by the Iberian peninsula, the Mediterranean is also protected from the desert to the south by a similar meseta: North Africa. The northern limits of the Mediterranean are bordered by the highest mountains of Europe: the arc of the Alps, repeated by the arc of the Apennines surrounding the Gulf of Genoa and the Adriatic, the latter being further barred in the east by the mountains of Yugoslavia.

The barriers round eastern Mediterranean are equally formidable: the whole of Turkey is another meseta, difficult of access and with poor communications. The coast of Syria, the easternmost coast of the Mediterranean, is bordered almost entirely by high mountain ridges which are in turn backed by a secondary defence, a *vallum* formed by the Dead Sea, Jordan and the Lake of Tiberias. Beyond this to the east lies the barrier of the desert, which human migrations have skirted rather than crossed. The Mediterranean's enclosure is thus almost complete, for the long gap towards the south-east, through Libya and Egypt, leads only to one of the emptiest deserts of the world. On the other hand, the Nile Valley opens the way to a succession of fine oases leading to tropical Sudan and the great lakes and forests of the equator. And parallel to this gap lies the isthmus-canal of Suez and the Red Sea, the great gate to the south-east.

In the north-west corner of the Mediterranean there is another double gateway that is equally important — to Europe. Between the Iberian meseta and the great Alpine arc, there are two corridors that by-pass the high bastion of the central massif: one leads through Languedoc towards the Garonne and into the Atlantic; the other follows the Rhône, the Saône and the Rhine and opens the only easy line of communication with the north. Both these gates pass through France, which explains why France has become a channel for all Mediterranean influences, both physical and human. Strabo called it 'the great isthmus of the West', as in earlier times Herodotus once called the Nile Delta 'the isthmus of the east'.

There is a strange symbiosis of a sea and a whole section of humanity, which could not exist in the same pattern anywhere except here, centred on a unique feature: a deep, enclosed sea stretching lengthwise from east to west, whereas other European oceans are shallow and run from north to south. The English Channel, the North Sea and the Baltic are seas 'over land' not 'between lands', whereas the Mediterranean has depths of more than 13,000 feet. The great Alpine flexure is intimately connected with it; it has helped to form its bed, and has almost completely surrounded it with the Alps, the Apennines, the Pyrenees, the Sierra Nevada, the Rif, part of the Atlas Mountains and the Taurus.

The Mediterranean is literally an enclosed sea, and the enclosure is so definite that it affects atmospheric phenomena. This is the only sea that has given its name to a climate. We talk about a 'Mediterranean' climate, and 'Mediterranean' vegetation, although we would never refer to a 'Pacific' climate or vegetation. But for the presence of this sea, the deserts would doubtless have extended much farther north, as in Central Asia; Rome and Athens, for example, would have been oases. Of course, the dominant factor in the climate is its most flexible element; the Mediterranean is the zone of the winds: the mistral tramontane, bora, sirocco, crivetz, cers and autan. These winds leave their mark on the landscape and influence vegetation as well as human life. Several continents have each established a sort of annexe on the shores of the Mediterranean, small in extent and termed 'minor', but often of major importance: Asia Minor, Africa Minor — one might even say, 'Europe Minor', for it is so near to the Atlantic seaboard that it has afforded some nations — France, Spain and Morocco — a double outlet to the sea.

Briefly, the Mediterranean is a privileged domain for humanity, so valuable that it has been, and still is, beset by rivalries; its very unity is the product of ceaseless political, racial, religious and ideological tensions. But these antagonisms, the source of temporary and superficial disruption, are the keystones of its vitality and progress, promoting contacts between Semites and Celts, Byzantium and Rome, Christianity and Islam, East and West. Here so many apostles have preached universal understanding and universal fraternity. Here, above all, the human species has formulated so many of its noblest causes and its fundamental objectives. It is here, too, that both early and later civilisations erected some of man's finest monuments: the Pyramids, the Parthenon, the Colosseum, Saint Sophia, the Mosque of Omar, the Pitti Palace, St Peter's.

Any study of these middle regions of the Mediterranean basin should include their desert surroundings, which have provided them with a framework rather than a frontier; for in the course of the more recent geological periods the degree of dryness and ardiity of these zones has varied, and these pulsations of the deserts have often had a valuable influence on both men and methods.

The real frontier lies rather beyond the deserts, in the savannas and the mountains of the tropical zones, the 'Sudans', where another world begins, the world of the great peninsulas that extend the Old World towards the south, as far as the equator and some even beyond, like Central and South Africa, and Asia's southern peninsulas: India, Ceylon and Indo-China. There is a further extension in Indonesia and Australia, around the Sunda Sea, where again we find repeated the physical dynamism associated with exceptional human dynamism. With its two annexes, the Gulf of Bengal and the Gulf of Tonkin, the Sunda Sea would appear to have surrounded the cradle of the first men, *Pithecanthropus,* whose remains have been found in Java. In historical times it sheltered ancient civilisations of singular brilliance, spreading as far as Madagascar and Oceania. This eastern 'mediterranean' is flanked, like its western counterpart, by desert prolongations towards the south — deserts in the south and west of the huge continent of Australia — while to the east it is surrounded, not by deserts but by the Pacific, the largest of all marine expanses, where islands take the place of oases.

# NORTH AFRICA

A narrow mountainous fold, 1,100 miles in length, runs across North Africa south-west to north-east, bordering the sea in the north and the desert in the south and covering an area of more than 300,000 square miles. Nothing could be more complex than this country of contrasts.

*A compact relief.* There is first the structural complexity. North Africa belongs to the vast Mediterranean geological complex produced in the Tertiary Era by the tangential thrusts and vertical movements that created the Alps.

The North African ranges together form an elongated parallelogram. The northern branch includes two linked systems: an outer ridge composed of Hercynian nuclei and calcareous sierras, like the Kabyle massif backed up by the Jurjura chain; and a complex of longitudinal ridges and depressions: the Moroccan Rif and the Algero-Tunisian Tell. The southern branch is divided by tectonic faults (Tamlelt and the Biskra gap) into the High Atlas, which rears its snow-covered peaks to a height of 13,000 feet, the Saharan Atlas, with short, widely spaced folds like a grid, and Aurès, reaching the highest point of Algeria, the Chélia (7,630 feet). The Middle Atlas forms the western branch: a group of narrow hills separated by wide valleys is aligned from south-west to north-east, forming a barrier between Morocco and Algeria, at several points more than 9,000 feet above sea level. Finally, the southern chains, going north beyond Aurès, close the parallelogram to the east. The wide ridge of domes and rock basins scored with transverse fractures which forms the Tunisian High Tell ends in the peninsula of Cape Bon, pointing into the Mediterranean towards Sicily.

This compact mountain complex can, however, be divided into three distinct parts. In the east, Tunisia, backed by the High Tell, which is flanked by the Steppe and the Sahel rising tier upon tier, lies open to the eastern Mediterranean; a coastal road, which provided a route for the Arab invaders during the eleventh century, links it to the Moslem world. Cape Bon, Pantelleria and Malta form a bridge towards Sicily. The surface relief canalises communications with the west: from Carthage the Romans used the north-east—south-west corridors formed by the folds of the High Tell to reach the Numidian plains. Later, the Bedouin tribes, skirting the shores of the great saline lakes, the shotts, entered Algeria by the Biskra gap. Today both roads and railways take advantage of the Medjerda valley. To the west, the greater part of Morocco is surrounded by a great arc of mountains curving towards the Atlantic from the Rif to the High Atlas. The Strait of Gibraltar, only eight miles wide, forms an easy line of communication with Spain; the Taza corridor leads to the heart of Algeria. In the centre, Algeria is imprisoned between the sides of the mountainous parallelogram. Stretched out in a long, narrow band, furrowed by natural east-west tracks, with mountainous partitions isolating north from south, it has no centre of gravity; its precipitous, unbroken coastline shuts it off from the Mediterranean, while its desert border, breached by corridors, brings it into intimate relationship with the Sahara, by which it is influenced far more than are its neighbours.

*South Mediterranean climate.* Climate is the factor which gives uniformity. The Mediterranean climate is influenced, as is well known, by the latitudinal variations of the Azores anticyclone, which produces the regular alternation of a hot, dry season with a cold, damp one, with no marked intermediate seasons. But North Africa, lying between latitudes 30° and 36°N, has a southern type of Mediterranean climate. In its coastal areas the temperature is high even in mid-winter. In the summer the temperature often rises to excessive heights: 49.4°C. (121°F.) in August 1931 at La Calle. Only the coast of southern Morocco, washed by a cool current, enjoys a temperate summer. The successive ridges of the surface relief, lying parallel to the coast, account for the rapid weakening of maritime influence in favour of continental conditions in the interior of the country: winter frosts make their appearance only a few miles from the shore and continue until spring in the almost enclosed basins

Most of Tunisia's population is crowded into the narrow coastal strip, where density is high. In contrast, the southern desert and inland steppe are almost uninhabited.

A *casbah*, or citadel, in the High Atlas mountains.

such as the high plains of Constantine and the Tadla; summer turns these areas into veritable 'frying-pans'. It is here that the highest temperatures have been recorded. Above the plains, the mountains form islets of cold with lengthy frosts and lingering snow.

In winter low pressure over the Mediterranean draws in a series of depressions from the west, the majority, from the north-west, bringing rain to eastern Algeria and Tunisia, while others, from the west, water the whole length of the country. In summer the return of the anticyclone of the Azores brings dry weather again, interrupted only by a few violent thunderstorms in the interior basins. Owing to the intervening relief rainfall lessens rapidly from the coast to the centre. Conditions of life are determined by the quantity and seasonal distribution of rainfall. Regions receiving at least 14 inches a year can grow crops without irrigation; these constitute the Tell, which includes a littoral and sublittoral zone where the rains of the cold season maintain deep-seated reserves, which in summer feed long-rooted plants (trees, vines,) and an interior zone where the rains, more regularly distributed over the year with a slight maximum in spring, maintain a surface humidity favourable to herbaceous plants (cereals). Where the annual average rainfall is less than 14 inches the cereals disappear and the grassy steppe takes possession of the soil; the Tunisian steppe, the high Algerian plateaus and the Moroccan meseta offer extensive pasturage for sheep. Acting as a screen in the path of depressions, the mountains are distinguished by their relatively high rainfall; the average annual rainfall at Bessombourg, in Lesser Kabylie, is 69 inches. But there is a violent contrast between the north-west facing slopes, abundantly watered, and the dry south-facing ones.

The desert hinterland is not without influence on the climate of North Africa; masses of Saharan air invade the north, drawn along by the passage of depressions over the Mediterranean. This is the hot, dry sirocco; arriving in the summer, it can destroy harvests in a few hours.

The low rainfall and its seasonal character and extreme variability from one year to another, combined with general conditions favourable to desiccation, creates semi-arid conditions in the greater part of North Africa. Intense capillary attraction has led to the sterilising of large areas by covering them either with a thick, hard calcareous crust or with a layer of toxic salts. The best agricultural soils are not those richest in fertile elements, but those whose physical composition helps to make up for the irregularities of the rainfall; sandy soils, for instance, allow the rain to sink in and form deep-lying reserves drawn upon by the vegetation in summer, whereas impermeable soils allow evaporation and increase aridity.

North African vegetation, reflecting the characteristics of the climate, presents a great number of transitional forms, succeeding one another from the wettest to the driest regions. A whole range of forests can be distinguished: dense forest of cork-oaks and cedars in the Rif, both Kabylie and Kroumeria; thinly planted forests of ilexes, Aleppo pines, thuyas of the Oran massifs mingled with junipers on the summits of the Saharan Atlas and the Anti-Atlas. A whole range of scrubs occurs too: olives and lentisks in the damp plains; dwarf palms; jujube trees as far as the Tell, beyond which lies the esparto grass and artemisia steppe covering the high Algero-Moroccan plateaus and the high Tunisian steppes. In addition there is degradation resulting from damage caused by human beings in the effort to extend their crops and pastures. Very often the soil has been deprived of its vegetable covering, and the bare rock has become exposed to a process of gullying by sudden rainstorms.

The violence of the erosion is revealed by the amount of alluvium. In spate during the rainy season, the North African wadis become tumultuous torrents, burdened with mud and stones, which rapidly block bridges and dams. In the summer they are reduced to a thin trickle of water running from pool to pool, unable to reach the sea. Even the largest of them, the Medjerda, the Chéliff, the Moulouya and the Sebou, retain this torrential character which makes them difficult to utilise. In regions too dry to send their

The most striking feature of the region is the concentration of agricultural activity of all kinds in the moister regions bordering both the Mediterranean and Atlantic coasts, in contrast to the increasingly blank areas, both in terms of human settlement and agricultural activity, towards the south, with the beginning of the Sahara. The presence of natural water or irrigation schemes corresponds almost exactly with the areas of intensive cultivation. Cereals, vines, forests and grasses make up the bulk of the crops. Wheat production fluctuates violently from year to year, dependent as it is on the irregular rainfall.

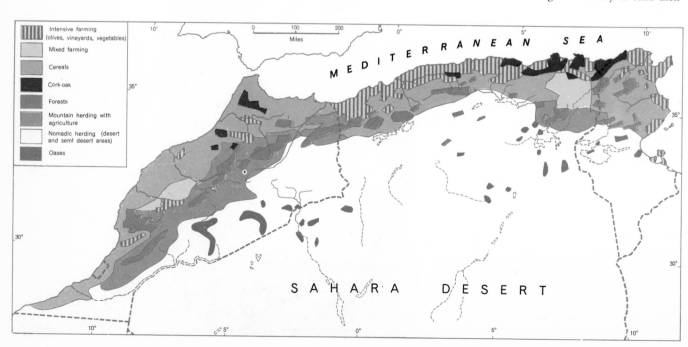

wadis to sea regularly, like the Tunisian steppes and the high Algerian plateaus, trickles of water accumulate in shotts and sebkhas in the enclosed basins, while their load of silt spreads out in an alluvial fan. From all of this it may be seen that in its marginal situation between the limits of the Mediterranean zone and those of the desert, North Africa is a land of transition. Like all Mediterranean regions, it exhibits a sharp contrast between mountain and plain, while farther inland, behind its maritime façade, its steppes form an introduction to the Sahara.

*The old Berber stock.* Being placed at the crossroads of Africa, Europe and Asia, North Africa has received contributions from all of these, superimposed on one another, which have resulted in a not entirely homogeneous civilisation.

The old aboriginal Berber stock remains. Retreating before invasion, it found refuge in more or less inaccessible massifs: Kabylie, Aurès, the Middle Atlas, the High Atlas, and in the heart of the Sahara. There it maintains its own culture, its language, of Hamitic origin, its artistic concepts, its beliefs in magic predating Islam, and above all its social organisation, based on the entire posterity of a single ancestor, formed into related families. Cohesion is safeguarded by respect for the juridical customs, the *Kanoun,* which have retained the force of law, by the duty of mutual aid and the enjoyment of collective possessions. Berber life has not been able to subsist in its original purity, however. The old beliefs are giving way to Islam, the language is losing ground in favour of Arabic. Finally, in contact with French civilisation, individuals are freeing themselves more and more from their ancestral constraints: both temporary and definite emigration is accelerating the disintegration of the old society.

*Orientalisation.* Orientalisation began early with the founding of Carthage and its empire; it was completed by the arrival of the Arabs in two successive waves, in the seventh and eleventh centuries, followed in the sixteenth by the reflux of the 'Andalusians' driven out by the Spanish reconquest. This annexation did not occur without causing disturbances, but the prodigious progress initiated by the Arab conquests must not be forgotten: the birth of new towns (Kairwan, Marrakesh, Fez, Rabat) succeeding the destroyed Roman cities; the development of a village life based on a skilled agriculture imported from Spain.

*Attempt at westernisation.* The country had already undergone an attempt at westernisation with the arrival of the Romans in the middle of the second century B.C. In the fifth century assimilation seemed near, but it was suddenly interrupted by the Arab invasions. The West did not regain a footing in North Africa until the fifteenth century, when Spain and Portugal began encroaching on the littoral opposite the Strait of Gibraltar. After 1830 France settled successively in Algeria, Tunisia, and Morocco. The colonial era which then opened saw the introduction of a large European population, the exploitation of latent riches, and the beginnings of relations with other countries.

Now, having attained independence, these three countries must achieve a balance between their oriental heritage and the developments of western society.

During this long history, with its alternating phases of eastern and western influence, tensions manifested themselves between different groups of the population, elements differing not so much in their ethnic origins as in the ways of life that had developed in the various geographical regions.

*Opposing elements.* Antagonism developed between settlers and nomads, the latter trying to convert to grazing ground the land cultivated by the former. It was by way of precaution against the incursions of the nomads that the Romans established their fortified *limes* on the frontier of the Tell and the Steppe.

Another antagonism was that between the mountain-dwellers and the inhabitants of the plains. The object at stake was the good land which the mountain peoples coveted in order to extend their winter crops and pasturages. From a spirit of independence and attachment to their traditions, and also to escape taxation, they refused to submit to the authority of the towns. The latter, owing to the permanent menace of incursions by the mountain-dwellers, had to surround themselves with ramparts. The North African mountains have been strongholds of revolt and disaffection throughout history.

Finally, all through the history of North Africa antagonism has existed between natives and conquerors. In the Roman period, the revolt of the *circumcellioni* was an agrarian insurrection against the great landowners, mainly Romans. In the Moslem period the Kahina led the Aurès tribes against the Arab army. In later times French troops were forced to crush the hostility of Abd el-Kader. The resistance of these populations, which refused to be assimilated, led to the recent Algerian war and ultimately to their self-determination.

The history of North Africa seems to have been paralysed in its development by the struggle between contrary elements; man has been caught between opposing forces he has been unable to reconcile.

In spite of its geographical unity, North America is divided politically into three: Algeria, Tunisia and Morocco, each with its own regional composition and its special problems.

On the sandy plain tents, camels and military lorries intermingle. At the crossroads of Africa, Europe and Asia, North Africa has features drawn from all three. Under tensions bred of the alternating influence of East and West, antagonism developed between settlers and nomads, between mountain dwellers and plainsmen, and—lastly—between indigenous peoples and a series of conquerors.

# ALGERIA

*Eastern Tell and the Kabylies.* It is in Algeria that the difference between the cultivable Tell and the sheep-raising Steppe is most plainly seen. Colonisation has further accentuated it, and the Tell is often reminiscent of the landscape of the south of France, especially in its western part, which had absorbed the bulk of the European population. The Eastern Tell consists of a vast depressed basin between two high mountain ridges lying to the north and south.

The northern ridge comprises the Kabylie Mountains, which reach great heights, as at Lalla Khedija in the Jurjura (7,570 feet). It is composed of great massifs dissected by deep gorges, which owing to their proximity to the sea have a high rainfall, nearly always amounting to over thirty inches annually. The siliceous soil bears huge oak forests. In sum, a combination of characteristics makes them difficult of access, and has enabled them to serve through the centuries as a refuge in which the Berber race has been preserved. Sheltered from external influences, their populations have maintained their ancient social organisation and their old nutritional economy, based on the cultivation of olives and figs. Constantly driven back to their fastnesses and multiplying among themselves, they have attained great densities, which continuous emigration to the neighbouring plains and even as far as France has not succeeded in lessening. Colonists established a footing only on the fringe, in the coastal plain of Bougie, the valleys of the Saf Saf, the Sebaou, the Summan, and in particular on the plain of Bône, where they left very productive vineyards and plantations of citrus fruits.

*The continental hinterland.* Behind the screen of the Kabylies, the high plains of Constantine are hollowed out into an almost enclosed basin, in which the wadis leave some of their water and alluvium in a multitude of minute shotts or temporary salt-marshes. The colonists had to depend for their subsistence on cereals and irrigated crops, as the Romans discovered. In the absence of vineyards, French colonisation had hardly developed there. The colonists lived also by mining the iron and phosphate deposits which abound around Tébessa. The fellaheen or peasants, whether landowners or partners with a fifth share, occupied most of the land, growing barley and breeding sheep, while the Saharan nomads pastured their livestock on the salt grazing-grounds which lie mostly in the middle of the plains.

*The Aurés, counterpart of the Kabylies.* In the south, the Aurès with its high peaks forms a counterpart of the Kabylie. It is another Berber massif; life there is concentrated in steeply built villages, where the terraced houses rise one above another to the *guélaa,* a collective granary and defensive redoubt combined. On the slopes there are fields of barley and wheat; along the wadis there are orchards of apricots and pomegranates, with palm-groves in the approaches to the desert. The mountain-dweller is a shepherd as well; when the summer crops are in he leaves his stone-built house for the high plains of Constantine where his sheep graze until the winter.

Situated in the centre of the province, on its calcareous rock carved out by a loop of the Rummel, Constantine preserves the rôle of capital city assigned to it in the days of antiquity, but its economic functions amount to very little. It is closely rivalled by Bône, whose expansion is due to the exploitation of the vast neighbouring plain and of the mineral deposits on the Algero-Tunisian frontier. Skikda (ex-Philippeville), Sétif and Bougie are towns of secondary importance.

*Western Tell and European colonisation.* The western Tell has only scanty rainfall, and when the French arrived the semi-nomadic inhabitants of the plains were living on unreliable crops of cereals and extensive stock-breeding. However, it became the supreme domain of European colonisation. This was due to two decisive factors: the arrival *en masse* of sober, hard-working Spanish immigrants and the progress of viticulture at the end of the nineteenth century. The vine, which needs no irrigation, was best fitted to make use of the sandy soils, which resulted from the decomposition of the sandstone formations covering considerable expanses of western Algeria.

The change in structure between the meridian of Algiers and the Moroccan frontier results in a characteristic division into zones parallel with the coast. First is the maritime zone, which, under the influence of the warm waters of the Mediterranean, has a warm winter and a hot summer. It was here, near the disembarkation ports of Algiers, Mostaganem and Oran, that the newcomers first settled in force. Bordering the coast from Algiers to Oran runs a light screen of plateaus and hills of largely undisturbed sandstone strata, the suitability of whose soil for wine-growing resulted in extensive settlement by the colonists and their almost total appreciation of the land in the Sahel of Algeria and on the Oran plateau. The nearness of the sea creates a warm, humid atmosphere well-suited to the growing of early fruit and vegetables, which are sold at a high price in the Paris market. To the south lies a long corridor of low alluvial plain forming a natural road westward. As the dryness increases towards the west, the nature of the soil becomes the overriding factor in the localisation of

Street scene in the *casbah* of Algiers. Like other old cities of Algeria — Constantine, Oran, Tlemcen — the capital consists of an Arab section, the *casbah* as well as a quarter built by the Europeans.

people and crops. The whole of the damp region of Mitija behind Algiers bears vineyards and orchards dotted with big villages and farms, but from the valley of the Chéliff onwards, dwellings and plantations take refuge on the piedmonts of ancient terraces and alluvial fans, where the loose soil remains cool, or for preference at the mouth of rivers, like Rélizane and Perrégaux, for the sake of the natural irrigation. The centre of these sublittoral plains is carpeted with fine, compact, chlorinised alluvium, from which the fellaheen reap a few precarious harvests of barley and on which they pasture their sheep. The erection of large dams will transform this situation.

The central zone comprises mountain massifs, sandstone plateaus and alluvial basins. The mountain massifs, which are damp, forested and difficult of access, are repellant areas, like the Blida Atlas and the Ouarsenis, where on the ravined slopes, the Berber communities have perched their wattle hamlets, their barley fields and their orchards.

The high plateaus of Médéa and Mascara provide conditions favourable to viticulture: sandstone soils, and temperatures enabling fermentation to take its regular course. It is here that Algeria harvests its best vintages. The alluvial basins of Eghris, Sidi-bel-Abbès and Tlemcen enclose the greater part of the population of the central zone, which depended for a long while on the local system of extensive stock-breeding and the cultivation of cereals, until the colonists planted large vineyards there. Sheltered from the north by the mass of the Ouarsenis, the Sersou plains with scanty rainfall present much the same natural conditions as the high plains of Constantine. Lentils and hard varieties of wheat are the chief crops grown here and in summer this pioneer zone is used by the flocks returning from the Sahara.

*The high plateaus: infertile steppe.* On the south of the western Tell, the high plateaus form an almost empty hinterland, in the dry, continental climate of which the only resource is an infertile steppe where the starveling flocks of the nomads wander to and fro in accordance with the seasons. The colonists were content for a long while to exploit only the natural crop of esparto grass, but they then engaged in the industrial exploitation of the mining region of Colomb-Béchar-Kenadsa.

Until this undertaking becomes fully productive, the whole economic life of western Algeria will continue to depend on its agricultural resources, especially its vines which, even today, are Algeria's greatest economic asset.

## ALGERIAN PROBLEMS

*Increase of population and urbanisation.* By her presence in Algeria from 1830 to 1962, France profoundly altered its conditions of life, especially its demography, first of all by settling a European population there, which grew by immigration and then by natural increase.

When independence came in 1962, the European population numbered about a million; today there are not more than 120,000 for in 1961 and 1962 great numbers of French returned to metropolitan France. The loss of these elements, which provided so much of

the enterprise and specialist knowledge Algeria needed, struck at the foundations of the country's economy. But, on the other hand, it has restored to Algeria its ethnic unity, a national identity, which will undoubtedly be an important factor in establishing an economically viable independent state. Most of the remaining European population is concentrated in the towns.

The Algerian population, which is extraordinarily prolific, has doubled its numbers in fifty years: in 1963 it exceeded ten million, not counting some 140,000 Jews who acquired the status of French citizens in 1870. The great majority of the Moslems are still rural people, despite increased urbanisation. The differences between Berbers and Arabs, which have often been exaggerated, tend to die out as contacts increase, and Arabisation proceeds rapidly.

The population of Algeria increases by nearly 145,000 a year: a demographic expansion of a nature to swell the currents of migration seeking to re-establish a balance between resources and local needs. The mountains, where the density of population has been increasing on the spot for centuries, the dry plains with their uncertain crops of cereals, the zones of extensive stock-breeding, where nomadism and the system of transhumance or moving flocks from one pasturage to another are both in decline, are all manifestly over-populated; the overspill finds its way into regions where mining or farming provide jobs on a seasonal or permanent basis. Offers of employment have been rapidly filled, and the trend is now towards the towns, which have been submerged by the flood of arrivals. Without regular employment, these people are too often reduced to living in shanties of sheet-iron and timber; huddled on scraps of waste ground, these 'tin-pan towns' in the heart of the cities form centres of poverty, epidemics and social unrest. Latterly emigration has actually crossed the sea; the Moslems went to France to seek the means of support that the Algerian economy could not procure them. As labourers, and occasionally as specialised or qualified workmen, they are employed in public works, and in the industries of the regions of the north

One of the few places in Saharan Algeria where there is sufficient water to support vegetation of any kind.
Where there is water there are trees, from dense forests in the wet east to the junipers of the dry Saharan Atlas.

and east, of Paris, Lyons and Marseilles. Their number is estimated at about 400,000.

The population density per square mile averages 15 in northern Algeria, but it is very unevenly distributed: density is least in the steppes of the high plains, the domain of nomadism, amounting to less than 2 per square mile. On the other hand, it may reach 7 in transitional regions like the high plains of Constantine and the Sersou, where stock-breeding is combined with intensive cereal cultivation. It usually exceeds 7 in the Tell itself, where there are scattered communities of more than 30 to the square mile. They occupy very different regions: barren mountains like the Kabylie massifs, sheltering prolific populations jealous of their racial peculiarities; lands intensively cultivated by colonists, like the Mitija; and, above all, the towns and their outskirts, which are undergoing a period of remarkable development, and which offer an increasing attraction to the Algerians.

*Algiers.* In 1839 Algeria possessed only a few towns: Algiers, Constantine, Oran, Medea and Tlemcen; these were administrative centres and Turkish strongholds surrounded by ramparts. The arrival of the Europeans and the economic development due to colonisation brought about a rigid urban expansion; new towns were added to the old ones, designed all of a piece on a geometrical plan. The earlier ones present a complex structure, in which two conceptions of urbanisation meet; they invariably consist of a native quarter, the *casbah,* and a European one: the former with a maze of dark alleys, medieval booths, little houses with a few barred windows, noisy crowds, smells, processions of little donkeys; the European centre characterised by the severity of its right-angled avenues, the tall façades of its buildings, big shops, tram-lines and long streams of cars.

Such a town is Algiers. It plays the part of a capital; it has grown up around the acropolis, formerly inhabited, along a narrow coastal plain, between Saint-Eugène on the north and Maison-Carrée on the south. The old town is in the centre; from the heights of the *casbah* it tumbles down in a helter-skelter of white cubes into the quarters first colonised, surrounding the harbour. The built-up area of Algiers contains more than half a million inhabitants, among which the Europeans form a small minority group. The city is closely connected with its port, which is sheltered from the prevailing winds behind the western tip of an immense sickle-shaped bay. Originally a mere anchorage for corsairs, protected by a jetty based on a few islets, the port grew rapidly in size in order to meet the needs of commercial development. Its south-east extension follows the shape of the shore. Between its two moles, several miles in length, the water level is adapted to its various functions as a passenger port, a commercial port, a port of call, a fishing port, and a harbour for coastal trade.

*Two human communities: two types of agriculture.* Two contrasting systems of agriculture still persist: an archaic type producing food for home consumption, and commercial farming which makes use of modern methods. Land tenure among the Moslems is very insecure and the land is much fragmented. Many farms consist only of a few acres of usually infertile soil, which are farmed as a joint undertaking by several members of one family. The largest are divided among the Khammès — tenet farmers sharing their produce with the landlord — who for long have received only a fifth of their total harvest. Most of the fellaheen are content simply to raise a few food crops for their own use. Their lack of savings makes it impossible to increase their output by improved methods; they must either emigrate or augment their incomes by working on the commercial estates.

Modern agriculture was developed by the colonists who owned or acquired 6,672,000 acres, distributed among 22,000 undertakings, as against 17,620,000 acres between 543,000 native farmers. The European property occupied fertile lands in the plains; its structure varied from the small farms of only a few acres, devoted to the intensive cultivation of early fruit and vegetables, to cereal crops commercially grown over thousands of acres. The largest estates belonged to companies controlled by banks: well furnished with capital, they were able to obtain the equipment they needed and recruited cheap native labour.

It is this type of agriculture which produces export crops, headed, as always, by the vine, which covers between 750,000 and 850,000 acres, gives employment to large numbers and provides Algeria with the greater part of its foreign revenue. But its outlets are mainly in the metropolitan market which imports the best grapes for blending; as the quality improves, this may one day become unnecessary.

Meanwhile it is fortunate that the Algerian climate favours other profitable crops.

The colonists expanded the cultivation of olives and figs which were traditionally cultivated by the natives in the Tell, and date-palms in the Saharan oases. French methods improved conditions of production and commercialisation. The Europeans also, over a period of many years, stimulated the cultivation of citrus fruits: today oranges, tangerines, lemons and clementines occupy, in all, more than 60,000 acres of good irrigated land in the favourable climate of the littoral.

The proximity of the French market, available during the slack months of the winter, has led to the cultivation by market-gardeners of early vegetables for export (new potatoes, tomatoes, artichokes, carrots) in the vicinity of the ports, on the warm, sandy soil near the seashore, particularly around Bône, Oran and Algiers.

Industrial crops have hardly got beyond the experimental stage, with the exception of tobacco, which the fellaheen cultivate on their own land or as tenant-farmers paying rent in kind.

Among food crops, cereals rank highest. Unlike agricultural products for export, food crops are by tradition the main crops grown. Cereals cover nearly 9,750,000 acres, 20 per cent of this total once belonged to the colonists, who grew soft wheat and oats, while the natives were the great growers of hard wheat and barley, which form the basis of their food. Average yields are small: from 7.5 to 9 bushels per acre in the native soils, against 12 to 15 in those once farmed by Europeans. Even with the extension of cereal lands annual harvests have increased but not sufficiently to keep abreast of the increase in population: each inhabitant could count on 18 bushels of cereals

TUNISIA: Date palms on Jerba Island.          A potter's shop in Mednine, southern Tunisia.          European dress in a typical Arab quarte

a year in 1871, 14 in 1900, less than 11 in 1956, in which year there was a record harvest of nearly 81 million bushels. In Algeria, cereals have reached, if not overstepped, the limits of the cultivable land.

Leguminous crops form a valuable contribution in food. Beans and chick peas are traditional crops; the Europeans, some thirty years ago, added that of lentils, which is grown in rotation with wheat in the dry regions. More recently they have introduced rice in the irrigable plains.

*Sheep-breeding climate.* The Mediterranean climate is little suited to stock-breeding; only sheep and goats can make use of the extensive feeding grounds with their meagre rainfall. The Algerian livestock comprises five and a half million sheep and two million goats, for only 623,000 head of cattle. This stock is at the mercy of epizootic diseases, bad weather, cold and drought. The deathrate causes great numerical variations from one year to another. The increase of colonisation on the borders of the steppes, administrative obstacles to seasonal displacements, and the impoverishment of the nomads of the south caused the decadence of stock-breeding: between 1889 and 1960 the entire stock fell from 16 to 10 million head.

*Modernisation of agriculture.* In the Mediterranean countries agricultural productivity is closely related to irrigation, and the public authorities have therefore financed large hydraulic works. The most important works are concerned with the Tell region, where water storage helps to make up for the irregular rainfall, increases the yields, and puts an end to the climatic fallowing of the land; it has been possible to introduce new crops, such as cotton and sown grasses. These results are obtained by the construction of reservoir-dams. Since the completion of the 1920 programme, Algeria possesses twelve dams with a total reservoir-content of 9,000 million cubic feet, supplying nearly 500,000 acres, of which 232,000 are completely irrigable. In the arid regions, small and medium hydraulic works, such as dams for the distribution of floods, pumping stations and artesian wells, have improved conditions of cultivation in the oases and of pasturing in the sheep-grazing lands.

Side by side with this there was a plan to modernise peasant holdings by setting up agricultural co-operatives, distributing to the native inhabitants lands appropriated from the vast estates, and establishing a Land Bank.

The political standpoint of the new government is much more radical: it is based on socialist principles of agrarian development. The National Bureau for Agricultural Reform today allocates more than 4½ million acres of land, most of it previously in the hands of colonists or wealthy native landowners. These operations are in the hands of 1500 committees of management and will eventually resettle 70,000 fellaheen.

Hastily conceived, this plan at first overlooked the big shortage of trained personnel and basic machinery: to avoid serious setbacks Algeria has to seek help from overseas technical advisers and agronomists, mainly from France, Bulgaria and the United States.

Even so, agrarian reform alone cannot solve all the economic problems resulting from population growth: industrial development must accompany it.

*Mining, power and industries.* Algeria has no great mineral wealth (apart from oil and natural gas, dealt with in the section on the Sahara, and some valuable deposits of phosphates).

During the colonial period, what capital there was went chiefly into agricultural and urban development; metropolitan France did not wish to see its industrial markets threatened. For this reason primary products were for long the chief export and manufactured goods were in fact imported at the expense of traditional skilled crafts. However, various four-year plans (covering the years 1949-56) stimulated economic development and industrialisation went ahead at a fairly rapid pace.

The Algerian government has continued these policies in an attempt to establish the economy of the independent nation and improve the living standards of its people.

Sources of energy, too, are few: small deposits of coal have been found in the Kenadsa basin: hydro-electricity provides only 45 per cent of the total power consumed. On the spot utilisation of oil and natural gas from the Sahara would supply the expanding needs of industry for a long time to come. Algeria possesses large deposits of phosphates in the region of Tébessa; iron ore of good quality is mined at Zaccar and Ouenza, and in lesser quantity, non-ferrous ores such as lead and zinc. But Algeria does not have the mineral wealth of Morocco.

Formerly Algeria drew the raw material for its processing industries from its agriculture. Cereals feed the flour mills, semolina and macaroni factories. When their export season is over, market-gardens supply the vegetable canneries; fruit crops have given rise to jam factories and factories for drying figs and apricots. The processing of by-products of the vineyards produces alcohols, oils and tartrates. The recent progress in sugar beet cultivation has led to the erection of a distillery and a sugar mill at Mercier-Lacombe near Sidi-bel-Abbès. There are industries processing hand-gathered produce: esparto grass for paper

Cultivation in the Tafna Valley. There are two types of agriculture in Algeria: an archaic type producing food for home needs, and a commercial type employing modern techniques.
The latter was until recently the monopoly of colonists who concentrated on intensive cultivation of early fruit and vegetables, and, of course, the vine.

manufacture and cork for bottling purposes and the manufacture of agglomerated cork.

The postwar policy of industrialisation has given a certain impetus to other industrial concerns, especially metallurgical ones. Smelting works, brass foundries, rolling mills, copper wire mills and general engineering works have increased in number. Chemical industries set up near the ports of Bône, Algiers and Oran manufacture sulphuric acid, phosphated manures and copper sulphate. To these may be added glass, leather, wood and building materials and their allied industries.

The general index of industrial production, building excluded, rose from 100 in 1950 to 141 in 1956. These results were encouraging, but they cannot be said to have had the social effects aimed at. The factories built in the last ten years maintained no more than 100,000 people, hardly equal to the demographic growth of seven or eight months.

Planned industrialisation continues on a sound basis: the rich mineral and power resources of the Sahara will play a major part in the development of all the adjoining territories.

*Commerce and port installations.* Trade between Algeria and France was controlled by economic agreements which allowed duty-free imports. France, Algeria's chief customer, supplied manufactured goods, metal goods and textiles, in return for raw materials and foodstuffs. Agricultural products were most important, especially wines and table grapes. In all, Algeria's trade with France accounted for 80 per cent of her total exchange. The remaining 20 per cent of exports consisted of phosphates, iron and alfa grass, Algeria receiving oil, machinery and textiles in return. In spite of an overall increase of exports, both in bulk and value, there would have been an adverse trade balance had there not been financial help both from France and from Algerians overseas, which more than restored the balance and accounted for Algeria's increasing wealth.

This situation remains broadly true since independence, but far reaching changes must be made to modernise the economy and end Algeria's economic dependence on metropolitan France: and if this can be satisfactorily accomplished a big search for new markets will be necessary. One answer may well lie in the reorientation of foreign trade towards black Africa, another in extending trade agreements with U.S.S.R.

Commercial activity is concentrated in the few large ports. Some are of regional importance, like Arzew, Bougie, Skikda and Mostaganem. The others serve as vast hinterland: Bône, linked by electrified railway to the mines of Kouif and Ouenza, despatches large quantities of phosphates and iron, which give it first place in terms of tonnage exported. Algiers and Oran exert the same functions — passenger ports, commercial ports, ports of call, fishing ports and coastal trading harbours — and they handle more or less the same goods: agricultural and farm produce, esparto grass and ores as exports; fuels, manufactured and food products as imports. They were rivals for pre-eminence for a long while; Oran is now second in rank.

The Algerian ports have added industrial activities to their commercial functions, for the purpose of increasing the value of the raw materials intended for export. They have become great urban organisms, attracting an ever-increasing population.

*Political problems.* Independence, has left the country with many problems. One of these is the process of 'decolonisation'; of developing a national identity to replace the patterns of life and thought imposed by alien settlement. The task is formidable: new world markets must be found now that production is no longer bound by the needs, both domestic and international, of France. Moreover, this new economic stability must be achieved in the face of increasing demands from a fast-growing population at home.

Finally there are the difficulties inherent in welding Algeria's heterogeneous peoples into one nation. The young Algerian government is treading the paths of socialism in an endeavour to achieve its goal of Algerianisation as quickly as possible and create from the varied strands of Moslem culture and the heritage of a hundred years of French rule, a united country.

The presence of iron, phosphates, oil, coal and natural gas in large quantities in north Africa, particularly in the east and south-east augurs well for the future economic development of these countries. But there are formidable problems to be solved before this wealth can be exploited. Scattered deposits, difficult terrain and climate, lack of transport and the distance from ports and markets are some of the difficulties encountered. But in many cases the mineral wealth is of sufficient importance to attract settlements and communications to even the most unpromising locations.

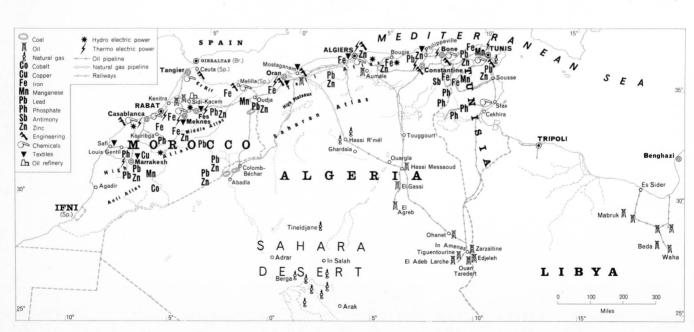

# TUNISIA

*Inner Tunisia.* The natural zones of Algeria stretch beyond its eastern frontier, to form an 'Inner Tunisia', as distinct from maritime Tunisia. Inner Tunisia comprises a number of rural areas living on stock-rearing and arable farming. Near relatives of the Lesser Kabyles, the mountain-dwellers live scattered in hamlets or isolated huts, in clearings and argilaceous depressions. They rear cattle and goats, cultivate patches of barley and sorghum with horse-drawn swing-ploughs, and exploit forest products. In the north the massifs fall steeply to a wild coast frequented by local fishermen; in the south they shelter the plains of the Middle Medjerda from the sea. These plains constitute a complex region including the river valley itself, the low valleys of the tributaries, and the slopes mounting progressively towards the surrounding mountains. The black soils and well-watered alluvia produce the finest harvests of the country, and afford the farmers the best conditions for mechanised farming. Stock-breeding, in particular cattle-raising, is carried on as well as arable farming. The population tends to scatter in small villages and even isolated farms, with a few small towns such as Beja acting as markets and administrative centres. The valley of the Medjerda is used as the line of communication with Algeria by road and rail.

The High Tell stretches from the hills of Ouergha and Teboursouk to the great Dorsal range; its structure produces a broken relief of plains and secondary chains. The climate, influenced by the altitude and the distance from the sea, resembles that of the high plains of Constantine, with its cold winters and some rainfall in spring and summer. Owing to its central position, the High Tell constitutes the water-tower of Tunisia. Its stepped zones of vegetation maintain many flocks of sheep and goats, some of which move seasonally from the south. Tents are giving way to houses, often scattered among the fields, instead of being grouped in villages placed on defensive sites. The only industry is that of iron- and phosphate-mining.

*Transformation of the steppe.* The Great Dorsal forms the southern limit of the Tell. South of it stretches the steppe, where the rainfall decreases rapidly from north to south, though the regional differences are due to altitude: in the west, between 2,300 feet and 1,000 feet, the high steppe has a harsh climate, with esparto grass in possession of the soil; in the east, under 650 feet, the lower steppe forms a distributary plain full of rocky humps and basins. A scrub region of jujube trees takes the place of esparto. For a long while almost exclusively given up to the nomads, the steppe today supports crops of cereals in the depressions and of olive trees near the sea. where the dews contribute extra humidity. Men are beginning to settle near their plantations; tents are giving way to huts, the land is being broken up and the tribe is losing its sense of cohesion.

South of the 8-inch isohyet, which marks the limit of olive dry-farming, the Tunisian Sahara begins: the sporadic vegetation affords pasturage only to a few camels and goats; most of the population is settled on the oases (Gabès, Djerid), and in the mountain villages where running water feeds orchards and cereal plots. The massif of Gafsa contains large deposits of phosphates. These are economically well worth exploiting.

*Urbanised Tunisia.* Maritime Tunisia is very different. Widely exposed to external influences, colonised by the Phoenicians and later by the Romans, it owns its vine and olive cultivation to these invaders, together with the birth of the towns strung out along its coast. City or village dwellers, the people concentrated on this narrow littoral fringe differ from the simple people of the interior by their urbanity and aptitude for progress.

The plains of the north-east and east, between Bizerta and Sfax, are dotted with a multitude of large villages, the inhabitants of which own carefully tended olive-groves, orchards, market-gardens, and cereal plots intersected by vineyards created by Europeans — a way of life and an organisation of the countryside introduced by the Andalusians. The group of large villages clustered round Sousse, Monastir and Mahdia constitutes the Sahel which is densely populated.

In the south, Sfax has enlarged its girdle of olive-groves, which are exploited by farmers' co-operatives; it exports phosphates.

## TUNISIAN PROBLEMS

*A rapidly increasing young population.* The rate of demographic increase in Tunisia is rapidly rising; the annual rate of increase is from 2 to 2.2 per cent, resulting in a very young population, 42 per cent of which is under fifteen. On the eve of independence the country had a population of 4,168,000, or an

Bedouins of Tunisia at market. As the Tunisian steppe is increasingly cultivated, nomadism is declining. The majority of the population now live in the oases or in mountain villages.

average density of about 87 to the square mile. Actually the almost empty desert of the south and the interior steppes contrasts with a narrow coastal strip which, from Bizerta to Sfax, has a population of 300-450 per square mile. A multitude of villages and towns are crowded together there, in which urban life has produced a sophisticated society. To help restrain the population growth the government has set up birth-control clinics throughout the country.

Tunis, the important Moslem town of North Africa, with its outskirts has a population of nearly 700,000. It rose to importance at the end of the seventh century. The site is a defensive one, an isthmus between a lagoon and a brackish marsh on a hill on which stands the citadel or *casbah*. Around

this the Arab quarter has grown up, a jumbled maze of alleys. At the end of the nineteenth century the European town was added, with its long avenues and intersecting streets. The contrast between two different forms of urban development is nowhere more striking. Its port is joined to the outer harbour of La Goulette by a sea channel five and a half miles long.

In December 1963, Bizerta, previously occupied by the French, was incorporated in Tunisia. An oil refinery is already operating. A major Mediterranean port, Bizerta will be a powerful industrial centre. There is already a new steelworks nearby under development.

*Economic structure.* Tunisian economy has long combined a modern section of capitalist type and European origin (to which, however, some of the native farmers and traders also belonged) and a traditional section of primitive type, an area of home consumption and of barter hardly disguised by cash exchanges.

Agrarian reform has begun in Tunisia. The nationalised estates, co-operatives and individual smallholders are being helped to improve production of the export crops: vines, fruit and olives. The vineyards are localised in the region of Tunis and Cape Bon, whereas the 26 million olive trees, covering more than 1,800,000 acres, are found in the coastal region. Tunisia is the second largest exporter of olive oil in the world. Stock-breeding, however, is even more important, ranking next to cereals in production. Moreover, unlike Algeria, which lives entirely on the land, Tunisia derives great profit from her fisheries, employing about fifteen thousand fishermen. Although agriculture occupies 75 per cent of the population, it furnishes only 40 per cent of the gross value of home production.

Twenty-eight per cent of this value is derived from handicrafts and industry. Some handicrafts retain traditional forms: weaving pottery, embroidery and tapestry afford a livelihood to nearly 600,000 people. European capital has been chiefly interested in mining, exploiting phosphates (Tunisia is the world's fourth largest producer), iron, lead and zinc ores. Important mercury deposits are a recent discovery. These raw materials are only partially treated on the spot: superphosphates are manufactured at Sfax, and there is a foundry at Megrine. But oil and natural gas from the Sahara will do much to stimulate industrial development. Factories are being placed and built for refining oil (Bizerta), paper-making, plastics, sugar-refining and textiles. As in Algeria, it is agriculture that feeds the chief processing industries: oils, macaroni, canned vegetables and fish.

There is much to be done before a national economy can be developed that is capable of raising living standards. The modernisation of agriculture is going ahead, together with extensive basic works designed to increase both the cultivated area and its yield. The setting up of agricultural co-operatives is encouraged.

To achieve these aims and to obtain the necessary equipment, the Government has intervened in commercial projects, for example, rationing the home consumption of olive oil in 1962, thereby achieving an export total of 39,000 tons. The indications are that Tunisia is surmounting many of the difficulties which face any newly independent country.

A central water trough feeds secondary channels to irrigate model fields in the Medjerda valley.

The industrial suburbs of Tunis, capital of Tunisia, a rapidly developing area containing half of Tunisia's industrial concerns.

# MOROCCO

Eastern Morocco, an arid continuation of the department of Oran in Algiers, owes its economic importance less to its traditional agriculture and stock-breeding than to mineral resources and its geographical position.

*The mountain region of Morocco.* The Taza corridor leads into Morocco proper, which forms an amphitheatre giving on to the Atlantic. The sharp contrast between plains and mountains has destroyed that sense of geographical unity without which any viable political entity is difficult to achieve. The mountains constitute a world of their own. The slopes exposed to the ocean winds receive abundant falls of snow and rain, which feed the Moroccan rivers; they bear forests composed successively, as the altitude increases, of oaks, cedars and junipers. These contrast startlingly with the slopes sheltered from the rain, on which ilexes, Aleppo pines and junipers, in mixed order, form a steppe-forest. The old Berber civilisation has retreated into the upper valleys which, being so isolated from one another, have fostered the fragmentation of social life into independent communities, whose resistence to all external authority has long delayed the social and political unification of Morocco.

The mountains describe an arc of a circle open to the ocean. To the north, the range of the Rif borders the Mediterranean like another Kabylie. To the east, the Middle Atlas intervenes between Algeria and Morocco: its limestone strata form plateaus traversed by long south-west—north-east parallel folds, over 6,500 feet in height. The steppe zones of vegetation, and the Saharan origin of part of the population, explains the preponderance of stock-breeding over agriculture. Animals and humans go down to the plain in winter. On their return, the families tend the crops round the villages, while their flocks spend the summer in high pastures, under the vigilance of shepherds. This traditional mode of life is giving way today to extended crops, settled stock-breeding, and work in the forests. To the south, the High Atlas raises a continuous barrier bearing the higher peaks of North Africa. It is broken only by cols, which make possible relations with the Sahara. The Chleughs, grouped in villages, grow irrigated crops at the edges of the torrents and cereal crops on the dry slopes; they also own flocks feeding on the spot or in transhumance; like the Kabyles, they emigrate to the rich plains and the coastal towns. The Anti-Atlas is a drier counterpart of the western High Atlas, to which it forms a buttress.

*The village Dir.* A transition interrupts the descent to the plains — the Dir, a piedmont of talus slopes and dejecta cones fringing the maritime façade of the Middle and High Atlas. On leaving the mountains the rivers spread out here and disperse: the abundance of water, good catchment, and a variety of soils and exposures, have led to a settled, rich cultivation of irrigated gardens and orchards. At the foot of the Dir stretches a line of high alluvial plains with a dry, continental climate, which would be devoted to pastoral nomadism if it were not for the water flowing down from the Atlas ranges. The populations of the Tadla are beginning to settle, thanks to the irrigated fields, whose creation has been accelerating since 1961 under the guidance of the *Promotion Nationale*. In the midst of the gardens and orchards of the Haouz, the old trade relations with the Sudan (now Mali) have led to the development of Marrakesh, the capital of the south.

*Central plateau and coastal plains.* In the centre of Morocco the crystalline bedrock, partly hidden under its sub-horizontal sedimentary cover, constitutes the *meseta,* a complex of plateaus hollowed out by deep valleys. The climate, harsh in temperature, becomes increasingly dry from the north to the south, where oak forests are succeeded by a scrub of lentisks, dwarf palms, and jujube steppes; cattle-raising and

A Moroccan woman cooking the family meal.

The barren landscape at the foot of the High Atlas, a barrier of the highest peaks in North Africa. Here and there the range is broken by cols giving rough access to the Sahara.

agriculture are rapidly replaced by pastoral nomadism. The deposits of phosphates in the Eocene strata are actively exploited.

The Atlantic plains form another world. Their suitability, together with the ease of circulation and of outside contacts, has favoured urban development. The plains form a sort of boulevard between the two capitals, Fez and Marrakesh.

The heart of the empire is in the north, in the plain of Sebou, where the richness of the soil, abundantly watered by rain and rivers, has resulted in the settlement of a dense rural population living on a variety of crops and on stock-breeding. It is from the convergence of the overland routes from the south via the coast and the mountains; from the east by the Taza col; from the north by the Habt, that the region has acquired its urban tendency. A geographic unity, the plain of Sebou exhibits nevertheless a great diversity of scenery: the wooded slopes of the mountains; the twin plains of Fez and Meknès, on the site of an embanked lake basin; the limestone hills of the pre-Rif; the alluvial plain of the Gharb, with a mixture of crops on the drained soil; the summer pastures in the merjas, and the ilex forests. The rectilinear coast is barred by a line of dunes, the growth of which tends to drive the mouth of the Sebou increasingly southwards.

South of Casablanca, the black soils of the central plain are not without fertility, but there is a constant lessening of rainfall from north to south. The land inhabited by the Chaouia and Doukkala bears fine crops of cereals and belongs to both Moroccans and Europeans; stock-breeding predominates among the Abda and the Chiadma. The intermixture of ways of life and social conditions is reflected in the juxtaposition of stone-built houses, cylindrical huts made of branches, and even tents.

The sub-Atlantic plains are prolonged by the plain of Sous, occupying a rift valley between the High Atlas and the Anti-Atlas. The climate, resembling that of the desert, favours only irrigated crops; the inhabitants supplement their incomes by fishing and trade, both concentrated at Agadir, but they often emigrate to the north.

Of Morocco's 12.5 million inhabitants, 75 per cent are rural. Berbers still form 30 per cent of the total, living in the mountains as settled or nomadic farmers and shepherds. The Arab population inhabits the towns and plains.

## MOROCCAN PROBLEMS

*Ethnic duality and population increase.* Of the three countries constituting the Maghreb, Morocco is perhaps the most individualised; it has its specific problems, not least among them the presence in the population of a large proportion of Berber elements. In spite of Arabisation, accelerated during the years of French administration, Berbers still form 30 per cent of the total; farmers or shepherds, sedentary or nomadic, they live in the mountains, whereas Arabic-speaking natives live in the plains and the towns.

Since 1936, the population of Morocco has increased at the rate of 1.5 per cent a year; it now has 12.5 million inhabitants, very unequally distributed. More than half are under twenty, and 75 per cent are rural. The development of the country by colonisation has produced certain displacements of population: the mountain-dwellers, especially those of the south, are migrating to the mining centres and towns. *Urbanisation and large towns.* The rapid urbanisation of the country is the most characteristic demographic event in the last forty years. Morocco possessed some ancient towns, political, religious and commercial capitals, cities with their medinas round the Great Mosque, their royal palaces and their closed *mellahs,* or Jewish quarters. Modernisation of the economy has given rise to new towns in European style.

While Fez and Marrakesh testify to the urban trend of Islam in the Maghreb territory, Casablanca is the most representative town of modern Morocco. Unprotected from the Atlantic surf, there was nothing about the site to suggest much future for it, but against the advice of technicians, Lyautey decided to build a port there. A long mole pointing north-east, together with a transverse one, now protect a fishing port, a dry dock and two wet docks from the breakers. As traffic increased, largely a result of the opening up of the interior, the town developed in rings round the old medina; semicircular boulevards mark the stages of this growth. Industries came into being at the same time: phosphates, sugar-refining, fish-canning, smelting. From 1917 to 1964 the population rose from 82,000 to 1,177,000. Since independence in 1956 the European population fell from 20 to 8 per cent.

In 1956 Tangier was integrated into the new independent and reunified state after 50 years as an enterprising and cosmopolitan 'free' town. Like so many North African ports on the Mediterranean, Tangier occupies the sheltered western tip of a sickle-shaped bay. It has a population of 142,000, and is linked by rail to the interior of the country. Tangier is developing both as an important commercial port for Morocco and an entrepot. A naval dockyard is planned and hinterland is being developed. It was reinstated as a free port in 1962.

*Morocco's economic assets.* Of the three North African countries, Morocco stands the best chance of escaping from its economic underdevelopment, thanks to its rich geographical advantages.

Admirably situated, it controls important routes linking Europe to Africa and South America, and the Atlantic to the Mediterranean and the Near East, which of itself explains Morocco's importance in western military strategy. But it also has mineral riches; the central plateau contains huge deposits of phosphates at Khouribga and Louis-Gentil, whose yield ranks second in the world; the eastern provinces have coal mines at Jerada, lead and zinc mines at Bou Beker and manganese mines at Bou-Arfa; oil output in the Gharb is falling, but it is rising at Essaouira. Total output is 150,000 tons annually and prospecting continues. The High Atlas has various ores, exploited in spite of transport difficulties: manganese at Imini, cobalt at Bou-Azzer, lead, zinc and copper, and in several places iron of excellent quality.

Agricultural assets are no less important: Morocco cultivates 60 million acres of land, some of which, especially the *tirs,* black clay soil, is among the most fertile of the Maghreb; all the cultivable land has not been developed yet, and still more will become available when irrigation is developed to make use of wadis fed by the high mountains of the Atlas.

The greater part of Moroccan agriculture, is however, still backward; left to themselves, the fellaheen as a rule produce only scanty harvests of cereals, and concentrate on cattle-raising, except at the foot of the mountains, where irrigation has given rise to rich villages surrounded by orchards. From 1921 onwards the French administration created native Provident Societies for the granting of mutual benefits and loans, then regional Savings and Loan Banks, for long- and short-term loans, followed by Production Co-operative Societies. In 1925 district areas were formed for the modernisation of peasant farming. Special mention must be made of the Office of the Beni Amir, which with the help of water drawn from the neighbouring wadis succeeded in transforming semi-nomads into peasant farmers cultivating their small farms intensively.

Modern agriculture was first developed by the Europeans. On the eve of independence they owned nearly $2\frac{1}{2}$ million acres devoted largely to export crops: cereals, vines, citrus fruits, olives and early vegetables, concentrated around railroutes and other natural links. The government has inaugurated a programme of agricultural reform and development, at the same time reclaiming pockets of land hitherto unproductive. These steps will make possible the distribution of plots and land large enough to be economically cultivated by modern methods. Each unit will be in the hands of a co-operative.

*A variety of industries.* Thanks to all these mineral and agricultural assets, which have attracted European capital, Morocco has reached a more advanced stage than her Maghreb partners. She possesses a varied range of industries: food, textile, chemical and metallurgical. Some are small-scale but others can compete with those of France, including the sugar-refineries at Casablanca (output 200,000 tons) and at Sidi Slimane (output 180,000 tons, from sugar-beet), the Lime and Cement Company (450,000 tons), cotton and wool spinning and weaving mills and the more recent manufacture of cellulose, cardboard and paper pulp.

The fishing industry deserves special mention; it ranks high in world production. From Casablanca to Agadir there is a line of cannaries whose products stand second or third in the list of exports.

The progress of industrialisation can be measured by the fact that from 1936 to 1960 the percentage of the working population employed in the mines, industry and handicrafts rose from 12.3 to 25.9 per cent of the total.

In order to establish its economic independence and further its development, Morocco embarked upon a five-year Plan (1960-64), whose success depended largely on foreign investment, particularly French and American. The Plan aimed at increased output of limestone and phosphates; development of electric power; the construction of a chemical complex at Safi, an oil refinery at Mohammedia, a dam on the Moulouya River and steelworks at Nadir. The Plan also embraced projects for modernising agriculture.

Since achieving independence, Morocco has been increasing its technical knowledge in order to provide a sound basis for industrial development. Phosphate deposits are extensive and of good quality. The discovery of oil on the same scale as that already exploited in Libya and Algeria would rapidly turn Morocco into an important industrial country.

Rabat, a coastal city of Moslem profile. Elsewhere rapid urbanisation in European style has accompanied the modernisation of industry.

# SPANISH WEST AFRICA

Spanish West Africa consists of two Spanish overseas provinces: Spanish Sahara, comprising Rio de Oro and Saguia el-Hamra, and Ifni. This desert territory, facing the Atlantic, extends from north to south, from the Dra to Cape Blanc, over a length of nearly 600 miles in a straight line, with a littoral of approximately 686 miles.

From west to east it has a width of 375 miles at the level of Cape Bojador. It is only 250 miles wide at the Gulf of Rio de Oro in the southern zone, and 270 miles at the level of La Aguera. The total area amounts to about 106,000 square miles.

It is an excessively hot country, akin to the desert, with hardly any rain. Only the littoral has a relatively temperate climate, under the influence of the Atlantic, and especially of the constant, very strong trade winds. Dryness and heat increase from north to south and from west to east.

In the interior, except in the depths of winter, maximum temperatures often exceed 43-45°C. (109-113°F.); minimum temperatures may occasionally drop to 10-12°C. (50-54°F.) at dawn, and the variations of temperature are very marked at all seasons. Rains may cause violent local floods after years of drought.

Camels, and a few small flocks of sheep and goats, live on temporary grazing grounds, in accordance with the nomadic habits of pastoral populations of diverse origin.

To the east are much dissected granite plateaus, to the north extends the Great Hammada (stony desert) west of the Tindouf depression, while unstable dunes fringe the coast. The few watercourses have eroded wide, indeterminate valleys. Altitude increases inland, but nowhere exceeds 1,570 feet.

The coast is generally much indented, being exposed to the violently erosive action of the sea — a rough sea, rich in fish. Where the plains of the interior descend to sea level, beaches take the place of rocks. The cliffs are often vertical.

The territory of the Rio de Oro (population about 13,000, chief town Villa Cisneros), and the territory of Saguia el-Hamra (population about 11,000), which lies to the north of the Rio de Oro, are both Spanish possessions. Although Spain has yielded to Morocco the territory formerly known as 'Spanish South Morocco', she has retained Ifni, which forms a metropolitan enclave inhabited by some 10,000 Spaniards (total population, 50,000); its capital is Sidi Ifni.

In the same way, on leaving the northern zone of her protectorate (ex-Spanish Morocco), she retained her old 'presidios' on the Mediterranean coast, the Spanish territories of Ceuta (population about 73,000), Melilla (population 79,000), le Peñón de Vélez, Alhucemas and the Zaffarine Islands.

# THE SAHARA

Between North Africa and the Sudanese belt and from the Atlantic to the Red Sea, on either side of the Tropic of Cancer, stretches the largest desert of the world, the Sahara. Politically speaking, the Sahara does not form a whole: occupied and pacified by the countries bordering it to the north and south, it has remained under their domination, divided between Algeria, Tunisia, Morocco, Mauritania, Mali, Niger, Chad and Libya.

The lack of any single political framework, and the persistence of radial frontiers, makes it impossible to assign definite limits to the Sahara, as distinct from the desert.

*The true limits of the Sahara.* In the north, the line of the first palm-groves stretches roughly from Goulimine to Gabès, following the foot of the Anti-Atlas and the Sagaran Atlas. Clearly marked in the central part, this line is much less clear at the two extremities, where the Sahara appears to retreat under the influence of the mountains and the sea. The whole southern border of the Anti-Atlas, as far as the cliffs bordering the rocky uplands of the Dra and the Guir, is merely an attenuated desert, a pre-Sahara. In the same way, at the southern end of Tunisia, the mountainous region of Matmata, the Djebel, and even the

The palm will fruit as far north as the south of France. Food, fuel, clothing, shelter, building materials, resin, oil, and wine are a few of the things the tree provides; hence its importance throughout the tropics.

A tomb of the kings of Touggourt, in the Algerian Sahara.

coastal plain north of Remada, with their esparto steppe and olive plantations, lie beyond the domain of the desert.

In the south, the *cram-cram* (*Cenchrus biflorus*) line with thick growths of thorny vegetation stretches from Nouakchott, on the Atlantic coast, to the north of Ennedi. Nevertheless the massifs occupying the southern Sahara, Adrar of the Iforas, Aïr and Tibesti, present a double aspect: the valleys are overrun with tall grasses, euphorbias and doum palms, an arborescent vegetation which at times assumes the appearance of a vaulted forest, while the plateaus remain absolutely bare. There is, therefore, some uncertainty as to the southern limit of the Sahara, though not enough to warrant putting it as far south as the Senegal, Niger, and Chad rivers.

Within these limits, the Algerian Sahara, with its Moroccan and Tunisian outliers, occupies an area of about 1,600,000 square miles, or about eight times the size of France.

By a law of January 1957 a Joint Organisation of the Saharan Regions (O.C.R.S.) was set up, for the improvement of these regions and the social advancement of their inhabitants. This organisation comprises, besides the former territories of South Algeria — now the departments of the oases and of the Saoura — the Saharan portions of the republics of Mali, Niger and Chad.

*The land of thirst.* Of all definitions of the desert, the most striking is certainly the expression 'land of thirst' seen on the old maps, by which the inhabitants still designate certains parts of it. In the spring of 1955, some travellers died of thirst in the southern Sahara because their car had broken down and there was no watering-place within a day's march. Springs and pools are few and far between, hidden among the rocks; rivers and lakes are non-existent. Water is thus the most precious of all possessions. It is carried in water-skins called *guerbas,* from which a little is drawn for drinking and cooking, but not a drop can be used for washing.

Within the boundaries described above, no point of the Sahara has an average annual rainfall of more than 4 inches, at least in the plains; many stations are even well below this total (Adrar, 0.5 inches; Bilma, 1 inch). On the mountains, however, maxima may reach 4 inches to 5.5 inches on the Asekrem (8,857 feet), in the Ahaggar and possibly more on the Emi Koussi (in Tibesti). To the figures for rain should be added the amounts of water received by the soil in the form of dew. It is very difficult to measure these, because condensation varies enormously according to the nature of the surface. They are certainly large in the massifs of the dunes, the beds of the wadis and everywhere along the Atlantic littoral; but it is doubtful whether this water penetrates far into the soil and helps to feed the water-tables.

More is known of the minima existing in the lower parts, exposed to the wind from the plateaus and mountains. Salah, at the foot of the Tademaït, has an average of 14.1 millimetres (0.66 inches); Djanet, at the foot of the Tassili n'Ajjer, has 19.1 millimetres (0.75 inches). Nowhere has an average of less than 5 millimetres been registered in a series of observations covering at least ten years. (It is different in the Egyptian Sahara, where several stations register averages of less than 5 millimetres: Kharga, 1.1 millimetres; Dakhla 0.4 millimetres.) There is no station without any rain at all.

These low averages are the result of thoroughly irregular rainfalls, irregular not so much in their distribution throughout the year as over the course of several years. Quite often there may be no penetrating rain for a whole year. In the Libyan desert several years may go by without any rain at all; and then rain storms may occur, all the more astonishing in that they are totally unexpected. Tents are carried away; houses collapse; the wadi rises many feet in a few minutes, tearing the earth from its banks, carrying away stones, roots and tree-trunks in a swirling torrent of mud.

*A hot desert.* The amounts of water falling on the soil during these cloudbursts could, if they drained away normally, feed the wadis for several months; actually, most of the floods, except on the Saoura, last only a few hours because the water that has spread out in pools is evaporated before it has time to penetrate.

Evaporation in the Sahara is conditioned by three facts: the dryness of the air, its movement, and the very high summer temperatures. The dryness of the air is, perhaps, what a traveller coming from a damp country notices most. After a few hours his nails will break, his lips will crack and his skin will become roughened; he feels the need to drink constantly and in great quantities, without any visible perspiration resulting. The summer temperatures are among the highest ever recorded in the world. The official record is held by Timimoun with an absolute extreme of 55.4°C. (131°F.). Most of the stations in the plain have July averages of more than 35°C. (95°F.); the thermometer goes up regularly to above 40°C. (104°F.) in the daytime, and at night, in spite of the wide thermic range, it hardly drops below 28°C. (82.4°F.). Human beings can live there in summer only by reversing their habits of the temperate zone: shutting themselves up by day in the house or in an underground tunnel, and lying out on the flat roof at night or at the foot of the dunes, which cools off more rapidly than buildings. The mountains alone enjoy an appreciable fall in temperature: Tamanrasset, at 4,592 feet, has no monthly average higher than 30°C. (86°F.). The Sahara is the hottest and the most extensive of deserts with uniformly torrid conditions prevailing in summer over a width of 1,250 miles and a length of 3,400 miles.

This gives rise to intense evaporation, further increased by aerial disturbance. In the desert the wind is sometimes pleasant and benign, sometimes cruel, but seldom at rest, at any rate during the day. Under these conditions evaporation on the surface of a sheet of water amounts to more than 13 feet a year, which means that the atmosphere of the desert can evaporate a depth of water a hundred to two hundred times greater than that it is possible to register on the rain-gauge.

During winter the greater part of the Sahara experiences northerly winds which carry desert conditions nearly to the Guinea coast. There the excessively dry, dusty wind, called the harmattan, is a welcome change from the humid heat, but often dries up and ruins crops and also the natural vegetation.

As a matter of fact the north-east wind seldom blows all the year round in the Algerian Sahara as it does in the Libyan desert and the Spanish Sahara. For six months of the year, in the north, it gives way to south-west or north-west winds, due in the winter to disturbance of the polar front; in the south, south-east or south-west winds occur in summer, connected with the northward movement of the inter-tropical front and the invasion of the continent by the Guinea monsoon; but in both cases geographical conditions are such that the Sahara does not benefit by them. The Atlantic and Mediterranean depressions make themselves felt only as far as the Atlas; beyond it, disturbances take the form of sandstorms, one of the most characteristic meteorological phenomena of the desert, and one of the most disagreeable. In the south, the Guinea monsoon, driving back the harmattan, penetrates as far as the Aïr and the Tibesti, sometimes into the Ahagger, 1,100 miles from the ocean; but by then it is exhausted, almost devoid of humidity, and the rainy season is reduced to a few tornadoes. North of the line Villa Cisneros-Semmour-Eglab-Ahaggar-Tibesti, there is practically no likelihood of any rainfall in summer. There is a wide gap between the southern limit of the polar front rains and the northern limit of the monsoon rains, except at the western end, where the two limits intersect.

The Atlantic Sahara is none the less arid, however; precipitation at Port-Etienne is only 0.394 inches and at Villa Cisneros (Spanish Sahara) 1.75 inches. It is widely exposed to the ocean winds, but all along the shore there is a cold current which cools on-shore winds, so that when reaching the continent these winds become warmed to the temperature of the land and give no rain.

Thus besides a general cause of aridity — the existence of an aerial current that sweeps and dries a wide zone on either side of the tropic — there are additional local factors: a mountain barrier, or distance from the sea and the influence of a cold current, will reduce or even eliminate the rainfall which the seasonal displacement of fronts generally causes in the border regions.

*Climatic changes.* If these factors had always existed they would have ensured the permanence of the desert climate. But in the course of a period as brief as the Quaternary, the climate of the Sahara has undergone a profound alteration. The wadis, dry and choked with sand today, once eroded gorges and spread sheets of stones over their banks. Lakes as big as Chad filled the basins of the southern Sahara and hippopotamuses, rhinoceroses and crocodiles haunted their shores; men strewed their tracks with chipped stones and covered the rocky walls with engravings that have preserved for us the image of a different civilisation from that of today. It is now an established fact that several times since the appearance of Man, in the Lower Palaeolithic and even the Neolithic ages, the Sahara has had the climate of regular rainfalls, probably of Sahelian type, while in the intervals the desert recovered possession of its present domain, or of a domain even wider towards the south.

The reason for these climatic changes is not known; at most it seems possible that they were connected with the glacial invasions of which Europe was the theatre at the time. Signs of recent desiccation have been adduced, on the north and south of the desert: failing wells, disappearance of forests, pasturages and inhabited places. But as a rule this evidence is not proof against criticism; it is man himself, with his wars, his flocks and herds, and his destructive exploitation of vegetable resources, that has laid the land waste.

## PLAINS AND MOUNTAINS

*Varied landscape.* The climatic conditions of the deserts are diversified by the relief, In the low-lying regions aridity reaches its peak; the plains radiate the heat like a furnace. The mountains enjoy cooler air and more frequent rains; their tall rock walls provide shade, thanks to which certain valleys of the central Sahara form cool pockets, in which animals and vegetation of the last humid period have been preserved.

But these fortunate mountains are isolated in the midst of far more extensive plains: the Ahaggar and its bastions of the Tassili n'Ajjer, the Immidir and the Ahnet, are surrounded by a belt of empty spaces, or *tanezrouft*; the Aïr rises between the plains of Tamesna and Ténéré, the Tibesti on the border of the Fez basin. This sharp contrast between plain and mountain, everywhere repeated, betrays the presence in the subsoil of two different elements, bedrock and mantle rock.

The bedrock consists of a mass of pre-Cambrian rocks, folded and more or less metamorphosed; gneiss, amphibolites, mica-schists, all interpenetrated by large granitic masses.

The mantle rock comprises the whole series of sedimentary layers that have been deposited on the bedrock, sometimes on the surface of the emerged continent, at other times in shallow seas (the last of which receded at the beginning of the Tertiary).

Volcanic eruptions have affected the central Sahara, especially from the Pliocene onwards, and contributed more than anything else to the formation of its relief. The Ahaggar, the Tibesti and the Aïr were the principal centres of eruption, and in each of these massifs the highest peaks, Tahat (9,840 feet), Emi Koussi (11,209 feet) and Greboun (6,167 feet) are volcanic centres. All the rest of the Sahara, except Libya and the Mauritanian Adrar, where there are eruption craters, has been free from volcanic activity.

The bedrock has the less differentiated relief, because the contrasts in hardness have been affected by several cycles of peneplanation. Wide areas constitute a first form of *reg,* or zone of easy passage, where the camel and the motor vehicle travel without difficulty over a thin covering of gravelly debris and sand.

The volcanic forms are of three sorts: overflows of lava which have poured into the valleys or over the slopes and fossilised the relief; cones formed by alternate layers of lava and projecta, the whole topped by a crater, the perfect curve of which proves its recent age; and needles pushed up through bedrock and mantle rock.

The Tibesti forms a most imposing complex. Above outflows of lava called *tarsos* rise the giant cones of the Emi Koussi and the Toussidé, topped by craters;

fumaroles on the flanks of the Toussidé show that volcanic activity is not quite extinct. As these high altitudes disintegration of the rocks by alternate frost and insolation is intense, but floods occasionally carry away the debris and the relief retains its freshness of outline.

It is quite different at the lower levels, where the relief has a congealed appearance. The sedimentary layers of the mantle mostly take the form of large, slightly dissected plateaus, which the Arabs call *hammadas,* a feature that consists of a hard layer — rock or hardpan — rising well above the surrounding plains.

Farther south, the plateaus surrounding the Ahaggar, which the Turegs call *tassilis,* are cut up to a greater extent by narrow valleys. Dissection is even more pronounced in the *chebkas,* which are patches of hammada intersected by a highly ramified network of ravines. On the fringe there is nothing left of this dissected plateau but *gours,* or outliers with tabular summits.

Plains of sand and drift boulders spread from the foot of the hammadas and form a second type of *reg,* which is not the result of disintegration of the adjacent rocks, but of the sweeping action of the wind over an alluvial surface. These regs follow the beds of the principal wadis, Saoura, Ighargar and Botha; their monotony is the despair of the traveller, and yet as soon as he is out of them his one idea is to return to them, for the sake of his mount or his car, if it were not for the potholes of soft sand, concealed by a flake of crust, these regs would be a motorist's paradise.

Going downstream, they give way to more or less extensive depressions, with closed basins entirely cut off from the ocean, which, according to whether their bed is of salt or not, may be *sebkhas* (often called *shotts,* a term which, in part of North Africa, refers only to the pastures of salt-loving plants surrounding the sebkha), or *dayas;* unlike the sebkhas, the dayas can be cultivated. Finally the wind plays its special part; hollowing out rectilinear, parallel lines in soft rocks, ceaselessly carrying away mobile material sand and even clay when it has been flaked away by salt.

*Eolian structures: Barkhans and ergs.* Sand is present everywhere in the Sahara: continuous drifts in the beds of the wadis, thin covering on the surface of the regs, crescent-shaped dunes, or *barkhans,* perpetually on the move; the only substantial accumulations are formed by the *ergs.* The ergs are formations of dunes, sometimes occupying an area of several thousand square miles, whose altitude reaches three or four times that of the highest coastal dunes. The principal ergs lie in southern Algeria, in Mauritania, south of the Eglabs, and in certain parts of southern Sahara, but they are practically non-existent in the central Sahara; in all, they cover less than one-seventh of the desert.

The dunes are the most permeable of all media; after rain, the sand is wet to a depth ten or twelve times greater than the height of rain registered by the rain-gauge. But in the interval between rains, evaporation and capillary action bring the water back to the surface; only very heavy rains can penetrate deeply and reach the level of saturation; the wells in

the ergs are not fed in the dunes but at their base, either in the alluvia of old wadis now choked by sand or in the permeable Tertiary formations.

## THE MEN OF THE DESERT

Men are not entirely absent in the desert, any more than vegetation, but they are few in number and widely scattered. Travelling by camel, one may sometimes go several days without meeting a soul; even the motorist is not always sure of finding a night's lodging. Over expanses larger than a French department such as Tanezrouft, Ténéré, and Chech Erg, there are no inhabitants. But in the grassy valleys and non-salt basins, density may grow to 28 per square mile, at any rate in a good season; in the palm oases it reaches 2,800 per square mile of cultivable area, though it must be admitted that this area could usually be fitted within our urban boundaries. Thus the contrasts in population found in civilised countries between town and country are seen

In a land of dry, sandy wastes the camel is well fitted to serve as beast of burden and to provide meat, milk, and skins for its nomadic owner.

Desert landscape, Bou Saâda, Algeria.

in the Sahara between the over-populated oases and the more or less empty parts of the desert.

*The Sahara's population of varied racial composition.* The distribution of races in the desert is not a zonal one; it is the result not only of climatic factors, but of invasions and migrations of various peoples, occurring in all directions.

The Berbers represent the old, if not the oldest, white element, for though it is certain that they came from the east along the line of oases running from Egypt to Tripolitania through Siouah and Aodjilah, it is not known what people preceded them in the Sahara. Today all Berber-speaking people are accounted Berbers, whatever their physical differences may be. Besides their language, there are certain customs proper to all Berbers, of which the best-known is matriarchy. Contrary to Arab usage, women are in law, and in fact, equal to men and the Berber woman of the Sahara, energetic, skilful and relatively educated, transmits a real form of civilisation to her descendents.

The most important of all the Berber groups in the Sahara is that of the Tuaregs. They number nearly 350,000, scattered over an immense expanse, from Gadames and Mourzouk (Lybia) in the north to Hombori and Dori in the loop of the Niger; but nine-tenths of them live in the Sahelian zone, outside the desert. Saharans or not, they wear the veil, raise livestock and recognise the authority of a chief elected by the Confederation, the Amenokal.

The Arabs in general are descendants of the warriors that conquered North Africa in the seventh century, and of the Bedouins that spread all over north-west Africa from the eleventh century onwards; actually, most of them are Arabic-speaking Berbers who have more or less preserved their old customs. The chief Arabic-speaking tribes are localised in the north and west. Those in the north form subdivided groups, mostly nomadic but beginning to settle. In the west, the Regueibats and other nomadic tribes of Mauritania form the group of the 'blue men', so called because of the colour of their clothes. More than the Arabs of Algeria, the Moors have preserved their old pastoral civilisation and a society hierarchy founded on the inequalities born of conquest.

From the economic point of view, the Arab invasions have been of far less importance to the Sahara than to the Mediterranean countries. Camels, date-palms and irrigation existed there before their arrival; of the plants introduced by the Arabs, oranges and bananas have hardly penetrated into the oases, and hard wheat has never succeeded in driving out the indigenous soft varieties. The political consequences were greater, but ephemeral; the sovereignty of the Moroccan sultans in Timbuktu lasted less than a century. The religious consequences are the only ones that have endured. The doctrine introduced by the followers of the Prophet has crossed the southern border of the desert and taken firm root in part of the Negro world, held up only by the dense forest and the zone infested by the tsetse fly. Islam, a religion of shepherds, found an ideal terrain in which to propagate itself in the desert and the surrounding steppes.

The coloured populations include the native Negroes of the Sudan, some descended from the black populations occupying the country in the Middle Ages. Other Negroes are descended from the slaves bought or raided in the Sudan by Arab merchants and held captive in the oases.

In most of the oases, alongside the Negroes, there are people of a bronze complexion, called *Haratin* (sing. *Hartani*, literally, 'man of dark colour') whom the other groups look upon as half-breeds. In the oases the Haratin form a different social class from both landowners and slaves. While the latter have domestic functions, the Haratin are essentially gardeners; they form a rural proletariat, very poor but not incapable of progress. Among the Tuaregs of the south, the liberated slaves (*Bella*) form whole tribes, incorporated and assimilated into Targui society.

While the Haratin can hardly be ranged amongst the Negroes, the Toubous are undeniably distinct from them. This group includes not only the inhabitants of Tibesti and Téda, but the peoples of the plains surrounding the massif, Dazas, Bideyats and Gaëdas. Their skin is black or reddish, but their features, much finer than those of the Negroes, remind one of Tuaregs or Abyssinians. These Toubous, who number about 100,000 are scattered over an immense area with no definite boundaries.

In all, there are about 1,700,000 people living within the boundaries defined above, less than three to the square mile. The smallness of the population has paralysed French administration for the last hundred years as much as, if not more than, the climatic difficulties.

*Traditional ways of life.* Scanty as it is, however, the population of the Sahara still represents a miracle, considering the country's resources. These amount to only two: a very infertile, practically unlimited steppe, and water reserves almost non-existent on the surface though sometimes abundant underground. These have formed the foundation of two different ways of life, at once inimical to each other and interdependent.

Ever since the domestication of animals, the exploitation of the steppe has taken the form of pastoral nomadism. Hunting has ceased to be a way of life.

Food-gathering has remained in favour, at least as a further resource. In years in which a relatively high rainfall allows the *drinn* to form ears, the Tuaregs store the grain, with which they make a sort of *couscous*: the Toubous gather colocynth seeds and doum-palm nuts; but there are no tribes in the Sahara living exclusively by hunting or food-gathering, like the Pygmies in the Congo.

This is because, since the Neolithic Age, a certain number of animals of the steppe have been domesticated, both cattle and horses. The magnificent paintings recently discovered in the Tassili n'Ajjer provide striking evidence of this earliest pastoral civilisation. The domestication of the camel may not go back further than the beginning of the Christan era; but this auxiliary soon enabled man to adopt the mode of stock-raising best adapted to natural conditions.

Except for monetary improvement due to penetrating rain or flood, the Saharan pastures are too poor to allow flocks to remain stationary in them for long at a time; they must keep on the move in quest of food. On the other hand, animals need water — the amount depending on season. Excellent grazing grounds may have to be deserted if there is no well for watering the sheep within a radius of fifteen miles. Moreover, all animals, including camels, must now and then take a salt cure either in vegetable form (salt plants) or in the form of minerals (salt springs in the southern Sahara). There are thus three reasons, each of them imperative, why stock-breeding must be of a nomadic character.

Pastoral migrations are undertaken in ways that vary from year to year according to the state of the pasturage, but retain their general character in any given tribe; the composition of the flock can therefore be classed according to four types.

*Different types of migration.* A certain number of tribes, on the north and south borders of the desert, breed mostly sheep; the Ait Khebbache of Southern Morocco, the Arbaa and Ouled Zekri of southern Algeria, the Merazig of southern Tunisia. Sheep can thrive on salt-plant pasturages; they can stand the winter cold on the hammada so long as they are well fed; but they must be watered regularly — in summer, at least every other day. So they can only live by remaining in the summer within reach of the wells, where they soon exhaust their pasture, or by moving to and fro between the desert and a humid region. A form of migration thus developed, known in Algeria as *achaba*, leading the flocks of the Arbaa, for instance, from the region of the dayas south of Laghouat, where they spend the winter, to the col-onised zone of Sersou, where they are taken to graze in the summer.

Other tribes, unable to spend the dry season outside the desert, breed only camels, e.g. the Regueibat of Algeria (Lgouacem) or of Mauritania (Sahel). In the winter the watering-place is no longer required, and in the summer it is sufficient to visit the wells from time to time. The herd can thus scatter in search of places that have grown green again, making the maximum use of the area; the tent-dwellers follow it, being themselves to some extent freed from the need for water by the camels' milk. A simple and economically perfect system, it allows the nomads almost total freedom of movement.

In the mountains of the central Sahara, Ahaggar and Tassili, where the vegetation is restricted, stock-breeding has to be confined to the valleys, and even these become unbearable if the drought lasts several years; in this case the Tuaregs who breed camels and goats send the camels to the Sahelian borders, not just to spend the dry season in *achaba*, but for an indeterminate period, while the goats, which are the personal property of the women, remain near the tents, often constituting the sole food resource.

On the Sahelian borders, the Tuaregs of the Ahag-gar join other Tuaregs, mostly breeding cattle. The feeding habits of the ox differ from those of the camel: it will not touch the *had* (*Cornulaca monocantha*), it disdains the *djerdjir* (*Schouwia purpurea*) but fills its paunch with cram-cram; long marches tire it, and it has to drink large amounts regularly, so that it can only remain in the Sahara when the winter rains have filled the pools and increased the number of water-ing places. On the other hand, it needs its annual salt cure as much as the camel.

Although it is true that the type of nomadism depends on the composition of the flock or herd, it

Six thousand feet below this part of the Libyan desert, near Cyrenaica, lies a thick layer of oil-bearing limestone.

A typical oasis of the Sahara. While the desert is almost uninhabited, the cultivable areas and the oases are overcrowded.

must be added that very few tribes breed only one kind of livestock. In any case the nomadic tribe must possess camels to carry tents and provisions. Indispensable to the nomads on the move, the camel affords them other benefits as well: milk, hair, and sometimes if there is an urban market in the neighbourhood, meat. Camels are used for commercial transport.

Camel caravans have been an essential of nomad activity for centuries. Travellers and merchandise travelled in groups, under the paid escort of the tribes across whose territory they travelled. At a time when closed economy was the rule in Europe, the caravans brought an open economy to north-west Africa.

In this way the nomadic tribes were able to obtain provisions from the settled tribes at an early period and this accounts for the part played by camels and dates in their food. In some cases the shepherds themselves are able to grow cereals. When the wadis have run dry, leaving a fertile layer of silt on their banks, some tribes cultivate these depressions: wheat or barley in southern Algeria; wheat or maize in southern Morocco; sorghum in Mauritania.

Sometimes the nomads buy palm trees, an understandable investment for people who consume, and always have consumed, great quantities of dates. They entrust the trees to a métayer or tenant who pays rent in kind, and merely go every year to fetch their share of the harvest.

*Oases, gardens and palm-groves.* While men tend to scatter over the pastureland, they crowd together in the oases. An oasis comprises one or several villages, each surrounded by a palm-grove. It is a permanently inhabited area, contrasting with those areas through which men only pass, and which alone constitute the Sahara in the eyes of the natives.

It has often been said that the symbol of this permanent habitation is the house, as the tent is that of nomadic life. But the house, regarded as a family possession as it is among the peoples of the West, exists only in the towns of the M'sab or Gadames, perhaps even Agadès, where there are artisans and middle-class people. Usually the Saharan settler has other interests; exclusively a farmer, he is attached to the land more than any to any building, and to water more than the land.

For if men are to live permanently at one place in the desert, they must find water there for themselves and their crops. Even if the springs are enough for daily needs of human beings, well-regulated farming requires the creation of reliable artificial watering-places.

This does not mean that irrigation, in the ordinary sense of the term, is an absolute necessity, because in certain regions of the Sahara farmers have contrived to do without.

The inhabitants of the Souf dig hollows, and plant palms straight into the wet sand, which saves them having to draw water. The same method is met with on the borders of the Great Western Erg, and generally in regions where the water table can be brought in contact with the roots without having to dig too deep. Even cereals can be grown in this way in valleys in which the alluvium remains wet, like that of the Saoura; but as a rule, all plants with shallow roots have to be watered.

Water for this may come from the surface or from underground. The surface water comes from springs and wadis. On the northern border of the desert there are some rivers which have water in them even in summer; among them are the Dra, the Ziz, the Gheris and the Guir. By means of primitive dams, people living on their banks divert some of the water into channels, or *seguias,* by a system in general use in Mediterranean regions. As these rivers reach their maximum in the cold season, the water in the seguias is then sufficient to water both cereals and palm-trees; in the summer all the water is reserved for the palm-trees, and even then it is often not enough to allow maximum growth.

In the interior of the desert, where there are only trickles of water, the system of dams has had to be adapted to a violent and intermittent flow. These are mostly diversion dams, generally mere banks of earth demolished by every flood. Sometimes the local inhabitants have erected real gravity dams which retain the water and force it to infiltrate. The government has recently built a few dams with a deep-level flow, whose underground walls force to the surface water circulating in the alluvium.

Where topographical conditions are not adapted to such undertakings there are other ways of utilising the water table.

The simplest of these is to sink wells in which the water is raised to the level of the ground, either by a counterweight balance-bar method used throughout the Mediterranean basin, or by a set of pulleys and ropes worked by an animal. Both these methods have the drawback of being slow and having only a small output.

If the water table shows a considerable gradient and does not lie too deep, it is possible to bring water to the surface by digging an underground channel with a lesser gradient than that of the table; this is the principle of the *foggara,* which acts as a drain upstream, and down stream as a conduit ending in a seguia.

Like ordinary wells, the foggaras have only a small output. Artesian wells alone permit extensive areas to be irrigated. The sinking of deep wells and utilisation of captive water tables were not European innovations; as early as the fourteenth century the Berbers of the Righ Wadi had obtained gushers from artesian layers. After 1850 wells increased in number—not only in the Righ Wadi, where since 1930 the number of sinkings has had to be controlled for fear of exhausting the reserves in the Neogenic, but at El Goléa, in the Tidikelt, in southern Tunisia, and recently in the M'sab, where fresh layers discovered in the Lower Cretaceous contain practically unlimited reserves. Unfortunately these wells do not always gush spontaneously and the high cost of pumping restricts their construction to the most favourable situations.

Except for artesian wells and floods, no method of irrigation produces more than a small quantity of water, which has first to be accumulated in a basin before it can be used. This fact has left a mark on the rural landscape, from the Atlas to the Mauritanian Adrar, and in the Tibesti. One of the largest oases in the Sahara, Ouargla, possesses 1,780 acres of palm plantations; the little oases of Saoura have on average 25 acres each; the seventeen centres of cultivation in the Ahaggar have a total of only 1,450 acres under cultivation, although the dependency is three-fifths the size of France. The fragmentation of the land is great: each holding occupies no more than 2.5 to 5 acres; the patches themselves are Lilliputian, from 9 to 54 square feet.

The economy of the oases sometimes resembles gardening not only in the restricted dimensions of the holdings but in certain features of intensive cultivation, such as the superposition of several levels of vegetation: cereals or vegetables at ground level; fruit-trees higher up (fig-trees, apricot-trees, peach-trees, with vines twining like lianas round them); lastly, towering above them all, the palm-trees, sometimes regularly spaced and aligned, sometimes planted at random, and so close together that their shoots touch. But these appearances are deceptive. The superposition of crops is far from being so general as is believed. Lest they should be too much in the shade, cereals are often sown on separate patches outside the palm-grove. The latter only shelters the vegetables and fruit-trees; actually, in the recent plantations in the Righ Wadi, any intercalary crops are prohibited: between palm-trees planted at regular intervals of 27 feet and land is left bare, frosted with salt. Even in oases of traditional type, the gardens are seldom cultivated all over at once; as a rule they are divided in two parts left fallow alternately to allow the land to rest. Sorghum never occupies as much space as wheat because there would not be enough water to irrigate it in the summer. Although theoretically the three principal crops — wheat, dates and sorghum — should afford a continuous supply of food, in practice they are never sufficient to meet requirements, and the Ksourians, once their provisions are exhausted, live by their wits and charity.

PROBLEMS OF TODAY. Since the occupation by France of the major part of the Sahara, several achievements have affected profound alterations in the conditions of life. First came the establishment of order and security. With the occupation of Tindouf in 1934 and the meeting of the columns coming from the north and south, the era of the *razzias* or raids came suddenly to a close.

Less immediate, but no less profound, has been the effect of the suppression of slavery. The military government shut its eyes for a long while to the persistence of domestic slavery. Even today it is not unusual to find among the Moors and the Turegs Negro servants whose condition is no different from that of captives. But customs are gradually altering under new political conditions; though the Negro is still obliged to have a master to feed him, he has been given the franchise and at least he is free to choose his master.

Another event, the appearance of the automobile, did have immediate repercussions. The camel cannot transport everything, and above all it is very slow: a caravan takes a fortnight to go from Gabès to Ouargla, fifty days from In Salah to Zinder, and few travellers will put up with the fatigue of a camel journey. The automobile journey may be no less tiring, but it shortens the duration of the ordeal: it brings the Niger Republic within six days of Algiers. A twenty-ton truck can transport iron, pipes and parts of machinery together with any number of individuals fleeing from the desert.

As a result of these different factors, traditional ways of life are no longer adapted to the necessities of life; a crisis has arisen which affects all the peoples of the desert.

*Decline of nomadism.* We have seen that even at a time when the absence of any organised government favoured it, the nomadic way of life bore certain seeds of disintegration within it; half a century ago, these found a favourable soil, and radical changes followed rapidly.

The suppression of slavery hit at the foundations of nomadic society. Among the Tuaregs of the south, the Negro slave was employed as a shepherd; once the shepherd had left the flock was in peril, for the owner could not himself draw water from the well without losing face; of all the grievances nursed by the Tuaregs against the French at the time of the 1916 revolt, the greatest in their eyes was the liberation of the Iklans. They thought better of it later, when in 1946 the Negro became the equal of the white man. At that time, too, the establishment of a regular government and a police force prevented the nomads from continuing to play a dual rôle as caravan escorts and as pillagers.

Apart from this decrease in their personal income, they lost certain advantages they had derived, as shepherds, from their social organisation. Until a few years before, a sort of feudal regime had subsisted, under which nomads descended from the conquerors levied dues in kind from those cultivating the soil, and sometimes from other tribes considered as vassals. However, the egalitarian spirit of French legislation was bound in time to overcome the conservative spirit of the chiefs; almost everywhere, the subordinate classes have freed themselves from the dues they used to pay to the lords of the land and established for themselves a degree of economic independence.

For this loss of revenue and prestige, the nomads might have found some compensation in trade, of which they had long enjoyed the monopoly. But caravan traffic had lost much of its former splendour. The fatal blow was given it by the automobile. Arab and Mozabite merchants immediately monopolised the transport of costly perishable goods, leaving the nomads only that of wood, dates and, above all, salt in the southern Sahara. The introduction of currency for transactions which up to then had been settled solely by barter also contributed to the dispossession of the nomads, to the benefit of established merchants.

Finally, therefore, the nomads have been reduced to a single activity, that of stock-breeding. It would be unfair to suggest that recent changes have all been to their disadvantage in this field. Now that raiders have disappeared, they have only the jackals to fear, and as a result they are spreading almost everywhere into areas that used to be closed to them. In addition, the Government has taken upon itself the maintenance of wells and watering-places. But there are more powerful factors operating against nomadism. Apart from the trouble with the shepherds already referred to, camel-breeding attracts fewer and fewer people now that caravan traffic has been restricted, and sheep-breeding is subject to terrible crises in years of drought. The tribe, which the need for defence no longer keeps together, is becoming scattered; the chiefs are no longer obeyed; families move about as they choose, and migrations are assuming a more and more anarchic character.

Nevertheless, two main features are becoming apparent in this evolution. First, a trend towards the separation of families from their flocks, which are entrusted to a shepherd for most of the year. If shepherds were not so difficult to come by, this separation would become the rule.

The second, more general trend is that towards settlement. As already noted, the cultivation of flooded hollows was leading to semi-nomadism in regions where the wadis undergo regular inundation. The same effect is achieved when the nomad who has made money buys palm-trees to make sure of his supply of dates and add the safer gains of commerce to the uncertain profits of stock-breeding.

Little by little these sojourns in the oases grow longer, the stock-breeder contenting himself with a return to the Sahara in the spring to take a milk cure; if the government encourages the movement, the last lap will have been covered: the former nomad will have become a settler. Sudden impoverishment as much as enrichment may lead to the liquidation of the flock and the end of migration.

As a rule the nomads have settled on their own initiative, especially where they could plant palm-trees at no great expense and reap the harvest without having to water them. But a settled shepherd does not become a peasant automatically; he still has to acquire a taste for agriculture as it is practised in the oases, and learn its methods. Moreover, a general settlement presupposes the extension of cultivated areas which is only possible in certain favoured spots. Neither the central nor the western Sahara can offer wide expanses of arable land or sufficient water layers for irrigation. This being so, the mass settlement of either Tuaregs or Moors would appear to be dangerously Utopian, since it would end by depriving these peoples of their natural resource, which is stock-breeding, without offering them any alternative activity on which they can depend.

Traditional nomadism was at once a method of stock-breeding and a social organisation. Both are in decline today because this way of life cannot be adapted to modern conditions of transport and exchange.

*Exodus from the oases.* Under a show of wealth, afforded by the shade of the palms and the crowded patches under cultivation, the oases often conceal a jungle of weeds or uncultivated gardens. Agriculture suffers there from various ills, some adventitious, like swarms of locusts and invasions by rodents, but two of them permanent: low productivity and uneconomic distribution of property.

The soil of the palm-groves, fairly rich in mineral elements, always lacks humus; the few plants that grow in it dry up and turn to dust instead of rotting. To make up for this absence of organic matter, a great deal of manure would be needed, but the Ksourians have no livestock except for the animal that draws the water from the well and a few goats. There remains human manure. Every year in October, there is a joyous to-and-fro of little donkeys and Negro children, bringing baskets of fresh sand and garbage in time for the sowing. Even so the soil is soon exhausted, especially if it is watered with pure water like that from the wells and foggaras, and the cereal product is very poor in spite of irrigation.

The yield of the palms depends much less on the soil than on irrigation. A well-watered palm-tree may produce 220 lb. of dates a year, but unfavourable atmospheric conditions and repeated plagues of locusts may lower the average by 75 per cent. Besides, in southern Morocco and southern Oran many palms are attacked by a disease, the *bayoud,* which has so far resisted treatment.

Date production in southern Algerian territories has dropped from 925 lb. a head (nomads included) in 1930 to 264 lb. in 1950 and 115 lb. in 1956.

So long as the oases remained isolated from the rest of the world, the Ksourians accepted famine as the will of Allah; now that contact with Europeans has revealed other conditions of life to them, and the truck offers them a means of escape, they are becoming conscious of their freedom and their poverty, and having decided that the ills their fathers endured are no longer tolerable, they are deserting their gardens *en masse.*

## DISCOVERY OF WEALTH IN THE SUBSOIL

*Coal, oil and ores.* Until a few years ago it was thought that the Sahara possessed no mineral resources except salt. Explorers had searched in vain for its legendary emeralds; the gold of the Sudan (Mali), which had given its name to a part of the Spanish Sahara (Rio de Oro), was either no longer mined, or had changed its direction; only the salt trade had lasted through the centuries. Unfortunately the Sahara salt, carried by caravans, costs as much in the villages of the Sudanese belt as that of the coastal salt-pans or the European salt despatched by sea or by rail and it is gradually losing the market in face of this competition.

Such was the balance-sheet of the desert's mineral resources when, at the beginning of the century, a geologist discovered coal at Kenadsa, about twenty miles west of Colomb-Béchar. Owing to Algeria's difficulty in obtaining an adequate supply of coal at that time, the workings, begun in 1917, did not acquire much importance until the Second World War, when a methodical survey of the basin was undertaken. The survey showed that the basin extended southwards from Colomb-Béchar with a fairly regular stratification. The measures are of rich coal, with a large percentage of ash and a little sulphur. Production amounts to 300,000 tons a year. The great obstacle to concentrated working lies in the thinness of the seams, which are usually less than eighteen inches in thickness, while the remoteness of the mines entails considerable cost in transport. Two rail routes connect Béchar to the coast, a narrow-gauge one across South Oran and a broad gauge one through Moroccan territory; only the latter is used for coal transport.

To reduce costs of transport it is proposed to burn the coal at a generating station now in course of construction, and convey the current to Oran by high-tension cable.

Certain ores found in the western Sahara could also be treated at Colomb-Béchar.

At Gara Djébilet, eighty miles south-east of Tindouf in Algeria, an enormous quantity of iron ore has been located, the iron content of which varies from 50 to 60 per cent with 0.8 per cent of phosphorous. The regularity of the deposit and the thiness of the overburden will render the working economical. But the ore will have to be exported in a crude state as far as the Atlantic coast (300 miles), and the total capital invested will amount to £8.6 million or U.S. $24.3 million; nevertheless the exploitation will be profitable if extraction reaches ten million tons a year. Another deposit is of manganese in Djebel Guettara, ninety miles south of Colomb-Béchar. The reserves are estimated at one million tons of ore with 45 per cent of manganese and a notable proportion of arsenic, which can be sublimated by roasting; treatment of this ore is soon to be begun at Colomb-Béchar.

In Mauritania discoveries have been made in two places. At Idjil (Fort Gouraud), there is a deposit of iron ore smaller than that of Tindouf, but with a higher metal content (more than 100 million tons of ore with 63 per cent of iron and very pure); transport is effected by a railroad built to Port Etienne. Part of this line could be used also for the transport of copper from Akjoujt, where 18 million tons of sulphide ore and 9 million tons of oxide ore have been located. The copper content is low (1.5 to 2.5 per cent), but the ore also contains gold and iron. Exploitation has been begun here; a pilot plant was started in 1954 for the treatment of the sulphide ore, and another is to be erected for the oxide ores.

There are signs that minerals are present in the rest of the Sahara; tin, south of the Aïr (the natural concentrates are now being gathered), tungsten, platinum and diamonds in the Ahaggar; but prospecting is not yet sufficiently advanced for explorable deposits to have been noted.

Exploitation of its underground wealth would be more advanced if the Sahara had been earlier able to do without imported liquid fuel, which makes motor transport very expensive, especially in the depths of the desert.

This explains the interest taken in oil-prospecting since the end of the war. Nothing suggested the presence of gas or petroleum oil in the Sahara; but experience gained in other parts of the world had shown that old rock levels retaining sufficient sedimentary cover may conceal large oil reserves. In 1949, therefore, a campaign of research on a large scale was opened. Five companies share between them a territory larger than France; three have obtained positive results.

To begin with, in 1954, the existence of considerable reserves of natural gas was ascertained in the Tidikelt, south of In Salah; this gas (methane) is an excellent fuel, but as there is no market for it on the spot, and transport over more than 600 miles would render it unprofitable, the wells have been closed. Production is now centred on the region of Hassi Rmel, south of Laghouat, nearer to the coast, where reserves of liquid gas are of the order of 500 thousand million cubic metres; but finding markets has been a serious problem.

The exploitation of oil is the most advanced. Two oilfields are now well known: that of Hassi Messaoud, east of Ouargla, where impregnated sandstones have been reached at a depth of 11,500 feet, in the centre

A Bedouin woman of the Tunisian Sahara. Traditionally itinerant, Bedouins are gradually being absorbed into the main streams of life.

Exploitation of oil deposits found in the Sahara was dependent on the rapid construction of pipelines to the Mediterranean. In 1960 output of crude oil from 200 production wells was almost nine million metric tons. By 1963 Algeria alone exported 21.7 million tons a year.

of an enormous, very flat anticline; and that of Edjélé-Zaraïtine, south-east of Fort Flatters, where oil is found at only 1,300–1,650 feet. In both cases the oils are of a light kind, with mainly white products. Exploitation was dependent on the construction of pipelines. Great progress has been made: oil pipelines have been laid from Hassi Messaoud to the coast at Bougie, with links to Edjélé, El Gassi and El Agreb, from Hassi-R'Mel to Arzeur (Algeria) and from Edjélé to La Skhirra (Tunisia), and a gas pipeline has been completed from Hassi Messaoud via Hassi-R'Mel to Mostaganem-Oran-Algiers. In 1960 about 200 wells were productive, and output of crude oil from Algeria and the Sahara was almost 9 million metric tons, or approximately one half of France's home consumption. By 1963 Algeria was able to export 21.7 million tons, three-quarters of it to France.

Thus the situation is being gradually defined. The Sahara possesses ascertained mineral wealth: coal measures of which the probable reserves—50 to 100 million tons in the only workable seams — are enough to ensure continued exploitation; iron deposits of world rank, comparable in tonnage to the Lorraine basin or that of Lake Superior, and another deposit of exceptional quality, equal to that of the best Lapland ores; deposits of copper and manganese that may well be workable in the near furture; enormous reserves of natural gas whose exploitation depends on the creation of markets in North Africa and in Europe; and — last, not least — two oilfields, whose output is conveyed to the Mediterranean by pipeline. These prospects are not only encouraging with regard to the supply of metropolitan France and the industrialisation of Algeria; they should mark the beginning of a resurrection of Saharan agriculture, since even the mines, oilfields and construction work cannot absorb the excess population of the oases.

*Towards a restoration of the oases.* This resurrection will undoubtedly be a long-term development. The semi abandonment of the palm-groves of Colomb-Béchar sinoe coal began to be mined in the neighbourhood suggests the probable first effects of more intensive industrialisation. But this is merely a transient consequence of the disparity between wages in agriculture and in industry; other factors are intervening which will soon palliate these effects and, subject to certain time-lag, agriculture can only benefit by the progress of hydraulics, new means of transport and the increase in purchasing power resulting from the wages paid by industry.

Of all the discoveries made in the Sahara in the last twenty-five years, the most important is undoubtedly that of large reserves of water in the Cretaceous layers of the mantle rock. It is estimated that this water table receives 225 cubic feet per second from the Saharan Atlas and the desert itself, whereas the total flow of the springs, wells and foggaras amounts at most to 59 cubic feet per second for the whole of the basin. There is therefore a large surplus of water in existence which could be tapped by new wells. Spectacular flows have been obtained north and east of the M'sab: 50 gallons per second at Guerrara, 54 gallons per second at Ouargla. The Ouargla well had to be restrained to 30 gallons a second because there was no means of storing so much water. Where the water layer does not gush, as in the Gourara and the Touat, modern methods afford means of raising the water mechanically.

A radical transformation of the system of cultivation may be expected, as traditional products no longer pay. Also these oases are in a good position to supply the urban markets with what the native workers and the European management require most — meat and fresh fruit and vegetables, which up to now have been sent by air from Algiers or Paris. The higher acreage under lucerne, made possible by the increase in irrigated areas, will allow livestock to be stalled, and the dung collected. But this will necessitate a complete transformation of agricultural methods, and possibly even of landed property. The Native Provident Societies (S.I.P.) and the District Areas of Rural Improvement (S.A.R.) point the way to this reconversion.

A FRESH CHANCE. There are moments when countries, like individuals, see new prospects opening before them; the Sahara has reached one of these. The exploitation of mineral resources, long ignored, and better utilisation of the hydraulic resources of the subsoil are beginning to alter the shape of the problem posed by the presence of man in the desert.

During the course of the present century, science has made such astonishing progress that it would be unwise to predict the ultimate extent of these transformations; the tapping of the sources of energy proper to the desert, in particular, opens almost infinite prospects, and it is not too far-fetched to suggest that man may some day alter the climate. The air conditioning of buildings, already effected at oil-drilling stations, is only a first step in that direction; the attempts now being made to provoke condensation and precipitation may perhaps lead in the near future to complete control of rainfall, and on that day the desert will be finally conquered. For the time being, with the climate as it is, and the Sahara still the most arid zone of the globe, stock-breeding activity will remain dispersed over vast expanses, while in one spot after another the genius of man creates fresh centres of life.

Women selling beads in the bazaar at Rissani in the far south of Morocco.

# LIBYA

Midway along the Mediterranean, between Malta and Crete, on the route from Europe to Central Africa and on the road to Chad, an outpost of Suez, between Bizerta and Alexandria, Libya occupies a strategic position that has made it a much coveted country. A Turkish territory, it was conquered by the Italians between 1912 and 1930; Mussolini made it one of the bulwarks of his African policy. As a result of the Montgomery-Leclerc offensive of October 1942, Great Britain was entrusted with the administration of Tripolitania and Cyrenaica, and France that of Fezzan. In 1949 the United Nations, owing to the lack of agreement among the Great Powers, decided to grant Libya its independence from 1 January 1952 at the latest. The administrative countries transferred their powers to Libya in December 1951.

*The face of Libya.* Libya comprises the former provinces of Tripolitania, Cyrenaica and Fezzan. Desert climate and maritime influences confront each other, but in the greater part of the territory the Sahara has the upper hand.

On the Jabal Akhdhar, the loftiest of the tiered plateaus of the Cyrenian mountains (over 3,500 feet), forests of cypress, ilex and juniper with an undergrowth of arbutus and lentisk alternate with denuded clearings coloured by the red ochre of the clays and the white humps of the chalky outcrops. The many valleys end in caverns and grottoes and the streams run underground. Rainfall is plentiful at all times (23 inches at Cyrene), and the summer, which is calm and restful, is free from the stifling heat of the south. There are few springs, and water lies deep; it is a pleasant corner of the Mediterranean.

At a lower level with an irregular rainfall of about 10 inches among the outcrops of rock, a bushy vegetation degrades to steppe. North of the Jabal Akhdhar the coastal plains such as those of Appolonia and Derna are narrow and salt.

The coast of Tripolitania is the richest region of the province, and the triangle Garian-Homs-Tripoli (rainfall 13 inches) seems the most favoured. The coast from Zuara to Taourga is a discontinuous string of oases, interrupted by lagoons and dunes. Farther south, from the Tunisian frontier to Homs, stretches the purplish cliffs of the Tripolitanian Jabal edging a rocky plateau, jagged at Dahar, pre-desert in the west (Nalut region), steppe in the centre and covered with olive-trees, crops and scrub from Garian onwards towards the east. While the coastal subsoil contains layers of water, the Jabal's numerous springs have only a scanty flow. The summer is long and hot and there is a violent south wind (guebli). In spite of a high degree of humidity one feels nearer to the Sahara than to the Mediterranean.

The rest of Libya — nearly the whole of it, that is — has a steppe or desert character. The arid, sandy plains of the bleak Jeffara stretch from Tunisia, between the sea and the Tripolitan Jabal; the beds of the wadis south of the Jabal and Sirte supply the nomads with a sparse shrub vegetation, and the plains south of Benghazi and Marmarica are covered with a poor bushy growth.

The oases of Fezzan, Jofra, Aujila-Jarabub and Kufra are alignments of palm-trees lost in a desert immensity of dunes, mountains and flat expanses. There is very little rainfall, watering-places are rare and crops are irregular. The El Hamra Hammada and the Libyan Sahara of Cyrenaica are so denuded as to be almost absolute deserts.

*Difficult conditions for agriculture and stock-breeding.* The desert climate — high temperatures in summer and cold nights in winter — the hot, drying south winds and irregular rainfall combine to make cultivation a hazardous undertaking over three-quarters of the territory. Except in the coastal zones, dry farming is impossible; the peasants are obliged to have recourse to a difficult, laborious process of pumping.

The soil of Tripolitania is mostly sandy and poor; that of Cyrenaica, more clayey, has the drawback of being more greedy of water; the desert soil is often salty. Only the coastal oases are truly fertile.

Cereals (wheat and barley) are grown in irrigated gardens (palm-groves), or after the rains, in the collective lands of the tribes. Olive- and almond-trees, grown in the Tripolitan Jabal, and the palm-trees on the Tripolitan coast and in inland palm-groves are well adapted to the climate. Citrus and soft-fruit trees and market-garden crops are grown only in the outskirts of the towns.

The livestock comprises goats, sheep and cattle in the maritime zone, the cattle being replaced by camels in the desert regions. The nomads or semi-nomads pasture their flocks and herds freely in the recognised ancestral territories of the tribe, and water them at collective or private wells.

Libya has few other resources. Fishing for sponges, tunny and sardines could be developed. Esparto grass is turned to account, and so are the castor-oil plant, and henna plant. A number of country craftsmen are employed in making carpets, mats and leather goods. There are not many processing industries.

Potassium salt is found in the soil not far from

Welding the last link of the pipeline from Zelten, the most important oilfield revealed by intensive prospecting.

In soft conditions like this
the wheeled vehicle sinks
into the heavy sand
and emphasises the natural
advantages of camel transport.

A back street in Tripoli,
capital of Libya.
Tripoli is an attractive town
and the only one in Libya which
can aptly be called a city.
A cluster of smaller townships
on the coast gives the region
of Tripolitania an urban character.

Marada (Sirtica) and natron in Fezzan. Intensive oil-prospecting by twenty-two companies has resulted in the discovery of a number of oilfields, the most important being at Zelten, 200 miles south of Benghazi, where production and export began in 1961, at Dahra, midway between Benghazi and Tripoli, and at Beda, just east of the Tripolitania-Cyrenaica border. In January 1962, 57 wells in Cyrenaica and 102 wells in Tripolitania were in production.

The splendid Roman cities of Sabratha and Leptis Magna, restored in recent years, and the graceful Greek ruins of Appolonia and Cyrene, bear witness to former prosperity in more pluvial periods.

. Although industries exist to supply local needs, exports consist chiefly of products of the soil — fruit, esparto grass, early vegetables and groundnuts (peanuts) — livestock and fish. Imports include cereals, foodstuffs (sugar, tea) and textiles, basic necessities in a society of Bedouin extraction where the family budget is balanced by barter. The other chief items of import, lubricants and petrol, as well as all manfactured products such as vehicles, have increased considerably since independence, but invisible exports through the oil companies offset this.

*Semi-nomads, farmers and townsmen.* In Cyrenaica the nomads and their rural brethren form two-thirds of the population, and are divided by themselves into two categories of tribes: the Saadi, representing the Beni Solaym nobility, and the Merabtin, their protégés, who include the old Berber tribes and some of whom pay tribute. The nomads (or rather semi-nomads) have taken possession of the rich soil of the Jabal Akhdhar, on which they pasture their stock and cultivate sown crops. Returning to the steppe south of the Jabal in November, they go to the uplands again for the harvests in the hot season.

The townsmen are outsiders who do not mix with the nomads, the great majority being composed of Tripolitans (in Misurata and Urfella), North Africans, descendants of Turks and Negroes and a few Jews, Cretans, and Maltese. The towns are markets for the nomads; Benghazi is still really no more than a large village.

In Fezzan the semi-nomads, forming a fifth of the population, live on the outskirts, with an eye to the settlers' palm-trees. The settlers, whether Negroes or half-breeds, from the serfs who draw water to the Islamic hermits, have always been a prey to the nomads. The oases of Gadames, Tunisian in character, and of Ghat, a Targui settlement, have sadly declined from their ancient splendour as caravan cities between Tripoli and the Sudan. No town has ever arisen among the palm-groves of Fezzan, and Sebha, the capital, is merely a crossroads.

In Tripolitania the settlers outnumber the nomads by seven to four and even have an influence on Bedouin life. The same national elements are found among them as in Cyrenaica, with the addition of Italians and Ibadhites.

The semi-nomads of the Jeffara, Guibla and Sirtica are poor and forced to add arboriculture to stock-breeding in order to live. This explains why they covet the olive trees of the Jabal and the palm of Fezzan, where they come into conflict with the settlers.

Tripoli, the joint capital, was smartened up by the

Italians, and is the only built-up area in Libya to count as a city. Tripoli and Benghazi will eventually be replaced as capital by Beida. The centres around Tripoli and the villages on the coast house a large population and give the province an urban character.
*Italian colonisation.* Individual and fragmentary from 1911 to 1921, capitalists from 1922 to 1927 (investment of private capital in private concerns), Italian colonisation in Libya had become demographic by 1928; that is to say, its purpose was to settle peasant families from over-populated regions of Italy.

In Cyrenaica the Italian colonists introduced into the Jabal Akhdhar poured out again before the British armies in 1942, and their farms were either rented by the Government (300), or abandoned (1,400). In Tripolitania there are still two types of farming, related to the two stages of colonisation referred to above: capitalist and demographic. The first comprises private 'concessions', which were, however, in receipt of assistance from the Government (up to 30 per cent), on condition of installing Italian working-class families (7,400 people in 1949); well equipped and managed, they are now suffering from lack of funds and wear and tear of implements. The second type is connected with the 'colonies' created by means of independent associations that made themselves responsible for all installations (houses. roads, water, schools, church), distributed holdings on the estate and advanced funds (to 11,000 people in 1949); working well from the technical point of view, they became Libyan property after the decision of the United Nations in 1955.

Today, however, the Italians tend to be regarded as foreigners in Libya. Italian farming is still recognisable by the rows of olive-trees alternating with almond-trees and citrus fruit which, together with cereals, groundnuts (peanuts), tobacco and vegetables, form the chief exports.
*Foreign contributions and technical assistance.* As soon as it achieved independence, the young state devoted its attention to economic problems and the development of education.
Besides various contributions from France, Britain and the U.S.A., the Libyans have the benefit of technical assistance from the United Nations, who supply experts and implements, of Point Four (United States aid to underdeveloped countries), of various gifts from Turkey and Egypt and loans from the 'Financial Corporation' — Italy, France and Great Britain. In this way the budgetary deficit has been largely made good.
*Federation or unitary state?* In the days of antiquity Tripoli, a Phoenician city, had no connection with Cyrene, a creek colony; whether under Roman or Arab rule, Tripoli belonged to Tunis, Cyrene to Egypt; they differed in climate, soil and way of life; it took the Italian conquest to unite them.

Libya is an almost empty country (about two people to the square mile), and life is concentrated in widely separated spots, true desert oases, Tripolitania has twice the population of the other regions situated in a marginal zone, mainly in the built-up area of Tripoli. The great distances reflect the geographical divisions, which in turn are marked by the diversity of the inhabitants.

In view of the natural compartmentation of Libya,

the constituent authorities first made it a federation; but in 1963 a unitary state was established.
THE FUTURE OF LIBYA. The United Nations confronted Libya with a dilemma: should it live in independence with a pastoral economy, or renounce certain freedoms and receive the assistance of powerful protectors? Was it possible to build up a viable state given the limited resources and marked internal divisions? The discovery and exploitation of rich oilfields has made the future seem more secure for the new state, for it no longer needs to rely entirely upon a precarious development of agriculture to support its growing population and raise the standard of living.

The discovery of oil in Libya has contributed to its initial economic development. Here, after drilling in the Raguba oilfield, flow is improved by pumping acid into the well and burning off the mixture of oil and acid until there is a flow of pure oil.

# EGYPT

The concentration of fellaheen in enormous densities in the Nile Valley does not alter the fact that 97 per cent of the area of Egypt is uninhabitable, and that Egypt itself is a geographical paradox.

Although bounded to the north by the Mediterranean and to the east by the Red Sea, it is really no more than an immense tawny desert forming part of the sub-tropical Saharo-Arabian belt.

In the winter, however, the Saharan high pressures retreat far enough to the south to make way for a Mediterranean rainfall. Alexandria's annual average is 7 inches, Cairo has 1.4 inches and Asyut 2 millimetres (0.079 inches); but the rain is not much use, indeed it is often harmful, because it falls in violent showers. The influence of the sea has a more definite effect on the temperature of the coasts, which are cooler than the interior; but the seas are warm, and do little to cool the summers. The dryness of the air always pro-

The Sphinx and an Islamic graveyard at Gizeh, on the edge of the Sahara and a few miles from Cairo.

Old and new in sharp contrast in Cairo.

duces vast differences between day and night temperatures: at Cairo this difference is 12°C. (53.6°F.) in January and 14°C. (57.2°F.) in August. Night temperatures in winter may drop as low as freezing-point, whereas in summer rocks exposed to the sun may reach a temperature of over 70°C. (158°F.). In addition, evaporation is intense and subjects all organisms to such a degree of desiccation that few plants are able to resist it without an artificial water supply.

## THE VALLEY OF THE NILE
## AND THE LEGACY OF THE PAST

*Hostility of the deserts.* The flat desert west of the Nile is the most 'desert-like' known. In winter its coastal fringe condenses enough moisture in the form of rain or dew to maintain the existence of a very loose steppe, and even the nomads' few crops of barley. Watering-places scattered along the coast mark the old route of the pilgrims coming formerly from the Magreb.

In the interior, enormous basins reach to the level of the artesian water tables, producing either brackish lagoons and crusts of salt or settlements in the palm-groves. Except for Kharga, these minute oases communicate only by nomad caravans, of which there are few. Faiyum is better off, being watered by an offshoot of the Nile, the Bahr Yussef.

On the east of the Nile the Arabian desert, which is narrower than that on the west, rises towards the east to form mountains, connected beyond the Red Sea with the massifs of Arabia and the Sinai peninsula. A close network of deeply eroded dry valleys, or wadis, runs down these mountains towards the Nile and the Red Sea. These wadis have temporary flows of water, especially in the heart of the mountains, which condense more rain; they preserve shallow layers of water in their alluvia, supporting a denser, less transient vegetation and feeding the rudimentary wells sunk by the miners of antiquity and the nomads of today.

The harshness of climatic conditions increases everywhere when, owing to migratory cyclonic depressions, the south wind rises, hot and dry, charged with electricity and full of dust and even sand. This is the Khamsin, which in spite of its name (which means 'fifty') rarely blows for more than twenty-five days a year, in the spring.

*A fairly simple geological history.* North-East Africa has a fairly simple geological history, during which the desert climate was frequently dominant, particularly between the Carboniferous and Cretaceous periods when thick Nubian sandstones accumulated above the worn-down folds of Archaean rocks. Later the seas of the Cretaceous and subsequent periods deposited limestones and marls over almost the whole of the region. Faulting over a wide area during the Alpine earth movements created the Red Sea and elevated the Isthmus of Suez and Mount Sinai (Jebel Katherina 8,664 feet) and the Arabian massif (Jebel Cheyeb 6,892 feet).

*The Nile.* The desert is populated by fewer than 50,000 people, including the oasis-dwellers (one to about eight square miles). Against this, 27 million, a veritable human ant-heap, are crowded together on a long south-north strip of land, the Valley of the Nile.

The Nile as we know it is not a very old river, but dates from the Alpine earth movements during the Tertiary period. These created the anticline of the Red Sea Mountains and, paralleling them to the west, a broad syncline into which the great Nile trench was cut. The present anomalous course, profile and character of the river are the outcome of the linking of a number of independent drainage systems, notably the great lakes of East Africa, the Sudd (the former inland drainage system of the Sudan), and the run-off from the Ethiopian highlands. The heavy early summer rains of East Africa and the Ethiopian highlands enable the river to maintain its flow across 1,200 miles of absolute desert, in fact, rising to a flood during these arid months. For centuries this late summer flood in Egypt, spreading widely over the valley and delta, distributed a layer of fertile silt of Ethiopian origin. The lack of tidal scour in the Mediterranean and the great volume of silt carried by the river has resulted in the development of a delta.

Thanks to perennial irrigation the Lower (Egyptian) Nile can now supply man at all seasons with the water the sky refuses him, but no longer lavishes on him the silt that forms the cultivable soil, the black *khemi* famous in the days of the Pharaohs.

*Men and the Nile.* The river swells rapidly between June and September; it increases from 523 to 8,500 cubic metres a second at Aswan, which means that it rises from 26 to 32 feet above its lowest water level. This seasonal rise formerly caused general inundation, but now it is made use of under the 'basin' system of irrigation.

Under this system, as soon as the river has returned to its bed, seed is sown in the mud left behind (October–November). The water is stored in a soil full of deep cracks, the low evaporation in winter and mild temperature enabling the crops to be harvested in April: this is known as *chetui* farming, and takes advantage of favourable natural circumstances. But the low relief of the flood-plain in effect reduces the useful area: from the pre-dynastic era onwards the Egyptians undertook collectively to separate huge enclosures or basins by means of earth dykes and to level their floors, so as to standardise the benefits of the floods and hasten the drying out of the low areas. Hard wheat, barley, beans, onions, flax and vines grow without much expenditure of labour. The livestock, chiefly cattle and donkeys, reduced in number, needed leguminous crops grown in rotation. A light swing-plough and a hoe (*fass*) formed the main equipment. In the uncultivated zones of the delta, hunting and, to a greater extent, fishing were sources of income. From April to July the land was forced to rest by the intense heat of the sun.

The exceptional conditions created by the Nile help to explain the birth of Egyptian civilisation — a civilisation that matured slowly, away from outside influences, before astonishing the Mediterranean world. The rhythm of men's lives was based on that of the river-god, whose caprices were feared. Demographic expansion led to the cultivation of the land above the high-water level by watering it with the *shadouf*, a balance beam with a bucket on a rope (*nili* or autumn farming), the lower-lying land being watered from wells reaching down to the water table (*sefi* or summer farming).

This system is still practised today in the south (Upper Egypt) over an area of about three-quarters of a million acres. It has been much improved by the pumping dams on the Nile at Isna, Nag' Hammadi and Asyut, from which channels with sluices feed a whole series of interconnected basins, which may be inundated for a period of thirty to sixty days. These features of an age-old past have been best preserved from Aswan to Asyut, where the valley is only half a mile to six miles wide.

## RISE OF A MODERN ECONOMY

*Influence of Europe.* Napoleon Bonaparte's expedition was a startling revelation of the weakness of the Ottoman suzerain, and led to the revival of Egypt under the strong hand of Mehemet Ali. His ambitious projects for the country and himself requiring prosperous finances, Mehemet Ali revolutionised the economy with the introduction of cotton. One of

The apex of the Nile delta. Since earliest times the Nile has been vital to the people of Egypt. Today twenty-nine million people crowd together along the north-south strip of its cultivated valley.

Cotton is the dominant element
in the Egyptian economy.
Yields are high and in an average
year cotton provides roughly one-
third of the net national revenue.

*Map opposite:* The Egyptian
economy revolves
almost entirely around the
River Nile and the irrigation
provided by its waters: hence the
concentration of population
around the fertile Nile valley,
so that, while the average
national density is 64 per
square mile, the figure is as
high as 1,896 per square mile in
the inhabited areas.
Successful completion of the
Aswan High Dam
provides sufficient power and
permanently irrigated land to
transform the entire economy.

Construction of the Aswan High
Dam. In early summer the Nile
is at its lowest and then rises
rapidly to its floods.
In order to store the flood-waters
for irrigation purposes during
the following dry season
the Aswan Dam, built in 1902,
has been enlarged several times
and supplemented with a system
of cataracts to raise the level
of the water locally. The valley
of the Nile is predominantly
rural, with agriculture, fishing
and stock-breeding,
the principal activities.

his successors, Ismail, took more interest in sugar and
in the Suez Canal. Europe, which in spite of France
had already checked Mehemet Ali's free expansion.
was even more perturbed by this canal, the fruit of
perseverance by de Lesseps. First France, and then to
an even larger extent Great Britain, took advantage
of the Khedive's financial difficulties to intervene in
his government, and finally to occupy the territory,
which had become a 'strategic' one. This led in turn
to Egypt's loss of the Sudan, stirred to revolt by the
Mahdi and then organised as an Anglo-Egyptian Condominium. The British Protectorate hastened the
economic transformation already begun, and gave it
a semi-colonial character.

*The reign of cotton.* Known to the ancients, but soon
supplanted by flax, cotton-growing was revived by
Mehemet Ali. In 1821 Jumel singled out a long-fibred
Ethiopian variety which became the only authorised
one. Its plantation even became obligatory, in order
to increase Mehemet Ali's national trade, but the negligence of the fellaheen soon led to its degeneration.
Varieties were imported from Malta, America (Sea
Island) and India. The War of Succession, by depriving
Europe of the American fibre set the Egyptian cotton
trade finally on its feet. Among the natural hybrids
'long-fibre' varieties (over $1\frac{1}{2}$ inches) and medium-
fibre varieties (over $1\frac{1}{8}$ inches) were selected, which
gave a good yield in the field and the spinning mill.
Research is now carried on by the Cotton Research
Board, and there is strict supervision of the quality
of the seed, of the ginning carried on in the hundred
provincial mills, and of the grading for export in
Alexandria.

Sown in February, the cotton is watered a dozen
times, harrowed and weeded. War against parasites,
waged by hand, does little to reduce losses, which
amount in some years to a third of the crop. The
double harvest takes place in September in Lower
Egypt, where early rains may be troublesome, and
in August in Upper Egypt, where it delays the inundation of the basins. The cotton harvest represents a
fifth of the total area harvested and 2 per cent of
world plantations, producing from 300,000 to 450,000
tons of ginned cotton (6 per cent of world production).
Average yield is remarkable: 7.45 bushels to the acre,
or twice that of the United States and almost four
times that of India.

Cotton eliminates the customary fallow break from
April to July and exhausts the soil, especially if it is
grown every other year. This difficulty has been more
or less solved by an increasing use of nitrogenous
chemical fertilizers. The maintenance of post-war
State control over the exchanges of the frenzy of
the speculators seriously disturbed the cotton trade
from 1948 to 1952.

These vicissitudes have proved prejudicial to the
Egyptian economy, since in an average year cotton
represents 35 per cent of agricultural revenue, or at
least 15 per cent of the net national revenue and 80
per cent of exports. Although it is not the only crop,
cotton is the predominant element in the economy,
a fact that all is the more dangerous in that its value
depends wholly on world trade. It is a luxury fibre,
and in recent years artificial textiles have had an
overwhelming success and offer a serious threat
to cotton-producing countries.

*Revolution in agricultural methods.* The Nile is at its lowest during the early summer and then rises rapidly to its flood. Consequently widespread cropping of the soil throughout the summer was impossible until a system of perennial irrigation utilising water stored from the previous flood could be instituted. To do this the Aswan Dam was constructed in 1902. It has been twice enlarged and now stores 5,500 million cubic metres of water. This supplemented by the dam at Jebel Aulia, in the Sudan, with a capacity of 2,500 million cubic metres. Downstream of the Aswan Dam a number of barrages or weirs have been constructed to raise the level of the water locally to facilitate the feeding of distributary canals. Such barrages are at Isna, Nag Hammadi, Asyut, Cairo (the Delta Barrage), Zifta and Edfina. From them water flows into the main canals, thence into distributary canals and finally by means of *shadoufs*, *sakkiehs*, Archimedian screws and mechanical pumps the water is lifted on to the chequerboard fields.

The water handicap having been overcome, cultivation goes on without interruption: temperate region cultivation during the winter months (*chetui*) is followed by tropical cultivation (*sefi*) in the summer. In the rotation of crops, cotton, bersim (Alexandrian clover), wheat and maize follow one another over a period of three years or, more often, two years. Wheat can share the *chetui* period with bersim, barley, beans, lentils and onions, while cotton yields to rice, sorghum or sugar-cane in Upper Egypt, and sometimes to groundnuts (peanuts) in sandy soils. The *nili* period of autumn farming is best suited to maize. Plots yield five harvests in three years, or four in two, according to the rotation.

By using these methods approximately 6,177,000 acres cultivated represent nearly 9,637,000 acres harvested. The fertility of the soil, now deprived of the benefit of silt and of fallowing from April to July, is only maintained with difficulty by means of nitrate fertilizers. In the low-lying regions, excessive watering has raised the level of the water table and brought about the deterioration of the soil owing to the rise of noxious salts. Considerable drainage provision is necessary, with arteries running parallel to those of irrigation. The altitude of the northern part of the North Delta necessitates costly pumping to discharge the sewers into the sea.

The Nile regime is irregular from year to year. At Aswan the August-to-October flow, which represents two-thirds of the annual total, may vary in September between 4,706 and 11,469 cubic metres per second. On average, the annual flow is 84 milliard cubic metres, while the need (for Egypt and the Sudan) is only half that amount; but in the spring the whole of the reserves stored up in the winter (7.1 milliard cubic metres) have to be used. A bad year, e.g. 1913, may provide no more than 46 milliard cubic metres, of which part, being too full of silt during the high-water flow, is drained out to sea again. On the other hand, in some years there may be too much water, and in spite of an alarm system for the riverside inhabitant, there is a risk of the earth dykes breaking down and flooding the perennial irrigation land. often 12 feet below the maximum level of the river. It is impossible to foretell precisely how the river will behave;  precautions can only be

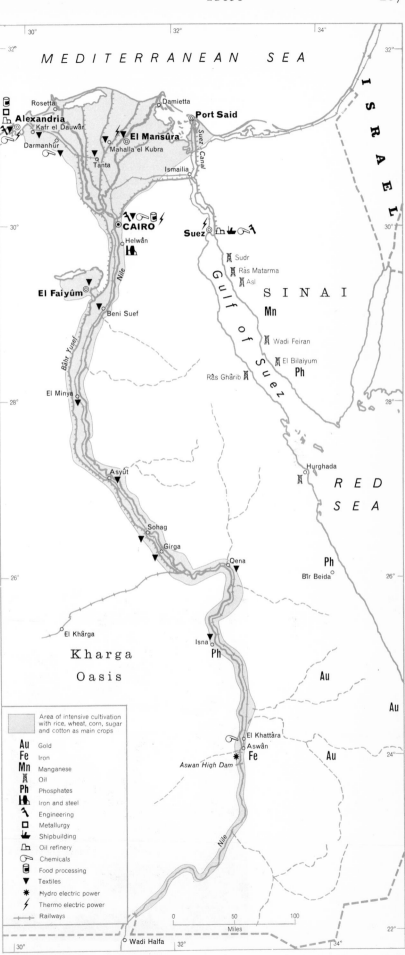

Area of intensive cultivation with rice, wheat, corn, sugar and cotton as main crops

Au   Gold
Fe   Iron
Mn   Manganese
    Oil
Ph   Phosphates
    Iron and steel
    Engineering
    Metallurgy
    Shipbuilding
    Oil refinery
    Chemicals
    Food processing
    Textiles
    Hydro electric power
    Thermo electric power
    Railways

taken a few weeks beforehand, when Cairo is supplied daily with the figures registered by the Nilometers in the Sudan, indicating the speed of flow of the tributaries. Thus besides difficulties resulting from fluctuations and crises in the cotton market, Egyptian agriculture suffers damage from a badly disciplined and unpredictable river.

*Agricultural and rural Egypt.* The condition of Egyptian agriculture today may be stated thus: wheat grows widely, except in the North Delta and Upper Egypt (fructification hampered by the heat); it covers 17 per cent of the harvested areas, but produces only one million tons (22.92 bushels per acre), because the choice of seed is left to the fellaheen. The 'wheat granary of Rome' is now obliged to import up to half of its requirements. Barley, which overflows the Libyan coastal fringe, is partly used up in brewing. Field beans (*ful*) help to supply the deficiency in animal proteins and keep the cattle alive during the summer; the Valley grows more of it than the Delta; and the same is true of onions, the third export product. Flax has almost disappeared. The highest acreage goes to bersim (2,224,000 acres); this fixes the nitrogen in the soil and feeds the livestock, but makes very poor hay.

Sugar-cane tends to take the place of cotton in the south, where it is sure of water (7,600 cubic metres per acre), and where the temperature is always above 4°C. (39.2°F.). A season of winter makes it necessary to select fast-growing varieties (Cuban, Javan, Indian), whose cycle is completed before flowering, in ten or twelve months; cuttings are planted and three successive harvests reaped in four years. Eighty-nine thousand acres yield only 180,000 to 250,000 metric tons of sugar produced in four sugar factories working

seasonally. Imports are increasing, to cover a third of requirements.

In the salt North Delta, rice used to be grown as a soil-improvement crop; but in time its good quality won it a place among Egypt's exports, and even in home consumption. However, it needs 6,600 cubic metres of water per acre during the period of its April-to-August cultivation. This is the lowest-water period, and it is the first to suffer from the capricious flow of the Nile. As a rule the yield of paddy is high (55 bushels per acre), although the seedlings are not thinned out. The exportable surplus is variable, sometimes nil. There is a market for the by-products of the rice fields.

Sorghum (*doura rafia*) takes the place of maize south of El Minya, and overflows into the Sudan. Maize (*doura chami*) grows well only in the *nili,* or autumn, period, when it is not stinted for water. The relative humidity of the Delta improves its yield and its area exceeds that of wheat, but production is becoming insufficient. The leaves are sometimes used as fodder.

Market-garden crops (tomatoes, marrows, beans, cabbages at all seasons) keep pace with the expansion of the towns. Potatoes have only recently been introduced; melons and water-melons are traditional. Fruit-growing covering only 89,000 acres, mostly in the neighbourhood of Cairo, includes cultivation of citrus fruit (50 per cent), vines and figs on the north coast, olives in Faiyum, bananas and mangoes.

Palms (about 6 million, chiefly in Middle Egypt) produce rather poor dates. Timber trees — acacia, tamarisk, sycamore and eucalyptus — are planted in the villages, and along the roads and canals. There is no true forest, and a considerable amount of timber is imported.

Apprentices at work in a refrigeration and air conditioning training centre. To speed up economic development, the Egyptian government has established a vocational training programme on a national basis for all industrial trades.

There is little stock-breeding, bersim being the only fresh fodder: in the summer, beans and chopped straw provide insufficient feed. Cow buffaloes (*gamousse*) and cows are used for labour and supply milk. There is little meat to be had except in large urban areas. Dromedaries are used to transport sugar-cane and cotton, but the herds are maintained by imported animals. Donkeys are ubiquitous, robust and equal to every task. Sheep are found everywhere, even on the borders of the desert. Goats do best in Upper Egypt, and small chickens, geese and pigeons are bred everywhere, the last essentially for the sake of their droppings. Bee-keeping is traditional. Altogether, although the consumption of animal food is very low, imports from the Sudan are a matter of necessity.

Fishing does not play a compensatory part as it does in the Far East: the 40,000 tons of fish come from lagoons and rivers rather than from the sea. Greeks gather sponges off the Libyan coast, and Sudanese the mother-of-pearl of the Red Sea.

The Valley of the Nile is predominantly rural, and the primary activities — agriculture, fishing and stock-breeding — supply an essential part of the national revenue (45 per cent), in addition to which they absorb a large part of the working population (53 per cent).

*Development of urban population.* Continued growth and excessively uneven distribution of her population are perhaps Egypt's greatest problems today. With an average national density of 64 per square mile, nevertheless, in the inhabited areas the density is as high as 1,896 per square mile. Such disparity of distribution creates many problems. The post-war period has seen a marked expansion of the towns, fourteen of which have more than 100,000 inhabitants. All but one of the towns are in Lower Egypt. They possess districts of Western aspect, especially Cairo, with a population of over 3 million, and Alexandria. In sixty years (1897-1957) the urban population rose from 13 per cent to 15 per cent of the total population. This increase was the outcome of new activities: connected with industries, commerce and administration.

The cotton revolution has thus upset the balance between the people and the land, permitted the introduction of elements, often luxurious ones, of Western life, and given rise to more and more serious problems of the land facing every fundamentally underdeveloped economy. The Protectorate was partly responsible: while food crops were restricted in favour of cotton, the peasant crafts declined under competition from European manufactured goods, and the embryonic Egyptian industry started by Mehemet Ali disappeared. Firmly linked with world economy, Egypt appeared to be doomed to suffer its vicissitudes but not to share its financial success. Some benefit must, however, be noted: a rail network as a security for the National Debt, permanent modernisation of the Suez Canal, the equipment of Suez, Port Said and Alexandria, the birth of urban development and of embryonic health and educational organisations. It is within this framework, and by contact with the colonies of Europeans engaged in business or administration, that the Egyptian middle class was born.

*Birth of Egyptian industry.* Most of the present enterprises were started after 1930, the year of the first protectionist law, which has since been strengthened. Sources of energy are still insufficient; no workable coal has been discovered. Oil is exploited only on the shores of the Red Sea, and prospecting in the deserts has hardly begun. Its production expands slowly, while the Near East has gone rapidly ahead and home demand increases apace. Electricity, which is mainly thermal in origin, is localised in the towns and round the pumping-stations. Mineral deposits (gold, zinc, copper, chromium and tin), although numerous in the Egyptian hills, are hardly profitable, except those of manganese in the Sinai peninsula, the output of which is sent to the United States, and of iron, recently discovered near Aswan. Phosphate is extracted in large quantities at Safaga and Kossier for export in a crude state, and bay-salt at Port Said. Natron from the Wadi Natrun is almost exhausted.

Manufacturing industries are better represented.

The population of Egypt is approximately 29 million. Even the agrarian reforms instituted by the military junta that assumed power in 1952 have done little to raise the standard of living.

Textiles are first in order, occupying four workers out of ten. Ginning and pressing are highly mechanised, and cotton spinning still more so, and highly concentrated. Weaving is distributed among 100,000 craftsmen. Wool is scarce, rayon is expanding; clothing and footwear complete this branch. If workers employed in the food industry (wheat mills, rice mills and sugar factories) are added, three-quarters of the total industrial labour force is accounted for, engaged in supplying though not satisfying the elementary needs of the population. Metallurgical industry is almost non-existent. An ironworks, set up by a German firm at Helwan, a suburb of Cairo, was started in 1958. A chemical industry has begun with oil-refining (Suez) and artificial fertilizer manufacture (Suez and Aswan). Urban development has favoured the building industries (cement, bricks, window-glass, lamps), and 25,000 factories employ 450,000 workers. Cotton yarns, footwear and salt are already seeking foreign markets, for demand on the home market is low. The localisation of industries is still restricted, with a few exceptions, to the areas of Cairo, Alexandria and the Suez Canal. Well under 6 per cent of the working population was employed in the secondary industries (processing) in 1947, the same proportion as in 1927; by 1960 the proportion was no more than 10 per cent.

*Political evolution.* In 1922 negotiations with Great Britain secured independence and in 1923 the monarchy became a parliamentary one. The control of the Suez Canal and the Statute of the Sudan provoked political and diplomatic disturbances, to which the approach of war put a temporary end by the treaty of 1936, restricting British troops to 10,000 men in the Canal zone and re-establishing the Con-dominium in the Sudan. Admitted to the League of Nations, Egypt secured the ending of the Capitulations. After some hesitation, she took part in the struggle against the Axis in the Second World War. Negotiations fraught with hostile incidents ended at last in the evacuation of the Canal by British troops (1956) and free determination in the Sudan, which chose independence rather than union with the Valley of the Nile (1953-56). Now Egypt plays a leading part in the Arab League founded in 1945, especially since the war she waged against Israel. In 1958 this leadership of the Arab world brought about a union of federal type with Syria (United Arab Republic) and one of confederate type with the Yemen. In September 1961, however, Syria broke away and resumed independence, and in December of the same year the union with the Yemen was also terminated. Political independence and economic growth have kept pace with each other, sometimes increasing the tendency to xenophobia and religious intolerance, and masking the aggravation of the social crisis.

## ACUTENESS OF PRESENT PROBLEMS

*Population and distribution of resources.* Estimated at 2.5 million in 1800, Egypt's population today amounts to at least 29 million, with an annual increase of 500,000 to 600,000, owing to a birthrate varying between 40 and 45 per thousand, while the deathrate has dropped from 27 before the Second World War to 19-16 per 1,000 between 1952 and 1956. The standard of living is very low and has been degenerating continuously for the last few decades. This can be seen from the fact that between 1938 and 1950, for instance, the annual consumption of maize per

A view from the Citadel, Cairo. To the right are two minarets of the Rifayeh mosque; in the centre, the mosque of the Sultan Hasan, built in 1356-63.

head dropped from 209 lb. to 154 lb., and that of wheat from 163 lb. to 132 lb., a decrease that is not offset by the rise in average consumption of rice (from 48 to 68 lb.).

This phenomenon is due not only to the increase in the birthrate, but to an ossified economy and a semi-feudal social structure: in 1952 from 200,000 to 300,000 people, out of 20 million, shared between them 37 per cent of the total of private income. But it is in the rural world that disparity is most apparent; at that time, 95 per cent of the landowners (two and a half million peasants) possessed only 35 per cent of the cultivated land between them, and seven out of nine of them had only a patch 130 feet square, whereas an area of five acres is required for the support of a normal family. Besides these, there were a million landless peasants seeking employment as day labourers, but seldom working more than 120 days a year. The effects of these conditions are apparent in the form of endemic diseases: trachoma, 90 per cent of the population; bilharziasis, 55 per cent (75 per cent in rural areas); hookworm disease, 30 per cent. The first gesture of the military junta that came to power in 1952 was to decree an agrarian reform, which shattered the ultra-conservative power of the landed proprietors by allowing the maximum family holding to be no more than 300 acres, expropriating the surplus and distributing it among landless peasantry. Only about 10 per cent of the farmland was thus redistributed to the benefit of no more than 200,000 landless peasant families. In 1961 more severe measures were enacted to reduce maximum holdings to 100 acres.

*Increase in production and Aswan High Dam.* The solution can only be found in an expanding economy, tending to a better balance between the three branches by displacement of labour. This presupposes an increase in agricultural production: the old hydraulic plans have given way to the Aswan High Dam scheme, providing for an immense reservoir south of Aswan (a dam 3 miles long and 327 feet high, giving a reservoir capacity of 130 milliard cubic metres). The lake, with an area of 1,150 square miles, will submerge the Wadi Halfa in the Sudan, and allow the entire discharge of the Nile to be used. This scheme has been planned with the Sudan, which will also receive more water. Agricultural yields can be improved by returning to triennial rotation, and by a greater use of chemical fertilizers and of dung (now used as fuel). Water will be available for reclamation of the desert edge into farmland and rice may one day surpass cotton as chief cash crop, and with market-garden and fruit crops transform Egypt into one immense *huerta*. The provision of fresh sources of energy (the Aswan High Dam will produce 10 thousand million kWh) may encourage industrial development, and better technical development and conditions of labour will be needed if the competition of Europe is to be withstood, and that of Israel.

Among the obstacles to be overcome is the lack of capital, only to be remedied by calling on foreign assistance. Discontinuity of effort is another hindrance to achievement: too many of the schemes proposed during the last fifty years have been pigeon-holed, and rapid action is called for in face of the constant increase in population. The problem calls for the active not to say passionate, participation of a whole people — accustomed to passivity for thousands of years — in the quest for a better social and economic stability of the country.

Founded by Alexander the Great in 331 B.C., Alexandria is today the principal port of Egypt and a busy commercial centre. Food processing, chemicals, shipbuilding and engineering head the list of its industries.

# AFRICA
# OF THE SAVANNAS
# AND FORESTS

# ETHIOPIA

Ethiopia has a history extending over three thousand years. It became Christian sixteen centuries ago and has remained so. It was for centuries the only independent country in Africa, and this gives it a special pride and prestige.

Until the end of the nineteenth century, Ethiopia was known as Abyssinia. It perches on a platform 10,000 feet in altitude, surrounded by deep deserts. The conquests by Islam from the seventh century onwards closed the Red Sea and encircled the high Ethiopian plateau. Ethiopia began to emerge from this isolation after the cutting of the Suez Canal; but the Great Powers at once established themselves on the coasts and imprisoned it on the continent. From 1936 to 1941 Italy occupied the whole of the territory. In 1941 the Emperor Haile Selassie I regained his throne. In 1952, by federation with Eritrea, Ethiopia acquired a wide seaboard on the Red Sea. Eritrea was in 1962 integrated into a new unitary Ethiopian Empire, with an area of 395,000 square miles and a population officially estimated at over 20 million.
*High plateaus and rift valleys.* From East Africa to south-west Arabia a huge shelf became upthrust and a very fluid lava spread out through fissures to a thickness of more than 6,500 feet, forming horizontal plateaus. In the Miocene and Pliocene Ages, fractures occured from Lake Malawi to the Taurus, and formed the largest rift valley of the earth. The shelf, with its covering of lava, was broken into three high plateaus separated by rift valleys. A second eruptive period in the trough faults followed these fractures.

The three high plateaus, Ethiopian, Galla-Somalian and Yemenite, have features in common: a high mean altitude of about 10,000 feet, with peaks exceeding 13,000 feet; mostly horizontal surfaces; asymmetry, with fault scarps of many thousand feet facing one another and having gentle slopes on the outer side; climatic features similar to those of tropical mountains, with moderate, even temperatures, and relatively heavy rainfall. But the Ethiopian plateau stands out by reason of its size, its position and its powerful rivers. It has also been important historically: all the political structures from which present-day Ethiopia is descended had their foundations within it, and for many centuries the Ethiopian Empire had the edge of its high plateau for frontier. This high plateau extends from 5° to 18°N., about one thousand miles. It is narrow in the north, where it drops almost straight down to the sea, widening until in the south its width is 300 miles. In the centre and the north, the mean altitude is about 13,000 feet, but it is considerably lower to the south of the Blue Nile. The high plateau rises to the east, where it dominates Danakil with an escarpment of more than 6,500 feet in places. In the west, the descent to the plain of the White Nile is far less steep; the plateau is prolonged by spurs from 3,000 to 5,000 feet in height, alternating with very wide valleys.

Owing to the upheaval of the eastern part of the plateau, nearly all the rivers run west, first in ill-defined valleys, with wide, shallow beds, which they overflow in every rainy season. At about 8,000 feet they plunge suddenly into gorges that drop to 4,250 or even 6,500 feet below the level of the plateau. These canyons of the Mareb, the Takkaze and the Blue Nile run north to south and break up the plateau into the great regions that have become historical provinces: Eritrea, Tigre, Amhara Gojjam and Shoa. In the east, above the escarpment, the line of watershed between the rivers flowing into the Nile and those that lose themselves in Danakil forms an almost unbroken belt of plateau, where erosion by the Danakil torrents has isolated table areas with very steep sides. This eastern edge of the plateau forms a sort of battlement, the width of which varies from six to sixty miles. It has played an important part in the history of Ethiopia. It is the meeting-place of the people of the valleys and of the mountains, the nomads and settlers, Islam and Christianity; the only north-south communications pass through it, including the road from Asmara, capital of Eritrea, to Addis Ababa, capital of the Empire. It is on this fringe that nearly all the capitals were built.

The climate of the Ethiopian high plateau is a tropical one, modified by the altitude and comparable to that of the Andean countries. Mean annual temperatures vary from 15°C. (59°F.) to 20°C. (68°F.), and increase with the distance from the Equator, while rainfall grows less from the Equator to the north and occurs in the spring and in the summer, when it is heaviest. The mean annual rainfall is 49 inches at Addis Ababa and only 18 inches at Asmara. This relative dryness of Eritrea puts it at an economic disadvantage.

As in the Andes, there are three distinct climatic levels: the hot lands, up to 6,000 feet; the temperate lands, up to 8,250 feet; and the cold lands above.

The Galla-Somali high plateau slopes steeply towards the south-west. The highest summits (14,000 feet), formed by piled-up lava, overlook the trough fault that separates them from the Ethiopian plateau. The climate resembles that of the latter, but is slightly drier. The slopes of the Galla-Somali plateau descending to the Gulf of Aden and the Indian Ocean are divided between former British Somaliland and

An Eritrean girl carrying water-skins. Eritrea is the most northerly region of Ethiopia's high plateau and is intensely arid.

former Italian Somaliland, now the Federation of Somali.

The Ethiopian and Galla-Somali high plateaus are separated by rift plains that contrast violently with them.

The trough fault of the lakes, a continuation of the famous Rift Valley of East Africa, extends from Lake Rudolf to the altitude of Addis Ababa. It forms a corridor rising from 1,500 feet in the south to nearly 6,500 feet in the north, on a discontinuous slope dotted with lakes, the largest of which are lakes Abaya and Zwai. North of Lake Zwai, the rift widens to form the vast triangular plain of Danakil, which is dotted with volcanoes, partly covered with recent lava outflows, and pitted with closed salt basins, some of which are more than 300 feet below sea level. The Red Sea is simply the submerged part of Danakil. The climate of Danakil and the coasts of the Red Sea is torrid, while that of the lake trough is tempered by the altitude.

*Diverse populations. A Christian Empire.* The first people whose displacement is mentioned in history are the South-Arabian Semites, who crossed the Red Sea and brought the elements of advanced civilisation to the Hamites of the north of the plateau. The history of Ethiopia is basically the history of these Semitised Hamites, the Amharas.

The Hamitic Semites founded a grest empire, of which the capital, Aksum, became a trade metropolis connected by tracks to the ports of the Red Sea. In the fourth century A.D. Aksum adopted the monophysite Christianity of Alexandria. The sixth century marks the apogee of the empire, which had made the conquest of Arabia. In the seventh century the

Persians took possession of Arabia and closed the Red Sea. But the final blow was dealt the Aksum Empire by Islam, which, starting from Arabia, became established in the valley of the White Nile and in Danakil, isolating the high plateau. The conquests by Islam had the same consequences here as in the West: they put an end to commerce and brought about the decline of the towns, regional contraction, and finally the establishment of the feudal system. In the sixteenth century the kingdom of Prester John, which the West isolated on the Ethiopian high plateau, came near to suffering the fate of Egypt and the Magreb, under the attack of a Moslem conqueror coming from Harar. It was saved by the intervention of the Portuguese, lately settled in India. But from the southwest, in the wake of the Moslems, came Galla Hamites, pagan shepherds who succeeded in occupying a large part of the Ethiopian plateau.

At the end of the nineteenth century, at the time when Great Powers were becoming established on the shores of the sea, Menelik brought his armies down from the Ethiopian plateau and enlarged his frontiers until they touched the Sudan, British East Africa, the Somalias and Italian Eritrea. The Ethiopian Empire was quadrupled in size.

Today, with universal adult suffrage, Ethiopia is attempting to achieve social unity. For long the Amharas dominated the other peoples: pagan Negroes on its borders, pagan Hamite farmers in the south and west; Moslem Hamite shepherds in the east.

ADDIS ABABA, THE CAPITAL, AND THE PRINCIPAL TOWNS. Addis Ababa, the highest city in Africa, was founded in 1889 — the year in which the King of Shoa, Menelik II, became Emperor — on a site whose disadvantages are obvious. It is built on a fault scarp with a drop of 984 feet, scored from north to south by deep ravines and broken up by hillocks. The site thus has many drawbacks for a modern capital; the altitude (8,200 feet) adds to them by fatiguing hearts and car engines. Many of the population of 450,000 have preserved purely rural establishments and activities in the city itself; 10,000 Yemenites trade there; and besides Greeks, Armenians and Indians, settled there from the earliest days of Addis Ababa, there are 15,000 foreigners, Europeans and Americans. These people represent almost every conceivable way of life.

The tangle of the three towns (that of Menelik, that of the Italians, who for prestige reasons made it the capital of their East Africa, and that of Haile Selassie I); the area, equal to that of Paris; the omnipresence of a forest of ten million eucalyptus trees designed to anchor the soil; and the lack of communications with the outside world and with the sea, all present problems. Addis Ababa should perhaps be abandoned and the capital built lower down on a less rugged site nearer the sea and at the same time nearer to regions which, if developed, would provide not only the energy needed for industry, but important products such as coffee, cotton, rice and sugar-cane. But any undertaking of this kind would conflict with tradition and the outlook of the Amharas. Fifteen centuries of isolation and defensiveness have developed a reluctance in the leading population to descend from the high plateau and this is holding up the development of the marginal regions and any dissemination of the economy.

The market in Harar, an important commercial centre.

The other important centres of Ethiopia are Harar, Dessye, Gondar and Diredawa.

THE FOURTEENTH PROVINCE: ERITREA. With Asmara as its capital, Eritrea consists only of the most northerly part of the high plateau, the narrowest and the nearest to the sea. We have seen that it is dry and poverty-stricken. Its population is around 600,000 But what chiefly distinguishes it from the rest of Ethiopia is the character given it by sixty years of Italian colonial occupation: it has railroutes, roads, ports (Massawa, Assab) and urban centres. This development no longer corresponds to its economic situation: in 1949, when it was still under the wardship of the United Nations, imports were twice the amount of exports, and the deficit was £1,600,000 sterling ($4,450,000). After ten years of federation with Ethiopia, it became an integral part of the Empire in 1962.

## ECONOMIC PROBLEMS: AGRICULTURE, IRRIGATION, COMMUNICATIONS

These problems are less serious and urgent here, it is true, than in some over-populated and famine-stricken countries. The problems of enabling 20 million people to live frugally in an area of 395,000 square miles was solved long ago. But the needs of the State, like those of the Ethiopians, are daily increasing, and Ethiopia realises that it cannot continue in a biblical way of life today, isolated from the outside world. Led into the road of progress, it may refuse to be driven along at too great a speed, but it can no longer stay still.

The development of the country must be begun with the Ethiopians themselves; for this reason the imperial government attaches the greatest importance to education, in order to give all Ethiopians a common language, Amharic, and to form an elite capable of remedying the under-administration of the country and modernising the economy.

Eighty per cent of the Ethiopians live on the high plateaus, and nearly all of them by agriculture and stock-breeding. Their very ancient method of cereal cultivation with the swing-plough is adapted to the rhythm of the seasons and the nature of the soil. It produces 4.5 million tons of cereals, almost half of which consist of *teff*, a kind of millet from which bread is made; the rest being barley, maize, sorghum and wheat. The production of all these could be increased.

Of far greater importance than cereals, from the commercial point of view, is the coffee that grows on the plateau between 5,000 and 6,500 feet. Ethiopian coffee, 90 per cent of which grows wild, is among the most favoured in the world: Ethiopia exports 50,000 tons annually, representing over 65 per cent of the value of all exports, and constituting (together with duty) the chief resource of the country.

The harnessing of the Blue Nile would allow an area the size of Belgium to be irrigated at an altitude of over 3,000 feet, and this land would produce sugar-cane, rice, cotton and oil-seeds; in addition, the hydro-electric production would assist the manufacture of agricultural fertilizer and the industrialisation of the country. Of more immediate interest in the harnessing of the Awash, flowing less than fifty miles from the capital. The Awash valley is being developed, with several dams, for irrigation. Already a Dutch plantation of sugar-cane has taken only a few years to meet home needs for sugar. Cotton too is grown.

But because of the lack of communications coffee is rotting in the underwood of the west and a large proportion of the 20 million cattle overburdening the pastures die of old age. There are less than 4,000 miles of good roads; Addis Ababa is connected with the sea by the one narrow-gauge railway, which ends at Djibouti in French Somaliland. Ethiopia has in fact gone over, almost without transition, from portage to air transport. Addis Ababa is directly linked with Cairo, Athens, Frankfurt, Lagos, Accra, Khartoum, Nairobi, Djibouti, Aden and Liberia. The inland lines serve forty places in the Federation and carry passengers, besides coffee, hides and imported products.

Foreign trade is still small in amount; 60 per cent passes through the port of Djibouti, and 25 per cent through the Eritrean ports of Massawa and Assab. Aden and Djibouti are distributors of Ethiopian exports.

The Federation has neither the technical nor the financial means required for its development; the international organisations for the assistance of underdeveloped countries come largely to its aid. UNESCO, the World Health Organisation, Point Four, and the International Bank for Reconstruction and Development work in Ethiopia. In addition several individual nations, including the United States, the Soviet Union, Yugoslavia and Britain, provide unilateral economic and technical assistance.

The reigning Emperor Haile Selassie has understood the need to liberalise his regime and associate with it the peoples of the outlying provinces. But though he remains firmly in control of all political decision-making he is advised by a parliament, has expanded the systen of education and is trying to break down the old semi-feudal relationship between Amharas and the other ethnic groups. His political and personal position remains virtually unchallenged, although an army-palace revolt in 1961 almost succeeded in ousting him from the throne.

The railroad connecting Addis Ababa with Djibouti, in French Somaliland. The narrow-gauge track is owned jointly by the Ethiopian and French governments, and carries more than half of Ethiopia's exports via Djibouti. Coffee (50,000 tons annually) is the major export.

# THE SOMALILANDS

The peninsula peopled by the Somalis is the easternmost part of Africa. It consists of the eastern slopes of the Galla-Somali high plateau, descending to Danakil, the Gulf of Aden and the Indian Ocean. In the north, the high plateau falls directly to the sea; at the Indian Ocean it ends in an escarpment some 330 feet high, dominating an alluvial plain. The coast, undoubtedly in process of emergence, runs in a straight line, and is edged with dunes, some of them extending up to twenty miles inland.

## THE COUNTRY AND THE PEOPLE

Despite its large area—over 280,000 square miles—the land of the Somalis has a fairly uniform climate. It is hot, arid or semi-arid, and characterised by the alternation of the monsoons, north-east in winter, north-west in summer.

The dryness of the climate and the permeability of the soil, which is often calcareous, account for the small number of permanent watercourses: the two big rivers flow down from the highest part of the Galla-Somali plateau in Ethiopia. They are the Webi Shibeli and the Juba. But the Webi Shibeli, which receives no tributary for the last 620 miles ot its course, does not reach the sea, while the Juba crosses the zone of coastal dunes with difficulty.

The land of the Somalis is a land of savannas, of acacias, gum trees, balsam trees and doum palms in the coastal region. It contains a population of about three million, 90 per cent being nomadic or semi-nomadic stock-breeders. The great majority are Somalis, almost certainly Hamites: that is to say of the same stock as the Ethiopians. They are mixed with Danakils in the north, Gallas on the Ethiopian borders, Negroes and Arabs on the coast.

Before July 1960, the Somali people were divided among five political areas: Italian Somalia, under United Nations Trusteeship; the British Somaliland Protectorate; the Ogaden and Harar provinces of Ethiopia; French Somaliland, which is an overseas territory of France with some local autonomy; and parts of the Northern Frontier District of Kenya. A movement for unification of all Somalis grew up in the 1940's led mainly by the militant Somali Youth League. On 26 June 1960 British Somaliland achieved independence; five days later, on July 1, Italian Somalia followed suit to unite with its neighbours in the Republic of Somalia. The capital is Mogadiscio, the old Italian Somalia capital, with a population of 100,000. The flag of the new republic has five stars, symbolising the desire to unite with it the Somalis in Kenya, Ethiopia and French Somaliland. Already this has brought the new state into conflict with its neighbours: the Somalis of Kenya refused to take part in pre-independence elections in 1963; while the Ogaden in Ethiopia is the scene of many conflicts. The French government refuses to concede independence and unification for French Somaliland, although there is some local agitation for such a solution.

*Former Italian Somalia.* This accounts for 181,625 square miles of the area of the Somali Republic and has a population of 1,270,000, of whom only 17 per cent are occupied in cultivating durra, sesame, vegetables and bananas. Banana production, organised by the Italians, forms the principal export commodity. Other commercial crops could be developed by means of irrigation: Kapok, sugar-cane, cotton and oil-seeds. Stock-breeding affords a precarious livelihood to a million nomads or semi-nomads. Fishing, especially

Shepherds of the Issa tribe watering their flocks in French Somaliland. Almost all the population is nomad or semi-nomad by tradition; but the number of nomads is decreasing.

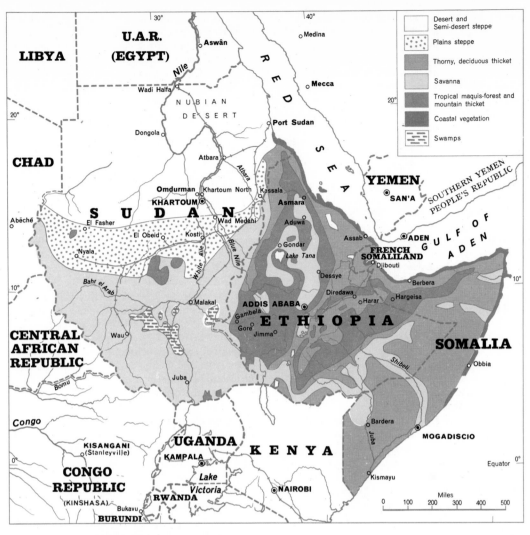

Agriculture, particularly livestock, is the basis of the economy throughout the countries of the Horn. From the north camels, sheep and goats are exported on the hoof, and hides and skins are an important source of wealth. In the more fertile south cotton, bananas and sugar make their appearance. Development of irrigation schemes and new methods would bring welcome diversity to the economy. Oil prospecting absorbs a considerable amount of time, energies and resources of private investors, but so far, apparently, unsuccessfully. In the Sudan cotton accounts for as much as 70 per cent of export revenues. Other crops (oil seeds, groundnuts [peanuts], pulses, salt) are much less important. Small amounts of iron, mica, manganese and asbestos are mined, but mineral wealth is not important.

shark-fishing, as well as salt-gathering and trade are pursued by the Arabs of the coast, some 30,000 in number.

*Former British Somaliland.* This part of the Somali Republic (68,000 square miles) has 450 miles of coastline on the Gulf of Aden. It is a very hot, dry region, in which 600,000 Somalis can subsist only by going up to the Ethiopian Ogaden in summer with their livestock. Hargeisa, the former capital, and the ports of Berbera and Zeila, are centres of little size.

*French Somaliland.* This is a little enclave in Danakil, with an area of 8,880 square miles and a population of 81,000. It has several features in common with Danakil: heights and depressions (Lake Assal, 570 feet below sea level), a torrid climate, great aridity, a population of more Danakils than Somalis.

All the importance of the territory is concentrated in Djibouti, with some 41,000 inhabitants, including nearly all the Europeans (about 7,000). Situated on the strait linking the Red Sea and the Gulf of Aden, Djibouti is a port of call for more than a thousand ships a year, and, thanks to a Franco-Ethiopian railroad, 60 per cent of the foreign trade of Ethiopia passes through it, in spite of the competition of Assab and Massawa, the ports of the Federation. Djibouti is also an international airport of importance, registering annually more than a thousand landings, at least half of which are by Ethiopian aircraft.

The main wealth of Somalia lies in its camels, sheep and goats. The arid northern areas export about £1 million ($2.8 million) worth of livestock on the hoof, as well as hides and skins. In the more fertile riverine areas of the Juba and the Shebeli, cotton and banana plantations, a legacy of Italian rule, produce export crops worth nearly £3 million ($8.4 million), of which the bulk is derived from bananas. With Italy the main market for bananas, the Somali economy is still closely associated with that country, which is also the chief source of foreign aid and investment. But Britain, the United Arab Republic, the Soviet Union and the United States, as well as international agencies, also provide assistance.

## THE SUDAN

The Sudan is an independent republic, which until 1956 was an Anglo-Egyptian condominium. Bordered by Egypt to the north, Libya, Chad and the Central African Republic to the west, the Congo, Uganda and Kenya to the south, and Ethiopia and the Red Sea to the east, it is only part of the climatic belt across Africa which geographers call 'Sudanese' and whose chief characteristic is heat.

*An 'African' country in the Nile basin.* The capital, Khartoum, has a mean annual temperature of 29°C.

(84°F.), one of the highest in the world. This extreme heat is explained by the latitude of the Sudan situated between the Tropic of Cancer and the Equator. Khartoum is sufficiently distant from the latter to have a very dry climate: that is to say an atmosphere that cannot affect the insolation as the equatorial zone does. The sun attains its zenith here twice a year, in May and July; except for the cold-season months, its rays are never far from the vertical at midday. This means that there is practically no shade to be found in the middle of the day. Vegetation needs a great deal of water to make up for increased evaporation. Thorny plants, which lose less moisture, do best; while crops can be grown in the damp valleys, which thus attract most of the towns and means of communication.

*A divided country.* The Sudan is typically African in its extensive reliefs. The basin of the Bahr el Ghazal is a long trough of the Nile that widens, especially to the west, as it approaches Egypt. The only exceptions are a semicircle of plateaus round the southern basin, the foothills of the Ethiopian massif in the east prolonged by the Arabian coastal massif, and on the south-eastern frontier the isolated Imatong mountains. But even these heights are in fact violently disrupted plateaus: their structure is fundamentally tabular, as is almost the whole of Africa, and of an antiquity that is attested by the abundance of laterites in evidence there.

The Sudan is African, too, in its essentially continental character, though it does possess an outlet about 200 miles wide on the Red Sea. The Sudanese coast borders a narrow sea, too hot to interrupt the continuity of the Saharo-Arabian desert. Moreover, the interior is separated from it by the screen of the Arabian massif, which no river crosses. The natural outlet of the Sudan was towards Egypt, by the valley of the Nile, until the construction of railroads transferred trade to Port Sudan.

Finally the Sudan is African in the skin-colour of its inhabitants. But the human and political differences between the northern and southern peoples are considerable and potentially dangerous, partly for historical reasons. The Nilotic peoples of the south are most closely akin to their close neighbours in Kenya and Uganda; by contrast the nothern peoples are Moslem and predominantly Arab. During the period of British rule, Catholic and Protestant missionaries tended to resist Islamic proselytising in the south, and this, together with the fact that Arabic was not spoken in this region, contributed to the southern feeling of distrust and separation from the north. When independence was granted in 1956, the south pleaded unsuccessfully for a federation rather than a unitary state. A few months later, as a result of an attempt to introduce Arabic into the Army in the south, a mutiny took place in the Equatoria province. Seventy Army officers and senior administrators from the north were killed before the revolt was crushed. But the underlying hostility between north and south remains; and many of the southern leaders have fled to neighbouring territories.

A special feature distinguishes the Sudan from other parts of the Sudanese zone — the existence of the Nile. It possesses only the middle course of the river, but this is a sector in which two important things occur: the enormous spread of its waters in the basin in which it is joined by the Bahr el Ghazal and loses half its flow; and farther downstream, the junction with tributaries pouring down from the Ethiopian mountains. Over the 2,000 miles of its course through the Sudan, the Nile bears three different names in succession (Bahr el Jebel, White Nile), grows smaller, then swells enormously, and finally acquires an excessive regime in which the high-water flow is fifteen times greater that that of the low-water period. Beyond Atbara it possesses all the features (including the summer floods) which led the Egyptions of the Pharaohs to deify it. But the Sudan gets little benefit from the Nile: below Khartoum the valley is too narrow, and the White Nile, above it, does not possess the same qualities. Besides this, the course of the river, very slow in general, is interrupted by six series of rapids, incorrectly termed 'cataracts', of which only the first is situated in Egyptian territory. Such as it is, however, the Nile is the great national artery, especially above Khartoum, and river navigation is the only usual means of transport in the Bahr el Ghazal basin. Thanks to the Nile, the Sudan has become a meeting-place and a scene of struggle between the civilising Arab influences of the lower valley and the less developed Negro tribes of the plateau of the great lakes.

*A recently created state.* The northern part of the Sudan, then called Nubia, very early came under the influence of the Pharaohs, who demanded gold, ivory and ostrich feathers from it. At a later period it temporarily renewed its connection with Egypt and, with the spread of Coptic Christianity, at the same time with Abyssinia.

Later conquest Islamised it and reduced the area to vassaldom. Its slave trade and the legend of its wealth of gold attracted Mehemet Ali at the beginning of the nineteenth century. Egypt unified the various principalities of the Nile basin by force, with the addition of the basin of the Bahr el Ghazal. The suppression of the slave trade ruined the Moslem traders, and this led to the Mahdist insurrection (1881-5), which was successful at the very time when Egypt was falling under the domination of Britain, who organised a slow reconquest (1896-8) and imposed an anglo-Egyptian condominium government. Stirred by Arab nationalism and anxious to imitate Egypt, although distrusting it, the Sudan localised its administrative structure under international control, and attained total independence in 1956. Although its economic and cultural relations with Britain are still close, it considers itself a member of the great Moslem family, and has a seat in the Arab League.

## VARIETY OF THE SUDAN

*The southern provinces and those of the western centre.* Within the country, relief, climate, ethnography and economy differ greatly, especially in the south. The Sudan is in fact a somewhat artificial state, although a diversity of resources and the presence of the Nile may in time succeed in giving it an organic unity.

The southern provinces extend as far as the latitude of Kaka. Thanks to a long rainy season (March to November), vegetation is continuous and perennial:

forest growing in tiers on the Imatong Mountains, forest attacked by denshering on the Congo-Nile ridge, grass in the basin of the Bahr el Ghazal (and aquatic plants during the summer floods). The ravages of sleeping sickness, caused by the tsetse fly, make stock-breeding impossible for the Azandis of the ridge, who raise crops on denshered land — bananas, sorghum, eleusine and manioc. In the basin, the Nilotic tribes of the Chillouks, the Nuers, the Dinkas and the Baris, mostly fishermen and stock-breeders, migrate in summer with their cattle from the high terraces and peripheral plateaus to the lower lands liable to inundation, where in the winter the marshes give way to grass. They still exert a sort of suzerainty over the intervening villages of the Bantus, who are purely cultivators. Difficult of penetration, flooded to a great extent and covered with aquatic vegetation in summer, the southern Sudan lives on its own resources, with a very primitive form of economy and social life.

The central provinces, on the left bank of the Nile, form an east-west strip of land 350-500 miles wide, which includes the transition between the semi-aquatic savanna in the south and the desert in the north, through an infertile savanna. The wet season is still briefer here; the grass is shorter and dies in winter, and the rivers are only temporary.

Among the plateaus and volcanoes of Darfur, the altitude improves the climate. Millet is grown as a food crop in the valleys, and on the borders groundnuts (peanuts) and tobacco are grown and camels and sheep are raised. But this province suffers from poor communications with the Nile.

Central Kordofan, less remote, is the millet granary of the Sudan and harvests half the world supply of gum arabic. Its fringes form the domain of briefly migrating shepherds, breeding cattle in the south and sheep and goats in the north.

*Provinces of the eastern centre and the north.* In the east, between the Nile and Ethiopia, there are numerous rivers. The plateaus have the same economy as those of the west. But since the construction of the Sennar Dam the blind deltas of the Tokar and the Gash can be irrigated as well as the triangle at the junction of the two Niles. Food crops are associated there with the growing of Egyptian long-fibre cotton. This is the heart of the Sudan, full of promise and well served by rail. The capital, composed of three cities (Omdurman, North Khartoum and Khartoum), is situated astride the junction of the rivers. The Jebel Aulia Dam, in the south, on the White Nile, is of use only to Egypt.

The northern provinces lie in the Nubian desert, whose inhospitality is tempered only on the coastal massif, where a little rain in winter supports a sparse nomadic population and the water that supplies the port towns. In the Nile valley (here barely 2½ miles wide), agriculture is carried on by summer flooding, as in the south of Egypt. The railroad makes up for the interruption of navigation by the rapids, and connects Wadi Halfa to Abu Hamad, which lies across the desert.

A branch line goes from Atbara to Port Sudan with connections to the most productive provinces of the Sudan. In spite of an inhospitable coast — bare, fringed by reefs, without fresh water — it possesses the slightly derelict town of Suakin, and Port Sudan (population 47,000) which, facing a great ocean route, serves as a port of call and monopolises 80 per cent of Sudanese foreign trade. But the interior is so desolate that many Nubians still travel north to seek work in Egypt.

*The economic situation.* With a sparse population, poor communications and financial backwardness, the Sudan has an annual per capita national income of £27 (75 dollars). It is largely dependent upon a single export crop, cotton, which brings in 70 per cent of its export revenues. Other exports include gum arabic, groundnuts, oil-seeds and millet. Livestock forms a small part of the export trade, although most of the people depend locally on goats and camels. Though iron ore, mica, asbestos and manganese have been found in commercial quantities, the Sudan is not rich in minerals. Economic diversification is a high priority of the government, and light industries, most of them based on local products — meat-canning, tanning, cotton ginning — are beginning to find a place in the economy.

A dhow on the Blue Nile, the Sudan's natural outlet towards Egypt until railroad construction transferred trade to Port Sudan.

A Moru tribesman with a large fish trap, near Amadi.

# WEST AFRICA

## PORTUGUESE GUINEA, LIBERIA, GAMBIA, SIERRA LEONE, NIGERIA, GHANA, SENEGAL, MALI, UPPER VOLTA, NIGER, MAURITANIA, DAHOMEY, TOGO, GUINEA, IVORY COAST

West Africa, like North Africa, is an area which has tenuous connections with the rest of the continent, partly barred by vegetation and by terrains that constitute a geological anomaly.

It is bordered to the north by the Sahara, a treeless expanse of shifting sands populated by nomads. To the south of this border the ground consists of rock or fixed soils where human and plant life can find anchorage. These damp lands are inhabited by Negroes; round the northern desert lies the fringe of the White world.

West Africa is washed on the west and south by a vast ocean, to which it presents an inhospitable littoral. Much has been said of the barriers of the sands in the north and the forest in the south; but the coast itself is the most forbidding frontier. Its three orientations correspond to three types of coast. North of the Cape Verde peninsula everything is obliterated by a fringe of sands stretching from north to south. Between Cape Verde and the Liberia-Ivory Coast border the littoral is broken up by a number of estuaries; but the estuaries are choked by mud and by the tropical mangrove. Between Liberia and Cameroun, the coast is again mostly obstructed by offshore bars. As seen on the map, unbroken coastlines are the most striking features of the seaboards of western Africa; on the spot, impenetrability proves the chief cause of their suffocation.

To the east, in the Chad region, there is some human continuity; but on the physical plane, west and east are sharply divided along the edge of Cameroun. From the Spanish island of Fernando Poo up to Lake Chad and even as far as the Tibesti mountains runs a real but discontinuous frontier. Its southern section is backed by the wall of the great Gabon forest; its northern course wanders among marshy zones and ill-defined catchment basins, live or fossil. Geologically it is marked by a straight row of outstanding volcanic heights, stretching from Fernando Poo and Mount Cameroon to the Tibesti Mountains at the north-east corner of West Africa.

## PHYSICAL FEATURES AND VEGETATION

This huge territory, nearly 2,500 miles long with an average width of 1,000 miles, is composed of a group of intertropical countries. Its imprecise northern limits wind along the Tropic of Cancer; its southern coast runs parallel to the equator, 4 or 5 degrees to the north of it.

Regions can be distinguished amid the monotonous landscapes of West Africa not by the space they occupy in this horizontal expanse but by climatic differences and the kinds of vegetation connected with them.

*Hot countries. Winds and rainfall.* Being intertropical, West Africa is first and foremost a hot region. The annual averages are around 26°C. (79°F.) in the south, and 30°C. (86°F.) in the north. In the south, the hottest and coldest months vary only slightly around the average; in the north, the winter months reach 20°C. (68°F.), while the summer ones exceed 35°C. (95°F.). But this dissimilarity is not itself enough to differentiate the various West African climates. They are distinguished rather by the rainfall, and the rainfall is conditioned by the winds.

The thermal equator corresponds to a ring of low pressure, while the tropic is an area of high pressure. These areas of different pressures, and their annual movement to and fro, regulate two of the winds that sweep these countries: the trade wind and the monsoon. Actually, these are both trade winds (due north trade in one case; modified south trade in the other).

The north trade blows from the Tropic of Cancer towards the Equator, curving to the west. In January it reaches its southernmost point, near the 15th parallel, the regions of the northern elbows of the Niger and the Senegal. After this it recedes farther and farther north, to reach the 22nd parallel in July, in the extreme north of West Africa. Then, between August and January, it gradually regains its lost positions towards the south. This northerly trade, exceptionally cool and damp on the seaboard of Senegal, and cool but dry everywhere else, brings no rain with it.

A trade wind symmetrical with the preceding one, the southerly trade, blows from the southern high pressures towards the equatorial low pressures. Up to the Equator it curves to the left, towards the west; but once past the geographical equator it curves right and heads north-east. But the geographical and thermal equators are not coincident, and this becomes more and more evident as one nears the heart of the northern summer: the south trade, which always to some extent crosses the geographical equator, goes farther and farther beyond it in pursuit of the low pressures of the overheated zones fleeing northwards. In July it reaches the neighbourhood of the north trade, expiring near the 22nd parallel north. In January, after a retreat of five months towards the south, it ceases to affect the southern coasts, which it will cross again one or two months later on resuming its advance to the north. This warm, damp sea wind brings the rains to West Africa. Originally a trade wind, it becomes a monsoon from the moment when it receives an impetus from the attraction of the superheated continental masses.

West Africa has thus a summer monsoon. It has no winter monsoon, because the north trades, which might blow towards a warmed Gulf of Guinea, are intercepted by a third wind, the harmattan, blowing direct from the Sahara.

*Fight between monsoon and harmattan.* From east to

Fulani women near Birnin Kebbi.
in Northern Nigeria.

Tropical forest in Sierra Leone.

west flows a great air current of equatorial type, which here takes the local name of harmattan. Fortunately for West Africa, this absolutely dry continental wind tends to seek high levels. It just permits the north trades to pass beneath it; from October to April it contends with them for the northern fringes of the country, barely allowing the trades to penetrate to the two great Sudanese rivers at the time of their farthest extent, and completely barring their progress farther south at all times.

But the harmattan is less potent when faced with the monsoon. The monsoon thrusts its wedge of moist air underneath it from February onwards, and obstinately drives it upwards and towards the north. In August it has totally ousted its adversary, which can no longer reach the ground at any point. But from September onwards, as the monsoon gradually falls back on the more southerly latitudes, the dry air of the harmattan descends again to fill southward positions in its wake.

It is this struggle for influence between monsoon and harmattan that regulates precipitation in West Africa. A wedge of warm, moist air is more or less buried under a vast hot, dry current, the base of which, however, is cool at a high altitude. The contact surface between these two masses is an oblique one, inclined from south to north. This front is critical around an altitude of 5,000 feet, where condensation turns to rain: in the north it is too near the ground; in the south it is too far from it. There are thus three main zones in the mass of the monsoon. In front, the thin edge of the wedge is an area not of monsoon rains but turbulence, where frequent imbalance between the air of the harmattan and that of the monsoon produces recurring squalls, or tornadoes. The middle sector is the most productive of rains, where the thickness of the monsoon reaches 5,000 feet. Behind this, where the base of the wedge is particularly thick, there is little rainfall.

The advance of the monsoon to the north up to August, and its regression afterwards, entail displacement of these three zones over West Africa, with the result that, once the 'winter' dry season is over, the south has two seasons of tornadoes and two of rain, coming and going, separated by a short dry season. The belt of land situated between the 8th and 12th parallels, which is the maximum latitude attainable by the 5,000-foot layer, has only one rainy season sandwiched between two seasons of tornadoes. The far north, between 15° and 18° N., is reached only by the thin edge of the monsoon wedge, and the single rainy season is one of tornadoes.

*The three climatic zones of West Africa.* Three belts, stretching from west to east, are the key zones of the West African climates.

South of the 8th parallel the climates are equatorial, pure or modified; they are those of the regions which the optimum rainy sector of the 5,000-foot thick monsoon crosses twice a year in its course, coming and going. The humidity of the air is always very high, even during what is known as the 'dry season'. As is inevitable under such a protective quilt, the temperature hardly varies, either from day to night or from one season to another; it is high, but not excessively so: round about 25.5°C. (68°F.), 26.5°C. (80°F.) or 28°C. (82°F.), as the case may be. It is only on its northern borders in the dry season that this equatorial region experiences the harmattan; elsewhere it is unknown, with remarkable exceptions in the region of Togo. From the end of November to April is the great dry season. From April to August is the great rainy season introduced by tornadoes. In August there is a short dry season: the zone of precipitation has slipped to the north, and temperatures have fallen after the great rains; the minimum is lower then than in January. Finally, from September to November comes a second rainy season, returning from the north, with its train of tornadoes.

North of this belt is another, known as the Sudanese climatic belt, stretching from the Senegal to Lake Chad. Its northern limit straddles the 15th parallel, north of it in the west, south of it in the east: this is as far north as the optimum rainy zone of the monsoon can reach. The humidity of the air is slight, sometimes very slight; the changes in temperature are violent. This is the Africa of two faces: these regions are the realms of the harmattan during the single really dry season, and are conquered by the monsoon during the rainy season, single likewise, the seasons being separated by periods of tornadoes.

Where only the thin edge of the monsoon wedge arrives, in the heart of the 'winter', lies the last belt of West Africa before the desert, south of the 20th parallel. This is the Sahelian zone, bordering the Sahara. Rigorous drought, wide range of temperature, slight rainfall over fewer and fewer months and brought by tornadoes rather than by the true monsoon, cold northern trade winds appearing in the midst of the very long dry season — these are the border conditions of West Africa.

Beyond this towards the north, in regions subject only to the great continental currents — the northern trade and harmattan — torn between extremes of temperature, less and less sure of seeing rain fall in summer, is really the Sahara, even if administrative conventions choose to extend the frontiers of West Africa to cover it.

*Tawny, dark red or bright red soils.* The soils of West Africa may be classed in three divisions lying in bands parallel to the three major climatic zones. Apart from some minor exceptions, the soil types belong to the Sahelian, Sudanese and equatorial regions respectively. The north is essentially a tawny region of sands that are stable, if not already supporting any vegetation, as in the northern Sahara. South of the 15th parallel are the red soils: the huge ferruginous dark red slabs of the shield, baked and rebaked by the Sudanese harmattan; and the brighter red, deep, mobile soils forming a surface layer over the rocky skeleton of the equatorial regions.

Four great rocky masses share these immense red or tawny expanses between them. Crystalline rocks — pure granites or metamorphic gneiss — reign over three vast areas. The first comprises Sierra Leone, Liberia, Upper Guinea and the western Ivory Coast. The second consists of the Mossi regions, inside the loop of the Niger. The third reaches the sea again either side of the lower Niger, in Dahomey and Nigeria. Defined as a 'shield' in both Nigeria and Liberia, this crystalline mass is an ancient platform.

The second group of rocks, the schists, also belong to this old platform. Almost non-existent in the east, their outcrops mostly fringe the crystalline areas elsewhere, while a long strip of schist forms a bridge in the west between the edges of the Nigerian shield and the crystalline massifs of the Rio de Oro.

The third group comprises two types of rock which do not belong to the West African platform, but merely rest upon it. These are non-metamorphosed sedimentary rocks. Siliceous sandstones form the most striking group, because they are more easily distinguished in the topography. They occur in Ghana and between the Aïr and the Adrar of the Iforas, more often around the south-western Sahara, and especially along the course of the Niger through Mali and in a wide strip between the upper Niger and Senegal, extending towards the south-west, where they form the Fouta Djallon Mountains.

The fourth group can be characterised as a complex of recent, rather soft rocks — clays, argilaceous sandstones, sometimes ferruginous sandstones: their outcrops appear widely along the borders of the West African platform.

*The northern regions.* West Africa is bounded to the north by three mountain ranges rising in the desert near the 20th parallel; the Mauritanian Adrar, the Adrar of the Iforas, and the Aïr

Lying hard against a granitic outcrop to the north is the Mauritanian Adrar, composed chiefly of primary sandstones which have formed elevated tabular areas, often steep-sided. In the Adrar of the Iforas, north of the elbow of the Niger, a crystalline massif of medium altitude between 1,500 and 2,500 feet, the crests are heavy in outline but jagged in detail and seem more like skeletons of dark rock mellowed by

The baobab, a tree native to Africa and one of the largest known species. A tough fibre for rope and cloth is obtained from its bark.

A Nigerian fishing festival during the seasonal spate of an affluent of the Niger, which at certain periods dries up completely. The semi-desert areas bordering these rivers mark the northern limits of West Africa.

Fulani cattle grazing on the Jos Plateau, in central Nigeria. The region is poor, suited neither to cultivation **nor** to extensive stock-rearing. At one time great hopes were aroused by the discovery of copper deposits, but these proved disappointing.

the desert, with patches of coarse scree here and there. Some 400 miles to the east lies the southern end of the Aïr, also a granite massif, infused here and there by recent volcanic intrusions. The volcanic appearance of the Aïr heralds another Africa, that of the east, to which belongs the Tibesti, a formidable Saharan bastion with peaks rising to over 10,000 feet.

From the line of high points running along the 10th parallel, a long slope descends to the north towards a chain of basins, preceding the Saharan moles and marked by important rivers, the Senegal, the Niger upstream and downstream from its elbow, and Lake Chad. These basins with their recent sedimentary rocks, and the slopes running towards them from the south, correspond more or less to Sahelian West Africa.

Whatever aspects these areas may have presented in the past, they are all alike today. This is flat, endless Africa, characterised by horizontal landscapes at low altitudes, belts of alluvial deposit, uncertain waters, marshes and lakes as much in Senegal as in the 'inner delta' of the Niger and round Lake Chad, with large networks of fossil tributaries east of the loop of the Niger and east of Lake Chad; semi-desert regions, in which rivers die out or run the risk of doing so, in which ponds swell at the time of the floods with reserves of water that they return to the rivers during the dry seasons. These areas mark the true northern limits of West Africa.

*The backbone and the southern slopes.* The southern part of West Africa slopes down to the coast from an uneven 2,000-mile backbone of very old crystalline or metamorphic rocks.

This backbone is best preserved in the west, where it is easily recognisable for 450 miles, from the region of Dabola, at the eastern foot of Fouta Djallon, to Man, in the western Ivory Coast. Here we have an insular shelf of high plateaus, sloping both north and south and dominated by mountains.

To the east, the backbone is less clear, but we can distinguish a continuous line of very depressed plateaus between 1,000 and 1,300 feet in height whose most significant feature is their double slope to the north and south. From these plateaus diminutive heights shoot up sporadically, in the form of hillocks or minor ranges, never reaching more than about 2,500 feet. At two points alone, one towards the middle and the other at the eastern end of the line, are there any reliefs comparable to those of the west. These are the long, thin chain of the Togo Atakora, and a granite massif situated in the northerly section of Nigeria.

The only notable mountain masses of West Africa are found along the east-west backbone, which is always detectable. Their common feature is that of rising at intervals from plateaus to which they do not appear to belong. This impression is less definite in the crystalline massifs of Man or Nigeria, but the anomaly strikes the least tutored eye at the sight of the diminutive elongated chains and minor ridges of quartzite or volcanic rocks rearing their steep walls above interminable flat expanses, along lines at right-angles to that of the main ridge, like rafters of a roof.

Of the panels the ridge must at one time have supported, very little remains. On one big mountain, however, the Fouta Djallon, the sandstone mantle is still to be found, dropping down to the sea in dislocated outliers.

In the north, the Sarakulle massif and that of the Manding Mountains form a counterpart to the Fouta, while to the east, as far as the loop of the Niger, the Dioulasso and Bandiagara plateaus are more or less of the same type — tabular sandstone plateaus ending in escarpments, a type of relief that differs profoundly from that of the regions of the long crystalline ridge.

Towards the south the land slopes down to the sea much more rapidly than it does to the Sahelian basins in the north. The southern slopes all follow a regular succession of three levels: plateau, hill and plain.

The plateaus lie within the Sudanese belt and are rigid, red, paved with ferruginous slabs or carpeted with ferruginous small gravel.

At their southern foot, undulating regions, with hills and spurs and river rapids, mark the line of attack of Atlantic erosion. They are the live zone of West Africa, the crucible in which the elements comprising the old Africa are combined in a modern pattern.

As for the littoral plain, whether a narrow fringe in Libya or vast delta regions in Nigeria, it presents the same appearance: marshy, and gaining on the sea. Owing to a combination of erosion and silting, it is always choked with deep, fine debris. It drives wide fingers through the belt of hills towards the northern plateaus, while the southern seaboard forms a long sandy dyke, protecting occasional dunes on the Ivory Coast and in Dahomey and Nigeria, and barring the estuaries even where the coast is rocky.

*Desert and Sahel. Bush and Savanna.* The types of vegetation exactly correspond to these three long belts determined by the relief. The zone of the northern basins is the yellow Africa of the Sahel and the desert; the ridge with its nearest foothills is Sudanese red Africa; the southern slopes are the green regions of the Guinea savanna and the dense forest.

The northern borders of West Africa lie in an area of total, interminable flatness, without rocks, covered with minute pebbles, over which shimmer pools of hot air. Vegetation appears only on the higher ground towards the Tagant and among the Iforas — a few blades of yellow grass, a group of date palms where there are human beings.

Then comes the hostile Sahel, an area of twisted stems, thorny branches, grey leaves. A baobab tree here and there heralds the south. The landscape is relieved occasionally by long green sheets of aquatic plants stretched over the blue surface of one of the two great Sahelian rivers.

Towards the south of the Sahel the size and density of thorny plants increases; the tufts of grass grow close together, their great yellow patches variegate a reddening soil. But the Sudanese bush really begins only with the appearance of trees and green leaves on the landscape.

The trunks remain twisted, but there are fewer thorns; the ubiquitous *karité*, the shea butter-tree, with its plumlike fruit, is characteristic of the Sudanese belt and in every landscape the absurd outline of the baobab occurs, an enormous barrel with a crest of stumpy branches from which hang great bell-shaped fruits on strings of endless peduncles. The steppe turns into a park-like savanna, then into a savanna of more and more trees, as one goes further south. The trunks are still twisted, covered with a thick bark that resists the bush fires, but the leaves increase in size, and fine trees shoot up: bastard mahogany, with twisted trunks, neres bearing long pods, kapok trees and silk-cotton trees with tiered foliage, palmettos whose fans rustle against a sky less blue than in the north. In the rainy seasons the scenery assumes a charming orchard-like character reminding one of Europe. Everywhere under the trees the grass reigns supreme: the red soil shows only here and there where a rent occurs in the gigantic herbage, which is green for half the year and tawny — no longer yellow — when the dry breath of the harmattan envelopes the region.

*A dense, perpetually green forest.* The bush has two faces according to the seasons, green or tawny, leafy or bare; but the forest is always green. This is its distinctive character, far more than its legendary giantism; a rich mantle of perpetual greenness covers everything.

The realm of the forest has advance posts in the areas of grass and little twisted trees; this is the zone of interpenetration between equatorial and tropical, the Guinea savanna, the pre-forest, or even the forest-savanna. The true forest area is marked by the total absence of grass. Trees, lianas and a few creeping plants reign supreme. In the moist, silent, oppressive atmosphere of a green twilight, one moves among enormous tree-trunks, often flanked by buttresses, sometimes supported on roots like stilts, among tiny young trees and very big ones, and among fallen, rotting trunks. One struggles with lianas, slender or monstrous, straight or coiled — latex lianas, prickly lianas and stinging lianas. But whether spongy, marshy, dripping, strewn with seeds, seed-pods or gigantic fruits, the soil is always free, without the vegetable carpet of moss and ferns of the temperate forests; in the tropical forest, all this grows higher up, rooted in the forks of the branches. The more dense and primitive the forest, the freer the ground will be from suckers and lianas. The picture of the great forest as an impenetrable chaos is an illusion. Tangle and impenetrability, sometimes absolute, are the characteristics of the secondary forest growing up again where man once made a clearing, where the sun has been able to reach the ground owing to the destruction of the high roof of foliage.

## HUMAN LANDSCAPES AND PROBLEMS

Human geography also distinguishes two major frontiers running from west to east across West Africa: one, at about the 15th parallel, between the white world and the black one of the savannas; the other, at about the 9th parallel, between the latter and the forest world. But inside these three long belts, so attractive to anthropologists, an incredible complexity of detail takes the form of other long strips stretching from west to east.

Anthropologists, linguists, ethnologists and sociologists all attempt to define large human groups. Leaving aside the outmoded concept of 'race', one clings to ethnic notions, another to linguistic relationships, and yet another to cultural ones, and the groups that each formulates are at variance with those of the others.

*Successive human waves.* The peopling of West Africa has been affected, as almost everywhere else, by successive waves, reaching and deserting fresh layers in turn, till the whole becomes stratified. Here these human waves appear to have come from the north and the east, reaching their maximum complexity between the 12th and 15th degrees of latitude.

It was thought for a long time that there had been a primeval occupation by Pygmies, but no valid trace of this remains, and it is wiser to think of them as perhaps passing through the regions while they were being driven towards their refuge in the Congo. There is abundant evidence, on the other hand, of an important prehistoric population of the western Sahara, and this human centre may well have been negroid. Traces of it may be thought to linger among the Moors in the west and the Toubous of the Aïr and the Chad basin in the east. Beyond some unknown frontier, Berber populations were in contact

Togolese women washing. The Togolese are heirs to an advanced type of African civilisation, and cultivate their land skilfully. Togoland is one of the most densely populated countries in Africa.

with it in the north. Drought and nomads drove the men living on wild fruit towards the wetter lands, and many Negroes spread towards the south.

Paleonigritic peoples established themselves in West Africa in ancient times, the earliest and most widespread living in and by the forest, while the latest arrivals lived in the savannas by a fairly advanced form of agriculture. Almost everywhere they were farmers, more sedentary in the savanna, more itinerant, dependent on wild harvests, in the forest, all keeping a precarious and true balance with their environment; peoples practising ancestor-worship, in awe of the elders, with families ruled by patrilinear succession, and a society governed by the old, without States or close attachment to their neighbourhood. Two strips of these remain. The one, comprising rural peoples chiefly, follows the stony soils and northern masses of the inner ridge, between the central Nigerian massif and the Fouta Djallon. The other, comprising forest-dwellers chiefly, borders the littoral from the Bandama River in the Middle of the Ivory Coast to the estuary of the Gambia.

A wave that is bound to be the subject of controversy for a long while yet cuts across these north-south movements. The Peul people, known as Fulani in Nigeria, are neither quite white or quite black, Ethiopian in some cases, Egyptian in others, or even Mesopotamian, and came via North Africa and the western Sahara, or else via the regions of Upper Egypt and Chad. However this may be, they are a Hamitic rather than a negroid people, pastoral though sometimes settled and living in a feudal or at least a caste society. They were often to prove most effective proselytisers of Islam.

*Civilisations and empires.* An east to west population movement reached the sea in the west, on the Senegalese littoral, and it was along its path that the great Sahelo-Sudanese empires grew up. That of Ghana dates from the fourth century, stretching between Niger and Senegal. It certainly appears to have been founded by northern Berbers, but these were quickly succeeded by the dark-skinned Sarakulle. In the thirteenth century Ghana was subdued by a young empire which, under the name Mali and in the hands of dark-skinned Mandingo sovereigns, was destined to dominate the whole of the western Sudan until the sixteenth and seventeenth centuries. Meanwhile a Songhoi state had asserted itself in the tenth century and reached its greatest power in the fifteenth, reigning over the loop of the Niger, from Niamey to Timbuktu.

The northern offshoot appears to have withdrawn again, but all along its passage the same oriental features are to be found, preserved among remote residual groups. These are highly hierarchised warrior or migratory peoples, organised in states under rulers with a halo of religious prestige, trusting only to matrilinear succession. They share the majority of these features with the peoples belonging to the southern offshoot.

There is a tendency to think of the man of the African continent as strictly conditioned by his natural surroundings: climate, the immeasurable size of an inhuman territory, the difficulty of establishing agriculture on a permanent basis, the suffocation of the forest, and impoverishing endemic diseases.

The reality would appear to be more complex. In its main lines, the population has certainly been shaped by such conditions; but social traditions have also had an important bearing on life among the tribes.

*Peoples of the desert and the Sahel.* The desert, in this part of Africa as elsewhere, is the domain of the dark-skinned nomad and the camel. The population wanders more or less to the north, and into a desert without oases to the west and the east, where higher ground is to be found. Moors in the west, Tuaregs in the centre, Toubous in the east, live as nomads on their northern borders and tend to settle in the south Sahel, exchanging their tents for huts or cabins. Their societies are hierarchical, with a light-skinned aristocracy, except among the Toubous of the Aïr. The population is dispersed, mobile, and restricted to the grazing grounds of the main sources of subsistence — sheep, goats and camels.

The man of the Sahel is the Peul; his animal is the ox. Almost exclusively nomadic in the north of his area, he, too, becomes settled in the south, but a caste society and a passion for the herd characterise him always. The Peul of the upper class owns a herd, dreams, sometimes lives a life of Islamic spirituality, and that is all; the cabin servants and the black serfs attend to the crops and the necessary chores. In the true Sahelian regions nomadic groups are constantly on the move for ten months of the year, carrying with them their hemispherical tents made of mats, and gathering around the watercourses during the dry season.

Farther south, the Peul is forced to fall in with the ways of life of the Negro peoples and a different countryside. Whether he be the owner of a personal herd or employed by a peasant proprietor, he must reckon with the tilled fields and the regular rhythm imposed by agriculture. This amounts to a transitional stage foreshadowing the Peul anomaly of the Fouta Djallon, far away in the south of the Sahel, where the spearhead of the wanderers has settled into a feudal state where they live by agriculture carried on by black serfs, among pernament groups of large round huts with tall conical, convex roofs, some constructed in village formation.

*The Sudanese. Huts, villages and towns.* Along the trail of the great Sudanese empires modes of life are found superimposed or intermixed, at times recalling that of the original occupants whose agricultural methods have survived, at others that of the cattle-breeder or the conqueror. Typical survivals of the last-named are the horses, mules or donkeys, which are as characteristic of this part of Africa as the camel is of the desert and the ox of the Sahel. Peasant peoples are found everywhere, in varying degrees dominated by an aristocracy, sometimes learned, sometimes religious, often migratory.

In these regions, traversed, except among the Mossis, by the tall priestly figures in Moslem dress that inspire such respect in the Negroes of the south, the settled population has begun to make its mark on the landscape. There are fields of groundnuts (peanuts) in the west; mixed crops combined with stock-raising among the Senegalese Sérérés; rice, and millet in the remote fields, vegetable plots near the huts, herds returning to the outskirts of the village in the evening in the Malinké region; acres of maize and vegetable produce, too, near the huts of the Mossis, where the crops consist, in decreasing importance, of sorghum and groundnuts (peanuts), with millet in the most distant fields. The human element is more evident in these cultivated lands; although there are no definite estates in the European sense of the word, there are enclosures and the forest has been selectively cleared to leave the wild fruit-trees.

Dwellings, too, are less primitive than in the northern zones. In the country, apart from the solitary huts of the Peul shepherds and the seasonal encampments round the crops, the buildings are grouped: little round, individual huts linked together by the walls of dried mud enclosing the entire family community among the Malinkés, large Mossi huts scattered about the Volta bush, and flanked by cereal granaries, miniature huts often perched out of reach of the ground and roofed like the larger ones by a cone of straw. Villages are the usual type of settlement; but there are towns too — Djenné, Gao, Ouagadougou, Kano — where the round hut with a conical roof of the Mossi or the Malinké or the hemispherical hut of many-coloured mats of the Songhoi is found alongside square or oblong buildings with flat roofs of beaten earth, dominated by the spiky minarets of mosques built of dried earth, topped by ostrich eggs.

*The true Negro peasant.* The Paleonigritic refuge zone stretching along the 10th parallel is full of paradoxes. A country of outcast peoples, its vitality is among the greatest in Africa; it harbours fierce warriors, primitive people living on wild products, and some of the best peasant farmers of Africa. Refugees in defensive sites, forgotten in the most arid lands, where the ferruginous rock mantle keeps breaking through, these people attain a surprising population density, commonly amounting to 150 per square mile, and sometimes to 600.

There is no political structure: social organisation has not got beyond the stage of the family and of gerontocracy; the individual is depersonalised, attached to one of the 'age groups' which make up the tribe; and initiation rites are an integral part of the social life.

These are the true Negro peasants. They do not consider themselves owners of the soil: they exploit it while respecting the delicate equilibrium between the spirits of all things: earth, rivers, rocks. They show fewer signs of modernisation than elsewhere; their only tool is the *daba* or African hoe. But in spite of the poverty of their domains, in spite of superstitious fears, their lands are among the most intensively cultivated in Africa. There is little question here of 'itinerant agriculture'; as a rule the land is well laid out and well exposed; the fields usually surround the village; only the fields sown with the poorest cereals lie scattered farther off.

With all these peoples, the dwelling suggests concern for vigilance if not defence. Where its form affords the least chance of defence, there is a grouping system, with a guard-house and sometimes a fence of mats. Almost everywhere, on his neatly laid out patch, man likes to feel his dependence on his group; he withdraws into his house, among his 'brothers', near the guarantees offered by his granaries, the authority of the elders and the cult of the ancestors.

*Invaders of the forest and 'gatherers of the fields'.* The forest and littoral area is another refuge zone, penetrated on the east by waves of invaders. The forest has encouraged the anarchic tendencies of the Paleonigritic world. The population is extremely scattered: the vegetation has assisted defence, increased suspicion and strengthened isolation. Crops are grown unsystematically in the highly fertile soil; always sure of gaining a living from a hitherto untilled field, and of seeing his clusters of bananas, his kola nuts and his oil palm seeds ripen, the Negro peasant has acquired a natural settler mentality.

This southern human fringe has three aspects. The region west of the course of the Bandama, in the Ivory Coast, is a land of outcast peoples, but the men of the western part of this refuge have features more reminiscent of the Paleonigritics of the savannas of the 10th parallel than those of the southern forest. They are still true peasants, and have transformed the mud of their mangroves into fields, with systems of dykes and drains and flooded rice fields. Here the population can reach 150 per square mile without exceeding the resources the country has to offer.

There is no question of diligent work among the other forest refugees, to the east of Lower Guinea; there are the people known as 'gatherers of the fields'. Here again, as in the Sahel and on the borders of the desert, the evidence of man fades out of the landscape; under the cloak of the forest or the secondary bush the fields lie buried, become scattered, tangled, badly fenced; population density drops to 6 or 9 per square mile.

Only among the peoples of eastern origin do we find intensive cultivation and well-marked estates. The Fons of Dahomey live in open country of extensive palm groves, planted and maintained above fields of maize and manioc. The Ibos of Nigeria have fields round their villages that they can cultivate without a fallow season, manuring them and surrounding them with low walls. Population densities in these areas regularly amount to more than 300 per square mile,

and sometimes reach 1,800; and, as in the regions of the great Sudanese empires, there are large built-up areas of truly urban character.

Among these diverse peoples, to whom commercial plantations of European type have introduced a fresh element of variety, there is a great diversity of housing: huts built around a courtyard with a water tank; crown-shaped huts; houses on piles among the fishing peoples. But the most common types today are the round huts with conical roofs and the rectangular huts with roofs having two, and sometimes four slopes; these may reflect Sudanese influence in the one case and European in the other.

*Early contact with the outside world.* It is through the eastern border of West Africa that the most important and least definable contributions have penetrated. A good deal of what is most authentically Negro in West Africa, both men and civilisation, certainly seems to have come from the east. But all is lost in the mists of a prehistoric Africa, and such eastern influences no longer operate.

More is known about contact with the outside world across the Saharan frontier. From the days of antiquity, caravans had been crossing the desert; the gold of West Africa was known to the Mediterranean world. With the appearance of the camel, the era of white incursions began, mingling conquest and proselytism.

*Spread of Islam.* In the Middle Ages Moslems began setting up their cells in Sudanese Africa. There were three active phases of this: in the tenth century, under the Ghana Empire, with Mauritanian Almoravides; in the fifteenth with the Askian sovereigns of Gao, followed by their Spanish-Moroccan conquerors; in the eighteenth, with the Holy War of the Peuls of the Fouta. In the intervals, diffusion proceeded as it proceeds today. The establishment of the European Powers in West Africa broke the warlike advance of proselytism at its height, but permitted, and even encouraged, Islamic infiltration through the Negro world. Islam may well have represented

Panorama of the Adobe buildings of Kano, seen from the minaret of the mosque. The fourth town in Nigeria, it is still the meeting place of caravan routes linking the Sudan in the east to Senegal in the west.

progress to some of the Negro societies, and the Moslems won their way southwards. Pedlars before they took to lorry transport, Sarakolés, Dioulas and Hausas traversed the forest from one to another of the towns that had sprung up from contact with Europeans, set up villages and finally reached the sea. Following in their tracks, the shepherd Peuls led their herds towards the urban centres. The village chiefs, aristocrats accessible to administrative notions, founded their authority on European confidence. The Islamic scholars taught in koranic schools. Following the pattern elsewhere the practical-minded Peuls and Malinkés married their daughters to the local Negro peasants in Mali and in Upper Guinea. Even agriculture, opposed as it is to the spirit of Islam, was laid open to Moslem influence by the attempts at groundnut (peanut) cultivation made in Senegal.

*Fresh influences.* The opening of the seaboard, which occurred later than that of its eastern and northern frontiers, proved decisive for the future of West Africa. It was in the fifteenth century, when they were forcing their way to India, that the Portuguese put these shores in touch with Europe for the first time. Henceforth West Africa quitted its insularity; it was opening itself to the world.

This occurred in stages. During the two centuries following the Portuguese discovery, navigators and merchants of every nationality and code of morals pillaged the warehouses of the coasts, as the natives of the interior pillaged their fields. This was the era of monopoly companies, with trade in wild produce, stealthy barter (spices, ivory, gold), and soon an attack on the flesh of Africa itself, with the slave trade.

The first settlements were peacefully ageing, especially after the abolition of the slave trade, when the second European influx took place, at the end of the nineteenth century. Capitalist and free-trade Europe was becoming entangled in competition; it discovered that new lands still existed in which to dispose of its surpluses, and from which to obtain new raw materials, and there was a race to cut Africa up into colonies. This was the era of imperialism; a profit economy was veneered over a traditional subsistence economy. The capital equipment of the country was undertaken, remarkable projects were carried out, but the majority of the population derived no direct benefit from this first attempt at development.

The Second World War made it clear that the day of colonisation was over. Almost everywhere, it was decided to work for the benefit of the local populations. This led first to an era of paternalism, the economic and social development of Liberia under the aegis of the United States; and of F.I.D.E.S. (Investment Fund for Economic and Social Development); the first four-year plan in the French territories; the Colonial Development and Welfare Fund in British territories. The fault of the system lay in its attempt to impose formulas planned from outside on a reality not completely explored from within.

After the failure of this paternalism, at a time when, paradoxically, the United States was leaving the field of action in Liberia to capitalist companies, the old colonising countries of Europe appeared to be taking this reality into more effective account. Their proposed solutions approached the African problems from the inside, as was evident in the second French four-year plan, which in 1953 set itself the task of developing the territories *in association* with the inhabitants, making use of traditional experience, empiric notions and natural balances to achieve a higher standard of living. In British territories the local population was being given participation in local and national government and by the mid-1950's the new patterns of government had been set and the way prepared for their independence.

Whereas the French authorities were working towards setting up independent territories inside the French Community with representation in Paris, the British Government had as its aim independent countries linked only tenuously by the permissive ties of the British Commonwealth.

Agriculture provides the basis for economic life and development throughout West Africa while in the poorest countries such as Gambia and Sierra Leone, it forms practically the whole wealth. Plantation crops are increasingly important — despite fluctuations in world prices — because they lend themselves to commercial production by modern methods. Ghana derives considerable wealth from cocoa, which employs 15 per cent of all agricultural labour, from forestry, chiefly hardwoods, and from fishing, which is carried on extensively elsewhere. Palm products and plantation crops — bananas, coffee, sugar, cocoa and cereals—are important throughout. The Ivory Coast, perhaps due to the large share of French aid it has attracted in the past, is among the most prosperous of the French-speaking countries in West Africa, as a result of which Abidjan has become an important port and the centre of considerable commercial development.

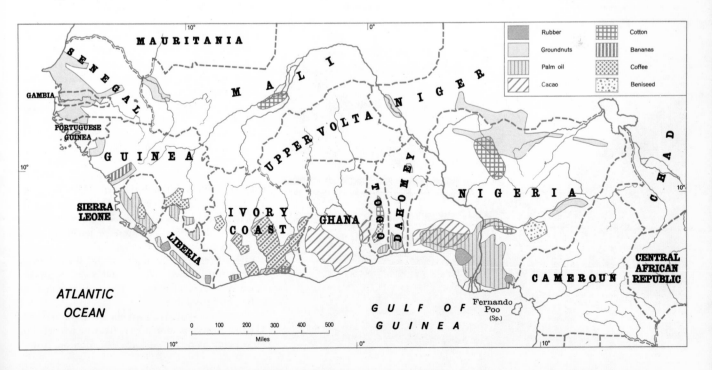

## WEST AFRICA IN EVOLUTION

While these countries were living under colonial government proceeding gradually from the simple export of primary products by the Companies to a more advanced economy, European ideas became current among them, indirectly through the transformation of their ways of life, and directly through the teaching in the schools. At the same time a country existed in West Africa that was set up as an independent unit run on democratic lines: Liberia was a concrete example of liberty set in the heart of dependent Negro Africa.

Yet the new nations of West Africa follow the administrative structures set up at random in the course of European expansion, though names have sometimes changed. Only by the uniting of the two Cameroons have boundaries altered.

**Portuguese Guinea.** Pinned to the western slopes of the Fouta Djallon, the colony was born of a Portuguese landing in the fifteenth century. A country of rivers and mangroves devoted to rice-growing and to oil palms on the littoral, with a hinterland divided between maize and manioc for local consumption and groundnuts (peanuts) for export, this little territory has the appearance of a survival from an older state of things, awaiting, or already seeking, some fresh stability.

In the past, after its discovery in 1446, it was regarded only as a coastal fringe from which the navigators provisioned themselves with slaves, gold and ivory; the interior plateaus were unkown. Today one of the most striking features of the country is still its division in two: low-lying regions given up to intensive rice-growing by a Paleonigritic forest people, the Balantes, and the interior regions divided between Mandingo peasants and former Peul shepherds, now settled. There is no modern Agriculture, either European or African. The few surpluses from local production are collected by a big trading company which exports them overseas, groundnuts (peanuts) and palm kernels forming the major colony's exports.

The former colony is now constitutionally a province and an integral part of Portugal, but with the franchise restricted to the Europeans and the African 'Assimilados' (who have passed the assimilation test which requires that they should be literate in Portuguese, practise the Christian religion, have a certain financial standing and be willing to give up native customs and live in a European manner). There is only one legal political party, the Government's own.

**Liberia.** Devastated at one time by the slave trade, this coast was chosen by American philanthropists in the 1820's as a refuge for recently liberated slaves. In 1847, Liberia became a free republic. Today, the country exports large tonnages of rubber and iron ore, but it is above all the first prototype of African democracy. The United States, however, continued to exercise considerable influence, assisting the local finances, establishing rubber plantations and building up the free port of Monrovia and the main airfield. Their interest in Liberia sprang in turn from strategic necessity, paternalistic goodwill and concern for their capital investments.

But the descendants of the former slaves, although black, were foreigners; they were not able to adapt themselves to their new country and were not recognised by the inhabitants as belonging to them. Like the original European colonisers, they remained as it were encamped on the coast: even today, the interior of Liberia forms one of the last relative 'blanks' on the African map.

For the sake of idealistic principles, the United States spent a long time financing a Government that could neither govern nor solve the problems of development. Now that Liberia stands on its own, traces of American procedure remain: but the rubber concessions of the Firestone Company are shreds of American land rather than modernised African centres.

Local government has, however, grown stronger; the iron mines near Monrovia, the capital, produce annual exports of over three million tons; rubber has not come up to original expectations, and no longer contributes more than half the export trade. The monopoly of the Firestone Company has now been broken and about sixty per cent of rubber produced is now grown on Liberian-owned plantations and half the shares of one of the biggest iron ore projects at Nimba are owned by the Liberian Government. And although in 1960 more than half Liberia's exports were going to the United States, Liberia no longer needs America to dominate its economy as in the past.

This, however, is not the country's major trouble, which is twofold: a nominally democratic but actually oligarchic government and an advanced Negro-American social fringe overshadowing the retarded peoples of the hinterland, more or less detribalised and up to now rigorously segregated.

Paradoxically, in the midst of the West African surge towards new political and social formulas, Liberia produces the impression of a country that has so far failed to evolve.

AUTONOMOUS EVOLUTION WITHIN THE BRITISH ORBIT. The first British territories were likewise restricted to a few points along the African coast; later on, British

Students of Ibadan University. The progress of West African independence has been marked by the establishment of national universities.

The paw-paw is a tree of the same family as the custard-apple, and its fruit has a taste similar to the bana

rule extended in the form of protectorates established over the regions of the interior. Unlike developments in Liberia, those in the territories of the former British West Africa suggest a natural ripening of human societies working out their own salvation along their own lines, for their own reasons, and with the guarantee of their own capacities.

This is due in great part to the fact that these territories were endowed with natural riches, various geographical and cultural potentialities, and great population densities. The most advanced among them were peopled by groups with a high degree of African civilisation, which had already succeeded in organising themselves into solidly constructed communities.

**Gambia.** This is a tiny strip of land surrounded by Senegal. Some English merchants established their trade there towards the end of the sixteenth century, at the mouth of the river offering the best means of penetration on the west coast of the West African bloc. Later on, the same site was chosen as a strategic position of defence against French enterprise and the slave trade.

As everywhere else in West Africa, the French worked round the inner side of the favourable sites chosen by the British on the coast; but here they did this before the British had established enough trading posts in the interior to form the basis of a large protectorate. Thus Gambia is merely a gate, which might have been valuable, into a hinterland that makes no use of it.

In this narrow territory, the food crops — rice, manioc, maize and millet — are hardly sufficient for local needs. Following the example of Senegal, groundnuts (peanuts) have been adopted as a commercial crop, and account for almost the whole of the exports. There are a few titanium-bearing deposits in the sands of the littoral; these were exploited briefly in 1956-7 but operations have now ceased.

Bathurst, the capital, at the entrance to the estuary, is confined to strategic and administrative functions; it serves as a port for the Gambian hinterland only; until recently much of its site was unhealthy.

Gambia became independent in February 1965, the last British colony in West Africa to do so; it faces the future determined to become more than the colonial trading post of the past.

**Sierra Leone.** The name of the capital, Freetown, which in 1787 was the first point of contact of the British with this part of the coast, bears witness to the origin of the colony, intended as a home for African waifs in London. At the end of the nineteenth century the hinterland was annexed as a protectorate widely enveloping the original nucleus. In 1961 the Colony and Protectorate became an independent and sovereign state within the British Commonwealth.

The Colony, now known as the Western Area, served at first as a reception centre for the slaves liberated by the British naval forces, which were using Freetown at the same time as a base in their pursuit of the slave-traders. The peninsula is now occupied by the town, an excellent port and cultural centre, surrounded by a narrow rugged terrain exhausted by too

A native woman of the Kru tribe with her child in a village near Monrovia.

Groundnuts being loaded at the wharf at Basse, Gambia.

Diamond workers washing the diamond-bearing gravel in a stream near Kenema, Sierra Leone.

EST AFRICA : A cattle market at Asni, Nigeria.　　　Gambian girl.　　　Two northern Nigerians meet on the arrival of their caravans in Kano.

intensive farming. Its future may depend on fishing, specialised poultry and pig-breeding and possibly the exploitation of titanium-bearing sands.

The lands of the ex-protectorate consist of low-lying ground and marshes along the littoral (Southern Province), and plains and plateaus in the Northern and Eastern Provinces. There is some hope of an agricultural future for the littoral, thanks to a planned increase in rice and palm-kernel production. The North and East have already given proof of mineral potential: diamonds, iron ore, chrome ore; there are reserves of bauxite, rutile, gold and platinum, which are being investigated. Diamonds, iron ore and palm kernels lead exports, followed by coffee, cocoa, piassava and ginger.

The economic potential thus appears substantial, yet Sierra Leone gives the impression of a country not actuated by any intense dynamism. As yet, apart from the mines there is little industry, even around the port areas, except that concerned with the primary processing of raw materials; types of food and methods of cultivation are mostly primitive.

This may in part reflect the lack of the highly developed African civilisation and definite social structure found farther east. In the peninsula, cultural and administrative evolution is mainly the concern of the descendants of former slaves, known here as 'Creoles'; the rest of the country is given up to peasants of the old Africa, still living their traditional life in small, scattered communities of Paleonigritic type; but much is being done by the government under the policy of equal rights for all Sierra Leoneans and a great part of both capital and recurrent expenditure has been spent on communications and education in the last decade.

**Ghana.** Ghana's history is the usual one: isolated posts and warehouses on the coast, creation of a colony (1874), establishment of a protectorate over the regions of the interior (Ashanti, 1896; Northern Territories, 1901).

It is a rich country, as far as the south-west region is concerned, with an old African culture developed in a solidly built state. In the north and eastern centre, together forming the basin of the Volta, soil, climate and seasonal floods combine to make a hostile zone, always rather thinly populated. It was therefore no great loss to submerge a good proportion of this arid land under one of the most daringly conceived barrage lakes in the world, the Volta River project. Its first purpose will be the establishment of a centre for the manufacture of aluminium, starting with the deposits of bauxite found farther west, in the rich Ashanti regions; in addition, it is thought that it might enable the land to be cultivated by irrigation, and even exert some influence on the climate. There are plans for rice cultivation on the banks of the lake (which will recede in summer), cheap transport systems along its 250-mile length and a fishing industry. Electricity production began in 1965.

The south-west, meanwhile, lives, and enables the whole country to live, on assured resources. This region, corresponding roughly to the domain of one of the most dynamic ethnic groups in African history, the Ashantis, is at the same time richly endowed by nature.

The old name of Ghana, 'the Gold Coast', bears witness to the original activity of the state. But in addition to gold, amounting to 3 per cent of world production, other mineral wealth has been discovered: this country is now the second largest producer of diamonds in the world and the third largest of manganese, while its bauxite deposits could ensure an annual production of 200,000 tons of aluminium by the industrial complex of the Volta. Besides these resources of the Ashanti region, lime is exploited along the coast, and there are deposits of iron ore, bitumen and asbestos, as well as salt.

All food products of forest type are represented in Ghana's agriculture, besides commercial crops, especially cocoa. The latter is the main source of profit, greater even than minerals; Ghana supplies one-third of the world's production of cocoa, and derives two-thirds of the value of its trade exports from this source. Lesser but still substantial resources are represented by timber and fisheries.

Cocoa trees at Dwinasi, Ghana. Cocoa is by far the most important of Ghana's crops, and covers about five million acres. It already supplies a third of the entire world supply, and there has recently been a considerable increase in yields as a result of control and the introduction of improved varieties.

The market mamies, well-known figures in the market of Accra, the capital of Ghana.

In spite of the damage suffered by the cocoa plantations, attacked by a disesae that has been controlled but may prove incurable, it is easy to see what has contributed to the accelerated evolution of the country. This evolution is all the more fundamental in that, as in Nigeria, the bulk of commercial production is in the hands of African associations — families or companies; all cocoa cultivation is African and half the gold and diamond mines belong to Ghanian companies.

Economic advance and cultural development are symbolised by the port of Takoradi, the modern harbour opened in 1962 at Tema, near Accra, and the three institutions for higher education including the autonomous University of Ghana. Accra, the capital, is a symbol too, of the conclusion of this advance: in March 1957 it became the capital of the first dependent African state to attain independence. The Gold Coast was henceforth Ghana.

Having achieved independence some years before its neighbours, Ghana, inspired by a strong and visionary political leader, attracted the alliance of many emergent neighbours by its policy of Pan-Africanism, a movement aimed at a United States of Africa. Among the opponents of the Ghanaian conception of political union has been Nigeria, which believes that its size and population entitle it to the economic leadership of all African states south of the Sahara.

**Nigeria.** This is a large country, and its population of 55 million is about half that of all West Africa.

It was not till 1820 that the British began to be interested in these regions, and the constitution of a colony in Lagos, the present capital, did not take place till 1851. During the whole of the end of the nineteenth century, relations with the interior were in the hands of a trading company. The usual regime of a protectorate was not established in the hinterland until 1900. Today, Nigeria is an independent federation within the British Commonwealth, consisting of four Regions, each with its own House of Assembly, with Lagos, the capital, a federal territory. The northern part of the former trusteeship territory of the Cameroons voted in 1961 to join Nigeria, while the southern part joined the Cameroun Republic.

Before the beginning of their common Afro-European history, four different civilisations had shared the country between them. The Hausas, peasants of Sudanese type, had been living in the north-west since the tenth century; in the thirteenth, the Peuls — shepherds, warriors and proselytes of Islamic faith — settled in the north-east. The history of these northern regions was related to that of the various empires of Sudanese type. The coastal and forest regions were divided between the two powerful ethnic groups, the Ibos in the east and the Yorubas in the west. The former, isolated until the nineteenth century, had not advanced beyond the unorganised stage of most of the Paleonigritic peoples, but the latter have had a brilliant civilisation, based on a powerful kingdom.

Western Nigeria is purely Yoruba; its minority peoples formed the Midwestern Region in 1963. The Eastern Region is largely Ibo, while Northern (Sudanese) Nigeria has a great variety of peoples, the the largest groups being Hausas and Peuls, or Fulani.

The sawmills at Dwinasi, Ghana. Timber forms a considerable part of Ghana's exports, but the destruction of unreserved forests by farming is threatening the supply. The Protected Timber Lands Act of 1959, as well as further reservation and afforestation, try to counteract this trend.

Tappers on the Avreboo rubber plantation, Ghana, bring in their collections for processing.

Lagos, the federal capital of Nigeria, seen from the top of the Federal Government building. The second largest town in Nigeria after Ibadan, it is a flourishing port and industrial centre. The University of Lagos was founded in 1962.

Western Nigeria is a rich Yoruba area of forest lands devoted to agriculture, and influenced by the plantation economy found in Ghana and the Ivory Coast. An area of big villages and some large purely African towns, it lives mainly on its food crops (bananas, manioc, oil palms, rice, yams, maize), and commercial crops (cocoa, pineapples, cola nuts, coconuts), from timber, and from the fisheries of the coastal regions. It has no mineral resources, but practises traditional handicrafts in addition to those introduced by modern ways of life. A few industries have sprung up alongside the capital Ibadan, which has the oldest of Nigeria's five universities, but most industry is found round the port of Lagos, the federal capital; these are concerned with foreign products (engineering works, fuel depots), or local ones (breweries, soapworks, oil and textile factories). This area will gain fresh prosperity from the Niger Dam project for which planning was completed in 1963. To be built at Kainji, some 64 miles upstream of Jebba, the dam, together with a power plant and navigation works, will provide electric power needed for industrial and domestic use (the 880,000 kW it is capable of producing should satisfy requirements until about 1980); it will afford partial flood control; provide enough water to double cultivable acreage; help fishery production; and allow the progressive development of navigation. A bridge across the Niger at the dam provides an alternative to the inadequate facilities at Jebba, thus not only reducing the traffic delays, but also allowing cattle to avoid tsetse infected areas through which they have hitherto passed to reach Jebba.

The Ibo territory, in the east, is quite different. Though more densely populated, it does not possess the same agricultural resources, so that there is a tendency towards Ibo migration throughout Nigeria and West Africa. Although the Ibo was considered backward compared to the Yoruba people, the Ibos have shown a remarkable adaptability to the twentieth century and quickly caught up once their geographic isolation ceased. On the other hand, the area appears

to offer the best hopes for mining and industry in Nigeria, with its deposits of oil (with an output of over 2 million tons in 1961), iron, zinc, lead and lime; the presence of coal, even though it is of poor quality, makes Nigeria exceptional in West Africa, where there are so few natural sources of energy.

Besides this ethnic division from east to west, there is a division separating two main human blocs between East and Northern Nigeria from north to south. In the south there is the prolongation of the belt of land with its mantle rock and its aboriginal peoples which crosses the whole of West Africa at about 9°N. This is an area of poor crops and insufficient stockbreeding, where the deposits of tin on the Jos plateau once raised high hopes, later to be disappointed. In the north is the Sudanese belt, consisting of the northern slopes of the West African 'roof' descending to the basins of the interior. More intensively cultivated in the west by Hausa peasants, more devoted to trade and a certain amount of industry in the east by the Peuls, the country is rich in all Sudanese food and commercial products, capable of satisfying local consumption, supplying the markets inherited from the past on its Saharan borders, and feeding processing industries, the creation of which at this distance from the coast is very significant.

Varied in relief, climate, vegetation, people and resources, Nigeria possesses the elements of stability; its cultural heritage and its dense population contribute dynamic elements. But it has concomitant defects: political and tribal loyalties have so far kept the members of this great whole relatively separate. The federal formula certainly stands the best chance of remedying this condition, provided its application tends to real communion and not to fragmentation, but there is danger that it has too far formalised the indigenous regional differences.

THE TERRITORIES WITHIN THE FRENCH ORBIT. The eight territories of the former French West Africa and the French part of the Trusteeship Territory of Togo have become since 1960 the independent Republics of

West Africa has a very varied mineral wealth but most of it is at present only in the early stages of exploitation. Gold has long been important in Ghana and iron ore is now being developed in Sierra Leone and in Guinea, which also has bauxite and diamonds. The completion of the Volta River Dam in Ghana will provide hydro-electric power for a variety of local industries as well as a major industrial complex which will produce aluminium. A similar project on the Konkouré will exploit the important iron reserves in Guinea, where bauxite is also mined.

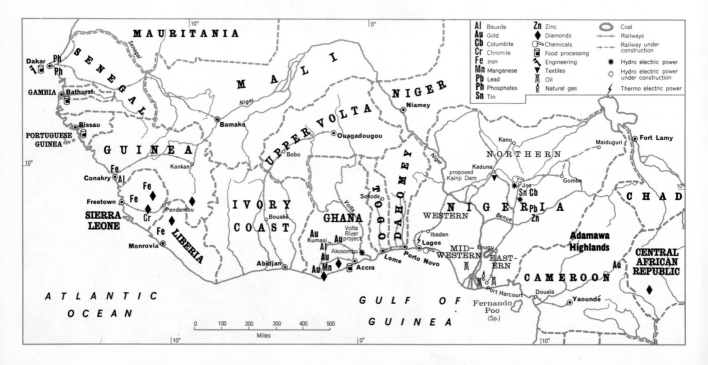

In Nigeria, workers prepare
bunches of bananas for shipment.
A good commercial bunch or
'hand' of bananas may
weigh as much as 120 lb.

Senegal, Mali, Niger, Mauritania, the Ivory Coast, Dahomey, Upper Volta, Guinea and Togo.

According to an amendment to the French Constitution adopted in 1960, member states of the French Community could become independent and sovereign while remaining within the Community. Of the former French West African territories all but Guinea chose to remain within the Community either as member states or by special agreements. The Republic of Guinea had already chosen to become independent outside the French Community in 1958.

**Senegal.** This small country on the western front of Africa comprises a desert, the Ferlo, surrounded by fertile borders: the valley of the Senegal in the north and east, the alluvial lands of the Cayor in the west and the wet lands of the Casamance in the south.

The oldest of the French colonies in Africa and one of the starting-points of French penetration into the interior of Africa, Senegal was the first territory to have suggested the possibility of mass exports, and was at one time the administrative pole of the whole of French West Africa. It is to these historical factors more than to natural advantages that the country owes its advance.

The whole of the interior, Ferlo and a good deal of Cayor was originally given up to nomad shepherds, or else turned into a desert by the cultivation of the groundnut (peanut).

The Senegal valley, in the north, is an attractive area for settled cultivators and nomad stock-breeders. Cattle are pastured there when the millet sown after the river floods has been harvested. But this alternation is not enough to ensure economic stability, and irrigation projects have been under consideration for the valley and the delta which would permit the expansion of millet and rice cultivation, and possibly the introduction of cotton production.

The coastal regions, more than any others, have seen the meeting of old ways of life and European economic influence: fishing and stock-breeding share their importance with groundnut cultivation and market-gardening; the fisheries are slowly becoming

industrialised and on the shores the titanium-bearing sands are being exploited.

South of the Gambian enclave is an area whose stability is due to the skilled cultivation of rice by the Diolas; there is no scope here for extension of groundnuts, which are spreading in the east, where the land is drier.

The economic weakness of Senegal lies in the single-crop cultivation that has established its reputation: that of the groundnut. This represents almost the whole of its exports, and makes it the fourth greatest world producer. But groundnuts have also exhausted the soil. Food products will have to be developed and the number of cattle increased.

The extent of Senegal's industrialisation was for a long time unique in West Africa, but these industries have been facing some difficulty recently in that they were built up as part of the French West African area, which has now split up into separate states. But there is room for development: a mining industry is being founded on the phosphates deposits — in 1962 output of phosphate rock was 639,000 tons; fishing, especially for tuna, is becoming increasingly important.

But it is the capital, Dakar, that gives Senegal its greatest importance. This city represents the opening of the country to the modern world. It is the fourth port in importance of the whole of the French Community; a commercial, administrative, industrial and strategic centre, it is also a university town and one of the chief ports of call on many sea and air routes; its notable urban advance has made it a residential centre in which the old Western world and the African world intermix.

**Mali.** This is a vast, composite territory, one quarter of which encroaches on the desert, while the rest covers the systems of the Upper Senegal and the Middle Niger and parts of the sandstone plateaus of the south, the northern slopes of the Fouta Djallon and the red, ferruginous expanses of the crystalline and metamorphic regions. Except for its desert regions, Mali is a bush and savanna country, where the Negro

peasant mingles with the nomad, the stock-raiser or the trader. As in the past, it forms a transitional area between white and black Africa within the French sphere.

During the period of French rule an attempt was made to substitute east-west relations along the Senegal-Niger axis for the old trans-Saharan relations from north to south. A system of railroads and waterways conveys the influx of modern life from outside across the immense expanses.

Along this axis lie the country's chief resources, development projects and towns. Besides the basic resources of millet, rice, fish and livestock, other elements have been introduced on European initiative in the hope of improving the country's economy. The west is mainly a region of markets and of trade routes; Bamako, the capital, is a market and a rail centre, road and air junction and a navigation terminus on the Upper Niger. The centre is divided into two major sectors: the region of the 'inner delta', with the town of Ségou, where the Office du Niger project, having renounced its hopes of cotton cultivation on a huge scale, is still engaged in furthering the cultivation of rice and increasing the conquest of land that is already maintaining 25,000 African settlers from the arid regions; further on, towards the bend of Timbuktu, is the lake region, where millet and groundnut (peanut) cultivation alternate with transhumant stock-raising. Finally, in the east, as in the west, lies a market region: Gao is a river and air stage, and the starting-point of the main road across the Sahara to Oran.

To the north of this axis lie the borders of the desert, given up to nomadic stock-breeding; to the south the ferruginous rock plateaus, an area of poor crops and a little nomadic stock-breeding.

Mali appears to be restricted, as far as its economy is concerned, to trade with its African neighbours: it has not developed any large scale commercial agriculture of international interest; its mining prospects are very modest — a little iron in the west, and traces of manganese, lead, zinc and poor phosphate. Its chief rôle may prove to be that of a transit station, a turntable in the heart of West Africa.

**Upper Volta.** In 1929 a small territory was marked out inside the loop of the Niger. An extensive crystalline plateau, slightly inclined towards the Niger, it is a true Sudanese country in respect of climate, soil, relief, vegetation and continental character. Its peculiarity is of a human kind: it includes the whole area of the feudal Mossi Empire, which still maintains a sovereign of sacred character, an intensely hierarchised administration, a people of peasants, monolithic, impermeable to Islam, grouped around its capital, Ougadougou. The Mossi comprise the majority of the population and are in conflict with anti-federalist non-Mossi minorities.

In the neighbourhood of Bobo Dioulasso, in the west, resources are modest: food crops of Sudanese type (millet, yams, maize), with some additional products such as groundnuts (peanuts) and cotton shared between local consumption and the markets. In the central, Mossi, areas of the country production is very poor, in spite of the hard labour of the peasants on

A Mali village at the foot of the Sangha Cliffs. The Dogons have followed the same way of life since the twelfth century, when they sought refuge from war here. The tall, square buildings are traditional.

Ploughing in the Upper Volta. Agricultural produce (with the exception of groundnuts) is mainly for home consumption: the principal crops are millet, sorghum, maize, yam, and karite. Rice, cotton, and groundnuts are of increasing importance.

their ferruginous rocks. Over-populated, the region forms a reservoir of labour for the favourable zones of the south, especially the Ivory Coast and Ghana.

Still more continental Mali, as no permanent river crosses it, it suffers from the conditions of the arid belt along the 9th parallel, has few export crops, and is hardly able to live on its own food products. It is difficult to see how the Upper Volta Republic can support economically the life of a modern independent state. It has a few mineral deposits, of gold and manganese, and exports some cotton, groundnuts, karité and especially cattle.

**Niger.** Made a colony in 1922, Niger is an immense country thinly peopled. Moreover, the population is localised on a narrow southern strip between the Niger and Lake Chad, along the northern frontier of Nigeria. Niger is the meeting-point of the Negro and the light-skinned nomads, the desert sands and the last thorny shrubs of the southern monsoon area. An Islamic country, it has been torn between the supremacies of the empires of Gao in the west, Sokoto in the south and Bornu in the east.

Its traditional capital, Zinder, once the starting point of the roads to the north, through the Air and Fezzan, still functions as a commercial capital, while the other caravan station, Agadès, is slowly dying, devitalised by the movement of economic activity towards the south and south-west. It is there that the modern capital, Niamey, has been established, where the land and air routes cross the waterway of the Niger.

The Niger Republic suffers, nevertheless, from its situation: thousands of miles away from the administrative complex to which it formerly belonged, cut off from the sea by the huge expanse of Nigeria, and thus often dependent upon the Nigerian transport system. Even the projected railway link between Dahomey and Niamey would still leave it with access only through another country, although one within the Customs Union of the former French West African territories. Dependent upon external aid even for its current budget and dependent on the existing goodwill of its neighbours for all outlets, Niger hesitates to commit itself politically. This may explain its relative aloofness from the French Community.

**Mauritania.** At the other end of West Africa is another vast, almost desert territory, with a largely nomadic population of only 1.5 per square mile. To the south, it is fringed by a border of cultivable alluvia on the right bank of the Senegal. This long ribbon of food crops and pastures was the area to which the Moorish Saharans withdrew and then expanded, and was the first line of French penetration to the interior.

Here the most traditional trade of the country developed, that of gum, alongside a second source of revenue, livestock. The old capital, St Louis, was established here.

On the outskirts of Nouakchott, the capital of Mauritania. Situated on the desert littoral, between Saint Louis, the former capital, and the fishing port of Port Etienne, Nouakchott is a true desert town, isolated and having little contact with the rest of the African world.

Today, Mauritania appears to be emphasising its Saharan character, and withdrawing to some extent from contact with the Negro world of the south. On the edge of the desert, about halfway between St Louis and Port Etienne, the new capital, Nouakchott, is a symbol of this trend. This sandy country, which was one of the poorest of French West Africa, refused to enter the short-lived Mali Federation, as did the Ivory Coast, the country that was the richest. On the other hand, Mauritania asserts its independence from its northern neighbour, Morocco, which lays claim to it.

This may have been because it expects to attain economic independence by adding to its traditional products, dates of the oases, the profits of a mining industry unmatched except in Guinea. In the Middle of the Sahara, in the hinterland of Port Etienne, the iron deposits of Fort Gouraud contain an estimated 150 million tons of ore, and there is enough copper, farther south, to provide an annual production of 25,000 tons.

Mauritania's atitude to its neighbours may also spring from the peoples feeling that they belong to another world, both ethnic and cultural, rather than to those of the black Africa of traditional cultivators and modern planters.

**Dahomey and Togo.** These are two narrow strips of country opening on to the Gulf of Guinea exhibit the paradox of countries in an equatorial latitude with open horizons and estates rigorously organised by a population that has inherited high civilisations and attained the greatest population densities of all West Africa. They are rich in both food and export crops (palm products, copra, rice, maize, manioc, yams, millet, shea butter, castor oil, cotton, cocoa and groundnuts) and their people are among the most open to new ideas and most preoccupied with their social and political future.

Since 1956, Togo, formerly under United Nations Trusteeship, has had a Legislative Assembly and a ministerial government; the French guardianship is at an end, and it is now an independent republic. Dahomey, with different origins and a quite different history, is now also an independent republic.

Both these young states have sufficient dynamism and consciousness of their individuality to remain truly autonomous in spite of their size. But they will have to rely heavily on external aid, especially from France, for their development. Dahomey must expand its agricultural capacity, for its mineral prospects are poor; the projected rail link with Niger and the expansion of the port of Cotonou are of great importance for it gains large revenues from its transit trade with Niger and Upper Volta, which could be diminished by a closer link between Niger and Nigeria. Togo, on the other hand, though smaller and with poor agricultural resources, has a promise of a sounder economy founded on the phosphate deposits now being exploited near Lake Togo and estimated at 50 million tons, much of it of a very high quality.

Peul tribewomen in Togo. The Togolese are among the most receptive of African peoples to modernisation, and their communities are well-ordered and constructive.

A lagoon in Dahomey, with the houses set on stilts to escape rising waters.

**Guinea.** This country, curiously twisted in shape, composed of mangroves, high plateaus, mountains, wide plains covered with rocks and Sudanese savannas, and undulating land buried in dense forest and peopled by equally dissimilar human groups, owes its shape and diversity, as usual, to the framing of African territories by European competition. Guinea became a French colony at the end of the nineteenth century.

Up to the Second World War, Guinea differed little economically from other colonies with the same climatic conditions. The country lived on the usual crops of rice, manioc and millets. It raised cattle, some of which it exported. Commercial crops included coffee, palm oil, citrus fruits and bananas, introduced in 1920.

The bananas of Guinea now cover French needs twice over, so that in spite of tariff concessions in the French market, other customers had to be found.

The face of Guinea took on a new look from the day when attention was centred on its mineral resources. Today it seems probable that this country, whose gold-washers supplied antiquity with precious metal, has every chance of becoming the most important industrial unit in West Africa. Its mineral wealth will not lie in gold, or even diamonds — successfully exploited on its eastern borders — but in the minerals required for a modern metallurgical industry.

The first of these to attract attention was the bauxite of the islands of Los, opposite the port of Conakry, and the iron of the Conakry peninsula itself. Today it is on the mainland, at the foot of the Fouta Djallon, that the interest in bauxite is concentrated; production amounted to 1,731,000 tons in 1963, and the reserves have been estimated at 600 to 700 million tons. As for

iron, reserves are expected to amount to thousands of millions of tons and the two mountain ridges of eastern Upper Guinea, the Nimba and the Simandou, formed of magnetite quartzite, are virtually mountains of iron.

The Konkouré and the rivers of the Fouta Djallon are, moreover, being developed to supply hydro-electric power, on the basis of which plans for industrialisation have been drawn up.

The iron of the Kaloum peninsula provided in 1962 exports of 700,000 tons; that of Upper Guinea is the object of valuation and negotiation with foreign companies, American, Swedish and West German. But for the moment it is bauxite that is the most important. Besides the exploitations on the islands of Los, two groups are in process of formation. In the west, at Boké, near the frontier of Portuguese Guinea, and in the hinterland of Conakry. This entailed the opening of new roads and railroutes, the creation of a port south of Boké, the expansion of the port of Conakry and the erection of a dam on the Konkouré. While all these projects were in course of execution the object was not to extract bauxite for export, but to transform it into aluminium on the spot.

All the problems attending the introduction of industrialisation into a rural, even tribal, country explains the Guinea government's policy of centralised planning and production of communal type.

Much of the external aid to Guinea has come from the Soviet bloc, but the Government continually affirms a policy of positive neutrality and readiness to accept investments from any country which attaches no political ties to them — a policy which its natural riches and the competitive aspect of the 'Cold War' makes possible.

**The Ivory Coast.** Comparable to Guinea by reason of its area and its population of something over three million, this country is the opposite of it in natural features and economy, and, today, in the political formula it has adopted.

Its history is the usual one: slave trade stations on the coast, exploration and penetration towards the regions of the Niger, struggles for influence among European competitors, establishment as a colony with arbitrary frontiers. Here, too, a subsistence economy was followed by a slave trade economy, then exploitation, then development.

In spite of this the Ivory Coast has a character all its own. It makes a first impression of being a densely forested country, but, in fact, the forest covers only the southern half. This forest has certainly marked its people and its history, and given a special character to the landscape. It engendered a way of life that would later welcome a plantation economy with enthusiasm, and make the Ivory Coast the richest of all the colonies of French West Africa. It also served as a gate to the sea and to the world for the vast hinterland.

Economic interest in the Ivory Coast shifted from the slave trade to gold and ivory, to the search for forest rubber and then to the exploitation of timber. Later the forest regions turned to the cultivation of cocoa and then coffee, which is now the basis of the country's economy. Later still the production of bananas and pineapples was widely introduced.

Today the economy relies in the main on the export of coffee and cocoa, but also substantially on that of timber and bananas, with pineapples as a sideline.

Even before independence the country derived enormous wealth from these products, compared with the rest of West Africa, and this had important consequences. The Africans of the Ivory Coast had themselves exploited rubber and timber, and they took a share in the plantation economy. Though European planters remain, more than 90 per cent of the coffee and cocoa is now produced on purely African plantations, and banana-growing is becoming increasingly an African concern. The farmers of the forest zone have nearly all become planters and exporters and lead a middle-class life in the villages and towns.

The Ivory Coast's rôle as a gateway to the interior was hampered by the lack of a real port. The port of Abidjan, the capital, was not opened until 1950, but its development has been rapid, and it now handles a higher tonnage than Dakar, giving a great impetus to the development of the country. Investors were as enthusiastic about the Ivory Coast as they were about the industrialisation of Guinea, and important works were started: renovation of the road network, extension of the river system, enlargement of the port, building of a hydro-electric dam.

It seems unlikely that the Ivory Coast will ever be able to depend on its mineral resources, though in 1963 213,500 carats were exported from the diamond mines in the north-west, exports of manganese amounted to 105,300 tons and there has been oil prospecting along the littoral. Although at present industrialisation is mainly confined to the processing of agricultural products, the inducements offered by the Government to private enterprise may attract new factory projects and there is already a German scheme for a chemical industry.

Sure of its economic potential, conscious of its cultural and social advance, the Ivory Coast may, however, rest content as a primarily agricultural country.

Abidjan, Ivory Coast. The new port which has been developed on the Ebrié lagoon.

# EQUATORIAL AFRICA

## GABON, CONGO (BRAZZAVILLE), CHAD, CENTRAL AFRICAN REPUBLIC, CAMEROUN REPUBLIC

The four territories which made up the former French Equatorial Africa (F.E.A.) are now the Republics of Gabon, Congo (Brazzaville) — formerly Middle Congo and for the purpose of this section described as Congo or Congo Republic — the Central African Republic (formerly Oubangui Chari) and Chad. They all achieved independence as Member States of the French Community in August 1960. Prior to full independence they had formed an economic, technical and customs union. Brazzaville, the capital of the Congo Republic, remains the de facto capital in the field of technical and financial assistance. To a great extent the future development of these four territories depends on their will to work together.

The 184,000 square miles forming the Federal Cameroun Republic were a German colony from 1884. In 1921 the territory was divided into two League of Nations Mandates, latterly under United Nations Trusteeship. East Cameroun, which was administered by France, became independent in 1960 West Cameroun (formerly called the Southern Cameroons), which was administered by Britain as part of the federal area of Lagos, decided, by plebiscite, to disengage from the newly independent Federation of Nigeria and to unite with the former French Cameroons.

In October 1961 they combined under a federal constitution as the Federal Cameroun Republic with special relations with Britain and France but opting out of both the British Commonwealth and the French Community. The former Northern Cameroons, which was administered by Britain, chose at the plebiscite in 1961 to become part of the Northern Region of Nigeria as Sardauna Province.

The straggling outline of this area of Equatorial Africa extends for about two thousand miles from Tibesti to the Lower Congo. The Federation of F.E.A., organised in 1910, perpetrated an accident of history: the success of French explorers in the race for the interior after the coasts had been occupied. But despite the efforts of nearly fifty years, the federation was a fragile link, which never overcame profound differences and divergent interests.

### THE PHYSICAL SETTING

*A fragment of the African shield.* As in the rest of tropical and Saharan Africa, the relief is dominated by the presence of a rigid Pre-Cambrian shield, either on or below the surface. The structure of this ancient shield, usually metamorphic or crystalline, is of great complexity. Over immense regions it is hidden by a virtually undistorted sedimentary covering. Continental formations predominate. In the north, they form the bedrock of Tibesti as well as that of Ennedi; in the south, the Bateke plateaus; and betwen them, a part of the Congo-Chad backbone.

Nevertheless the gravel, sand, marl, limestone and dolomite, lying in a series of rings behind the Cameroun and Gabon coasts, are associated with a chalky marine formation. Quaternary formations of clay and sand have accumulated in the two large areas of subsidence: the Chad basin and the Congo punchbowl.

The relief is as peculiar to Africa as the structure. Its salient features are flatness and monotony; only minor irregularities occur in the whole of the enormous plains of the Chad and the Congo. The Logone, in the Ere region, and the Chari, further east, flow along ridges; in the space between stretches a vast depressed 'tray', flooded in the rainy season. To the north of Lake Chad, dunes and dune-like massifs to some extent break up the flatness of the extensive Congo Basin.

Immense plateaus of sandstone or volcanic rocks separate the river basins. But enormous eroded areas cut at varying altitudes into the folded or raised formations of the Pre-Cambrian shield. Peneplains stretch almost uninterruptedly across the whole of western, southern and central Cameroun. In the Central African Republic is a related peneplain. Viewed in detail the surfaces are divided between glaciated hills with convex slopes and digitate glens with flat bottoms. Here and there residential reliefs rise up. Exposed to the action of the humid tropical climate from a remote epoch, the soils of the peneplain have undergone marked lateritic weathering and continual change.

At the edge of the plateaus the descent usually consists of one clear-cut, comparatively undissected step, a typical feature of tropical relief. Seen from the coastal plain of Cameroun, the high plateaus of Bafang and Yaoundé look like a wall, giving the impression of a great chain of escarped mountains; but in fact there are few genuinely mountainous regions. The most remarkable reliefs are of volcanic origin: the Manenguba and Bambuto Mountains on the frontier of the former British Camerouns. The Alpine prairie of the peaks shelters numerous nontropical species, including clematis, brambles, violets, scabious and clover. Comparatively intact volcanic cones crown the high plateaus of the Tibesti massif, whose highest point is Emi Koussi (11,209 feet). Above 6,500 feet, the winter frosts are severe; temperatures of −10°C. (14°F.) to −15°C. (5°F.) have been registered. Above 5,500 feet, the flora includes Mediterranean species: myrtles, asphodel, lavender, et cetera.

*The West African Rift.* How can we explain the 'West African Rift'? From Mount Cameroon (13,353 feet) to the Bambuto Mountains, the great volcanoes in western Cameroun form a definite alignment. The alignment continues into the sea: Fernando Poo, Principe, São Tomé, Annobon, are also volcanoes whose upper part alone emerges from the sea. The volcanic

A Chad herdsman. For the most part little care is taken of cattle, though in Chad and northern Cameroun there are some specialised stock-breeders.

extrusions mark an enormous fracture, parallel to the Benue rift. The major volcanic axis is flanked by two other approximately parallel faults, themselves signposted by minor volcanic emmissions. Between these two facing faults is a rift due to subsidence, comparable to fragments of the East African rift valley. On its edge, the ancient shield rises symmetrically to a height of 5,000 feet in the great horst of the Roumpi Mountains (western Cameroun). Only at a distance of 125 miles inland does the rift become less sharply defined, before giving way to a faulted system continuing as far as Chad.

*Lake Chad.* The Chad punch-bowl is a perfect specimen of a region with internal drainage. The punch-bowl structure shares the responsibility for this with the arid or nearly arid climate. The southern half of the punch-bowl sends a large part of its waters into Lake Chad, mainly via the Logone and the Chari. The lake is only a film of water; in normal years its average depth is no more than six feet. Its Sudanese banks are black and clayey, ill-defined and flat, while on the Saharan side they are of tawny sand, heaped into little dunes covered sparsely with mimosa and acacia type bushes, divided into an endless number of islands and peninsulas, tangled in a labyrinth of stinking stagnant water. Finger-like prongs of stagnant water called *bahrs* reach between the lines of the dunes in Kanem and are prolonged in garlands of pools. On both sides, it is impossible to say definitely where Lake Chad begins and ends. Rain and water from the rivers raise its level every year until the beginning of December; its lowest level is reached during the month of July. Moreover, the level of the lake is subject to slow but considerable variations following a regular rhythm. In a few years, the surface area has been known to vary from 5,500 square miles ('little Chad') to 10,500 square miles ('big Chad'). To the east of the lake and the Lower Chari, several other depressions are flooded by temporary watercourses in the rainy season.

At an altitude of about 780 feet, Lake Chad is by no means the lowest point in the punch-bowl; the altitude decreases to about 600 feet in the Bodélé depression south of Borko. A trough, called Bahr-el-Ghazal or Soro, joins the lake to the depression. At one time the excess waters of Lake Chad flowed away through it.

Now, since the discovery of a communication at high water between the Logone and the Benue through an affluent of the Benue, some think it possible that the Logone will eventually make a capture at the expense of Lake Chad.

*All the climate zones of tropical Africa.* Owing to its great extent from north to south, equatorial Africa covers all the climatic vegetation zones of tropical Africa with the climatic belts running from southwest to north-east. The equatorial climate of the textbooks is not found in its classic form until farther east, in the former Belgian sector of the Congo punch-bowl. At Impfondo (Congo Brazzaville), at approximately latitude 2°N., the rains slacken off in June-July and from December to February. In January, the driest month, the rainfall is 2.5 inches; there is no real dry season, but the low rainfall affects the vegetation. The mean minima reach 20.4°C. (69°F.); the mean maxima do not exceed 31.2°C. (89°F.). In this type of climate ombrophilous forest predominates. The especially well-known forest of Gabon resembles all the Equatorial-Guinean forests of the Ivory Coast, Ghana, Nigeria and Cameroun. The primary open forest is a heterogeneous mixture of species. On a concession of 2,250 acres on the Lower Ogoué 6,484 large trees divided into 42 different species have been counted. The enormous mahogany trees, the iroko and the tali are especially remarkable. Two extremely common trees are not natural inhabitants of the ombrophilous forest: the okoumé and the oil-palm. The okoumé, plantations of which are scattered from Spanish Guinea to the Congo, is a species requiring light; but for man and his cultivation, it would have stayed confined to the marshy parts of the coastal region, its natural habitat. Man has played a similar and even more active part in the propagation and cultivation of the oil-palm.

Towards the south, the equatorial climate begins to decline. The rhythm is still based on four seasons, but the dry southern season increasingly predominates. It

The M'bali falls, Bangui, Central African Republic.

almost stops raining for three months (June to August) at Brazzaville. September, with 1.4 inches which quickly evaporate under the blazing sun, does not help the vegetation much. However, the hydrometric degree never falls below 70 per cent in any given month. Dibuncha, on the coast at the foot of Mount Cameroon, has a rainfall of 404.6 inches, among the highest in the world; Douala receives 155 inches; Cocobeach, on the frontier of Gabon and Spanish Guinea, 151 inches. But these are notable exceptions due to the relief. From an average of 78 inches near the Equator, precipitation falls to 53 inches at Brazzaville, and even less at certain places in the plain of the Niari. The climate of Brazzaville, the Niari and Pointe-Noire marks a transition between the equatorial climate of the north and the tropical climate with its two clearly demarcated seasons. The same regions have a complex vegetation pattern, in which a savanna poor in trees predominates.

Bangui, in latitude 4°N., has a rainfall of 63 inches. A brief dry season occurs in January; there is also a slight falling off in rainfall in the dry southern season, during the summer solstice. At the foot of the Tibesti, Faya-Largeau (latitude 18°N.) registers only just over half an inch, and almost half of that in August, a faint echo of the season of tropical rains. Between these two extremes occurs every gradation of tropical climate. As the dry season is prolonged, so the annual range of temperature increases. Abéché, in latitude 14°N., has an average maximum of 45.5°C. (114°F.) in April despite its altitude of 1,950 feet. High altitude and the forest areas afford the only relief from the intensely hot and dry climate.

*Vegetation.* Climatic variations are matched by variations in flora. The forest proper, whose large trees shed their leaves individually, as a rule during the period of one to three weeks, ends near the fourth parallel except where it has been cleared by man for purposes of cultivation.

The extreme north of Cameroun and the whole of the north of the usable parts of Chad belong to the Sahelian zone; thorny shrubland dotted with acacias alternates with marshy steppe in periodically flooded depressions; this passes into desert; thinning out more and more beyond the 14th to 15th parallels.

In between, central Cameroun, Chad to the south of the 11th parallel, and a large part of the central African Republic are the domain of wooded savannas, a mixture of trees and giant grasses in varying proportions. The Central African Republic savannas have a great wealth of flora: about 250 species of trees and shrubs. The wooded savannas seem to be of man's creation. They probably derived, by stages, from a deciduous forest, intermediate between the primeval forest and the thinly planted woods of thorny species. The humidity of the subequatorial forest and the spacing out of Sahelian acacias have enabled them to resist fire, whereas this dry forest has been the victim of man-made fires. However, there are still important traces of it left in the east of the Central African Republic and on the slopes of the Cameroun plateau. In appearance it is an open timber-forest with scanty or non-existent undergrowth, reminiscent of the forests in temperate countries. Every year, brush fires sweep the wooded savanna; in the long run only the most sturdy of species can stand up to this regime.

## MEN, HOUSES AND TECHNIQUES

VARIOUS HUMAN GROUPS. RELIGIONS AND LANGUAGES. Up to a point, the climatic and vegetation regions are matched by variations in population. The striking fact is the isolation of fair-skinned peoples, Arabs and Peuls (Fulani) in the north. The cleavage between nomads and settled tribes cuts across the classification of Arabs by origin. The nomads, whose stronghold is the Yadé massif, have lived in relative isolation and their original type has been well preserved. With their tall slender figure, fair skin, aquiline nose and thin lips, they resemble the Peuls of Mali. But the settled tribes in the south, around Marona, on the Upper Benue and in the north of the central Cameroun plateau have interbred to a large extent. Arabs or Peuls, the fair skinned peoples are in a minority, and are slowly being assimilated by the surrounding population. Another people, the Pygmies of the jungle, form a strong contrast with the Negro background. They live, dispersed in small groups, in a large part

of Gabon, the Congo and the forest-clad parts of Cameroun, but never in the savanna proper. The forest is undoubtedly more of a hiding place for them than an essential environment. But the Pygmies, too, are undergoing change through interbreeding with other racial groups.

Islam makes an even clearer division than race. Arabs and Peuls have been its propagators and champions. Of their own accord or by force, out of fear, conviction, or a wish to better themselves, many Negroes have been converted; but there is less intermarriage between religions than between ethnic groups. In the north, Moslems predominate; the south is largely heathen; in between is a large zone of interpenetration. The Boudouma of the islands of Lake Chad are the most northerly of the fetishists; the Peuls of Ngaoundere Banyo and Tivati are the southernmost tip of Islam. In Chad, Islam is not simply an attitude; it is a political force with which France has had to reckon and often come to terms.

Nevertheless, the greater part of the area and the majority of its population remain outside Islam.

Felling an okoumé tree in Gabon, the richest of the equatorial territories. As in the Ivory Coast, Ghana, Nigeria and Cameroun, the primary forest is a source of wealth and supports a thriving timber export trade.

Animism and fetishism are commonly used as convenient labels for the beliefs held in this area, but little is really known about them. The missions, both Catholic and Protestant, which cover a wide area, have made a comparatively small number of firm converts.

The great linguistic groups are also arranged according to latitude. Arabic is less widespread than Islam. The mother tongue of the Arabs and some interbred groups, it is confined to the north. The major division is between the Bantu tongues of the south, and the Sudanese dialects of the north. The division runs more or less along the 4th parallel.

Natural boundaries have acted as obstacles to the propagation of men and cultures. The example of the Peul, dispersed from Baguirmi to Senegal, shows how easy diffusion along the parallels is. But the nomadic stock-breeder who pushes southwards has to change his camel for the ox, then the ox for agriculture. The cultivator of the savanna who penetrates into the forest has to serve a hard apprenticeship with the axe, accept a new environment and overcome his fear.

A caravan of porters carrying ivory tusks at Fort Rousset, in the Congo (Brazzaville).

HOUSES. Human 'zoning' is reinforced by many of the features of material civilisation. Some of them are merely a reflection of the natural environment. The significance of others is less simple. The most striking example is that of the dwelling hut. By and large, the plan adopted is circular north of the forest, rectangular in the forest and farther south. Sometimes a mixed type appears on the boundary line. In the far north we see the reappearance of rectangular buildings; but the earth walls and flat roofs have nothing in common with the forest huts built of vegetable materials and crowned with a ridged roof having two or four slopes. Each category embraces countless local and ethnical variations. The northern populations have managed to remain truer to their traditional architecture than the southern peoples. In the forest and the Congo savannas, evolution of the habitat is going on rapidly. Vegetable materials are used traditionally for building purposes but these are being progressively abandoned in favour of walls of mud or bricks dried in the sun, a change advocated by the administration for sanitary reasons.

AGRICULTURAL METHODS. Gathering vegetables and berries, hunting and fishing are seldom the basis of nourishment and the way of life. In the north of the Congo (Brazzaville), the negrillos of the Middle Sangha dig up wild yams with a 12-15-foot pole at the end of which are fixed two wooden blades, gathered into a cone and lashed in with creepers. They hunt elephants with assegais (wooden spears), or, from high up in a tree, drop a hanging block of wood armed with an iron head. They procure arms and iron tools by barter with the 'tall Negroes'. Some tribes specialising in fishing live on the banks of the big rivers.

Except in the desert zone, the area shows the characteristic agriculture of hot countries. The renewal of fertility depends on a long-term cycle of land lying fallow. Implements are confined to the hoe, the axe, the machete and (more rarely) the dibble. Within this general framework two climatic types are contrasted.

The Bantu system of agriculture predominates in the rainy zone of the south. To make their fields they cut down the forest, then burn the trees and branches on the ground twice. The shallow, light soil does not need tilling. Land clearing takes place at the two periods when the rains slacken off. The main crops are manioc, plantains, yams — all plants with a long development cycle. Maize is the only cereal. Many plants are cultivated as mixed crops; their harvest is staggered over long months. In a single field, the lifting of manioc can continue for more than a year. Consequently there is no seasonal shortage. After one banana harvest and two of manioc at the most, the fields revert to forest land. A few plots of groundnuts (peanuts) occupy the recently abandoned 'plantations' or the sites of former villages. In the immediate neighbourhood of inhabited huts small plots of various vegetables and plants are fertilized with domestic rubbish and ordure. When the axe has done its work the women bear the full burden of the agriculture. This picture is valid for almost all the forest. In the remote regions of Gabon and the Congos the banana heads the crops; along the coast and in the Congos it gives way to manioc. In the south of the

ZAMBIA and RHODESIA: The Kariba Dam and part of the lake reservoir behind

Congos, several peoples cultivate the savanna; their plantations are made or renewed three times a year. Gourds, leguminous plants — groundnuts (peanuts), haricots, etc. — are important crops. Clearance of the savanna requires very careful labour. Slash and burn cultivation is practised in various forms. Ridging, raftering, and digging-in green crops are common practice. This type of cultivation is only a variant of forest agriculture: manioc is still the basic crop everywhere, and maize the only cereal; the close succession of tilling the soil and harvesting leaves no room for a rest period. A similar pattern exists on the northern edge of the jungle.

Farther north this agriculture of the forest and its verges gives place to an entirely different type. The annual succession of a period of intense activity and an agricultural dead season mirrors the climatic division into two clear-cut seasons. The rhythm of the rainy periods suits cereals. The plantations are almost exclusively under sorghum, which is the basic food. Sorghum is sown from May to August and harvested in December. Sweet potatoes, coleus (fairly common throughout the region), gourds and haricots are subsidiary crops. As elsewhere, clearing the brush consists of taking up the grass, cutting down the shrubs and part of the trees, drying them and burning them. The major problem, peculiar to this agriculture based on cereals, is to protect the seeds from birds, during the sowing period and when the ears ripen; watchmen have to stay on the fields permanently. As elsewhere, the gardens round the huts contain a wide variety of plants, but in small quantities. Farther north, where the rainy seasons do not last so long, small-grain millet becomes one of the basic crops. The tribes on the shores of Lake Chad grow subsistence crops on stretches of sodden muddy soil. The seed-times, staggered to match the lake's withdrawal, take place out of season, from the end of November onwards. Rice has recently been introduced on the banks of the Logone. It is cultivated on level ground, together with millet, on denshered ridges, near the edge of the area of annual floods. Everywhere, concentration of the harvest within a short space of time poses a problem of storage. Hence the granaries of various shapes so characteristic of the region with two seasons. Despite these and partly owing to extravagance at harvest-time, a few months later there is a food shortage. While waiting for the first harvest (early varieties of millet), the inhabitants of the Chad punch-bowl live on *kreb,* a mixture of seeds of wild grasses the size of a semolina grain which are harvested with the aid of a special basket.

The northern boundary line of dry crops passes slightly to the north of Lake Chad. Beyond it, agriculture is concentrated in the oases. There is a series of palm plantations in Kanem. Borko, south of Tibesti, has larger and better plantations, Between the date palms, immaculately kept gardens are irrigated by Shadoufs, a pole-and-bucket method of raising water. The soil, divided into squares separated by banks, produces successively wheat (in winter), small-grain millet and maize. Caravans bring an additional supply of milk from the south in exchange for dates grown in the oases.

Stock-breeding is left to nature. The animals are not fed; their muscular strength is not made use of for cultivation; their manure is not collected. Many farmers own a few head of cattle of which they take very little care. But in Chad and northern Cameroun there are also groups of specialised stock-breeders. Traditionally, the stock-breeders barter products with the settled tribes or have the soil tilled by their servants. In Borko, the nomadic Gorans, who own palm plantations, do not arrive in the oases until the time of the date harvest, in July-August. The rest of the year they leave it to their servants to look after the trees in a perfunctory manner. The composition of the herds changes with the latitude. Sheep and goats are common everywhere; but pigs assume especial importance in the extreme south of the Congo. Trypanosomiasis prevents the breeding of cattle south of the tenth parallel. Two detached islets in the Sudanese region form areas free from the disease, the high plateau of the Adamaoua and the Bambari country (where herds were recently introduced). To the north of Lake Chad and Ouadai, oxen, ill adapted to desert conditions, give way to camels. The Sahelian lands at the northern extremity of Cameroun and Chad are the great stock-breeding zone. Family herds frequently contain several hundred or even several thousand animals. The herds on the move towards the pasture lands and the watering-places are accompanied by part or the whole of human communities who consume the milk and butter. Farther north, without agricultural support, population density falls rapidly. Farther south, the importance of stock-breeding decreases steadily from Chad to Gabon and the West. Pigs, sheep and goats serve as a means of payment in specific cases (fines, matrimonial negotiations) and provide some meat for great occasions. But as soon as the herds are larger than a few head they are ravaged by parasites and epizootic diseases.

## HUMAN AND ECONOMIC PROBLEMS

*A skeleton population.* Africa has a low population density, as is well known. But the figure of 18.4 inhabitants per square mile in tropical Africa is high in relation to the figures for this area: Gabon, 4;

Groundnuts are cultivated as a commercial crop in the valley of the Niari, Congo (Brazzaville).

Congos, 6; Chad, 5; Central African Republic, 5. The Cameroun Republic alone rises to a population density of 22. The physical environment is certainly not responsible for such a scanty population. The best proof is given by the following examples, where regions in no way distinguished from their neighbours, or distinguished only by more difficult conditions, have a much higher density. In the north of Cameroun, the Mandara mountains, in spite of the handicap of their steep slopes, are islands of heavy population. About half a million people are concentrated in the once restricted area of the Bamileke country; the density reaches 208 in the Dschang regions; 338 in the 1,250 square miles of the plateau proper; 298 and 419 in the two chieftainships of the subdivision of Bafoussam. The density appears to be just as high on the granite shield as on the parts of the plateau covered with ancient basalt. In Congo (Brazzaville) Koukouya are 18 to the square mile on their little plateau. The neighbouring Bateke plateaus, physically similar, have a density in the neighbourhood of 2.6. The granitic

fortresses of the Sahelian region have obviously served as refuges. In addition, the Paleonigritic peoples of the Chad mountains have perfected methods of agriculture with crops on terraces, intensive stock-breeding, thorough collection of manure and rotation of crops. But Bamileke agriculture conceals many weaknesses. And the Koukouya techniques are similar to those of their Bateke neighbours. In any case, the most primitive agriculture is capable of feeding more than six and a half inhabitants per square mile. The narrow localisation of high densities, then, is not caused by the soil or technical inferiority.

The slave trade has undoubtedly been partly responsible for sapping the population. According to estimates, 13,250,000 natives of the Congo Basin (in its broadest sense) are said to have made the voyage to the Americas in the course of five centuries. The demand on the coast had its repercussions hundreds of miles inland. Slower in reaching the savannas of the north, the slave trade caused equally great ravages there in the 1870's. At the same period, the eastern Oubangui was emptied by Arab merchants operating towards the Nile with the complicity of the local chiefs. To the west, the Adamaoua Peuls carried out parallel operations. Some of the captives were resold at Bornu and Sokoto, with a consequent increase in the population of what was to be British Nigeria.

Another factor of major importance is sleeping sickness. In the past it does not seem to have been very virulent and was confined to clearly demarcated districts. With colonisation and the development of traffic, it spread. The losses were enormous. Infection rates of 20, 30 and even 54 per cent were observed. The epidemic ceased only for lack of human fuel. It was not until after the First World War that the authorities received the technical and financial means for an effective campaign, although it had to be constantly renewed.

Demographic stagnation is a third factor militating against a numerous population. Medical and administrative investigations have often revealed an alarming situation. Among the Bahoumbo Bakota of Franceville (Gabon) the proportion of children is about 45 for every 100 adult women; in the Bahou village of Malima, which had 92 inhabitants in 1947, it was observed that only one child was born in four years.

The situation is no better among various groups in the north of the area. In some cases colonisation has been balanced by a demographic collapse. In others, in the coast regions of Gabon, for example, the problem seems to be of long standing, but its medical or social causes cannot be easily ascertained. Admittedly, there are many flourishing populations: the Bakongo, the Bakamba of the Niari valley, the Cameroun Bamileke, etc. But their rapid progress is offset by the recession of many others.

It is doubtful whether this area has ever been much more populated than it is now. It is only part of a vast semi-desert region, which runs from Chad eastwards into Zambia and Angola; straddling the climatic zones, a great void separates the human concentrations of East and West Africa.

*Economically backward countries.* The countries of this area are even less advanced than their underdeveloped neighbours. In spite of progress made, export figures

A young tribeswoman of Chad, a land-locked semi-desert country. Population density in equatorial Africa is low: in Chad (total population 2¾ million) it is 5 to the square mile.

remain low. Basically the great majority of the population consumes what it produces. And even among agriculturally hard-working tribes it rarely produces enough food to satisfy its hunger throughout the year. Wage-earners in the towns, the only ones fully integrated with the monetary economy, are in a wretched state. Slow development is related to scattered population, difficult communications and shortage of money.

## DIFFICULTIES OF DEVELOPMENT

*Too few people.* The low population density is pregnant with economic consequences. In an underpopulated region it is impossible to find the manpower for a large undertaking or a big workshop on the spot, to collect enough products in the same place to justify commercial planning or pay off the cost of processing

In general these territories must still rely heavily on foreign aid for economic development since their own mineral resources, although in some cases of considerable importance, are as yet largely unexploited. Primary products and timber are, therefore, often disproportionately high on the list of exports.

plant, or to supply sufficient traffic to make transport less expensive.

In this scantily populated area the densest groups have a tendency to settle in the mountains and remote regions; there are not many people along the coasts and the major routes to the interior — the navigable Ogoué, Congo, Lower Oubangui, Upper Chari, etc. Yet that is where the best chances for commercial agricultural development exist, at the lowest cost and in the shortest time. French colonists found that even where there were people, they were not readily available; wages were too low, trading products too low in price and imports too dear to induce them to work, once they had paid their wife's dowry, settled the capitation tax and satisfied the few needs which seventy years of colonisation have introduced. In the south, the egalitarian nature of Bantu societies reduced the attraction of earnings still further: anyone who grows rich has to share his wealth or face accusations of sorcery. Subtle or brutal administrative pressure forced recalcitrant villagers to work: compulsory taxes and crops, statute labour on the highways, 'recruitment' of manpower through the chiefs. Without his commercial crops such as cocoa in western Cameroun and cotton in the Central African Republic and Chad could never have been grown. In some cases workers were recruited hundreds of miles from their place of work. A more far-reaching policy consisted in shifting not only individual workers but also settled villagers. This today facilitates both the maintenance of roads and the harvesting of products (especially cocoa). Certain unexploitable regions were emptied of their population for the benefit of other regions. Post-war investment has made towns shoot up like mushrooms. Attracted by city life, the country dwellers have made a massive response to the call for manpower. The eight major cities of the area have a combined population of 540,000. Such compulsory methods are not in favour today. 'Recruiting', apart from its disastrous social and demograpic implications, was expensive in men or in money, according as the workers were poorly or well paid. The flow of country dwellers into the centres correspondingly diminishes the number of producers. Mechanisation seems ultimately to be the only genuine solution. The timber concessionaries have realised this: Gabon exports more okoumé than before the war, with superb equipment and half the manpower. But machines were very expensive. Often they did not exist; people had to invent, build, test and perfect them before beginning to use them; in other words, it meant an expenditure of time and money. And money in particular was lacking for the preliminary stages of mechanisation.

*Not enough money.* The rudimentary economy of these five new countries is quite incapable of financing their development, in spite of the heavy taxes and import and export duties. It is a vicious circle: without a vigorous economy, no money; and without money, no expansion. Money can come only from abroad, but apart from Gabon, which possesses an enormous deposit of manganese near Franceville, none of these countries offer investors the mineral wealth which has set several African territories upon the road to wealth. Hydro-electric power is the only resource which may one day claim to play the part of copper

in ex-Belgian Congo or gold in South Africa: the Edea dam on the Sanaga (coastal Cameroun) supplies a large aluminium factory; in the Congo (Kinshasa) France, West Germany and U.S.A. have begun work on harnessing the Kouilou Falls at a remarkable site. On the Atlantic coasts, trade is much more ancient than colonisation. In the interior, trade has followed exploration closely and sometimes preceded it. In 1899-1900 some forty companies were given a monopoly for the exploitation of immense territories in Gabon, the Congos, Chad and Central African Republic. Many companies failed, the sale of ivory and rubber not having sufficed to keep them going; some of them have outlived their concessions. They have been joined by the more powerful West African companies. The companies have a network of shops 'in the bush', where they trade, i.e. buy up native products. Others confine themselves to import-export; the small Portuguese, Greek or French shopkeepers act as their intermediaries. Among the products drained off towards the ports, three are especially important: cocoa (Cameroun, 60,000 tons); groundnuts — peanuts (north Cameroun, the Niari valley); palm nuts and oil (Cameroun, the Congos). Cotton is a maginal crop, with the Central African Republic exporting the largest share (35,000 tons). Chad sends cattle on the hoof to neighbouring countries and also meat by air. Generally speaking, commercial demand stimulates the African producer without improving his ments, the governments of the Congos and Central return to lying fallow and accelerates the exhaustion of the soil in the Central African Republic. The export companies, anxious for immediate profits and afraid of doing each other's work, leave the heavy task of agricultural education to the various governments, the governments of the Congos and the Central African Republic being particularly active in this respect.

Timber exploitation was born of trade, and the Europeans bought the trees before cutting them. Since 1930 and especially since the war, the 'cutters' have given way to a powerful industry. The area exports about 120,000 tons of undressed timber annually, not counting sawn timber and plywood. But the timber business confines itself to exploiting an existing resource; it does not renew it. The cutting of okoumé in particular is more like 'tree-picking' than agriculture. After the cutters have passed, they leave behind an impoverished forest.

The same remark holds good for the mines. The firms working gold and diamonds do not make lasting investments: they 'cream off' the alluvial deposits with the help of mobile plant. The gold of the area is not competitive and its production is diminishing. Diamonds, on the contrary, are making progress. Under the aegis of two large companies established in the Central African Republic, output rose from an average of 100,000 carats to 400,000 in 1963. Zinc and lead are extracted to the south of the Niari in what were the only genuine mines in the former F.E.A. Very little private capital has participated in the creation of new wealth. Crops introduced by Europeans are essentially the work of courageous planters, settled in the south of the Cameroun Republic (coffee, plantains, bananas) and Central African Republic (coffee, sisal), although in the former British Camer-

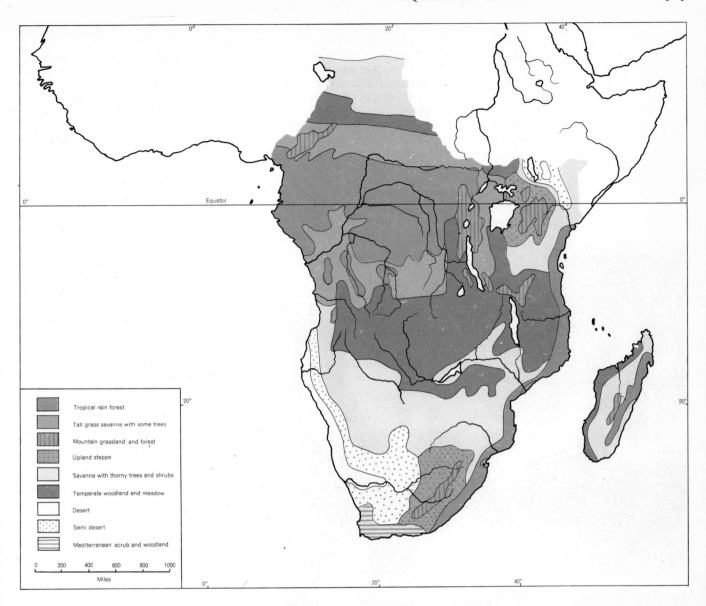

Tropical rain forest

Tall grass savanna with some trees

Mountain grassland and forest

Upland steppe

Savanna with thorny trees and shrubs

Temperate woodland and meadow

Desert

Semi desert

Mediterranean scrub and woodland

0   200   400   600   800   1000

Miles

oons the old German plantations were taken over and considerably improved after the war by the Government-aided Cameroons Development Corporation. In spite of large Government subsidies, the colonisation of the Niari has not succeeded in producing a paying form of mechanised agriculture with groundnuts (peanuts) and jute substitutes. Sugar-cane is the one exception, being on the increase. Apart from the immediate processing of agricultural products, industry remained in an embryo state. The cotton mill at Bouli (near Bangui), which gets its supplies and sells on the spot, figures as one of the most notable achievements.

Public investment has also sinned by omission. The French Government granted credit in fits and starts. Consequently short periods of feverish activity have alternated with long periods of sluggishness. No new effort begins to be effective until the personnel is recruited and trained, plant ordered and imported, and preliminary studies completed. Because of a desire to make too rapid progress by cutting short the preparatory stages, money has been wasted in occasional dubious achievements. Too many simultaneous efforts in 1950-51 led to a bottleneck on lines of communication and a manpower crisis; enough supplies for months piled up in the warehouses of Pointe Noire. French Government funds have principally served to establish modern transport routes.

*Transport difficulties.* As the crow flies, Yaoundé is 125 miles from the coast, Brazzaville 250, Bangui 625 and Fort Lamy 685. These distances would be negligible if they could be covered by rivers all the way and by boats of large enough draught. But the watercourses are navigable only in divergent isolated sections, burdened with physical or political obstacles. So the authorities had to opt for road or rail, for a land road from end to end or the incorporation of navigable sections of rivers.

River transport from the coast was made impossible in Cameroun by the escarpment to be climbed and was impeded elsewhere, as on the Ogoué, by a series of rapids. For a certain time navigation service functioned in the Niari. The Germans built two roads on to the Cameroun plateau. The idea of a railroad started by Brazza in 1882, rapidly won the day. While the layout was still being discussed, the Belgians built a line from Matadi to Kinshasa (Leopoldville). Since a competing line was not essential, the French

Zones of intensive cultivation follow closely the valleys and settlements. Timber is commercially valuable, especially in the Congo basin and also in Swaziland. Elsewhere the open savanna takes over; extensive grassy uplands corresponding in some measure to the prairies found in the south of the central United States. These are the regions of tall elephant grasses. Occasional clumps of trees and shrubs break the monotony of an otherwise unbroken horizon. These, too, are the regions of the famed National Parks, the game reserves where determined efforts are now being made to save from extinction many species of wild life, whose numbers have been dwindling for years as a result of indiscriminate hunting and the activities of poachers.

The horizontal loom is still used among certain tribes in north Cameroun, such as the Doayes.

A smelter at work in an aluminium factory at Douala, the principal southern port. In 1964 the Cameroun's output was 53,000 tons.

projects slumbered. The 'Congo-Ocean' railroad (1921-43), through wooded Mayombe territory and down the Niari valley, was not built until experience showed the inadequacy of the Belgian line.

As soon as the conquest and pacification of Chad had been completed towards 1910, the centre of interest shifted towards the north. Since then, the great problem has been to link the Central African Republic and the Chad plains (including the northern tip of Cameroun) with the coast. These regions, which are the most populous and the richest in economic potential, are still the most isolated. Communications could be improved in three directions: towards Kinshasa and Brazzaville; towards Douala across the Cameroun plateaus (which at present seems the most likely); and towards the Nigerian ports (Port Harcourt and Lagos).

The federal authorities of F.E.A., anxious to control the traffic from one end to the other, always favoured the north-south axis: it was Oubangui (Central African Republic) and Chad which had the Congo-Ocean line built, although it was not justified by purely Congolese traffic. A point in the favour of the federal route was that it would connect with the best port on the whole coast: Pointe Noire, with its roads opening into the high seas, its five deep-water berths and its modern equipment. This route also makes extensive use of river navigation, an economic method of transport: the recently renewed and modernised Congo fleet links Bangui directly with Brazzaville; farther north the navigable Chari makes some hundred miles more available. But there are many disadvantages. In spite of work on rock clearance, for several months in the year the low level of the Oubangui prevents large vessels from crossing the Zinga sill (50 miles downstream from Oubangui). The Chari is navigable only during the rainy season, when the Chad lowlands are transformed into marshes and cut the incoming routes. Even if a Bangui-Chad railroad were to be built, the north-south route would be slow, interrupted by costly trans-shipments. As for the Benue, though it has no rapids, steamers can pass up it only during the short annual floods (July-September). In 1964 Cameroun, Nigeria and Niger agreed to co-operate in a comprehensive improvement of the Niger river basin.

Built during the Second World War, the Fort Lamy-Maiduguri-Jos road carries some forty thousand tons of freight to the Nigerian rail lines in the dry season. Douala contests for zones of influence with Pointe Noire and also with the Nigerian ports. It was easy to build good laterite surfaced roads across the comparatively unforested and sandless Cameroun plateaus. Today powerful diesels link western Central African Republic with Yaoundé and Douala (with or without partial trans-shipment). The groundnuts (peanuts) from the region of Maroua (northern Cameroun) were once transported via the Benue; now they are sent south by goods train. Studies are being made for a Douala-Chad rail line. This route would guarantee Douala the lion's share of the traffic of the northern regions. But quite apart from the political difficulties its construction would cause, such a line would be highly expensive to build. And, in addition, it was recently decided to extend the Douala-Yaoundé line as far as Ngaoundéré, with a line to Chad too.

A network of minor routes joins the major traffic routes: some navigable waterways accessible to small steamers; but mainly a large number of makeshift roads where drivers and springs are severely tested. And aircraft? Numerous stations are linked weekly, or even several times a week, to the main towns and the ports. Aircraft have provided the best answer to the problem of transporting people. On little-used itineraries they compete with the roads for goods traffic, including the transport of manganese from Franceville, but they are still incapable of competing with a modern well-made land route. It is doubtful whether air traffic can contribute effectively to opening up Chad, apart from the very special case of fresh meat.

ATTEMPTED REMEDY. Too few men, too many miles, too little money: these factors have had cumulative effects. In the majority of productive fields capital can count only on a risky return; it has tended to invest in better endowed territories. Stagnation has made a part of the small population flee. Fortunately in the last few years the problem has been recognised. A considerable financial effort and aid from overseas, mainly from France, has enabled the governments to attack all aspects of the problem. Errors have regrettably been made in the past: towns have alloted a part of their capital out of proportion to their economic importance to costly constructions; grandiose road plans, conceived from too far away and at too high a level, have proved liabilities in Gabon and the Congos, and all there is to show for a prodigious waste of machinery and vast sums of money are a few stretches of motorway undermined by seepage.

But positive results have been obtained. The topographical map has made immense progress; geography, hydrology and soil have been the subject of serious investigations. A modern port has come into being at Brazzaville; the ports of Douala and Port Gentil have been enlarged. Industrialisation is beginning: there is already a sugar factory, and other projects are under review. The waterways have been opened for longer annual periods. The Congo-Ocean line has been renovated. The installation in the Congos of the first peasant co-operatives is a good omen for the future of commercial crops. With first-class equipment, the lumber undertakings of Gabon are no longer haunted by the shadow of shortage of manpower. Near Franceville exploitation of one of the world's biggest manganese deposits began in 1962; the ore is taken away by air, by an overhead railroad and a line attached to the Congo-Ocean railroad. There is talk of a railroad line intended to open up the iron at Mekambo, where a very high-grade deposit is located; another deposit, less rich but quite near the coast, near Tchibanga, could supply 4 million tons a year; exploitation should begin in the 1970's. There are uranium deposits near Franceville, and Franco-American finance has opened the way to exploitation of large pottassium deposits near Holle (Congo). Oil has gushed near Port Gentil in Gabon and exports already total 900,000 tons annually. Several hydro-electric stations are already functioning. The one near Bangui gas enabled a large cotton mill to be set up. Close to Douala, the Edea station, on the Sanaga, provides the kilowattage for a battery of aluminium tanks.

A similar project, but of quite different scope, on the Lower Kouilou near Pointe Noire, will supply an industrial complex.

There is growing hope that in the not too distant future these newly independent countries may play a major rôle in financing their own investments A close link between Chad, better equipped for food production and better populated, but badly placed to sell, and the republics of the south, which have power, industrial raw materials and good communications at their disposal, would be economically logical. For collaboration between the republics is necessary in the interests of each one. But Chad is drawn by the Moslem and stock-breeding elements in its population towards Nigeria and the Sudan.

# THE CONGO (KINSHASA) RWANDA, BURUNDI

Former Belgian Africa consists of the large territory of the Congo, with its capital at Kinshasa, and the two former United Nations Trust Territories of Rwanda and Burundi. Each is now a separate independent state.

### THE CONGO REPUBLIC (KINSHASA)

The Congo is an enormous country with an area of 910,000 square miles, and it is crossed by the Equator in the north. Broadly speaking, it corresponds to the basin of the Congo River, including in the east the edge of the East African mountains. The relief presents no serious obstacle to communications with the neighbouring countries, except perhaps in the east. The sources of the Nile are in Congolese territory and in Rwanda and Burundi so that these countries have an outlet to the Mediterranean. Despite its size, the Congo has a coastline only twenty miles long. The river estuary is a maritime gateway without great value, for above the port of Matadi the river quickly becomes blocked by impassable rapids. The mines, which lie 1,250 miles from the sea, are hampered by their dependence on easy access through foreign territories. The Congo is surrounded by Angola and by Zambia towards the south and south-west, by Tanzania, Rwanda, Burundi and Uganda in the east, by the Sudan in the north-east, by the Central African Republic in the north and by the Congo Republic (Brazzaville) in the north-west.

*Physical features.* Structurally, the Congo consists of a vast central wooded punch-bowl, bordered by grassy plateaus. Smooth unbroken landscape is the rule. But the Congo is not wholly flat; the central punch-bowl,

Open savanna in the Congo (Kinshasa). Beyond the mountain range lie the rain forests.

the uniform and frequently marshy plain, occupies only one third of the territory. A typically African feature, the Crystal Mountains, rising 2,000 to 3,250 feet, cuts off the central depression from the littoral. In the north, towards Chad, the barrier is not very pronounced. In the south, the slope is more marked towards the plateaus of Luanda and Katanga, while beyond the boggy zone of Lake Upemba, in Katanga, rounded folds and tabular massifs reach a height of 5,000 to 6,500 feet. The relief becomes most pronounced on the eastern borders, on the edges of the great African subsidence zones marked by Lakes Tanganyika, Kivu, Edward and Albert; here the edges of the plateaus sometimes look like mountain ranges. To the north of Lake Kivu rise the mighty volcanic cones of the Virunga Mountains (11,000 to 15,000 feet), and between Lakes Edward and Albert, almost on the Equator, the summit of Ruwenzori (16,794 feet) disappears beneath sparkling glaciers.

Almost the whole area of the country is drained by the Congo and the vast network of its tributaries.

One of the volcanoes of the Virunga mountain chain in the Congo (Kinshasa). The volcanoes are worshipped locally in the belief that the craters represent the urn in which thoughts are crystallised and the melting pot in which the souls of the dead are resting.

The Congo occupies fifth place in the list of great rivers with a total length of 2,700 miles; but its volume — 810,000 to 2,430,000 cubic feet per second, depending on the season — is second only to that of the Amazon. In the plains, the courses of the rivers flow calmly and are navigable, but they are interrupted by falls and rapids when they cross the edge of the plateaus. Even the Lower Congo is no more than a gigantic torrent between Stanley Pool and Matadi.

The part of the Congo between 4°N. and 4°S. belongs to the equatorial zone. The heat there is intense and unvarying though not as strong as in the Sudan. The copious rainfall, distributed fairly regularly throughout the year, reaches from 71 to 86 inches. This is the domain of dense evergreen equatorial forest and the only large quadruped which can get through it is the elephant. To the north and south this region gives way to another with a Sudanese climate and two rainy seasons, and this gives way in Katanga to a region where a single rainy season alternates with a single dry season of about six months each. On the high plateaus, the trade winds from the east blowing for three-quarters of the year moderate the temperatures considerably and at night in the dry season it may even freeze slightly. The alternation of the seasons in these two climatic belts produces savanna with giant grasses; this savanna is always more or less wooded, except in the highest eastern and southern areas. This is the habitat of the large herbivores (antelopes, buffalo, zebras, elephants) and the large carnivores like lions, leopards and hyenas.

These landscapes and their fauna are threatened everywhere by man's intervention, which has often been thoughtless: itinerant agriculture, over-grazing, brush fires, wastage of timber and over-hunting. To preserve wild life, parks have been established such as the Albert Park between Lakes Kivu and Albert, Garamba in the north-east, Upemba in the Katanga and various other game reserves.

*Population.* With about 15 million people, the Congo is not highly populated and population distribution is very uneven. Certain regions of the punch-bowl and Katanga are practically deserted, but in the Lower Congo, the Kasai, and the northern and eastern plateaus, the growth of mining and industrial activity have concentrated the population.

The majority of the Congo's inhabitants are Bantu, but towards the northern borders they give way to Sudanese peoples. Generally speaking it is possible to contrast the Bantu of the forest, living in small groups, with those of the savanna, who like the Sudanese form large, well-organised tribes and sometimes kingdoms.

In the forest, especially the Ituri forest, about 150,000 Pygmies are to be found. Their height varies between 4 feet 6 inches and 5 feet 2½ inches. In contrast, on the borders of Uganda and in Rwanda and Burundi, there is a giant race of Nilotic origin, called the Watutsi, whose average height is 6 feet and many of whom reach 6 feet 6 inches. Although they constitute a minority, their superior tribal cohesion gave them a social and political domination over the Bantu in the past. Today however Bantu community life has been developed considerably under European influence.

Congolese living in rural areas still represent nearly four-fifths of the total population. They are chiefly occupied in cultivation but also raise a few goats and some poultry; hunting and fishing often provide supplementary food. Stock-rearing is practised on a large scale only on the plateaus of the south and east. In spite of the efforts of Belgian administration to improve them, agricultural techniques have in general remained primitive, and poor fertility and rapid deterioration of the soil often mean that farmers have to seek new land to work after two or three years. *Towns and villages.* Villages are fairly small. Among the Sudanese in the north and the Bantu in Katanga, they consist of circular huts with conical roofs; elsewhere the houses are rectangular and the roofs are arched or have two or three flat panels. Tree-trunks, grass, leaves and clay are used as building materials.

Towns are rare, but they are real towns, not rural agglomerations, being of quite recent origin and established by European colonists. About one-fifth of the total population lives in the towns. Kinshasa, the capital, situated opposite Brazzaville on Stanley Pool, is the seat of the federal government, and extends for six miles. 1966 saw extensive administrative reorganisation accompanied by the name changes of major towns, including that of the capital to Kinshasa. Lubumbashi (Elisabethville), situated in the southeast corner of Katanga, owes its prosperity to the development of minerals, Kisangani (Stanleyville), capital of the agricultural North-East, on the upper reaches of the Congo River, stands one degree north of the Equator.

Other main towns in Katanga are Jadotville and Kolwezi (mining centres), Kalemie (Albertville), a port of rail head on Lake Tanganyika and Kamina, the vast former Belgian military and air-base.

In the Kasai region, where diamonds are mined, the major towns are Luluabourg and Mbuja-maji. The capital of Kivu is Bukavu, and that of the North-West is Mbandaka (Coquilhatville), on the Congo. *Early history.* The Congo was founded by King Leopold II of the Belgians. He recognised the immense potential of the country and decided to take personal possession of it, after the British had displayed no interest in it. He formed a private company, called the International Africa Company, to exploit the territory. Shortly afterwards the company's name was changed to the Congo International Association, and soon recognised as a sovereign independent state by the United States, France, Britain and Germany in June 1960.

It was a state with very fluid frontiers at first. Towards the Atlantic, Portugal, which had claimed the whole of the coastal zone, was finally satisfied with the left bank of the Congo River and the enclave of Cabinda. France took back Kouïlou-Niari, which had been occupied by the Belgians, and later stabilised the frontier at the Oubangui River (1887). Inland the 'occupation race' for Africa between the Great Powers continued. It led the Belgians to the great lakes in the east, where they were forced to withdraw from Bahr-el-Ghazal. However, they retained Katanga, with its great mineral wealth, when the frontier of Rhodesia was traced in 1894. The Belgians also retained the Kasai basin, another area of vast mineral wealth, when the boundaries between the Congo and Angola were agreed to by the Portuguese.

The methods employed in the Congo Free State — an often ruthless exploitation, forcible recruitment of native labour, division of the land into huge concessions — were certainly not blameless, but in this respect the Congo resembled many other colonies at the same period. The benefits of colonisation in the territory were often overlooked. They included the pacification of a country ravaged by incessant tribal warfare, the suppression of barbaric customs, military campaigns against the Arab slave-traders and the official abolition of slavery, the achievements of Catholic and Protestant missions and medical services. But determined press campaigns exaggerated the evils of the administration — and invented some. In 1889, preparatory to requesting a loan from the Belgian Parliament, Leopold announced that he would bequeath the Congo to Belgium. Criticism of Leopold's rule in the Congo steadily increased in Belgium and abroad. In 1908 he agreed to hand over the administration to the Belgian State, a year before his death.

*Brief history of the Congo before independence.* The Belgian administration between 1908 and 1960 was much more enlightened than Leopold's had been. Under its rule an extensive system of primary education was developed, largely through Catholic and some Protestant missions. At independence the Congo had the greatest degree of literacy in Africa. Excellent medical services had come into being, a high quality of housing for the Africans prevailed and their average standard of living was the highest in Africa. The vast mining and agricultural research establishments and enterprises such as the Union of Minière in Katanga and Huilever helped economic development. However, the Belgian administration in the Congo was essentially paternalistic. Although it was often pointed out as an example to other countries whose colonies were evolving in a more turbulent fashion, this turned out in retrospect to be a weakness. No provision was made for the advancement of the African beyond low levels of responsibility. There was little secondary education, no universities until Lovanium was

*(See map on page 320.)*
The Congo is one of the few exceptions (Rhodesia and South Africa are others) to the general economic pattern of Africa where exports are chiefly of agricultural produce. Copper in Katanga, an extension of the Zambian Copper Belt, provides the chief mineral wealth. Oil and diamonds offer opportunities for future development as does the prospect of hydro-electric power from the Lower Congo (Kinshasa).

There are about 150,000 Pygmies in the tropical forests; they are a minority group but tribal solidarity has been their strength in the past.

established in Kinshasa (Leopoldville) in 1954, and a University in Lubumbashi (Elisabethville) in 1956. While the Belgians determined to preserve the economic structure of the country, they neglected to ensure that there would be Africans who could accept responsibility in administration, medicine and the army.

*Independence*. But the Congo could not escape the political ferment of Africa as a whole. After World War II politics began to be discussed by the Africans, especially those, who, by virtue of their secondary education, were known as *évolués*. By 1959 it was clear that some political rights had to be conceded, and local elections were held. But riots in Leopoldville, and a widespread upsurge of nationalist demands for independence, indicated that even this was not enough. Thus in January 1960 the Belgian Government invited the leaders of the main political parties to a round-table conference at Brussels to discuss the demand for independence. So overwhelming was the pressure from all but a few moderate leaders that the Belgian Government, somewhat to their own surprise, announced that independence would take place on June 30th that same year.

National politics were new to the Belgian Congo. There was not a single political party with support throughout the country.

The election produced two strong, and roughly equal claimants for power. Each tried to form a government without the other, and each failed.

The history of the Congo Republic since independence is the history of international efforts, through the United Nations, to re-establish a political unity and economic stability in a country which fell into disorder with the sudden departure of the Belgian authorities. It is a complex and eventful history, which cannot here be described in detail. The principal difficulties were the attempted secession of Katanga and Kasai which, if successful, would have deprived the central government of valuable mining revenues, and the fact that the political parties fell back into their tribal hostilities.

The problem of Katanga's seccession almost destroyed the U.N. effort in the Congo, but finally, in January 1963, this secession was declared at an end and the U.N. forces left the Congo in June 1964.

Relations between the Congo and Belgium have been resumed and in the framework of the United Nations Belgium provides grants and some technical and educational aid.

*The economy*. The Second World War considerably speeded up the country's development. During this period the Congo had to meet large orders for raw material and it was forced to establish local industries to supply the commodities that it was no longer able to import. Similarly, during the political upheavals of 1960-62 industrial output rose by thirty per cent. Again the reason lay in the country's inability to import goods during that period owing to lack of foreign exchange. Today, with an exceptionally diverse economy, it is the third most important industrial state in Africa, coming after South Africa and Egypt.

The copper of Katanga and the diamonds of Kasai form the principal wealth of the Congo. The copper reserves are enormous, the metal content extraordinarily high and the presence of cobalt, zinc and other metals increase the value of the ore. At present the largest quantities of ore come from big open-cast mines to the west of the basin, in the neighbourhood of Kolwezi, as well as from the underground workings of Kipushi, to the south-west of Lubumbashi. Crude copper and cobalt are mainly produced near

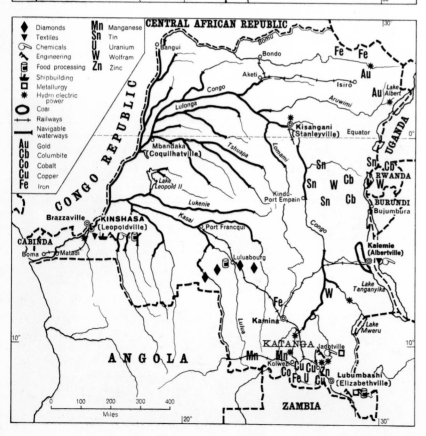

Lubumbashi and Jadotville. Part of the crude copper is refined in Katanga; the rest is exported. The production of zinc and silver has been started at Kolwezi. Pitchblende or uranite is worked near Jadotville. Manganese ore is found in the south-east of Katanga and cassiterite, associated with precious metals (tantalum, wolfram), is found farther north, as well as at Maniema. Gold mines exist in various regions of the periphery, mainly at Kilo and Moto in the northeast, but they produce only twelve tons a year, or one per cent of the world's production. The gravel pits of the Kasai basin yield half the diamonds in the world, but they are small stones, principally black diamonds used in industry.

Mining in the Congo is dominated by the Union Minière concern, which produces seven per cent of the world's copper and two-thirds of its cobalt.

*Agriculture and secondary industries.* The Congo is the world's second largest producer of palm-oil, which comes from trees grown in Mayumbe, Kasai, and the equatorial regions. Tea and coffee plantations are to be found in the central basin. Other products include cotton, rubber, sesame, groundnuts (peanuts), kapok, raffia grass, agave, sisal, pyrethrum, timber, manioc and bananas.

In the Lower Congo, in the north, and alongside the railroad in Kasai and Katanga, there are large ranches which raise beef-cattle, supply the towns with dairy products and also breed pigs as a sideline.

The Congo's industrial enterprises include flour mills, breweries, cement works, construction firms and shoe factories in various centres, large textile factories at Kinshasa and Kalemie and a shipyard at Kinshasa. But Congolese industry is handicapped by shortage of fuel; the Luena basin in Katanga supplies poor quality coal and the Katanga mines depend on coal imported from Wankie in Rhodesia. Fortunately the Congo possesses vast hydro-electric reserves — twenty per cent of the world's known resources — of which only a minute part is used. Powerful hydro-electric plants have been set up near Kinshasa and in Katanga to meet the needs of industry. A project has been adopted for harnessing the falls of the lower reaches of the Congo at Inga, near Matadi, which will eventually generate over 20 million kWh.

*Transport.* Navigable waterways cover about 8,500 miles, of which more than 1,500 are accessible to ships of 800 to 1,200 tons. However, navigation is hindered by rapids which occur at the edge of the plateaus bordering the central basin. The River Congo between Kinshasa and Kisangani and the Kasai as far as Port Francqui are the principal navigable watercourses. Kinshasa is the country's main river port; the major sea ports are Matadi, Boma and Ango-Ango.

The rail system is fairly comprehensive and the major lines are from Kinshasa to Matadi, Port Francqui on the Kasai to Katanga, between the Congo River and Lake Tanganyika, and the narrow gauge lines which operate in the north-east of the Congo. A line runs from Lubumbashi to Lobito in Angola, which handles a considerable proportion of the Congo's foreign trade. The road system is being extended; at present mileage exceeds 90,000 miles.

A street scene in Kinshasa, capital of the former Belgian Congo and the seat of the Government.

Copper mines at Ruwe. Copper and diamonds form the principal wealth of the Congo. Copper reserves are enormous. Some of the crude ore is refined in Katanga; the rest is exported.

A dried-fish market in Kisangani (Stanleyville), capital of Haut Congo Province, a rich agricultural area. Kisangani lies half a degree north of the Equator.

The Congo is well served by air and most major airlines flying to Africa from Europe stop either at Kinshasa, Lubumbashi, or at Brazzaville, connected to Kinshasa by ferry. Air Congo links all the provincial capitals.

## RWANDA AND BURUNDI

The former U.N. Trust territories of Rwanda and Burundi (known before independence as Ruanda-Urundi) were administered (each as an independent kingdom) until 1960 as part of the former Belgian Congo. The area was originally annexed by Germany and became a mandated territory after the First World War, and a United Nations Trust Territory in 1945. Attempts failed to persuade the two territories into a federation before independence in 1962. The capital of Rwanda (now a republic) is Kigali, and that of Burundi (also a republic) is Usumbura.

With a population close to 5 million, it is a crowded area: the density is 236 to the square mile. Two main races predominate: the immensely tall and slender Watutsi, making up a fifth of the population, and the smaller, less skilled Bahutu, who for centuries have been regarded as serfs by the aristocratic Watutsi. As the Congo achieved its independence in 1960, and it became clear the same would soon follow for these Trust Territories, tribal hostility broke out between the Bahutu and the Watutsi. In Rwanda bloody warfare ensued, resulting in the flight of several hundred thousand Watutsi to nearby territories. The Bahutu gained control of the government at independence in 1962. In Burundi tribal hostilities were less severe and the independence government was a coalition between the two tribes.

Both countries are primarily agricultural and pastoral. Crops include maize, sweet potatoes, manioc and groundnuts (peanuts) for local consumption and coffee as the principal export crop (24,000 tons). Subsidiary exports are cassiterite, cotton and hides. The economy is still heavily dependent upon Belgian subsidy, and the United Nations agencies are helping with a programme of training technicians and civil servants.

A woman working in the fields in Rwanda, with her baby on her back.
Coffee and cotton are both produced here, but methods of cultivation are primitive and yields are low.

A commercial school at Astrida, Rwanda.
The country urgently needs trained workers, and these students will find ready employment at the end of their training course.

# SPANISH GUINEA AND THE PORTUGUESE ISLANDS OF THE GULF OF GUINEA

SPANISH GUINEA. Spanish Guinea comprises two entirely different types of territory: the islands of Fernando Poo and Annobon, both the cones of extinct volcanoes fertilized by the ashes, and a mainland region, Rio Muni, which forms an enclave between Cameroun and Gabon.

The profound difference between the economic, administrative and human problems which arise in the islands and on the continent explain the creation of the post at Bata of a Vice-Governor, who exercises his power with some degree of autonomy, under the authority of the Governor General at Santa Isabel. The difference between Fernando Poo and Rio Muni were emphasised during the 1936-9 Civil War, when Fernando Poo was pro-Franco, whereas continental Guinea was republican for a long time and even repulsed an attack by Franco elements from Fernando Poo.

RIO MUNI. The territory of Rio Muni, situated just north of the Equator, experiences the hot, humid climate characteristic of southern Cameroun and Gabon, its neighbours. The forest covers almost the whole of its 10,000 square miles, broken only here and there by patches of savanna. Consequently timber working is the country's main economic activity, far outstripping in importance the few industrial crops, which include coffee and cocoa. The population belongs to the Fang tribes, which also inhabit the neighbouring territories. The Government and religious missions have made a start in improving their living standards, providing hospitals and schools.

The Guinean population is backward, especially in relation to that of Cameroun, and it is difficult to close this gap because of the laws in force: most Spanish Africans are legally minors. In order, officially, to protect him from himself, he is forbidden to buy or sell anything above a certain low value or to dispose of his land. If, however, he reaches a European standard of living, he may be assimilated and become a Spanish citizen. But the number of *assimilados* is as yet tiny — about 150 — in relation to the number of inhabitants — 246,000. The timber-growers and European planters make use of Nigerian manpower, working under contract and coming mainly from Calabar. These workers are mostly young bachelors who want to earn the sums necessary for paying the dowry required on their marriage.

The capital of Rio Muni is the port of Bata, the terminus of the shipping lines linking the colony with Cadiz and Cartagena. The largest airport in Spanish Guinea is also situated at Bata, pending the construction of a new airport on Fernando Poo, near the capital, Santa Isabel.

In spite of the absence of natural frontiers, continental Spanish Guinea has managed to preserve a very special character little affected by outside influences in equatorial Africa. If tension can be expected in the future, it will probably stem not from local natives, but from Nigerian workers conscious of their individuality. Meanwhile, Guinea, in spite of its small dimensions, makes a valuable contribution to the Spanish economy, especially by the massive export of plantation products, such as cocoa and bananas.

THE ISLANDS OF THE GULF OF GUINEA. We shall deal in the same section with the Spanish islands of Fernando Poo and Annobon, and the Portuguese islands of São Tomé and Principe, since they form a geographical whole regardless of their political allegiance. The Cameroun fault, in which Mount Cameroun also rises, is prolonged by four lofty islands of volcanic origin stretching in a general north-north-east and south-south-west direction. The southernmost of these islands, Annobon, is situated south of the Equator, but an identical equatorial climate, hot and rainy, with a short 'dry season' in May, characterises them

Spanish Guinea has two territories: the hot, humid, forested Rio Muni mainland, and the islands of Fernando Poo and Annobon. Following the plebiscite of 1963 they became autonomous provinces of Spain, with local self-rule.

all. This climate is modified only locally by the great altitude of the mountains of São Tomé (7,800 feet) and especially the cone of the Pico de Santa Isabel on Fernando Poo (9,350 feet).

The fertile volcanic soil, the climate and the proximity to the ports have encouraged intensive tropical agriculture based on export in these islands. The shortage of land and lack of communications have slowed down this development on the island of Principe (46 square miles) and Annobon (6 square miles; 1,800 inhabitants). The ancient cover of forest has been riddled or destroyed everywhere to make way for cocoa, coffee and banana plantations. Agricultural developments have, on the other hand, profoundly changed the islands of Fernando Poo (808 square miles; 61,000 inhabitants) and São Tomé (381 square miles; about 60,000 inhabitants). Especially at Fernando Poo, the yield and quality of the cocoa reach a very high standard.

Their different histories and political allegiances— Fernando Poo and Annobon are Spanish (since 1774 and 1778 respectively) while São Tomé and Principe belong to Portugal — have imposed two quite distinct faces on what, geographically, is an entity.

Fernando Poo alone was inhabited by a native people, the Bubis, at the time of its discovery by Portugal in the fifteenth century. The Bubis still form traditional villages in the southern and eastern cantons of the island, but their society has greatly decayed, mainly owing to the effects of alcoholism, and they now constitute only one-third of the total population of the island. The remainder of the agricultural population is composed of workers under contract, mainly recruited in the region of Calabar (Nigeria) and working on the large European estates. The forests provide mahogany, ebony and African oak, whilst the undergrowth includes indigo, cotton and sugar cane to supplement the staple foods: millet, yams, bananas and rice.

Fernando Poo's only real town, Santa Isabel, is the seat of the General Government of Spanish Guinea and the most important port in these Iberian possessions. Grouped around a marvellous natural harbour, an ex-crater with a breach, Santa Isabel has about 5,000 Spanish inhabitants and an equal number of descendants of slaves freed by the British fleet after the Treaty of Vienna (1815). Natives of Calabar and ex-British subjects have given Fernando Poo its mixed character, marked by the prevalence of English or pidgin English.

The social structure of São Tomé is quite different. A country where inter-breeding took place early, the island possesses an agricultural proletariat with Negro or mixed blood, completely detribalised and assimilated. There is also a small group of middle-class shopkeepers, and bureaucrats from Lisbon. The Governor of the province resides at São Tomé, which is also the island's principal port, situated in the extreme north-east.

Fernando Poo and São Tomé are linked with their respective metropolitan territories by air and sea. The islands of Principe and Annobon, on the contrary, remain isolated: European population is almost non-existent (fewer than 10 Europeans on Annobon) and the small African communities brought there in the past by the slave trade lead a precarious existence.

Tristan da Cunha, the tiny Atlantic island whose volcano was supposed extinct until it erupted in 1961. Its whole population was evacuated to Great Britain, but later chose to return to Tristan in 1963.

# ST HELENA, ASCENSION, TRISTAN DA CUNHA

The island of St Helena (47 square miles), which lies 1,200 miles off the west coast of Africa at latitude 16°S. longitude 6°W., is little more than 10 miles long and 6½ miles across at its widest point. Like Ascension and the archipelago of Tristan da Cunha, it is of volcanic origin, part of the huge crater being now submerged. The 450 to 2,000-foot cliffs which surround the island are constantly eroded by the sea. Jamestown, the capital, is situated in the north-west in an indentation in the cliffs at the only accessible point. A submarine platform about three miles wide extends round the island at a depth of some 300 feet; beyond it depths reach as much as 13,000 feet.

The island was discovered in 1502 by the Portuguese João da Nova. The first colonists, in 1513, were Portuguese deportees and some Negro slaves. The Dutch occupied the island, abandoned at the time, towards 1651. Shortly afterwards, the British East India Company, seeking ports of call for its ships, acquired the island from the Dutch in exchange for the Cape of Good Hope and built a fort. English families began to settle there, especially after the Great Fire in 1666. Chinese and Malayan colonists later arrived to swell the population. Towards 1860, it numbered nearly 7,000 inhabitants; but the prosperity of Cape Colony attracted emigrants and at present there are only 4,648 inhabitants.

Britain took over the government of St Helena in 1815 and interned Napoleon there from 1815 to 1821.

Today it is administered by a Governor, assisted by an Executive Council and Advisory Council. Ascension and the archipelago of Tristan da Cunha are attached to it for administrative purposes.

The surface of St Helena, on a granite shelf, is very broken up. Diana Peak in the centre of the island rises to a height of 2,336 feet. About 8,600 acres are cultivable, approximately 3,500 of them under flax, which is processed in seven small mills. Fruit trees, as well as cedars, eucalyptus and pines flourish in a mild, pleasant climate, with adequate annual rainfall (30 inches) and a mean annual temperature of 21°C. (70°F.). Goats, introduced into the island when it was discovered, have multiplied and caused great damage to the forests. Enough livestock is raised to meet the needs of the population.

Trade is limited to exchanges with the United Kingdom. The island mainly exports products made of flax (tow, twine, cord), leather, skins and some lace, and imports manufactured products. This trade has developed considerably since the Second World War. Nevertheless, the number of ships stopping at St Helena has decreased steadily since the disappearance of sailing ships (38 ships in 1955). Apart from radio communications, the island is connected by cable with Cape Town and St Vincent in the West Indies.

Ascension, 700 miles to the north-west of St Helena, on latitude 8°S. and longitude 14° W., was discovered by João da Nova on Ascension Day 1501.

Uninhabited for three centuries, it was occupied by the British in 1815 to make the supervision of Napoleon more complete. Later it served as an anchorage for ships detailed to control the slave trade. The population is increasing (374 in 1963 against 162 in 1949). The climate is temperate and rain is frequent.

This volcanic island of 34 square miles, dominated by a summit 2,739 feet high, has an exceptionally broken relief and only ten acres are cultivated, producing vegetables and fruit. Hares, partridge and wild goats, together with some domestic animals, complete the food resources.

Every year between January and May giant sea turtles come in large numbers (about 2,500) to lay their eggs in the sand, Sooty tern or 'wideawake' also lay their eggs there every eight months.

The group of islands consisting of Tristan da Cunha, Gough, Inaccessible, Nightingale and a few rocks, is situated on latitude 37°6′S. and longitude 12°1′W., out of the path of the big shipping routes, but on almost the same parallel as the Cape of Good Hope (1,750 miles) and Montevideo (2,300 miles). It was discovered by chance in 1506, by the Portuguese admiral Tristão da Cunha, and passed into British possession in 1815.

Tristan, the largest of these islands (40 square miles), consists of a volcano rising to a height of 6,760 feet with a base circumference of 21 miles. This volcano was believed to be extinct until 1961, when it erupted unexpectedly. The whole population of 281 was evacuated to the United Kingdom, but decided to return in 1963. The island is bordered by abrupt cliffs except in the north-west, where a plateau some hundred feet above sea level afforded about 30 acres of cultivated land, mainly under potatoes and a few fruit trees. Bullocks, sheep and geese were reared and fish completed the islander's diet. A South African crab-canning factory was established in 1949 and provides a little extra income.

The archipelago is attached to St Helena for administrative purposes. The main island is the seat of an important meteorological and radio station, known as H.M.S. *Atlantic Isle*.

St Helena, a small island of volcanic origin, offers a striking contrast in landscapes — wild, rocky, fissured hills alternating with gentle, cultivated slopes. In this picture, flax is drying in the distance.

# ANGOLA

Angola, situated on the western flank of Africa, has proved a major racial flash-point. Since 1960 an African revolt in the northern areas has assumed the proportions of a civil war, the African rebels receiving assistance from other nations of Africa, while the cost of the war threatens to cripple Portugal, the metropolitan power. The territory covers an area of 481,351 square miles. The district of Cabinda, separated from Angola by the Congo estuary, is nevertheless regarded politically as a part of this Portuguese bloc.

*Physical features.* The country's relief is simple: a coastal plain of varying width (between 15 and 62 miles) climbs rapidly to a high plateau with an average height of 3,500 to 4,225 feet, which descends in a very gentle slope to the east. A group of *serras* (ranges) and *morros* (mountains) is superimposed on a T-shaped plateau, the cross of the T coinciding with the western edge and the upright pointing eastward. Morro Moco (8,515 feet), the highest peak in Angola, is situated at the intersection of the two lines, to the north-west of Nova Lisboa.

The hydrography of Angola is determined by the relief. The central region forms a 'water tower'

The Sena de Chela, one of Angola's many mountain ranges.

where, in close proximity, the watercourses belonging to the basins of the Congo, Zambezi, Cubango, Cunene and Cuanza originate. The last-named is the largest of the purely Angolian rivers (600 miles), navigable for 95 miles.

The marked relief and the Benguela current are responsible for a coastal climate which is abnormally dry for the latitude. The great extent of the country from north to south creates sharp contrasts between the various regions. Cabinda and the banks of the north Congo have a tropical climate; on the latitude of Luanda candelabra-like euphorbias appear, decorating the littoral; while Moçâmedes, in the south, is situated well into the Namib Desert, with flora such as the strange *Welwitschia*, which looks like a giant mushroom. Rainfall remains high on the edges of the high plateaus and because of the altitude frost is not uncommon above 5,000 feet. In spite of large forests along the valleys in the north of the country, Angola is primarily a land of savannas which become thin as they extend southwards.

*Population and economy.* Administratively, the country has been an Overseas Province of Portugal since 1951 and divided since 1954 into thirteen districts. Luanda, the capital, is the seat of the Governor General, who is assisted by a Legislative Council, in control of finance and internal administration. All major policy decisions are taken in Lisbon.

Angola is very sparsely populated. The population in 1960 was 4,833,000 including 200,000 Europeans, and 50,000 mulattos, or people of mixed blood; distribution is difficult to assess during the current civil war since the government is engaged in a policy of regrouping and redistribution of population, especially in the north. However, vast expanses in the south-east are completely uninhabited and the highest concentrations are found in the western centre of the high plateaus, around Luanda and in the coffee-growing regions of the north. Apart from 10,000 Bushmen in the southern semidesert, the 4,500,000 Africans belong to the Bantu family, divided into numerous tribes. Of these the most important are the Ovimbundu, grouped in the centre of the country and making up one-third of the total indigenous population, and the Bakongo in the north. The non-African population is almost entirely Portuguese (200,000 before the revolt) but two small national groups have marked individual characteristics: the Germans (500), who specialise in sisal and coffee, and a curious group of about a hundred Boer *voortrekkers*, who mark the extreme limit of the Great Trek towards the north, and who live in the Huila district.

Angola is still an essentially agricultural country. The main food crops are manioc in the north, maize and haricots in the centre and millet in the south and east. Coffee is the main export crop — 50 per cent of the total value of exports — and half of it goes to the U.S.A. It is concentrated in the mountainous region north of the Cuanza. Sugar-cane is cultivated on a few large plantations in the irrigated valleys of the coastal plain and sisal on the edge of the high plateaus south of the Cuanza. To these key products we may add the growing of cotton in the Malanje region, groundnuts (peanuts) and oil-palms. Stock is raised in the hinterland of the southern coast. Here, too, is an important fishing and salt industry, although other scattered fisheries and salt-pans are found as far as north of Luanda.

Until 1955, the diamonds of Luanda, in the north-east, along the affluents of the Kasai, were the only mineral resource of major importance. Copper from Bembe in the north-west and a few deposits of manganese and asphalt to the north and east of Luanda were of a little account in the country's trade. But the discovery of oil in the immediate neighbourhood of Luanda transformed the economic future of the country. In 1962 production was about 337,000 tons. Since 1956, Luanda has been exporting crude oil. A refinery with an annual capacity of 550,000 tons, and the installation of a tanker harbour in the Bay of Luanda, have created an important centre of economic activity.

*Communications.* Angola suffers from inadequate communications and consequent serious neglect of the interior. The road system, though extensive, is very poor. An internal air service copes with a large passenger traffic and links Luanda with all the important towns and with Kinshasa and Windhoek in South West Africa. In the south, the Moçâmedes railway links the high plateaus with the coast and the line has been extended as far as Vila Serpa Pinto.

Products from the Malanje region (cotton, manganese and coffee) are sent to Luanda by railway. A new line connects the coffee-growing region of Vila Marechal Carmona with Luanda. Most important, however, is the Benguela line, which crosses the whole of the high plateau from west to east. It starts from Benguela and Lobito on the coast and ends at Lubumbashi in the Congo.

Lobito is Angola's major port. It is used by ships loading goods from the Congo. Other major ports are Luanda and Moçâmedes.

Secondary industries are concentrated around the ports. Factories producing textiles, paper, cigarettes, chemical products and shoes and a brewery are found at Luanda, while cement works, shipyards, canning factories and grain mills operate at Lobito. Fisheries and canneries are to be found at Moçâmedes. The only large inland town is Nova Lisboa, situated in the region of the high plateau on the Lobito-Lubumbashi railway. It handles produce from the agricultural areas.

*Political problems — a legacy of the past.* Slow though it has been, Angola's economic development is being considerably handicapped by the revolt. Its cause lies as much in the history and psychology of Portugal as in the indigenous population of Angola. Portugal is the oldest African colonial power, having had possessions there since the fifteenth century. Partly for this reason, partly because of the extensive nationalism of the Portuguese government, its overseas territories have been regarded as an integral part of Portugal itself. No local political autonomy was conceded; and independence has been considered unthinkable. But as successive African territories became independent, African nationalism took root in Angola; and with Belgium's grant of independence to the Congo in 1960, the revolt exploded with the murder by Africans of over 1,500 Europeans in the northern area. In the first reprisals several thousand Africans were killed; and the war has continued intermittently ever since.

Apart from the denial of political rights, African grievances were largely economic. Although there is no official colour bar in the territory, an African is required to pass several tests in order to qualify for the status of *assimilado* or 'assimilated' European. The paucity of good education — 95 per cent of the people are illiterate — and the lack of widespread economic development meant that when the revolt started there were only 35,000 *assimilados* in a total African population of over 4 million. A more specific grievance was the system of contract labour, under which Africans not regularly employed were rounded up by the authorities for poorly paid compulsory labour for at least six months of each year. It is estimated that over 1½ million Angolans work in other territories in order to avoid the contract labour system.

The leaders of the revolt, though themselves divided, aim to achieve independence; at present Portugal has no intention of conceding it. The war, meanwhile, costs both sides considerable losses in men and resources.

Pouring salt into barges for transportation to salt storage piles, Angola. Of the annual production (about 25,000 tons) most is used for preserving fish.

A view of Luanda, the capital of Angola, situated on the Atlantic coast. Founded in 1575, it is now an attractive and ultra-modern city.

# EAST AFRICA

The former British East Africa consisted of three mainland countries—Kenya, Tanganyika and Uganda—which had certain geographical features in common, together with the offshore islands of Zanzibar and Pemba. The area forms the equatorial section of the eastern façade of the continent; but its eastern features are more pronounced than its equatorial ones. The striking physical characteristic of the area is its high relief, tilted blocks, fractures and rifts. Though near the Equator, it has not the heavy rainfall of the Congo punch-bowl on the same latitude; indeed, rain shortages are not uncommon. Single in the north (Abyssinian Rift) and in the south (Lake Malawi), the East African faulted corridor is divided into two rift valleys in its central sector: the western rift valley, bordered by Lakes Albert, Edward, Kivu and Tanganyika, and the eastern rift valley, which is especially associated with the name of the geologist Gregory and where a series on minor lakes (Baringo, Nakuru, Magadi, Natron, Eyasi), are situated, the majority of them being salt. The two rifts are by no means as continuous as is often supposed. The Tanganyika rift does not extend as far as Lake Malawi but is connected with it to one side by a new rift farther east, in the vicinity of Lake Rukwa. The eastern rift extends southwards in a fantail of escarpments which merge progressively with the plateaus of the Tanganyika shield.

A typical cross-section of one of the rift valleys shows a more or less flat bottom of varying width bordered by steep, high slopes which mark two facing faults. The high plateaus on either side of the rift drop away in a gentle slope, with which the sharp drop into the rift valley makes a strong contrast. Volcanoes and lava-flows are often associated with the faults.

This simplified but convenient picture does not stand up to detailed examination. At the bottom of each rift valley, the altitude varies considerably from one part to the next. Lake Malawi is 1,568 feet above sea level; Lake Tanganyika 2,534 feet; Lake Kivu 4,790 feet; Lake Edward 2,999 feet; and Lake Albert 2,030 feet. But Lake Kivu is separated from Lake Albert by a mass of lava rising to about 6,000 feet in Belgian territory. The valley of the Ruzizi, between Lake Kivu and Lake Tanganyika, is no more than a V-shaped indentation in a mountainous block. The deepest hollows are concealed by the lakes: Tanganyika reaches a depth of 4,663 feet. The eastern rift is broken up locally into a mosaic of unevenly sunken blocks, more or less tilted, and demarcated by escarpments parallel to the general direction of the rift. Several lakes have no outlet. The lowest is Lake Rukwa.

With few exceptions the highest of the mountains in East Africa are situated on the edge of the rifts. They fall into two categories. The first are horsts: sections raised from the granite-gneiss shield. To the east of the eastern rift, the Aberdare Mountains, once the refuge of the Mau Mau rebels in Kenya, reach more than 12,000 feet. Ruwenzori, on the frontier of Congo (Kinshasa) and Uganda, is a full-scale mountain range eighty miles long and forty wide; springing

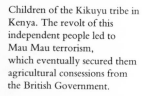

Children of the Kikuyu tribe in Kenya. The revolt of this independent people led to Mau Mau terrorism, which eventually secured them agricultural consessions from the British Government.

from the bottom of the rift it reaches a height of 16,794 feet with Margaret Peak. Its gleaming snows can be seen from the Semliki valley. We may also mention the Ufipa Mountains, between the parallel rifts of Tanganyika and Rukwa. Other mountains are volcanic: those to the north of Lake Malawi, a whole group of volcanoes (the Great Cauldrons) scattered among the area of faults; this group stretches to the south of the eastern rift, and includes the famous Ngorongoro. In certain regions the edge of the rift is not very pronounced. The most distinctive characteristic of the border reliefs is their discontinuity: they form an ineffective barrier against both human and climatic influences. One one of the most remarkable breaches opens up south of Ruwenzori, linking the region of Lake Victoria to that of Lake Edward and running in an east-west direction.

Controversy is widespread about the nature of these rifts. Only one thing seems to be clear: the East African rifts are a very ancient topographical feature. Not only have the great border faults shrunk several times since the Cretaceous Age, but in addition the rifts follow the lines of weakness of the Pre-Cambrian shield.

Between the two rift valleys a level area covers the western of Tanzania and a larger part of Uganda. It is an ancient shield, raised en masse but left intact. In the south this shield reaches a height of 4,500 feet and assumes a convex shape. In the north the punch-bowl appears framed by the border reliefs of the two rift valleys. The bottom of the punch-bowl is occupied by Lakes Victoria and Kyoga (3,717 feet and 3,289 feet respectively). Lake Kyoga, as its digitate outline clearly shows, is a network of submerged valleys. The relief of the northern half of the shield is extremely monotonous, an endless succession of tabular or rounded hills and valleys with flat bottoms flooded for at least part of the year. The large volcanic cone of Mount Elgon (14,178 feet) rises at the approaches to the eastern rift.

Plateaus of uneven altitude extend towards the east, beyond the rift valley: in the north, they vary between 5,500 and 9,000 feet and the highest consist of masses of basalt. Farther south, the Masai Steppes, straddling Kenya and Tanzania, reach between 3,000 and 4,500 feet. Isolated but formidable volcanic mountains dominate the plateaus. The summit of Mount Kenya reaches 17,058 feet, although the mountain is an ancient and relatively dismantled volcano. With its peaks, its ridges and its glaciers, it is a paradise for equatorial mountain climbers. Kilimanjaro, of more recent formation, dwarfs the surrounding countryside with its 19,565 feet; two summits, Kobo, a vast icy cone, and Mawenzi, a strongly escarped and jagged peak, are separated by a high denuded saddle, about six miles long.

In the north, the region between Lake Rudolf and the high plateaus of Kenya on the one hand and the frontier of Somalia and the Indian Ocean on the other hand, forms an immense plain broken up here and there by ranges of hills, some of which are quite high. Farther south, the descent to the coastal region from the Masai Steppes and the Tanganyika shield is less regular: it is broken up by a series of steps, a faint echo of the structual features of the rift. Some blocks, tilted towards the coast, show a very abrupt face to the interior, for example Mounts Usambara and Pare, south-east of Kilimanjaro.

*A predominantly dry equatorial climate.* North-east winds blow across East Africa from October to March. The product of the Asiatic continental anticyclone, they contain less humidity than the maritime trade winds whose place they take. From June to September, East Africa is swept by the southern trade wind, blowing from the south-east. Contrary to what we might expect, the south-east trade wind brings only a low rainfall in its train, for unlike the West African monsoon, the trade wind meets the coast obliquely, not head-on, and this reduces its effectiveness. Once it has met the continent, it is caught in the orbit of the Asiatic summer areas of low pressure and continues its descent by curving inwards instead of coming up against the inter-tropical front, which would produce rain. Thus the only rainy months come in the intermediate seasons, periods of calm favourable to rains formed by convection. An arid strip extends from the borders of Ethiopia and Somalia to Lake Tanganyika on the one hand and from the coast to Mozambique on the other. Precipitation increases slightly towards the south: in Tanzania, Tabora (4,013 feet, 5°3'S.) receives 35 inches; but across the Equator at Mandera, in north-east Kenya, the rainfall drops to 8 inches. These figures are paltry in comparison with those of the Congo punch-bowl and the West African basin. Only the temperature, which is very constant from one month to another, shows which latitude the area is in.

This aridity has a marked effect on the landscape. Equatorial forest is out of the question. The densest formation on the dry ridge is the *miombo* of the north-west and south-east of Tanzania, thinly planted deciduous forest or wooded savanna, and it needs a minimum rainfall of 32 inches. In the central part of Tanzania and Kenya, in proportion as the aridity increases the trees grow rarer and give way to bushes. There is a change from well-wooded savannas to a savanna with scattered trees, next to a thorny bush, then to a steppe of low shrubs and stunted trees, succulent and thorny plants, and scattered tufts of grasses. This last kind of scenery prevails in the region of Lake Rudolf, stretching up to the borders of Ethiopia.

More abundant rainfall and more luxurious vegetation is first found along a narrow coastal strip between 2°N. and 8°S., straddling Tanzania and Kenya. The island of Pemba, north of Zanzibar, receives 76 inches, but on the nearby mainland the humid strip, originally wooded, extends only five to ten miles inland. In the west, one vast, continuous region enjoys an adequate rainfall. It includes the area round Lake Victoria and the greater part of Uganda. Entebbe, on a peninsula on the north shore of Lake Victoria, has an annual rainfall of 58 inches; the rainfall in any one month is never less than 3 inches. Except in the south-west (the highlands of Kigezi and Ankole), the west (the rift of Lake Albert and the Albert Nile) and the north-east (Karamoga Steppes) the rainfall in Uganda always exceeds — often considerably — 39 inches. The climate with four seasons continues almost up to the Sudanese frontier. The western borders of East Africa are favoured locally by the humidifying effect of Lake Victoria, but far more by their position

The Ruwenzori Mountains,
a range eighty miles long
and forty miles wide, in the rain
forest area of Uganda.
In the foreground are tropical
plants — giant groundsel
and lobelia. Uganda has a varied
landscape: fertile fields round
Lake Victoria, semi-desert
in the north, and the splendid
mountains of Ruwenzori.

Cattle at Ankole,
in the south-west of Uganda.
Stock-rearing is one of the
main activities of Uganda's tribes.
The quality of the herds is low,
however; the grazing lands are
poor and the beasts emaciated
and parasite-ridden.

The centre of Nairobi, capital
of Kenya.

in relation to atmospheric currents. They benefit from a permanent flow of humid equatorial air coming from the west.

This improvement is shown in the vegetation. Admittedly the ombrophilous forest is not well represented. Beyond the mountains, it is found only on the banks and islands of the north-west of Lake Victoria, in scattered patches in southern Uganda, and in the Semliki valley, upstream from Lake Albert. And it exists only in the fairly narrow corridors. But the elephant-grass savanna forms a dense and continuous enclave from Ruwenzori to Mount Elgon. It has very probably taken the place of the primitive forest, almost entirely cleared by a large population. It also affords considerable protection for the soil from the danger of erosion.

So far only the regions of the plain and the plateaus of medium height have been considered. Where the altitude increases or the relief is very pronounced, the rainfall rises. On the Kikuyu plateau, adjoining Mount Kenya, the 39-inch isohyet corresponds virtually to the 6,000-foot contour. In Tanzania, the raised blocks on the edge of the rift valleys and in the tectonic foreland are islets of rain forests in the middle of savannas and the *miombo*. In the Masai Steppes, the slightest hills act as condensers. The rainfall drops again above a certain altitude on the highest slopes, but the temperature falls regularly, hence the formation of glaciers. On Ruwenzori, the lower limit of perpetual snow is about 14,450 feet. The Credner glacier on the northern slope of Kilimanjaro descends to 14,625 feet.

The variability of the climate according to altitude affects the vegetation. Clearly differentiated layers are superimposed: mountain forest, with its arborescent ferns at the lowest level; then bamboo thicket (which, however, is not found on Kilimanjaro); then open forest; then scrub; and lastly the alpine layer with its giant lobelias, its arborescent groundsel and its everlasting flowers. The aridity of the depressions and rifts is accentuated by the mountain winds. In winter, drying winds from Upper Egypt enter the western rift valley.

## KENYA

Lying on the east coast of Africa and bisected by the Equator, Kenya is bounded to the north by Ethiopia and Sudan, to the west by Uganda, to the south by Tanzania and to the east by the Somali Republic and the Indian Ocean. There are four main areas: an arid scrub-covered plain, with a small nomadic population, in the north-east; low arid land, but including Lake Rudolf and a mountainous area, in the north-west; a dry, almost uninhabited stretch of land in the south-east; and in the south-west, where 85 per cent of the population and nearly all the economic production is concentrated, a plateau rising to 10,000 feet and supporting Mount Kenya (17,058 feet), Mount Elgon (14,178 feet), and the Aberdare Mountains (12,000 feet). This is cut by the Great Rift Valley, 30 to 40 miles wide and 2,000 to 3,000 feet lower than the land on either side. West of the rift the plateau falls to Lake Victoria, and eastward Kenya's two main rivers, the Tana and the Athi, flow towards the Indian Ocean.

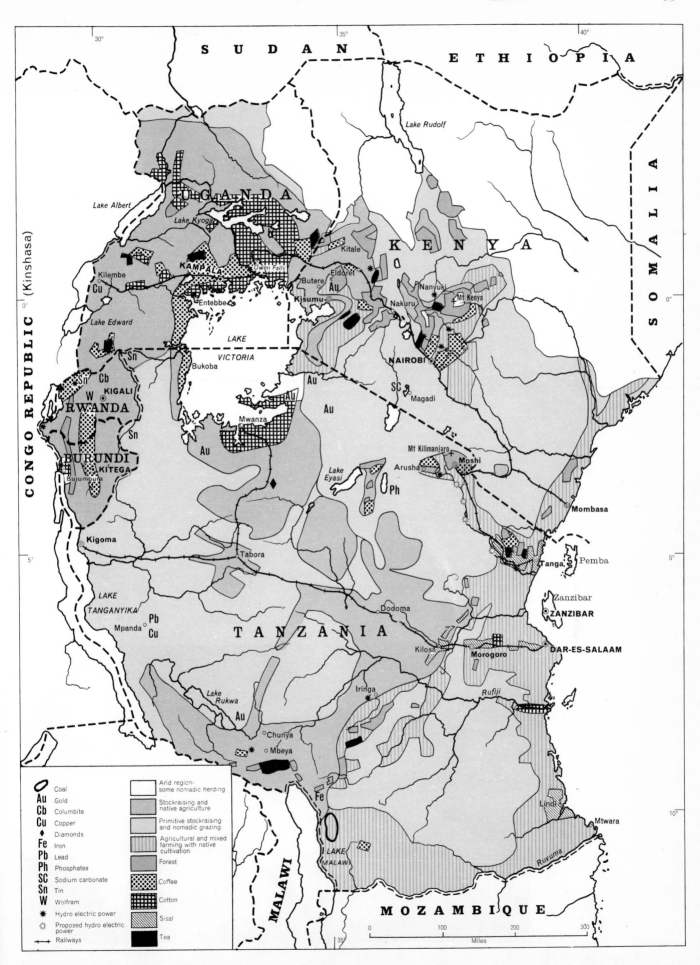

**SUDAN**

**ETHIOPIA**

Lake Rudolf

**SOMALIA**

CONGO REPUBLIC (Kinshasa)

U G A N D A

Lake Albert

Lake Kyoga

**KAMPALA**

Kilembe

Cu

Entebbe

Lake Edward

Owen Falls

Butere

Kisumu

Au

Kitale

Eldoret

Nakuru

K E N Y A

Nanyuki

Mt Kenya

**NAIROBI**

Sn

LAKE

VICTORIA

Bukoba

Au

SC

Magadi

Sn

Au

Au

Mwanza

RWANDA

KIGALI

Cb

W

Sn

**BURUNDI**

KITEGA

Bujumbura

Lake Eyasi

Au

Mt Kilimanjaro

Arusha

Moshi

Ph

Mombasa

Kigoma

Tabora

Pemba

Tanga

Zanzibar

**ZANZIBAR**

LAKE TANGANYIKA

Pb

Mpanda

Cu

T A N Z A N I A

Dodoma

Kilosa

Morogoro

DAR-ES-SALAAM

Lake Rukwa

Iringa

Rufiji

Au

Chunya

Mbeya

Fe

Lindi

Mtwara

LAKE MALAWI

Ruvuma

**MALAWI**

**M O Z A M B I Q U E**

| | | |
|---|---|---|
| ⬯ | Coal | |
| **Au** | Gold | |
| **Cb** | Columbite | |
| **Cu** | Copper | |
| ◆ | Diamonds | |
| **Fe** | Iron | |
| **Pb** | Lead | |
| **Ph** | Phosphates | |
| **SC** | Sodium carbonate | |
| **Sn** | Tin | |
| **W** | Wolfram | |
| ✳ | Hydro electric power | |
| ✿ | Proposed hydro electric power | |
| ⊢⊣ | Railways | |

Arid region-some nomadic herding

Stockraising and native agriculture

Primitive stockraising and nomadic grazing

Agricultural and mixed farming with native cultivation

Forest

Coffee

Cotton

Sisal

Tea

0    100    200    300

Miles

(See map on page 331)
Subsistence farming remains the most important single occupation in terms of the number it employs. There is, also, some fishing. Cash crops were at first exclusively in the hands of the white farmer as, for example, in the Highlands of Kenya. Kenya is the poorest of all the East African territories, in terms of mineral deposits. Coffee, tea, sisal, cotton and sugar are among the crops commercially grown throughout East Africa. Uganda has a flourishing agriculture based on cotton, coffee, sugar and, to a lesser extent, tea and cocoa. Tanzania has diamonds, lead, gold and tin, while in Uganda copper is mined and hydro-electric power from the Nile supports a cement industry, some copper mining and smelting, and textiles; and the power is also shared with Kenya. Zanzibar still derives 80 per cent of its foreign earnings from the clove crop alone and, despite considerable efforts by the Government to diversify the economy, farming and fishing for subsistence or local exchange still occupy all the rural population.

A ten-mile-wide coastal strip extending from the Tanzania border to Kipini, together with the Lamu Archipelago islands, comprised the mainland dominions of the Sultan of Zanzibar, until the Sultan voluntarily ceded his sovereignty there in exchange for a fixed annual income.

Kenya has a total area of 224,960 square miles which includes 5,170 square miles of inland water. The population is over nine million, of whom the majority are Africans. The main tribes are Kikuyu (Bantu), Luo (Nilotic), Baluhya, Kamba, Meru and Masai (half-Hamitic). There are also 49,000 Europeans, 183,000 Asians, and 40,000 Arabs and others.

The capital of Kenya is Nairobi (population 297,000), standing 5,475 feet above sea level, and the other major towns are Mombasa, which has a deep-water harbour, Nakura, Kisumu, Eldoret in the Highlands, and Lamu on the coast.

*Economy.* The basis of Kenya's economy is agriculture and stock-breeding. Most plantation cultivation is concentrated on the eastern slopes of the high plateaus, the high plateaus themselves and in the Rift Valley, where the volcanic soil and the climate favour the principal cash crops. Products include coffee, tea, sisal, hides and skins, dairy produce, maize and wheat. Under the impetus of the 'Swynnerton Plan' for the intensification of African agriculture, introduced in 1954, African farmers are already making a big contribution to the production of cash crops as well as to subsistence agriculture. In 1960 an intensive programme of land settlement for Africans was undertaken on the lands of Europeans who wished to leave the country following African self-government. Industrial activity has been increasing fairly rapidly and there are now in the country over a hundred main types of manufacturing and industrial concerns producing goods both for internal consumption and for export. There is a small output of several mineral products. In order of value they are: cement, soda ash, copper salt, lime and diatomite. The main manufacturing and industrial concerns make metal goods, food products, cement, cigarettes, clothing, footwear and furniture. The main exports are coffee,

tea, sisal, wattle bark extract, pyrethrum, meat and meat products, raw cotton, hides and skins, and sodium carbonate. The tourist trade now ranks as Kenya's second 'export'.

*Communications.* Public roads total 26,000 miles, about 4,000 miles being all-weather roads, but this figure excludes roads and tracks maintained by the Forest Department, the National Parks Organisation and from local resources. Nairobi Airport carries international traffic.

*Political history.* As early as 1823 the inhabitants of the Mombasa area asked to be placed under British protection, but it was only in 1895 that a formal declaration of protection was made over what is now Kenya and Uganda. The Kenya over which the British declared a Protectorate was sparsely populated. During the nineteenth century, tribal feuds, drought, disease, and the Arab-run slave trade kept the population low. A railroad to Uganda was completed in 1901 by the British Government. which encouraged white settlement and development of the virtually empty Highlands. Land was sold to white settlers but was held according to native tenure practices, whereby any land not under beneficial use was at the disposal of the Crown. The large and over-crowded Kikuyu tribe who lived in the Highlands were not alone in resenting European intrusion, and an agitation began for the restoration of 'stolen lands'. This was one of the grievances which led to the Mau Mau uprising in the early 1950's. In 1960 the Highlands, hitherto farmed exclusively by Europeans, were opened for African settlement but were still subject to legal restrictions.

More than any other tribe, the Kikuyu had a deep sense of political and social frustration over the land question, the colour bar, and various bans such as one forbidding Africans to grow the profitable cash crop of coffee. A series of political movements started in the 1920's led finally to the Kenya African Union, an extremist wing of which created Mau Mau. This was a nationalist movement dedicated to removing European domination from Kenya and establishing majority rule in the country. The State of Emergency,

Coffee beans drying near Nyeri. Coffee is one of Kenya's principal exports.

proclaimed by the then colonial government, lasted from 1952 to 1960. Thousands of people, mainly African, lost their lives during the uprising.

After Mau Mau the country was deeply shocked, and despite the reintroduction of constitutional government in 1956, tribalism and racialism have dogged Kenya politics and political parties since then. In 1960 the foundations were laid for African majority government. By 1963 an African government was elected to take the country into independence, on 12 December 1963; a year later Kenya became a republic with a President as Head of State. The constitution upholds the rights of minority tribes and the principles of parliamentary democracy. One grave tribal question remains: the Somali population, which inhabits parts of the northern frontier district of Kenya, demands secession, and refuses to take part in elections. This may become a serious problem.

## UGANDA

Uganda lies astride the Equator in the heart of East Africa and covers an area of approximately 94,000 square miles. It is bounded to the north by Sudan, to the west by the Congo (Kinshasa) to the south by Rwanda, Burundi, and Tanzania, and to the east by Kenya. Nearly half of the world's second biggest lake, Lake Victoria (area over 26,000 square miles), lies in Uganda, and the White Nile has its source there. Other large lakes are Lakes George, Edward, Albert and Kyoga. On the western frontier lies the 80-mile-long Ruwenzori range (the Mountains of the Moon) whose highest peak is 16,794 feet; on the eastern frontier lies Mount Elgon (14,178 feet).

Although Uganda lies acros the Equator, the tropical heat is tempered by an average altitude of over 3,500 feet. Most of the country has a rainfall of at least 40 inches annually and the land is potentially very productive in most districts.

The towns of Uganda are all the creation of the immigrant races, Europeans and Asians, and have grown up around administrative and trading centres; in recent years, however, there has been a concentration of Africans around the urban areas. There is virtually no settled European population in Uganda, the 11,000 or so Europeans being mainly civil servants, missionaries, teachers, technicians and the representatives of the larger expatriate commercial enterprises. The Asian population numbers about 72,000 and controls a large part of the trade and commerce of the country. There are nearly 6½ million Africans, of whom the Baganda, a Bantu group, are the most numerous, numbering over one million. They are also the most highly developed. Other tribes closely related to the Baganda are the Basoga, the Bunyoro and the Batoro; while in the north, and of different origin, are the Iteso, the Lango, the the Acholi and the Karamojong. The latter are a nomadic, cattle-rearing people.

Uganda is now divided into four provinces — Buganda, Eastern, Northern and Western—and contains the four seaprate Kingdoms of Buganda, Ankole, Bunyoro Toro. The capital is Entebbe, but Kampala, 22 miles away, is the commercial capital and the largest town. Other main towns are Jinja, at the source of the Nile, and Mbale in the Eastern Province.

*Economy.* Uganda is primarily an agricultural country of peasant farmers, whose main cash crops are coffee and cotton. Farmers, especially in the south, are the most prosperous in the whole of East Africa owing to the growth of these two crops. Cotton was first introduced in 1903 and exports now vary between £15 and £20 million ($42 and $56 million) annually. Coffee, which is native to Uganda, has been developed more recently but very rapidly and exports exceed £20 million ($56 million) (91,000 tons) per year, making Uganda the largest coffee producer in the British Commonwealth. These crops are marketed through statutory marketing boards: price assistance funds are maintained and guaranteed prices are paid to the growers. There are a few plantations producing sugar, and attempts to diversify the economy are being made by the introduction of tea and cocoa.

Plantains, millet, sorghum, sweet potatoes, groundnuts (peanuts), beans, maize, cassava and sugar are grown for local consumption. Cattle-rearing is rapidly

A cotton mill in Uganda. A sound export trade in cotton and coffee gives Uganda's people the most stable prosperity in East Africa.

The Owen Falls Dam at Jinja, Uganda. The entire industrial expansion of the country is based on the hydro-electric power provided by the Owen Falls Scheme.

increasing, and a profitable fishing industry has grown up on the lakes of western Uganda. Local manufacturing industries include cement, brick and tiles, engineering, printing, sawmilling, soap-making and textiles. Copper is mined in western Uganda. Other minerals exported are wolfram, beryl, salt and tin.

In 1954, the Owen Falls Dam at Jinja, on the Nile, was opened. The hydro-electric plant has at present a capacity of 120,000 kW, and will eventually produce 150,000 kW. It has been estimated that the full generating capacity will be in use by 1969. The project has also made possible improved storage capacity for water needed to irrigate areas in Egypt and the Sudan. A smaller hydro-electric station is situated on the Kagera River at Kikigate. More than a third of the electricity sold by the Uganda Electricity Board is exported to Kenya.

*Political history.* Uganda, which was under British protection for about sixty years, became independent in October 1962. Executive and Legislative Councils were first established in 1921 and their scope extended progressively from 1951 onwards. One of the most serious problems has been the strong regional interest in the country. In 1955 a major constitutional crisis arose between the Kabaka of Buganda (the king of the largest and most important of the kingdoms) and the British Government over the latter's constitutional responsibilities, which led to the temporary exile of the Kabaka.

Though constitutional changes had granted progressively greater representation to Africans, difficulties over the terms of the association of Buganda with the central government continued. Early in 1959 disturbances broke out in parts of Buganda and led to the proscription of a number of political organisations and to the declaration of the Buganda province as a disturbed area, with certain restrictions imposed on the population. In the following year the Buganda Government made further claims for Buganda's development as a separate state, and also for the termination of British protection. These were rejected by the British Government, but it was agreed to reopen the constitutional discussions.

In March 1961, in accordance with the new constitutional arrangement, elections were held throughout Uganda, although Buganda boycotted them. Nevertheless, a strong central democratic government was set up under the guidance of the departing British, with Buganda in a federal relationship (i.e. with its own parliament) and the three other kingdoms (Toro, Ankole and Bunyoro) in a semi-federal relationship with the central government. Buganda was constitutionally compelled to send representatives to the National Assembly. This carefully balanced constitution was specifically designed to uphold Uganda as a united country.

*Communications.* There are over 11,000 miles of road maintained by the Public Works Department and by the provincial and local authorities. Uganda's railroads form part of the rail system controlled by the East African Railways and Harbours Adminstration. The main route runs from Kasese to Mombasa on the coast of Kenya and there are two branch lines — Tororo to Soroti and Liva and Mbulamuti to Namasagali. There is a short branch line from Jinja to Bukonte. There is also a comprehensive lake steamer service which connects Uganda with Kenya, Tanzania and Congo (Kinshasa). The United Republic of Tanzania was formed in 1964 by combining the former territories of Tanganyika and Zanzibar.

## TANZANIA

*Tanganyika,* lying just south of the Equator, between the Indian Ocean and the great lakes of Central Africa, has an area of 362,690 square miles.

In general Tanganyika is a land of plains and plateaus, but it includes within its boundaries the two extremes of topographical relief of the whole continent of Africa: Kilimanjaro, with a permanent icecap rising to over 19,000 feet above sea level, and the deep trough-like depression filled by Lake Tanganyika. The coastline is some 500 miles long, and inland, beyond the coastal plain, the land rises gradually to a central plateau about 4,000 feet above sea level, sharply defined along its eastern and western margin by steep eroded escarpments, which reach in some places heights of over 7,000 feet. Towards the west the land falls away to the level of the lakes which lie in the Great Rift Valley.

Tanganyika has numerous rivers, although few are navigable for any considerable length and many dry out during part of the year. The two main river systems rise in the central plateau, one flowing east to the Indian Ocean and the other west or south to enter the Great Lakes.

Much of the central part of the country is under open woodland or bush and thicket and large areas are uninhabited and infested by tsetse fly, except where measures to eliminate or control this pest have been taken. Less than ten per cent of the land is at present cultivated, although a larger proportion is under grazing.

The territory falls into three main climatic zones. On the coast and in the immediate hinterland, conditions are tropical and humid, with an average temperature of 24°C. (76°F.) and a rainfall of about 40 inches. The central plateau is hot and dry, although with considerable daily and seasonal variations in temperature. In the mountainous regions the climate semi-temperate, with occasional frosts. Much of the country has a one-season rainfall, from about December to May, but amounts vary greatly from year to year. Only about one-third of the territory is reasonably well supplied with water throughout the year.

The capital and chief port of Tanganyika is Dar es Salaam (population 129,000); other important towns of Tanganyika consist of Tanga, the second port, and Mwanza, the port on Lake Victoria.

*Population.* Apart from some 21,000 Europeans and a little over 150,000 peoples of other nationalities (mainly Asians) the 9.4 million people of Tanganyika are all Africans. They are descended from many intermingled ethnic groups: Nilotic and Hamitic tribes, which came at different periods from the north, and Bantu. Today there are 120 different tribes of which the largest, the Suguma, accounts for about 12 per cent of the African population. Among the other large tribes are the Nyamwezi, Makonde, Ha, Gogo, Haya and Chagga. Swahili, the language of the coastal area, is widely understood, and is most generally used for communications within and between different tribes.

The African population is mainly agriculturist, producing enough food to meet its own needs and a limited amount of cash crops for sale. Many Africans are also cattle-owners, and a few tribes are entirely pastoral. The Asians are engaged mainly in commerce and trade, and over 80 per cent of them live in the towns. The Europeans, today mainly British, include farmers, civil servants and missionaries, as well as many engaged in industry and commerce.

*Tanganyika's history up to independence.* In about the middle of the eighth century Arab settlement and control of the coastal area of Tanganyika began, and continued up to 1885 when the Germans occupied the territory. It was not until 1907, however, that Germany was able to achieve effective control. After the First World War Tanganyika became a League of Nations Mandate Territory, and was administered by Britain. Its adminstration continued to be carried out under the terms of the mandate until 1946, when it became one of the first territories to be placed

The snows of Kilimanjaro. The highest peak in Africa, Mount Kilimanjaro rises to a height of 19,686 feet.

A youth of the Gogo tribe, near Dodoma, capital of Tanganyika's Central Province. The country's African population is made up of more than 100 tribes, each with its own distinctive dialect and customs.

Sisal fibre drying in the sun near Moshi. An important cash crop, sisal contributes one third of the total value of Tanganyika's exports, and about one half of the world's supply.

under the trusteeship system of the United Nations.

Constitutional development followed the general pattern adopted by United Kingdom dependencies. In Tanganyika, the final stage of advance to full independence was reached with a speed and smoothness which reflected the harmonious relations between its various races and tribal troups. As early as 1926 a Legislative Council was established; but though nomination to the legislature was from the start open to members of any race, it was not until 1945 that an African sat in Council. Progressive developments culminated in the 1961 Constitutional Conferences at Dar es Salaam and in London which led to the independence of Tanganyika in December of the same year. The country adopted a republican form of government in 1962.

*Agriculture and minerals.* As Tanganyika is a country with very wide variations in climate and soils, it is possible grow most tropical crops of economic importance, plus many requiring temperate conditions. Agriculture and livestock together are the mainstay of the country's economy, accounting for about four-fifths of all domestic exports.

In general, African farmers practise a form of subsistence agriculture, growing such crops as maize, rice, sorghum and pulses, using fairly primitive methods of cultivation and producing little more than enough for their own requirements. However, with government aid and considerable community development efforts. better techniques are gradually being introduced and higher yields are resulting. African farmers grow the whole of Tanganyika's cotton crop, much of the coffee and most of the oil-seeds, cashew and rice.

Sisal, the country's staple export crop, continues to be grown almost exclusively by immigrant farmers, who also grow nearly all the tea, and much of the tobacco and pyrethrum — but African farmers are now taking an increasing share in the production of tobacco and pyrethrum, and are beginning to take an interest in tea cultivation.

Diamonds, gold, lead and copper are at present the minerals making the largest contributions to Tanganyika's economy; but the prospects for further mineral development are hopeful. Diamond, mined near Shinyanga in the lake province, account for more than 60 per cent by value of all the minerals exported.

*Manufacturing industries.* Tanganyika's forests contain some valuable trees such as mahogany and camphor These occur both in the relatively small area of tropical rain forest and in the savanna forest lands (*miombo*). Some of this timber is exported. Mangroves are used for poles on Arab dhows and for tanning bark. There has been substantial growth in the manufacturing industry since 1945, although it is still limited mainly to processing local raw materials. Processing of sisal, tea and sugar and the treatment of mineral ores is for the most part carried out by the producers themselves, but cotton ginning and coffee and tobacco curing take place at commercially run establishments to which the raw material is brought. Oil, rice and flour milling are carried out extensively and soap industry is run in conjunction with copra milling.

Among other industries now represented in Tanganyika are: beer and soft drinks; aluminium ware; block flooring; bricks and tiles; metal containers; gas;

leather goods; nails; paint; pre-cast concrete; shoes and textiles; cigarettes; cashew nut processing; and a tyre factory.

*Communications.* The railroads of Tanganyika are run in conjuction with those of Kenya and Uganda and rail routes link Dar es Salaam on the coast with the inland towns of Kigoma on Lake Tanganyika, Tabora south of Lake Victoria, and Mwanza on Lake Victoria. The Tanga line, which runs inland to Arusha, has recently been linked with the line and so with the rest of the Eeast African rail system. There are about 30,000 miles of roads and it is planned to spend more than £3 million ($9 million) on road construction and improvement.

Tanganyika is well served by air, for East African Airways operates internal air services to all the more important towns in the area as well as to Central and South Africa and to Mozambique. It also has regular flights to London, Bombay and Karachi.

The major sea harbour is Dar es Salaam, but other major ports are found on the coast at Tanga and inland at Mwanza, on Lake Victoria. A deep-water port has been constructed at Mtwara, and in conjunction with the Southern Provinces rail line provides an outlet for the varied agricultural export produce of a large area.

*Zanzibar*, twenty-two miles at its nearest point from the East African coast, consists of two main islands, Zanzibar (640 square miles) and Pemba (380 square miles) together with one uninhabited outcrop known as Latham I. It was formerly a British Protectorate, and the most important trade centre of East Africa. The population of 300,000 comprises 77 per cent Africans, 16 per cent Arabs, 6 per cent Asians and 1 per cent Europeans. It is almost exclusively Moslem in religion and atmosphere. Zanzibar is potentially a rich tourist resort, with its coral beaches and brilliant coastline. At present, however, it is dependent almost entirely upon the export of cloves, an uncertain and declining product. Attempts are being made to diversify the present economy. Zanzibar attained its independence in December 1963, and following a revolution in January 1964 joined with Tanganyika to form the new Republic of Tanzania. The town of Zanzibar, with a population of 58,000, is Tanzania's second largest urban settlement.

EAST AFRICA FEDERATION. As early as the 1920's, ideas were discussed for some form of closer political association between the three former British East African territories, and possibly, Northern Rhodesia, Nyasaland and Zanzibar. But all attempts foundered, as the Africans feared such a scheme would be used simply to subject them to the relatively large settler population of Kenya. After the Second World War, an East African High Commission was established by the British Government to co-ordinate certain common functions — communications, customs, etc. — for Kenya, Tanganyika and Uganda. In 1960 it became a political body, headed by the elected Ministers and known as the East African Common Services Organisation, with wider terms of reference. In June 1963 a joint declaration by the three Prime Ministers of Kenya, Uganda and Tanganyika set out their intention of forming a Federation, to be worked out over the coming year. Zanzibar was also invited to participate, and other independent countries will be free to join.

Gathering the cocoa harvest in Zanzibar. The pods are sorted, some being retained for propogation and the rest are exported to Britain for processing. Some food-processing industries are being developed.

Zanzibar produces 80 per cent of the world's supply of cloves. Here they are sorted for size and quality before being exported.

A potter in Zanzibar. Most of the population (300,000) lives at subsistence level only. Cloves and coconuts are exported, and coffee and tea are grown. Efforts are being made to diversify crops and there is some tourist trade.

SOUTHERN AFRICA

# MOZAMBIQUE

Mozambique is a huge, irregularly shaped wedge of territory bisected by the Zambezi River and almost cut in two by the the southward thrust of Malawi. It has an area of 297,731 square miles and is bordered to the north and north-west by Zambia and Malawi to the north by Tanzania, to the west by Rhodesia and to the west and south by the Republic of South Africa. Along the coast the landscape is flat, but towards the north this coastal plain gives way to uplands rising to a chain of mountains (Namuli, Msenga) whose highest peaks are Namuli (8,200 feet) and and Lichingo (over 6,500 feet).

When Portuguese fleets sought a half-way port of call after the discovery of the route to India, geography pointed to Mozambique. The deserted coast of South West Africa offered no region suitable for replenishing stores; the Cape was dreaded because of its storms. The coast of Mozambique, on the other hand, offered a number of advantages. Citrus fruits, introduced by the Arabs, made it possible to treat the crews' scurvy; ships could await the winter monsoon (from the south) before continuing the voyage to India; and the ports of Mozambique and Sofala exported Rhodesian gold previously bought by the Arabs. By the mid-sixteenth century, Portugal supported three commercial markets on the borders of the empire of Monomotapa, the producer of this sought-after gold.

But the Portuguese empire of the Indies was already lost. The annexation of Portugal by Spain put a stop to her expansion eastwards; however, it was tacitly agreed that Portuguese possessions extended across the whole of Zambezi Africa as far as Angola. The explorer Serpa Pinto linked Lourenço Marques with Luanda and so reinforced the Portuguese claims. But Rhodes brought these areas into the British sphere of influence by annexing to the British South Africa Company the lands now forming Rhodesia, Zambia Malawi. A frontier between the British and Portuguese spheres of influence was fixed in 1891.

In 1919, Mozambique was enlarged by the Kionga triangle taken from what was at that time German Tanganyika.

*The land and its native inhabitants.* Mozambique has a coastline of about 1,500 miles. The influence of the summer (southern) monsoons and the warm Mozambique current makes itself felt far in the interior. Thanks to a rainfall which remains above 40 inches nearly everywhere and to a relatively high and constant temperature, Mozambique's climate contrasts with the desert conditions found on the same latitude on the western façade of Africa, which is not subject to the same maritime conditions.

The lowlands (49 per cent of the total area) are covered with forest or thick brush, behind a coastal fringe of coconut plams. The forest becomes dense in the centre, between the Zambezi and the Pungue Rivers. The inland plateaus are divided into three blocks. The largest is in the north, towering over the *graben* of Lake Malawi. In this region, the rounded summits sometimes reach over 6,500 feet. To the west of the Lake Malawi rift is a plateau sloping towards the valley of the Zambezi. The third section consists of a strip of highlands on the other side of the Zambezi, along the frontier of Rhodesia.

The main river of Mozambique is the Zambezi, which has its source in Zambia and flows almost through the centre of Mozambique to the Indian Ocean. Other rivers and their sources are the Limpopo (South Africa) and Save (Rhodesia). The Rovuma, the Luria, the Ligonha and Licungo rise in the upland plains of the north.

Mozambique has a tropical climate, but owing to the altitude and to the summer monsoon conditions vary from region to region. The main rainfall occurs in summer and is heavier in the north. On the high plains and the south the climate is more temperate.

There are more than six and a half million people in Mozambique of whom only about 70,000 are European and 60,000 are Asians or mulattos. The remainder of the population is African, and can be divided into four major tribes, all of which are Bantu. The Tonga in the south have been markedly influenced by the Zulu. The Caranga, to the north, are less well developed. They are divided into savanna- and forest-dwelling tribes and are only beginning to practise regular agriculture. The Nhaga occupy the whole of the Zambezi Valley and the plateaus on the edge of Lake Malawi; and the Macoua live along the broad coastal strip which extends from the Zambezi to the Rovuma. The latter tribe show a marked oriental influence (Arabic and Indian) and are nominally Moslem. The capital of Mozambique is Lourenço Marques, which has about 120,000 inhabitants. Other major towns are Beira, with a population of 25,000, Quelimane, Nampula, Nacala, Tete and Inhambane.

The official language of Mozambique is Portuguese, which is understood and spoken by the majority of the coastal-dwelling Africans. There are diverse African languages and dialects.

*Communications.* The major ports of Mozambique are Lourenço Margues and Beira. The former provides an outlet to the sea for the Transvaal and the latter for Rhodesia, (Zambia and Malawi) which are completely landlocked.

A comprehensive rail system runs between the

The main square of Lourenço Marques, capital of Mozambique, a large wedge-shaped territory bisected by the Zambezi River.

Republic of South Africa and Rhodesia and Zambia, with five major lines: Johannesburg-Lourenço Marques; Beira-Umtali-Salisbury; Beira-Port Herald, in Malawi; Lourenço Marques-Bannockburn; and the Porto Arroio line on Lake Malawi which runs to Nacala on the coast and gives Malawi another outlet to the sea.

There is a fairly well developed road system. Both Lourenço Marques and Beira are served by air. The South African and Portuguese airlines fly to Johannesburg and Salisbury, thus providing a link with international flights.

*Economy.* Agriculture among the indigenous population is still largely confined to semi-nomadic cultivation of subsistence crops such as manioc, groundnuts (peanuts) and maize. Large-scale agriculture is controlled by Portuguese or foreign concessionaires using cheap local labour. Cotton is the most successful of these plantation crops. Rice has been introduced on the same system but suffers from the lack of assured export markets. Sugar and coconuts are also grown by monopolistic companies. Tea is gaining inportance and is chiefly grown on the high plateaus east of Lake Malawi. Sisal is grown on smaller plantations in the poorer plateaus to the north of the tea region. Other plantation crops recently introduced are citrus and bananas, in the Lourenço Marques area.

Apart from its export trade of cotton, sugar, maize, tea, copra, cashew nuts, sisal and vegetable oils, most of which goes to Portugal, the Mozambique economy relies largely on income derived from port and railroad services to the rich landlocked hinterland of the Transvaal, Rhodesia, Zambia and the Congo. Currency earned by these services, together with deferred pay and remittances from African labourers working in South Africa and in Rhodesia and Zambia, and the proceeds from tourism, more than cover the trade gap.

Mozambique is essentially an agricultural country, but there has been an appreciable growth of local manufacturing industries. Factories are situated in the vicinity of Lourenço Marques and Beira. They include mills for ginning and spinning cotton, sugar refineries and alcohol distilleries, soap factories, breweries and cigarette factories, cement and fibro-cement works and metallurgical firms.

Mining carried on on a small scale. Coal is mined at Moatize (Tete) and limited quantities of beryl are found at Alto Ligonha (Zambezi). Gold and bauxite are also exploited on a small scale.

A POLITICAL ASSESSMENT OF MOZAMBIQUE. The Portuguese have been in Mozambique for over 450 years. Like all other Portuguese territories in Africa, Mozambique is regarded not as a colony or a protectorate but as an integral part of Portugal. In its capacity of province, Mozambique is governed by the *Ministerio do Ultramar* in Lisbon. There is an unbroken flow of authority from the Ministry through a Governor-General to the administrator of each district. Education, medical services and housing are almost non-existent for the Africans, and it is estimated that only three per cent of the Africans are literate. Six months' labour every year is compulsory for all African male adults. This provides plentiful cheap labour for the undercapitalised Portuguese farmers and makes it hard for Africans to develop their own cash crops. The system

is rigorously enforced and produces widespread resentment. The Government also fixes the price of African-grown cash crops well below the level of world prices, to ensure their cheap import to Portugal.

In contrast to the extremely retarded development of Africans in Mozambique, there has been a boom in peasant immigrants into the country. The new immigrants have a capacity for hard work and have contributed to an increase in the agricultural wealth of Mozambique. This class of peasant forms therefore a block to African advancement and is even introducing a colour bar, although the official *assimilado* system has prevented racial discrimination against the small number of educated Africans (0.08 per cent) who have surmounted the barriers which divide the *indigena* from the *civilizado*.

The result is considerable discontent, aggravated by the lack of political rights. Some European intellectuals and administrators see the need to end forced labour and other abuses, as well as to secure provincial autonomy, with the aim of creating a genuine multiracial state within a Portuguese Commonwealth African nationalism has grown over recent years; and two Portuguese African nationalist associations are receiving support from other African countries to enable them to function in exile. To prevent the situation from exploding, as it has done in Angola, Portugal keeps over 30,000 troops in Mozambique, especially in the north, near the borders of Tanzania and Malawi.

# RHODESIA

Rhodesia, named after the indefatigable Empire pioneer Cecil John Rhodes, is a landlocked country occupying 150,333 square miles, and is surrounded ' to the east by Mozambique, to the south and west by South Africa and Botswana and to the north by Zambia, from which it is separated by the Zambezi river. Between 1953 and 1963 the colony was joined with the British territories of Northern Rhodesia and Nyasaland in the Central African Federation. The Federation broke up in 1963 owing to intransigent African opposition. In the following year Northern Rhodesia and Nyasaland attained independence and changed their names to, respectively, Zambia and Malawi. Thereafter Southern Rhodesia was known simply as Rhodesia.

*The physical setting.* Rhodesia is bordered by the Zambezi rift in the north and by the Limpopo valley to the south. It forms the watershed between these two river systems, and its mountain backbone, a plateau known as the highveld, which runs from south-west to north-east and which is 400 miles long and 40 miles wide, belongs geologically to the Transvaal, whose gold-bearing formations it prolongs; in the west, too, the strata of the Karroo conceal gold deposits. The tropical climate is tempered by the altitude of the plateau. The mean monthly temperature at Salisbury, 4,500 feet above sea level, varies between 13°C. and 20°C. (56°F. and 70°F.). In the middle of winter nocturnal radiation is so intense that frost may occur. The coldest months are June and July and the hottest October and November;

*See map on opposite page*
Mozambique has few mineral resources. Cotton heads the list of crops, providing 20 per cent of all exports. Others include sugar, tea, copra, and sisal. Trade is largely with Rhodesia and South Africa and revenues from port and rail services with this rich hinterland more than balance the revenue account.
Zambia's great wealth — shared with neighbouring Katanga — is copper, which provides much of its revenue. The success of the Kariba Dam project has encouraged manufacturing and processing industries. Commercial agriculture includes tea, cotton, tobacco and cereals of all kinds.

but temperature also varies according to altitude, latitude and distance from the Indian Ocean. Except in the south-west and the eastern border, most of the rainfall occurs in summer, especially January and February, with the arrival of the oceanic monsoon. The annual totals, higher in the mountains than in the valleys, are mostly between 30 and 36 inches, though they may drop to as low as 20 inches in the south, on the borders of Botswana, an area of scrubland.

*Conflict of peoples.* Rhodesia was the cradle of the African Monomotapa Empire of the thirteenth century, to whose advanced civilisation the ruins at Zimbabwe bear witness. From the seventeenth century onwards the territory saw successive waves of conquest from the Barozwi and later the Zulu. These people, now known as the Matabele, dominated the local Mashona peoples. Rhodes' British South Africa Company hoped to discover in Matabeleland and Mashonaland an extension of the rich mineral resources of the South African Rand. In 1888 the Rudd Concession gave Rhodes a monopoly of all minerals in the territory in return for supplying Lobengula, the Matabele chief, with a subsidy and arms. In the following year Rhodes obtained a royal charter to enable him to assume governmental powers north of the Zambezi. Difficulties followed Lobengula's renewed

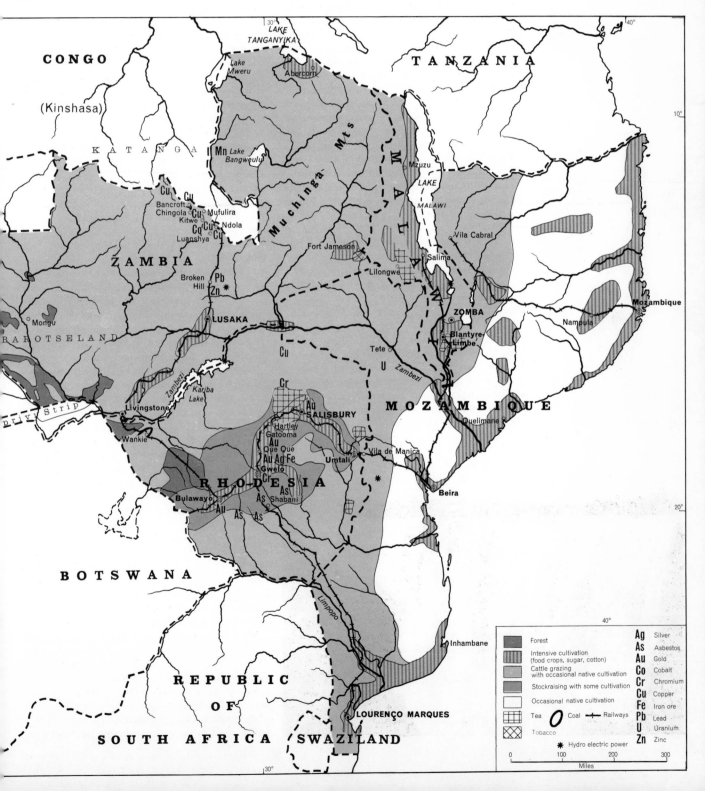

attempts to crush the Mashona, but in 1893 he was defeated by the small band of settlers already established there. The crushing of a further combined uprising of the Matabele and Mashona in 1896 finally established the rule of British law.

In 1923, under pressure from the local settlers, the British Government granted Southern Rhodesia self-government, with a Parliament elected by the white settlers. (Although Africans were theoretically not excluded from the franchise, only a handful reached the educational and property qualifications required for a vote.) Britain retained reserve powers in relation to foreign affairs and certain internal affairs, but these were in practice never used. In 1961, a new constitution was negotiated, for the first time introducing fifteen seats on a 'B' roll (in practice an African roll) as well as fifty 'A' roll seats (predominantly European voters). Under that constitution Britain lost almost all its reserve powers. Negotiations between the Rhodesian and British governments for a constitution under Rhodesia could attain independence broke down principally over the issue of how rapidly African majority rule should develop. In November 1965 the Rhodesian government, rejecting rapid African political advancement, unilaterally declared itself independent and announced repressive emergency measures. Britain retaliated with economic sanctions. These were made mandatory by the United Nations Organization in December 1966. Early in 1967 the the Rhodesian Cabinet established an independent and impartial commission to make recommendations for a revised constitution.

Apart from the exclusion from effective political power, the chief grievance of the Africans of the territory stems from the Land Apportionment Act of 1931. This Act, subsequently slightly modified, regulated land distribution into exclusively African and exclusively European areas. Though the proportion granted to each race is roughly equal, the disparity between four million Africans and 225,000 Europeans means that in practice the Africans are starved of land, while 'European' lands lie fallow. Consequently Africans are forced to find industrial or agricultural employment in European areas.

The main falls at Victoria Falls, Rhodesia.

The white population is settled largely on a strip some thirty miles long on either side of the Bulawayo-Salisbury rail line, built on the heights which separate the basin of the Zambezi from the basins of the Limpopo and the Sabi. However, the Europeans live mainly in the towns; 64 per cent are concentrated in six urban regions: Salisbury, Bulawayo, Umtali, Gwelo, Que Que and Gatooma.

*The Economy.* Rhodesia is well endowed with natural resources. Minerals, including coal, asbestos, chromite, tin, copper, gold and emeralds, are extracted for local processing and for export. Climate and soil combine to support a range of crops, varying from the temperate to the tropical.

It was the discovery in 1894 of gold, scattered in a mass of small deposits between Bulawayo and the Portuguese border, that first attracted mass settlement and determined the extension of the railroad from the Cape. There are nearly eight hundred mines, of which seven hundred extract less than 1,000 oz. per year. After reaching a maximum of 833,000 oz. in 1940, production is diminishing appreciably (1964: 574,000 oz.). Today asbestos is more important than gold: the production of 153,400 tons in 1964, taken from two mines at Shani and Mashaba, places Rhodesia third among world producers. The coal reserves in the strata of the Karroo, around Wankie, are estimated at 2,690 million tons; extraction is about 3.3 million tons per annum. The output of copper and chrome ore is also valuable.

Rhodesia's main commercial crops are coffee, tea, cotton, oranges and above all tobacco, which makes up 40 per cent of the value of Rhodesian exports. The extensive raising of cattle in areas unaffected by tsetse fly serves a refrigerating works at West Nicholson. Cotton and sugar production are expected to rise rapidly after the completion of irrigation projects in the Sabi-Lundi river basin. The forests supply tropical hardwoods, coniferous softwoods and wattle extract.

Important manufacturing industries are based on local raw materials, the most important sectors being metals and metal products and textiles and clothing.

The economic fortunes of Rhodesia have fluctuated with political events. After the Second World War the progress made by industry opened up a phase when large-scale immigration was encouraged, largely from Britain and South Africa. The settler population rose from 83,500 in 1946 to 224,000 in 1963. The economic boom, encouraged by the influx of skill and capital, was given a further boost with the formation of the Federation in 1953, with its capital at Salisbury and its industrial and commercial heart in Southern Rhodesia. During the decade 1953-63 the economic growth rate averaged 9.2 per cent per annum. Large-scale foreign investments were made. The £68 million Kariba hydro-electric project, which began operation in 1960, was an outstanding example. This supplies electricity to both Rhodesia and Zambia.

With the collapse of the Federation in 1963 and the ensuing political uncertainty, a serious economic decline occurred, with rising unemployment and a fall in markets in Zambia and Malawi.

Rhodesia is at the centre of lines of communication that link the different parts of Africa situated south of the Equator. Through Bulawayo passes the rail line which connects the Cape, via Botswana, with Port

Franqui in the Congo. Offshoots of this major line are the lines from Bulawayo via Salisbury to Beira on the Indian Ocean and to Lobito on the Atlantic Ocean. Rhodesia and Zambia are joint owners of a comprehensive rail system.

# ZAMBIA

Zambia, formerly Northern Rhodesia, is one of the richest of the newly independent nations of Africa. It owes this almost entirely to its rich copper reserves, which are an extension of those of Katanga in the Congo, which projects into the north-western part of the country. Zambia's area of 290,586 square miles, which is also surrounded by Tanzania, Malawi, Mozambique, Rhodesia and Angola, occupies diverse terrain. The dominant feature of the southern border is the Zambezi and Luangwa rift, which experiences high temperatures and extreme humidity in the wet season and which supports a dense forest of mahogany and teak trees, whose shade and moisture encourage the breeding of tsetse flies and malaria-bearing mosquitos. Most of Zambia, however, is healthy country, consisting of an undulating plateau, 3,000 to 4,000 feet above sea level. In the north-east the land rises to mountains over 5,400 feet high dominating the rift valley of Malawi and Tanzania. To the west, the Barotse river lands grow increasingly arid near the Angola border. As in Rhodesia, the year includes a cool, dry season and a warm, rainy season, between November and March. Rainfall varies from 50 inches in the north to 30 inches in the south. Temperatures, modified by latitude and altitude, vary from maxima of 15°C. to 27°C. (60°F. to 80°F.) in the cool season to 27°C. to 35°C. (80°F. to 95°F.) in the hot season. In all seasons the temperature drops sharply at night.

*Political development.* The principal tribes of Zambia are the Lozi of Barotseland and the Bemba of the Northern Province. Quite unlike the Southern Rhodesian tribes, these peoples were not conquered; but early settlers and missionaries were not resisted, and Northern Rhodesia was declared a Crown Colony in 1924 and included the Protectorate of Barotseland, established in the 1890's.

With the entry of the first two Africans to the Legislative Council in 1948, the situation in Northern Rhodesia changed radically. Since 1924 the colony had been ruled by a combination of British colonial administration and the local, relatively small, settler community (77,000 in a total population of 2.5 million). The Africans of Northern Rhodesia, like those of Nyasaland, opposed the setting up of the Central African Federation, which they regarded as a means of extending Southern Rhodesian traditions of white domination to the north. Thus when the African political parties won a majority of elected seats in the elections held under the 1962 constitution, they announced their intention of taking the territory out of the Federation as soon as possible.

*The economy.* The early colonisation of Northern Rhodesia was based largely on agriculture. It was relatively late that the country's mineral resources were discovered. The opening of routes to the copperbelt in the 1920's unleased a fresh wave of immigration, and the European population grew from 3,600 in 1921 to

A native fisherman on the shores of Lake Tanganyika, near Abercorn, Zambia's only port.

Citrus fruit plantations in Mazoe, in Mazoe, Rhodesia. The orderly layout is characteristic of this farming area twenty-five miles from Salisbury. Irrigation is provided by the Mazoe Dam.

African workers stacking asbestos-cement ridge pieces for corrugated roofing in a factory in Salisbury. Asbestos mining is now an important industry in Rhodesia and has overtaken that of gold. The 153,400 tons of asbestos mined at Shani and Mashaba has placed Rhodesia third in world production.

A mine at Roan Antelope in the Copperbelt of Zambia. Copper, together with recently developed secondary industries, accounts for over 80 per cent of the total volume of Zambia's export trade.

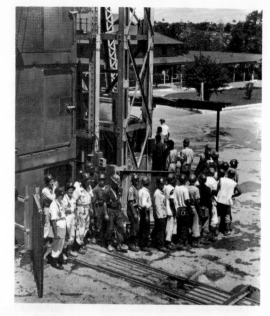

An aerial view of Mount Mlanje, the highest mountain (9,840 feet) in the Shire Highlands, in south-east Malawi.

11,000 in 1930. As in Southern Rhodesia, industrialisation after the Second World War was accompanied by a new phase of immigration.

Cotton, groundnuts (peanuts), tea and fruit and vegetables are now growing in importance as cash crops. Cattle-raising is developing slowly owing to the prevalence of tsetse fly over two-fifths of the country, despite efforts to control it. The forests supply large quantities of teak and other hardwoods both to the mining industry in the Copper belt and to the sawmills at Livingstone in southern Barotseland.

Copper, lead, zinc, cobalt and manganese are the principal mineral products of Zambia, but copper is by far the most important. The frontier between Katanga and Zambia splits a vast copper-bearing field, the Copperbelt, about 200 miles long from north to south Though less than half of the field belongs to it, Zambia's proven reserves amount to over 700 million tons of ore, with an average metal content of 4.5 per cent, divided between the mines of Mufulira, Nchanga, Nkana, Chibuluma, Bancroft, Chambeshi and Roan Antelope. The mining industry gives work to 8,000 Europeans and 42,000 Africans. At the present time production reaches 640,000 tons of crude copper which, after being treated on the spot, is exported via Beira. Minerals account for over 90 per cent of exports.

Apart from various minor hydro-electric projects, notably at Livingstone and Broken Hill, which serve the needs of Zambia's developing metallurgical and other industries, the giant Kariba project has revolutionised the country's power potential.

# MALAWI
## (formerly Nyasaland)

Malawi is a narrow strip of land and water extending approximately from latitude 10°S. to 17°S. Its narrowness is an echo of geological structure: the country is moulded on a grandiose rift valley, the last *graben* of the series which begins in Jordan. Lake Malawi, at an altitude of about 1,500 feet, occupies the bottom of the rift. Three features point to its tectonic origin: the fact that it is depressed to more than 600 feet below sea level, its remarkably parallel sides, and the two mountainous folds which enclose it. To the south-east, above the plain, forming an extension of the lake, the undulating Shire Highlands rise to 3,500 feet, towered over by Mount Zomba and the granite mass of Mount Mlanje (9,840 feet). In the west the massif of Mount Dedza (7,786 feet), the Vipya plateau and the Nyika plateau succeed each other. In a typically tropical rhythm a rainy season (November-December to March-April) alternates with a dry season which is cool at first and later extremely hot and humid. The extreme heat is tempered only in the highlands. Between 1,800 and 3,600 feet, the landscape is completely covered with open *brachystegia* forest; its deciduous trees turn green again after the annual fire which is deliberately lit.

Connected with the Lower Zambezi by the River Shire, Lake Malawi points obliquely at the heart of Africa, a feature which considerably helped European penetration. From 1861 onwards, in answer to appeals by Livingstone, missionaries set out to fight the slave trade which centred on the lake. Somewhat later, Scottish missionaries, hoping to combat the slave trade by normal commerce, founded the African Lakes Corporation, whose operations marked the beginning of economic development. Towards 1890 the Germans moved into Tanganyika and the lake lost its function as a routeway of the British Empire. In 1891 the British Government reluctantly established a protectorate to safeguard its own nationals in their humanitarian and commercial activities, and to bar the way to the Germans.

*Uneven agricultural development.* The only developed regions are those connected by rail with a maritime outlet. The Shire Highlands form the area most intensively developed by Europeans, most of whom live there.

The *arabica* species of coffee and tobacco provide increasing sources of cash income to Malawi's small farmers, especially since their encouragement by the new African government. But the most profitable crop is still tea, grown on plantations in scattered blocks, and, increasingly, tungs (trees yielding a siccative oil used for varnishing). Blantyre, on the rail route, is the commercial capital, while Zomba, the administrative capital, climbs the lower slopes of Mount Zomba forty miles away by road. With some difficulty, authorities of the then protectorate succeeded in introducing cotton among African farmers on the alluvial plain of the Lower Shire. The main centre of commercial crops is situated south-west of the lake, around Lilongwe and Kasungu, behind a line of highlands. A few European colonists settled there; but the villages are responsible for most of the produce. Maize and tobacco, the former earmarked for feeding the southern province, which is short of crops, the latter for export, reach the rail terminus at Salima. The cultivation of rice, introduced long ago around Kota Kota, a former slave port where an Arabic nucleus still exists, is making progress. Farther north, economic activity is largely limited to subsistence farming, though there are some hopeful experiments in fisheries. Wherever there is enough local demand, shops owned by Indian and European traders have been developed.

*One resource: the population.* Malawi's geographical position has been a barrier to its development. Though the British constructed a costly bridge over the Lower Zambezi, it is isolated from world markets; the only rail route terminates at the Portuguese port of Beira. Private foreign capital is scarce, for there are less than 2,000 permanent settlers out of some 8,000 Europeans (including women and children), and the Government has had difficulty in balancing its budget; however, the grant-in-aid on which the territory depended before the introduction of the Federation has been renewed. In addition, grants from the United States increased from $1.8 million in 1964 to $3.2 million in 1965.

Malawi is fortunate in having a population of nearly three million industrious people. Density reaches about 63 per square mile as against 9 in its nearest neighbour, Zambia. The climate, which is slightly more humid and better for agriculture, is to a large extent responsible. But the comparatively dense population poses problems. In several regions where the population is concentrated, agriculture of a traditional type on lands cleared by burning is not able to feed it adequately. In the Shire Highlands, which were almost empty when the Europeans arrived, the partially unexploited properties of planting companies raised political problems. Over the years the government bought back land and distributed it to farmers who had none. The agricultural services are making efforts to intensify peasant techniques and multiply local resources. Since the African Nationalist government was elected to power in 1960 its exhortations to the peasants to grow more food and more cash crops has resulted in a threefold increase in most areas. Nevertheless, the task of making Malawi economically viable will be long and arduous. For too long it has depended on the export of its manpower. No one pretends that Malawi on its own can become a rich industrial nation, but it is already a cohesive and industrious one. Its future depends to a large extent on developing communications.

Politically, Nyasaland's chief asset was its tribal integrity and cohesiveness. Its inclusion in the Central African Federation was effected partly to relieve Britain of an economic burden, and to allow the territory to share the resources of the richer Rhodesias. But the process angered and united the Nyasas as never before. Their unflinching refusal to value the economic benefits of Federation more highly than self-government produced serious disturbances in 1958, followed by Britain granting them a constitution in 1960 providing for a majority African government. In 1963 the territory became self-governing. Full independence was attained in July 1964, and the name Malawi was adopted. The first demand of the new African government was met in 1963—the break-up of the Federation. The resultant economic burdens have been accepted.

The Liwonde Ferry. River transport is important in a country with only one rail route.

# THE REPUBLIC OF SOUTH AFRICA, SOUTH WEST AFRICA, SWAZILAND, BOTSWANA AND LESOTHO

The geographical area of southern Africa has been dominated, economically and politically, by the Republic (formerly the Union) of South Africa, which has several unique features. Of Africa's five million Europeans, three million live in South Africa. Based on its production of 64 per cent of world gold output, South Africa's economy is the strongest, richest and most diverse in Africa Since 1910, when it achieved its independence from Britain, policies have been determined by its European population with no reference to a colonial power: such non-Europeans as were enfranchised in 1910 were later deprived of the vote. Traditionally its policies have been based upon racial discrimination; but since 1948 this tendency has been formalised as a policy of strict separation or *apartheid,* intended, in theory, to provide for the future racial division of South Africa.

The former German territory of South West Africa has been governed by South Africa since 1920 under a mandate from the League of Nations. Since 1945 South Africa's policies in the territory, and latterly her sovereignty over it, have been questioned by the United Nations. The Republic of Botswana (formerly Bechuanaland), the kingdom of Lesotho (formerly Basutoland) and the kingdom of Swaziland are surrounded or partly surrounded by South Africa. Political union with South Africa is unlikely under present conditions, but all these territories have been sucked into the vortex of the dominant South African economic system. All three are self-governing states and Commonwealth members. Swaziland was granted internal self-government in April 1967 and full independence in 1968.

## TROPICAL AND 'MEDITERRANEAN' REGIONS

*A vast inland plateau, tilted towards the centre.* The Republic of South Africa, the League of Nations mandated territory of South West Africa, and the three British protectorates of 'Botswana, Swaziland and Lesotho, cover a total of over a million square miles. They form a vast, largely arid plateau, access to which is barred by the escarpments facing the coasts. Accumulations of ancient granite make up its bedrock. The latter, raised at a very early date above the seas which merely covered its edges, experienced a long period of sub-aerial erosion, during which it disappeared beneath thick layers of continental debris. Those of the Karroo are the largest and today occupy nearly half the surface area of South Africa and measure more than 19,500 feet at their thickest point. The shield and its covering resisted the secondary foldings which produced the range of the Cape at the extreme tip of South Africa. However, they underwent mass deformations, changes of level, and fractures from which abundant eruptions of basaltic lava escaped.

One of the world's most striking panoramas—the Cape Peninsula, with Table Mountain in the middle foreground, Devil's Peak to the left, Signal Hill to the right, and the city of Cape Town in the foreground.

The Great Escarpment forms the dominant feature of the South African relief. It is a continuous arc girdling the inland plateaus. In the east it appears as a range of high mountains. The Drakensberg, an enormous accumulation of lava outflows cut into precipices, contains the highest peaks in southern Africa: Thabana Ntlenyana (11,425 feet) and Mont aux Sources (10,822 feet). To the south it loses height and recedes owing to the effects of regressive erosion, leaving behind it isolated secondary chains: Compass Berg, and Winterberg. It is interrupted by breaches which follow the lines of access to the interior. In the west, the escarpment, generally formed of granite, becomes smoothed off in places.

On the other side of the Great Escarpment, the slopes descend gradually towards the centre of the South African continent. The edges of this vast basin reach a height of 4,000 to 6,000 feet in the east and south, where the High Veld backs on to the Basuto massifs.

In the west, the Orange River gouges its canyons through the horizontal plateaus of Namaqualand, whose lonely expanses of stone and sand are used for pasturage by the indigenous Bushmen tribes. In the north the plateaus of Damaraland, dotted with trees and bushes, contain numerous mountains, among them Etjo and the Great Omatoko, whose escarpments rise as inselbergs. In the neighbourhood of Angola, the appearance of dolomitic rocks gives rise to a karst type of landscape which retains sufficient rain to support a grassy covering scattered with trees.

The centre of this semicircle of raised plateaus is occupied by the closed basin of the Kalahari Desert, where internal drainage has accumulated enormous thicknesses of red sand which the winds pile up into barkhans (crescent-shaped dunes) and vast longitudinal dunes. A certain amount of Tertiary buckling created the depressions, since enlarged by wind erosion, in which the courses of the wadis terminate. The multitude of basins forming the salt water lagoons of Makarikari cover nearly 5,700 square miles.

*Marginal regions and the Drakensberg.* Between the Great Escarpment and the coast is sandwiched a strip of marginal regions, which, unlike the inland plateaus bear a series of Secondary and Tertiary marine sediments on which a riot of folds and fractures has occurred. The recession of the escarpments under the effects of erosion has left a relief of terraces descending rapidly to the coastal plain.

The coastal plain of Natal, in which the penetration of the rivers has cut a series of terraces, spreads out at the foot of the Drakensberg. A fold probably determined the original outline of the coast, which is almost perfectly regular today. The folded ranges of the Cape form the backbone of the southern region. They describe arcs parallel to the Great Escarpment, towards which they have been thrust back. In spite of erosion over a long period, some peaks are still dramatic formations; among them are Langeberg and Swarzberg, both over 7,000 feet. The Karroo, between the ranges of the Cape and the Great Escarpment, with its plains of debris scattered with escarped hillocks, is a preview of the arid landscapes of the interior. To the south of the Cape ranges, the coast, which cuts across the folds obliquely, is considerably broken up and reaches its southernmost point at Cape Agulhas.

Donkeys grazing in eroded land in the Nqutu rehabilitation area of the Republic of South Africa. These animals are being eliminated in large numbers in the Nqutu district, as they accelerate soil erosion by cropping the grass close to the roots.

The Cape of Good Hope is a spur of Table Mountain, an ancient rocky island now re-attached to the continent. The coastal region of South West Africa comprises the Namib Desert; the uniformity of desert conditions does not exclude a variety of features — delicately sculptured rocks, sheets of sharp pointed pebbles and great expanses of sand dunes.

The Great Escarpment, keystone of the edifice, also forms the boundary of the hydrographic zones. It constitutes a line dividing the waters between the short, swiftly flowing rivers of the coastal regions and the two main rivers of the interior, the Limpopo and the Orange, which leave the Escarpment via canyons broken up by waterfalls. The dividing line is shifting, in so far as the coastal river waters are sometimes diverted into the interior.

*An arid climate.* The climate, however, is the decisive geographic factor. It determines not only the sort of erosion that occurs, but also the vegetation and the methods of working the soil. Situated between latitudes 18°S. and 34°S., South Africa belongs almost entirely to the tropical zone, with the exception of its southern tip, which has Mediterranean characteristics. The Cape peninsula receives its rainfall in winter during the passage of depressions along a front from west to east; upward latitudinal movement of the Atlantic anticyclone determines the summer dryness. Everywhere else, by contrast, this season is humid. On the overheated continent areas of low pressure of thermal origin prevail, and attract the trade wind produced by the anticyclone lying southeast of Madagascar. This mass of sea air reaches the eastern coast to the north of Cape Agulhas and climbs the terraces of the eastern highlands, causing heavy rain in Natal where it passes. Once it has crossed the Drakensberg, it starts to descend to the inland plateau. In the course of its advance westwards, precipitation becomes increasingly rare. In winter, a wide belt of low pressure with its axis along the tropic of Capricorn ensures dry anticyclone weather from one ocean to the other.

South West Africa has a climate in which sea

breezes and continental winds alternate. The latter, hot and dry, cause a slight rise in the temperature of the coastal waters, though the predominant influence is still the cold Benguela Current. On the same latitude the mean January temperature is more than 8°C. (14°F.) lower than on the east coast, past which flows the warm Mozambique Current. These conditions explain the scanty rainfall, which is not compensated for by the profusion of dew and fog.

*Herbaceous vegetation and mineral wealth.* Thus the Republic of South Africa includes widely varying climatic regions. The Cape Province, Mediterranean in its southern part, becomes steppe-like in the Karroo, which grows grass only in a humid year. Natal is tropically humid: Durban, on the latitude of Cairo, has a climate which produces bananas and sugarcane. The Orange Free State, the territory of which forms the high veldt, is windswept. It registers a scanty summer rainfall which permits at the most a seasonal herbaceous vegetation, and the Veldt turns into bushy scrub towards the west. Continental

At the heart of South Africa's racial problems lies the antagonism of ten million Africans for the small white minority which preserves a dominant political rôle and pursues a policy of apartheid or segregation.

situation and altitude explain the intensity of the radiation, which produces low temperatures and frosts in winter. In spite of its aridity, the Kalahari Desert is not completely barren: it has a mantle of grass dotted with trees, beginning to look like a savanna towards the north. As for the Namib, it would be nothing but a cold desert without the hidden condensation which supports a scanty vegetation of xerophytes. The balance is very favourable: two-thirds of the Republic of South Africa, and all of Botswana and South West Africa, are arid or semi-arid. This land, covered with sand or stones, with escarped slopes, and receiving only a low and irregular rainfall, is primarily used for pasturage. The herbaceous vegetation, precariously balanced in the natural background, rapidly deteriorates and disappears with excessive pasturage; and bad crop-growing methods deliver up vast denuded areas to wind and water erosion.

In these conditions, it was impossible to base a solid state simply on extensive agriculture and stock-raising, for they were threatened with exhaustion sooner or later. The development of the region's abundant mineral wealth has been a determining factor in its whole development during the last eighty years. The discovery of diamonds and gold built small, traditionally agricultural-cum-pastoral communities into a modern state whose power today is based on the booming progress of large-scale modern industry.

## HUMAN FACTORS

*A divided minority of whites.* At the heart of South Africa's problems lies the intention of a white minority, whose settlement in the country goes back three centuries, to maintain its dominant political position. To do so, it has devised a unique programme of racial separation known as apartheid — the Afrikaans word for 'separateness'.

The population of South Africa is 16 million. It includes 10.9 million Africans, 3 million Europeans, 1.5 million Cape Coloured (people of mixed or Malay blood), and 477,000 people of Asian stock. This means that the Europeans make up only 20 per cent of the whole. Moreover, they are not themselves a homogeneous community. The Afrikaaners are the descendants of Dutch and German settlers, supplemented by Huguenots driven from France by the revocation of the Edict of Nantes. They speak Afrikaans, which derives from Dutch, and belong to the three Dutch Reformed Churches. Traditionally they were the country's farmers, but now nearly half of them are urban dwellers. The English-speaking South Africans have kept their native tongue and predominate in most of the towns. Although it is difficult accurately to determine the origin of individuals, the Afrikaners are estimated at just over 60 per cent, and the English at 40 per cent of the European total.

The character of the Afrikaners was formed during their Great Trek inland from the Cape, when they lived in small, isolated, almost biblical communities, believing themselves chosen by God to lighten a dark continent. Their attitude to the Africans is determined partly by fear and partly by contempt for their pagan past. They blame the English for having tried to destroy their rigidly paternalistic relationship with the

Africans. The English, by contrast, tend to regard the Afrikaners as rustic reactionaries, opposed to the personal and economic freedoms upon which the economic growth of the country depends. Not that the average English South African has a liberal attitude to the African by modern standards, but he is opposed to the kind of restraints which reduce the rate of economic growth. For if the Afrikaner regards himself as the guardian of 'white civilisation' in Southern Africa, the English South African sees himself as the guardian of its wealth. True political liberals constitute no more than five to ten per cent of the white population — for the human history of the area has encouraged the notion that the African is useful chiefly as a source of labour.

The Cape Coloured, ten per cent of the population, are the result of intermarriage between settlers and the indigenous women or slaves imported from Madagascar, Angola and the Malayan Archipelago. Most of them live in Cape Province, speak English or Afrikaans, and have adopted the Christian faith. They tend to regard themselves as a cut above the Africans, because their skins are paler, and some try to pass for white. But on the whole they are a somewhat pathetic community, feeling themselves unacceptable to either European or African. People of Asian stock form a minority representing only three per cent of the total population. They are largely concentrated in Natal, where the successful cultivation of sugar-cane led to the indenturing of Indian workers on a three-year contract. They were recruited between 1860 and 1913 and remained in the country once their contract was terminated; since then their number has increased steadily. Today they live mainly in the towns as workers or shopkeepers, and they make up nearly a third of the population of Durban.

The Africans, nearly seventy per cent of the population of South Africa, are not indigenous in the strict sense of the word. Their settlement is the result of successive invasions from Central and East Africa. The Bushmen and the Hottentots were succeeded by the Bantu at the end of the eighteenth century, just when the Europeans, starting from the Cape, emerged on to the inland plateau. The encounter resulted in many bloody battles. It was not until 1879 that the colonists became undisputed masters of the land. South African Africans fall into the Bantu group of tribes. Their diversity of natural potentialities was matched by a great variety of ways of life, until the coming of the European. Some led a nomadic life in the scrub; others hunted, picked fruit and gathered roots; others grew millet and sorghum. But all of them raised cattle or goats, whose possession conferred wealth and social status. They lived in village communities in their groups of huts (kraals). There they were submitted to a strict collective discipline under the authority of traditional chiefs. But the absorption of Africans into the European economy and urban life has destroyed the old way of life, and, more than anything else' in Africa, broken down the old tribal loyalties and traditions.

The policy of racial separation, expressed in the intention to allow each race to 'develop along its own lines in its own area', and reinforced since 1948 by a spate of legislation, has brought increasingly vocal criticism from many countries.

## THE ECONOMY

*Agriculture*. Before the discovery of gold and diamonds the South African economy was based on agriculture and stock-raising, natural conditions favouring the latter. About 8 per cent of South Africa is cultivated: i.e. about twenty-five million acres. The rest is made up of forest (just over 2 million acres, or a little more than one per cent of the total area), and immense steppe-like or semi-desert expanses with no agricultural potentialities.

Agriculture comprises two distinct sectors. The African Reserves, which make up approximately 13 per cent of South Africa, maintain the traditional Bantu system combining food crops and stock-raising. Families, or groups of families, cultivate the land which belongs to them or which the chief periodically redistributes; the pasture lands remain collective. Since the majority of able-bodied men work as migrant labour in the mines or the towns, it is left to the women and old men, whose chief implement is the

A farm in the low veldt of the Transvaal, where sub-tropical conditions allow cultivation of a variety of orchard crops and garden plants uncultivable in high veldt conditions.

hoe, to cultivate small fields of maize in the humid regions and sorghum and millet in the dry regions. There is no fallow period, for land is not plentiful; furthermore, it is not enriched, for manure is used as fuel. The pasturages are badly over-grazed. Exposed to this destructive exploitation, the soils become exhausted and deteriorate owing to the effects of extremely severe erosion. Conditions vary considerably from one reserve to another, but none of them can support their population. It was estimated in 1955 by a government commission known as the Tomlinson Commission, that at least a third of the people living in the Reserves would have to be removed in order to rehabilitate the land; and that £10 million a year ($28 million) would have to be spent on development. Although some modernisation of methods has been carried out, it is negligible when compared to the Commission's recommendations.

Eighty-seven per cent of South Africa is reserved for Europeans. As individuals they own over 70 per cent of the total area: in 1959, 228,724,000 acres divided into 106,220 properties, giving an average of more than 2,150 acres per farm, more than 70 per cent of them developed directly by their owners. With an abundant supply of African labour, about one-third of the native population works on European farms. The immense farming properties of the Transvaal have adopted the system of the mining companies: their seasonal workers, all recruited under contract, are fed and housed in strictly disciplined compounds, though regular workers still live on the farms.

After the Second World War, European agriculture suffered a shortage of manpower, owing to the attraction offered by the towns and the high wages of expanding industry. To some extent mechanisation has been adopted in response to labour shortage. But South African agriculture is still less mechanised than agriculture in Europe; and since the introduction and tightening up of apartheid laws in the late 1950's and the 1960's the shortage of farm labour has been somewhat relieved.

Cereals have a predominant place among South African crops: maize, wheat and oats take up over one-third of the cultivated area, and about a fifth of the annual production is exported. However, since the summer aridity does not encourage stock-raising, the land lacks manure: after a few harvests yields fall unless artificial fertilizers are used.

Increasing demands from abroad since the war, and the tendency of town-dwelling Africans to abandon maize for wheat bread have made it necessary to sow this crop on unfavourable soil: the cultivation of wheat is becoming more and more extensive, though production is still only about one-sixth that of maize.

The 'Mediterranean' zone in Cape Province contains almost all the 150,000 acres under vines. Viticulture, introduced in the middle of the seventeenth century, developed with the arrival of the Huguenot settlers. Confined at first to the humid regions, it subsequently spread to irrigated land east of Worcester. Grapes are exported and also used for wine.

South Africa's orchards are even more important. In the south-west of the Cape, at the foot of the folded ranges, the slopes of sandstone scree and the perennial springs decided the choice of trees from temperate countries: pear, apple, plum, peach and apricot. The area growing citrus fruit — oranges, lemons and grapefruit — is very much larger. It embraces the Transvaal, Natal and the Cape. With a climate where coconut palms grow wild, the east coast produces all kinds of tropical fruits which are consumed locally. Its alluvial and sandy soils also support plantations of sugar-cane which, thanks to the Mozambique current, spread as far south as latitude 31°S. On either side of Durban, 400,000 acres produce 600,000 tons of sugar. With yields of 24 tons of cane per acre, giving 13.43 per cent of sugar, it is a most efficiently grown crop.

Tobacco is another important crop, annual production being about 27,000 tons. It and maize are, however, in some places giving way to cotton, which is more drought-resistant.

Stock-raising, the principal resource when colonisation was in its infancy, has retained its importance: the estimated gross values of animal and vegetable production are approximately equal. Vast semi-arid regions have no other activity. There are over one million head of cattle in Bechuanaland, two million in South West Africa and twelve million in South Africa; large numbers of them are Afrikander cattle excellent draught animals capable of living in the most impoverished veldt, but poor milk producers.

Wool farming is highly profitable. The merino sheep, introduced in 1789, has adapted itself admirably to the veldt, the value of which it has re-established. It has prospered in spite of periodic droughts. Today it forms the major part of a flock of 38 million head. The dry regions support another 5 million goats and 620,000 angora goats yielding mohair.

Nevertheless, agriculture and stock-raising pose some difficult problems. The most serious is the loss of soil by erosion, so advanced in certain areas, especially the African reserves, that it has assumed the proportions of a national crisis. The Soil Conservation Act of 1946, described by the late Field-Marshal Smuts as the 'Magna Carta of South Africa', was the official reaction to the danger.

*The age of gold and diamonds.* The real wealth of South Africa is to be found in the subsoil which conceals almost inexhaustible resources: they are contained in the rocks of the ancient sub-stratum and the volcanic formations. The great strides made by the mining industry in the second half of the nineteenth century have radically altered conditions of existence in the country.

Diamonds are extracted from mines in the Cretaceous volcanic seams and Pre-Cambrian conglomerates of Witwatersrand, around Kimberley and Pretoria, but alluvial deposits have also supplied some of the finest specimens. Those which were discovered in 1927 between the mouth of the Orange River and Port Nolloth are directly exploited by the State. Annual production is more than three million metric carats, over half being industrial diamonds.

Gold abounds in the strata of the Witwatersrand. Recent additions to the gold-bearing fields grouped around Johannesburg are those of the extreme western Rand, Klerksdorp, and the Orange Free State, making a total of fifty mines. Annual production is 665 tons or 64 per cent of known world production. Its extraction requires the handling of millions of tons of low-grade ore and the application of a costly technique which can be carried out only by companies with a very large capital. These companies are grouped into holding companies: the Anglo-American Corporation of South Africa, the most powerful, has shares in seventy-three companies. One of its subsidiaries, de Beers of South Africa, has an almost complete world monopoly of the sale of diamonds (over 80 per cent of all sales).

The birth of this capitalist economy transformed a region previously devoted to agriculture and stock-raising. European technicians and African labour from as far afield as Malawi flocked to the industrial centres, which grew on an American scale. The Rand, linked with South African ports by a network of railroads, emerged from its isolation into a world commercial centre for the collection and distribution of the valuable mineral wealth.

The rocks of the Karroo hold coal deposits whose workable rreserves exceed 25,000 million tons. The principal mines are situated in the Transvaal, the Orange Free State and Natal. They supply about forty million tons annually. Because of the cheapness of manpower, the horizontal direction of the coal strata and their nearness to the surface, the cost of extraction is exceptionally low. South Africa is able to export part of its production.

Iron is abundant: the reserves of ore, with an average metal content of 40 to 60 per cent, reach 6,000 million tons. Manganese, tin, copper, tungsten, chrome and nickel are also found in good commercial quantities. Lastly, discoveries in the late 1950's proved that the greatest gold field in the world is also the largest uranium field. Today, several factories extract this extremely valuable ore as a by-product of gold.

*Industrialisation. Urban development.* But South Africa is no longer only a supplier of raw materials. The mining industries initially required the support of a series of subsidiary industries, but it was the Second World War which encouraged the development of manufacturing industries by stopping the importation of British manufactured goods. The total value of industrial production in South Africa increased by over six hundred per cent in the twenty years from 1939 to 1959. Today it equals the combined contribution of agriculture and mining.

The greatest strides have been made in the metallurgical industry; the Iron and Steel Corporation (ISCOR) meets almost all the nation's steel needs. Remarkable progress has been made in the production of electricity, which reached 19,630 million kWh in 1961. The expansion of the textile industry is even more striking: today South Africa supplies one-third of its requirements in cotton goods, and three-

Built on a foundation of rich mineral wealth—gold and diamonds, coal, iron ore, uranium and small deposits of many other minerals, South Africa today has a sound and expanding economy. The development of secondary industries since the Second World War has underlined this prosperity. Commercial agriculture on a large scale (forests, cereal crops, vines, livestock, and fruits of all kinds) contrasts with the subsistence farming of the Bantu, who grow millet, sorghum and maize for their own needs.

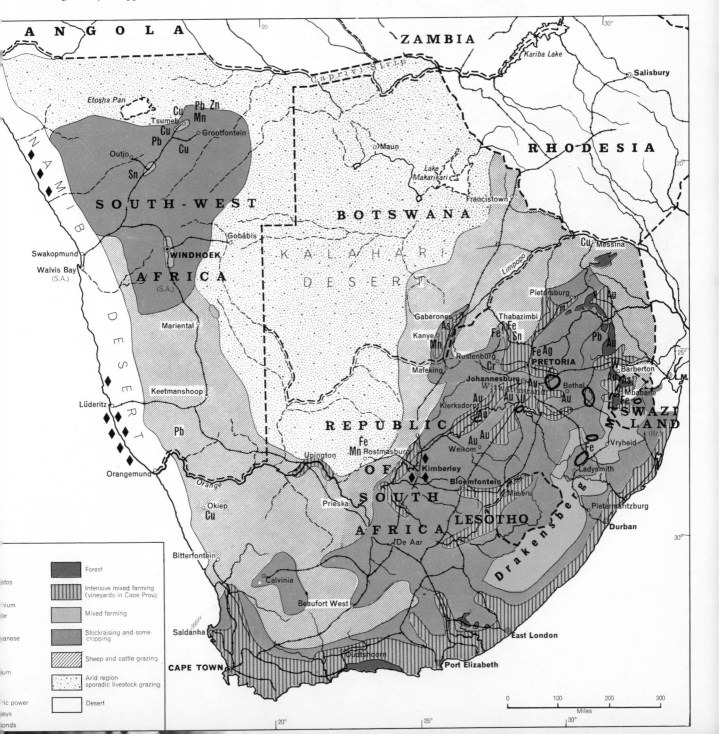

Forest

Intensive mixed farming (vineyards in Cape Prov.)

Mixed farming

Stockraising and some cropping

Sheep and cattle grazing

Arid region sporadic livestock grazing

Desert

Workers picking diamonds out
of heavy residue at
Alexander Bay. Annual
production from the Cretaceous
volcanic seams and alluvial
deposits is more than
three million metric carats.

Rustenburg Platinum Mines,
South Africa. Underground
haulage of the platiniferous ore
is by electric locomotive
and trains of four-ton trucks.
South Africa's mineral resources
are considerable, with gold
production well in the lead.

the industrial labour market. This in turn has in the
past five years seriously inhibited the internal market,
for the majority of the population are not allowed to
earn enough to buy the products of industry. A programme of white immigration has been set in motion
by the Government to try to remedy this situation.
But since non-white workers constitute 95 per cent
of South Africa's labour force, the attempt to replace
them altogether would seem an impossibility. Ever
since the discovery of valuable minerals, and especially
since 1939, Africans have tended to leave their impoverished Reserves to seek work in the towns. Today
only 3 per cent of the adult male African population
is classified as peasant farmers in the Reserves. The
urban African population is over 4 million. About a
third of these workers are migrant labourers, who
have left their families on the farm or in the Reserves.
Those who work in the mines live in special communal compounds, where they are well looked after
and highly regimented. Others live in the so-called
'native locations' outside the main towns.

Between 1912 and 1959, the share of agriculture
and the mining industry in the national income fell
from 17 and 27 per cent to 11 and 13 per cent respectively, whereas the share of industry rose from 6 to
25 per cent. The national income increased fivefold
in value between 1939 and 1959. Nevertheless, because of the uneven distribution of income the average
income per head is not high. In 1939 it stood at £138.1.
Since 1947 the average earnings of non-Europeans have
declined as a percentage of European earnings. On
average the European income is ten times the African,
seven times the Coloured, and five times the Indian
income.

It is clear that the South African economy is exceptionally well based and diversified. The chief obstacles
to an even faster rate of growth are shortages of
labour, especially skilled labour, and lack of economic
confidence. Both these obstacles stem from the country's political problems.

## POLITICAL PROBLEMS

In 1910 South Africa was granted its independence
by Britain through an exceptional act of magnanimity
towards the defeated Afrikaners, only seven years
after the end of the Anglo-Boer War. It was hoped
that this gesture would mark the beginning of recon-
ciliation between the Afrikaners and English South
Africans. Non-European races were not enfranchised
in any numbers, though a handful of Africans, Coloureds and Asians, enfranchised at the time, were not
excluded. But all African voting rights were removed
by the South African Parliament in 1936 and all
Coloured and Asian voting rights in 1955. Racial
discrimination, inherent in the original settlement of
independence, has been strengthened in South Africa
ever since. It was aggravated in the 1930's when the
Depression years produced the so-called 'poor white
problem' and resulted in the beginnings of a policy
of reserving jobs for white workers. Throughout this
period, and right up to 1948, successive governments
introduced increasingly rigid laws for the control of
the movement, residence and employment of Africans.
But with the election of the Afrikaner Nationalist

quarters in woollen goods. Most mills process cotton harvested on their own plantations. Co-operative
and private canning factories have built up a considerable export trade in products grown in South
Africa.

In effect, international captialism has been the basis
of the development of the Union's extractive and
manufacturing industries. Between 1870 and 1936 the
amount of foreign capital invested in them was estimated at £525 million sterling ($1,450 million). By
1959 total overseas investment was estimated at £1,400
million ($3,900 million), of which over £800 mil-
lion ($2,000 million) came from Britain. Since then
British investment alone has reached over £1,000
million ($2,750 million). But since 1950 an increasing
amount of investment is supplied by local savings.
By 1957 South Africa provided 95 per cent of gross
domestic investment.

The biggest obstacle to industrial growth is the
shortage of skilled labour, resulting from the Government's refusal to allow non-white workers to rise in

Party in 1948, what had been a pragmatic and *ad hoc* process became a doctrine of *apartheid* or 'separateness'. Already the Europeans had established exclusive land rights over seven-eighths of South Africa. The rest consisted of scattered Reserves in which only Africans were permitted to own land.

The chief purposes of apartheid are: to preserve the identity of the white races, and prevent their being swamped by the majority races; to segregate the ethnic groups into their own areas where each is intended to develop as a self-sufficient unit; to halt the process of detribalisation of the Africans, and restore the old tribal systems of authority and loyalty; and to turn all Africans working in the 'white' areas into temporary migrant workers without political or social rights. It would not be possible to list the laws which have been introduced to carry out these aims. They include separate and different educational facilities, the nature of which varies with the group for which it is indended; restriction of jobs which non-whites are allowed to take; restriction of areas in which Africans may live or work; and a ban on miscegenation. Since many of these laws have proved highly unpopular, not only among the Africans but also with the minority of sympathetic Europeans, other laws have been passed restricting the right of individuals to form political movements, to speak freely or to protest openly.

At the same time the Government has established the principle that the Reserves will become 'Bantustans' or 'African homelands', with a certain amount of local autonomy. The attempt to develop the Bantustans to the point where they may be able to support even their present population, let alone those now working in the 'white' areas, has so far made little headway. This is partly because it has not proved possible to move hundreds of thousands off the land in order to rehabilitate it, without at the same time starving them—for there are no sizable industries within the Reserves, and very few on their borders.

In 1961, following a referendum, South Africa became a Republic, and left the British Commonwealth because other members were not prepared to entertain its continued membership while apartheid was practised.

Thus, while the split between the Afrikaner and the English South Africans has not been finally healed (the formation of a Republic, for example, angered most non-Afrikaners), the true conflict in South Africa today is between the white man and the black. The Afrikaner Nationalist Party can hardly be ousted from power by the main opposition party—the United Party, previously led by General Smuts—since the former holds two-thirds of the seats in the Assembly. Meanwhile, although their political organisations are banned, the Africans are steadily organising underground movements for the overthrow of the Verwoerd regime. These problems may be aggravated by South Africa's relations with the other territories of southern Africa — South West Africa, Lesotho, Swaziland and Botswana— and by the hostility of the newly independent nations in the rest of Africa. It is becoming increasingly difficult to forecast a peaceful solution to South Africa's problems in view of the present conflicting aims.

## SOUTH WEST AFRICA

Originally colonised by Germany in the middle of the last century, South West Africa was adopted as a mandated territory by the League of Nations after Germany's defeat in the First World War. Mandates for former German territories were parcelled out among the major powers to administer them 'as sacred trusts of civilisation' (Preamble to the League Charter) until they were able to become independent. South West Africa was put under the administration of South Africa. Since then it has been subject to most of South Africa's laws, though the territory has its own Legislative Council with roughly the same powers as a South African Provincial Assembly. In particular, apartheid has been applied throughout the territory.

When the League of Nations was succeeded by the United Nations Organisation in 1945, the Mandate System was converted into the Trusteeship System. Every other mandatory power submitted its mandated

A general view of Johannesburg with some of the mine dumps in the background.

territory to the authority of the Trusteeship Council, and all of them are now either independent or making progress towards independence. But South Africa refused to admit that she had any obligations to the United Nations Organisation: her agreement, she claimed, had been with the League, now defunct. She has refused to undertake any of the obligations of a Trustee power. Every year since then, the U.N. General Assembly has passed a condemnatory resolution calling on South Africa to carry out its obligations. Since 1960 these resolutions have included the demand for United Nations intervention of some kind to remove South African authority over the territory. Two advisory opinions of the International Court have declared South Africa to be legally in breach of its obligations.

South West Africa is potentially one of the richest areas in Africa, despite its climate. The mining industry—diamonds and base metal—contribute over half its £45 million ($125 million) export revenue. There is also a flourishing trade in cattle and dairy

Tribeswomen and children in the Transkei.

products, Persian lamb pelts and fish products. The total population was officially estimated in 1960 at 544,000, of which 464,000 are Africans, 21,000 are Coloureds, and 69,000 are Europeans, mostly of Afrikaner stock. The capital, Windhoek, has a population of 38,000, and the chief ports are Walvis Bay and Swakopmund.

Although the economic potential and strategic position of South West Africa are at present considerable assets to the South African government, it is not unlikely that the territory will turn out a liability if the United Nations resolves to enforce its rights over the territory.

## BOTSWANA
## SWAZILAND AND LESOTHO

Botswana, Swaziland and Lesotho are also potentially a thorn in the side of the South African Government. Since South Africa's independence, its successive governments have pressed for the incorporation of these territories into South Africa;

this the British Government has refused without the concurrence of their inhabitants. Because of the possibility of incorporation, their economic and political development has been relatively retarded.

Botswana is 275,000 square miles in extent, with a population of 320,000, including 3,000 Europeans. The Constitution, approved by the British Government, came into effect in March 1965. The cabinet is presided over by the Prime Minister. Lesotho, surrounded entirely by South Africa, covers 11,716 square miles and has a population of 685,000 of whom 2,000 are Europeans. In April 1966 it became the Kingdom of Lesotho with the Paramount Chief as king. Swaziland, the richest of the three, covers only 6,704 square miles, and has a population of 260,000, including 6,000 Europeans. The territory was a British protected state but is now independent. The executive authority is vested in the king and exercised through a Cabinet which consists of eight ministers, including the prime minister and his deputy.

Only Swaziland, with its iron ore and rich forest and sugar resources, is potentially capable of providing a prosperous and rising standard of living for its population. However, the importance of these territories lies not in their economic strength but in the fact that they are not subject to the laws of apartheid and could be used by South Africa's opposition organisations as an escape route and a channel for assistance. They are seen by the outside world as islands of progress in a sea of political conflict. For that reason they represent a potential 'fifth column' to the South African government; and the pressure against them is building up inside South Africa.

# THE SOUTH-WEST OF THE INDIAN OCEAN

The south-west of the Indian Ocean is occupied by a mass of islands of all sizes marking lines of submarine fracture along which volcanic activity still continues Between the Equator and the Tropic of Capricorn, they come under the successive influences of the trade wind and the monsoon. This alternation produces two clear-cut seasons, one relatively cool and dry, the other hot and humid. Situated between Africa and Asia, towards which the winds blow alternately, the islands of the south-west of the Indian Ocean have served as ports of call for European navies; geography has thus placed them at the meeting point of the most varied influences.

## MADAGASCAR
### (The Malagasy Republic)

Madagascar, the largest of these islands, has an area of 227,602 square miles. Stretching between latitudes 12° and 25°S., the island is about a thousand miles long and takes the form of an asymmetrical spine of highlands sloping towards the Mozambique channel. The crystalline formations which make them up have been worn away by years of erosion after being folded in the Primary Era. Reduced to blunted ridges and broad shallow valleys, the highlands were subsequently affected by vertical movements which thrust them to an average height of 3,000 feet and at the same time tilted them from east to west. Slow subsidence hollowed out basins in their interior, the plains of Tananarive and Antsirabe. Situated on fractures, volcanoes form the highest peaks: Tsaratanana, 9,450 feet; in the Ankaratra, 8,675 feet; and Andringitra, 8,740 feet.

Towards the east the structure of Madagascar takes the form of terraces: the cliff of Angavo and the cliff of Betwimisaraka, which separate the depressions of Lake Alsotra and of the Ankay valley, border closely on a narrow alluvial plain terminated by the sea in a low rectilinear coast fringed in turn by lagoons.

In the west, Secondary and Tertiary sedimentary strata occur on the highlands sloping towards the Mozambique Channel. Above the depressions hollowed out in the soft strata are escarpments of hard strata which continue inland as rocky plateaus. In the north-west, the last submersions and the action of the tides have produced a coast with estuaries and heavily indented bays, such as Diego-Suarez, fringed with coral reefs and volcanic islands such as Nossi Bé. In the west, currents and counter-currents clashing in the Mozambique Channel have favoured alluvial accretion on the coast and the extension of deltas.

In the south of the island, sub-horizontal strata of Tertiary limestone make up the plateaus of Mahafaly and Androy. The action of the sea has broken them off into cliffs.

*Contrasting coasts.* This relief closely determines the climatic phenomena. The eastern façade raises its screen of cliffs in the path of the trade winds: it is a windward coast which has abundant rainfall in all seasons. Once past the Angavo Cliff, the trade wind becomes an increasingly dry wind in the course of its rapid descent towards the west. The Sakalave area thus has to rely on the hot season monsoon for rain. However, Sambirano and Nossi Bé in the north-west, under the influence of a barometric depression which settles permanently leeward of Tsaratanana, have no dry months. The south-west, out of the range of the monsoon, though affected by the passage of southern depressions which produce a few storms there, is a semi-desert region. As for the central highlands, they are distinguished from other parts of the island by their tropical mountain climate with clearly separated thermal seasons: Tananarive has a hot season of five months and a cool season of seven months, in the middle of which July registers a mean temperature of 14.4°C. (58°F.) Lastly, Madagascar is in the path of the cyclones which develop in the south-west of the Indian Ocean: Tamatave is one of the most exposed points.

The asymmetry of relief explains the hydrography of the island: the well developed rivers of the western slope contrast with the short torrents in the east. The Betsiboka, the Tsiribinina and the Mongoki in the west are the chief rivers. Harnessed with dams, they are able to supply motive power and water for the dry season crops, especially beneficial for the dry areas of the south-west.

These differing climatic conditions determined the distribution of the original flora. However, in the hills the clearing of land by burning for rice cultivation, and elsewhere the periodic fires lit by cattle breeders, have ravaged the primitive vegetation. Over vast expanses, a kind of brush called *savoka* has replaced the great humid forests of the east; wooded savanna has taken the place of the open forest of the Sakalave area, and in the south the desert is gaining ground at the expense of the natural bush of thorny plants. But denudation is more complete in the highlands than anywhere else. Deprived of their vegetation, these highland ridges are exposed to severe erosion.

*An African island populated by Asians.* Long uninhabited Madagascar was belatedly populated by people coming from all corners of the Indian Ocean. The first immigrants were probably African: these Bantu peoples were joined from the sixteenth century onwards by large numbers from Mozambique, introduced by the slave trade. Meanwhile there had been a whole series of invasions from Indonesia, the last of which most probably took place after the introduction of Hin-

Preparing Madagascan rice fields in the dry season.

duism in Java and Sumatra between the seventh and fifteenth centuries. Moslem influence, radiating from Arab colonies settled on the coast of Africa, was also felt. After the sixteenth century the Europeans began to take an interest in Madagascar, which was admirably placed on the route to the Indies.

Certainly, however, the most important elements in the formation of the Madagascan people were of Indonesian origin.

*The tendency to political unity.* The only lasting political structure, the Merina kindom, was born in the middle of the island. It was based on the colonisation of the plains of the Ikopa and its affluents, the use of which for the irrigated cultivation of rice enabled a numerous peasantry, strongly attached to its village communities, to take root. It was from this social and economic organisation that the State drew its power: crossing its own frontiers, it undertook the political unification of the island, but at the same time laid itself open to the European influence of the Protestant missions established on it. In the middle of the nineteenth century it seemed that the Merina monarchy was in a position to equip Madagascar with modern institutions modelled on the British system. But at the decisive moment, the kingdom was unable to resist the impact of French expansion.

*Colonisation.* The development of Madagascar was the work of large companies planned to carry out a great variety of activities and of private individuals who settled on concessions. Small planters from Réunion were able to make do with family labour; the larger farms had to have recourse to native labour. The major difficulty was the recruitment of manpower in a population with a density of only 24 per square mile: farm labourers engaged under contract came from the central regions paying rent in kind.

As for commerce, its best employees were found among the Indian and Chinese immigrants. The import-export companies still carry out their operations through them. As small shopkeepers established in even the smallest hamlets in the bush, they also lend the peasants money against the harvests at exorbitant rates of interest.

French colonisation was uneven, leaving vast regions untouched by its direct influence. Moreover, it was not organised round a core of directors, technicians and officials. Hence the low European population of 55,180 Frenchmen concentrated in the towns; in the country, colonisation was often represented only by a single Chinese moneylender. Asians form only 1.8 per cent of the total population. The four and a half million native Madagascans can be divided into some twenty groups. Starting from what is undeniably a common base, the peoples have acquired their own characteristics as a result of being placed in relative isolation in different natural settings. They form a great number of variants of a single civilisation native to the Far East, and based on the cultivation of rice and the raising of oxen.

## VARIED LANDSCAPES

*The Central Highlands.* The peasantry left behind in the central highlands at the fall of the Merina kingdom still lives by intensive rice cultivation with the aid of irrigation. The spade is used to till land fragmented into a multitude of small plots, which produce a dry or humid season harvest depending on their situation in relation to the irrigation canals. Crops are grown in the valleys, while the depressed basins in the middle of the bare lateritic ridges are given up to cattle and reforestation.

The plains of Tananarive and their mountainous surroundings support a dense population of villages established on rocky islets safe from flooding. The levelled alluvial lands are devoted to ricefields, while vegetable allotments, manioc and fruit-trees occupy the low terraced slopes. Tananarive lies to the east, dominating the flat country, and its houses with their verandas cover the escarped sides of an enormous granite-gneiss hump almost completely isolated from everywhere else. It is a large town with multiple functions and a population of 248,000, including 20,000 Frenchmen. Besides being the headquarters of the government and the banking and commercial establishments, it is the starting point for road and rail networks; and it redistributes merchandise from Tamatave. Industries have sprung up in its suburbs: rice mills, oil works, tanneries and canned meat factories.

To the south, fragmented into a multitude of valleys winding between rocky humps, the scenery of Betsileo is reminiscent of the Far East with its terraces

A panorama of Tananarive, capital of Madagascar, the largest island in the Indian Ocean. Tananarive is situated on the high plateau of the Imerina (the central massif of Madagascar) at an altitude of 4,593 feet, on a hill overlooking the Ikopa.

of ricefields arranged in tiers on the slopes. Although there are also villages grouped on the top of a hill or bordering a road, the rural population is mainly dispersed in an infinite number of small farms. Rice, sugar-cane, sweet potatoes and manioc are the chief crops.

To the north and south of these two eminently agricultural provinces are regions where stock-breeding predominates: in the north, a humid verdant country; and in the south, an area which experiences a long dry season. Throughout the central highlands, European colonisation planted deep roots in only a few places: the volcanic district of Itasy and above all the depression of Lake Alaotra where it was based on the cultivation of rice, groundnuts (peanuts) and manioc. But Europeans are now mainly concerned with industrial activities such as the extraction of graphite and mica, the processing of agricultural products, and stock-raising.

*The great escarpments of the east. The isolated north.* The traditional domain of colonisation is the eastern façade of the island: at the foot of escarpments carpeted by dense forests where the Tanala still live by gathering roots and berries and growing rice in clearings made by burning, the humid, hot coastal plain is suited to luxuriant plantations of vanilla, coffee, sugar-cane and cloves. They were introduced there by immigrants from Réunion. After a period of prosperity, economic crises, native competition and the 1947 revolt struck these European plantations a hard blow: today, export crops are largely in the hands of the Betsinisaraka, one of the most important Malagasy peoples. The European planters are numerous only in the districts of Brickaville and Tamatave. Commercialised by the intermediary of Chinese crop-dressers, brokers and shopkeepers working for companies, crops are exported through Tamatave, whose port handles nearly half the external trade; with its 40,000 inhabitants it takes third place among Madagascan towns.

The north of the island, isolated by the powerful forest-clad massif of Tsaratanana, has as its chief town Diego-Suarez (Antsirane). The Antakarana mainly live by breeding oxen. European colonisation is represented by a few large groundnut (peanut) and sisal plantations, and especially by dozens of small mixed crop family farms installed in the valleys radiating out from Ambre Mountain. Diego-Suarez owes its importance to the strategic position of its excellent bay in the Indian Ocean and at the entrance to the Mozambique Channel.

The north-west of Madagascar today forms the most important region of commercial agriculture, thanks to its natural conditions: a tropical climate with a not too pronounced dry season, and fertile soil of volcanic or alluvial origin which made possible the development of valuable export crops. In addition to the small concessionaires, usually permanent settlers, the area was developed by companies which invested their capital in establishing plantations of sugar-cane, cocoa, coffee, vanilla, and plants used in perfumery.

*An African landscape in the west and desert scenery in the south.* For a century the west of Madagascar has been a zone of immigration and colonisation. It is a patchwork of peoples and intermingled ways of life. The only authentic native population of the island is the Sakalave, who remain oxen breeders and whose basic methods consist in burning the pasturelands at the end of the dry season. Among the immigrants, the Merina and Betsileo are tenants paying rent in kind on land occupied by irrigated ricefields where they also cultivate tobacco, maize and Cape peas, and the people of the south — Antaimoro, Antaisaka and Antandroy — work on concessions. Once their contract is terminated they often try to settle. As for European and Indian colonisation, it thrived in Boina where it was based on the production of rice, sisal and sugar-cane, and thinned out and deteriorated south of the Ambongo. A whole range of varied agriculture supplies a number of factories: oil works, soap mills, flour mills, rope work and spinning mills grouped around Majunga. Although requiring modernisation, this port holds second place in the maritime traffic of the island. The urban population amounts to some 34,000 inhabitants.

The south is the poorest natural region in Madagascar. In its semi-desert climate, Mahafaly and Antandroy lead a poverty-stricken life, combining cattle-raising on the transhumance system and cultivation of many food crops. They supply most of the man-power used in the island. Colonisation is represented only by sisal plantations and mica workings — pending the development of the Sakoa coal mines and the recently discovered deposits of thorianite.

*From regional variety to unity.* Thus Madagascar is made up of several regions differing from one another in their natural conditions, their resources, and the way of life of their populations. However, regional division perpetuated by the federal system imposed by French colonial rule could not stand in the way of the historical tendency to national unity. The Merina monarchy had been very close to effecting it; it fell to the Madagascan people as a whole to realise it and this was behind the disturbances of 1947. In June 1960 the Malagasy Republic achieved independent status within the French Community, and so today unification is a *fait accompli*.

## CHANGING THE COLONIAL ECONOMY

Previously an exploited colony, Madagascar was forced to export the products of its agriculture, its stock-raising and its subsoil, and to import manufactured goods. Most agriculture and stock-raising has now been left to the native population, some of whom still use primitive techniques of burning forest and brush to clear land for agriculture and pastureland; sometimes no reserves of fodder are kept, so that the herd dwindles during the dry season. The cultivation of cloves and coffee degenerates into the gathering of wild fruit. The peasant, an easy prey to traffickers, is not rich enough to provide himself with adequate equipment. One remedy which might have worked was the extension of credit and of agricultural co-operatives: but this failed. Great hopes have been placed in plans for modernisation and capital equipment, for which France has supplied credit. Agricultural reformers aim to organise the inhabitants of a single region into communities of different types, from peasant co-operatives to modernised native collective farms. The part played by European colonisation in agriculture is reduced to a few large plantations of sugar-cane, sisal or plants for perfume, and to concessions handed over to the native tenant farmers.

Capital has gone into industrial and commercial investments. Industry is represented by the extraction of graphite, mica, precious stones, and especially by the processing of agricultural and livestock products. As for commerce, controlled by three or four large companies, it still often smacks too much of old-style trading operations.

Nevertheless Madagascar gets most of its income from agriculture, with mineral products accounting for less than 6 per cent of its income. Of a variety of agricultural products, three — coffee, vanilla and sugar — total 48 per cent of the value of exports. But the island still has almost all its foreign trade within the franc zone and depends heavily on France for grants to cover government expenditure. A chronic deficit characterises the balance of trade of this closely dependent economy. Chief imports are metal goods, vehicles, textiles, cement and liquid fuel, electrical appliances and foodstuffs. Four-year plans exist which are intended to put an end to Madagascar's situation as an underdeveloped country. Textile and foodstuff industries have been among the first new developments. The biggest effort, however, is directed towards developing and equipping the infrastructure: reclamation of marshy land, construction of hydraulic works, mineral prospecting and above all improvement of communications. This island has 19,728 miles of roads, of which over 16.000 miles are practicable all the year round; about 540 miles of one-metre-gauge railroad and only one well equipped port. The lack of an adequate communications network leaves the island divided into compartments and isolated from the outside world. The programme of social development includes plans for building more schools, hospitals and dispensaries in the bush.

However, the four-year plans have run up against a major difficulty. Madagascar has a small population: the density is only 24 per square mile. The great problem is the recruitment of the necessary manpower to carry out the work. On the other hand, the distribution of the population into islets leaves vast spaces empty and they remain unexploited. Although an improvement in public health ensures a continuous increase in the excess of births over deaths, the regions of Soavina, Itasy and Ankaisina especially are seriously underdeveloped. Families from Réunion have recently settled in the Sakay valley.

# THE COMORO ISLANDS

A host of little islands form an extension of Madagascar, some at the entrance to the Mozambique Channel, others right in the Indian Ocean. Among the former, France owns the volcanic Comoro Archipelago, comprising Mayotte, Moheli, Anjouan and the Grande Comore.

It belongs to the Moslem world. Africans, Malays, and Arabs have come together under the aegis of the Shafite sect of Islam. The colonial era which began here in the middle of the nineteenth century saw the arrival of Europeans, European settlers from Réunion, Indians and Chinese. There are 183,000 inhabitants on 836 square miles, giving an average density of 218 per square mile. Owing to the reduction of native inherited land property in favour of the colonists, and the rapid deterioration of soil submitted to primitive practices, the islands are over-crowded. Nowhere is this more serious than in Anjouan, where there has been agrarian unrest. Comorans have flocked towards other lands, particularly Madagascar. Agriculture is the foundation of the whole economy. Food crops are staggered according to altitude: tropical fruit trees, maize, manioc and sweet potatoes grow up to 1,300 feet, in the shade of the cocoa trees; above that, mountain rice predominates. The products exported — plants for perfume (citronalla, ylang-ylang, jessamine), vanilla, cloves, sisal and copra — are partly harvested by French companies who monopolise the trade in them. Sugar-cane has lost its previous importance. A former dependency of Madagascar, the Comoro Archipelago has acquired administrative, financial and customs autonomy. Moroni is the chief town of Grande Comore.

# REUNION

Réunion, 420 miles east of Madagascar, is a French Overseas Department which has preserved its traditional colonial economy. When discovered, it was uninhabited, and its first population consisted of the French colonists who settled there three centuries ago.

Violent volcanic eruptions, active in the Burning

Once the rice fields have been flooded the whole area is churned into a sea of mud by herds of cattle

SOUTH AFRICA: Rigging a winch mechanism in a gold mine in Orange Free St

Crater, have constructed a complex of juxtaposed cones: the roughly circular island rears up to a height of 10,068 feet in the Piton des Neiges. Explosions, subsidence and especially erosion have opened gaping wounds in the sides of the cone, which close up into narrow gullies lower down: they take the form of cirques surrounded by precipitous lava ramparts. The torrents which radiate fron the heart of the island have left an accumulation of pebbles on the sea shore and this has produced a discontinuous fringe of coastal plains. Access is difficult to the alluvial coast, carved out of the lava outflow, defended as it is by reefs.

The tropical oceanic climate varies according to exposure and altitude: the north-east half of the island, lashed by the full force of the monsoon, is better watered than the south-western part. Above 3,000 feet minimum temperatures fall below freezing point and the climate is similar to that of the temperate zone. The combination of these natural conditions results in division into several regions with different potentialities. The coastal plains and lower slopes are a typically tropical domain, where the coffee plantations ravaged by a parasite have been replaced by sugar-cane, vanilla and tobacco. As the height increases they give way to geraniums (used in perfumes), to the market-garden crops of the temperate region, and to vines grown on trellises. The sale of wine provides the major part of the income of small farmers in the cirques.

The population of Réunion is the result of gradual cross-breeding between European settlers, Negro slaves from Africa and Madagascar, Moslem workers recruited in India, and Chinese. A small white minority has remained racially pure and controls business and politics. This essentially rural population lives in wooden huts forming small mountain hamlets, or in villages along the roads of the coastal plain and the lower slopes.

There are some towns on the edge of the sea, in particular St Paul (29,000 inhabitants), St Pierre (28,000 inhabitants) and the capital St Denis (42,000 inhabitants). These have kept the appearance they had in the colonial epoch: a chessboard street pattern, houses with verandas at the far end of gardens shut off from the street by wooden fences.

About 330,000 inhabitants live on 970 square miles To support a density exceeding 340 per square mile, agriculture, which occupies only a third of the total land area, is the single resource. Side by side with some fifty major planters, each owning more than 1,000 acres, is a multitude of smallholders short of capital, farmers who share the produce of their farms with the landlord and farm labourers.

The larger and better part of the land is devoted to sugar-cane; sugar production has grown steadily, today fluctuating around 200,000 tons annually. It constitutes almost the whole of the island's exportable wealth and is controlled by some fifteen mills, the most powerful of which belongs to three very large French companies. Rum is produced as well as sugar. A one-crop system and over-population combined with a high birthrate have produced severe poverty and stagnation. One of the remedies proposed is large-scale emmigration to Madagascar but it is doubtful that this would alleviate the situation greatly.

# MAURITIUS

Although only some 150 miles to the north-east, Mauritius is quite different from Réunion. It is smaller (720 square miles), and also less broken up. The outflows of lava accumulated since the Cretaceous appear as a rounded central dome surmounted by scattered stumps seldom over 2,500 feet high. The general relief, consisting of gently sloping plateaus, is not pronounced but it is given variety by a whole series of caverns, waterfalls, lakes, peaks and coastal indentations.

Although they do not produce the wide range of climates observed on Réunion, differences in altitude and exposure influence the geographical distribution of rainfall and temperatures: the plateau which forms the highest region around Black River Mountain (2,710 feet) is also the coolest and most humid in the island.

Since 1810, when it was ceded by France, until 1968 it was a British Crown Colony. However, French culture and traditions have been faithfully preserved. In 1966 the population was of 768,692. About 67 per cent are of Indian descent (both Hindu and Moslem), 26 per cent of African or Eurafrican descent, 4 per cent Chinese, and 3 per cent European. The ethnic problem is aggravated by the high population density of about 1,000 per square mile.

The island's only major resource is the sugar-cane crop which, although efficiently produced, does not support such densities without a very low standard of living. Moreover, it is periodically badly damaged by hurricane; in 1960 Mauritius was hit by a devastating cyclone. More than 87 per cent of proprietors own less than 6 acres; together with farm labourers and farmers sharing the produce with their landlords, they form a sizable agricultural proletariat. Large properties (more than 100 acres), including factory domains exceeding 5,000 acres, make up 70 per cent of the area under cane. Even more than in Réunion, the concentration of landed property for the benefit of the factories ensures industrial capitalism's domination of the economy.

The export of 500,000 tons of sugar each year feeds all commercial activity, which is concentrated at the capital, Port Louis (with suburbs 113,000 inhabitants).

The island and certain dependencies, including Rodrigues, are administered by a Governor-General with a council of ministers and a Legislative Assembly of seventy members. Though the Government encourages foreign investment in new industries the rapidly expanding population has made it think in terms of large-scale organised emigration, perhaps to former British territories in East Africa. Although independence was attained in March 1968, most islanders know that the future of their country is extremely uncertain unless it is associated with other territories — economically, if not politically.

Great Britain still possesses a scattering of volcanic rocks and atolls in the Indian Ocean: Albatross, Aldabra and Amirantes. The Seychelles group together about a hundred granite islets which supply copra, cinnamon and guano: Mahé, the most important (not to be confused with the town of Mahé in India) possesses the port of Victoria.

MEDITERRANEAN ASIA
AND
THE MIDDLE EAST

# TURKEY

The rectangle representing the Turkish Republic on the map is as satisfying to the eye and the mind as the 'splendid hexagon' of France. Like the latter it has deep coastal indentations opening to the west, and plays the part of a continental shelf facing a maritime state — that of Greece — which possesses nearly all the interlying islands. Like France it has long continental frontiers which gave access to the great populations of history, and expose its weakest flank to the north-east and the north. Like France, again, it has formed contacts, both hostile and civilising, in the south-east, in this case with Iranian and Arab peoples.

But we must avoid the temptation to carry the comparison too far. Whereas France forms a bridge between the Mediterranean and the Atlantic, Turkey, on the one hand, constitutes a difficult, rugged passage between Europe and Asia, while on the other it forms, with the straits, the easiest route from Eastern Europe to the warm seas. Finally, while the geographical shape of France today is the outcome of slow historical agglomeration, that of modern Turkey is the result of distinct changes of fortune; it was formed by an ancient conquest, followed by an age-long shrinkage, and, finally, by the quite recent partition of the Ottoman Empire. The Turkish state of today, with a population of 28 million occupying an area of 294,502 square miles, contains less than half the total of the Turkish people. The founder of modern Turkey, Mustafa Kemal (known as Atatürk, or 'Father of the Turks') turned this radical reduction of Turkish territory into one of the principles of the rebirth of the State. Atatürk's reforms, carried out from 1923 (abolition of the Sultanate and proclamation of the Republic) to 1928 (adoption of the Latin alphabet), and after, effected a profound alteration in every aspect of the country, changing the Turkish people's ideas of its destiny, transforming political and social life, remodelling the territory and giving a fresh direction to the exploitation of resources.

## A LAND OF CONTRASTS

*Seaboards: the Anatolian 'horseshoe'.* The present-day territory of Turkey consists of a vast tableland, Anatolia, frayed out on the west towards the Aegean, surrounded in the north, and still more solidly in the south, by two mountain barriers — the Pontic arc and the Tauric arc — and rising sharply in the east to the Ararat ridge, or Armeno-Kurd massif, which connects it to the continental platform of Asia.

The wide maritime surroundings, the relief, and the rainfall they produce between them, divide Turkey into three quite distinct main zones: the 'horseshoe' of the Anatolian coasts in the west, the Armeno-Kurd insular shelf in the east and the steppe plateaus in the centre.

The Anatolian 'horseshoe' bordering the coasts of the Mediterranean, the Aegean, the Sea of Marmara and the Black Sea, forms a littoral strip almost entirely open to the sea, separated from the interior, and broken up throughout by mountain barriers; lying entirely within the zone of an annual rainfall of 19 inches — and even, in the case of its two eastern extremities, the Taurus in the south and the Pontic Forest in the north, in the 31-inch zone — it has presented favourable, if very diverse, conditions for human development.

*The Bosporus and the Dardanelles.* The west coast is particularly indented and characteristic. Its northwest buttress is breached by the 'Straits', which form a connection from the Black Sea (Karadeniz), through the Sea of Marmara, to the Mediterranean (Akdeniz or 'White Sea'), on a course that has varied up to a recent geological period. The lower course of the Sakarya, the attractive Lake of Sapanca (Sapanja), and the long, narrow Gulf of Izmit, running from the Sea of Marmara deep into the sombre, wooded Anatolian hills, mark the former outflow of the Black Sea. During the time this shelf was rising to a height of 150 feet above the present level of the sea, the breach of the Bosporus opened, 87 miles to the west; its width, which averages 1,650 yards, is reduced to 650 at certain points. The Black Sea, fed by the great Russian rivers, and subject to less evaporation than the Mediterranean, continually pours its less saline waters into the latter, producing a north-south surface current in the Bosporus, with an undercurrent running the other way; these differences in the temperature and salinity of the waters, varying according to the season, favour the existence of a great variety of fish. Exposed to the north wind, which often brings violent storms from the Black Sea, the area is cool, even in summer; but fashion is deserting it to some extent for the beaches of the Asiatic coast and the islands (Adalar) exposed to the south and so warm until later in the tourist season.

Istanbul stands on a triangular peninsula between the southern end of the Bosporus, the north coast of the Sea of Marmara and the deep indentation of a flooded valley, the Haliç, or Golden Horn. Like Rome the ancient site of this historic city is broken up by seven hills, but for centuries now the city has overflowed on to the north shore of the Golden Horn and along the neighbouring coasts; its maritime suburbs, served by ship transport, thus extended into two continents. Its situation is one of the most picturesque in the world, and to Napoleon its geographical position marked it out to be 'the seat of universal sovereignty'. Today, however, it has ceased to be even a capital.

At the western end of the Sea of Marmara lies the Strait of the Dardanelles (the ancient Hellespont), longer (nearly 49 miles), wider (an average of $2\frac{1}{2}$ miles) and more harsh in appearance than the Bosporus. Even since the Turks crossed the Strait at Canakkale, where it is only 1,390 yards wide — even before they had taken Istanbul — they have mounted a guard on the Dardanelles, and it has never been forced; in 1915 the British and French fleets were held up by drifting submarine mines, while on the hills of Anafarta (Gallipoli — Gelibolu — Peninsula) General Mustafa Kemal drove back the Anzacs. Turkey was confirmed in her rôle of guardian of the Straits by the Treaty of Lausanne (1923). The existence of this Turkish 'bolt' across her only access by sea to the Mediterranean explains Russia's age-long ambition to lay hands on the Straits or to force Turkey into an unequal alliance.

*The 'European' coast of the Aegean.* Between the mouth of the Dardanelles in the north and the latitude of the island of Rhodes the distance is only 154 miles in a straight line, but the actual length of the coastline is five times as great. Although the alluvia of the coastal rivers continue to silt up the gulfs, the coast is deeply indented and ramified into peninsulas; beyond it, innumerable islands and islets lie scattered, all of which, with the exception of Imroz (Imbros) and Bozcaada (Tenedos), are now outside Turkish territory. Geographically and historically, this coast is chiefly European in its associations. One has only to think of Troy (south of the mouth of the Dardanelles), Pergamos (now Bergama), Phocea (Foça), Clazomenae (round present-day Izmir, formerly Smyrna), Ephesus, Miletus, Halicarnassus (now Bodrum), and Cnidus, at the tip of the southernmost and best articulated of the promontories. The easy outlets to the sea, the mildness of the climate, the variety of resources (fruit crops, stock-breeding, fisheries, navigation), and the encircling mountains, have all favoured the development, apart from the nearby oriental satrapies, of a civilisation of cities looking towards the west.

The compartmentation of the terrain has preserved the native character and for a long while ensured the survival of districts and provinces corresponding to geographical realities. Mysia is rugged and massive in the north, but possesses a certain number of fertile rift basins and a more broken coastline in the south. Lydia presents a sharp contrast between its young mountains with their sharp relief and its many alluvial plains, fertile but formerly unhealthy; the coast is extremely indented, and two small rivers, the Gediz (the ancient Hermos) and the Menderes (the famous Meander), open a way into the interior and water the good lands of Aydin, Ödemiş and Alaşehir. Izmir, magnificently sheltered at the head of a very fine gulf, provides the local transport service of this prosperous littoral, but much of its traffic has now been attracted away to Istanbul.

Caria, though well defined, is limited in extent, cut off by a high massif; pine forests and scrubland are more in evidence here; this is where the southern arm of the 'horseshoe' opens. The general line of the coast runs henceforth from west to east, although broken by wide headlands (Lycia, coastal Cilicia) and vast gulfs (towards Pamphilia and rural Cilicia). The magnificent curved bar running out beyond Iskenderun (Alexandretta) affords the fleets one of the safest anchorages of the eastern Mediterranean, sheltered by the Amanus; but beyond these there are very few of the indentations and the islands so favourable to navigation and to local activities. Except during the winter rains, the climate is drier; trees are scarce on the limestone mountains, which are lofty and narrow, young in shape, and rise gradually higher to form the powerful barrier of the Taurus. Two coastal plains, however, have a more favourable soil: the smaller one, round Antalya (Adalia), has been compared to the Roman Campagna; the larger one, that of Çukorova in Cilicia, the 'hollow plain', a damp and torrid terrain, is watered by the Seyhan and the Ceyhan (two river names found in Central Asia as well); now reclaimed and drained, the soil is excellent for cotton-growing.

The Dolmabahce Mosque in Istanbul, once the historic city of Byzantium, the centre of Christendom.

It is here that the lines of communication connecting Anatolia with the Arabian steppe and the Levantine littoral force their way between the high mountains; the German-built railroad (formerly the Baghdad Railway) drags out its long ascents, with its bridges and tunnels, near the Gülek Pass and near the famous Cilician Gates, which lie at a height of nearly 6,500 feet.

*The narrow Black Sea coast.* The coastal outline of the northern arm of the 'horseshoe' reproduces the curve of the southern one; like the latter, it exhibits only minor indentations. Here, too, the folds run from west to east; a few gorges cut across them at right angles, with three considerable rivers, the Sakarya, the Kizilirmak and the Yeşilirmak. But although the fertile basins are relatively small, they support good crops of tobacco, flax and fruit trees (the north is the home of fruits), and the climate and living conditions are far less harsh than in the south. Owing to the prevalent north and west winds, rain is copious and falls in summer; the mountains are regularly wooded: this is the Pontic Forest, with tannin oaks, very large nut bushes covering thousands of acres, and timber trees.

*The centre of Turkey: an elevated tableland.* The Pontic Chain and the Taurus join the eastern ends of the 'horseshoe' almost imperceptibly to the formidable complex of the Armeno-Kurd mountains, which form a part of the great massif that rises higher still towards the east, and is succeeded, across the conventional frontiers, by the chains of Armenia, Azerbaijan and Iran.

The high peaks are all in the east, with the legendary pyramid of Ararat (16,945 feet) dominating the valley of the Araks and Russian Armenia. Farther south, lying on either side of Lake Van, the volcanic massifs of the Aladag and the Suphandag, the water tower of the Bingöl (the 'thousand lakes') and the Botan and Hakkari Hills form the typical habitat of the Kurd people. The massif falls away to the south, between the Tigris (Dicle) and the Euphrates (Firat), to join the Mesopotamian steppes by a series of terraces, some of them steep; it remains compact towards the west, as far as the Dersim (about 11,246 feet), and contains some of the highest and least accessible peaks.

The region, copiously watered, acts as a water tower, sometimes without an outlet (bitter waters of Lake Van); it provides the headwaters of the Araks, which flows into the Caspian, the Euphrates (Firat, with its two branches, Kara Su — 'black water' — and Murat) and the Tigris which reach the Persian Gulf via Syria and Iraq.

It is not surprising that this country should have sheltered tough communities, clinging fanatically to their independence, though it afforded them only a precarious existence. The heat of the summer allows the vegetation to make up for the long delay of the terrible winter; barley grows even beyond the 6,500-foot line, and the fine pasturages support millions of sheep and goats and are suitable for transhumance; the crops and orchards of a few fertile interior plains and the handicrafts of the large villages have provided the scanty population with an almost self-sufficient livelihood. There are only a few small towns — handicraft centres and citadels, but full of historical interest: Erzurum, Bitlis, Muş, Diyarbakir; the low

hovels of the villages, often built into the rock, lie one above another on the terraced slopes, their flat roofs giving access to the upper tiers; but in the summer tents are unfolded in the high pasturages, and the most active members of the population lead the life of the ancient warrior shepherds.

Lying to the west of the eastern shelf, the inner plateaus of Anatolia present a vivid contrast to the surrounding country; here, in a harsh climate, the steppe, sometimes more or less green but bereft of trees, alternates with the salt desert, grey and yellow, dotted with brackish lakes. Living conditions in general still resemble those of Central Asia; the Seljuks established a dominion here which they maintained long after the Ottomans had seized the western curve of the 'horseshoe'; their steppe capital, Konya, still bears witness to their civilisation, sterner and less ornate than that of the Ottomans. At the other end of the steppe, towards the north-east, present-day Turkey has built her new capital on top of the old citadel of Ankara, the object being to bring the heart

Turkey suffers from a serious shortage of water, though the position has been greatly improved by a vigorous programme of dam- and well-construction.
Here an early morning queue forms at a suburban well.

of the country nearer to its geometrical centre, thus ignoring the geographical void.

## 'TURKIFICATION' AND MODERNISATION

*The ancient ethnic mosaic.* Under the Ottoman Empire this land of contrasts sheltered the most disparate peoples. The Ottomans, coming from Central Asia, subdued them and submitted them to the rules of classic Islam; the Moslem community represented the State and the conquered groups constituted tolerated 'lateral groups'; their members were both protected and harassed, autonomous under their religious heads, but in an inferior social position. But the Armenians for example, were not excluded from any public office.

In the territory forming the Turkey of today these 'minorities' formed the majority, and sometimes the entire population of whole provinces: Greeks on the coasts of the Aegean and the Sea of Marmara, Armenians and Jacobites between the Tigris and the Euphrates, Assyrians in Hakkari. Large non-Turkish

A broad valley in Anatolia, the central plain of Turkey.

Moslem groups joined them: Lazes around Trabzon (Trebizond), Kurds in the mountain massifs of the east, besides various elements from outside, Jews from Spain in Istanbul, Circassians and other Caucassians and even Armenians fleeing from the Russians.

In the multi-national Ottoman Empire the question of 'Turkification' had never arisen, but spontaneous or forced migrations had brought about an extensive mingling of races; in order to build up the population of the only capital, Istanbul, a contribution from eighteen towns had been called upon, whence the name given to one of the quarters of the city, Aksaray, peopled by the inhabitants of that Anatolian town. In general, the Jewish and Christian 'minorities' flocked into the towns and villages, where they controlled trade and most crafts, together with the foreign 'colonies', which owing to the weakness of the Ottomans were constantly on the increase.

*The transfer of the capital.* During the second half of the nineteenth century, national feeling awoke. This movement gathered strength and led to the attempted reform of the Government by the 'Young Turks' (1908). But Turkish national feeling, inflamed by Turkism and the consciousness of danger from Russia, led to increasing hostility towards the minorities. This was no doubt stirred up by foreign powers. A huge massacre of Armenians took place from 1894 to 1895, and further killings followed during the First World War, repaid fiercely by the Armenians and Russians. Today, however, 60,000 Armenians live peacefully in Turkey, mostly in Istanbul.

The Kemal regime organised a systematic Turkish reconquest of the whole quadrilateral. Not only did it thwart Greek expansionism but the defeat of the Greek armies in Ionia (recapture of Izmir, September 1922) brought about the eviction of the Greek populations of Anatolia, exchanged by the Treaty of Lausanne (July 1923) for the Turks of the Kingdom of Greece, with the solitary exception of those living in Thrace.

The only Turkish exceptions were the inhabitants of Istanbul. While transferring the rank of capital from this city to Ankara, Mustafa Kemal left Istanbul its rôle as a commercial centre and point of contact, its mixed population and even its cosmopolitan nucleus at Pera, now Beyoglu. Except for a few picturesque details such as dress, and apart from the extension of modern quarters towards the north and some urban redevelopment designed to open up vistas or give better views of monuments, Istanbul has retained much of its former appearance.

The new, modern capital, Ankara (formerly Angora), built below and at the side of an old citadel and an austere Anatolian country town, forms a complete contrast to Istanbul.

Since the reforming spirit of Atatürk was not merely concerned with the elimination or isolation of non-Moslems, but with making Islam a private cult, the remodelling of the territory was equally concerned with Moslems of non-Turkish race and language, especially if they remained attached to traditional Islam. While the Lazes, already largely 'Turkified', presented no problem, these considerations explain the policy followed by Kemalism towards the Kurds, though they do not justify its excess. Militant Kurd nationalism obliged the Turks to face strong popular movements, which they repressed systematically. The Kurds were deported and driven out of western Anatolia and Rumelia, and replaced by Turks coming partly from the Balkans. Time has softened the expression of these popular movements without suppressing the underlying causes.

*Internal 'reconstruction', external claims.* The task of unification entailed the construction of a great system of public transport. Owing to limited resources, an initial choice had to be made between the development of the railroads and of the roads. The latter would ultimately have resulted in easier penetration into the regions of difficult approach. Atatürk, however, gave preference to the railroads, partly because a network existed in embryo, but chiefly because roads might entail ruinous imports of automobiles and petrol (gasoline), uncontrolled circulation of people and ideas and the formation of a proletariat of motorists. On the other hand, the railroad, which could be equipped and maintained largely with Turkish resources, would throw a network of disciplined officials over the whole territory and canalise the movements of foreigners.

The preference given by Atatürk to internal reconstruction over external enterprises was, however, a matter of expediency rather than principle; it did not prevent a vain attempt by Turkey, before 1925, to obtain the Vilayet of Mosul, partly peopled by Turks and Kurds, nor, after 1937, to claim the Syrian sanjak of Alexandretta. This territory was finally reunited to Turkey in 1939 as Hatay.

Atatürk's successors relaxed the rule of 'Anatolism' whenever they could. During the Second World War, at the time of the German invasion of Russia, 'Turkism' made great strides in right-wing circles, and a lively interest in the Turks of Central Asia was aroused. However, the Russian victory at Stalingrad (1942) put an end to these aspirations; in the summer of 1945 it was the turn of the Soviet radio at Tbilisi (Tiflis) and Yerevan to claim the return by Turkey of the Vilayets of Kars and Ardahan, which had been Russian from 1878 to 1918 and were represented as natural complements of the Soviet Socialist Republics of Georgia and Armenia; these claims helped to make Turkey side with the West in the cold war.

Turkey supported the Turkish minority in Cyprus (100,000 people, or one-fifth of the population) in resisting the plans for uniting the island to Greece, and in 1959 she obtained a compromise (independence of Cyprus, with local Turkish interests safeguarded). Between 1950 and 1960 the Democratic Party in Turkey retained the main institutions and structures of Kemalism, but Islam, though no longer the official religion, is regaining some of its state importance (evidenced in religious teaching, building of mosques and flourishing confraternities). Faced with growing discontent among some sections of opinion, stern measures (especially against the press) have brought accusations of reactionism, even totalitarianism. Revolution in May 1960, led by a coalition of the army and the intellectuals, seemed to foreshadow a return to Kemalism; but the elections of 1961 revealed divided opinions. A Government of National Unity was formed and a new constitution was approved by plebiscite, which appears to have achieved a degree of political stability.

## RESOURCES AND PROSPECTS

*Towards democratic liberalism.* Turkey possesses only average resources, but they are more varied than those of most eastern countries.

Agricultural production and stock-breeding are fairly favoured by the climate (abundant rainfall in the Anatolian periphery, warm, well-sheltered littoral plains); trees are relatively plentiful, except in the central steppe (15 per cent of the land is wooded). The tobacco from the shores of the Aegean, the Marmara and the Black Sea, the cotton of Cilicia and the cereals of the north-west supply a few industries and a considerable export trade; the dried figs and raisins of Ionia and the nuts of the Black Sea are less easily disposed of; the sugar-beet of Thrace, the olives of the Aegean and the trees of the Pontic Forest supply local demand for sugar, oil and timber. Stock-breeding is carried on in half the territory and permits a few exports, although its extensive character does not give it a

corresponding importance in the country's economy.

The subsoil, too, is valuable more for its variety than for any general wealth. Sources of energy come first in importance: there is oil in the south-east, at Raman Dag—though the deposit is small; on the coast of the Black Sea at Eregli Zonguldak lies the only coal basin of the Near East; there is a good deal of iron at Divrigi, unfortunately rather far from the coal; and some small deposits of copper (Maden-Ergani), sulphur (Keçiborlu) and mercury. Turkey's only mineral wealth of world importance is chromium, widely distributed over a number of places in the mountains of the west and south, but difficult to transport because it is so scattered and because contorted relief makes communications difficult.

'Western' modernisation of the Turkish economy began under the Ottoman Empire, mainly owing to the influence of the minorities and renegades; European traders, financiers and contractors played a leading part at the time of the decadence of the Empire, and had destroyed Turkey's economic independence

A young Turkish girl at the family loom in the troglodyte village of Ortahisar, where the dwellings are hewn out of soft, volcanic rock. Here, as in many parts of Turkey, unbetrothed girls wear their hair in long plaits until their wedding day.

by the end of the nineteenth century. Anxious to restore national independence, and basing their policy on the six-point programme of the 'People's Republican Party', the Kemalists decided in 1922 to eliminate businessmen and concessionary companies, and to seek economic self-sufficiency as a complement to political independence. In particular, with a view to the needs of national defence, they encouraged industrial development based on the utilisation of local raw materials and also of available manpower.

State control was really another basic principle but it constantly met official objections and private criticism. Attempts by the Agricultural Bank and the Business Bank to assist timid or badly equipped private enterprises were soon completed by direct State action. However, a reforestation plan failed.

When war broke out in 1939 the planned development of Turkish economy had not yet had time to bear fruit. Though she signed a Tripartite Treaty with Britain and France, Turkey tried to maintain her commercial relations and to profit by the opportunities for equipping herself offered by the rival belligerents (airfields and a basic trunk-road system). But it was impossible to avoid financial burden on the State and a rise in prices. State control lost favour. The People's Republican Party, which was still in power, allotted a larger share to private enterprise in 1945, and accepted economic assistance from America in 1947, with the obligatory supervision and publicity this entailed. It welcomed American experts and solicited the assistance of the Import-Export Bank and that of the Bank for International Reconstruction and Development (B.I.R.D.). Closely associated with American strategy, Turkey had the benefit of considerable assistance in its equipment, both military and general, and, entirely deserting Atatürk's ideas on the subject, it put in hand the construction of a road system, at the same time improving certain sections of the railroads (electrification of the lines round Istanbul).

When, after the elections of May 1950, the Democratic Party came to power, it relied heavily on American aid to provide much-needed development of the country's basic equipment. Roads, airfields and ports were built. The Government tried to attract foreign investment, to encourage evolution towards economic liberalism; and, presenting itself as the Party of the 42,000 tractors, it launched a programme of agricultural modernisation aimed largely at increasing cereal production. But this plan, over-ambitious and under-organised, and often hampered by partisan interests, has brought impoverished soils, lower yields and depopulation of rural areas. Slums, built overnight, surround many towns (a thirds of Ankara's population lives like this). The growing population, under-employment, the national debt and the adverse trade balance all present formidable problems.

*Achievements and difficulties.* The Government formed under the new constitution of 1961 grappled realistically with these problems, and in 1963 inaugurated Turkey's first coherent economic plan. This 'new deal', calling for a major onslaught on economic planning and organisation, and aiming, above all else, at the country's industrialisation, will probably cause considerable immediate hardship. Substantial aid for this programme is being sought from Europe. Turkey is an associate member of the European Economic Community.

The American alliance, and Turkey's inclusion in the Western strategic and political system, considered necessary for the protection of her frontiers as well as for economic advance, have greatly modified the character of the country's national life.

As far as external affairs are concerned, Turkey has accepted the rôle of champion of the Anglo-American policy of defence in the Near East, which was given a concrete form by the Baghdad Pact of 1955 concluded with Iraq and soon extended to Great Britain, Iran and Pakistan; her policy is still based on this diplomatic instrument, but the attitude adopted by Iraq since 1958, in which extreme left-wing movements made themselves felt, coupled with claims on the part of the Kurds, induced the Turkish Government to modify its contacts with the Arab world.

The resurgence of the Cyprus question in 1963 exacerbated relations between Greece and Turkey. Much economic and technical assistance is received from the U.S.A., and some of late from the U.S.S.R.

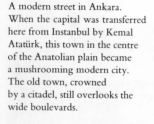

A modern street in Ankara. When the capital was transferred here from Instanbul by Kemal Atatürk, this town in the centre of the Anatolian plain became a mushrooming modern city. The old town, crowned by a citadel, still overlooks the wide boulevards.

# ISRAEL

A visionary, Theodore Herzl (1860-1904), stirred to pity by the vicissitudes of the Jews in Europe, gave concrete form to the aspirations that linked them to Palestine by founding the World Zionist Organisation, with the object of 'creating an asylum in Palestine for the Jewish people, guaranteed by Civil Law'. From the end of the nineteenth century onwards, the Jews began repeopling Palestine, which, occupied for nearly twenty centuries by Romans, Byzantines, Arabs, Crusaders, Egyptians and Turks, had in part become rather like a desert peopled by nomads.

Towards the end of the First World War the collapse of the Ottoman Empire enabled Great Britain to proclaim in the Balfour Declaration (November 1917) her intention of promoting the establishment of a national home for the Jewish people in Palestine. The British mandate for Palestine, under the aegis of the League of Nations, accelerated the return of the Jews and the rebirth of their country in the midst of the combined difficulties of Hitler's persecution and the conflicting interests of the British and the Arabs. In November 1947 the United Nations recommended the creation of a Jewish State in Palestine. But the Jews still had to undergo the ordeal of war against the combined armies of Egypt, Syria, Lebanon, Transjordan and Iraq, before their final victory and the creation of the State of Israel, solemnly proclaimed in May 1948.

## THE LAND OF THE BIBLE

*Diversity within a small area.* Israel is situated on the western edge of the continent of Asia, on the north-west border of the Arabian peninsula, on the east coast of the Mediterranean. It is a small country, whose total area of 8,048 square miles is about equal to that of Wales, or a little over that of Massachusetts; it stretches from north to south over a length of 265 miles; its width from east to west varies from 71 miles in the south to 6½ miles in the littoral plain of the centre. Its frontiers, fixed by the armistice agreements of 1949, have preserved the territorial division then prevailing. In relation to the total area of the country the frontiers are extraordinarily long: 590 miles of land frontiers and 159 miles of maritime ones. Its neighbours are Lebanon to the north, Syria to the north-east, Jordan to the east, Egypt to the south and the south-east. Dovetailed into the very heart of professedly hostile Moslem countries and alongside the half-Moslem half-Christian Lebanon, Israel also embodies the presence of the West in this exceptional meeting-place of continents, peoples and ideas.

It is a country in which geography and history appear inseparable. Every region, every landscape recalls some moment of the Biblical past, and the attraction of the country to many lies in the ancient presence of this spirit.

The geology of the country is of calcareous strata intermixed with marl formations; their upthrust has produced two chains of plateaus, separated by a deep, narrow rift valley. There are three very distinct geographical units: the central region of plateaus and mountains, the coastal plain and the Jordan depression.

The region of central mountains and plateaus, now mostly included in Jordan, comprises the hills of Samaria, Ephraim and Judea. The central plateaus rise to an average height of 2,300 feet over a width of about thirty miles; dry and barren, they are intersected by a few narrow valleys. In the south, the steep massif of Hebron (3,323 feet) is bordered on the west by the impressive empty stretches of the Judean hills, in which Jerusalem stands, divided today between Israel and Jordan. Farther north, Galilee forms a transitional region with the outliers of the mountains of Lebanon, a hilly region rising gradually from west to east, to culminate at 3,962 feet in Mount Meron, near Safad in Upper Galilee. In the mountainous regions the principal valleys are those of Lake Hula, well-known for its marshland, now drained; of Zebulum, which includes the industrial region of Haifa; and of Yisreel (plain of Esdraelon, 'Haemek' in Hebrew, watered by the Qishon), round the

In 1947 the United Nations recommended the creation of a Jewish State in Palestine. Jews from 74 countries make up its population, many of them professional men turned labourers in order to help build up the new Promised Land. This quarry worker was once a schoolteacher.

urban centre of Afula. The Plain of Esdraelon is bordered on the south by Mount Carmel, of no great height (1,790 feet) but with a rocky spur running out into the sea to form the roadstead of Haifa.

The coastal plain extends from Mount Carmel to the Egyptian frontier, and includes the plains of Hefer, Sharon and Shephelah. It is the traditional region of the country's agricultural wealth, where wells are easy to dig: olive gardens and citrus fruit plantations lie alongside the cornfields and the meadows reserved for livestock. Tel Aviv/Jaffa, on the coast, the most important town of the state, with a population of 393,000, is surrounded by the secondary centres of Hadera, Natanya, Petah Tiqva, Ramat Gan, Ramle, Lydda and Rehovet—all in process of rapid development. The coastal plain is succeeded in the south by the Negev desert, between longitude 30°30′ and Eilat, on the Gulf of Aqaba. This vast triangle, which occupies half the total area of Israel, has a subtropical climate and desert landscape. Structurally, the Negev is similar to the northern part of Israel: mountains in the centre (Mount Ramon, 3,396 feet), coastal plain, and the depression of Wadi Araba. Two thousand years ago this desert was largely populated; the pioneers of today have started to reclaim it, in order to make it the garden of the new Israel.

The total length of the River Jordan is 157 miles, of which 73 miles lie within the territory of Israel, where it forms three lakes: Lake Hula (5½ square miles; 229 feet above sea level); Lake Tiberias (102 square miles; 695 feet below sea level) and the Dead Sea (652 square miles; 1,286 feet below sea level), forming the deepest land depression in the world. The Ghor—or depression of the Jordan—runs from north to south through a mountainous, wild landscape.

The extraordinary variety of the scenery, ranging from the attractive hills of Galilee to the apocalyptic vistas of the Dead Sea, and from the eternal snows of Mount Hermon to the palms and banana-trees of the south, is matched by an uncommon diversity of climate. The land between 20° and 33°30′ N. is in a subtropical zone. But the character of its climate is complicated by the ceaseless battle waged in the mountains, the plains and the depressions of the region between the winds of the Mediterranean and those of the desert. A meeting-point of continents and climates, between the Mediterranean and the Arabian desert, Asia Minor and Africa, Israel is also the meeting-place of an extraordinarily rich flora and fauna, mostly Mediterranean and subtropical, but of desert character in the south and tropical near the Dead Sea.

## THE RISE OF ISRAEL

Established in 1948, the Republic of Israel is a democracy whose legislative body is a parliament elected by universal suffrage and whose government is headed by a Prime Minister. The growth of the nation—for which everything had to be provided, everything created, the land itself as well as the agriculturist and the agriculture, the worker as well as his craft or his industry—is maintained by the Jewish Agency, a product of the World Zionist Organisation, which assembles resources favourable to the national renascence in the Jewish communities of the Diaspora.

The new Israel is compounded of the blood of all the nations of the earth. The vast majority of its population of 2,430,000 is composed of Jews, from seventy-four countries of the world. Escaped from the trials of exile, Jews at every stage of historical development have joined together to found the new state: Yemenites with their patriarchal customs, Africans like contemporaries of Christ, Poles out of the Middle Ages and Americans of the atomic era; here, every human type is to be found, including Negroes and Indians, and every stage of cultural evolution. The non-Jewish communities are in the minority; they comprise 190,000 Moslems, 56,000 Christians and 27,000 Druses. On the religious side there is a similar profusion of churches, sects and tendencies: Judaism, which is the religion of the majority (the Sabbath and the feasts of the Synagogue are kept as

Wadi Timna, in the Negev Desert, near King Solomon's Mines. Until recently the Negev was an entirely desert region of sand and eroded rocks such as these; but, as all over Israel, a spectacular land reclamation and development programme is now under way.

holidays), restored to life in freedom after two thousand years of development within the closed compass of the ghettoes, is tending to break its traditional bounds; hence a profound religious crisis, a multiplicity of trends and an exaggeration of extremist movements. Israel witnessed the death of Christ and the birth of the Christian Church, and in consequence every Church is represented there, and probably every Christian sect—Catholic, Orthodox, Maronite, Armenian, Coptic, Ethiopian, to say nothing of the multitude of Protestant sects. These Christians keep vigilant watch over the Holy Places, which, as it happens, are situated chiefly in Jordan.

Chief among demographic problems is the necessity of admitting immigrants from all quarters of the globe and integrating them into their new way of life, mostly by encouraging them to work on the land. Between 1948 and 1962 more than a million immigrants had broken with the habits of former days of exile in order to co-operate in the work of bringing the Promised Land to life again.

The Hebrew tongue itself, reborn after being a dead language for over two thousand years, is the national tongue of the new Israel, and the most powerful factor in uniting the nation. This extraordinary rebirth of the language of the Bible is accompanied at the University of Jerusalem by a renewal of biblical studies (encouraged by the discovery of the Dead Sea scrolls).

The resurrection of the people and the language has brought about a profound revolution in the geography of Israel. In his fight against the aridity of the sand and the barrenness of the rocks, man is transforming the centuries-old desert landscape. The area under cultivation has risen from 487,275 acres in 1948 to 1,058,650 acres in 1961. Twenty-eight towns of more than 11,000 inhabitants have been built at a feverish pace, together with 800 rural localities; other improvements include the afforestation of the hills, where more than 40 million trees have been planted in the last few years. The harnessing of the waters, which enables channels to be directed to every point of the territory where the immigrants wish to settle, has been achieved by conrol of all drinking water and of waste water for use in irrigating the land, and by draining the marshes of Hula. Plans have also been made for harnessing the flow of the Jordan and of various torrents and underground sources of water to ensure the irrigation of 741,000 acres of land still desert today; a long-term scheme for a canal connecting the Mediterranean to the Lake of Tiberias is directed at harnessing the water of the Jordan and creating plant with an annual production of hydroelectric energy amounting to 594 million kWh. These achievements and projects, born of the courage and faith of new men, aim at maintaining the existence of a rural population of a million, living on 1,482,000 acres of irrigated land under intensive cultivation, for a total population that might amount to 4 million within the present frontiers. In the reconquest of the deserts the collective settlement (*kibbutzim*) and the co-operative settlements (*moshavim*) play a leading ans increasingly important part.

The industry of Israel, like everything else in the country, is itself a modern creation. The co-operation of the State, of trade unions grouped in the powerful Histadrut, and of private enterprise, has made it possible to set up and develop manufactures and factories: textiles, leather, plastics, chemical products, food products, tobacco, building materials, diamond-cutting, electrical industries and automobiles. Exports in this domain rose from 29.7 million dollars in 1949 to 240 million in 1961. Oil discovered in the Negev will help to bring economic independence.

PROBLEMS AND THE FUTURE. Israel embodies the triple paradox of the rebirth of a people, a language and a country. It constitutes, in every domain, a creation *ex nihilo*, or nearly so, which thus assumes an experimental character. Natural difficulties are increased by the hostility of the neighbouring Arab states, which force Israel into a defensive effort that may well compromise her present growth. The creative work of the pioneers, aided by the Jews of the whole world, is, in spite of every difficulty, one of the greatest truimphs of human geography: at the crossroads of Christendom and Islam, the West and Asia, Israel illustrates the power and virtue of hope.

Pioneers removed stones, built terraces against erosion, drained swamps, wiped out malaria, planted forests and built reservoirs in the drive to rebuild their national land.

# SYRIA

Situated between the Mediterranean and Mesopotamia, of which it comprises a large part, covering 72,234 square miles, Syria was for long a state which the Great Empires fought over. Of mixed character, but desert for the most part, it is covered with the sites of decisive battles, and with the traces, both in the heart of the towns and the desert solitudes, of the civilisations that have succeeded each other for four thousand years, as in the Tells of the Jazira; the ruins of dead cities (Mari, Doura Europus, Ugarit, Apamea, Palmyra), of temples and basilicas (Baetocecea, St Simeon), of fortresses (castles of Marqab and Sahyoun and the Krak of the Knights Hospitallers) and the holy places of Islam. After the 1914-1918 war, the period of the French Mandate (1930-1914) witnessed the beginning of a rapid material advance, and prepared Syria for its part as a modern nation. It was given a democratic constitution, elections for the

President of the Republic being held every five years, and a single-chamber Parliament sitting at Damascus; it obtained complete emancipation in 1945. But in the struggle to achieve political equilibrium in the face of perpetual disturbances due to the rivalries of parties and factions, several military dictators came to power. In February 1958, the Syrian Parliament ratified the provisional Constitution associating Egypt and Syria in a single State to be known as the United Arab Republic (U.A.R.), but following a revolution in September 1961 Syria seceded from this union.

*Western Syria.* The vital regions of Syria, forming part of the fertile crescent that is more or less bounded by the 7-8 inch isohyet, lie east of the mountain chains of the Levantine Mediterranean, and south of those of eastern Turkey. Syria is Mediterranean by reason of its climatic conditions—winter rains—that lessen the drought of the interior. It is Mediterranean, too, through much of its past and through the links with the West from which it has drawn the elements of modernisation. It possesses, nevertheless, only a narrow seaboard, 100 miles in length, overlooked by the massive dome of the Jabal Ansariyeh (or Ansariya). On either side of this barrier is a passageway; in the south, towards the Lebanon, a corridor littered with basalt rocks, through which passes the road from Homs to Tripoli (in Lebanese territory); in the north, towards Turkey, the valley of Nahr el Kebir, which gives Aleppo access to the sea. Latakia, a growing city destined to supplant Beirut in Syrian trade, and even now attracting almost the whole of northern Syria's exports, is the only modern port on this coast, alongside the old harbours of Djéblé, of Baniyas (reanimated today by the tankers at the outlet of the pipeline from Kirkuk) and of the island of Rowad, opposite Tartus. The Jabal itself has little economic value. It is the refuge of the Alawites (still sometimes called Nosairis) and the Ismailis, both dissenters from Islam. Mostly poor, they grow mulberries, tobacco and vines on moorland slopes and scrubland, among the vestiges of Frankish fortresses.

The eastern face of the Jabal Ansariyeh drops down to the tectonic rift of the Orontes (El Aassi) which prolongs the fracture of the Palestinian Ghor and the Lebanese Bekaa. The river, which is relatively narrow, winds its way among fine farms and villages—sometimes large built-up areas with houses made of dried brick, and shaped like sugar-loaves—to be lost for a time in the marshes of the Ghab, where it is overlooked by the boat-like huts of the silurus-fishers. Beside the banks of the river lie two towns: the first, Homs (Emesus), seems dark and dull beside its lake, and is tending to become industrialised; the second, Hama (Epiphania), has mostly white buildings, seems dominated by its enormous cemeteries and its norias, and is famous throughout the country for its strict religious observance.

South of the Ansariyeh the Lebanon intervenes between Syria and the sea. The frontier follows the crests of the Anti-Lebanon and the Hermon, leaving Syria with only the harsh rearward slopes. But rainwater seeping into the calcareous rocks reappears in the form of springs of shallow pools at the foot, giving rise to oasis towns. Damascus, in the midst of its green Ghouta, an oasis of multiple crops, owes its

A Syrian village near Aleppo, in which the dwellings are built in a conical shape hardly altered since medieval times. Built of coarse brick, they are covered with whitewash.

existence to the Barada, which, like its neighbour the Nahr el Aouaj, is lost eventually in the salt depressions of the interior. Still farther south lie areas of black basaltic soils. Above the plains of the Djolan and the Hauran the eruptive dome of the Jebel Druz bears volcanoes still recent in shape (Tell Gheine, 5,904 feet). Volcanic activity did not cease until the Quaternary. Like the persistent earthquakes, it betrays the tectonic instability of the central rift valley, of which Syria's territory occupies the eastern edge, along a line of politically tense contact with Israel.

The Hauran formed one of the granaries of the Roman Empire. From 1860 onwards, the Jabal now known by their name was settled by a great number of Lebanese Druses. Here and there, houses built of lava stand beside the remains of Roman cities (Suweida, Chaqqa, Chabba; Bosra in the Hauran, famous for its citadel and its theatre). The restored reservoirs (*birket*) form a precious water supply, and the fallen monuments provide building materials A few Circassian groups, established in the Djolan, add to the ethnic peculiarity of this region, which is even visited in summer by nomads with their black tents.

*Mesopotamian Syria.* North Syria has a quite different appearance, heralding the monotony of the desert. The discontinuous fertile belt runs eastwards to the foot of the Turkish mountains. From their high ridges, copiously watered, streams run down to throw strips of verdure across the steppe. The Kuweik, after supplying Aleppo, disappears in the marshes of the Matk. Less than 125 miles from the sea the Euphrates, a majestic monster, instead of attempting to cross the mountains that bar its way to the Mediterranean, turns away to the depressions that lead it to the Persian Gulf. From a flow of 735 cubic metres it reaches a maximum, in March and April, of 5,000 cubic metres, and covers the whole extent of its main bed with silt. If a too early melting of the Anatolian snow happens to coincide with a fresh spell of rain, its floods may be formidable.

From the Balikh to the deep, picturesque trough of the Tigris stretches one of the most beautiful regions of Mesopotamia, the Jazira. The water table does not lie very deep, and wells can be dug in great numbers. The agricultural promise of this Syrian borderland has attracted many different tribes: Bedouins (Tays, Jeburs) now semi-sedentary and, more recently, Kurds, Assyro-Chaldeans, and Armenians. It is easily exploited by the speculators of the big cities, landgrabbers taking advantage of the greed of the tribal Sheiks, owners of hydraulic pumps and machines. Except for Hassetché, the administrative capital, the urban centres are aligned near the Turkish frontier and the Aleppo-Baghdad railroad. Qamichliya, a new and attractive town, is the liveliest centre of this promising region, still only thinly peopled but slowly expanding.

*The desert.* Elsewhere lies the Hamad, a steppe rather than an actual desert, decked in the spring with a multi-coloured carpet of flowers—grasses, anemones, asphodels, umbellifers, devoured later by the burning heat of the summer. Here the Bedouin is king: there are 150,000 to 200,000 nomads. The camps of black tents, following the itineraries determined by the few watering-places, or wandering in quest of fresh pastures, move about regardless of frontiers.

*The towns.* Without her two largest towns, Damascus (the capital) and Aleppo, which between them contain nearly a quarter of the population, Syria would be no more than an artificial assembly of disparate regional units, more or less clearly defined, on the periphery of the Syro-Arabian tableland. The geographical position of these two cities in relation to the sea is analogous; each of them commands a rail junction of great importance; both of them, too, jealous of each other's importance and to some extent rivals, are rapidly expanding in trade and industry. Damascus (population 475,399), the second Holy Place of Islam, is proud of her Mosque of the Omayyads, in the heart of the old city, and of her young university and new residential quarters—models of contemporary urban development—rising from the right bank of the Barada to the slopes of the Jabal Qasyun, from which the whole of the great Ghouta can be seen. Her prestige in the past gives her incontestable political supremacy. Aleppo (population, 466,026) is less favoured than Damascus by her

immediate surroundings, and destitute of gardens, but gains more through the increasing economic value of northern Syria, which lies within her sphere of influence. As a caravan centre ever since the dawn of history, she, too, has her monuments—her tall citadel, her great mosque, the Firdaus, and her suks (markets), the finest in the East. The cotton industry is expanding and more mills are going up. The construction of an outlet to the Mediterranean will establish her commercial importance.

Working the salt resouces at Lake Djerond, near Aleppo in the Syrian desert.

## THE SYRIAN ECONOMY

*Contemporary economic progress.* Agriculture occupies by far the largest place in the Syrian economy. Nowhere in the Middle East is a greater average area utilised per head of the population (about 2½ acres). Syria is able not only to feed herself but even to export foodstuffs. The area under cultivation is, however, still small compared with the potential acreage, and the yields, as in the whole of the Middle East, are below the general average. The necessary improvement in the people's standard of living, and the demographic pressure foreshadowed by a high birthrate (in some places up to 40 per thousand) and a rapid reduction in the deathrate (due to hygiene and antibiotics) call for a massive increase in food supplies.

The extension of cultivated areas has certainly been considerable during the last thirty years. Astonishing progress has been made in the large expanses won for cereal monoculture by mechanisation, spectacular results obtained with private capital. Attention is constantly drawn to the poverty and incapacity of the peasant of the eastern plains, eternally victimised, once by his rulers and now by the rapacity of rich townsmen, to whom he is bound by debts subject to high rates of interest. The abandonment of the ancient community system of joint estates, entailing a periodic redistribution of the land, has resulted in the crumbling of these estates and their seizure by big buyers who are not interested in making improvements. Today estates of more than 25 acres represent more than 85 per cent of the total cultivated area, and those of more than 125 acres 52 per cent. Although small properties are relatively numerous in the south and the region of Damascus, they are very few in number around Aleppo, and almost nonexistent in Jazira and the Orontes region, where Hama offers the most striking example of concentration of the land in a few hands (86 out of 114 villages in the hands of four owners). The mountain-dwellers are less victimised, for they look for protection to chiefs quick to use their guns. A very inadequate attempt was made at agrarian reform under the Chikakly Government, limiting the extent of domains to 123 acres; but it came to nothing, and benefited only a few speculators. At the end of 1958 the Government of the U.A.R. promulgated fresh laws, which led to unrest and contributed to the break between Syria and Egypt.

It is by an extension of irrigated territories, in particular, that Syria hopes to increase her agricultural production. Every brilliant period of her history is remembered for great hydraulic works, the destruction or abandonment of which does more to explain the contraction of the fertile belt than the hardly tenable theory of a very pronounced deterioration of the climate. Irrigation is even at present almost entirely dependent on traditional techniques: ingenious but rudimentary elevating machines (noria, nasba), small dams and gravity leats, and foggaras (kanayet); but the use of motor pumps is increasing. The French mandate period saw the construction of the reservoir-dam of the Lake of Homs. Since 1952 the canal of the Tell Maghass has been watering 20,000 acres on the left bank of the khabur. Drainage works have been started on the Ghab. The principal project has reached only the planning stage so far; it envisages systematic harnessing of the flow of the Euphrates and the Khabur, and conversion of the marshes of the Madk and the Rudj.

Since the Second World War Syria has derived large revenues from industrial crops. Sugar-beet comes from the Hom region, where a refinery has been at work since 1948, and new prospects have opened with the sudden extension of cotton cultivation. Cotton is a hazardous crop, closely linked to the fluctuations of the international market, and often affected by the cruelty of the climate, but it was stimulated by the coincidence of suddenly increased demand with unhoped-for harvests, and has spread over immense areas (the Orontes, Aleppo and the Euphrates regions), finding its way into the rotations. This has made Syria the second producer of the East, next to Egypt, and one of the principal suppliers of France.

Sheep and goats are the most important domestic animals in the Syrian economy. Camels are used largely for transport though the milk is also drunk.

A *young and enterprising industry*. If they could be modernised, agriculture and stock-breeding would afford Syria a degree of prosperity for which all its neighbours would envy it. It is on these two basic sources of wealth that a young and enterprising industry is being founded, centred on the principal towns. The cotton industry takes first place, with excellent equipment and rapid vertical integration. Food industries come next—oil-works, soap factories, tanneries. Handicrafts, although on the decline, are still lively; they include almost the whole of the woollen manufacture. The suks (markets) of Damascus and Aleppo still have articles of quality to offer: hand-worked leather and metal, silks, chests and old-style furniture. The inventory of subsoil resources is far from being completed: no coal, only lignite (Damascus and Aleppo regions, southern Syria); deposits of bitumen and asphalt in the province of Latakia and the Jabal Bishri; a few metalliferous deposits—iron, copper, chromium, lead, manganese—neglected at the moment. It is not without bitterness that the Syrians, waiting for the 'liquid gold' to gush from their own soil, see the pipelines of the Iraq Petroleum Company and Aramco crossing their territory. The last word has not been said on the subject, however, and the presence of hydrocarbon near Latakia and in Jazira is considered a favourable sign.

*Insufficient means of transport*. The present economic advance is hampered by insufficient means of transport. The rail system, left undeveloped since the war, is not adapted to current needs. There is only one passenger express line: Tripoli - Aleppo, via Homs and Hama. The others, with worn-out equipment and endless mileages, have only a small capacity. The line connecting Aleppo with Qamichliya and Kotchak, a branch — in part Turkish — of the old Berlin-Baghdad Railway, laboriously transports some of the products of northern Jazira. The Hijaz rail line, from Damascus to Medina, is being reconstructed jointly by Syria, Jordan and Saudi Arabia. The planned opening of a line from Latakia to Jazira via Aleppo would ensure and regularise the traffic of Aleppo and that of the Euphrates region. Traffic by road is far greater than by rail, but except for a few tarred highways connecting the larger towns, most of the territory is traversed by rough tracks used by the heavily loaded motorbuses (*bousta*), heirs of the caravans. A modern highway is under construction between the Lebanon border and north and east Syria. Internal air services are regular and increasing use has been made of this form of transport in recent years.

Issuing from the Ottoman Middle Ages, Syria has plunged into the modern revolution. The old social structure, incompatible with this renovation, is breaking almost automatically with the advent of a moneyed middle class educated on Western lines, whose example tempts the feudal population to the conquest of quick, high profits. Meanwhile, foreign problems are of the greatest urgency. In the imbroglio of international politics, Syria's exceedingly heterogenerous elements make it dangerously weak. Uneasy, hostile to the influences and enterprises of the West, it is endeavouring to find support elsewhere. Because of the enthusiasm of the mass of the people and the tacit anxiety of the minorities and of some leading factions, Syria today favours unity of the Arab world.

# THE LEBANON

The Lebanon is a mountain land running down into the sea. This fact has contributed to its love of independence, its character as a refuge, fostering a spirit of tolerance, and the precariousness of its resources, compensated by the ingeniousness and commercial sense of its sons, scattered all over the world. On the other hand, the position of the Lebanon on the Mediterranean, and the existence of a large Christian nucleus in Mount Lebanon itself have made of it an intermediary between the East and the West. Lebanon's importance in the world thus appears to be out of all proportion to the area of its territory (3,400 square miles) and its population of 1,626,000.

## A MOUNTAIN OF MANY CLIMATES

The Lebanon coast, stretching from north-north-east to south-south-west, and less than 125 miles long, is remarkably uniform, though a few promontories, creeks and islets provide shelters which early encouraged the seafaring vocation of the Phoenicians. Though narrow in places, the littoral leaves room for a main highway. Immediately behind this rises a mountain wall, even straighter in direction, the crest of which, at a distance of about twenty miles from the sea, rises to a height of 10,000 feet. Terminated in the north by the wide pass of the Nahr el Kebir (frontier with Syria), along which, in summer, the Arabs sometimes carry their tents as far as the sea, the mountain drops towards the south, turning into the Hills of Galilee beyond the frontiers of Israel. This massif is Mount Lebanon, the 'White Mountain', crowned with snow for much of the year. On its flanks, climate and ways of life are stepped into widely differing zones.

Terraced cultivation in the mountains on the Beirut-Tripoli road. The price of arable land in the Lebanon is among the highest in the world. However, projects for increasing agricultural output are under way and harvests are improving.

The littoral (Canaan of old), has only one large town, Beirut (population, 500,000), now with a greatly modernised port, whose magnificent airport, built on flattened dunes, is one of the busiest in the East. But it has many small towns and important villages that were formerly famous harbours (Tyre, now Sur; Sidon, now Saida; Byblos, now Jbail; and Tripoli) and agricultural and handicraft centres, like Kaferchima, Choueifat, Juniya and Batrun, which with their olives, oranges, vines, and soap factories afford a livelihood for a very dense population on this narrow strip of land.

The valleys, very deep and narrow at their outlets, offer no easy access to the interior; but the roads winding up over the slopes serve human settlements on the stepped terraces and ridges, which are almost as densely peopled as those on the coast. Half-way up, between 650 and 4,000 feet, the intermediate zone of the Wossout, which from the coast looks like a scattering of big villages, forms the most characteristic part of the Lebanon. The varied structure of the mountain, built of limestones, dolomites, sandstones and marls, and scarred with fractures, has encouraged the particularism of the historical cantons, often accentuated by the diversity of the ruling religious communities. The urban centres here are proud cities whose horizon, narrowed at home by stubborn inter-clan quarrels, extends over the whole world through their emigrants. These emigrants send back enough money to double the meagre local resources, and their ideas tend to disturb traditional social life. The profits from the summer season and, more recently, from winter sports, have the same results. According to the nature and degree of these influences, and in spite of a common Lebanese stamp, these little cities differ enormously from one another: Mukhtara is Druse and traditional; Jezzine and Bikfaya are Christian and harmoniously balanced; Bhamdun and Aley are typical summer resorts; and there are a hundred others, no less individual.

Higher still, in the Jurd, the mountain grows rugged; up to about 6,500 feet the valleys are still inhabited and cultivated and, besides occasional wooded stretches (the famous cedars of Kadisha and Baruk), there are Alpine meadows that sustain a frugal pastoral community.

Beyond this, Mount Lebanon falls sheer, on the east, to the plains of Beka'a (formerly Coele-Syria, 'Hollow Syria'), which is itself high, at an altitude of about 3,250 feet over a width of some twelve miles; a second mountain barrier, parallel to Mount Lebanon, but from 1,300 to 1,650 feet lower, is formed by the Anti-Lebanon and in the south by majestic, wooded Mount Hermon, the crest of which marks the frontier with Syria.

Some cantons of this hinterland are much like Mount Lebanon in character: Hermel in the north, which is Shiite, tribal and harsh, and rises from the delightful valley of Zahle (Greek Catholic); and, in the south, the districts of Rashaya and Hasbaya (mixed in religion, mostly Druse and Orthodox Greek). But Beka'a proper, round Baalbek, resembles the Syrian countryside in its physical aspect and its population (chiefly Moslem). Indeed its physical geography is inseparable from that of Syria, within whose natural boundaries it appears to be situated.

## AN 'ISLAMO-CHRISTIAN' STATE

Mount Lebanon forms the nucleus of a region populated by Druses and Maronites, whose chief centres are Kadisha, Kesruan, Chouf and Jezzine. Surrounding this area are regions less distinctly characterised and with more mixed populations: Moslem on the north and south of the mountain; elsewhere the religiously composite towns and plains of Beirut, Tripoli, Saida and Beka'a.

The mountain has for centuries served as an asylum for nonconformists of all religions. In modern times, the Lebanon increased its ties with Europe and asserted its independence of the Mamelukes, and later of the Ottomans, and after 1861 enjoyed the status of an autonomous province. The balance between the different communities, instinctive to begin with, thus became statutory. Order was maintained and, under a military Governor and an elected Council of Ministers, the Lebanon has enjoyed peace and relative prosperity.

The 'air of freedom', which was characteristic of the mountain, was for some time extended to the neighbouring areas. These were united to the traditional Lebanon in 1920 to form Greater Lebanon, which in 1926 became the Lebanese Republic, and was placed until 1943 under French Mandate. The 'Islamo-Christian' State thus constituted founded its socio-political structures on the balance of communities, public offices being distributed in proportion to the effective strength of each section. A definite number of seats in Parliament is thus alloted to each community, the deputies themselves being elected from an inter-community list by a single college; ministerial portfolios and government staff appointments are distributed in the same way; an unwritten law, the National Pact, lays down that the President of the Republic shall be a Maronite Christian and the President of the Council a Sunnite Moslem. The traditional mutual tolerance has thus been consolidated, but the modernisation of the country is thereby impeded: a social organisation in which feudal relationships and clans subsist combines uneasily with a parliamentary system copied from the West and the constraints of a community regime which often degenerates into denominationalism.

The Lebanon was schooled in Western ways at an early date by the missionaries, Lazarites and Jesuits, settled in the country since 1734, who founded the university of St Joseph in Beirut in 1875; and by other institutions, including an American university, functioning in Beirut since 1868. The country was also affected by Western influences through its emigrants, scattered abroad for a century and now looked upon as the state's 'other half'. Its Christian elements enabled it to play a pioneer part in the renascence of Arab letters, and later in the development of nationalist movements in the East. The number and importance of its *élite*, its double culture (the French language playing a prominent part), the perfect religious equality exists within it, and its widespread international relations make the Lebanon, in spite of the difficulties of its internal political life, the most advanced state of the Middle East, a link between East and West and an example to the world of true religious and natural tolerance.

KUWAIT: A gathering centre at Kuwait. Exploitation of oil has brought both social and economic change in the Middle Ea

## A PRECARIOUS ECONOMY

It is to its skilfully played rôle of intermediary, far more than to its scanty natural resources, that the Lebanon owes its prosperity; this, however real, is felt to be paradoxical and insecure, and a more conventional foundation should be given by increasing the regular national income.

The Lebanon possesses no mines, a lack that at one time favoured its independence. Of some 2½ million acres, 672,390 are cultivated, and of these 118,612 are irrigated. The population depends on imports for all heavy industrial goods, many light industrial goods, and essential foodstuffs. Three-quarters of the wheat consumed is purchased abroad. The annual deficit in the balance of trade is a large one, exports covering only a quarter of imports. But the balance of payments shows increasing surpluses: the Lebanon lives on its services.

The Lebanese economy is systematically liberal. The Exchequer, very 'easy-going', levies taxes that are 80 per cent indirect and hit consumption rather than enterprise. Beirut stands third in the gold traffic of the world (reshipment is mostly to Kuwait, for clandestine transmission to India); traffic in currencies is equally free and carried out with consummate skill. Two oil pipelines converge on the Lebanon: that of the Iraq Petroleum Company, from northern Iraq to Tripoli, and the 'Tapline' from the Arabian coast of the Persian Gulf to Saida. The port of Beirut has tripled its traffic in the last few years. Customs revenue has also notably increased. The airport handles about half a million passengers annually, more than a quarter of them in transit. Remittances from emigrants amounts to 50 million Lebanese pounds a year, and income from summer tourists and winter sports is considerable.

So great a variety may be reassuring, but continuous expansion in such sources of income cannot be relied on. Certain special trades, like that of gold, have reached their ceiling; taxation on oil in transit cannot be increased beyond a certain rate. In any case Beirut owes its prosperity as a junction more to the spirit of enterprise of its inhabitants than to its natural advantages; its port is cut off from the interior by the mountains; Syria by encouraging Latakia, and Jordan by developing Aqaba, hope to free themselves from its agency. The economic unity of the Arab countries, which would greatly benefit the Lebanon, is still merely theoretical.

The Lebanon intends therefore to try to increase its production, which would improve social stability at the same time. National revenue per head is one of the highest of the Near East, but only one-third of it derives from local production (agriculture 19 per cent, industry 16 per cent), and it is very unequally distributed (only one-fifth among four-fifths of the population, the working classes). Profits from services are mostly invested in real estate; only 10 per cent of the emigrants' remittances are invested in industry, and the price of arable land is among the highest in the world (1,000 to 3,000 Lebanese pounds per acre for dry-farming land, and from three to five times as much where there is irrigation).

Agricultural progress must thus be encouraged; the irrigated areas can be tripled by a planned use of water; cereal yields have increased (56,000 tons of wheat on 165,300 acres in 1955, as against 35,000 tons on 172,000 acres in 1954); the production of fruit (oranges, apples, bananas, etc.), technically improved, permits considerable exports. A Franco-Lebanese agronomic station at Tell Amara (Buka'a) plays an important part in this advance.

The development of light industries, much to be desired, is hampered by the insufficiency of electric energy, which will be doubled by the harnessing of the river Litani, planned with the financial and technical assistance of France. Under the aegis of Fouad Chehab, President 1958-64, and helped by economic missions, systematic and vigorous efforts are being made. Given adequate capital, new industries and reforms in the administration, this mountain land will be able to achieve a considerable degree of economic self-sufficiency.

Street scene in Beirut. The capital of the Lebanon is a flourishing Mediterranean city set in a magnificent bay. It is one of the busiest ports on the Levantine littoral, and has tripled its traffic in the past few years. It is also a thriving commercial centre and increasingly attractive to tourists.

# JORDAN

An artificially created state, Transjordan was born of the liquidation of the Ottoman Empire after the First World War, and the division of the Arab world into states under French or British mandate. The frontiers of this kingdom, allotted to Abdullah, son of Hussein, King of the Hijaz, were marked out geometrically between Syria, Iraq, Arabia and Palestine, solely in order that the southern leg of the Iraq Petroleum Company's pipeline should be entirely under British control. In 1946 Great Britain granted it independence, but by a treaty of alliance the British kept control of the instruction and command of the army (the 'Arab Legion'), as well as a great degree of economic and political influence; this treaty was terminated in March 1957.

The end of the British mandate in Palestine resulted in the formation of the State of Israel (1948), the Arab-Israeli War and the partition of Palestine along a line which runs through the middle of Jerusalem, so that half the city is now part of Jordan and the remainder is in Israeli territory. In 1949 Transjordan annexed Palestinian Samaria and Judea, but excluding the Gaza strip, and thus became the Hashemite Kingdom of Jordan.

With an area of 34,750 square miles, Jordan can be divided into four different types of landscape from west to east.

The Palestinian plateaus form the area known by the biblical names of Samaria and Judea: all bare hills, separated by narrow valleys. The climate, which is Mediterranean, is influenced by the altitude, which tempers the summer but often makes for snowy winters. The rainfall (24 inches a year at Jerusalem) would be sufficient if it were not broken by a summer drought and did not fall on limestone soils. The archaic conditions of cultivation, on terraces and on the floors of the valleys, of cereals, olives, vines, citrus fruits and tobacco, have undergone hardly any change. One-third of the cultivated area is devoted to fruit, and irrigation is much less extensive than it might be — in sharp contrast to the neighbouring regions colonised by Israel. This is also a region of towns, the land of the Holy Places, Christian and Jewish as well as Moslem: Jerusalem (the old city only, the new one being in the Israeli zone), Bethlehem, Hebron, Ramallah, Nablus and Jinin. The United Nations wished to make the Jerusalem-Bethlehem sector an international zone, but the plan did not materialise.

The rift valley from the River Jordan to the Dead Sea and the Wadi Araba is a long, narrow, sunken area between deep faults, dominated by the Palestinian plateaus and the heights of Transjordan. The River Jordan meanders through it, in the midst of a quasi-tropical bush, in a valley that reaches a width of nearly ten miles in the south, and runs into the Dead Sea, 1,286 feet below sea level, surrounded by salty wasteland. South of this, the rift is prolonged by the wide depression of the Wadi Araba as far as the Gulf of Aqaba on the Red Sea, Jordan's only outlet to the sea.

At the bottom of this deep valley the summers are torrid, but the very mild winters have made a winter resort of Jericho, which is surrounded by gardens and citrus groves. Rainfall everywhere is below 8 inches a year. Sparsely inhabited and often wild, the region would be rich if it harnessed the water of the Jordan, but this development awaits a political settlement constantly deferred by the persistent tensions between Israel and the Arab world.

The plateaus of Transjordan dominate not only the rift valley (by about 3,500 feet), but also the heights of Palestine, and thus receive the moist air of the Mediterranean, at least in the north. Chiefly formed of marl and chalk in the centre and the north (where they are also covered with basaltic outflows from the Jebel Druz) and of sandstones in the south, the plateaus slope gently down, becoming drier towards the arid basins of Qazr Azraq and Jafr. They consist of two distinct regions: in the north and the centre, between the railroad and the edge of the rift, a strip of fertile, cultivated land, thirty miles wide near the Syrian frontier, but narrowing towards the south and degenerating into an arid steppe near Ma'an; and beyond this, a desert steppe, the domain of nomad Bedouins, where the irregular rainfall is sufficient for scattered stockbreeding only up to the point where it merges into desert proper.

A camel caravan on the Jericho-Amman road in the Mesas Desert that lies between Jericho and the River Jordan—one of the many desert regions of Judea.

## NOMADS, FARMERS & TOWN-DWELLERS

In 1948 Transjordan had only 400,000 inhabitants: in 1961 a census of the new Jordan showed a population of 1,690,000. With only a slight addition to her useful area, she had acquired 972,000 Palestinians, of whom only 400,000 were residents established in Samaria and Judea, while 572,000 were exiles, driven out of Israel; among the latter, 100,000 have succeeded in establishing themselves in the country on their own resources; the rest (472,000) live on international aid, on the rations distributed by the U.N.R.W.A. (United Nations Relief and Works Agency for the Palestine Refugees), in huge camps.

The future of these refugees is the main problem: there is no land on which to house the rural workers, and no industry in which to employ the others. Their redistribution appears to depend on the materialisation of plant for harnessing the Jordan. The gravity of the problems is worsened by the very high birth rate, and an annual population increase of at least 2 per cent.

The greater part of this population is Sunnite Moslem; there are, however, some 100,000 Christians (Orthodox, Catholic, Armenian), mostly grouped in Palestine.

Ways of life are in course of evolution: the census of 1952 showed (refugees excepted) 65,000 nomad and semi-nomad stock-breeders (the latter becoming settled), 400,000 sedentary agriculturists and 450,000 city-dwellers. The agriculturists are landowners with small or medium sized holdings, or tenant farmers of big city landowners. In 1950 the whole of the land was in the hands of 90,205 people, 70,686 of whom had less than 25 acres, and 386 more than 250. Forty per cent of the villagers had no land at all in the most favoured regions. In consequence, the villages are poor, and the houses until recently sheltered the family and its livestock in a single room divided in two. The rise of the towns dates from 1949, the influx of refugees having suddenly swelled the population of Nablus, Jericho, and above all Amman, which from a little town of 30,000 inhabitants in 1930 is now a busy city of 240,000, spreading in all directions.

## INSUFFICIENT RESOURCES

The drama of Jordan consists in the fact that this suddenly over-populated country sees no means of increasing her resources. Agriculture and stock-breeding still form the basis of her economy: with archaic methods and scanty yields (as capricious as the rainfall), the country produces wheat, barley, millet, maize lentils, beans, peas, tobacco, sesame, grapes and olives. Stock-breeding, chiefly in the hands of nomads and semi-nomads, falls far short of the results possible under a sedentary system.

Industry is only beginning: at Kallia, on the Dead Sea, there is a factory extracting potassium and magnesium from the supersalted water; phosphates are mined at Resafe, north of Amman, manganese ores have begun to be mined at Wadi Hasa. But these are difficult to ship from Beirut (this led to Jordan's decision to build the port of Aqaba); they will, moreover, suffer competition from the Israeli Negev.

Processing industries (vegetable oil extracting works, flour mills, breweries, cigarette factories and mineral water factories) are few in number but meet home consumption. An oil refinery has been built and there are plans for the construction of a cement works, a textile factory and some tanneries, which would have the advantage of reducing unemployment

There is an enormous deficit in the balance of trade: exports (live animals, cereals, lentils, vegetables, leather and hides, wool and phosphates) are worth about twelve times less than imports (cotton materials, sugar, automobiles, coffee, cement, iron, motor fuels). The circulation of money has doubled since 1949; prices have gone up, while wages have gone down, owing to the influx of refugees.

Jordan is thus less and less able to do without foreign aid: the precarious balance of this artificial state is ensured by enormous subsidies. Though Jordan aims for economic independence by 1970, she is meanwhile supported by a British subsidy; by dues from the oil companies (Iraq Petroleum Company and Aramco) for the pipelines crossing the territory; by American aid (assistance to underdeveloped countries) which provided 45 million dollars in 1964, not repayable; and by contributions from the U.N.R.W.A. This assistance is obviously conditional, which places Jordan in a delicate position between her Western money-lenders and the other Arab states, which would like her to adopt a more anti-Western policy.

Amman, the capital of Jordan, which sprawls across several valleys and hills.
In 1930 it was a small town of 30,000 inhabitants: today the population is 296,000.
An artificially created state, Jordan is heavily dependent on foreign aid and therefore in a delicate political position.

# IRAQ

Iraq, born like the neighbouring Arab countries of the dismemberment of the Ottoman Empire in 1920, has like them been given arbitrary frontiers; but it is more varied than any of them in physical structure, ethnic composition and natural resources.

## THE LAND OF TWO RIVERS

In the west the territory of Iraq covers part of the Arabian steppe; there are a few fine oases like Shithatha, and the intricate network of grazing grounds belongs to the great nomads, apart from a neutral zone which has had to be created at a certain point between Iraq and Saudi Arabia. The nomads are, however, increasingly settling. In the central plain the two great alluvial rivers, the Euphrates and the Tigris, flow north-west to south-east; they first gave the country its distinctive name of Mesopotamia — 'between rivers', More than 186 miles apart where they cross the frontiers, they draw nearer together at the level of Baghdad and soon mingle their waters in deltas, lakes (*hor*) and marshes, before uniting in the Shatt al Arab; their alluvia have been silting up the Persian Gulf for five centuries over a length of 185 miles. Al Jazira ('the island'), lying between their northern course, is a steppe country dominated by the beautiful Sinjar mountain, isolated and peopled by Yezidis; but it has a high enough rainfall, especially towards the north-east (5 to 16 inches) to permit arable farming as well as stock-breeding. Along the two rivers, and their tributary, the Diyala, irrigated fields are gradually gaining on the marshes; the climate, tropical towards the south, is favourable for rice and even for date-palms.

To the east the land rises rapidly towards the high mountains of southern Kurdistan and the Zagros, themselves outside Iraq territory until north of the Baghdad parallel. This is the land of the Kurds, who traditionally practise transhumance, but are becoming more and more settled; beyond relatively fertile and well-watered hills (north-east of the line from Mosul to Kirkuk the rainfall exceeds 16 inches) lies a steep and intricate mountain system, with narrow, sometimes cultivable valleys, high summer pastures, and plateaus and peaks difficult of access, where tribal autarchy and Kurdish pride defend their last refuges.

Amounting in 1947 to about 4,600,000 settlers and more than 250,000 nomads, the population of Iraq is now about 7 million. It is far from being homogeneous: although the census made no mention of religious or ethnic categories, Moslems may be reckoned at over 6 million. In addition, there remain more than 50,000 Christians (two-thirds of whom are Assyrians, belonging to the Nestorian community, not united with Rome, and the Catholic Chaldean community), 20,000 to 30,000 Yezidis (Kurds summarily characterised as 'devil-worshippers'), and only 5,000 Jews left of the original 140,000, after a mass exodus in 1950-51 to Israel.

The Sunnite Arabs constitute the ruling classes of the country; they form two-thirds of the population of Baghdad, the capital, and fill the greater part of the government and administrative offices. The Shiites are in the numerical majority, but except for a small number of feudal tenants, they lead the life of needy peasants, and even, in the outskirts of Baghdad and the marshes of the province of Amara, of the utmost poverty. The Kurds, who until recently have hardly had any assistance in improving their land, are doing their best to preserve the use of their language; they maintain an avowed particularism which admits, however, national solidarity with their racial brothers across the frontiers; meanwhile, the provisional Constitution promulgated in 1964 associates them with the Arabs on an equal footing in the Iraqi nation.

Nearly a quarter of the Iraqi population is concentrated in the four largest cities: Baghdad has more than 860,000 inhabitants and Mosul 260,000; Basra has 329,000, and Kirkuk nearly 222,000.

## THE 'FERTILE CRESCENT' AND ECONOMIC EXPANSION

Encouraged and assisted by Britain, Iraq assumed from the first the rôle of champion of Arab nationalism and aimed at Arab leadership. Freed from tutelage in 1932, but not from British influence, ruled by a Hashemite dynasty founded by the adroit Faisal I (d. 1933), and thus closely related to the Jordanian dynasty, Iraq has been working, especially since 1941, for an Arab association of which it seeks to secure the leadership by first bringing about the unity of the 'Fertile Crescent' (Union of Syria with Jordan, possibly with the Lebanon and in principle with Israel, under the aegis of Iraq), which would allow it to counter-balance the power of Egypt. By way of reaction against Arab 'neutralism' in the Cold War, the conservative government of Iraq associated itself entirely, though without any popular support, with the Anglo-American plans for Eastern defence and, in February 1955, signed with Turkey an agreement which constitutes the basis of the Baghdad Pact. The other signatories to this agreement, which was intended both as a defensive alliance and as an instrument of technical and economic co-operation, are Iran, Pakistan, Great Britain and, to

The black tents of the Bedouins are still a familiar sight in certain parts of Iraq. They serve as a shelter for man and beast alike.

some extent, the United States. While the latter makes use of the alliance as an instrument of financial, technical and military aid, and of the battle against subversion, British influence is centred on its economic aspects — creation of a system of main roads, planning of hydraulic resources to be shared between Turkey and Iraq, and so on. A military coup d'état in July 1958 brought to an end the rule of the Hashemite monarchy, and the substitution of a Republic.

A fresh coup in February 1963 saw the rise of the Baath Party, later succeeded by the army. Attempts were made to effect a tripartite union between Syria, Egypt and Iraq. These plans, however, were only partially successful. The restiveness of the Kurds, a minority group in the north-east, who had rebelled in the summer of 1961 because of their failure to achieve the independence promised them in 1958, is a continuing drain on the resources of the country.

The momentary interruption of Iran's petroleum production in 1951, the opening in 1952 of a new pipeline serving the oilfields of the north (Kirkuk) and trebling the flow capacity to the Mediterranean, the opening up of the deposits in the south around Basra, and the adoption of the rule whereby the Government takes 50 per cent of gross profits, have resulted in an increase in Iraq's annual oil production from 9 million tons in 1951 to 58 million in 1963, and a corresponding increase in the resources this affords the Treasury. Not less than fifty per cent of the sums paid in is devoted to building up an independent economy, with the advice of foreign experts. An autonomous Development Board was set up to this end. One-third of the Board's expenses was first devoted to the control of the disastrous floods of the Euphrates and the Tigris, diverting them by dams towards the reservoir-depressions of Habbaniya and the Wadi Tharthar. The drainage of Lower Iraq, the regulation of irrigation in Mesopotamia, and the storing and utilisation of water from the Kurdish mountains have been undertaken at the same time. A start has also been made in industry: manufacture of chemical products and fertilizers, but chiefly industries independent of mineral oil (cement works, sugar refineries, weaving mills, and so on).

The effects of these development plans were considerable, but their orientation, under the pre-1958 government, appeared far more economic than social: the big landowners were the main beneficiaries of the rural improvements, the peasantry still poverty-stricken and passive; the people of the suburbs and the intelligentsia were growing restless. The Board was dissolved in 1959, following the coup d'état of July 1958. A second five-year economic plan 1965-70 envisages investments of 750-850 million Iraqi dinars allocated chiefly to agriculture, industry, transport and communications, and housing. Oil revenues are to provide 385 million Iraqi dinars, and Soviet and Czech loans 80 million. In December 1961, after the breakdown of prolonged negotiations, the Iraq Goverment banned the foreign oil companies from prospecting or exploiting any region where they were not actually producing already. This development is still disputed by the oil companies, but it represents an important effort on the part of Iraq to establish a national oil industry and lessen her dependence on foreign aid.

Gathering dates in Mesopotamian Iraq, where they flourish along the banks of the Tigris and Euphrates, particularly towards the south.

A tunnel under construction, on the road from Erbil to Derbend-i-Khan in northern Iraq. It is being built by a Düsseldorf company, which is also laying down a road to the Kirkuk oilfield. In the same area a Bulgarian team is laying another road.

# IRAN

With an area about seven times that of Great Britain or almost that of Texas, Iran is orientated north-west to south-east, from the latitude of Madrid (Spain) to that of Rio de Oro (Western Sahara). Two great mountain shafts form the framework of this main orientation, between the almost inextricable 'knots' of Armenia in the north-west, prolonged by the volcanoes of Azerbaijan, and those of Hindu Kush in the south east, heralded by the widely indented upthrusts of the Khurasan. One of these chains is the Elburz, in the north, where limestones alternate with sandstones and schists; the other, in the south, is the Zagros, which extends in small parallel limestone ridges over nearly 620 miles and is accompanied by a volcanic central chain.

These heights surround the greater part of a vast desert central plateau, with a mean altitude of 4,250 feet. Nevertheless the country possesses two seaboards, one in the north, on the Caspian, the other in the south, on the Persian Gulf. The former is very well watered, but only a narrow coastal strip, wedged between the coast and the slopes of the Elburz, gets the benefit of the rainfall. The latter enjoys only a minute amount of condensation.

Iran is therefore a dry country on the whole, formed of a certain number of regional entities agglomerated around a still arid central desert, more hopeless even than the Gobi. These characteristics, which suggest an exaggerated Spain, give the country its powerful originality; they have influenced the course of a history in which the centrifugal tendencies of the provinces have always been opposed to the unifying will of successive sovereigns.

*An ancient civilisation.* At the time when a major part of Europe was still covered by glaciers, prehistoric man, traces of whom are found in strata dating from before 5,000 B.C., came down from the mountains to settle in the plains lying between the ridges of the Zagros and those bordering a central sea, waning by evaporation to become the present great salt desert Dasht-i-Lut which now covers a vast portion of the total area.

In 4000 B.C. an Iranian civilisation made its appearance, nearly ten centuries before the Aryan invasion that overran the whole plateau, and the area began at that early date to play its destined part as an intermediary between East and West. For although the mountain chains isolate the outer provinces, the country lies open along most of its sides.

A sixty-mile-wide gate, Atropatene of the ancient world, opens to the north-west in Azerbaijan, between the Elburz and the Zagros; and through it poured successively the Medes, the Persians, the Mongols, the Tatars and the Turks. At the western end of the chain, the Khurasan forms another passage, through which came the peoples of High Asia, those of the steppes, and of the Touran, more or less kept in check in the course of struggles that have passed into legend. In the south-west, too, the Mesopotamian plain saw the mixing of the races that penetrated into Iran through the passes of the Zagros, used by the Arabs in the seventh century when they brought Islam to the country. These currents did not run in one direction only: from the midst of these mountains and the arid plateau of Fars, the Persian conquerors set out to attack the ancient West; they achieved its conquest and organised it by founding the first of the really great empires.

*The mixture of races.* This country, seemingly so difficult of access, is therefore really an open one, a fact that has resulted in a mixture of peoples of the most diverse origins, The Persians, peopling the provinces of the central plateau, live alongside Turks, Mongols and Kurds in the north-east, Arabs in the south, Turkomans and Hindus in the east and south-east. There are also the Armenian, Jewish and Assyro-Chaldean minorities and nomadic tribes. It is easy to understand therefore why neither religious nor linguistic unity has been achieved. The official language and religion of the greater number are Parsee and Shiite Islam. But besides these there exists a mosaic of languages and beliefs. The Kurds, who are Sunnites, speak an idiom of their own. The other minorities have preserved theirs: Azeri Turkish in

The courtyard of one of the ancient mosques of Isfahan. Situated at an altitude of 4,600 feet on the Iranian plateau, to the east of Zagros, Isfahan is famed for the beauty of its ancient monuments.

Azerbaijan, Turkoman dialects among the Qasqais and in Khurasan, Arabic in Khuzistan, Baluchi on the shores of the Persian Gulf.

The Assyro-Chaldeans speak Aramic and are Christians. Besides these there are Nestorians, Jews, Zoroastrians and Bahais. But in spite of this extraordinary complexity, the genius of the Iranian race has succeeded in assimilating the contribution of successive invaders, and producing a most original synthesis constituting a culture proper to the country.

*The water problem.* The general dryness of the climate and the scarcity of perennial rivers have restricted human habitations to limited territories. Only one river can be navigated: this river, the Karun, takes its source at an altitude of more than 13,000 feet, and flows towards the Persian Gulf; its volume is increased by the Diz, which drains the Middle Zagros, and by the Markheh, which descends from Luristan. The combined volume of these rivers, which amounts to more than 4,000 cubic metres per second in periods of flood, runs into the Shatt el Arab at the level of Khorramshahr.

On the Caspian seaboard, the rivers flowing down from the Elburz are torrential and very short. The waters of the other regions collect in interior basins, the best example of which is that of the Lake of Rezaiyeh (formerly Urmia), which is exceptionally saline. That of Darya yi-Namak, the 'Sea of Salt', receives most of the condensation that collects on the southern slopes of the Elburz.

The border regions have played only a minor part in the elaboration of the Iranian geopolitical complex. The basin of the Karun, whose alluvia, brought down from the Zagros, form the fertile plain of Khurzistan, leaned first towards Mesopotamia but is claimed by the Arab world. The oases lying at the foot of the two mountain arcs, on the desert side, where the rivers can still be used, have always harboured most of the population. All the capitals of Persia have been situated there: Ecbatana, now Hamadan; Qazwin, Tehran (which was first Rey, then the Rhagae of the Medes) and Hecatompylos, all in the northern arc; Pasargadae, Persepolis, Ispahan (Isfahan) and Shiraz, in the south. The Elamite capital, Susa (Shush in Parsee), is an exception.

Several forms of a geographical nature (water scarcity, climatic conditions) have helped to concentrate habitation. Vegetation of European appearance, consisting mainly of fruit trees, beeches and poplars, lends a very special character to the orchard villages and the oases; but the permanent humidity of the Caspian seaboard, where there is a regular rainfall of more than 60 inches a year, gives rise to an entirely different manner of life, founded on rice-growing in flooded fields and extensive exploitation of the forest, and this gives the way of life of the inhabitants of Gilan, Mazanderan and Gorgan a family likeness to that of monsoon Asia. As for the desolate shores of the Persian Gulf, which are accounted among the hottest and most scantily watered in the world, they are inhabited by an outcast population. Towns like Bandar Abbas, Bandar Lingueh and Bushire, long moribund, are to have their ports modernised.

Conversely, man has altered the surface geographical characteristics of the country, unfortunately before the implementation of the land reform laws, not always for the better. Successive invasions have helped to turn districts formerly cultivated and fertile into deserts again. There, as elsewhere, the Arab inroads were followed by the devastation of the forests. Worse still, the Mongol raids by Genghis Khan and Tamerlane utterly destroyed the patient work of irrigation and land maintenance built up by generations. Provinces like the Seistan, in which the entire system of irrigation channels was systematically destroyed, have never recovered. The forests of the north slopes of the Elburz, which are dense, have been endangered by the lack of planned exploitation.

*Political and economic revolution of 1921.* Rich in a past of many thousand years, having ruled the world and seen its dynasties founder one after another under the impact of invasions from every quarter, Persia awoke only quite recently to modern life. In February 1921 an officer of the Persian Cossacks, Reza Khan, seized power and soon afterwards mounted the bejewelled throne of massive gold of the King of Kings, assuming the name of Reza Shah Pahlavi. This was the signal

for a bloodless revolution, somewhat in the Kemalist style in Turkey. The creation of a political system on the European model, a regular army, a police force, secularisation, roads, railroads and ports, are among the most notable achievements of this energetic monarch.

Today, proceeding along this initial line, and becoming fairly rapidly modernised, Iran has turned resolutely towards the West, and taken the form of a constitutional empire reigned over by the Shah-in-Shah, assisted by a two-chamber Parliament (Majlis) and a government presided over by a Prime Minister and comprising the various ministerial portfolios of a modern state.

In the political sphere the Shah is giving a strong personal stamp to the decisions of his government and is instituting many reforms. The social structure of the country is in course of evolution. The political personnel in office and the Cabinet consist almost exclusively of members of the great families, often associated with the history of preceding reigns. They

Iran is the home of a diverse mixture of races — Turks, Turkomans, Mongols, Kurds, Arabs and Hindus, as well as the indigenous nomadic tribes. These Turkomans live in eastern and south-eastern Iran, and speak their own dialect.

have had their influence in parliament diluted since the 1963 elections by representatives of other social groups — and even by women deputies — for a general redistribution of land is being undertaken, which will give the peasants and racial minorities considerably increased representation in political matters.

Growing industrialisation, the difficulties of rural life and the governmental order now ruling over the tribes, have all brought about increasing settlement, and a rise in the urban proletariat, especially in Tehran.

Another factor in this evolution lies in the aspirations of a young generation now becoming generally educated; these young people often undergo voluntary exile for the sake of studying abroad, and bring new ideas back with them. Such social changes, whether they are brewing or already partly achieved, are also connected with the economic situation of the country.

*Poor farming, nomadic stock-breeding.* Nearly always separated by considerable distances, the villages can only be centres of rather poor mixed farming, with small yields. On the Caspian seaboard, however, rice growing lends unity to the agricultural map of the province. Production is large enough to allow some of it to be exported. The irrigated lands of Azerbaijan and the orchards of Khurasan produce a great deal of fruit. Among industrial crops, cotton is produced in exportable quantity and quality (exported mostly to the U.S.S.R.). At one time, poppy-growing placed Iran in the front rank of opium producers, but as addiction to the drug was spreading, the government had to adopt restrictive measures.

In this land of immense steppes, still so pastoral in character, stock-breeding naturally plays a great part, but there are no actual nomads. The majority are sheep-breeders practising transhumance, and often breeding goats and horses as well. Owing to the competition of motor trucks, camels are losing ground. *Importance of road transport.* One of the most outstanding features of the Iranian economy is the importance of road transport. The Trans-Iranian Railway — a remarkable succession of engineering works — connects Bandar Shahpur on the persian Gulf, with Bandar Shah on the Caspian, and includes a recently completed branch to Tabriz; but it can convey only a small proportion of the required tonnage, as it is chiefly needed for the transport to the north of fuel oils, indispensable to the life of the country. Khorramshahr and Khanaquin (on the highway to Baghdad) stand at the only doors open to the west, so that all imports arrive through them; thus nearly all transport is by road, and the road system being very sparse and its substructure inadequate, it is overworked and in bad condition. All this hampers trade and increases costs enormously. This situation will be partly remedied by the improvement of the inland road system, the development of the railroads, the creation of fresh ports on the Persian Gulf, and the restoration of existing ones. As it is, the construction of the Trans-Iranian pipeline and the completion of the branch railway from Tehran to Tabriz, with its connection to the Soviet system through Djolfa, show that progress is being made.

*The importance of oil.* Generally speaking, the whole Iranian economy is dominated by the question of oil. It was in Iran, in 1917, at Masjid-i-Sulaiman, in the Bakhtiari Hills, that the first oil gusher of the Middle East was found. This discovery was destined not only to disturb the Iranian economy but to upset world equilibrium. The outstanding characteristic of the Iranian oilfields is their extraordinary output. This will be seen from the fact that daily production averages about 3,000 tons per well, whereas that of the American wells is only 2 tons. In 1950 Iran was fourth in rank of world producers, with 33 million tons of crude oil. After the 1951 crisis, production, which had almost ceased, rose again rapidly, In 1961 Iran had dropped to sixth place, but production had risen to over 57 million tons in the zone of the Consortium, and to 93 million in 1965, Abadan yielding 18 million tons. The crude oil is either treated on the spot in the refinery at Abadan, one of the largest in the world, or exported direct from the port of Bandar Mashur. The oil wealth is now nationalised, but exploited for the most part with the assistance of an international consortium, which has taken the place, in the technical

Pipelines from the oilfield of Agha-Jari to the refinery of Abadan, running across the mountains of southern Iran. Oil is the principal factor in Iranian economy; the abundant yield of the oil wells will largely determine the country's future.

sphere, of the Anglo-Iranian Oil Company (A.I.O.C.). The revenue from oil will be the main factor in raising the standard of living of the whole population. Iran's immediate future is largely dependent on it.

By reason of its geographical position, Iran has served, from the dawn of history, as a link between East and West. Traditionally open to the flow of ideas from without, the Persians have always shown a remarkable aptitude for tolerance and synthesis. The human, social and economic problems of the country will always be closely connected with the constants of its soil and its climates. It is a meeting-place and melting-pot of combined influences: the vastness of the steppe of pastoral High Asia, the evolution of the Slav world, the Arab and Indian mystiques and the technical demands of the twentieth-century West.

# ARABIA

In the westernmost corner of Asia, the Arabian peninsula (Djezirat el Arab) consitutes a veritable subcontinent. It is bounded to the east by the Persian Gulf and the Gulf of Oman, to the south by the Indian Ocean, to the west by the Red Sea and to the north by the Syrian Desert (Iraq and Jordan). With an area estimated at more than 1,150,000 square miles, this immense platform became detached from Africa at a relatively recent geological epoch. Its physical, climatic and human features relate it for the most part to the Sahara, but in the south-west it shows great resemblance to Abyssinia, lying opposite.

Arabia is a plateau, tilted down to the east. Along the Red Sea, the highest mountains rise abruptly from a narrow, unhealthy coastal plain (Tihama). Bare and desolate in the north, the mountains grow higher and become peopled in the south, reaching more than 10,000 feet in central Yemen. Limestone plateaus intersected by deep valleys (*wadi*) lie along the Indian Ocean. From west to east the huge Arabian plateau slopes gently and regularly, reaching the level of the sea at the Persian Gulf. Along the south-east coast, in Oman, another mountain ridge, reaching 9,850 feet, separates the littoral from the rest of the peninsula.

*Arabia Felix and Arabia Deserta.* The southern part of Arabia was once the seat of flourishing empires and was known as Arabia Felix ('Fortunate Arabia'). With the advent of Islam (A.D. 622) the focal point of the peninsula moved northwards. But Asir and the Yemen, in the south-west, and Inner Oman, in the south-east, form a natural contrast to the rest of the peninsula. Consisting of well-watered highlands, these regions enjoy a temperate climate favouring a highly developed agriculture and a sedentary way of life. Between the mountains of the Yemen and Oman, the south of the peninsula, except for the limestone belt, is occupied by the immense sandy desert of the Rub' al-Khali (the 'empty quarter'), the 386,000 square miles of which form the least known region of the world. This, with the rest of the peninsula, is the Arabia Deserta ('Desert Arabia') of the ancient world. In the centre is the Nadi, a stony desert intersected by a number of valleys and dotted with oases, which lies between the mountainous Hijaz in the west and Hasa, Kuwait and the Pirate Coast, a sandy, marshy littoral, in the east. Towards the north the sandy desert

reappears, with the Great Nafud, bordering on the Syrian Desert.

Two-thirds of the eastern part of the Arabian subcontinent consists of sedimentary rocks, the ideal lodgement for oil deposits. The Arabian subsoil is estimated to contain 50 per cent of the world's hydrocarbon reserves. The exploitation of this natural wealth, begun before the Second World War, is beginning to alter the appearance of Desert Arabia, which may some day become 'Fortunate Arabia' in its turn. Numerous oil wells are being exploited along the east coast (Kuwait, Hasa, Qatar and Bahrain), and prospecting is continuing towards the south-east, on the Pirate Coast and in Oman, as well as offshore in the Persian Gulf.

*The civilisation of the desert.* At a rough estimate, Arabia has a population of between 10 and 12 million, of which about half are in the south and the south-west (Yemen, Aden, Southern Yemen People's Republic). Although two-thirds of this population are settled, the Arabian subcontinent is still the home-

The refinery at Aden. Overlooked by high volcanic mountains, the refinery stands on a sandy peninsula. Beyond lies the oil harbour, while across the bay is Aden Port.

land of nomadism. Settlers live mainly in the highlands of the Yemen, Asir and Oman. In central Arabia, towns like Medina, Mecca and Riyadh, and the many oases, were for long merely trading and stopping places for caravans and nomads.

The Bedouins (*Badawi*: inhabitant of the desert) are tribes of nomad shepherds, dividing their time between stock-breeding, transport and pillage (rezzou). An acute sense of their own nobility, a sense of honour and of community, and the law of hospitality, dominate the existence of these men of the desert, who maintain a fierce independence in their battle with nature. Although Arabia—with Mecca and Medina in the Hijaz—is the spiritual centre of Islam, the Bedouins have remained much attached to their traditional customs, and pagan survivals are not unusual. Until the recent introduction of motor vehicles, the Bedouin camel-drivers were an essential element of the economy, maintaining a continual shuttle service across the deserts.

Except in central Yemen, the life of the settlers is

greatly influenced by nomadism. Trade currents, production and institutions reflected, and still reflect, this fundamental aspect of the greater part of Arabia. But the governments are tending to settle the turbulent nomads, the area in which they may wander is becoming restricted, and the civilisation of the desert is breaking up on all sides.

*Unity and diversity of Arabia.* Of Semitic race, the inhabitants of Arabia are divided into two main branches, corresponding to their two ancestors, Ismael and Qathan. The Ismaelites live mostly in the centre and the north, and are subdivided into Modariids and Rabiids. The Qathanids inhabit southern Arabia, and also spread to the north.

Linguistic unity appears to be complete, all the inhabitants of the subcontinent speaking Arabic; but there are great differences in dialect, and the survival of proto-Arabic dialects has been noted, especially in Oman and in Hadramaut.

Since the departure of the Jewish Arabs of the Yemen to Israel (1940-50), the entire population of

Arabia has been Moslem, but there are lively differences between sects and schools. There are sharp dissensions between the puritan Wahhabite zealots, who consider themselves to be the only authentic Moslems, and all the other sects and schools, whether Sunnite or Shiite. Wahhabism is not a new sect in itself, but it prides itself on being the most rigorous expression of the doctrine of Mahomet.

The peninsula is divided politically between Saudi Arabia, occupying at least two-thirds of it (Hijaz, Najd, Asir and Hasa), the Yemen, the former British Protectorate of South Arabia (now Southern Yemen People's Republic), the Sultanate of Muscat and Oman — under British influence — the Pirate Coast, Qatar, Kuwait and two neutral zones. The Pirate Coast, Qatar and Kuwait are protected by Britain, and so is the Bahrain archipelago, in the Persian Gulf. Many frontiers have never been fixed, and sovereignty remains unsettled around the Rub' al-Khali.

## THE EMPIRE OF IBN SAUD

The kingdom of Saudi Arabia (Al Mamlaka al 'Arabiya as-Saudia) is a Moslem theocracy founded in 1927 by the Emir of the Nadj, Abd el Aziz Ibn Saud, but it did not assume the name of 'Kingdom of Saudi Arabia' officially until 1932. It unites the Hijaz with the Nadj and its dependencies (Hasa and Asir).

Setting out from Kuwait in 1902 to retake Riyadh, the capital of his ancestors, Ibn Saud conquered successively the whole of the Nadj, the Hasa, the Hijaz with its holy cities, and Asir. To encourage his partisans he revived Wahhabite puritanism, an intransigent interpretation of Islam. In 1912 he founded the fighting confraternity of the *Ikhwan* (the Brothers); these fanatical settled Bedouins, grouped in over a hundred agricultural colonies, formed the main instrument of his power and the true backbone of his empire.

Ibn Saud reigned as absolute monarch until his death in 1953. The original dualism of the kingdom has been partly preserved; the Hijaz is a viceroyalty, with Mecca as its capital, Riyadh being the central capital. The diplomatic missions reside in Jidda, the chief port on the Red Sea. Asir and Hasa have a quasi-autonomous government, with governors responsible to the king. There are no political parties, and public opinion finds no expression in Saudi Arabia.

*The Holy Land of Islam.* Every year, hundreds of thousands of Moslems of every nationality travel to the Hijaz to visit Mecca and Medina, where Mahomet lived and preached. The pilgrimage (Hadj) is a source of revenue to the Saudi Kingdom, which levies dues on the pilgrims and imports all kinds of merchandise to sell to them.

Arabia, together with the Yemen, is also the cradle of the Arabs. Even before the Christian era, and to a greater extent after Islam, the Yemenites swarmed over all the countries known as 'Arab' today, and as far as the Maghreb. Very hard-working and intelligent, they are still given to emigrating to order to make their fortune abroad. Their country is essentially agricultural, but recent prospecting has proved the existence of oil, iron, coal, uranium and other minerals. Until the revolution of September 1962, the

A street in Jidda, Saudi-Arabia. Although Riyadh is the capital of this oil-rich state, Jidda is the principal port on the Red Sea and the headquarters of all diplomatic missions.

form of government was theocratic, with an Imam (religious head), disliked by the Shafiite (Sunnite) majority of the population because he belonged to the Zeidite (Shiite) sect. After the country gained independence in 1934, the Yemem's Imam had followed a policy of rigorous isolation; in 1955, however, he agreed to grant concessions to several foreign companies. The Yemen is considered the least developed of the Arab countries, but its agricultural substructure and its mineral and human potential could allow it to make rapid progress. The attempt to establish democratic government in 1962 together with economic aid from China (for road building), Russia (port installations) and America (road building and water supply) will pave the way for such development.

## SOUTHERN YEMEN PEOPLE'S REPUBLIC

Before 1967 the extreme south of the Arabian peninsula consisted of the little State of Aden (75 square miles), which was created a Crown Colony in 1937 and governed directly by the British Government, and also a collection of nineteen states comprising the Aden Protectorate. In 1959 most of these combined to form the Federation of South Arabia.

Between August and October of 1967 the seventeen sultanates of the Federation were ousted from their positions by the forces of the National Liberation Front. Civil war broke out between the NLF and FLOSY (Front of the Liberation of Occupied South Yemen) and the British forces in Aden. By November the NLF took over throughout the country, British troups departed from Aden and the Yemen People's Republic was proclaimed.

Aden's situation at the mouth of the Red Sea won for it the name of 'Arabian Gibraltar.' One of the most important ports of call in the world, halfway between the Suez Canal and the largest known oilfields, it had great strategic value. Since 1954 it has had a refinery with an annual capacity of 5 million tons.

The Republic is a semi-desert region with an area of 61,890 square miles. It has a total population of around one and a half million. The capital is at Madinet al-Shaab. Subsistence agriculture is the main occupation of the people — sorghum, sesame, millet, wheat and barley being grown with the help of large irrigation schemes. Cash crops are becoming increasingly important and cotton is now the country's main export commodity. Aden is still important as an entrepôt.

## SAND AND OIL ALONG THE PERSIAN GULF

All the south-east corner of Arabia is occupied by the crescent-shaped territory of the Sultanate of Muscat and Oman. This country belongs incontestably to the world of the Persian Gulf, the entrance to which it commands. The sultanate is an ill-defined, little known entity. The mountainous interior of the Jabal Akhdhar (the 'green mountain') has never been properly explored, because of the fierce character of the inhabitants. The authority of the Sultan of Muscat over it is nominal rather than real; but since 1955, oil-prospecting has led Britain to help the sovereign

Nomadic Bedouin tribesmen beside a section of the Trans-Arabian pipeline which stretches for hundreds of miles without a bend, linking the Mediterranean oil port of Saida with the oilfields of the Middle East.

to extend his authority over the mountain tribes. The strategic position of the sultanate and the near-certainty of finding substantial deposits of oil there have excited world-wide interest in it, given concrete shape since 1949 by the struggle between Saudi Arabia and Britain for influence in its borders (Buraimi oasis).

North of Oman, the Arabian shore of the Persian Gulf comprises the seven principalities of the Pirate Coast, the Qatar peninsula, the Bahrain archipelago, the Saudi province of Hasa, and Kuwait. It is an arid, desert coast, where stretches of sand alternate with salt marshes; there is no fresh water to be found anywhere. The coastal settlements are inhabited by a maritime population living by fishing and navigation; the pearl industry, once flourishing, is dying out, while oil exploitation is altering the appearance of the region and the life of the people. Enormous economic and technical improvements do not prevent a certain political and social stagnation.

PROBLEMS OF THE FUTURE. The prosperity and the

Fahad al Salim Street, the main street in the town of Kuwait, on the Persian Gulf. On this arid desert coast, stretches of sand alternate with salt marshes. Fishing and navigation are the main occupations of the coastal population; the pearl industry is on the decline.

upheavals brought about by petroleum have not affected equally all the states bordering the Persian Gulf, now the Oil Coast. But in the last few years the whole of Arabia has entered a phase of rapid development that is bound, sooner or later, to put an end to its traditional ways of life and autocratic regimes. Tremendous changes are everywhere to be seen in the mode and level of life, in mentality, and in social structures. Trucks, aircraft and railways have outclassed the camel; some Bedouins are becoming specialised workmen; ultra-modern hospitals and schools have been built, and Western methods are penetrating everywhere. In the whole of this area, the evolution from the traditional ways of life which have endured for centuries to an unindustrial civilisation is bringing a general but unequal increase in wealth, combined with unprecendented social and cultural changes. A middle class is coming into being, the proletariat is becoming restive, and intellectuals are propagating democratic ideals and beginning to demand political and social rights.

The Khyber Pass, with the Landi Khotal in the background, and a caravan of dromedaries in the foreground.
This is the communications route between India and Afghanistan, and is situated in the north-west frontier of Pakistan with peaks rising to a height of over 20,000 feet.

# AFGHANISTAN

With an area of 250,000 square miles, Afghanistan is a relatively small nation, considered on the Asiatic scale.

It is situated on the edge of Western Asia, and joined to Central Asia by mountain ranges which extend to the east into the Pamirs and Tibet; it is also sited on the watershed between Turkestan and India, between Central Asia and monsoon Asia. A transitional area, it also has well-defined characteristics of its own relating to its relief, climate and people.

History has had a vital effect on the country. It was from these high lands that the Aryan tribes came who occupied the greater part of India. Afghanistan witnessed the contact between Hellenism and Buddhism; it was conquered in turn by Persians, Arabs, Turks and Mongols; routes were forced through it and then were closed. But the mountain refuge was never conquered. This was much more than an invasion route of the conquerors: it was the essential route centre between Turkestan and the Indian world or even distant Mongolia; this north-south route was cut at right-angles by the ancient Silk Road, running between the Mediterranean and China.

*A region of contact and refuge.* The high ranges with mountain peoples of warlike tradition were to serve as a buffer state to two empires, the Russian and the British, which were more concerned with consolidation than further conquest. During the last quarter of the nineteenth century the frontiers of Afghanistan were defined, and the political independence of the country under a constitutional monarchy was established in 1921. The population, estimated variously at 7-8 and 13-14 million, is predominantly Sunnite Moslem, though a minority of one million Shiite Moslems live in the west of the country. Two official languages are used, Pushtu and Persian, which are closely linked Indo-European languages, and a Turkish dialect is spoken in the north. Within the present frontiers are Turks, Uzbeks, Tadjiks, the first Indo-European settlers, Hazarahs, mountain peoples of the Pamir and Tibet type, and Pakhtun, a partly settled and partly nomadic people of the south and south-east of the country who formed the nucleus of Afghan unity. In West Pakistan, where they number 7 million, they are known as Patans.

*A mountain relief.* The state of Afghanistan is situated astride a mountain mass known as the Hindu Kush, which spreads out like a fan towards the south-west. Really an extension of the Pamirs, these mountains reach 23,000 feet in the north-east but gradually drop towards the Iranian Plateau; in the north-west they are continued by the Khurasan mountains in Iran. The most northerly ranges dominate the great steppe-like depression of Turkestan and part of the area south of the Amu Darya. The eastern frontier is formed not by a river but by a north-south range known as the Sulaiman Mountains, which forms a barrier against the climatic and human influences of monsoon Asia. Between the Hindu Kush and the Sulaiman Mountains stretches a series of high plains separated by high watersheds. West of the central mountains the plains separating the ranges gradually become broader and lower with the final steep slopes overlooking the great inland basin of the Iranian Plateau. The altitude of this vast flat area gradually decreases towards its centre, where the Seistan Basin forms an undefined frontier between Afghanistan and Iran.

*An arid land.* While Afghanistan is situated at the focal point of Asian relief, climatically it is almost entirely within the large part of Asia known as the 'arid diagonal'. This huge area which establishes a desert barrier from one end of Asia to the other, from the shores of the Red Sea to the gates of Peking, includes Afghanistan and its neighbours, with the exception of Pakistan, much of which is in monsoon Asia. The monsoon has little effect in Afghanistan, for hardly any rain crosses the barrier of the Sulaiman Mountains. No part of the country receives more than 16 inches of rainfall annually; this comes in winter from westerly depressions which form or redevelop over the Mediterranean and Caspian Seas. Passing across central Iran these depressions cause precipitation when they meet the barrier of the Afghan mountains. Low-lying areas like the Seistan remain arid deserts.

Throughout the country the mountains are bare except in the ranges of the Hindu Kush, where the northern slopes bear scattered forests of pistachio and conifers. The only pastures which remain green in summer are found in the Afghan Pamirs. The valleys are desert or semi-desert. The dry farming of wheat pays only on limited areas in the north; it is risky or impossible in the remainder of the country.

The winters are very cold; there is not much snow, but the temperature falls to –30°C. (–22°F.) under the influence of the continental air masses. Summer is very hot in the valleys and the temperatures are still high enough in the central mountains to make cultivation possible at an altitude of 11,000 feet or even higher.

*A central 'water tower'.* The high mountains of the centre and east provide a well supplied reservoir. From it flow numerous temporary or permanent streams or even actual rivers, the most important being the Helmand, which supplies Lake Hamun in the centre of the Iranian Plateau, and the Kabul, which drains the eastern part of the country towards the Indus; but most of the water drains into Central Asia, to join the Amu Darya. This river forms the frontier between the Soviet Union and Afghanistan before entering Turkestan to flow into the Sea of Aral. The two longest tributaries from Afghanistan, the Murghab and Hari Rud, no longer reach the main river, for their waters have been diverted earlier for irrigation purposes.

*Regional diversions of the country.* Relief makes a multiplicity of divisions in Afghanistan; but uniformity is imposed by climate and the almost exclusively agricultural economy. Ethnic differences are obscured by the Moslem way of life. Four general regions can, however, be distinguished on the basis of relief, anthropology and present-day economic development: the great central mountain ranges, the high plains and mountains of the south-east, the western plains and valleys, and Afghan Turkestan.

The great central mountain ranges continuing the western projection of the Himalayas, the Koh-i-baba and Hindu Kush form an inhospitable area and an enormous barrier to communications. This has been the place of refuge for the Pamir Tibetans; they are skilful farmers but too numerous, and they would benefit from some migration to more favoured regions. The important mineral reserves and hydro-electric potential should soon make this the centre of a national industry.

The mountains and high plains of the south-east have formed the heart of Afghanistan for a thousand years; its high basins, valleys and foothills have been developed by the settled Tadjiks and Pakhtun, while the eastern mountains have been the home of the nomads and Pakhtun warriors. The lower valley of the Kabul (1,600 feet) is the only part in all this highland low enough to have an almost tropical climate. Most commerce and craftwork is concentrated in the three successive capitals of Afghanistan: Ghazni, Kandahar and Kabul. Kabul is the political, administrative and intellectual centre, and its position between Soviet Asia and India has made it an important trad-

ing centre. All these factors and the proximity of mineral deposits should result in its industrial expansion in the near future.

The western valleys and plains of Afghanistan are physically part of central Iran, and they show the effect of Persian influence quite strongly. Where the numerous large rivers flow from the mountains into the desert, there are valleys which grow some of the finest fruit in the world, especially the temperate fruits. Herat in the north is an ancient and beautiful city which forms the western gateway to the country In the south irrigation systems have been constructed along the Helmand River.

Afghan Turkestan, situated south of the Amu Darya and centred on Bactria, forms the extreme south of Central Asia. Historically important, this region has been in decline since the Mongol invasions and occupation by the peoples of the steppes, the Turkomans and Uzbeks. In the present century agricultural development has revived and the Afghan population has increased. In the centre of the region, Mazar-i

Afghanistan forms part of a desert barrier stretching from one end of Asia to the other. Except in the Hindu Kush the mountains are bare. The valleys are desert or semi-desert.

Sharif has become an important transit centre for U.S.S.R. aid and trade and Maimana in the west is the most important market for astrakhan.

## TRANSFORMATION OF THE LOWLANDS

Afghanistan is one, if not the last, of those Moslem countries whose traditional way of life has not been upset by the introduction of Western capitalistic methods.

As two-thirds of the country receives inadequate rainfall, the settled people were forced to irrigate, and through the generations built thousands of terraces in the valleys, collecting water from springs, underground sources and rivers, to give perennial irrigation. The villages look like wonderful gardens with a complete range of all temperate and sub-tropical crops and a large variety of fruit trees.

The continuous historical vicissitudes since the fifth century hindered this painstaking development but did not cause its decline. Internal peace and the settlement of the nomadic peoples during the last sixty years has allowed an extension of the irrigated areas, based on traditional methods.

The simple equipment consists mainly of a swing-plough and a sickle, but this does not imply primitive agriculture. Rotation systems are effective and quite complex. The basic crops are wheat, maize and sometimes rice, but vegetables, cotton and leguminous crops are also grown. The yields are reasonably good for agriculture without artificial fertilizers, and production is sufficient for home demand and for some export of fruit and cattle products.

The nomadic life, encouraged by the arid climate and the variety of relief, has almost disappeared, though about 2 million nomads still wander between Pakistan and Afghanistan. But most of the settled cultivators practise transhumance between the winter grazing period when the herds are of necessity largely restricted to the pastures within close proximity to the village with its surrounding fields, and the summer pastures. During this season the whole Afghan population gives the impression of being continually on the move, accompanied by flocks of sheep or goats. Women, children and baggage are carried on the backs of camels or sometimes donkeys.

*A closed field for foreign capital.* Local instruction and certain foreign technicians and administrators have since 1921 guided the country more and more towards a mechanical civilisation. Until the last few years the economy of the country was almost exclusively agricultural, agriculture yielding 90 per cent of the national revenue. The crops were essentially for home consumption, and the only exports apart from fruits were a little wheat and cotton. The nomadic stock-raisers had a more open economy, especially in the north where production of astrakhan proved profitable. The only industry was carpet manufacturing.

Between the two World Wars foreign capital was reluctant to enter Afghanistan because of the difficulties arising from independence, unstable government, the absence of skilled workers, a small local market and the serious problems of internal communication. Germany and Czechoslovakia alone helped the industrial development of a country which, in 1945, had only one hydro-electric power station, two textile factories and a sugar refinery.

Self-help through technical education has been backed by substantial foreign aid and capital from the United Nations, United States, U.S.S.R. and others. The health of the people has been improved; irrigation has been increased and several large dams are nearly complete in various parts of the country.

*Marked economic progress.* More than 3,750,000 acres of irrigated land have been added to the 20 million cultivated acres, of which over half was already irrigated. This new land will be under State control and it is hoped to use it to reduce the large numbers of pure nomads and unemployed farmers by extending the area of permanent cultivation.

Irrigation has always been important in the Middle East, where precipitation is generally deficient or intermittent—often both—and evaporation high. The 'fertile crescent' — Israel, Jordan, the Lebanon, Syria and Iraq — derives its fertility from precipitation along the mountain curve marking its outer edge. Here open forests, grasslands and scrubs are found. The desert, either rocky or sandy, covers much of Saudi Arabia and the territory along the Gulf of Aden and the Persian Gulf, apart from coastal areas and the main river valleys.

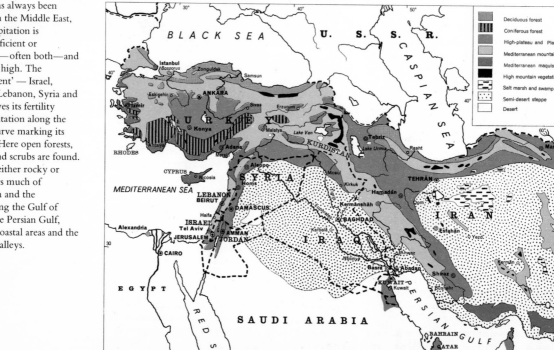

Mineral reserves are very important in this part of
Asia, where the outcrop of old rocks is widespread.
So far the land has been little prospected, and the
minerals hardly developed at all. The lack of ser-
viceable roads has prevented the exploitation of the
richer coal deposits and has forced the newly developing industries to use the poor-quality deposits
accessible. The reserves of coal at the deposits being
worked are less than 25 million tons, but the reserves
at Para, 10,000 feet above sea level, are 500 million
tons. Those of high-grade iron ore are equally good,
and will be able to supply home consumption for
a long time, with perhaps some for export. Oil has
been found in the northern region of the Hindu
Kush.

The two main rivers, the Helmand and Amu Darya,
could produce enough hydro-electricity for a population of from 12 to 15 million, with an average consumption comparable to that of Western Europe;
development programmes are in hand.

Textile industries have developed; the chief centres,
Pul-i-Khumri on the Surkhab and Gul Bahar near
Kabul, produce cotton goods; and Kandahar and
Kabul, woollens. Engineering and heavy industry are
still no more than projects.

Construction of a road network will be of prime
importance for future development. Already there is
a motorable road from Russia to Kabul and thence
through Pakistan and Kashmir to India. In all the rest
of the country paths are impassable for vehicles, and
transport, even of coal, is by pack camels.

A HEALTHY BASIS FOR DEVELOPMENT. Afghanistan, with
a healthy agriculture and important power and mineral resources, seems to have reached a turning-point
in its economy, thanks to its strict political neutrality
and wise domestic reforms. Distinctive features are
the restricted use of agricultural machinery which, if
introduced, would only create unemployment, and
the formation of a technical élite.

# OIL
# AND THE MIDDLE EAST

Since the beginning of the century, when the
Australian prospector d'Arcy, following up sugges-
tions of the French archaeologist Jacques de Morgan,
discovered the oil deposits in southern Iran, the map
of the oriental oilfields has become greatly complicated and diversified: all the countries on the coast of
the Persian Gulf and the Arabian Sea, with the exception of the Sultanate of Muscat, where little progress
has been made on the question of royalties, will henceforth be sharing, in often varying proportion, in the
production of petroleum. Immediately after the
1914-1918 war, oil was being produced only in the
countries of the north, Iran and Iraq; on the eve of
the Second World War, the American prospectors'
discoveries switched the interest towards Saudi
Arabia.

From 1951 to 1954, the interruption in the production of oil in Iran, nationalised by the Iranian Government, encouraged increased output in Saudi Arabia,
Iraq, and above all in Kuwait; this tiny Emirate is today
the leading producer of crude oil in the Middle East.
Thanks to fresh discoveries, Iran reconquered a place
in the front rank in 1955. Prospecting is being carried
out in many places in shallow sea beds, along the
southern shore of the Gulf, and in the deserts of
eastern Arabia, on the indefinite borders of the kingdoms of Saudi Arabia, the Sultanate of Muscat and
the Sheikdoms of the Pirate Coast. The most important production areas lie around the western side
of the Gulf, with the deposits of Iran and southern
Iraq (Basra is developing faster than Kirkuk), of
Kuwait and Saudi Arabia accounting for more than
three-quarters of the 'crude' extracted in the Middle
East. Deposits in Egypt are relatively small, and those
discovered in Israel and Turkey are still smaller.

The traditional way of life
has not been disrupted
by the introduction of Western
commercial methods
into Afghanistan.

A discovery well at Minagish,
South Kuwait.
Exploitation of Middle Eastern
oil deposits is shared between
Western companies, with
American interests predominating
in Saudi Arabia,
and British interests in Iraq.

Kuwaiti drillers at work.
The exploitation of oil gives rise
to social changes: here wider
education, there lavish spending,
and, of course, the establishment
of a new class, the skilled worker.

## COMPETITION FOR OIL: EXPLOITERS AND LANDOWNERS

The exploitation of these deposits is divided between
Western companies; these are sometimes associated,
but their rivalries often betray the divergence of
national interests. The United States finds a complement in the East to a national production that
has reached its maximum; Great Britain requires
petroleum payable in sterling, to ensure her autonomy
in the matter of fuel oils; France, through the Iraq
Petroleum Company, and now Italy (in Iran), are
trying to obtain supplies under the best conditions
by taking part in the exploitation. Local refineries,
a large one at Abadan (Iran) and two others at Bahrain
and Aden, meet the fuel oil requirements of the

inhabitants of the coast of the Indian Ocean, and
are more or less controlled by Britain.

A study of the value and direction of overseas
investments in the oil wealth of the Middle East
demonstrates in particular the American monopoly in
Saudi Arabia and the British preponderance in Iraq.
But the distinction must be viewed in the light of
other considerations, and is not so simple as it appears
at first sight. Bahrain Oil, for instance, with American
capital, is registered in Canada, and, in spite of an
equal share in operations, Britain dominates the Kuwait
oil industry, which supplies 'sterling' petroleum.

In the areas still under exploration, the limits of
which often coincide with ill-defined political frontiers, conflicts arise, whose seriousness can often be
explained only by reference to oil resources, such
disputes being concerned with the extent of the
territorial waters of the countries bordering the
Persian Gulf, ownership of the Buraimi oasis, status
of Oman, and so on.

The Middle Eastern states, at first very compliant
towards prospectors, gradually realised what revenues
they could derive in the form of royalties from the
exploitation of the oil on their land by the Western companies, and these companies were thus soon
forced to raise their offers. In 1948-1949, the American 'Independents' offered a hitherto unusal rate
of dues, as a bid for the concession in the neutral
zone south of Kuwait. Immediately afterwards,
Aramco adopted the formula of sharing profits with
the grantor state on a fifty-fifty basis, likely to appeal
to the imagination and sensibilities of the Middle
Eastern states. In 1951 the Anglo-Iranian Oil Company was evicted from Iran for not having accepted
this arrangement in time. But it was agreed to by
private contract with Iraq Petroleum, and has lately
become the rule. The non-producing states, whose
territories are crossed by the pipelines (Syria,

Agriculture and pastoralism
(mostly nomadic) are the
traditional economic activities
throughout the Middle East.
Fruits, cereals and oil seeds of
various kinds are grown and
cattle, goats, sheep and
camels provide meat, milk,
transport, clothing and shelter.
The discovery of oil (Egypt
began producing in 1911) has
largely altered the economic
picture. In 1951 reserves were
estimated at 23,075 million tons,
but since the geology is
suitable, the total is likely to be
substantially more. Some oil is
refined locally but most is
exported crude. World
demand is such that oil from the
Sahara (discovered in 1956) is
unlikely to affect the Middle
East as a European supplier.

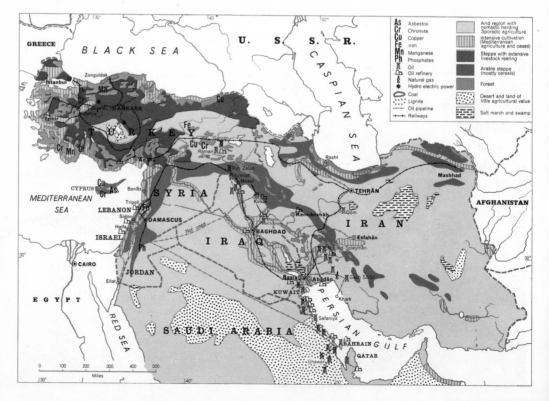

Lebanon, etc., also lay claim to a fifty-fifty share, which entails delicate calculations, and often gives rise to trouble.

## REVENUES FROM OIL: SOCIAL CHANGES

The Middle Eastern countries thus derive considerable income from oil; every ton extracted brings in 3.70 dollars in Kuwait, 7.45 in Iraq; oil furnishes Kuwait with four-fifths of the national revenue, Bahrain with three-quarters and Iran with a third.

But those resources are put to widely different uses. Iraq has preferred to employ them (at the rate of 70 per cent) in the systematic build-up of an economy independent of petroleum, and Iran has now begun to follow this example.

Elsewhere, a large portion is first set aside for the benefit of the dynasties (one-half in Qatar, a third in Kuwait) — unless the sovereign, as in Saudi Arabia, more or less regards the State treasury as his own. In these states, large luxury spending comes first: yachts, palaces, jewellery and, especially in the little Emirates of the Gulf, paternalistic schemes for building schools and hospitals, or, in the case of Saudi Arabia, the grant of political studies abroad. Some of this immense wealth is not spent, however; it is either paid into the Treasury, or invested on Western advice: the City of London administers large capital sums on behalf of Kuwait. A relatively small amount is then left to be devoted to local improvements, either because there is no natural opportunity for this (Kuwait), or because the sovereign, to suit himself, intends to make only moderate changes in the traditional state of affairs (Saudi Arabia).

Nevertheless, the exploitation of oil does give rise to social changes, large or small. Sometimes they are instigated by local authorities: extension of education at the suggestion of paternalistic sovereigns, as in Kuwait and Bahrain; or large expenditure for show by the dynasties and leading classes in the Arabian peninsula. This has led to partial Westernisation of material life. But it is chiefly the exploiting companies that set the movement going; the oilfields themselves, in Saudi Arabia especially, constitute enclaves of modern life in the heart of the traditional civilisation; local wealth is increased by the payment of relatively high wages, and the management attempts to train the local hands employed, and even to give them technical instruction; there is also an influx of more highly developed foreign labour, often Indian or Pakistani.

Although many of the local workers, expecially in the Arabian peninsula, are still only 'temporaries', who come for the sake of acquiring a transient surplus income and then return to the traditional way of life to which they are attached, a class of 'modern' workers is coming into being in the Middle East. These workmen or minor clerks and a growing number of local skilled workmen are gradually becoming organised to back their claims by a movement towards trade unionism, and even by strikes (Saudi Arabia, Lower Iraq). The Middle East thus contains the germ of social changes, at present only localised, but which may be profound and greatly influence its evolution.

Tankers alongside the quay at Kuwait.

## FUTURE OF MIDDLE EAST OIL MARKETS

The Middle East today contains the great majority of the proved oil reserves of the free world; it can guarantee, normally, almost the whole supply of crude oil to Western Europe, whose overall consumption is increasing.

Its prosperity through oil seems therefore assured for the present. As regards the future, however, it must reckon with new sources of energy (atomic, solar, etc.), which may to some extent replace petroleum and thus reduce the demand for it, and also with the discovery of fresh deposits (Western Europe, the Sahara, etc.), which are nearer, safer, perhaps cheaper, and may diversify the supply.

The Suez crisis in 1956 showed Western Europe the extent to which its oil supply depended on its good relations with the Middle Eastern states; not only the producing ones, but those through which oil is conveyed: Egypt, with the Suez Canal; Syria, Lebanon, Jordan, with the Iraq Petroleum's pipeline ending at Tripoli and Baniyas — the Haifa branch being out of service owing to the Arabian blockade of Israel — and the Tapline running through Saudi Arabia, Jordan and Syria, and ending at Saida in the Lebanon. The total annual capacity of the pipelines is hardly more than about forty million tons, and the Suez Canal, although being enlarged, in its present state allows only medium-sized tankers to pass through. The solution for the immediate future has been the building of very large and therefore economical tankers, which take the Cape route and reach Europe at deep-water oil ports (Milford Haven in Britain, La Pallice in France).

The range of American holdings and growing oil production from the Sahara, besides the probable consequences of Russian intervention in the Arab countries, and even the possibility of a Chinese market for Middle Eastern oil, all raise the future of oil production in the Middle East to the level of a world problem.

# THE PENINSULAS
# OF SOUTHERN ASIA

# THE INDIAN SUB-CONTINENT

## INDIA, PAKISTAN, CEYLON, NEPAL, BHUTAN

In the southern part of Asia, India, Pakistan and Ceylon together form a separate and distinctive region. For thousands of years this vast area, from the Khyber Pass to southern Ceylon, seems to have been the home of a separate people, living in fairly uniform conditions; in modern times the whole of this vast area came under British influence, and this has helped to standardise its ways of life. At present one-sixth of the world's population lives here, divided among India, Pakistan and Ceylon, which are member states of the Commonwealth, and the frontier states of Nepal and Bhutan.

The uniformity of conditions of the area appears to be derived in particular from the fact that the Indian sub-continent is sufficiently isolated and has a sufficient variety of resources to live an independent existence. It is a world of its own, extensive yet enclosed by marked geographical boundaries, bounded to the south by the sea, and in the north by the remarkable natural feature formed by the Himalaya mountains, which are both very high and difficult to cross. They are continued to the east in the tightly grouped ranges of Burma, and to the west in the arid and contorted mountains on the edge of the Iranian Plateau. The passes in the west, such as the Khyber, though very few in number, have allowed some invasion as well as communications overland with the rest of Asia. Sea routes played only a limited part until modern times, because of the large distances from the nearest shores, though the Cochin Christians arrived in India in the second century A.D. and Arab trade was important on the west coast in the fourteenth century.

There is no doubt that the Indian world was not entirely closed; there were even periods of expansion during which its influence spread towards the Far East. Buddhism, for example, originated in India and spread over a large part of Asia; it is still practised in these areas. In India it nearly disappeared but is now spreading again.

*Aridity tempered by the monsoon.* The sub-continent is subject to great climatic variety. In the extreme south in latitude 8°N., the annual range of temperature is only 2°C. (3.6°F.), while in Lahore it is 45°C. (81°F.). But there is one feature common to the whole country, and that is the monsoon climate, whose principal characteristics are regular seasonal winds and rainfall pattern. In the north and on the west coast it is customary to distinguish six seasons: from mid-November to mid-March it is cold and dry; this is followed by a hot dry period, and then by very hot conditions; in June masses of black cloud advance from the south-west and steadily cover the whole sub-continent bringing torrential rain; during the month of August the showers become more intermittent and the sky gradually clears; then from mid-September to mid-November there follows the autumn, which is a very pleasant season and the only one which could be considered temperate. The main monsoon bursts every year at the same time to within a few days. Usually in Malabar it is June 3rd, Bombay June 5th, Rajputana and Bengal June 15th and so on. Delays and deficiencies do occur but they are unusual.

This rainfall regime is of fundamental importance, for India is really situated in the arid zone. Between latitudes 15° and 25° the world shows a succession of deserts, the Mexican, Saharan and Arabian Deserts, all inhospitable areas. India is the only land in these latitudes to be so highly populated, for its regular rainfall has brought life to it.

However, the rainfall is unequally distributed; it is excessive along the west coast and in Bengal and Assam, where Cherrapungi holds the world record

for rainfall, with an annual total of 450 inches. The rainfall is deficient over much of the Deccan Plateau and in the area of Rajasthan between Karachi and Delhi. The country often looks arid or semi-arid.

Dramatic contrasts are typical of the pysical geography of the sub-continent, which has the highest mountain range in the world and one of the longest, overlooking one of the world's most extensive and monotonous plains. It has the record for altitude, rainfall and high temperature, and almost that for drought. There is extensive river flooding, which is often dangerous because of its suddenness.

*The population and the future.* The population, which is already excessively dense in many regions, has been increasing at a high rate for the last thirty years; there were 305 million people in India and Pakistan in 1921, 338 million in 1931, 388 million in 1941, 437 million in 1951, and 532 million in 1961. The problem of subsistence is becoming more and more acute. The Indian Government has attempted to deal with the serious situation in a series of five year plans.

Tea estates at 7,500 feet in the Western Ghats, on the borders of Kerala and Madras States. Climate here is equatorial.
In the hill country tea estates follow every contour.

With a population already extremely dense in many regions and increasing rapidly for the last thirty years, India has tried to solve the problem of subsistence with a series of five year plans.
Increased food production, accelerated industrialisation and diversification of products are their two main features.
This atomic reactor, Bombay, is a symbol of India's effort to bring about economic and technical change.

India and Pakistan have taken important steps to increase the production of foodstuffs and to speed up industrialisation. The problem does not simply consist in increasing the production of rice. Very important for local consumption are the vegetables and the varieties of millet which include sorghum, bajra and the small black millet which often yields quite good crops on infertile soils, especially in the Deccan. In this connection improved methods as well as small irrigation schemes will help to increase yields. Japanese agriculturists were invited to introduce the soya bean and improved methods of rice cultivation. As for meat, a large part of the population will not eat it on religious grounds, so that 200 million cattle will continue to be more of a liability than an asset, even if milk yields are raised above their present low levels.

A number of large dams intended for both irrigation and the production of electricity have been built or are under construction. The rivers of the Himalayas have high power potential, so far little developed.

Industrialisation in Pakistan may be based on its production of natural gas, which was discovered in 1954, while in India there are huge reserves of coal which, although rather low grade, occur in shallow deposits. India also has iron ore and one of the largest reserves of manganese in the world.

Promising oil deposits in both India and Pakistan, particularly India, are now only beginning to be discovered and exploited. India is well endowed for atomic power production and has stations at Trombay, near Bombay, and Alwaye on the Malabar coast. It possesses most of the ancillary raw materials for atomic power production (e.g. beryl, graphite) and even some fissile material.

An industrial revolution is under way in the sub-continent which will affect profoundly not only the lives of its people but also the balance of power in the world. Communications are outstandingly easy owing to the construction of roads and railroads by the British, and have been further improved by air transport, which brings Calcutta within four hours of Bombay instead of forty-eight, and in particular by the country bus, which is increasing the contact between the countryside and the town. Some of the symbols of the new era are the imposing bus stations and the ever-expanding bus networks with vehicles which are not always dilapidated, and whose traffic is increasing strikingly.

There are about 580 million Indians, Pakistanis and Ceylonese; most live in poverty-stricken villages. In India rural unemployment and underemployment is incalculable but vast, affecting perhaps a quarter of the rural population. For the past twenty years a gradual shift of the ever-increasing population into the cities has been going on.

# INDIA

Since the beginning of the 1950's, India has been making a sustained effort to modernise her economic and social structure. Although still the world's largest supplier of tea and jute goods and a major source of simple manufactures like textiles and leather goods, she has been trying to diversify her production and exports. To this end Government planning has centred on major industrial ventures like steel plants, machinery factories and the thousand and one items that go into a modern manufacturing economy. The attempt has been made with the help of substantial aid from both Western and Eastern countries.

Modernisation has meant more than economic change. India is trying to rid herself of the caste system, in which individuals are born to a social status, and to adopt one which allows more freedom to individual initiative and achievement. She has outlawed 'untouchability' and 'unseeability', opened educational and religious institutions to the socially underprivileged — all within a unique framework of a parliamentary democracy. This is probably the largest experiment in social engineering ever attempted, the results of which are not yet realised.

### THE DECCAN OR PENINSULAR INDIA

The Deccan (which means South) is the farthest south of the three main regions of India. Broadly speaking, the Deccan is a huge triangle, washed on two sides by the sea, its northern boundary extending a little beyond the Tropic of Cancer. Geologically it is the oldest part, a plateau which emerged from the sea in earliest times. It appears to form a whole, a relatively closed world, where nature is generally kinder and where Indian civilisation may have had its deepest rrots.

Initially its description appears simple; it is an eroded plateau, highest in the south and gently inclined from south-west to north-east, so that the western edge is appreciably higher than the eastern. More careful examination reveals considerable variety, mainly based on relief, soil and climate. Apart from the coastal strips, the plateau proper can be divided into the southern block cut off from the remainder by the Palghat Gap; the plateau, highest in the south in the massif of the Nilgiri Hills and descending in the direction of Bengal; the lava plains towards the west; and, lastly, the northern border, which separates the plateau from the valley of the Ganges.

THE SOUTHERN BLOCK. This triangular massif, which forms the backbone of the most southerly part of the Indian peninsula, includes the highest peak in the Deccan, Anai Mudi (8,841 feet). The peaks are flat-topped or gently sloping, often bare, and can be likened to the head of an Indian elephant (Anai Mudi means 'elephant's head').

The slopes are very steep and the massif is lined with deep ravines. The general result is a very attractive region with tourist features comparable with those of Ceylon, with which it has much in common. The hill station of Kodaikanal, from which the whole of the eastern plain can be seen, is noted for its temperate climate. The western slopes, with much heavier rainfall than the eastern, are covered with dense vegetation, which includes spices, tea, coffee and valuable trees such as rubber.

The massif creates a formidable barrier in spite of the Shencottah Pass, which is used by a narrow-gauge rail track. Though lightly populated itself since about the tenth century, it has formed a natural barrier between peoples, particularly between those speaking Malayalam in the west and Tamil in the east.

The hydro-electric power potential is considerable and is being developed; this will supplement thermal power stations in the major towns of the area, such as Coimbatore, Maduri, Cochin, Trivandrum, and is now the country's leading source of power.

The 13,000-foot Palghat Gap links the states of Madras and Kerala and is used by the railroad joining Madras to both Mangalore and Cochin. Along this route are market towns like Coimbatore, which is also a rapidly developing industrial centre, and Palni, the strange holy city of the Tamils, at the foot of Kodaikanal.

THE CENTRAL PLATEAU. In the south is the massif of the Nilgiri Hills, whose bare summits rise to 8,640 feet; the rocks have massive and also more compact features than the southern block, but surrounding slopes are just as steep, and in the north are separated from Mysore by the deep gorge of Moyar. Farther north the plateau rises in a gentle slope to form the eastern flanks of the Western Ghats, whose slopes fall very abruptly in the west to the coastal zone. No less surprising is the contrast between the torrential rain of the west and the occasional showers of the plateau, with luxuriant vegetation merging into poor savanna within a few miles. At about 13°N. there is the exception of the Coorg massif, a leafy enclave with a more equable climate; its shady valleys are not too wet and are suitable for coffee trees.

The Western Ghats continue northwards across Karnataka. They become steadily lower and are cut by a few gaps, but remain steep to the west and soon after Konkan are covered with lava flows.

To the east of the Western Ghats the plateau spreads out at a height of 2,000 to 3,000 feet, monotonous, stony and supporting poor savanna which almost merges into semi-desert in Mysore and Andhra Pradesh. The relief is usually gentle and the impermeable surface is strewn with rounded boulders; there are hollows filled with water or alluvium in the valleys. Several large rivers flow towards the east, eroding with difficulty narrow, shallow valleys in the gneiss; it is surprising to see rivers without flanking valleys, flowing along without bringing life to their surround-

A low literacy ratio makes the scribe a vital person in the community. Here, a scribe in the state of Rajasthan works in the street.

ings. The upper valley of the Godavari, flowing on lava, creates strange landscapes near Nasik, the holy town of the Marathat, with its impressive flights of steps.

There are three main river systems, the Cauvery, the Godavari, and the Kistna, with its right-bank tributary, the Tungabhadra, and left-bank tributary, the Bhima.

The rivers of the Deccan are not really suitable for navigation for, like many African rivers, they are interrupted by rapids caused by crossing crystalline rocks. The gradient of these rivers makes them less suitable than those of the north for hydro-electric generation. These disadvantages have, however, been overcome. The impressive falls at Sivasamudram on the Cauvery were relatively easy to develop and a start was made in 1900; other early dams were those at Chamrajsagar, and at Mettur in southern Mysore. The rivers flowing into the Bay of Bengal are not of much use for power except in the south; the most developed resources so far are those of the torrents which flow from the Western Ghats into the Arabian

Sea. Six hydro-electric projects were completed in the area during 1951-61, and another fourteen projects in 1962-66.

The Deccan is striking for the basic uniformity of its plateau landscape. But it is not all steppe and bare rock; round the edges there are forests of varying density. Karnataka, the eastern border of the Maratha country, Andhra Pradesh, the region of Hyderabad and the Plateau of Orissa, each has its own individual character.

Cultivation is largely dependent on reservoirs of rainwater called tanks, but big river developments are in progress. The sparse population lives mainly on millet. A little cotton is grown, and castor oil and other oil-yielding crops. There are some fairly important minerals; at Kolar in Mysore gold is mined and there are scattered deposits of iron, manganese and other minerals.

Cities have flourished here since ancient times, thanks to the relatively dry climate. The ruins of Halebid, Sravana Belgola, Golconda and Vijayanagar, near Hampi, bear witness to a glorious history. Among the modern towns, most of which are growing rapidly because of new industries, there are two large cities which have been increasing at an outstanding rate since the beginning of the century. The first is Hyderabad, with a population of over 1,200,000; the other, the beautiful city of Bangalore, with its ideal climate, has a population of 1,207,000 and has aircraft, electrical and engineering industries. Mysore is away from the main routes and its growth has been slower. On the borders of the Maratha cotton region, Dharwar, noted for its high-quality cotton, has failed to develop, unlike the region of Hubli nearby.

THE WESTERN OR WINDWARD COAST. The coastal plains which border the plateau on the west are quite unlike those of the east, for they form only a very narrow fringe at the foot of the steep slopes of the Ghats.

*Kerala: equatorial India.* The western plain widens only in Kerala, where it extends for about 200 miles from the southern extremity to the outskirts of Mangalore. At the foot of the rocky slopes and high lateritic areas this alluvial plain stretches flat, fertile, overflowing with water and fringed with lagoons. The climate in Kerala is equatorial, fairly similar to that of the west coast of Ceylon. The rainfall is very high, reaching 200 inches a year on the hills and 120 inches along the coast; in the north it is badly distributed, for most of it falls with the summer monsoon, but in the extreme south the rainfall is lower and more evenly distributed, being affected by both monsoons.

Rice is carefully cultivated even on the laterite soils; irrigation is required in the extreme south but drainage elsewhere. Protection is necessary against the water, and near the sea against the seepage of salt water. The luxuriant vegetation is dominated by the coconut palm, all or nearly all of which is used for dwellings, umbrellas, flooring and floor coverings, rope and lighting oil as well as food. Other trees are the slender Areca palms, nutmeg trees and palmyras. On the higher ground are rubber trees and forests with teak, rosewood and other rare species; there are also tree ferns, lianas and giant bamboo; pepper, coffee and tea grow well. Here the tiger and elephant are also to be found.

The population density reaches an average of 1,127 per square mile; in many parts of the plain the 'rural' density is over 1,500 per square mile. The semi-urban population cultivates gardens rather than fields; it is hardworking but there is not enough work. The fisheries provide for a large consumption of fresh and dried fish, and also for export; this fish diet is supplemented by rice, usually from Madras. The proportion of Christians among the population is very high; there are two Jewish colonies at Cochin, one of which is darker-skinned than the other. The continuance of St Thomasite (Christian) worship is proof of ancient connections with the Near East. With Goa it forms the most important Roman Catholic part of the whole of India.

The towns include Cochin, sited on a lagoon, which has been modernised at great expense. One of the six major ports of India, it has a military base and handles 2,360,000 tons of cargo a year.

To the north of Kerala the alluvial plain is replaced by lateritic highland; in some places the Archean rocks

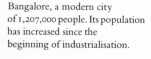

Bangalore, a modern city of 1,207,000 people. Its population has increased since the beginning of industrialisation.

outcrop, and in Kenara they reach the sea and form offshore reefs. The summer monsoon rains are heavy, about 120 inches or over, but the crops are poor and the population fairly sparse. Mangalore has a population of 170,000 and exports timber and coffee from the Coorg highlands.

*Goa: an historic enclave.* Goa was a Portuguese colony until December 1961, with an area of 1,250 square miles and a population of 550,000. It has a good harbour in a bay at the convergence of several small rivers whose deltas make fertile ricefields. Old Goa is a gloomy city, with buildings in the baroque style. The export trade is important and includes coconut products, iron and manganese ores.

*The Maharashtra coast: the Konkan.* North of Goa the Konkan widens to form the coastal part of Maharashtra. Though still high, the rainfall decreases progressively towards the north. Rice flourishes in the valleys; elsewhere millet and vegetables are cultivated. Many Maharashtrians are sailors or fishermen.

The whole region is dominated by Bombay; this over-populated city with over four million inhabitants is situated on a narrow peninsula. It owes its spectacular growth during the last hundred years or so to the advantages of its port. Bombay imports oil, industrial raw materials and manufactured products which are distributed by rail or coastal shipping. It exports less raw cotton than it used to, but a considerable quantity of cotton goods, vegetable oil and manganese. It is surrounded by an industrial region producing mainly textile and metal manufactures, and with an abundance of hydro-electric power available from the Western Ghats and relatively large thermal power resources it will certainly continue to expand in future years.

*The cotton lands: the lavas of the west.* The north-west part of the plateau is a triangular region with a covering of lava from 2,000 to 5,000 feet thick; the surface has the gentle relief of a crystalline plateau. Hills are found in some places, as for example in the Maratha Ghats.

The fertility of this area owes much to the fact that the monsoon winds are able to cross the Ghats more easily here, and so they penetrate farther eastwards. There are also irrigation schemes round Poona, Sholapur and Ahmadnagar. The soils are not fertile everywhere; the famous black earth which is well suited to cotton is only found in the broad east-west valleys. Elsewhere the red lateritic type of soil is common. Very little rice is grown, but much sorghum, wheat and millet. Cotton production is declining at present, but that of sugar-cane is increasing; the production of sesame oil is important, especially in Khandesh.

Tilting of the northern edge of the plateau has had important consequences: two rivers, the Tapti and farther north the Narbads, flow from east to west in two broad, deep valleys; the abundance of alluvium deposited in these trough-like valleys has been the basis of prosperity in Khandesh and encouraged an extremely intensive system of agriculture.

The population of the Maharashtrian plateau, which corresponds to the volcanic soils, is denser than elsewhere, and is grouped into large villages, fairly well spaced out and built of stone; they often have the remains of fortifications. The chief towns began as

Women threshing rice, the pricipal crop of India. Agriculture has always been India's chief industry, with about 70 per cent of the population dependent on the land for a living. A production increase of 2 per cent per annum is needed to keep pace with the rising population.

Bombay, an overpopulated city of more than four million inhabitants. Its spectacular growth in the last century has been the direct result of the activities of its port. Oil, industrial raw materials and manufactured goods are imported; cotton, vegetable oil and manganese are exported.

fortresses; much later they enjoyed a period of prosperity with the rise in importance of cotton; today they have ceased to develop. Ahmadnagar and Aurangabad are provincial towns living on memories; Kolhapur, with bauxite deposits nearby, has a more promising future. The three large towns are situated on the edges, Poona in the Ghats, Sholapur, a cotton town, in the south, and Nagpur, a metallurgical centre, in the east. Poona is an industrial town, intellectual centre and hill station.

Maharashtra is not confined to the plateau; it includes the Ghats, which are inhabited by mountain people, and the coastal zone with Bombay, the capital. In its population and culture this region forms a separate unit.

*Gujerat.* Gujerat is bounded by the Maratha lands to the east and the Kathiawar peninsula to the west. The basaltic lava extended this far and some even occurs in the peninsula. The Gulf of Cambay is fringed with estuaries which are partly silted and fertile. Climatically there is a rapid transition between the heavy rainfall in the east and the arid, healthy lands of Kathiawar, or farther west the semi-desert conditions of the Rann of Kutch. The rainfall is also unreliable and famines have occurred more than once in pre-independence days. In the centre of Kathiawar some rocky hills stand out, sometimes capped by the delicate sculptures of Jain temples; the hills are now covered with scanty woodlands and here live the only lions found in India inhabiting the lower slopes of the Kirthar Range.

Apart from some rather unimportant ports which include Porbandar, the birthplace of Gandhi, and the former Portuguese settlements of Diu and Damão, the main towns are Ahmadabad, the cotton centre, and Baroda. Surat, once the centre of European trade, declined but is now reviving with the aid of its textile industry. Kandla is a modern port on the Gulf of Kutch. Gujerat is the second oil-bearing state, after Assam.

THE COASTAL PLAINS OF THE EAST. To the east, along the Bay of Bengal, the Deccan is bordered by a series of plains which are rather more than a simple coastal strip, for in some places they are 80 miles wide.

The Eastern Ghats have very few characteristics in common with the Western Ghats. They are lower than the Western Ghats because of the general slope of the plateau, minutely dissected and of different origin. The alluvial coast is usually low and fairly smooth. The climate is generally dry except towards the north; it would be very poor country without the fertile ricefields of the deltas.

*The Tamil plain.* The Tamil Plain or Tamiland is mainly in the State of Madras. In the middle is the valley and delta of the Cauvery; north and south of this river it is drier.

Descending from the plateau there is a peneplaned region of hill country formed of gneiss, with isolated hills; below these is the alluvium extending to the sandy beaches. The climate is fairly dry, most of the rain coming with the north-east monsoon from mid-October to mid-December. However, the north-east monsoon sometimes fails.

In the extreme south there is a little fertile black earth, but the rainfall is slight. The highland of the southern block makes a complete rainshadow of the area during the summer monsoon. The palm is one of the chief resources of the region. Conditions are very similar in the area between the sea and Madurai; a shady plain extends the low desolate dunes of the seashore more than forty miles inland: but though the rainfall is heavier, for most of the year it is hot and dry.

The soils are poor and would produce little were it not for the very large number of reservoirs. Innumerable crescent-shaped ponds, each fringed with green and surrounded by a sea of sand, make a strange sight viewed from the air, especially after the first rains. The streams and rivers descending from the mountains are liable to rapid flooding, but for most of the time are almost dry.

The city of Madurai, where the river leaves the hills, is surrounded by rice fields. It is the ancient capital of Pandya, the intellectual centre of the Tamils, and is one of the most attractive towns in India, with huge temples whose towers are visible far away on the plains. A textile industry which has not entirely replaced the high quality hand-woven product is responsible for its present growth. In the hill country the town of Dindigul is the centre of a tobacco-producing area.

The Cauvery is not one of the largest rivers of India, but it is almost 500 miles long and has a basin of about 27,000 square miles. It rises in the Ghats of Mysore, quite close to the west coast; it follows a winding course with gorges and falls, but by the time it enters the lowland at Erode it is a broader, powerful river. It has an ample flow all the year round and flooding is relatively slight, the area affected being restricted by dykes. It passes near Tiruchirapalli and its rock; this is a centre with important locomotive workshops, a cement works and textile factories. Two miles away, on the large island of Srirangam, is one of the largest temples in India. The delta has many branches and is densely populated.

Ever since the dawn of history this delta has been as much the work of man as of nature. The most important outlet enters the sea towards the north, near Porto Novo. There are many man-made channels which divert water from the right bank of this outlet directly to the sea. This area of paddy fields is dependent on the Cauvery, for rainfall is low. Oddly, this very humid delta also produces groundnuts (peanuts), which are much better suited to the neighbourhood of Pondicherry. Bananas are also grown on the plain as well as in the hill country, the annual total averaging around 673,700 tons a year.

Farther north the plain is narrower. The Salem Plateau, which reaches quite close to the sea, is dry and rather infertile but is valued for its mineral resources of iron, mica, magnetite, steatite, copper and gold. Pondicherry, capital of the former French settlement on this coast, has a rather dry hinterland.

From Pondicherry to Madras stretches a region of stony uplands with aloes and palm trees and vast bare spaces, with a rather swampy alluvial coast.

Madras has not a very good natural site, chosen as it was so as not to arouse the jealousy of the Dutch, and also in order to trade cheap cotton goods. The harbour is entirely artificial. Nevertheless, a great city has sprung up which is developing rapidly; the population was 527,000 in 1921, 777,000 in 1941, and

*See map opposite:* India has one of the largest populations in the world, despite the high deathrate due to poverty and disease. The population density is greatest in the well-watered plains of Uttar Pradesh to the north, and in the pockets down the east coast around the mouths of the rivers, as far south as Madras. Between the areas of high density there is continuous settlement all along the Indian coast, in contrast to the dry interior plateau which is more sparsely populated.

The great majority of Indians are Hindus, and there is great diversity in the practice of this religion. The Moslems form a smaller but stricter sect. There are a number of Christians especially around Madras, the converts coming chiefly from among the lower-caste Hindus. The Sikhs, who are almost as numerous as the Christians, are found mainly in the Punjab and adjacent states and form a very distinctive minority. There are also small communities of Jains, Buddhists and many other tribal religions scattered throughout the country.

1,725,000 in 1961; the new suburbs along the coast are linked by electric trains and all kinds of industries have developed.

*The coast of Andhra Pradesh and Orisa.* Between Madras and the River Krishna passing through Nellore and stretching back towards Cuddapah, the plain is infertile, supporting only a thin savanna with some sparse woodland. In some valleys it is possible to grow millet and even rice with irrigation. The surrounding hills contain minerals such as asbestos, barytes, antimony and copper. The rainfall is inadequate even on the west-facing slopes of the highland, which do receive a little more rain.

The population as far as the Krishna, whether in the hills or on the plains, is sparse and backward; in nearly 40,000 square miles there is not one settlement worthy of being called a town.

There is a considerable difference in the region of the united deltas of the Krishna and Godavari, which leaves the plateau in a broad valley whose ancient sedimentary rocks load the waters of the Krishna with silt. The rice-growing delta is fairly restricted in area, and with low and unreliable rainfall the whole of the state of Andhra is infertile, even near Hyderabad.

Farther north the coastal plain is constricted by wooded highlands; this is the beginning of the area

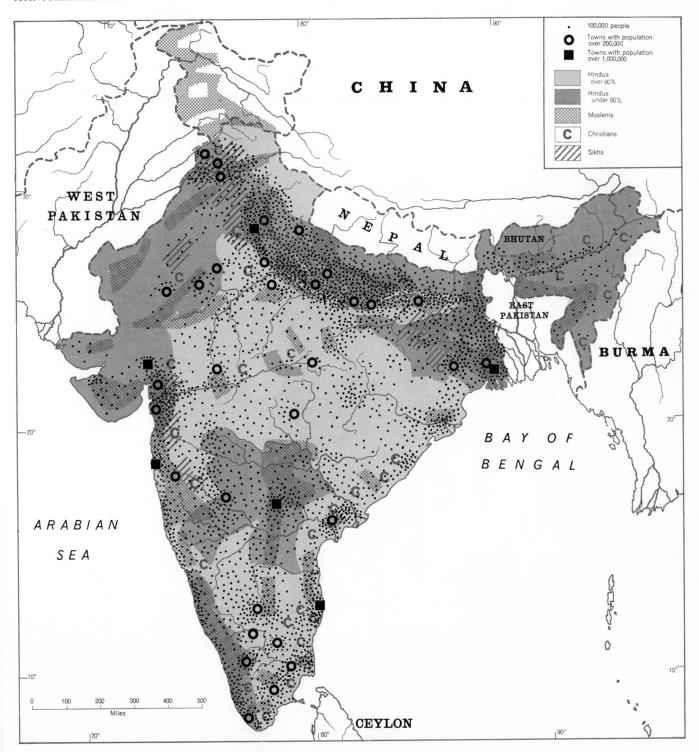

dominated by the main south-west monsoon, and the humidity increases steadily as far as Bengal. Jute begins to appear. A modern port with naval dockyards has been built at Vishakhapatnam. This area marks the boundary between Andhra and Orissa, between the Dravidian languages and the Indo-Aryan.

The state of Orissa regained its unity in the reorganisation of 1956. It includes part of the plateau with forests, some of which have hardly been explored, and along the coast the fertile adjoining deltas of the Mahanadi, Brahmani and Baitarani, where rice can be grown without irrigation. The population density in the deltas is over 500 per square mile: the town of Cuttack and the new adminstrative town of Bhubaneswar should develop. The old city of Puri, with its temple of Jagannath, is still a centre of pilgrimage.

The coastal plain narrows again, and at Balasore the gneiss nearly reaches the sea. The rivers, including the Mahanadi, are full of silt, some of which has been spread over their lower valleys.

Infertile soil and inadequate rainfall make the coast of Andhra Pradesh a region of extreme poverty and famine.
In 40,000 square miles there is not a single settlement that could be called a town.

THE NORTHERN BORDER OF THE DECCAN. *Barrier or link?* The transitional area between the Deccan Plateau and the Ganges Plain forms a triangle between Gujerat and Bengal, with Delhi at the apex.

During many different eras, mainly before the folding of the Himalayas, this region was a buttress against pressure from all sides, and consequently it is of complex structure.

The whole of this area is transitional from a human point of view. The population, especially in the east, includes primitive peoples speaking Mounda or Dravidian languages or sometimes both; each group has been isolated by the Indo-Aryan advance, which followed the natural routes and most fertile valleys. Even the people speaking Indo-Aryan languages in Rajasthan and Malwa towards the west, or in Bundelkhand in the centre, have survivals of the past in their feudal social structures.

The population is usually not very dense, especially in the sandy areas of the west; however, it has often collected near what were once forts, the capitals of independent kingdoms as well as the stopping-places on the caravan trails.

Except in the west, the rainfall is fairly adequate, and where the soil permits it supports savanna and sparsely wooded tropical grassland; there are some more densely wooded forests. The big difference between east and west is that the monsoon rainfall, which is reliable in the east as far as Chota Nagpur, becomes progressively unreliable towards the west.

The most attractive part of the whole region is undoubtedly the highland area formerly known as Malwa, stretching north from the Vindhya Range; this forms the watershed between the rivers flowing to the Indian Ocean and those flowing towards the Ganges Basin. The southern part, especially the area covered with lava, is fairly fertile and well cultivated. Historically it played an important part as a route between the Gulf of Cambay, with its sea connections with the West, and the Ganges valley. Ujjain was the capital of the Gupta Empire, and it was here that Sanskrit poetry and Indian sciences achieved their first development. Today it still has a population of 145,000. In the reorganisation of the political divisions in 1956, Malwa was incorporated with parts of the central area to form the extensive and poor State of Madhya Pradesh, known for its traditional village and home industries.

Among the transitional zones is the north-east corner of the plateau, the region of Chota Nagpur, which is one of the most remote and little-known parts of India.

This highly dissected mountain area includes the Damodar valley, which together with the surrounding country is exceptionally rich in minerals. Apart from mica, of which the Hazaribagh Hills are the leading world producer, the depression of Damodar contains coal of moderate quality in large accessible deposits. Bauxite is important, as well as iron ore deposits, particularly in the region of Singbhum. A great metallurgical industry, the Tata Steelworks, has been established in the heart of the jungle at Jamshedpur, which had under 6,000 inhabitants in 1911, 148,000 in 1941, and 332,000 by 1961. Also present are manganese, chromium, silica and ganister (fire-clay). The manpower comes from a very wide area. Other metallurgical centres are Assansol, Durgapur, Rourkela, and Bhilai. Ranchi is now a heavy electrical and metal-working centre.

The Damodar valley has also been chosen for comprehensive development on the lines of the Tennessee Valley Authority project. Dams have been built for irrigation and electrical power.

*The wealth of the Deccan.* Not all the mineral resources of the Deccan have been mentioned yet. There are, for example, the ilmenite and monazite used in the production of atomic energy, which are found in the sandhills at Waltair, near Vishakhapatnam, and on the beaches of southern Kerala between Quilon and Cape Comorin, where they occur with zircon. Graphite and beryl, also used in atomic plants, are plentiful in the Aravalli Hills near Ajmer.

It is in the Deccan that the most valuable treasures of Indian art are preserved. The South, including the Tamil regions of the extreme south, has been the main artistic and intellectual centre of India. There are advanced institutes for research, the Science Institute at Bangalore and the Gokhak Institute at Poona. Finally, most of the pilgrimage sites are to be found in the Indian peninsula.

## THE GANGES PLAIN

The Ganges Plain lies between the northern edge of the Deccan, which plunges abruptly into the alluvial plain, and the huge and lofty wall of the Himalayas; it is one of the largest plains in the world and stretches almost horizontally for a thousand miles from Amritsar to Calcutta, monotonously flat without a ridge or hill worth mentioning. It covers an area of 135,000 square miles and supports a population of 100 million.

The whole region is dominated by the River Ganges itself, which forms a natural demarcation line between the differing northern and southern parts of the valley. There is considerable climatic variation from east to west.

*The Indus-Ganges watershed.* The area of the Indus-Ganges watershed is a transitional zone between the Sutlej, a tributary of the Indus, and the Jumna, a tributary of the Ganges, with the Himalayas to the north and the Thar Desert to the south. The actual watershed between the Indus and the Ganges is at Sirhind, in East Punjab, at a height of only 680 feet. But it was not the relief which made the traditional routes of trade and invasion pass this way; it was mainly the aridity of the Hissar region, a northern extension of the Thar Desert, that was responsible for the concentration of communications and population at the foot of the Himalayas. The towns are sited along this route: Delhi, which is situated approximately in the centre of this region, in what is primarily a strategic position; Amritsar, the religious capital of the Sikhs, its temple roofed with solid gold; Jalandhar, Ludhiana and Ambala. The choice for the new capital of the State of Punjab fell on Chandigarh, which lies even closer to the mountains, below Simla. It is only in a zone parallel to the Himalayas that there are in the Punjab green and fertile fields where the people live in relative comfort, well fed on wheat and proud of their tractors.

Before long the giant installations of the Indian Government at Bhakra Nangal will lead the waters of the Himalayas far south across Hissar to create thousands of square miles of fertile fields, and also check the advance of the desert sand, which every year creeps a little closer to Delhi.

In spite of a few small industries, Delhi is primarily an administrative city with some elegant buildings. It regained its old position as capital in 1912. The rapid increase in population has led to the growth of satellite towns since 1950. In 1964, with New Delhi, it had a population of 2,659,000.

Compared with the Lower Ganges and southern India, the climate of Delhi is continental, with frosty winter nights and intense heat and dryness in April and May. There are about nine dry months, with monsoon rain from mid-June to the end of September *The Ganges Plain.* The River Ganges, rising in the Himalayas at a height of about 14,000 feet, is nearly 2,000 miles long and has a drainage basin of 350,000 square miles. At first it is a mountain torrent, but

This gigantic hydraulic power station, constructed by the Indian Government at Bhakra Nangal, is designed to channel the waters of the Himalayas across the Hissar, far to the south, and thereby to irrigate thousands of square miles and halt the advance of the desert which every year creeps nearer to Delhi.

when it enters the plain at Hardwar the height is only 1,000 feet, and it still has more than 1,500 miles to flow. It winds rather sluggishly across the plain, broad and deep with a good run-off all the year round. There is a marked rising of the river during the summer monsoon, due both to rainfall and to melting snow. During the dry season the river is sunk into its flood bed, which is often two or three miles wide.

Most of the left-bank tributaries flow at first almost parallel to the main river, which they join farther downstream. These tributaries, fed by Himalayan torrents, have worn courses for themselves in the unconsolidated sedimentary rocks, and are fairly regular except for a few violent floods and changes of course which leave useless swamp. The Gumti, which does not rise in the Himalayas, flows in fairly mature meanders; but Kosi rises on the slopes of Everest and flows straight down an alluvial fan on which it frequently changes course; as Bihar is a region of heavy rainfall there are sudden floods. Besides, the Kosi is continually spreading micaceous sand over the plain, making useless fields that were formerly fertile and productive.

The Jumna, a right-bank tributary which rises in the Himalayas, is joined by rivers from the northern edge of the Deccan carrying little alluvium, and because of this the Jumna, which has a regular flow, discharges into the Ganges water much clearer than that of the main stream. Another right-bank tributary is the Son, which joins the Ganges near Patna. Below Patna the Ganges is both wide and great in volume; at its confluence with the Brahmaputra it has a flow of 600,000 cubic feet per second.

Before entering Bengal the river meets the obstacle of the Rahmahal Hills, and the southern part of the river valley, which is often narrow, disappears completely.

*The transition of climate and region.* It is very difficult to define the east to west divisions of the Ganges Plain, for usually the change is imperceptible. The most striking difference is that of climate, with a marked drought and range of temperature in Rajasthan, and a high rainfall and equable temperature in Bengal. However, to base the intermediate divisions simply on isohyets would be quite arbitrary and misleading. A more acceptable division of the Ganges Plain is into rice- and wheat-growing regions. The wheat-growing region of the Upper Ganges extends roughly as far as Allahabad, and the rice-growing region of the Middle Ganges as far as Bengal. The Delta is also primarily a rice-growing area.

*The Upper Ganges wheat-growing region.* Though some rice is grown in this area, the people of the west use it only as a supplement, not as their basic food.

Annual rainfall in the Upper Ganges rarely exceeds 40 inches; while irrigation is highly developed in the region, it is almost absent below Allahabad, except for a small area south of the river near Patna. Between one-third and one-half of the agricultural production here depends on the elaborate irrigation system. The Ganges and the Jumna are utilised by a canal network over 7,500 miles long, supplying about 8 million acres which were developed mainly in the nineteenth century. The water fron the canals is supplemented by wells, either artesian or semi-artesian, which are bored deep into the water table.

Parts of the area are arid and useless; bordering the foothills there are gravelly areas and swamps; in some places even the better soils have been spoilt by the accumulation of alkaline salts. However, altogether there is much very fertile soil, forming one of the most highly cultivated regions of India. The average temperature for January is about 17°C. (63°F.) and for May 33°C. (91°F.). Most of the area receives nearly 40 inches of rainfall, which is sufficient for wheat to be grown without irrigation. But the centre of the valley receives much less rainfall; the area with less than 40 inches penetrates a long way down the river itself—Agra, for example, has only 25 inches. Nearly all the rain falls during the monsoon between July and August, but there are occasional short storms in February.

In the spring the wheat and barley are harvested; these are the crops of the dry season. In the autumn, after the monsoon, rice, millet and maize are the main crops. On the basis of area cultivated, wheat is the leading crop, with a slightly larger area than the millets, and almost twice as much as rice, chick-peas or barley. Maize, sugar-cane and oil-bearing crops are also grown. Cotton is declining and is not very significant, but tobacco is quite important. The feeding of livestock presents a serious problem, for there is about one head of cattle for every acre cultivated. The methods of cultivation and stock-rearing need to be improved.

*The towns and villages of the Upper Ganges.* Population densities are very high, reaching 1,000 per square mile in places. The system of land tenure has for long allowed the exploitation of the small peasants by the large landowners; reforms introduced since 1954 are producing some improvements by consolidating holdings and introducing community projects.

These high rural densities are all the more serious for a population living almost entirely on agriculture. The typical community is a village with from 500 to 5,000 inhabitants, cultivating the surrounding lands of less than 1,000 acres and sometimes of less than 50. A typical village consists of a cluster of habitations having poor communications with the outside world; only a few local dirt-tracks exist; nearby is water from a river or pond, or a small number of wells. The village, composed chiefly of tiny mud huts, is often surrounded by wall of dried mud and a strip which serves as the communal meadow. There are a few shops, some local craftsmen and one or two moneylenders. The administration is by a 'Council of Five' (panchayat). A small group of untouchables will live in a separate part. In the Oudh region alone there are over 24,000 such villages. General hygiene is poor, and the population is increasing in spite of a high, though falling, death rate. With a total of 65,000 square miles, this region forms the greater part of the State of Uttar Pradesh (population, 74 million).

There are five large towns: Agra, Lucknow, Kanpur, Allahabad and Benares. Agra, on the Jumna, is proud of its magnificent monuments, its fort and the famous mausoleum of the Taj Mahal; today it barely survives by weaving cotton and carpets; it is also a market for wool and leather. Lucknow, the centre of Oudh, is the political capital of the region, with a population of 656,000.

Kanpur, on the Ganges, has grown at an astonishing rate, largely owing to the cotton industry founded in 1869 and stimulated by two world wars; it had a population of 971,000 in 1964. Now it is the third greatest textile centre after Bombay and Ahmadabad, and the largest market in India for wool and leather, with sugar refineries, oil works, flour mills, chemical industries and brush factories. As in many of India's rapidly growing cities, social conditions here have not been satisfactory and serious troubles have occurred. Allahabad, at the confluence of the Ganges and the Jumna, is more an administrative and intellectual centre, and has printing works; the city has scarcely stirred from its provincial calm.

Finally, Benares, on the fringe of the wheatlands, marks the transition to Bihar. It is primarily the holy city of the Hindus, with the temples and steps of 'ghats' down to the River Ganges. A continuous throng of pilgrims keeps it busy. Since 1956 the city has been known officially as Varanasi. Its textile industry tends to produce luxury articles, as, for example, saris woven of gold thread.

Throughout this region the Moslems have remained numerous, even after the partition of 1947, and the Hindus themselves have been strongly influenced by Moslems for a long time. Hindi, which has been proclaimed the national language of India, is native to these parts, especially in the towns. This language has been strongly affected in vocabulary by Arab-Persian influence: it has two forms, Hindi in Devanagari script with part of its vocabulary drawn from Sanskrit, and Urdu with Arabic characters and an Arabic and Persian influence on its vocabulary.

*The rice-growing region of the Middle Ganges.* Apart from the eastern edge of Uttar Pradesh, the Middle Ganges region consists mainly of the State of Bihar, which has an area of 67,000 square miles, incorporating both Bihar and Chota Nagpur.

The climate is dominated by the monsoon, which brings ninety per cent of the rain, much of it in July. The borders of the Himalayas are wetter: while the north of this area receives at least 60 inches, the banks of the Ganges in the same longitude have only 45 to 55 inches. Altitudes never rise above 500 feet and are as low as 100 feet at the approaches to Bengal. The left-bank tributaries, especially the Kosi, are fairly unreliable. Along the Nepal border the swamps of the Terai are unhealthy to live in and also difficult to cultivate.

There is less variety of crops than in the upper part of the valley and the whole of the region is more flourishing. Rice is by far the most important crop, and jute makes an appearance. Millet disappears rapidly, but wheat continues to be grown in the western districts. Sugar-cane does well in the humid northern zone. The monsoon has the disadvantage of stopping suddenly in October, which makes the harvest of the wet season uncertain. There is some irrigation, particularly on the south bank where the Son supplies a vast system of canals.

Farther east a new stage is marked by the appearance of three annual harvests. In the nineteenth century this area was noted for commercial colonial types of crops such as poppy for opium and indigo, which have almost disappeared today. Market-gardening has developed along the Ganges in response to the

One of the community block villages of Nawanshaher, India, which aim at greater prosperity through shared resources. In these villages, hand-pumps are becoming common.

The Ganges at Benares. This holy city of the Hindus has a constant flow of pilgrims visiting its temples, descending its *ghats* and bathing in its river. It lies on the fringe of the wheat-lands.

increasing needs of the heavily populated Calcutta.

The average density of population is higher than 500 per square mile, and it rises to 1,200 in regions such as Tirhut.

There is no large city; Gorakhpur and Darbhanga are only big market towns. Patna is a rather dull administrative centre with a population of only 363,000, though it is the capital of Bihar, which has 46 million inhabitants.

There are numerous associations with Buddhism in this region; Kapilavastu, the birthplace of Buddha, is close to the Nepal frontier near Gorakhpur.

*The Delta.* The 30,000 square miles of the Ganges distributaries form one of the largest deltas in the world, and this area with the immediate surroundings is known as Bengal. Partitioning occured in 1947 and West Bengal, or that part of the delta now in India, is primarily under consideration here.

The Ganges turns towards the south-east and is joined by the Brahmaputra, after which the river is called the Padma and flows in Pakistan. Before this,

Laying a water pipe in Calcutta to feed a large-scale project undertaken fifteen miles away to relieve the critical water shortage.

some distributaries flow south through Indian territory, the first being the Bhagirath, which becomes the Hooghly. The area can be divided into four regions: firstly, the foot of the Himalayas, drained by the Tista, a tributary of the Brahmaputra; secondly, the highlands consisting of Barind, between the Ganges and the Brahmaputra (shared with Pakistan), and Bardwan, a relatively dry area of lateritic soils which is the edge of the Deccan Plateau; thirdly, the centre of the delta with its many waterways—those in the east or Indian part declining through silting, because the main stream has moved towards the east; finally, the Sundarbans, where several million people live in danger of the waters, at the mercy of the high tide.

The progressive change in climate along the Ganges valley is completed here in Bengal, where it is very wet and continually hot. The rainfall is especially heavy in the Assam Hills, in East Bengal.

The regularity of the monsoon is slightly modified in West Bengal, for north-westerly depressions, in Calcutta for example, bring sudden downpours of heavy rain, and sometimes hail, in April or May. These showers are very useful for the cultivation of rice and jute.

Bengal grows sugar-cane, tobacco and oilseeds; cotton has almost disappeared. However, it is primarily an area where there is marked competition between rice and jute growing, more noticeable in Pakistani Bengal than in Indian Bengal.

The population density is high; West Bengal has 35 million inhabitants, an increase of 33 per cent since 1951, which gives an average density of 1,030 per square mile, and this includes the thinly peopled borders of the Himalayas. Fields are small, and the economy of Bengal is always in a critical situation; in 1943 famine due to the cessation of deliveries of Burmese rice led to the death of about two million people.

Calcutta, with a population of 2,926,000, and Howrah on the right bank with 514,000 form a conurbation of some 6 million, which extends in dense suburbs along the banks of the Hooghly. Calcutta is a product of the colonial period, like Madras and Bombay; it was founded in 1692 in a loop of the Hooghly, and, though far from the centre of India, acted as the capital of British India from 1773 to 1912, when it was replaced by Delhi. It owes its importance and growth entirely to special historical circumstances and the conflicting interests of trading companies. Calcutta is a very bad port; it is costly to maintain, the winding estuary is more than 75 miles long, and is made dangerous by continual changes in the position of the sandbanks and by storms. Nor does it have good communications with the rest of India, for it stands on the left bank and the metal bridge which eased this problem was not built until 1943; the terminus for all the important rail routes is at Howrah. As for the site and atmosphere, the original swamps have been cleared only at great expense and the water is scarcely drinkable. Oppressive mists hang over the river and its neighbourhood; there is no breeze, and any winds occur only at gale force at the turn of the monsoon season.

Yet, in spite of the growth of Bombay and the development of new ports, Calcutta retains a high volume of traffic. It has a future as a river port, the outlet for the Middle Ganges, to which it is linked by quite large steamships to Patna. Partition dealt it a severe blow, reducing its exports of jute for three or four years and causing unemployment in the majority of jute mills—but jute is a generally depressed industry. However, the development of the iron and steel belt to the west (Bengal, Bihar, Orissa) should maintain Calcutta's activity. Its airport continues to expand, and sited symmetrically with Karachi, it plays an important part in the world's airways.

The varied industries of Calcutta include engineering and paper manufacturing. Long in contact with the West, Calcutta has a tradition of keen intellectual interest, for the local Bengali culture was highly developed and autonomous. Characteristic political interests are shown in a particularly keen local patriotism. The economic difficulties of the port and the influx of refugees combined to make Calcutta a major centre of extreme left-wing tendencies.

*Assam.* Assam, or the valley of the Brahmaputra, is cut off more than ever, for partition has almost isolated it from the rest of India, to which it is linked only by a narrow corridor in the south. A new railroad had to be built, which makes a long detour. Rather narrow (60 by 400 miles), consisting of the valley and the rain-drenched mountain slopes, Assam is a rather different region, not very Indian, but transitional to Indochina, and to a certain extent to Central Asia and the East. The Brahmaputra, imposing and wide, like an arm of the sea, acts as a line of access; it is navigable by steamships for over 750 miles.

The climate is relatively moderate; showers in April and May, which correspond to the storms of the plains in the north-west, are quite heavy and so prevent the high temperature common to the rest of India. The Plateau of Shillong intercepts the winds and receives enormous amounts of rain; Cherrapungi has the highest rainfall in the world with an average of 457 inches. But in the rainshadow, Gauhati has no more than 68 inches. The country appears fertile and village follows village among the small copses and clumps of bamboo. This is the land of bamboo; loads are carried with a supple piece of bamboo balanced on the shoulder, at the ends of which two trays of equal weight are suspended; this is a method used throughout South-East Asia.

Besides jute and rice, Assam produces large quantities of tea. The forest products are important. There is also a little coal and a considerable amount of oil in the Digboi-Nahorkatiga region in the extreme east. Coal deposits probably, and oil certainly, are of much greater importance than those being developed at present.

The population contains a varying mixture of Asian peoples. Assamese, an Indo-Aryan language related to Bengali, has peculiarities which may be explained by the proximity of Tibet and Burma.

The Shillong Plateau is a detached block of the Deccan. It is formed of slaty schists and quartzite with granite intrusions, and is inhabited by relatively backward tribes which are all quite distinct from most of the Indian peoples. Shillong, the capital of Assam, is a hill station nearly 5,000 feet above sea level, with more than 100,000 inhabitants.

## THE MOUNTAIN BORDER

To the north east, India is isolated from the rest of Asia by an almost impenetrable mountain barrier. There is hardly such a good natural frontier in the world. In the north is the huge arc of the Himalayas, with groups of folds extending nearly 2,000 miles without an appreciable gap. In the east is the group of convex folds in the Assam-Burmese mountains, lower but quite as difficult to cross. Both were elevated during the Tertiary Era and their youthful relief features are illustrated by the continuity of the ranges and the steepness of their slopes.

The Himalayas may be divided into a number of quite different regions. There is the eastern or Assam Himalaya, the central or Nepal Himalaya and the western or Kashmir Himalaya. It is convenient to consider together the Assam-Burmese mountains and the eastern Himalayas.

THE MOUNTAIN RANGES OF BURMA AND ASSAM. A compact group of parallel folds separated by deep longitudinal valleys stretches for over 450 miles, with a width of 80 to 125 miles, from the far northeastern corner of India to Cape Negrais on the south coast of Burma, and apparently into the Andaman and Nicobar Islands. The average height is a little over 6,500 feet; Mount Saramati on the Indo-Burmese frontier is the highest point, over 11,700 feet, and it is often snow-covered. Passes are few and of little use.

The western slopes receive heavy rainfall, which gives rise to luxuriant vegetation and an unhealthy climate; but the rainfall is not so excessive on the ridges and plateaus. The tropical forest is generally very dense, sometimes impenetrable. There are no roads, and for thousands of square miles there is nothing but mule tracks, usually along the ridges. Rail projects linking India and South-East Asia have been considered, but abandoned.

The only parts of these ranges which are in the Indian Union are the Patkai Bum in the north, the

A delegation of tribal people from Assam in New Delhi for Independence Day. The practice of headhunting is now dying out in Assam and will soon be only a part of Assamese folk-lore.

The main river flowing through the district of Nagar, in Kashmir. Most of the villages lie along its banks, as does Srinagar, the capital of Nagar, where the Mir, or ruler, has his summer palace. The route to Srinagar comes from Gilgit, 80 miles to the south; following the course of this track, a jeep road is being constructed.

Naga Hills and the grassy Plateau of Manipur. The hills of Lushai and Chittagong on the western edge belong to Pakistan.

Little of the land can be cultivated. On the drier plateaus like those of Manipur, mainly oranges and potatoes are grown, with a little rice and millet. Methods of farming and the mode of life of the people have similarities with the Shan State of Burma farther to the east. The population is fairly sparse and very mixed; as a result of the difficult communications there is a large number of linguistic subdivisions from valley to valley and sometimes in the same valley; all these languages are connected with the Tibeto-Burmese group.

The people practise extensive agriculture which results in a more or less slow migration. There are few towns of any size apart from Kohima, the Naga capital, and Manipur (Imphal). Manipur, with a population of over 100,000 is nothing more than a collection of villages without any real urban character. The air links with India are the only practical means of travelling beyond the national frontiers.

These peoples of Tibeto-Burmese orgin are very different from those of India proper. Their civilisation is advanced and complex, not at all primitive, though with peculiarities which are disconcerting to the Hindus. Like the peoples of the Shillong Plateau, they practise matriarchy; though Buddhists, they are warlike to the extent of being head-hunters. These regions raise delicate political problems for the Government of India, for though they are constitutionally integral parts of India, with representative government, taxes usually cannot be collected; the Indian police and army have suffered sometimes serious surprise attacks. There are quite strong feelings for autonomy; the Nagas, for example, persistently demanded independence. In the State of Tripura Communists number twelve out of thirty elected representatives. In the winter of 1962 the North-East Frontier Agency was the scene of Chinese incursions.

THE EASTERN HIMALAYAS: BHUTAN AND SIKKIM. The right bank of the Brahmaputra valley is dominated by the steep slopes of the Himalayas. The extreme eastern end of the range differs from the rest in its north-easterly curve and in the narrowing of the folds so that there are hardly any level areas. This part of the mountains has the simplest structure, with two zones, the outer or Lesser Himalaya, averaging from 6,500 to 11,000 feet, and the Great Himalaya usually over 20,000 feet. The mountains are dissected and crossed by the gorges of the Tsang-po, which becomes the Dihang after making a hairpin bend at the foot of Namcha Barwa (25,445 feet), and eventually becomes the Brahmaputra. The areas to the east of the bend and the mountains surrounding the eastern end of Assam have not been explored completely, forming as they do a complete physical and national boundary.

The Mongolian population in the eastern mountains is very sparse, though scarcely more so than in the state of Bhutan, to the east, where there are 700,000 inhabitants in 18,000 square miles. Bhutan is very hilly and dominated in the west by Mount Chomo Lhari (23,930 feet); it is a land of wild mountains, partly forested, with fortified Buddhist monasteries or castles standing on the edge of precipices. Yaks are reared, and somehow millet, maize and even a little rice is grown. Bhutan, which in principle is independent, is claimed by China. India maintains close diplomatic relations with the rulers of Bhutan.

In the west of Bhutan several rivers are incised deeply in the Lesser Himalayan Range; the valley of the Chumbi gives access to the best route to Tibet, via Gyangtse.

In the main Himalayan range there are numerous summits over 23,000 feet; they are dominated by Kanchenjunga (28,146 feet), a wonderful snowy peak which can be viewed from the hill station of Darjeeling, itself 7,300 feet above sea level. Darjeeling, which is included in Indian Bengal, has a cool and very wet climate. The monsoon rainfall is very heavy, with a total higher than in the extreme east of the Himalayas. The rainfall is particularly heavy on the slopes overlooking the plain of Bengal and adjoining Bihar.

The slopes leading to Darjeeling are covered with tea plantations. The people eat rice grown at this

Singapore River flowing through the centre of Singapore, a busy international por

unusual height, and maize. However, a large proportion of the land is not developed. The lower slopes are covered with dense tropical forest with clumps of giant bamboo; above 5,000 feet are oak forests, evergreen because of the high humidity. Above 10,000 feet these give way to conifers and then to giant rhododendrons. Over 13,000 feet there is hardly anything but alpine shrubs and pastures. The snow-line usually begins at 17,000 feet and all animal and vegetable life ceases. Only a minute proportion of the forest resources has been developed because of the difficult access.

The small Indian protectorate of Sikkim is covered by a network of torrents forming the River Tista, and has hardly an acre of flat land; it has the privilege of controlling Indian access to Tibet. The population of 161,000 in an area of 2,818 square miles is of Tibetan and Nepalese stock; Nepalese immigration has been going on for two or three hundred years and these people now account for 75 per cent of the population. Gangtok, the capital and a caravan centre, is only a village. The diurnal range of temperature is appreciable even during the rainy season; during the day there is a stifling heat in the enclosed valleys. There is widespread cultivation of millet and rye; wheat and barley are grown in the gardens around the houses, and terraced cultivation of rice has been introduced. Oranges and European fruits grow quite well. Cattle are reared and yaks kept on the highlands. Mineral wealth, which appears to be important, has been little developed. The Indian Government exercises a protectorate over Sikkim, which makes it responsible for external affairs, though Sikkim is autonomous with regard to internal affairs.

THE CENTRAL HIMALAYAS FROM EVEREST TO SIMLA. The highest peaks of the main range are grouped together in eastern Nepal; apart from Kanchenjunga they are: Annapurna, 26,429 feet; Dhaulagiri, 26,795 feet; and Everest, the highest mountain in the world, 29,028 feet. The distance between the two ranges is sufficient to form quite extensive plains in spite of some transverse mountain ridges. The valley surrounding Katmandu is the essential part of Nepal. From Sikkim to the western end of the Himalayas there is a line of foothills, called the Siwalik Range, composed of recently folded, permeable sedimentary rocks about 3,000 feet high. Between the Siwalik and the Lesser Himalaya the longitudinal valleys are sometimes quite broad and usually humid. Along the foot of the Siwalik Range extends the very humid and unhealthy zone of the Terai.

The structure of the Himalayas is very complex. North of a fairly clear fault beyond the Lesser Himalaya the ancient crystalline rocks reappear; these are in fact the base of the great Tertiary folding which has been exposed by erosion. This is the reason why the central zone with its peaks of heavily dissected crystalline rocks is very contorted, while the northern edge of the Great Himalayan Range is not so high as the rest, and is much more regular with smoother slopes and uniform heights.

The central Himalayas extend beyond the 550 miles of Nepal, bending north to Kumaon and Himachel Pradesh.

The Great Himalaya in Kumaon (administratively part of Uttar Pradesh) includes some high mountains such as Kamet (25,447 feet) and Nanda Devi (25,645 feet). Glaciers are more important here than in the east. The mountains have been heavily dissected by glacial erosion, the dissection being continued by the rivers. The process goes forward rapidly; the beds of the torrents are deepened quickly even in quartz, and in the steep ravines there are continual landslips. The improvised bridges are unstable suspension footbridges swaying above the chasms filled with rushing water.

The valleys are quite densely populated; the towns are either hill stations sited on the crest of the Lesser Himalaya, or agricultural centres and staging posts, Dehra Dun at the foot of the Himalayas being the most important of these. Also important is the holy town of Hardwar, where the Ganges enters the plain.

The monsoon is still very marked here, but rainfall is heavy only on the highland over 10,000 feet; at the foot of the mountains the climate is hot and humid — stifling in summer and foggy in winter. The alluvial valleys yield good crops of cereals. Stock-rearing plays only a minor part except in the heart of the mountains, where it becomes almost the only means of livelihood.

Himachal Pradesh overlooks the area of the watershed between the Indus and the Ganges and is very similar to Kumaon, except that the climate is much drier, and the mountains more dissected by numerous broad valleys. This area helps to supply the river network of the Punjab, and is the source of various irrigation schemes.

The population is slightly less dense than in Kumaon; the capital is Simla, a summer residence at 7,000 feet, an artificial town perched on the mountain top. The great hydro-electric projects in progress should help to improve the economy of this region because of the demand for labour and the distribution of electric power. Forestry is quite important; the famous Kulu valley produces most of the temperate fruit.

THE WESTERN HIMALAYAS: KASHMIR. The western Himalayas coincide almost exactly with Kashmir. A notable feature of the mountains is the broad syncline in the centre; the Jhelum, flowing north-westwards parallel to the folds before crossing the lower range, is the only Himalayan river with such a wide valley, and the only one which, in its upper course, is sufficiently graded to be navigable. A general lowering of the mountains is noticeable here in the Lesser Himalaya and in the Great Himalaya, called here the Zaskar Range. Beyond the longitudinal valley of the Indus is the Karakorum Range, which has thirty summits over 24,000 feet, among them the second highest in the world, K2 (28,250 feet): the strange name perpetuates the memory of a local intelligence agent who was killed on a mission.

The large State of Jammu and Kashmir (86,000 square miles) consists not simply of the famous Kashmir valley but also contrasting regions which from north to south are the Karakoram Range, the Indus valley, Ladakh, a kind of small Tibet, the Zaskar Range, the Jhelum valley and the borders of the plains.

The region below the Himalayas includes the fairly dry districts of Punch and Jammu, with limestone slopes exposed to the heat of the sun. Wheat, barley, maize and millet are grown. The dense population is composed mainly of Hindus of the Dogra caste who, during the nineteenth century, ruled over the Moslem majority in the Kashmir valley. The Moslem population of Jammu in 1961 was 50,000. Jammu, the chief town, is a religious centre and a very important military base since the partition in 1947 and the conflict with Pakistan.

Access to Kashmir from India is quite difficult; since 1948 a winding road has been available, though difficult to maintain and blocked by snow in winter. Air links are vital both from a political and a military point of view.

The famous Kashmir valley is almost level, stretching some 80 miles by 25 at an average altitude of 5,200 feet. The soil is partly composed of fine alluvium of lacustrine origin and also, in places, morainic materials. The whole surface is covered with a close network of streams and canals.

The climate is continental with cold winters, temperatures at about freezing-point in January and February, and snow even in April. Total precipitation is only 26 inches and is not monsoonal; the greater part falls during the winter months, much of it as snow, and May to September is the driest period. The amount of rain is barely sufficient for cultivation and over half the crops are grown with irrigation. Rice is quite common but requires much labour, especially for weeding; maize is the crop on the drier lands. There is some good wheat land where the crop can be grown on the moisture from the melting snow. Around the capital, Srinagar, are wonderful fields of market-garden crops and flowers, with waterways along which tourists can travel by boat. There are also winter sports.

Apart from the tourist industry, the chief resources of the country are stock-rearing — some cattle, but mainly sheep — and forestry. The manufacture of woollen cloth and of carpets are of equal importance also curious for visitors and for export. Agriculture has difficulty in supplying the needs of a population which is very dense in the valley. The bulk of the 3,600,000 people is crowded into either Jammu or the Kashmir valley. The smaller peasants, usually Moslems have long been exploited by the Hindu feudal system and the law relating to land ownership was a serious problem in addition to the many internal and external difficulties; this and the wish to keep the allegiance of Kashmiri Moslems were the reasons why Kashmir undertook in 1950 the most radical land reform legislation — and the first undertaken under the new Indian Government.

Kashmir has strategic importance through its control of access to north-west India. It is hardly surprising that since the departure of the British it has been the source of keen dispute between India and Pakistan. From November 1947 until the truce of 1949 and again in 1965 there was warfare here. It is only the provisional line of ceasefire which now separates Indian Kashmir from Pakistan Kashmir (treated in the chapter on Pakistan).

For centuries the Chinese Buddhists have come through Kashmir on pilgrimages to the lands of the Ganges where the Master lived. A considerable volume of trade also passes along this route. The bazaar at Srinagar is a meeting-point of different civilisations, and here a cross-section of the peoples of Asia can be seen. There are the Kashmiri Brahmans with fair complexions, who have imposed a language rather like Sanskrit on the country, and the Punjabi Moslems with long hooked noses; there are also quite different Moslems, traders and caravaneers from Afghanistan and Iran, as well as the yellow-skinned men from Ladakh and the Indians from the plains of Rajasthan and the Punjab.

In Srinagar wooden houses along rutted, muddy paths wet with melting snow give an impression of a small Russian town; the onion-shaped domes of the mosques complete the illusion.

Ladakh, with Leh its capital, is inhabited by yellow-skinned Buddhists. The mountainous terrain and lack of communications, as well as cultural differences, make it difficult for India to administer it. A large part in the east is in dispute with China, which has built a strategic road through the area since 1957. The aridity of the climate is very marked, with only three inches of rain a year; the range of temperature is considerable and the cold severe in winter.

Ama Dablam, in the Everest region of Nepal. One of the mountains of the Greater Himalaya, it reaches a height of 22,494 feet.

# NEPAL

Of the numerous kingdoms which existed in India before the advent of the British, only the State of Nepal retained its independence, defended by its mountains and the courage of the inhabitants.

There are no detailed maps or precise statistics concerning Nepal, but it includes more than five hundred miles of the arc of the Himalaya mountains. It is situated almost in the middle of this arc, between Sikkim to the east and the River Sarda to the west. From north to south it includes zones which differ greatly: the marshy Terai at the foot of the mountains; then the Lesser Himalaya, followed by quite a large central valley; finally the Great Himalaya with several very high peaks such as Dhaulagiri, Everest and Kanchenjunga. It is the valley of Katmandu in the centre, with an average altitude of 4,500 feet, which is the real heart of Nepal. It is shaped like a rectangular amphitheatre, about 15 miles by 8 miles; it is fertile and intensively cultivated, especially with rice. In this small area live about 600,000 people, with three towns, each with an historic past and well known for the attractive sculpture of the wooden buildings, both public and private.

The most important of the three cities, Katmandu, has a population of about 200,000. It is noted for its military activities, with barracks, parade grounds and armament workshops; it also contains the imposing palaces of the Ranas or the family of hereditary Prime Ministers, deposed in 1951. The other two towns are Patan in the south and Bhatgaon in the east.

Even today surface access to the valley is not easy; however, the air routes have put Katmandu less than an hour from Patna and a few hours from Delhi.

The Terai is very unhealthy because of the malaria there; its typical vegetation is tall grass. Wild animals including tigers are common. In some areas which have been cleared, the crops include rice, a little wheat, sugar-cane, tobacco and jute. The Terai remains thinly populated.

In the Lesser Himalaya the population is found in the narrow but fertile valleys, where rice, barley and maize are grown. North of Katmandu there are extensive orchards with some tropical fruit, such as mango and banana, and temperate fruits, especially the gooseberry. Stock-rearing is less developed than might be expected. The climate is similar to that of Kumaon and cooler than that of Sikkim. The Great Himalaya is inaccessible and little known.

The Nepalese people are mainly of two elements one of Tibetan stock and Buddhist, the other made up of Gurkhas who became predominant in Nepal in the sixteenth century. Buddhists and Hindus live side by side.

Nepal exports leather, opium, resins and dyestuffs, timber, jute, rice and saltpetre. It imports cattle, cotton cloth and other manufactures. Little is known of its mineral wealth but it is probably quite important. Plans for development, financed chiefly by foreign aid, cover improved farming techniques, irrigation, hydro-electric projects, road building and schools.

Special agreements have been made to allow Great Britain and India to continue recruiting young

Every square foot of cultivable land in Nepal is used, and monumental staircases of terraces follow every contour, as in the Pelang valley shown here.

Sherpanis (Sherpa women) feeding naks after a snowstorm. (The nak is female, the yak male.) The Sherpas, of Tibetan stock and Buddhist faith, and the Ghurkas, who are Hindu, are the two principal elements of the Nepalese population.

A street scene in Katmandu, capital of Nepal. A town with a population of about 200,000, situated 75 miles from the Indian frontier, Katmandu is an active military centre with a barracks and armaments factories. Katmandu will be linked to Llasa by a new road being built and air communications put it within a few hours' journey of Delhi.

Nepalese for Gurkha units, which are noted for their endurance and courage.

From a political point of view Nepal was under the double authority of a monarchy and the Rana family, hereditary Prime Ministers until 1951, when the King proclaimed a constitutional monarchy and put an end to the long despotism of the Ranas: this did not, however, stop the sporadic action of rebel bands in the areas far from the capital. In 1961 Panchayet (village council) democracy was introduced. With government policy thus based on the principle of decentralisation, it is hoped that the people will unite in the task of developing Nepal's resources.

# CEYLON

*The insularity of Ceylon.* Ceylon is a large island of high relief about 270 miles by 125 miles and covers 25,000 square miles. Separated from India by a shallow strait and on the same continental platform, it has similarities with southern India. Ceylon and India have similar civilisations and languages; Singalese, spoken in the southern part of the island and in most of the west, is an Indo-Aryan language originating from Sanskrit and obviously linked with the languages of the Ganges Plain, such as Hindi and Bangali. Tamil, the language of south-east India, is dominant in the north and north-east of the island.

Ceylon's history has been separate from India's. It was the site of a Portuguese and then a Dutch trading post before becoming a British Crown Colony in 1802, separate from the Indian Empire. The Dutch occupation exercised a strong influence and has left visible traces, including a Eurasian population of about 30,000 known as Burghers. There are 6,500 Europeans, most of whom are tea planters. Ceylon came under European influence more than India; the widespread use of English betrays British influence, and the common occurrence of Portuguese names is a reminder of distant Portuguese occupation. In the Middle Ages there were close relations with Indonesia, so that there is an appreciable Malay element

in the population. To this should be added an Arab population of half a million, resulting from the sea links with Arabia and the Near East.

The feature most typical of Ceylonese insularity is the continuance of Buddhism, which almost disappeared from India, apart from the Himalayan frontier areas, at least eight centuries ago. The religion was originally introduced from India in the 3rd century B.C.

Since 1948 Ceylon has been one of the nations of the British Commonwealth, in which it has the same status as India or Canada.

*Relief and structure.* The general structure of Ceylon is simple: the highest parts lie south of centre, and are surrounded by an upland belt and then by a coastal fringe. It is a massif of eroded crystalline rocks which has been partly rejuvenated. The centre and summit of the massif takes the form of a depression, the plain of Nuwara Eliya. The alluvium and detritus eroded from the mountain forms most of the surrounding soils; in the east it covers an area of gneiss. Only the northern part of the island, including the Jaffna Peninsula, is composed of sedimentary rocks, which are partly covered by sand.

On the east coast the crystalline rocks are eroded into bays which resemble rias. The best example is Trincomalee, one of the most attractive and safe roadsteads in the world. The bay at Jaffna is too shallow for anything larger than a barge; the port of Colombo, the major commercial port, is mainly artificial.

*Variety of climate.* The climate of Ceylon is hot with very small seasonal ranges of temperature, but in some places, especially on slopes where the sun is strong, large diurnal ranges of temperature are recorded.

Ceylon is influenced in turn by the south-west monsoon from the end of May to the end of August, and the north-east monsoon from November to January. These winds distribute the rainfall unevenly.

The south-west region receives heavy rainfall from both monsoons, so that the annual distribution of rainfall shows a double maximum and no dry month. The winds rise against the south-west slopes of the mountains and showers are almost daily throughout the year, while atmospheric humidity is usually between 90 and 95 per cent. This relatively small and low highland attracts all the rainfall and acts as a complete barrier to the eastern part, which receives practically no rain during the summer monsoon. Even more surprising is the dryness of the eastern part of the southern coast, which receives only some passing showers.

Half of the eastern part receives rain from the northeast monsoon; this small monsoon is rather irregular and may fail partly or completely.

The extreme northern region and Jaffna are liable to severe droughts; average figures are of little use in this context, but experience shows that this region has very little rainfall.

The contrast is nowhere shown better than along the west coast; luxuriant vegetation gives way to savanna-type vegetation with small scattered shrubs, and soon there are sand and palm trees. The sandy Manaar peninsula projects into the blue seas under a burning sun.

Ceylon is divided politically into a number of provinces which are distinct from one another, and which coincide fairly closely with the natural regions. There are three main regions: firstly the mountainous centre, including the tea and rubber plantations, secondly the humid lowlands of the south-west producing rice and rubber, and continued in the coconut belt from Negombo to Chilaw, and thirdly the dry lowlands which form three-quarters of the coastal belt from Puttalam to Tangalla, and include the dry region of the north central area.

There is no river of any importance. The Mahaweli Ganga, the longest, drains the eastern slopes and flows into the head of Trincomalee harbour.

*Tea and rubber in the economy.* In general, Ceylon has a plantation type of economy, in which commodities such as tea, rubber, coconut products and spices are produced largely for export. Cocoa production is relatively unimportant; rice and some other cereals occupy about a quarter of the cultivated land; both fresh and dried fish are eaten. But rice production and home fisheries cannot meet the demand and both rice and dried fish are imported. Ceylon also has to import many manufactured goods, as industrialisation has not yet had time to develop as the Government plans.

The balance of trade is precarious; fluctuations in world prices, especially of tea, have a profound effect on Ceylon's economy. The price of rubber is also vital; at one moment rubber trees are being planted feverishly, at another they are left standing without being tapped. Recently acreage has increased little.

*The growth of population.* The population of Ceylon is increasing very rapidly. In 1921 it was 4,500,000, with a density similar to that of France. In 1946 it was 6,650,000; in 1952, 8,089,000; and at the 1963 census, 10,625,000: this 3 per cent annual rise is exceptionally high. With Ceylon's existing resources the problem of food is becoming more and more acute; every day it is necessary to buy more rice in the world market.

Apart from the overall growth, which is serious enough, there is internal migration which seems even more alarming. In face of increasing economic difficulties the people of the dry eastern area are moving to the Colombo region, the Western Province. The density of population here rose from 250 per square mile in 1881 to 1,265 in 1946 and is now higher than 1,800 per square mile. The growth of industrialisation, centred on Colombo, is inadequate to employ all this manpower. In this way an uprooted working class has been formed, which the Government wish to resettle on the lands which will be available as a result of the large irrigation projects now under construction.

The population problem is complicated in the mountain area of the south centre because the tea plantations employ labour which was originally foreign; the workers are Tamils, usually from India, of whom there are about a million. The growing population and the sharpening competition for work has made Ceylonese society unhappily subject to racial or community conflicts — between the Singhalese and Tamil-speaking peoples. Under a recent agreement 550,000 Indian immigrants were repatriated to India.

The name Colombo Plan was given to a kind of economic link of certain countries in South-East Asia which was founded in 1950. At first it included some members of the British Commonwealth, and later other countries in the area were added. Ceylon has a special interest in the utilisation of its resources in co-operation with the other countries of South-East Asia, especially in spheres where common projects can reduce costs.

*The strategic importance of Ceylon.* Ceylon has always been of great strategic importance. During the last few centuries the navies of Holland, France and then England fought for control of the harbour of Trincomalee, which is still the key to the Indian Ocean. For a century the pleasant climate of the hills enabled the European crews of British ships to rest here and keep in good health. In 1956 the Ceylon Government demanded the return of military bases from Great Britain, and the naval base of Trincomalee and the air base at Katunayake on the west coast were handed over. In spite of the existing agreements for the joint defence of the Commonwealth, the ceding of these British bases appeared as an important event in world strategy. One of the consequences was the development of bases in British East Africa as well as the establishment of others on the Maldive Islands.

The tremendous strength of the elephant has long been exploited by the Ceylonese, but even in Ceylon their use is becoming rarer.

Picking tea in Ceylon. Tea is the second crop on the island, after rice, and the principal export. In 1963, 484 million pounds were harvested of which over 436 million pounds were exported, the principal customers being the United Kingdom, Australia and the United States.

*See map opposite:* With government and some foreign aid, modern large-scale industries are being developed especially in India — textiles, iron and steel, general and electrical engineering. India's mineral wealth includes copper, mica, bauxite, china clay, phosphate and silver, all with their associated industries. Ceylon has limestone, graphite and a wide variety of precious stones, while in Afghanistan the search for natural gas continues and copper, lead, iron, coal, silver and oil are being developed. The other side of the picture reveals a host of traditional crafts and small industries, weaving of cottons, silk-worm rearing, shawl and carpet making, metal-working and wood carving.

# PAKISTAN

Pakistan gained independence under the British law of 1947 which established independence of the Indian Empire and partition into the states of India and Pakistan. Though Pakistan became an Islamic Republic by the Constitution of 1956 it remained within the British Commonwealth.

Pakistan comprises those parts of the Indian sub-continent mainly inhabited by Moslems and is composed of two territories which are 1,000 miles distant from one another, and very dissimilar. West Pakistan consists mainly of the Indus valley bordered on the west by the edge of the Iranian Plateau; East Pakistan is the eastern half of Bengal.

Intercommunication is not easy because of continual political friction between Pakistan and the Indian Union. The use of the Indian railroads is subject to many restrictions; the distance by sea is over 2,500 miles. Non-stop air links and radio communications are therefore important.

Population is much denser in East Pakistan. Of a total of 94 million in 1961, East Pakistan has 51 million crowded into 54,000 square miles, while West Pakistan, the most important part politically, containing Karachi and other major towns, has a population of 43 million in a area of 310,000 square miles. East and West Pakistan differ profoundly in the people, both ethnically and linguistically, in their way of life, and in the physical surroundings. East Pakistan is part of monsoon Asia; a flat, sub-tropical delta, hot and humid, over-populated and rice-growing, it is subject to torrential showers at the June solstice. West Pakistan is really linked with continental Asia, and in particular with Iran, of which it forms the eastern fringe; much of it is mountainous and usually arid. It is hardly affected by the monsoon: conditions vary from semi-desert, passing through the almost temperate climate of the Punjab, to mountains with extreme temperatures. A great part of the population consists of shepherds and farmers. The agrarian reforms of 1959 brought West Pakistan, previously an area of large landed proprietorship, more into line with East Pakistan, where holdings were already smaller.

Only historical events and the bond of the common Moslem religion can account for the union of these two regions into the same state. Like her big neighbour, India, Pakistan has embarked on a series of five year plans to modernise and industrialise the country. Poorer to begin with, and with fewer resources in men and machines, her efforts have been more modest. They have also attracted less foreign aid, partly no doubt because Eastern-bloc countries have, until very recently, felt unable to help a country linked in a formal military alliance with the United States.

## WEST PAKISTAN

Throughout most of its history the Indus valley has either been entirely independent politically or linked with Afghanistan and Iran. The Middle Indus, which was formerly more humid and fertile, was and remains separated from the rest of the Indian sub-continent by the Sutlej, an important river, wide and violent when in flood, and by the arid land beyond the left bank of the Sutlej which becomes semi-desert still within the sight of the Himalayas. Western Rajputana is arid, stony or sandy and often hilly; it forms a wide barrier from the marshes of Kutch to the neighbourhood of Ferozepore, almost cutting off and isolating the Indus valley. There are no communications except along a corridor less than 65 miles wide at the foot of the Himalayas, indicated by towns such as Jalandhar, Ludiana, Patiala and Sirhind. The present frontier of Pakistan swings sharply east

A street bazaar in West Pakistan, three miles from the Khyber Pass, which leads from Kabul to Peshawar. A rocky and desolate region, its climate is one of extremes.

between Lahore and Sialkot; in this area the frontier is not a geographical one but the result of the political decisions taken in 1947.

Towards the west Pakistan includes the extensive, mountainous and sparsely populated region of Baluchistan; its western and northern boundaries across the plateau and then the mountains are not easily defined. In the north-west the frontier mostly follows the crest lines, but this is being disputed by Afghanistan. Since 1947 the future of Kashmir in the north has been in constant dispute and is still divided by a provisional ceasefire line. In the extreme north Pakistan includes the territories of the tribes of Gilgit

who are claiming a degree of autonomy, and extends a narrow tongue right up to the foot of the Karakoram Range.

The main regions of West Pakistan are the North-West Frontier area including the Himalayan parts, the Punjab, Sind and Baluchistan.

*The north-west: a gateway.* The North-West Frontier area forms the threshold to India and Pakistan and is the historic line of entry. It forms a rough triangle, one side resting on the Afghan Plateau and another on the Himalayas. It is hilly with an average altitude of 1,600 feet.

The Indus divides the region into two parts; in the

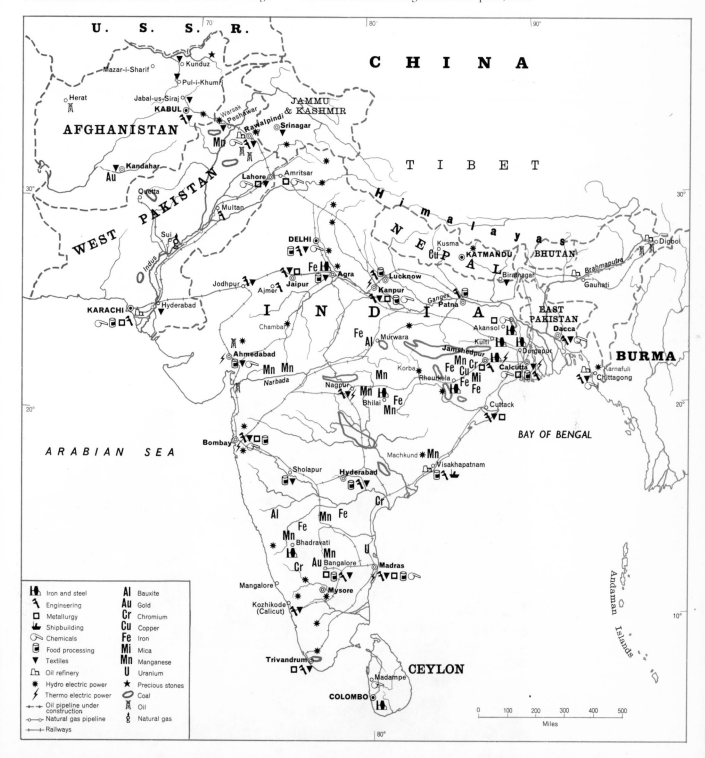

| | | | |
|---|---|---|---|
| ⚒ | Iron and steel | Al | Bauxite |
| ⌐ | Engineering | Au | Gold |
| □ | Metallurgy | Cr | Chromium |
| ⚓ | Shipbuilding | Cu | Copper |
| ⌐ | Chemicals | Fe | Iron |
| ▤ | Food processing | Mi | Mica |
| ▼ | Textiles | Mn | Manganese |
| ⌂ | Oil refinery | U | Uranium |
| ✳ | Hydro electric power | ★ | Precious stones |
| ⚡ | Thermo electric power | ⬤ | Coal |
| ⚡ | Oil pipeline under construction | ⛏ | Oil |
| ⟜ | Natural gas pipeline | ⚲ | Natural gas |
| ⊢ | Railways | | |

*See map opposite:*
Agriculture remains, as it has
always been, the chief occupation
throughout peninsular India.
About 16 per cent of the
land is irrigated by some
60,000 miles of canals and
irrigation is continually
being extended. Cereals,
pulses and oil seeds are
widely grown followed by
cotton, sugar, jute and
tobacco, coffee rubber, and
wool. Tea, grown on the
hill estates, employs nearly a
million people and accounts for
about 25 per cent by value of
all India's exports. Forests,
including valuable hardwoods,
cover an area more than
three times the size of the
United Kingdom.

west a succession of plains, in the east the Plateau
of Potwar.

In the west the plains of Peshawar, Bannu and
Dera Ismail Khan cut into the fringe of the mountains. The first two of these plains are fertile, being
watered by the rivers from the Afghan Plateau; in
the south is an arid clay plain surrounding Dera
Ismail Khan.

The climate of this western region is harsh, with
extremes of temperature including severe cold. The
population consists of farmers producing both crops
and stock, and their food is basically wheat and millet.
Peshawar is the capital of the province and an important strategic centre; it has an attractive and busy
bazaar which is one of the major crossroads of Asia.
Other much less important towns are Kohat, Bannu
and Dera Ismail Khan.

The surrounding hills are inhospitable: the rocky
Khyber pass, the gateway to India which leads from
Kabul to Peshawar, is by no means the most desolate
part. Rainfall is confined to light showers. The
stock-rearing Patans who live in this highland are
strong warlike people with white or bronze skins.
Most of their income is derived from external sources:
subsidies paid by the authorities to the tribes so that
they keep the peace; military pay, and pensions, for
these areas are a nursery for soldiers. A further source
of income is the remittances sent home by men of
affairs pursuing their professions and trades elsewhere
in Pakistan and in India.

East of the Indus stretches the Plateau of Potawar,
whose surface is made up of sandy rocks much eroded
by water. Aligned along the edge, overlooking the
Punjab Plain to the south, are the hills of the Salt
Range, looking like giant sand dunes.

As the rainfall is lower here than on the other side
of the Indus and there is little opportunity for irrigation, the chief crop is millet, which needs little water.
The poverty of the economy in this area has to a
certain extent been lessened by important garrisons
and military installations. Since the first years of independence the Pakistan Government has built imposing
factories, especially armament works, on its huge terraces; the land is cheap, the climate healthy and the
main problem, water supply, can be solved. Also
there were prospects of mineral wealth in the area;
for a long time there has been a small, languishing oil
industry with wells at Khaur and Dhulian, and a
refinery at Rawalpindi; oil prospecting is continuing
in this region as in the rest of the North-West. The
salt deposits of Kalabagh on the Indus, and Khewra
on the Jhelum are enormous. At Khewra there is a
bed of almost pure salt 300 feet thick, which is at
present being developed for home consumption and
for quite distant exports, to East Pakistan, India and
other countries of Asia; this could become the basis
of a chemical industry. In the vicinity are also deposits
of potash, gypsum and coal at Dandot not far from
Khrewa; the coal is a lignite of only 40 per cent
carbon content occurring near the surface in seams
about three feet thick.

Rawalpindi, interim capital of Pakistan, is primarily
a military centre. It is situated on the main line of
communication which has always been the focus of
life in this area. The road proceeds to Lahore and is a
small but vital section of the route linking Peshawar
and Calcutta. Its line is followed by the railroad; in
the rest of the North-West region the rail network,
often influenced by strategic considerations, is more
developed than the roads. Rawalpindi itself is sited

Kinyang Chish, a 25,000-feet
peak of the Karakoram
Mountains in the Himalayan
chain of Pakistan.

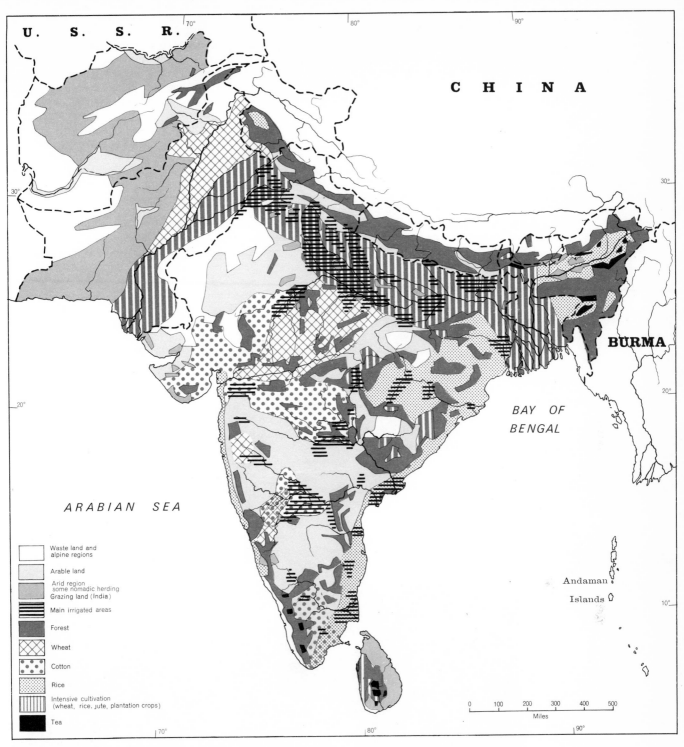

U. S. S. R.

C H I N A

30°

30°

BURMA

20°

BAY OF
BENGAL

20°

ARABIAN SEA

| | Waste land and alpine regions |
| | Arable land |
| | Arid region some nomadic herding |
| | Grazing land (India) |
| | Main irrigated areas |
| | Forest |
| | Wheat |
| | Cotton |
| | Rice |
| | Intensive cultivation (wheat, rice, jute, plantation crops) |
| | Tea |

Andaman
Islands

10°

0    100    200    300    400    500

Miles

70°                    80°                    90°

on a crossroads and also controls the best routeway to Kashmir.

*The Himalayas and Kashmir.* The rivers of the North-West Province and the Punjab, such as the Indus and Jhelum, have eroded the lowest and widest valleys of the whole Himalayan Range. These rivers have established a link between the mountains and the plain which does not exist to such a degree anywhere else in the Himalayas.

Thus it is to be expected that Pakistan should claim Kashmir, for it seems to be the natural outlet. However, the war which started in 1947 between India and Pakistan over the control of Kashmir, and which

has still not been settled, divided the country into two very unequal parts. The provisional frontier which divides Kashmir leaves to the west the smaller, very mountainous and poor part, which has become a kind of protectorate of Pakistan, with the name of Azad Kashmir (Free Kashmir); its capital is Muzaffarabad. Pakistan controls the pass along the valley of the Indus as far as Gilgit territory in the heart of the mountains. Gilgit, which recognises the authority of Pakistan, has a strategic importance as an observation post over neighbouring Soviet Union and China. The sparse people of Gilgit, the Hunzas, are energetic and hard-working; they live by cultivating small terraces, many of which are devoted to fruit trees.

The Himalayan region provides Pakistan with fine constructional timber.

*The Punjab: the 'Plain of the Five Rivers'.* The huge plain of the Punjab stretches south from the Potwar Plateau. About 65,000 square miles of the plain are Pakistani territory, the eastern districts having gone to India after partition.

The Punjab is basically the region of the 'Five Rivers': besides the Indus there is the Chenab with its right-bank tributary the Jhelum, and left-bank tributary the Ravi, and the Sutlej with its tributary the Bias. These rivers, rising in the Himalayas, have very irregular régimes; in their upper courses in particular they are mountain torrents and more like seasonal 'wadis' than perennial rivers. In the hot season, the monsoon and snow melt-water make them liable to violent floods, but in winter they are reduced to a mere trickle of water in the middle of a vast, sandy river bed. Their courses are changing either suddenly or slowly, as for example the river Ravi, which is slowly moving farther and farther from Lahore. The Indus is the only river which crosses the North-West Plateau, often in narrow gorges, before entering the plain at Mianwali; after leaving the Himalayas its tributaries flow across an almost flat landscape before joining the main river.

This huge alluvial plain, 475 miles long and 375 miles wide, consists of three zones: a green fertile belt, a desert and an irrigated area.

The area in the north-east between the Chenab and Sutlej and below the Himalayas is green and fertile; with an almost temperate climate it makes fine wheat land. With copses and hedges, careful cultivation, well nourished cattle and numerous sturdy horses, this area and Kashmir are the most European parts.

In the west the land between the Indus and the Chenab is surprisingly arid; it is intended to improve this region of the Thar desert by irrigation.

Towards the south the plain is just as dry; here one of the most important irrigation systems in the world has reclaimed thousands of square miles within the last hundred years, a colonisation which is shown by the exceptional increases in population; for example, the Montgomery district had a population of over 400,000 in 1891 and 1,800,000 in 1951. South of the Multan district, irrigation is struggling against the invasion of sand, especially from the tornadoes of the hot season. Bahawalpur is also very arid but has been partly improved by irrigation.

Since it has been an independent state, Pakistan has endeavoured to increase the irrigated area. In 1961 the area dependent on irrigation was 24 million acres. Under the Indus water treaty of 1960, and with funds subscribed by Australia, Canada, Germany, New Zealand, U.K. and U.S.A., canals will be constructed to divide the water power of the Indus and its tributaries; the Indus and two western tributaries will serve Pakistan, and the three eastern tributaries India. This provided the basis for irrigation development plans due to be completed in 1973.

Temperatures in the Punjab are less severe than in the North-West, but the range is greater than anywhere else in the Indo-Ganges Plain. The fairly low annual rainfall is monsoonal and falls mainly in July, but like the North-West the Punjab also receives some winter rain.

In general the Punjab is agricultural, and apart from wheat it produces maize, millet, a little sugar-cane and cotton, especially in the irrigated area of the south. The yields are quite high but the land is divided into very small holdings averaging one and a quarter acres.

Terraced cultivation in the Swat Valley, Pakistan. Wherever possible, land is cultivated in Pakistan, three quarters of it given over to rice and nearly all the rest to jute.

Following the agrarian reforms of 1959 some of these uneconomic holdings have been enlarged. The rural population densities are too high for comfort; the district of Sialkot is almost entirely rural, yet in 1951 it had a density of 1,020 per square mile. In the newly irrigated areas of the south the land has been divided into rectangular plots of 7 to 10 acres, where power and fertilizers are used, thanks to the existence of large estates with modern administration or of the co-operative societies.

The rural population lives in large, well spaced out villages, in huts made of mud because of the lack of stone. Lahore, with a population of 1,296,000 in 1961, is both an ancient capital and a modern city: it is an important intellectual and commercial centre and the capital of West Pakistan. It has the disadvantage, however, of being only 20 miles from the Indian border and is thus extremely vulnerable.

The other towns are the old city of Multan and the new towns of Lyallpur and Gujranwala. An important cotton industry has developed in all these towns and partly accounts for their rapid growth. Apart from this, the bazaars are centres for craft industries; Sialkot has a world-wide reputation for sports equipment.

*Sind: an irrigated desert.* Sind is the name of a former province of lowland stretching between the Punjab and the sea along the lower course of the Indus. As it is composed of alluvium it would be quite fertile were it not so dry; but its annual rainfall is only 5 inches and it experiences scorching temperatures. It is primarily dependent on irrigation. The whole economy of Sind was transformed by the construction of the Sukkur Barrage in 1932 which dammed the water near Rohri. The present irrigated area is nearly 4 million acres and will be almost 8 million acres when all the canals are constructed. The barrage is also a source of hydro-electric power.

Where there is no irrigation the landscape is desolate and desiccation is increasing. The Indus flows slugglishly towards its mouth in a valley sometimes sandwiched between the rocky spurs of the western bank and the desert-steppe of the eastern. In the northern part of the delta the survival of an old irrigation system has maintained a degree of prosperity around Hyderabad, a prosperity which has been renewed by the barrage of the lower Indus built at Kotri. Farther south the diminished Indus ends its course in huge areas of salt mud and marsh. This same depressing landscape stretches more than 125 miles farther east and is continued by the lagoons of the Rann of Kutch, which was the former outlet of the Indus.

With the aid of irrigation Sind produces considerable quantities of wheat in the north and rice in the south; there is some cattle-rearing, especially on the meadows in the south which are not too saline. Cotton plantations have increased recently. Huge reserves of natural gas have been found at the foot of the Iranian Plateau.

Sind has two important towns: Hyderabad, a major commercial centre, and Karachi, the former capital of Pakistan. Karachi is an almost entirely artificial port, situated some distance from the Indus delta and not far from the foothills. Even before the creation of Pakistan in 1947 its growth had been rapid, for its

In the Adamji jute mill near Dacca, East Pakistan. An old farmer turned skilled labourer. The Adamji is the largest jute mill in the world, but jute cultivation and production is declining in Pakistan.

Wheat is the main crop in West Pakistan. The extensive plains with their temperate climate make excellent wheat-growing lands.

The Mangla Dam Site, in West Pakistan, with the River Jhelum in the foreground.
On the extreme right are the Mangla Head Regulator and the Canal. At present the hydro-electric station at Mangla has a capacity of 45,000 kW., and will eventually irrigate three million acres.

port served as the outlet for the whole of the Indus valley where the production of wheat and cotton was increasing continuously; Karachi had a population of 216,000 in 1921 and more than 359,000 in 1941. It acquired unexpected importance in 1947 when it became the capital of the new state, and had to receive many Moslem refugees from India, so that its population was just over a million in 1951 and 1,913,000 in 1961. Urban problems have become very serious here. Some secondary industries have been developed in Karachi and its suburbs, but the very dry climate is not suited to textile manufacture.

Karachi airport is important and continues to grow, for it is a port of call for all the lines to the Far East and Australia, being on almost the only routeway between the West and the East outside Russia. In 1959 it was decided to create a new federal capital, to be called Islamabad, on the Potwar Plateau, near Rawalpindi. Government headquarters are meanwhile at Rawalpindi, and the National Assembly sits at Dacca, in East Pakistan.

*Baluchistan: an arid plateau.* In the west, Pakistan includes part of what is called the Iranian Foreland. Known as Baluchistan and covering nearly 120,000 square miles, this plateau is very dry and sometimes quite hilly; it has a population of a little over a million. It can be divided regionally into the western basin, the north-eastern mountains linked with the Afghan ranges, and the southern coastal region of Makran.

It is an inhospitable land, some places having no rainfall at all, and the people are mainly pastoral nomads. What little irrigation there is depends on ingenious systems of water collection with the help of underground canals; this accounts for the relative prosperity in the neighbourhood of Quetta, the only important town. Quetta, north of the Bolan Pass, has an almost entirely military function; however, some

deposits of quite good coal are developed nearby.

A methane deposit at Sui, 60 miles north of Sukkur and in Baluchistan, was discovered in 1951 and has been developed rapidly; pipelines have been built between Sui and Karachi and Sui and Multan.

Baluchistan is a meeting point of languages and races, where Indian and Iranian influences intermingle or are contrasted.

## EAST PAKISTAN

The partition of India and Pakistan in 1947 resulted in the division of Bengal. The western third went to India, the eastern two-thirds were allocated to Pakistan. To this was added the larger part of the district of Sylhet, taken from Assam. Before 1947 Bengal consisted almost entirely of a huge delta, with a geographical unity, and the people shared similar physical characteristics, traditions and language. Only the religious difference between Hindu and Moslem was taken as the basis of the division, so here and there minorities, sometimes exceeding 45 per cent, were forced to follow the lot of the local majority. There is therefore no natural frontier between the two Bengals, and neither of them has any marked unity.

Yet the political division does correspond to a certain number of geographical divisions. One significant political fact should be noted: many of the Hindu refugees who fled East Bengal when the Moslems assumed control were unable to adapt themselves to life in West Bengal and after a time large numbers left the houses and agricultural settlements which had been provided for them, and either dispersed to other parts of India, or even returned to their original homes, in spite of religious differences. In part this seems to have been because West Bengal was too dry for their liking; in part because jute is no better acclimatised in West Bengal than the people from the East. The jute India is endeavouring to produce in West Bengal is inferior in yield and, more especially, in the quality of the fibre obtained.

The partition had widespread effects on the economic stability of the entire subcontinent, for it interrupted the pattern of trade developed over many years. Attempts were made to restore the balance, and in May 1948 a settlement was reached which gave effect to the plan for exchanging essential commodities. Under this plan India supplied coal, and cotton textiles to Pakistan; and received in exchange jute, raw cotton and grain.

East Bengal is wetter than Indian Bengal because it has heavier rainfall and more active rivers. While West Bengal consists of the dead part of the delta, Pakistan Bengal is mainly the live part, including the most active distributary, the Padma, which after its confluence with the Brahmaputra carries the water of the Ganges farther to the east. Also, hundreds of streams flow down from the hills in the east. The result is luxuriant vegetation: unending thickets with continuous rows of houses along the paths or, more often the canals, for communications are mainly by water. The houses are made almost entirely from local vegetation, usually bamboo, with steeply pitched roofs and raised on platforms to avoid floodwaters.

These features are typical of a large part of the flat land, especially in the east. However, Barind, to the north between the Ganges and the Brahmaputra, is fairly dry and covered with savanna, while farther north still the Himalayan torrents cause the River Tista to be alternately dry and in flood.

East Pakistan includes high land, especially in the south-east in the hills of Chittagong bordering a coastal plain. Tea is grown there, especially near Assam.

Many areas are unsuitable for cultivation: the swamps along the southern shore, which extend into India, the marshlands of the western border near India, and the savannas of the north. Intensive farming is practised wherever possible. Three-quarters of the cultivated area produces rice, the remainder almost entirely jute, but the rice is hardly adequate to feed the population. There is serious competition for land between rice and jute; jute earns foreign currency and is favoured by businessmen and often the Government, while fear of famine and social difficulties encourage farmers to cultivate rice.

There are 51 million people to feed, and about 82 per cent are employed in agriculture. Power resources are much inferior to those of West Pakistan; hydro-electricity has made a beginning with the barrage at Karnaphuli. A little oil has been discovered in the region of Sylhet. Only ten per cent of the population is employed in industry and it is difficult to see what industries could be started. At present the textile industry is making progress with products including jute and cotton goods, and traditional manufactures, such as fine quality muslin at Dacca, where the humidity is favourable to production. Before partition the jute was processed at Calcutta and it is still mainly exported raw; Pakistan's new mills have the capacity to process only part of the country's jute crop of over 950,000 tons (80% of the total world production).

The population is both dense and dispersed, for there is no important centre. Calcutta served as the capital of all Bengal before partition; now the capital of East Pakistan is Dacca, which also houses the National Assembly. It is an old provincial town which had a population of over 213,000 in 1941 and 556,000 in 1961. Chittagong is rapidly developing as a port.

It is not always easy to maintain political harmony between the two parts of Pakistan; there are recurrent fears that East Pakistan will secede. East Pakistan opposed the use of Urdu in Bengal and demanded the continuance of Bengali, so that two national languages of equal importance had to be recognised.

East Pakistan includes a large Hindu minority of about 10 million, while West Pakistan is composed almost entirely of Moslems. The Constitution which came into force in March 1956 made Pakistan an Islamic Republic, but not a theocratic state; equality of rights for all is clearly stated, especially the right to work; the one exception is that only a Moslem may be President. The subsequent 1962 Constitution makes no change in this. It tends to centralisation, which can be explained as the wish to maintain the unity of the two parts of Pakistan through a strong government.

Rural life in the Lahore district.

# THE INDOCHINESE PENINSULA

The Peninsula of Indochina, between India and China, includes Burma, Malaya and Singapore, Thailand, Cambodia, Laos, North Vietnam (Vietminh), and South Vietnam.

This peninsula is one of the monsoon regions of Asia experiencing alternate seasons of heavy summer rains and winter drought. These conditions, common to all countries of the peninsula, encourage the widespread cultivation of certain crops, notably rice. However, there is great variety in the relief, soils, and mineral and industrial resources of this large region, and the differences are further increased by the various political régimes whose policies have important effects in the economic sphere.

## BURMA

Burma became an independent country of South-East Asia in 1948, and is now known as the Union of Burma. After the Second World War and liberation from Japanese occupation Burma first became a member of the Commonwealth and then, leaving the Commonwealth, a republic.

The total area of the Union is 261,798 square miles and the population was 23,735,000 in 1963.

Numerous mountain ranges make access difficult from all sides. Roads were built to link the north of Burma with Assam and the north-east with China, but there are no rail connections with neighbouring countries and the usual approach to Burma is by way of the sea.

*The growth of the Union of Burma.* Burmans inhabit the centre of the country, the surrounding mountain areas being occupied by groups of people different in many ways, though with certain affinities. All are, in fact, descendants of Mongolian tribes who migrated southwards in prehistoric or early historic times. The Burmese proper are the most advanced of these peoples, and were converted to Buddhism two thousand years ago. Since that time the Buddhist monastic system has dominated the life of the country.

In the seventeenth and eighteenth centuries, Burma had trade connections with the Portuguese, Dutch and British, but it was not until the beginning of the nineteenth century, when internal dissensions threatened the peace of the neighbouring regions of India, that the First Burmese War with Britain took place. In 1826, the coastlands of Arakan and Tenasserim were ceded to Britain, and the province of Pegu was added to these after the Second Burmese War in 1852. Upper Burma remained an independent kingdom until 1886. Since the British conducted these operations from India, Burma became a province of British India and remained so until 1937. It was in fact the largest province although it differed in its population, and in almost every other respect, from the rest of India. Union with India was always distasteful to the Burmese and it was terminated by the British government in 1937. In 1941 the Japanese invaded the country and the British forces retreated northwards carrying out a scorched-earth policy as they withdrew. Burma once more suffered severely when in 1945 the Allied armies crossed the mountains from the north and invaded the country again to drive out the Japanese. The once flourishing oil industry was completely destroyed, and when the independent government of Burma assumed control, the country was still largely disorganised.

The use of the term 'Union of Burma' refers to the union between Burma proper and five bordering states occupied mainly by non-Burmese. Burma proper is the largest and most productive unit. It covers about 160,000 square miles, and consists of the former British territories of Upper and Lower Burma. The other units are the Shan State in the east, Kachin State in the north, the Kayah State in the south-east, the Karen State farther to the south, and the Chin territory in the north-west. By granting semi-independence to these, the Burmese Government endeavoured to avoid conflicts which hindered the recovery of the country.

### THE LAND AND ITS RESOURCES

*The tortuous relief.* The Union can be divided into three main physical regions: the Arakan Yoma, the Shan Plateau and the Central Basin.

The Arakan Yoma and the Arakan coastlands bordering the Bay of Bengal are a series of fold ranges extending in a great curve more or less parallel to the coast; the succession of high forested ridges and deep valleys separate Burma from India and Pakistan; a series of short torrential rivers flows directly to the Indian Ocean. Both relief and the unhealthy, fever-ridden lower slopes make this a formidable barrier.

The Shan Plateau massif with its folds aligned from north to south occupies the whole of the east of the country and extends southwards into Tenasserim, the peninsula region. Some of the higher ranges are intrusive granite masses containing the famous tin-bearing ores, notably in Tenasserim. There are several lakes on the plateau, but these are steadily decreasing in size. The great River Salween flows across the plateau, whose western edge is a great escarpment, probably a fault line, which often reaches a height of more than 3,000 feet, and for long cut off the hill tribes that inhabit it from modern influences and control by the central government.

The mountainous region in the north of Burma includes the source of the Irrawaddy and its principal tributary the Chindwin. The altitude decreases southwards and the forested mountains of the north, including the wild country sparsely inhabited by the Kachins and Shans and still only partly administered, gradually give place to lower hills and fertile valleys inhabited by the Burmese.

The Central Basin, or Burma proper, lies between the Arakan Yoma in the west and the Shan Plateau in the east. It was once the gulf of a Tertiary sea, and is now extensively covered by light shady soils. Subsequent folding, particularly in the centre of this gulf, resulted in a north-south line of hills known as the Pegu Yoma. The oilfields of Burma are found in the gently folded rocks in the western half of the basin. The most recent period of Tertiary folding was accompanied by volcanic activity. Mount Popa, an extinct volcano in the heart of the country, reaches a height of nearly 5,000 feet. Central Burma is drained by the Irrawaddy and its main tributary the Chindwin.

The coasts of Burma can also be divided into three sections. The Arakan coast extends in a north-south direction and is a 'Pacific' type of coast; the Tertiary folded ranges parallel with the shore often rise precipitously from the ocean, and there is only a narrow fringe of lowland where man can settle and farm. The coast is closely indented, with headlands, rocky islands and stretches of mangrove swamp. There are many natural harbours, but the difficulty of communication across the Arakan Yoma has prevented the development of important ports, with the excep-

tion of Akyab with its alluvial hinterland. Beyond Cape Negrais the coast aligns in a west-east direction, and consists of the ever-changing front of the Irrawaddy delta. The immense quantity of alluvium which this powerful river brings down is accumulating at its mouth and the delta is constantly building up southwards. The third coastal region is that of Tenasserim, similar to the Arakan coast; but here the mountain ranges are formed of older rocks, especially granite. The coast is sheltered by a fringe of small islands, and the bamboo huts of the fishing villages are often built over the water. The most extensive area of cultivable land, where rice is the main crop, is in the immediate hinterland of the chief port, Moulmein.

*A tropical monsoon climate.* Though much of Burma lies north of the Tropic of Cancer, its position is such that the entire country experiences a tropical monsoon climate very similar to that of India, and with the same seasons. There is the cool and relatively dry season which lasts approximately from November to mid-February, when gentle breezes blow down the valleys from the north. The cool season gradually gives way to the hot dry season, which becomes progressively hotter and drier as the land heats up. The highest temperatures are recorded in the dry centre of the country during April or May. The storms of May are the forerunners of the monsoon and the heavy rains of mid-June. The Arakan and Tenasserim coasts are exposed to the full force of the south-west monsoon and receive heavy rainfall, often causing soil erosion. So, also, does the delta region, but farther north and on the leeward side of the Arakan Yoma annual rainfall decreases within a short distance from 200 to only 20 inches. This is in contrast to the hill country of the north where rainfall again rises. Along the coast diurnal and annual ranges of temperature are slight. The range of temperature becomes much more marked as distance from the moderating influence of the sea increases, and this is particularly true of the dry belt in the centre; the annual range at Mandalay is 11.4°C. (21°F.).

*Natural vegetation.* The irregular distribution of rainfall has produced a great variety of natural vegetation. Above the frost line at 5,000 to 8,000 feet there are forests of evergreen oak, with occasional pine forests and extensive areas covered with bracken and grass. At even higher altitudes there are rhododendron forests. Below the frost line the natural vegetation depends on the amount of rainfall and the types correspond to those of India.

Evergreen tropical forest occurs where the rainfall exceeds 80 inches. The timbers are hard and little used. Monsoon forests, which lose their leaves in the hot season, grow in the regions with between 40 and 80 inches of rain. They are the home of the valuable teak and other useful timber trees. Where rainfall is less than 40 inches the forest yields to scrubland and semi-desert. There is very little true grassland. Extensive areas of the Irrawaddy delta are covered with tidal mangrove forests adapted to saline conditions, but some of the trees are over 100 feet high and of considerable value.

In the past, wasteful methods of agriculture led to the destruction of huge stretches of valuable forest in an attempt to extend the area suitable for crop cultivation.

Under the torrential rain, a Burmese cyclist is inadequately sheltered by his umbrella. Burma has a tropical monsoon climate, with storms in May heralding the monsoon rains of mid-June.

A cane bridge in the dense jungles of Northern Burma. In spite of its fragile appearance it is strong enough to allow mules to cross it.

The forest rarely re-established itself on deserted clearings; it was usually replaced by a tangled mass of bamboo, bracken or grass. However, for more than eighty-five years now, the Forest Department has been working to improve the forests, and all the valuable forested areas have been declared Government Reserves. Fine teak timber is easily the most important forest product and usually comes second or third in the country's exports.

*An agricultural country.* A large part of the country, including huge areas as yet undeveloped, has fertile soils. Extensive alluvial lands in the valley of the Irrawaddy and the delta region provide excellent soils for the cultivation of rice, when they can be drained. Outside the alluvial regions, a thick layer of red laterite often covers the underlying rocks. In the dry belt, in the centre of the country, the soils are often poor; the surface tends to form a hard crust, and in the driest areas the presence of black alkali makes unproductive lands which could otherwise be fertile. On the slopes of the hills and mountains and in the wetter regions, there is constant danger of erosion and rock outcrops occur.

Forest and woodland still cover 57 per cent of Burma proper, and this does not include the Shan, Kayah and Kachin States and other areas. Cultivated land represents only 12.5 per cent of the area of the country; however, it is estimated that this figure could be raised to 25 per cent.

Agriculture is concentrated on the alluvial lands of the delta and in the valleys of the Irrawaddy, Chindwin and Sittang. Rice is by far the most important crop, and is grown on two-thirds of the cultivated area. Annual rice production now reaches the pre-war figure of 7 million tons, or over 800 lb. per person. There is thus a considerable surplus for export. Where the rainfall is less than 40 inches rice cannot be grown without irrigation, and in the dry belt the farmers concentrate on sesame, millet, groundnuts (peanuts), cotton and pulses. Nearly 1,500,000 acres are irrigated in the dry belt.

In the mountains and plateaus of the north and west poor crops of maize, millet and upland rice are grown on small temporary fields. Throughout Burma, fruits, vegetables, tobacco and sometimes fodder crops are grown to supply local needs. There are rubber plantations in the south, especially near Mergui and Tavoy.

Small humped oxen are used everywhere for transport and ploughing, but in the delta and the wetter regions they are usually replaced by the more powerful water buffalo; dairy-farming is little developed as yet. In the dry belt there are numerous goats and some sheep, generally of poor quality.

*Fisheries.* Food production is influenced by the religious beliefs of the population as well as by the physical nature of the country. A Buddhist is forbidden to take life, so there is practically no production of meat for human consumption; but a fish brought out of the sea simply dies, it does not have to be killed, and this partly accounts for the importance of fish in the daily diet of the Burmese.

Fishing and fish-curing are practised along the coasts and rivers, and as many as 100,000 people are classed as fishermen; however, the industry is not yet organised on a modern scale. Most of the fish are salted and dried and, with the strong-smelling paste known as *ngapi,* add variety to the basic diet of boiled rice and vegetables. The fisheries are likely to become much more important in the future.

*Mining.* British companies were responsible for the development of mining in Burma; in 1941 the oil wells and other up-to-date installations were deliberately put out of action to prevent their falling into the hands of the Japanese invaders. The restoration of the mining industries has been slow, owing to the unsettled state of the country.

By far the most important mineral produced before the war was oil; from 1909 to 1939 annual production from fields in the Irrawaddy basin was approximately 1 million metric tons; despite the total destruction of the industry during the war annual output has by now reached half a million tons.

Extensive deposits of brown coal or lignite, found in the Chindwin valley and in old lake basins in the Shan Plateau, have hardly been touched. These basins also contain oil shales. Since 1954, attempts have been made to develop better quality coal deposits in the Chindwin valley. Silver, lead, zinc, copper and nickel come from mines at Bawdwin. The rivers of Tenasserim first produced large quantities of tin and tungsten during the First World War, but later fluctuations in the price of these metals resulted in corresponding fluctuations in output. Iron ore is found in many places and was once worked by the inhabitants of the country for local use.

In the Mogok or ruby mines district, alluvial rubies and other precious stones have for long been obtained by washing superficial deposits. Later, systematic mining and washing was carried out. Changes in fashion and the development of artificial rubies dealt serious blows to the industry.

The jade used in China is found in the north of Burma and is exported overland to China. The mines are situated north of Kamaing and all the miners are Kachins. The old river workings used to produce better quality jade than the quarries, but the latter produce larger quantities.

Gold is found in most of the rivers in Upper Burma; but the washing of alluvial gold is done only sporadically between farming operations. Amber is extracted by the Kachins in the Hukawng valley, but the quality of the fossil resin is poor. There are salt deposits in various parts of Upper Burma, and also in the Shan States and at Bassein.

## THE PEOPLE AND THEIR WAY OF LIFE

The population of the Union is about 23,750,000, giving a density of only 90 per square mile compared with 346 in India.

The population is still mainly rural. Following the huge influx of refugees, Rangoon had 1.5 million inhabitants in 1963, 126,000 Indians, and Mandalay 213,000 inhabitants. Moulmein is the only other town whose population reaches 100,000.

*The variety of people, language and religion.* The inhabitants of Burma belong to many races and speak many different languages. The indigenous people are Mongolian in origin; the Burmese are the most advanced and occupy the fertile lowlands; other races live mainly in the mountain regions.

A young Burmese.
The country is inhabited by
several population groups, but
only the centre of Burma is
populated by true Burmese.
In the mountain and outer regions
are peoples descended from the
Mongol tribes which emigrated
southwards in prehistoric and
early historic times.

The literacy figure in Burma
is high, partly because the poor
can obtain a free education
by joining classes at a monastery.
This lesson is being held at the
monastery-school maintained
by the oil company at
Chauk oilfield.

Over a long period, large numbers of Indians have
been attracted to Burma by the prospect of higher
wages and the opportunities for commerce and trade.
Rangoon was said to be the largest immigration port
in the world during the period between the two world
wars. The majority of the immigrants were men
who came to Rangoon to work as labourers, and this
created difficult social conditions since men outnumbered women by up to ten to one. Indians almost
monopolised middlemen trade, particularly milling
and trading in rice. Relations between the newcomers
and the indigenous population were not always harmonious, and when the British withdrew from Burma
many Indians returned to India. Thousands more
departed following nationalisation of all retail trade in
1964.

The Burmese, together with the Arakanese of the
Arakan coast, the Mons of the region round Moulmein and the Tavoyans of the Tavoy region, all of
whom are closely related, comprise 80 per cent of
the total population. They have broad, flat faces like
the Mongolians, but not the almond-shaped eyes of
the Chinese. Their skins vary in colour from light to
dark brown.

The Burmese are Buddhists and religion plays an
important part in their lives. The spiritual head of
each village is a yellow-robed monk. The monastery,
usually just outside the village, also serves as the
school. Each village has its pagoda and almost every
hill is crowned with whitewashed pagodas, but there
are no temples in the accepted sense of the word.
Owing to the large number of village schools few
men are completely illiterate. Burmese women enjoy
a degree of freedom unusual in non-European races.

The hill tribes are generally less advanced than the
Burmese; the most advanced are perhaps the Karens
who inhabit the Pegu Yoma and the Karen State,
and have also settled in the delta. Trouble between
the Karens and the Burmese was one of the difficult
features of post-war Burma. The Shans occupy most
of the Shan Plateau and the upper Chindwin valley
The Kachins settled mainly in the extreme north, the
Chins, who were noted for their fierce inter-tribal
conflicts, in the western mountains, and the Padaungs
and Was are found on the Chinese borders. The Was
were, and perhaps still are, head-hunters. These mountain tribes are not Buddhists; their religion may be
described by the general term 'animism'. Christianity
has spread rapidly among these peoples.

The Indians have settled chiefly in the delta region,
in Arakan, and along the rivers and railroads. They
provided almost all the unskilled labour, except in the
most remote areas. There were about a million Indians
in Burma before 1941 who had mainly come from
Madras, Bihar, Orissa and Bengal. This situation has
changed since the departure of 300,000 between 1964
and 1966.

The Chinese are an important community. Some
of them live as peasant farmers near the north-east
frontier; but most belong to the artisan and merchant
classes in Rangoon and the larger towns.

*Industries.* Agriculture is the main occupation in Burma
but many farmers are also craftsmen during slack
periods in the farming year. In addition to rice cultivation, lumbering and fishing, the main occupations
are rice-husking, silk-weaving and dyeing. Hand

weaving has almost disappeared with the setting up of factories for the production of cheap cottons and silk fabrics, and aniline dyes are replacing the native vegetable product. The best silk weavers are found at Amarapura, and for many of the population this industry is the sole means of subsistence. In all parts of Burma both men and women make and smoke cheroots. The chief traditional Burmese arts are wood-carving and silverwork, and lacquer work at Pagan.

Although Burma remains essentially an agricultural country, modern industry is developing. Beginning with the exploitation of natural resources — oil refining near Rangoon, timber, rice milling — and going on to engineering and rail building, it now extends to cover a whole range of light industries. Silk and cotton weaving, under competition from western synthetic fibres are, however, declining and now employ only half as many people as at the beginning of the century. The principal oil refineries are at Syrian near Rangoon and at Chauk.

## TRADE AND COMMUNICATIONS

*Railroads and roads.* From time immemorial the chief highway of Burma has been the Irrawaddy and its tributaries. Rail transport has supplemented rather than replaced the river as a trade route. There is a state rail network of 2,000 miles with a gauge of one metre. The main line runs from Rangoon to Mandalay, where it was formerly interrupted by the Irrawaddy, and though it has now been extended on the opposite bank of the river to Myitkyina it still falls 390 miles short of the most northerly administrative centre. Yenangyaung, the centre of the oilfields, is still inaccessible by rail, and the Burmese system is not linked with those of neighbouring countries.

There is a good road link between Rangoon and Mandalay. The famous Burma road runs from Lashio in Burma to Kunming in China and is 800 miles long. The Stillwell road, built during the war from Ledo in Assam to Myitkyina in Burma, and the road from Manipur to Kalewa are now disused. Great progress in road construction has been made since the 1930's when there were practically no roads: there are now about 9,000 miles of all types. However, much more remains to be done.

*Burma's trade.* The new money introduced by the Government of the Burmese Republic is the Kyat, which has the same value as the Indian rupee.

Rice has always been the principal export, greatly exceeding in value all the others put together. These are, roughly in order of importance, teak, cotton, minerals, vegetables, rubber, hides and skins, and a variety of hardwoods. Some changes have taken place in Burma's export trade, for in the pre-war years rice was the chief product (two-thirds of the total in value), followed by petroleum products (now much less important), teak, minerals, cotton, hides and skins.

Textiles are by far the major import, followed by jute bags, foodstuffs, tobacco, machinery and vehicles, non-precious metals, mineral oils, chemicals, paper, vegetable oils, coal and coke.

Rangoon handles the bulk of the foreign trade. Other ports are Bassein, the rice port to the west of the delta; Akyab, the outlet for Arakan, and Moulmein, Tavoy and Mergui, which serve Tenasserim.

# THE MALAY PENINSULA

The term 'Malaya' is generally given to the area which came under British influence in the southern part of the Malay Peninsula, which forms the south-eastern extremity of the continent of Asia. The Isthmus of Kra is geographically part of the Malay Peninsula but belongs to Thailand.

## THE PHYSICAL FEATURES OF MALAYA

Malaya is 50,680 square miles in area and is therefore almost exactly the same size as England. Its total population is about 7 million. At the southern end of the peninsula of Malaya is the island of Singapore, once a British Crown Colony and now self-governing. In 1963 Malaya and Singapore joined with British North Borneo and Sarawak in the new independent state of Malaysia, but in 1965 Singapore seceded. *A central massif bordered by coastal plains.* Geologically

Malaya is part of the central core of South East Asia, and is therefore quite different from the island of Sumatra which lies to the west. The mountain ranges are composed of masses of granite, and run north-south. To the east, the quartzites of Pahang form rugged mountain ranges, in contrast to the sedimentary rocks of the valleys and plains. In the west of the peninsula some remarkable masses of limestone rise almost vertically to heights of many hundreds of feet. They are often riddled with natural caves, and overlook large valleys, many of which coincide with outcrops of shale. Ancient volcanic rocks often cover large areas, such as the Pahang volcanic series, but there are no recent volcanic deposits such as those found in Java or Central Burma. Among several small basins of Tertiary rocks, those of Rawang in Selangor contain coal seams formerly extensively worked. The alluvial valley gravels, especially those in the west of the peninsula, are important, since they contain almost all the tin ore produced by Malaya, and in some places gold is also found.

Tapping latex on a Malayan rubber plantation. The latex takes over three hours to drain into the cup. The tapper tips the latex into a large can and proceeds to the next tree.

A relief map of Malaya shows a central mountain mass bordered by coastal lowlands wider in the west than in the east. The central massif consists of a series of ranges gradually rising towards the west.

The east coast receives the full force of the violent north-east monsoon, and there is therefore little human activity along this shore, except for a few villages where the farmers and fishermen take advantage of the six months of calm weather. In contrast, the west coast is sheltered from the south-west monsoon by the high mountain ranges of Sumatra, which is separated from Malaya by the Strait of Malacca. The rivers flowing towards this western coast have brought down large quantities of alluvium. Much of the coast is bordered by extensive mangrove swamp and forest, while several estuaries provide harbours that are convenient though subject to silting. The most important natural harbour on this coast is formed by the strait of calm water between the island of Penang and the mainland.

*A typical equatorial climate.* The climate is essentially equatorial with the rainfall well distributed throughout the year, though in the northern region, including Penang, it is transitional between the true equatorial climate of Singapore and the monsoon climate of Burma, with a period of lower rainfall occurring between December and March.

The relief of the country is also responsible for marked local variations in the amount of rainfall and the seasonal incidence. As altitude increases temperatures become pleasantly cool, and for this reason there are hill stations in some of the highest parts of the peninsula; however, the land is nowhere high enough to be affected by frost.

But in general the climate of Malaya is hot and humid throughout the year. It is never cold but never very hot, with little seasonal variation except perhaps on the east coast, where seasonal changes are caused by the monsoon winds, It is essentially a monotonous climate, healthy for the robust, but injurious to the health of many because of its very monotony. Owing to the high humidity, dense mist often occurs between 6 or 7 o'clock and 9 or 10 o'clock in the morning, and the air seems cool despite the temperature of 24°C. (75°F.) or more. Later, when the sun breaks through, the heat becomes intense although the thermometer rarely registers temperatures of over 33°C. (90°F.). In the afternoon, especially during April and May, clouds gather and heavy rain occurs, often with thunder. The sky clears again in the evening and the nights are fine and starry.

*The dense equatorial forest.* The natural vegetation of Malaya is equatorial forest with broad-leaved evergreen trees often of considerable height. Many of them are hardwoods. The undergrowth is thick with a profusion of woody climbing plants, one of which provides the strong rattan or Malacca cane. The Malayan forests are extremely difficult to penetrate, and they are the natural refuge of the primitive aboriginal tribes.

On the hill slopes where the forests have been cleared much fertile soil has been swept away by heavy rains. Where erosion has occurred, rough grasses cover the land and it takes a long time for forest to become re-established. The alluvial valleys though limited in extent, contain rich fertile silt and have naturally been cleared for cultivation, but the paddy fields do not produce sufficient rice to meet the needs of the population. In the sheltered valleys on the western side of the peninsula large areas are covered by rubber plantations, one of Malaya's chief sources of wealth. On the sandy eastern coasts are belts of coconut palms and casuarina (horsetail) trees, while mangrove swamps are common along many of the western shores.

## THE DIVERSITY OF PEOPLE

*Malays, Chinese and Indians.* Apart from the few primitive tribes who still live in the depths of the forest, the Malays are the native people of the peninsula. They belong to the race of peoples with dark skins and Mongolian features, and are related to the Burmese, Siamese and Javanese. The country is organised in States and the Malay ruler of each State is known as a Sultan. The Malays were converted to Islam at an early date, and fine mosques were built in the towns, while most villages have a small mosque. During the last hundred years Malaya has attracted Chinese immigrants. On the whole Malays are peasant farmers and love the country, while the Chinese are town-dwellers mainly from Canton and southern China, and they are now crowded together in large numbers in the towns, which they have more or less created. Much of the industry and trade of the region is in their hands as well as the production of tin.

With the growth of the rubber plantations, the necessary labour was brought from India, often on short term contracts, so that there were times in the inter-war period when Malaya was populated by Malays, Chinese and Indians in approximately equal numbers. The geographical distribution and social status of these three groups of people are very different.

There are two groups of Chinese: those born in Malaya, and recent immigrants who were born in China. The Malaya-Chinese play an important part in the life of the community and many have risen to positions of great wealth and influence, though they have been constrained to leave political and administrative affairs to others. The many newly arrived immigrants from China need time to settle into their adopted country, and the problem of their assimilation is not easily solved. The influx of workers from China and India explains why men outnumber women in Malaya in the proportion of five to three. The Malayan population is relatively rich for South East Asia. Income per head is three to four times that in surrounding countries, and the demand for cars, bicycles and transistor radios reflects the comparative prosperity.

*An historical summary.* The story of European penetration into the Malay Peninsula is a long and complex one, in which Portugal, the Netherlands and Britain took part. In 1826, the ports of Malacca, Penang and Singapore were united for administrative purposes under the control of the East India Conpany, but they were separated from India in 1867 and became a Crown Colony, under the name of the Straits Settlements. The colony later included the Cocos Islands, Christmas Island and Labuan, off the north-west coast of Borneo.

British protection of the Malay States began in 1874

when Residents were appointed to Perak, Selangor, Negri Sembilan and Pahang. In 1896 a treaty was made between the British Government and these four states, which united to form the Federated Malay States, with the capital at Kuala Lumpur; but the powerful State of Johore remained outside the Federation. The four remaining States (Perlis, Kedah, Trengganu and Kelantan) are situated along the Thai border, and the rights of suzerainty and protection were handed over to Britain by Siam (now Thailand) by the Anglo-Siamese treaty of 1909.

All the British territories were captured by the Japanese in 1941-42 and occupied by them until 1945. After the defeat of Japan, it was clear that the country needed to be reorganised with much greater co-ordination than in the past, and so a new Constitution was prepared. In 1948 the Federation of Malaya was created, composed of the nine States of Perak, Selangor, Negri Sembilan, Pahang, Johore, Kedah, Perlis, Kelantan and Trengganu, and the two British settlements of Penang and Malacca, with Kuala Lumpur as the federal capital. Singapore became a separate Crown Colony and Labuan was joined to North Borneo. Thus two political units, the Federation of Malaya and the Colony of Singapore, replaced the divisions which existed before 1941.

In 1948 the office of Commissioner-General for the United Kingdom in South-East Asia was created, with headquarters at Singapore. The five territories which came under this authority were the Federation of Malaya, the Colony of Singapore, the Colony of Sarawak (in Borneo), the colony of North Borneo including Labuan, and lastly the Protectorate of Brunei In 1955 the Cocos Islands were placed under Australian administration, followed by Christmas Island in 1958.

Independent status within the British Commonwealth was attained by the Federation in 1957 and by Singapore in 1959. North Borneo and Sarawak became independent in 1963 and joined with Malaya and Singapore as equal partners in Malaysia. North Borneo taking the new name of Sabah. Singapore left the Federation in 1965.

## COMMUNICATIONS AND RESOURCES

The economic prosperity of Malaya today depends partly on agriculture and partly on mining. Agricultural prosperity is closely linked with the great expansion of the rubber plantations and the rubber industry, while mining is almost synonymous with tin mining, for Malaya is the leading world producer of this mineral.

*An excellent system of communications* The British Government made use of the revenue produced by the development of agriculture and mining to build an excellent system of all-weather roads. The road network was naturally more extensive in the valleys in the west of the peninsula, where most of the plantations and tin mines were situated, but there are roads in the east too. Only in the forested and mountainous central region are communications poor. A railroad system was also developed. For a long time it depended on the local supplies of coal, but now diesel-electric locomotives are increasingly used.

*Tropical agriculture.* The people of Malaya practise both

A jungle camp in North Pahang, at Fort Telanok, Malaya. On the left are the huts of the aborigines; on the right, those of the Special Air Service. Helicopter landings are made on the T-marks.

subsistence and commercial agriculture. Malayan agriculture caters chiefly for local needs, producing fruits, a great variety of vegetables, spices and tea, as well as coconuts and fibres. The Chinese introduced their own particular method of intensive agriculture, which is more like gardening, and were the first to cultivate crops such as pineapples, manioc, gambier and pepper. Today Chinese market-gardens are found near all the important towns. Much of Singapore island is occupied by market-gardens.

The three commercial crops of the peninsula are rubber, coconuts and rice, or paddy as it is called in this region. Rubber is the leading export product and the rubber plantations are mainly under European or sometimes Chinese management. Some progress has been made in the organisation of coconut plantations but these are of comparatively minor importance. Most of the rice is grown by the Asian peoples, both Malays and Chinese. The hill slopes and even the undulating lands are constantly exposed to the danger of serious erosion from torrential rains. Once the surface soil, which is relatively rich in human and plant food, has been removed, the process of restoring the natural fertility of the land is very slow. The farming methods used in Europe or the United States are usually unsuitable because large areas cannot be spared to be ploughed up and left completely free of vegetation. The land has to be prepared for cultivation in strips or circles to prevent gully erosion by heavy rains, and trenches, embankments and terraces are constructed for the same purpose. The cultivation of cover crops is one of the best methods of soil conservation. This is done extensively in the rubber plantations, where a leguminous crop is sown, for this practise also enriches the soil with valuable nitrates.

*The dominance of rubber.* Malaya is the leading world producer of rubber. The rubber tree, or *Hevea braziliensis*, was introduced into Malaya from the Botanic Gardens at Peradeniya in Ceylon. The story of rubber is well known. Seeds were smuggled to England from the Amazon lowlands in Brazil in 1876, and a large number of plants were successfully grown in the Botanical Gardens at Kew, London. The Botanic Gardens at Peradeniya received a consignment of nearly 2,000 plants and in 1877 seedlings from Ceylon were successfully planted in Malaya. However, it was twenty years before rubber was cultivated on a large scale, for world demand was then small. Equatorial Africa and the Amazon region supplied wild rubber at a low price, and the planters did not yet fully appreciate the value of the new crop. At the end of 1925, however, the total area under rubber in British Malaya was about 2,250,000 acres; in 1960 it was over 3,500,000 acres. Much has been replanted with high-yielding rubber, with a potential annual yield of 1,500 to 2,000 lb. an acre instead of the usual 500 lb. Crises and booms affected the rubber industry during its development. The first great boom lasted until 1919, when world-wide depression caused a slump in prices. At that time Malaya and Ceylon produced three-quarters of the world's rubber and they were able to control prices by restricting output. Then increasing world demand brought a general rise in rubber production. After the Japanese occupation, rubber exports were nearly a million tons;

since then they have declined (818,000 tons in 1964).

Most of the rubber plantations are in the lowland regions, especially in the once forested valleys of the west, on land which was formerly unproductive, where they stretch almost continuously from Kedah to Johore. This transformation was achieved by the efforts of a great army of Indian labourers, and Chinese and Malays. The young rubber trees are selected and planted with great care, about a hundred to the acre. Later they are thinned, so that by the twelfth year about half the number remain, and this is considered the ideal. The uniform climatic conditions in Malaya allow a steady output of latex throughout the year. There are various methods of tapping the latex, but the most usual one is to make a cut halfway round the circumference of the tree every other day. The latex flows into small glazed earthenware cups which are made locally. About an hour after tapping the Indian coolies collect the latex in buckets. One coolie looks after three to four hundred trees and is usually paid according to the weight of the latex brought in. The latex is diluted with water at the collecting centre and coagulated by the addition of acetic acid. Then the coagulated latex is made into sheets of rubber or long strips of crepe, which are washed, drained and smoked or dried. Most of it is exported as sheet or crepe rubber.

One of the great changes which have occurred in Malaya and in the neighbouring regions of Indonesia in recent years has been the increased production of rubber on smallholdings. In 1958 there were 565 European-owned estates, with a total area of 1,255,000 acres, 1,837 Asia-owned estates with a total acreage of 735,000, and 2,400 smallholdings with a total area of 1,989,000 acres. In 1953 a fund was set up to assist smallholders to improve quality and yield by replanting. Such a project has become necessary in order to reduce production costs, for Malaya faces serious competition from synthetic rubber.

About 900,000 acres in Malaya are under rice, which is equivalent to less than one-eighth of an acre per person. The Federation produces only sixty per cent of its total requirements. Even this proportion is a great improvement; the Federal Government has encouraged the expansion of locally grown food supplies and diversification of agriculture to make Malaya less dependent on rubber growing. Only the more remote States, Kedah, Kelantan and Perlis (where Malays are predominant) are self-supporting in rice. Ricefields are generally irrigated, so as to give greater yields The land is ploughed and the weeds dug into the soil; the fields are then flooded and trampled by buffaloes or rolled, then raked to remove the weeds, until they reach the firm, muddy state best suited for planting the young rice seedlings. These are grown in nurseries and transplanted by hand as in China.

Coconuts do well all over Malaya, but especially in the coastal districts of the west. In the east the winds are too strong.

The African oil palm has been introduced, mainly on estates, and by 1958 covered 122,000 acres.

Pineapples are grown throughout Malaya, but only in Johore, Selangore and Perak are they grown for canning. This export industry was important before the

Second World War in Singapore, but now has to meet increased competition. Much of the canning is still done in Singapore, though the fruit is nearly all grown in the Federation. On the island of Singapore itself the land is needed for the cultivation of food crops for an ever-increasing population.

Other cash crops could easily be developed, for example, bananas. Spices, which once made Malacca famous, are relatively unimportant now.

*The leading world producer of tin.* Apart from the former coal mines of Selangor, bauxite in Johore and gold in several places, Malaya has phosphates or guano obtained from the bat-infested caves of the limestone region. Kaolin from the granite areas is used to make coarse pottery, especially the cups for collecting the latex on the rubber plantations.

The mining of tin ore (cassiterite) is the second most important industry in Malaya. Chinese records show that tin was known and worked from the fifteenth century at least. As early as 1860 or 1870 the Chinese were particularly interested in the rich tin deposits of Malaya, and from that time onwards frequent disputes between different groups of Chinese caused serious difficulties for the Malayan rulers. This was one of the reasons for their appeal for British help in governing the region.

Nearly all the tin mined in Malaya is alluvial tin. Lode mining is still relatively unimportant. Long ago the tin was washed out of the rocks where it originated and carried away by the rivers with other alluvial materials; because of its high density tin ore or cassiterite is usually found in the lower lying layers of gravel deposits. It consists of rounded fragments varying in size from that of a pea to the finest sand. The richest deposits are in the valleys in the west of Malaya where the granite is in contact with limestone and other rocks.

There are several methods of mining, depending on local conditions. Sometimes a great thickness of overburden has to be removed, which increases costs. In the oldest mines, such as those owned by Chinese, the coolies remove the upper layers of gravel, and shovel the tin-bearing gravels into baskets, which are taken to the washing sheds. Mechanisation has been introduced into the European-owned mines. Where possible hydraulic mining is carried on; a powerful jet of water is directed on to the alluvial deposit which washes away the soft gravels, leaving a concentration of the much heavier tin ore. Dredging is another method, used mostly in the flat valley lowlands. A pit is excavated and filled with water on which the dredger floats. The tin-bearing gravel is brought to the surface by a continuous chain of buckets, and the washing and sorting is also done on the dredger. The ore is then sold to a local buyer (perhaps Chinese) or to one of the two big smelting companies. Most of it goes to their big smelting works in Singapore and Penang where they also process tin concentrate imported from Thailand and elsewhere.

When the European mining centres were being developed, between 1900 and 1908, Malaya produced about 50,000 tons of tin ore annually, more than half the world's total. The development of tin mining in Bolivia, Nigeria, Indonesia and the Congo reduced Malaya's share of world production, although in fact her output continued to increase. Today Malaya is again the world's largest producer of tin, accounting for a third of total world tonnage. The actual quantity varies enormously under government control of output in relation to the violent fluctuations in world tin prices. Production in 1956 was 62,295 tons; in 1959 37,525 tons; but rose in 1963 to 59,900 tons.

*Islands and towns.* Penang is a beautiful, rocky island reaching a height of nearly 3,000 feet. The central part is still forested, but there are many rubber and coconut plantations on the lower lands. The chief town, officially known as Georgetown, faces the mainland and the narrow strait provides a sheltered anchorage. Prai, on the mainland, is a terminus of the Malayan railroad, and from here Singapore can be reached in less than 24 hours and Bangkok in less than 36 hours. Although of narrow gauge these railroads are excellent. Penang is also a free port. Malacca has little commercial importance today, but it is of great historical interest. Kuala Lumpur is the largest town in the entire Federation and an

A tin dredge, seeking alluvial tin deposits north of Kuala Lumpar, Malaya.
Tin concentrates are the foremost product of Malayan mines.

important commercial centre. It is connected by rail and road to its own port, Port Swettenham, but the exports pass chiefly through Singapore and Penang. The main products of the surrounding region are rubber, rice, coconuts, sugar, tapioca and pepper. Ipoh is an important mining centre.

## SINGAPORE

The island of Singapore, which is now an independent democratic republic, lies to the south of the Malay Peninsula from which it is separated by the Johore Strait, less than a mile wide. The city and port of Singapore, where three-quarters of the island's population is concentrated, is on the south side and is separated from the Indonesian islands of Bintang, Batam and Bulang Besar by the Strait of Singapore. The island is 26 miles from west to east and 14 miles from north to south. The south-west is hilly with a fringe of mangrove swamps, while the east is flat and sandy or marshy. Most of the island is cultivated, with rubber plantations, coconut groves on the sandier areas, and market-gardens which supply vegetables for the population of Singapore, a city expanding so rapidly that it threatens to spread over the whole island. Estimated population in 1964 was 1,820,000. Pineapple cultivation is now only of minor importance: tobacco and pepper are two other cash crops.

The British owed their possession of this valuable island to Sir Stamford Raffles, who purchased it in 1819 from the Sultan of Johore; it was then almost uninhabited. Its importance is due to its position at the meeting-point of the world's great trade routes and to its fine anchorage. Johore Strait, although narrow, is deep at the eastern part, and a naval base for the British Admiralty was built on this side of the island. A railroad crosses the island from Singapore to Woodlands and is connected to the Malayan rail system by a causeway across the shallow part of Johore Strait. A main road and an oil pipeleine follow the railroad tracks.

The industries concentrated at Singapore include tin smelting, rubber manufacture, saw-milling, and a wide range of minor industries, but it is particularly famous for the great commercial activity of its port, which brings associated engineering and shipfitting industries. Much of the trade of the mainland of Malaya and the neighbouring countries of the East Indian archipelago passes through this port. The docks are constantly being expanded, and the civil airport to the north-west of the city, opened in 1955, has become a great international crossroads. Singapore has benefited considerably from being a free port (one where goods are free from customs duties).

Singapore's departure from the Malay-dominated Federation of Malaysia followed racial and political tensions arising from the feelings of Singapore's 75 per cent Chinese population.

Panorama of Singapore, capital of the island of the same name, south of the Malay Peninsula, from which it is separated by the Strait of Johore, 1¼ miles wide. Singapore is a port of considerable commercial activity, and an important market for rice, oil, sugar, cocoa and rubber, as well as a British naval base.

# THAILAND

Known as Siam until 1939, Thailand lies in the centre of the Indochinese peninsula and covers an area of nearly 200,000 square miles. It is divided into seventy-one provinces (changwads).

The kingdom of Thailand broadens out in the north between Burma to the west and Laos and Cambodia to the east, and in the south extends far into the Malay Peninsula. The distance from the north to the south, between latitudes 21° and 5°N, is over 1,000 miles. It is 500 miles wide at its broadest point in the centre, and narrows to a strip only 20 miles wide at the foot of the Khao Luang, the highland near the Burmese frontier. A region of such irregular shape cannot be considered a well-defined physical unit.

The fertile and well populated central plain is the heart of the country. It is crossed by the Chao Phraya and surrounded by very dissimilar peripheral regions, which often belong geographically to areas extending beyond Thailand's frontiers. Neither ethnically nor physically can Thailand claim to be called a homogeneous land.

*The origin of the Kingdom of Thailand.* Thailand became a political unit relatively recently. The Thais, who originally came from Yunnan, reached the fertile lowlands along the valleys of the Menam and its tributaries, and having freed themselves in the thirteenth century from Cambodian domination they founded for the first time an independent nation ruled by a Thai dynasty. The successive rulers and dynasties passed through various vicissitudes and had to endure long periods of conflict with the Burmese; but they maintained absolute rule until 1932 when a coup d'état substituted a constitutional monarchy.

Siam was fortunate in being able to preserve its independence throughout the period of colonisation, situated as it was between two European possessions, and it experienced only short-lived occupation by the Japanese during the Second World War.

Culturally the Thais were influenced by China, their country of origin. Later their civilisation was strongly affected by the Indian culture from which they borrowed their religion, art, sciences and writing. Only much later, in the seventeenth century, was Siam tentatively opened to European influences and it is mainly since 1932 that the country has been extensively modernised. Having chosen English as the country's second language, the Siamese enlisted the help of Scandinavian technicians to give them a better chance of preserving their independence; but it is American influence that has become predominant, at least in the economic sphere. Although Bangkok and some provisional towns have experienced great changes during the present century, the rural areas still retain their traditional way of life. Thirty miles from Bangkok, which is as bustling as any great Western city, all the features of rural life in Asia still remain.

## FIVE MAIN REGIONS

Five large physical regions can be distinguished: the Central Plain, the mountain region of the north and west, the Korat Plateau, the Chanthaburi region and the Thailand Peninsula.

*The fertile central plain.* This extremely fertile alluvial plain, where most of the country's rice is grown, includes the major part of the Chao Phraya river basin. This is the real heart of Thailand, and the river, which is navigable throughout the plain, makes a fine waterway. In the north of the plain and along the borders the lowland is sometimes abruptly interrupted by steep hills and ridges. These are a characteristic feature of the Thai landscape, and are formed of old rocks, usually Permian limestones, which are rugged and riddled with caves, and covered with a special type of scrub vegetation.

The delta itself begins ninety miles from the coast and is completely level and well drained. It is crossed by irrigation canals which also serve as waterways, and these are bordered by rows of palms and large bamboo clumps. Farther north the Chao Phraya plain is still partly forested and many of the rice fields scattered among the tree stumps have been established relatively recently.

*The mountain region of the north and west.* The north and west of the country between the Salween and the Mekong belong to the folded mountain system extending from Tibet into Burma and finally forming the backbone of the Malay Peninsula. Numerous streams flow southwards between the mountain ranges and unite above Nakhon Sawan to form the Chao Phraya River.

*The Korat plateau.* The north-east of Thailand is a

desolate region occupying one-third of the total area. It is an extensive, slightly undulating basin with a few scattered ranges of hills facing south-east. The average altitude of the central part is less than 600 feet. It is bordered in the north and east by the river Mekong which forms the boundary with Laos, and by ridges of highland in the west and south forming the southern frontier with Cambodia.

The plateau, formed mainly of sandstone tilted towards the centre of the basin, is infertile and semi-arid. It receives the same amount of rainfall as the other regions but the natural drainage is poor, so that during the rains large areas are flooded and during the long dry season there is drought. Research is

An extensive panorama of part of the great rice plain of central Thailand, viewed from the foothills along its western edge.

being carried out to find ways of making use of underground water supplies.

*The Chanthaburi region.* This region lies between the Gulf of Siam and the Cambodian frontier, and the Phanom Dongrak mountains in the north. It has a varied relief, a sparse population and is still largely forested. Between the Khao Khien and the Cardamom Mountains, which lie mainly inside Cambodia but whose western branches form high limestone country in Thailand, there is a broad gap. The road and railroad from Bangkok to Phnom Penh make use of this routeway, but they carry only a limited amount of trade.

The Chanthaburi region receives heavy rainfall and is one of the wettest parts of Thailand. Crops grow well here, particularly rubber and pepper. The town of Chanthaburi is a small port where fishing is the main activity.

*The Thailand peninsula.* The Thai portion of the Malay Peninsula begins at the lower course of the Mae Klong, which comes from the western mountains and enters the Gulf of Siam at approximately the latitude of Bangkok. The Tenasserim range is an extension of the Thanon Thong Chai which marks the border of Thailand further north, and extends south as far as Phuket Island. From here the mountains lie on the east side of the peninsula and form a series of ranges separated by broad valleys, while the coastal plains become wider. Here and there sheer limestone out-crops rise impressively from the lowland.

Dense equatorial forest covers most of this very wet part of the peninsula, and the population is sparse. The main settlements are on the coast.

*The monsoon climate.* Thailand has a monsoon type of climate and most of the country belongs to the wet tropical region. It is influenced alternately by the hot wet south-west monsoon winds which bring cloudy skies and heavy rains, and the north-east monsoons which bring warm dry air from China with clear skies. Between the warm dry season (November to February) and the rainy season (May to October), there is a transition period when conditions are still dry but extremely hot. This period, from March to April, is the time of the year when the climate is most unpleasant. Thus Thailand experiences three distinct seasons.

Temperatures are constant in the southern half of the country, moderated by the high humidity and the proximity of the sea. Mean monthly temperatures are very similar to the mean annual temperatures, varying between 26°C. (79°F.) and 27°C. (81°F.).

The northern half is more continental and temperature ranges are more marked. Temperatures reach a maximum of 45°C. (113°F.) during the hot season, with prolonged drought, in contrast to the pleasant warm period when temperatures may fall to 10°C. (50°F.) or at times even lower.

For a country in the wet tropical region Thailand's rainfall is not excessive. The north, which is relatively sheltered from the rain-bearing monsoons by the highlands along the Burmese frontier, in general receives between 35 and 60 inches of rain depending on the relief, spread over a period of 85 days; some parts, however, have considerably less. Rainfall increases in quantity and frequency towards the Equator. At Bangkok rain falls on 125 days and totals 80 inches. The peninsular region receives the heaviest annual rainfall, the total varying from 60 to 120 inches. Rainfall occurs regularly throughout the year in the peninsula and the dry season is short.

*The forests.* Originally Thailand was a forested country, the heavy rains from the south and south-west favouring the growth of dense equatorial forest or rain forest, with a great variety of species. In the north, where the climate is more continental and the dry season more pronounced, a semi-deciduous type of forest is found on the lowland and on the mountains below 3,000 feet. In the driest parts, particularly on the limestone areas, the forest thins out and gives place to scrub.

This semi-deciduous forest, known as monsoon forest, covers about 70 per cent of the forested area. Economically it is the most important, providing timber for piles, railroad sleepers and fuel. It is also the home of the teak, which grows well on the mountains in the north where it is worked on a large scale

Thailand's monsoon forest, about 70 per cent of the forested area, is economically important. Teak, a wood with a wide market, is one of the most valued of its products. Elephants are often used to haul heavy loads.

and floated down the rivers to Bangkok. But extensive felling, the destruction of the forest by charcoal burners and the huge clearings necessary for the expansion of rice fields and other cultivation have considerably reduced the areas of this type of forest. Where it still exists it has greatly deteriorated, and in many areas has been replaced by scrub vegetation where bamboos predominate.

Besides rain forest and monsoon forest there is the wet tropical mountain forest consisting mainly of rhododendrons on slopes above 3,000 feet; there is coniferous forest on the mountains of the north between 2,000 and 3,000 feet; there are extensive mangrove forests along the southern shores of the Gulf of Siam and the Andaman Sea. Only the mangrove forests have so far been exploited and produce timber for building, for making charcoal and for use in the fishing settlements.

*The peoples of Thailand.* Various ethnic groups have shared in the formation of Thailand's population. The original inhabitants of the country probably belonged to the Negrito race who were driven southwards by successive Mongol invasions, from whom are descended the Mons, Cambodians and Annamites. Later, though before the Christian era, came a migration of Tibetans and Burmese. In the sixth century, Indian cultural influences reached Siam directly, and Indian immigrants came via Java. Another powerful wave of people, the Laos Thais, who came from the upper Yangtze-kiang valley and had been strongly influenced by Chinese culture, spread over the territory in the ninth century, and the present-day Thais are their descendants. These people are today numerically superior, but they are far from being the only inhabitants of the country.

Thailand is unusual in being one of the Far Eastern countries with a population density that remains well balanced in relation to its size and potentialities. However, this population is very unevenly distributed. The mountains of the north and west and the peninsular region have a low population density while the deltaic lowland of the Chao Phraya has a very high density, especially in the south.

The true Thai peoples live in the centre of the country while most of the other peoples live in the regions surrounding the central plain. The mountainous northern zone between Burma and Laos is inhabited by a great variety of peoples.

The majority of the people in eastern Thailand are Laotians, who are closely related to the Thais and Cambodians. Large numbers of Cambodians are found in the south-east near Cambodia, and about the same number of Vietnamese have settled here.

In the extreme south the people are mostly Malays of Moslem faith, who have settled mainly along the east coast, where they are engaged in rice cultivation and fishing.

The exact number of Chinese living in Thailand is not known, but it is probably about three million, including those of mixed Chinese and other ancestry. The Chinese have played an important part in the country's economy and most of the trade is in their hands. They are mainly town-dwellers, and in Bangkok form half of the population, but they are also numerous in the coastal villages, where most of them live by fishing, and in the mining districts of the south, where they are the chief source of labour.

The Chinese tend to form closed communities, exposed to some hostility on the part of the Thai population and its rulers. However, recently the latter have shown a more conciliatory attitude and taken steps to facilitate assimilation of the Chinese.

## THE PRINCIPAL RESOURCES AND COMMUNICATIONS

*An agricultural economy.* Thailand is still primarily an agricultural country and 85 per cent of the population are farmers. Rice is the country's staple product and has been since remote times. Over seven million tons of paddy are produced annually, of which about 1,750,000 tons are exported, representing 48 per cent by value of the total exports. Thailand is in fact the third largest world producer of rice, and a great deal is done by the government to develop the irrigation systems essential for this important crop.

A young Akha tribeswoman with her baby. Thailand's population is well balanced in relation to the country's size and economic potential. Distribution is, however, uneven.

Rice occupies three-quarters of the cultivated land and monopolises most of the lowlands. The traditional method of shifting cultivation still continues without irrigation on the highlands. A great variety of crops is grown but exports are small in comparison with rice. Maize production, for example, is only one tenth of that of rice. Other crops include manioc, ground-nuts (peanuts), castor oil, plants and soya beans, which are grown in the north, as are tea and tobacco. Market-gardening has developed particularly in Bangkok. Sugar-cane grown in Thailand provides 35,000 tons of sugar annually and this meets half the home consumption. Palm sugar makes a substantial contribution and creates a family industry of treating the sap of the *borassus*, which is grown on the lowlands in plantations, near all the populated areas. The coconut is widely distributed even some distance from the coast, its natural habitat, but there are no large plantations. The nuts are used locally for food and only a very small proportion is used for the preparation of copra for export.

Industrial crops include various textiles such as cotton, ramie (the grass cloth plant), jute which is widely grown on the Central Plain, and kenaf in the north-east. In 1901 rubber was introduced to the southern provinces from Malaya, and today Thailand ranks third among the world's rubber producers.

*Industries and natural resources.* With a few exceptions, industry has kept its domestic character and is mainly concerned with the manufacture of consumer goods such as pottery, baskets and silk. Silk is manufactured round Chiang Mai, with raw materials imported from Japan. A highly developed industry is rice-milling.

There are also some new modern industries such as cement-making, spinning, brewing, sugar-refining.

The timber industry is fairly important. Various timbers are exported, teak being the most valuable.

Mining operates on a small scale as yet. About 8,000 tons of tin ore (cassiterite) are exported annually, especially from the island of Phuket, the centre of Thailand's tin industry, and also 700 tons of wolfram, the ore containing tungsten. These ores, which are commonly found together, are usually alluvial, but they are derived from the granite rocks which out-crop in many places in the Thai part of the Malay Peninsula. Granite also occurs farther north, in the mountains along the Burmese border as far as the district of Mae Sariang, which produces mainly wolf-ram. Small quantities of monazite, columbite and diamonds are found in the tin-bearing alluvium at various places. Precious stones such as sapphires, rubies and zircons are mined in small quantities in the alluvial deposits of Chanthaburi. There are various deposits of lignite, especially at Mae Moh in the north-west, which has to produce 200,000 tons annually to supply the power station at Bangkok. Copper, iron, lead and zinc are known to exist in various parts of the country but they are not mined at present.

Electricity for industrial and domestic pruposes was long produced only at Bangkok and in the chief towns. Much has still to be done before the country districts are supplied with electricity. A large dam and the Yanhee power station have been constucted at the outlet of the gorges on the Mae Ping. By 1964 the dam had been completed and two generators had been installed to provide electricity for the Central Plain.

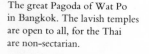

The great Pagoda of Wat Po in Bangkok. The lavish temples are open to all, for the Thai are non-sectarian.

*The development of communications.* Water transport has always been important in the Chao Phraya Basin, and today the lower reaches are still used extensively between Nakhon Sawan and Bangkok. The upper courses are now little used except for floating teak logs and for a small amount of local trade.

There are 2,200 miles of railroad which serve the different parts of the country and converge at Bangkok; a further 300 miles are under construction. Road building has been slow for various reasons. Apart from the competition of the railroads, inherent difficulties were encountered in the delta region, which has periodic floods and a clay soil, and there is a local shortage of material suitable for road metal. Good modern roads are of recent construction, but several already provide good communications to some peripheral regions. Ten years hence the road system should be much more extensive.

BANGKOK. The capital of Thailand, Bangkok, is, like Singapore, one of the largest centres of population in Southern Asia, with nearly 1,660,000 inhabitants. Owing to its geographical position it has become a very important airport, and a tourist centre.

Two worlds exist here side by side, that of the East and that of the West. In Bangkok, a sprawling city surrounded by rice fields, the past and the present are closely associated. The East is represented by the colourful crowds, the busy life of the rivers, the swarming markets along all the thoroughfares, the pedlars and the eating-houses; also typical of the East in this Buddhist city are the processions of young, thin-faced monks in bright yellow robes collecting alms, and the many beautiful and brightly decorated pagodas. These lavish temples are open to everyone, for the people of Thailand are non-sectarian. Formerly Bangkok was entirely a city of waterways, as the densely populated suburb of Donburi still is. Its intersecting *klongs* or canals are bordered by dwellings raised on piles, intermingled with a profusion of tropical vegetation, and busy with the coming and going of sampans and barges. In contrast, the modern parts of the city have large avenues built over the old canals, and these serve the new districts, where there are imposing buildings, universities and hospitals, built in the old Cambodian style of architecture with red-tiled overlapping roofs, lofty pinnacles and ornate decorations.

It is not necessary to go far beyond the outskirts of Bangkok to see the traditional Siamese countryside. On the delta chequered with ricefields, in turn green, golden or newly ploughed, the settlements are scattered along the irrigation canals, perched on high piles and often concealed by large clumps of bamboo. Flocks of domestic duck may be seen swimming or waddling about, and children mounted on the backs of grazing water buffalo. The women, protected by wide hats of white straw and dressed in dark cotton clothes, work in the nearby rice fields, or search in their sampans for the water plants widely used in Thailand for food. Fishing is done on a large scale along the coasts and waterways, and also among the rice fields on the delta, for fish is an important part of the diet. Industry supports a fishing population of 30,000. Fishermen can often be seen handling huge nets which are raised and lowered by an ingenious system of pulleys.

# CAMBODIA

The Kingdom of Cambodia, 70,000 square miles in area, is the smallest country in the peninsula of Indochina. It consists of a basin drained eastwards by the Mekong, with lakes occupying the central part, and is almost entirely surrounded by highlands.

## THE LAND AND ITS PEOPLE

*The highland rim.* In southern Cambodia the Cardamom Mountains, aligned from north-west to south-east, and the Kirirom and Elephant Mountains, aligned from north to south, cut off the central plain from the Gulf of Siam. This great mass of sandstone, in places 3,000 feet thick, has been uplifted and tilted towards the south-west. Much of the sandstone covering has worn away and the underlying old rocks, complex in character and intensely folded, form the relief. The mountains of southern Cambodia, completely covered with dense forest, are still largely unexplored and are a formidable obstacle to communications.

To the east of the Mekong, sandstones form plateaus of lower altitude which rise gradually towards the Vietnam frontier. This region is an almost perfect peneplain, preserved beneath basaltic lavas, and massive bare ridges outcrop, covered with savanna.

West of the Mekong a well defined escarpment, the Dangrek Mountains, extends in an almost straight line from west to east and separates Cambodia from Thailand. The land slopes gently on the Thai side

forming the Korat Plateau, but the southern slope is almost vertical. There are a number of difficult passes. Farther south there are low plateaus of sandstone and ancient alluvium, with a lateritic soil and dotted with hills.

*The Cambodian plain.* The low plateaus of the north merge imperceptibly into the Cambodian basin, which consists of the Tonle Sap Plain and the Mekong Lowland. The plain contains a large lake, the Tonle

A family meal in Cambodia. No meat is eaten, for religion forbids the killing of any living thing.

Sap, which is 100 miles long and 20 miles wide, and the Veal Phoc or Plain of Mud, a marshy region whose numerous rivers flow into the lake. The average depth of the lake is 30 feet and here and there islands appear.

Several hills divide the Tonle Sap Plain from the Mekong Lowland, where at Phnom Penh four waterways converge: the Upper and Lower Mekong, the Bassac and the Tonle Sap. These rivers flow between levees which they have built up to a height of 30 feet. During the rainy season the rivers fill the area between these natural embankments, but for most of the year they are uncovered. There is a gentle slope outwards from the levees towards low-lying areas of lakes which are linked to the rivers by channels. The lowland in the east of the Mekong Plain is only 6 to 30 feet above sea level, but to the west the land rises quickly to a height of 130 feet at the foot of the hills.

Rocky hills or buttes, called *phnoms*, rise like islands from the Tonle Sap Lowland and the western part of the Mekong Lowland. To the north of Kompong Cham an extensive basaltic plateau is divided by the Mekong valley.

The coastal region, isolated as it is by highlands, is quite different. There are several small lowlands, often marshy, like the Kampot plain. The coast itself is flat with large bays, and there is much silting; the sea here is shallow.

*Rainfall and flooding.* The central part of Cambodia has a dry, sunny climate. The total annual rainfall is low for a tropical country and the rainy period is short. There is a long season of drought: from December to May Phnom Penh has only 7 inches of rainfall and there is practically no rain for four months of the year. The north-east winds which blow during December and January bring cool but desiccating conditions, while in February, March and April the heat becomes oppressive and storms occur frequently. Although the skies are grey it rarely rains and the rivers are almost completely dried up. The rainy season begins in May. However, this month, so vital in the cultivation of rice, has only 11 days of rain. In July or August there is much less rain and this is known as the short dry season. The really heavy rains do not occur until September and October. This is the time when Buddhist monks go into retreat. The effects of the drought are often aggravated by the irregularity of the rainfall from one year to the next. The rain is accompanied by thunderstorms.

The highlands of eastern Cambodia receive more than 80 inches of rainfall, and the mountains of the south more than 160 inches. The whole of the coastal region has heavy rainfall and the dry season is shorter. These mountains form a barrier in the path of the depressions brought by the monsoons and this explains the relative dryness of Cambodia's climate.

Even so, the Cambodian lowland is partly flooded from August to October. The rivers flowing into the lake area become torrents and are locally disastrous. However, the main floods are caused by the Mekong. The melting snows of Tibet cause the river to rise from mid-June onwards, and it is fed by the numerous tributaries. Soon additional water is brought down when torrential rain falls on the mountains of Szechwan, Yunnan and Upper Laos. The rivers are very full by the beginning of August and reach their maximum at the end of September. The water at Phnom Penh is then 26 feet higher than at low water level. Some of this enormous volume of water therefore floods the country. The rivers rarely flow over the top of the levees, but the water escapes along the channels cut into them. Under the grey September sky the Mekong Lowland is an immense sheet of grey water with villages sticking up in rows along the top of the levees. The floods are responsible for an unusual change in drainage in this area. After mid-June the waters of the Mekong hold back the waters flowing from the Tonle Sap, thus reversing the normal flow; from then until the beginning of October, the river, which normally drains the lake, flows northwards. The waters greatly increase the size of the main lake and the smaller lakes flanking the levees, and flood the lakeside forests so that only the tops of the great trees can be seen; altogether an area of about 4,000 square miles is flooded. By mid-September floodwater covers 8,000 square miles. The floods begin to subside in mid-October, the Tonle Sap resumes its southward course and gradually the lakes empty. At the November full moon a great festival is held to celebrate the retreat of the waters.

The Mekong rises slowly, taking 150 days to rise 26 feet, and is not destructive. The river is loaded with silt, which is deposited when the water subsides, renewing the soils near the river and enriching them, particularly in lime.

*The growth of population.* The population, estimated at nearly six million, is growing rapidly, having doubled in forty years; it is not homogeneous and is unevenly distrubuted.

The Cambodians or Khmers are an indigenous people of Indochina who have intermixed with other groups, especially the Chinese. Physically, they are distinctive; fairly tall and sturdy, with a dark skin, high forehead, straight eyes and often wavy hair. They speak a variant of the Khmer language, their writing is of Indian orgin, and their religion is Hinayana Buddhism. The Cambodians are deeply religious people and 60,000 of them are monks or priests.

The population also includes Moslem groups, among them 85,000 Chams. They form closed communities living on the levees of the Mekong between Kratie and Phnom Penh, and along the Tonle Sap between Phnom Penh and Kompong Chhnang. There is a great variety of fairly isolated peoples living in mountain borders who have been variously influenced by the Cambodians, Laotians and Vietnamese.

Two strong foreign minorities have settled in Cambodia: 500,000 Vietnamese and 300,000 Chinese. The Vietnamese, most of whom came from South Vietnam, live in Phnom Penh and on the banks of the Mekong south of Banam. Some work in the rubber plantations, others are fishermen on the large lakes or main rivers. Another unit of Chinese population consists of the many emigrants from southern China in Phnom Penh, and in the pepper plantations of Kampot; elsewhere they live as merchants among the Cambodian peasants.

For a country in eastern Asia the overall population

density of 84 per square mile is low, but two-thirds of the country is unpopulated, or nearly so. The lack of population in the mountain regions is not peculiar to Cambodia, for highland areas are sparsely populated in all the countries of South-East Asia. The feature particular to Cambodia is unequal distribution of population even in the alluvial lowlands. The Tonle Sap Plain has less than 80 inhabitants per square mile, and huge areas covered with thin forest, especially by the lakes, are unpopulated except for the small settlements along the rivers. In the east of the Mekong Lowland the population density is 180 per square mile. The density in the west and south is generally over 260 per square mile. Lastly, the banks of the Mekong and Bassac have a density of over 520 per square mile, and one-tenth of the population is concentrated in Phnom Penh.

## THE RURAL LIFE AND ECONOMY OF CAMBODIA

The uneven distribution of the population can be accounted for historically, for the Tonle Sap Plain was depopulated by the Thais. But the chief reason is economic; 80 per cent of the Khmers are peasants who cultivate either the rice fields or the *chamcars*—the land along the levees — but though almost half the country's area is cultivable, less than ten per cent is under crops.

*The rice plantations.* Each year three million acres of land are under rice, yielding an annual output of 1,300,000 tons, of which almost 200,000 tons is available for export. Ricefields almost entirely cover the Mekong Lowland, and extend into the forested areas on the Tonle Sap plain, with a marked extension round Battambang.

Methods of rice cultivation have remained traditional. Species vary according to the soils, climatic variations and the preference of the peasant; this produces serious difficulties in the rice-husking mills, where there is a high percentage of fragments, for machinery must be adjusted to the average size of the grain. There is no scientific selection of seed and no fertilizer is used, not even manure. Only the rice nursery is irrigated and the plantations often suffer from water shortage during the short dry season. The soils are not very fertile, being deficient in chemicals and often unsuitable in texture, for the sandy soils are too permeable and the clay soils too heavy for the small wooden Cambodian plough. Yields are low and rice is generally the only crop.

However, almost everywhere the peasant plants the sugar palm. It grows to a height of 40 or 50 feet and its grooved trunk is crowned with fronds. This is the national tree. It provides fruit, fronds for roofing houses, and the sap from which wine and sugar are made. It is grown on a large scale in the west of the Mekong Plain where most of the country's 30,000 tons of sugar is produced. Along the rivers which flow into the Tonle Sap are fine groves of coconuts, areca palms, citrus fruits and betel trees.

*The chamcars.* Cultivation on the 'chamcars' is very different. They occupy an area of about 675,000 acres along the main rivers. Two harvests a year are produced on many of them. The excellent texture of the soils allows water to rise by capillary action during

Cambodian women gathering rice plants for transplantation. Well over two million acres of Cambodia are devoted to rice cultivation: the paddy-fields are dressed in May and June, transplantation takes place in August and September, and the harvest from December to February.

the dry season, and a great variety of crops is grown, including tobacco, maize, beans, sesame and ground-nuts (peanuts). During the period preceding the floods only one crop is grown, red maize. On the tops of the embankments above flood level are the dwellings and tree crops which take a long time to mature, like kapok, areca palm, banana and mulberry, sugar-cane and ramie. On the slopes behind the levees maize is grown on the heavy clay soils.

These mixed crops are carefully cultivated; though not indigenous, they are adapted to existing conditions, and yields are satisfactory. The majority were introduced recently, but maize, tobacco and groundnuts (peanuts) were introduced by the Portuguese in the sixteenth and seventeenth centuries.

Production for sale rather than home consumption is also important. The crops grown vary from year to year according to the state of the markets; for example, since 1945 cotton has almost disappeared in favour of tobacco, kapok and sesame, and maize production has declined sharply. Farming on the levees is much more profitable than rice cultivation alone and provides more food for the population.

*Stock-rearing.* The Cambodian peasant eats practically no meat, for his religion forbids him to kill living things. His staple diet is rice and fish. Domestic live-stock are unimportant. A few hens are kept, ducks are reared by the Chinese, and there may be one or two pigs per household.

On the other hand, Cambodia has large herds of cattle, about 980,000 head, and 320,000 head of buf-falo: that is, one animal to three peasants and 25 per square mile. Cattle are used entirely for draught pur-poses; water buffalo in the rice-growing lowlands, and oxen in the higher rice fields or on the levees. Milk is not part of the diet, so cows are not particu-larly useful to the peasant.

*A rural society.* The peasant society is homogeneous and there is very little difference in social status among the people. Peasant holdings are 2 to 10 acres on the rice lands and 1 to 3 acres on the levees, and each holding is worked with primitive tools by the family. Most peasants own their land, but there are some tenant farmers in the Battambang region and on the levees.

The smallholder is dependent on usually extortion-ate merchants, generally Chinese, who control prices and lend him such things as seed, cloth, jewellery, salt, harness, etc., rather than ready money. The merchant is repaid in kind at harvest time at 100 per cent rate of interest for one season's production—that is, nine months.

Along the Mekong and Bassac rivers women and girls add to their income by weaving cotton, and in the province of Takeo they weave silk. Domestic industries, however, are being replaced by factories.

Settlements are varied; they may be isolated but usually take the form of a row of houses along the river, set apart from each other and surrounded by fruit trees. The houses are built on six-foot stilts to escape the floods. Rural life is centred on the pagoda with its curved roof, built in the shade near a lake. The school is often found here, and this is the place where festivals and gatherings are held, and where every man at some time undergoes a period of instruction.

*Plantation crops.* In marked contrast to the traditional rural life is the cultivation of two important crops of foreign origin, pepper and rubber. Pepper cultivation is concentrated in the east of the province of Kampot, where the dry season is not too long. This crop gives good returns and the price of Cambodian pepper is higher than the world price; but the plantations are old and attacked by disease. Annual production has fallen from 3,500 to 1,000 tons.

In contrast, the cultivation of rubber is increasing rapidly. It was introduced only in 1921 and thrives in forest clearings. Grown scientifically as a plantation crop, it gives a yield of 1 ton per acre, the highest in the world. Production in 1960 was 40,475 tons, and it was all exported. The latex is treated on the spot and today there is a tendency to specialise in the pro-duction of rubber for crepe soles and liquid latex rather than in the production of the customary smoked sheet rubber.

The plantations are owned by large companies, mostly French, and are mainly under French manage-ment. The chief problem for a long time was labour supply, for plantations were started in unhealthy regions where there was little population. Systematic efforts have been made to improve both health and social conditions, and villages have been built. At first it was necessary to bring in workers from outside the area, and until 1945 they came from the delta region of Tonkin Vietnam. Today more than half of the 13,000 labourers working in the plantations are Chams and Cambodians.

*The lake fisheries.* Cambodia has the richest freshwater fishing grounds of South-East Asia. Almost every peasant is also a fisherman, and fishing is done on a family basis with very simple equipment.

Fishing is also an important organised industry About 100,000 tons of fish are produced annually, two-thirds of which comes from the lakes. Some of the fish is eaten or sold fresh, the rest is dried or smoked. It is estimated that about 25,000 tons of salted and dried fish are harvested from the lakes alone, this being in some years almost a quarter of the total annual catch.

When the floods occur the fish and fry swim up to the lakes. Conditions are favourable to their devel-opment in the lakeside forest, which is a spawning ground and a source of plankton. When the floods subside the fish leave the lakes for the rivers. How-ever, when the floodwaters retreat from the sill formed by the mud flats of Snoc Trou at the end of January, the Tonle Sap lake becomes isolated and acts as a huge net from which the fish cannot escape until May. It is said to be the richest fishing ground in the world, with a maximum area of 6,250 square miles producing approximately 15 tons of fish per square mile.

Large scale freshwater fishing with seine nets, or by building barrages, occupies at least 30,000 fishermen. The great majority are Vietnamese. They live in sampans at the outlets of the rivers, or on the lake in villages floating on rafts. Unfortunately these rich fishing grounds are threatened by excessive exploita-tion and since 1945 the fishing regulations have con-stantly been invaded. The consequences are disastrous when fishing is continued during the rising of the floodwaters, for it destroys the young fish and the females about to spawn. The result is already clear: the fish are becoming smaller in size and so is the catch.

Sea fishing has been of limited importance till now, but it is an industry that could be greatly increased.

*Other resources and communications.* The forests, which cover over half the country, are a further resource. So far these have not been much exploited and where they have little attempt is made at conservation. Bamboo and rattan grow almost everywhere, but it is believed that the forest could also supply more valuable timbers. Other forest products are resins and wood oils, bark and natural products, such as nux vomica and cardamom.

Industry is as yet unimportant, but is developing. Light industries were the first to be set up: spinning and weaving mills, a paper mill, a match factory, a plywood factory and agricultural produce processing industries. The present five-year plan includes a tyre factory, a jute mill, an iron and steel works and a general engineering factory. There are high-grade iron ore deposits in the north, but these have until now not been exploited commercially because of transport difficulties.

Cambodia's economy is therefore simple. Rubber, rice and maize are the chief exports, and manufactured goods and fuel (such as petroleum) are imported. There is usually a balance between imports and exports. The chief markets and sources of imports are the neighbouring countries of Asia, France (rice and rubber) and the United States (rubber).

Communications in Cambodia are fairly good and include some fine waterways. The Mekong is navigable throughout the year for junks and Chinese longboats from the Vietnam frontier to Kratie, and the Tonle Sap is navigable as far as Kompong Chhnang. A railroad 240 miles long links Phnom Penh with the Thailand frontier. There is a good network of roads (2,380 miles) linked with those of the neighbouring countries and tracks serving all the populated regions. Until recently, however, Cambodia has had no sea port, and her foreign trade passed through Saigon. Since 1947 the river port of Phnom Penh has increased its trade, but its position on the Tonle Sap is a disadvantage and it is ill-equipped. Besides this, numerous technical and political difficulties affect navigation on the Mekong, as the international status of the river has not yet been defined. A sea port has been created from nothing at Sihanoukville, on the Gulf of Siam, with economic aid from the French mission. This was a difficult task in an undeveloped and unpopulated area. It is connected with the capital by a main road built under the United States aid programme.

PHNOM PENH. Apart from Phnom Penh the main settlements in Cambodia are only small towns, where the Cambodian pile dwellings are found, together with a market, a Chinese quarter and an administrative centre. The most important of these are Battambang, with 25,000 inhabitants; Kompong Chhnang, with 20,000 inhabitants; Kompong Cham, a busy town with a population of 15,000; and Siemreap, with 10,000 inhabitants, near the ruins of Angkor, which is the most attractive.

Phnom Penh is a city of about 500,000 which has increased from 120,000 in 1942. It is a cosmopolitan centre and only about 200,000 of its inhabitants are Khmers. Is is well situated where four rivers meet, and it was built on top of the levee to the east of the main river and west of an area of large lakes. The town has a curiously elongated shape, dictated by the site. Nearly all the factories in Cambodia are concentrated in Phnom Penh, as well as great many craftsmen who work in the Chinese quarter in the centre of the city. It is also the chief administrative and commercial centre. All the trade of Cambodia converges here and the port is busy mainly with inland water transport. These activities are insufficient to support such a large population, though some are not fully developed.

Cambodia's economy is simple but sound, and it has been spared the most serious population and social problems. Industrialisation should improve conditions but the greatest efforts must be made to modernise agriculture for the benefit of the large and still growing peasant population.

Fishing on the Mekong, the river to which Cambodia owes its very existence; the Cambodian lakes are in the richest freshwater fishing grounds in South east Asia.

448

# LAOS

Laos is a mountainous country covering an area of about 90,000 square miles. From north to south there are four main natural regions: Upper Laos, the Annamite mountain range, the alluvial lowlands of the Mekong, and the sandstone region of southern Laos.

## THE PHYSICAL SETTING

Upper Laos is a folded highland region with the ranges aligned north-east to southwest, and is drained by the Upper Mekong and by its chief tributary the Nam Ou. The underlying rocks mainly consist of a complex of slates, schists and sandstones which often contain salt. Forest remains only in the valleys; it has been steadily removed from the highlands by the practice of clearing land for cultivation by burning; as a result of subsequent erosion the highlands are now covered with savanna or poor steppe.

Luang Prabang,
'city of a hundred pagodas',
and former capital of Laos.
It lies at the confluence of the
Mekong (seen in the photograph)
and the Nam Khan.

The Annamite mountains within Laos are formed of crystalline or granite masses which include the highest peaks of Laos. They receive heavy rainfall at all seasons and are densely forested. The eastern slope of the Annamite range is drained to the Gulf of Tonkin by the headstreams of the Song Ma, and the western slopes by numerous tributaries of the Mekong. The Plateau of Tranninh is an extension of the Annamite range; farther south the mountains are crossed obliquely by a spectacular outcrop of Permian limestone eroded into sharp ridges, chimneys, peaks and caves. The steep sides of the escarpments bristle with stunted trees and shrubs in contrast to the luxuriant vegetation which flourishes lower down. To the north of Thakhek there are rich deposits of tin ore (cassiterite) found in the hills, and this is mined at Phon Tion.

While the Mekong valley lowlands are formed of sands and clays or old lateritic alluvium, the sandstone region of southern Laos which includes part of the lowland area consists of extensive arid plains covered with deciduous open forest, and high plateaus or peaks. The underlying sandstones of the Bolovens Plateau are covered by a thick layer of recent basalt, which produces red soils suitable for all kinds of crops, especially coffee.

The ancient rocks of Laos are almost everywhere overlaid by younger sedimentary rocks which have themselves been covered in places by volcanic lavas or which contain volcanic intrusions.

*The monsoon climate.* Laos comes under the influence of the monsoons. The dry season from November to March, a period of continuous fine weather, relatively low temperatures and cool nights, is pleasant. In April and May the atmosphere is oppressive and temperatures are high. This is followed by the rains from June to October, which help to lower the temperature. Annual rainfall varies from about 150 inches on exposed areas near the mountains to about 50 inches in the region of Luang Prabang. Everywhere the rainfall is sufficient to support dense forest but the nature of the sandstone and lateritic soils often prevents its growth.

*The vegetation.* Climatic and soil variations and man's activities explain the existence of many different types of vegetation. In the lowlands the most common type is dense humid forest, with the trees linked by numerous lianas and climbing plants.

When the natural forest is destroyed by burning or by felling, it is replaced by a secondary type of vegetation or dense scrub of eupatorium bushes. This scrub vegetation, about six feet high and originating in Central America, establishes itself with great rapidity in the deforested areas. It is in turn supplanted by woody shrubs and young trees, and a secondary type of forest is then established. Where lateritic or sandstone soils occur the vegetation is open forest, most of the species being deciduous. At the height of the dry season, in March, forest fires are widespread. But the vegetation recovers quickly, for it is adapted to such conditions and rapid growth is encouraged by the ensuing wet season.

A third type of forest is found on the lowlands, a moderately thick deciduous forest which usually contains teak. In Laos such forest is found particularly in the region of Pak Lay, on the the right bank of the

Mekong, and farther north in the region of Ban Houey Say, on the left bank of the river. Attempts have been made to reforest various regions with teak, which is able to flourish outside its natural habitat.

As altitude increases the dense forest gives way successively to areas of transitional forest, dense forest of laurel-like trees, and oaks, mixed dicotylous and coniferous forest.

In the mountainous regions, where clearing land for cultivation is the usual custom, secondary forms of vegetation are again burned and eventually replaced by scrub and grass savanna, or 'pseudo-steppe' similar to prairie, the final stage in deforestation, when the only vegetation to grow is poor, coarse grass.

Man has also introduced in the populated areas particular types of vegetation of a useful nature which have become more or less naturalised. The food-producing species are the coconut, areca palm, mango, pawpaw, and tamarind. The oil-producing plants include the castor oil plant, which has become naturalised on the embankments of the Mekong near Vientiane, and among those producing textiles is the kapok, whose beautiful red flowers bloom on the bare branches in January. Decorative trees include the frangipane, whose flower is a national emblem.

## POPULATION AND PRINCIPAL RESOURCES

*The various ethnic types.* Laos has a total population of about 2.2 million, giving an average density of 20 inhabitants per square mile. It is composed of a variety of ethnic types.

The valley peoples are generally Buddhist Laotians, related to the Thais and the Shans of Burma. They live in settlements raised on piles and practise rice cultivation, fishing and stock-raising. Subdivisions of this group can be recognised by differences in costume and dialect.

The primitive Kha tribes are widely dispersed in the areas between 1,500 and 3,000 feet above sea level. They are Indonesian aboriginal peoples who were probably driven back into the highlands by invading peoples. The Meos, who came originally from China or Central Asia, live at even higher altitudes. Although they settled in Laos relatively recently, about a hundred years ago, they now form an important minority of about 50,000 who are spreading southwards. The Khas and Meos cultivate their crops almost exclusively on land cleared by burning.

Besides Laotians there are 35,000 Chinese and 25,000 Vietnamese, many of them working as craftsmen or merchants.

*Chief settlements and political regime.* The administrative and political capital, Vientiane, is a small wood and brick town with a population of 100,000 spread along the Mekong River among areca palms, coconut palms and mango trees. At the confluence of the Mekong and the Nam Khan stands 'the town of one hundred pagodas' or Luang Prabang, the royal residence of Laos, with a population of 8,000.

Thakhek, Savannakhet and Pakse are small towns of commercial importance on the banks of the Mekong. Tin from Phou Tiou and from Boneng, about 40 miles farther north, passes through Thakhek.

Savannakhet handles trade passing between Thailand and central Vietnam. Pakse is an agricultural centre for the products of the Bolovens Plateau.

In the north, Xieng Khouang and Samuea are likely to develop when communications give easier access to this region, which is of some economic importance; stock-raising and agriculture are carried on in the Tranninh region, and gum benzoin comes from Samuea.

Laos, which became a French Protectorate in 1893, is now an independent country governed by a constitutional monarchy. Under French administration the king of Luang Prabang was able to gather together under his rule the ancient fiefs of Vientiane and Bassac and thus to achieve national unity. This unity, both threatened and precariously upheld by the major protagonists of the Cold War, rests in the final analysis on the political evolution of South-East Asia as a whole.

*Agriculture and industry.* The staple crop is rice, mainly grown by irrigation on the lowlands and without

irrigation in the mountainous regions, but some is irrigated on terraced land. Rice production is not sufficient for local requirements and has to be augmented by imports from Vietnam and Thailand.

In the mountainous districts of Xieng Khouang and Samuea the cultivation of maize is fairly important, and it often takes the place of rice as the staple food of the Meos.

Vegetables cultivated for local consumption include mungo beans, stick beans, Chinese cabbage, various tubers, sweet potatoes, yams, white radish-turnips, popular everywhere in the Far East, and cucumbers and water melons. The principal condiments and spices grown are pimentos, which are exported to Thailand and Vietnam, cardamom, various species of curcuma, galingale and ginger.

Women pounding rice in Laos, using traditional equipment. This mortar combination is used in most houses where there is no rice mill.

Industrial crops are of minor importance although there is quite a variety. Opium poppies are grown by the Meos in northern Laos. Part of the crop is disposed of as contraband; the rest, about 3 tons, is purchased by the government. Tobacco grows well in the alluvial lowlands of the Mekong valley and cigarettes are manufactured and exported to Saigon. Coffee is grown mainly on the red soils of the Bolovens Plateau but in the unsettled conditions in this region the output fluctuates. The tung tree could be cultivated on a large scale in the Tranninh region, but because there is no cheap means of transport existing plantations are unable to find outlets for their production. The most interesting resource of northern Laos is styrax, the tree which produces benzoin. Some of the trees grow wild, others are cultivated. This region almost has a monopoly of benzoin, known as Siamese benzoin, which is in great demand. Output varies but it is about 40 tons annually. The production of 'sticklac' or gum lac is chiefly localised in the Samuea region. Cotton is grown throughout Laos but the annual output falls far short of the needs of the population. Ramie is cultivated on the red soils of the slopes of the Bolovens Plateau in the province of Saravane, and many other textile-producing plants, such as hemp, jute and kapok, are cultivated for local use.

Forestry provides more than enough timber, fuel and charcoal for the country's requirements and some is exported to Vietnam.

Stock-raising is fairly important in spite of disease, which often affects the cattle. There are about 350,000 cattle, 400,000 buffalo, and 800,000 pigs.

There is a number of small craft industries, such as the making of gold and silver ware, basket making, the weaving of cotton and silk—for every family has a loom—and the manufacture of palm sugar and fish paste.

Except for tin-washing at Phon Tiou and several rice-husking factories, industry does not yet exist on a large scale in Laos. The mineral resources, especially iron and copper deposits in the Xieng Khouang region, cannot be worked, owing to lack of power and good communications.

*Communications.* In spite of numerous rapids which impede navigation, the Mekong is still the vital artery of the country between Ban Houey Say and the Khon Falls. A road runs parallel with the river for nearly 1,250 miles, linking Luang Prabang and Saigon, and is intended to overcome the difficulties of river navigation.

The maintenance of the 2,200 miles of stony or embanked road is difficult, for great damage is caused every year by the rains, especially in the mountainous regions. There are no roads suited to motor traffic north of Luang Prabang and Xieng Khouang, only tracks for the traveller on foot or on horseback and rivers suitable for small craft.

Because road transport is unreliable, air transport has developed considerably in the interior of the country. There are five aerodromes and thirty airstrips of over 1,800 feet.

The large deficit in the balance of trade shows that there might be a case for Laos to become part of a larger commercial system, to expand all types of production and to gain economic independence.

# VIETNAM

The entire eastern border of the Indochinese peninsula forms a distinctive region of human geography whose inhabitants pursued their own economic development from the tenth century onward. Greatly hindered by internal conflicts until the realisation of political unity at the beginning of the nineteenth century, Vietnam owes its position to the fact that the Vietnamese made no attempt to penetrate the mountainous and forested interior to the west.

The Vietnamese are a lowland people. Mountains and high plateaus do exist in Vietnam, in fact the greater part of the country is highland, but these regions are sparsely populated and even today are inhabited only by people racially distinct from the Vietnamese.

Vietnam is 126,000 square miles in area and has a population of over 30 million. It was formerly divided into three: Tonkin with an area of 45,000 square miles, and Hanoi as the capital; Annam, with an area of 57,000 square miles, and Hue as its capital; Cochinchina, with an area of 24,000 square miles, and Saigon as its capital. It stretches over a thousand miles from north to south, and at its narrowest is 38 miles from east to west. It has a long coastline and land frontier bordering China, Laos and Cambodia.

The territory is now divided into two: North Vietnam, which includes Tonkin and the northern part of Annam, has an area of 61,000 square miles, a population of 16 million, and is an Eastern Bloc country; and South Vietnam, which includes central and southern Annam and Cochinchina, has an area of 65,600 square miles, a population of 14,000,000, and is allied to the West. The frontier between the two territories follows the 17°N. line of latitude passing south of Dong Hoi, and was fixed by the armistice agreement of July 1954 but the Government of Vietnam did not sign and military conflict still continues.

## CONTRASTS IN CLIMATE AND RELIEF

*The monsoon influence.* The whole of Vietnam is affected by the tropical monsoons. The heaviest summer rainfall is in the high mountains of the north at Chapa, on the coast of central Vietnam and on the Annam highlands. The region with least rainfall is on the south-east coast around Phan Ri and Phan Thiet.

From north to south the mean annual temperature increases and the mean annual range of temperature decreases. However, temperatures are modified by the relief.

*The folded mountains of the north.* There is a striking contrast between the relief of the sparsely populated highlands of the interior, and that of the succession of fairly narrow and densely populated coastal plains. The highlands, still thickly forested, cover three-quarters of the total area of Vietnam.

The outstanding features in the northern part of Vietnam are the folded mountain ranges. In spite of the complexity, certain major relief regions can be distinguished.

North of the Red River the ranges form convex

curves. The most southerly one, the Dong Trieu anti-cline, curves towards the sea and on the coastal slopes there are deposits of anthracite, worked by open-cast mining. The thousands of tiny islands and isolated rocks in Along Bay and the neighbouring bay of Fai Tsi Long are remnants of a limestone plateau destroyed by erosion. Between the mountains and the Red River delta is a lower region of plains, small hills and isolated massifs.

Between the Red River and the Black River there is a succession of massifs which, beginning with Fan Si Pan (10,315 feet), the highest point in Vietnam, become progressively lower towards the south-east. The region between the Black River and the upper course of the Song Ma is formed of limestone plateaus which descend in steps from the frontiers of China and Laos in the north to the fertile delta and the Gulf of Tonkin.

South of the Song Ma, where the country is confined to a narrow belt along the coast, the relief consists of the lower slopes of the highlands of eastern Upper Laos.

*The plateaus of the south.* The highlands of South Vietnam are predominantly tabular in structure, in contrast to those of the north. The whole highland region in the south is asymmetrical. Elevated in the east, it falls steeply towards the China Sea between Cape Batangan and Cape Padaran. Westwards the land falls in a series of plateau steps.

All these plateaus, which are basically sandstone, are largely covered in the centre and south by basaltic lavas, which have weathered into the rich red soils suitable for the cultivation of rubber, tea and coffee. Large areas were once densely forested, but forest has now been replaced by savanna or open woodland. This is big game country, and the Darlac Plateau is one of the world's best-known hunting grounds.

*The alluvial plains.* Only 20 per cent of Vietnam is lowland. These fertile lowlands and deltas support 90 per cent of the total population, of which only one-sixth live in the towns.

The extent of the alluvial plains depends on the size of the rivers which built them up. They are the plains of Tonkin and northern Annam, which includes the Red River delta and the plains of Thanh Hoa and Vinh; the plains of central and southern Annam, south of the Annam Gate; and the plain of Cochinchina, the delta of the Mekong.

*The plains, deltas and coasts.* The northern delta was mainly built up by the Red River and the Song Thai Binh. The delta alone is 57,000 square miles in extent. Song Ma and Song Ca have formed the smaller alluvial plains of Thanh Hoa and Vinh. The three deltas are only separated by ridges, which become lower and more broken up towards the coast, where the deltas almost merge.

Outcrops of hard rock on the coast have fixed sandspits, in front of which is the exposed foreshore formed by alluvial deposits from the Red River — deposits that are extremely fertile and much disputed by the farmers. Farther inland the plain is very low, with numerous lakes. This low-lying part of the Tonkin delta, extending from Phat Diem to Hai-phong, was the last to be formed and is continually developing. Behind it is the middle delta region, lying north of the Bambous Canal and Nam Dinh and

The valley of Langson, in North Vietnam, near the Chinese frontier.

stretching as far as the Rapides Canal and the Song Day, a distributary of the Red River. These plains, which are slightly higher than those near the coast, are divided up by embankments to protect them from flooding and by smaller banks which control irrigation water.

From Hanoi north to Vietri the alluvial region at the head of the delta slopes more steeply towards the foothills.

The deltic lowlands of Thanh Hoa and Vinh extend from the foothills of the Annam range to the straight sandy shore. This is an extremely inhospitable coast, battered by the typhoons of the China Sea, especially from July to November.

South of the 'Annam Gate' the coastal features change. The 'Annam Gate' is an historic gateway which was part of a large defensive system, and marks the true geographical boundary between northern and central Annam. South of this the mountains are near to the coast, the rivers are short and bring down only small quantities of alluvium.

The lowlands are small and irregular, dotted with hills, and shut in between the wooded slopes of the Annam range and the white dunes fringing the shore.

The coastal plains are bordered by lagoons as far as Cape Batangan. Tourane (Da Nang) is the only major port. Farther south is Faifo, historically important as the point of departure for ships leaving Vietnam for China and Japan, avoiding the Gulf of Tonkin.

Between Cape Batangan and Cape Padaran the mountains come right down to the sea, and this part of the coast has very attractive scenery. Cape Varella, halfway along the coast, is the most easterly point in the whole Indochinese peninsula. South of this Cape lies the bay of Nha Trang, whose wealth of aquatic life led to the establishment of an Institute of Oceanography in 1927. It is also a popular holiday resort. North-west of the Cam Ranh inlet is the port of Ba Ngoi, the natural outlet of the Lang Bian region.

South of Cape Padaran the mountains begin to withdraw from the sea, and the coast takes a south-westerly direction. Bordered by dunes, it shelters numerous small fishing ports. There are large salt works in the region of Binh-Thuan.

The plain of Cochinchina has been built up by the Mekong. The delta begins at Phnom Penh in Cambodia, 250 miles from the sea. The alluvium brought down by the river, estimated at 1,300 million cubic yards per annum, is carried south-westwards by a coastal current, and is extending the spit at Camau at the rate of 260 feet a year. On the coast, deposits of black mud are fixed by mangroves. Between Saigon and the Bassac, where the land has been silted up, huge areas are covered with vegetation called *tram*, whose rot-proof trunks are used for piles; where the land is still regularly flooded there are extensive mangrove forests.

The best cultivated land is in the eastern and central parts of the delta. Efforts are now being made to develop rice cultivation in the Transbassac region, particularly at Cai San, where numerous refugees from the North have settled.

*The Red River and the Mekong.* The basins of the two important rivers, the Red River and the Mekong, extend far beyond the boundaries of Vietnam The coastal rivers of central Vietnam are very much smaller. The regime of all these rivers is dependent on the monsoons, and there is low water at the end of the dry season in May and flooding in summer from July to October. All the rivers form deltas which are constantly growing and extending the eastern coast.

The Red River rises in the high plateaus of Yunnan in China, at an altitude of 8,000 feet, and is 750 miles long. From Lung Po to Lao Kay, about 30 miles, it forms the frontier with China. At Lao Kay, 300 miles from the sea in enters Vietnam, and is already only 260 feet above sea level. As far as Yen Bay, its valley, which is followed by the railway from Yunnan, is narrow and confined between parallel ranges of hills. Here it is navigable only for sampans. Then below Phu Tho it receives its right-bank tributary the Black River, 575 miles long, and at Vietri the River Claire, 275 miles long, joins it on the left bank. Both these tributaries rise in southern China. Vietri is 140 miles by river from the sea (93 miles as the crow flies), and

32 feet above sea level. The delta begins here and the river winds across it leaving many abandoned meanders. The levees of the main channel have been strengthened and raised in the course of time, and a system of dykes controls the floodwaters. The smaller delta of the Song Thai Binh joins the Red River delta. Numerous distributaries join together the various branches of this complex delta. At Hanoi, on the right bank, the average depth of the river at low water is 7 feet 2 inches and the discharge 700 cubic metres per second. Floods raise the water level to 39 feet, i.e. 20 feet above the level of the streets, and the discharge reaches 28,000 cubic metres per second.

Each year the Red River carries about 80 million cubic metres of alluvium to the sea. It is so named because in floodtime the alluvium colours the waters red. A coastal current carries the alluvium towards the south west and the delta is growing outwards at an average rate of 300 feet a year in the region of Phat Diem. The Red River is navigable for junks and launches as far as Vietri.

The basins of the coastal rivers of central Vietnam are very small and, since they flow from highlands near the coast, they are short, with steep longitudinal profiles and torrential flow. The most important rivers north of the 'Annam Gate', the Song Ma (287 miles) and the Song Ca (312 miles), have built up the plains of Thanh Hoa and Vihn, which, together with the Red River delta, form the great plains of the north.

The Mekong, which rises in Tibet and is nearly 3,200 miles long, is the most extensive river basin, covering an area of 313,000 square miles. It is the largest river in Indochina, but only the lowest oart of its course passes through southern Vietnam. Its two main distributaries, which divide at Phnom Penh in Cambodia, form the Lower Mekong and the Bassac. The river is tidal as far as Phnom Penh in the dry season, and as far as Xuyen and Cho Mo in the flood period. The Lower Mekong, which takes three-quarters of the total discharge (about 13,000 to 17,000 cubic metres), is the deeper distributary and that most used by shipping. Below Sadec it divides into several branches, of which the most northerly is the only one used by cargo boats.

Since 1956, when the possibilities of developing the Lower Mekong basin for triple purposes of irrigation, shipping and power were first considered, the Government has been able to call on the help of a number of countries to implement the project.

In addition to the network of distributaries there is a system of artificial canals which extensively is used for inland water transport.

All these plains are extremely important in terms of human geography, for they support and feed the greater part of the population.

## THE HUMAN ENVIRONMENT

*Chinese and Indian civilisations.* The region now known as Vietnam has not always been populated solely by Vietnamese. Like the rest of Indochina it has been the scene of great migrations of people from the continent of Asia or from the sea, who met here but did not mix.

The earliest inhabitants are related to the people who now populate the Pacific islands. In ancient times migrations took place continuously over a period of centuries, generally from north to south, the migrants being successively Austronesians (e.g. Chams), Austro-Asiatics (e.g. Khmers) and Mongolians.

From the end of the second century A.D. the present territory of Vietnam came under two spheres of influence. In the north was the kingdom of Champa, whose people, the Chams, spoke an Indonesian language; there was Chinese political influence, which sometimes involved intervention even as late as the beginning of the fifteenth century. In the south was the kingdom of Founan, where there was cultural influence from India, but no political or military intervention. Hinduism and Buddhism were successively dominant, and the chief vassal state was the kingdom of the Khmers, the direct ancestors of the Cambodians. The country was divided under successive dynasties until 1802, when the whole of Vietnam was united for the first time.

*The peoples of the mountains and the plains.* In addition to the fundamental racial diversity of the population, there is a remarkable contrast in the geographical distribution of the population, due to the relief.

The mountain peoples of the north include the Thais, who are the most numerous and live by the rivers in the high valleys, cultivating flooded rice fields; the Mans (or Yaos), who live on the upper slopes; the Meos, who occupy the highest slopes, and the Muongs, who occupy the foothills close to the delta, west and south-west of Hanoi. The mountain peoples of the south, until recently referred to as the 'Mois' (the barbarians), live in separate tribes in the mountains and high plateau lands, grouped in villages built on piles, and cultivate their crops on land cleared by burning.

In origin, language and tradition, these mountain peoples of the north and south are quite separate and do not attempt to mix with one another. They are even more opposed to the peoples of the lowlands who have built up powerful and homogeneous societies; among these are the Chams, whose civilisation has left clear traces in central Vietnam, the Khmers, who form fairly important minorities in south Vietnam, and finally and most important the Vietnamese, who besides being the most numerous in the country are also the most dynamic.

*A densely populated country.* Vietnam has the second largest population of any country in South East Asia, after the Republic of Indonesia. It has a total population of over 30 million, of which about 20 million are Vietnamese, compared with Indonesia's total of 96 million.

The non-Vietnamese who have settled in Vietnam can be divided into three groups: the radial minorities of the North and South (the Thais, Mans, Meos, Muongs, Chams, the southern mountain tribes, and the Khmers), who number about 2,200,000; more than 700,000 Chinese and other Eastern peoples, some of whom have Vietnamese citizenship; and about 10,000 French. There are many of mixed blood.

Were it not for wartime casualties the Vietnamese population would be growing still more rapidly, since the birth rate remains high (estimated at 30 per 1,000) and the natural death rate has declined considerably in recent years.

*Opposite page:* A small-town market day.
Only one fifth of Vietnam's long strip of territory is lowland but it supports 90 per cent of the population.
Vietnam has the second largest population of South-east Asia, and the birth rate is high.

A Vietnamese farmer and his
children at the gates
of the hamlet of Cu-Chi.

lands. In North Vietnam peoples are crowded into the delta, where the average density exceeds 1,250 per square mile, and in certain parts is as high as 2,500, or even 3,750. In South Vietnam the population is concentrated on the delta and in the lowland region of the central part. The average density is lower in the southern delta, 500 per square mile.

These densities for 1940 are in general still valid. However, since partition in 1954 an important movement of people, mainly Vietnamese, has been going on from North to South, with a much less important migration from South to North. Besides these internal migrations, some Vietnamese have left the country. The growth in population in the South has led to the settlement and development of the scantily populated region of Transbassac and the high plateaus.

There have always been some Chinese in Vietnam. Most of them live in the towns and are engaged in trade, crafts and transportation. The reasons for Chinese immigration to Vietnam and its extent and character have varied in the course of time. Today most Chinese families come to settle permanently. All those born and resident in South Vietnam became citizens from April 1957; it is estimated that half the Chinese living in South Vietnam were affected by this regulation.

## THE MAIN GEOGRAPHICAL REGIONS

*The lowlands and highlands of the north.* The Northern plains were the cradle of the Vietnamese nation. Their soils and climate are similar everywhere from Dong Trieu to the 'Annam Gate' and, as already stated, they are the most densely populated regions. The people have cultivated rice here for centuries and are engaged in many very specialised crafts. There are numerous villages and some important centres like Hanoi, the historic capital, Haiphong, the leading port in the North, and Nam Dinh, the centre of the textile industry. There are large and varied mineral resources which are being developed.

The highlands of the North were always partly inhabited by mountain peoples of Vietnamese origin, mainly Thais in the high valleys, Muongs in the south-west, Mans and Meos on the higher slopes. Of the mountain peoples of the North all except the Thais practise shifting cultivation. They destroy the forest and grow vegetables and opium poppies. The lands they acquire by burning off the natural vegetation are never irrigated or fertilized, and are soon exhausted and then abandoned for fresh clearings. In contrast to the shifting method of cultivation on the hillsides is that established by the Thais living in the valley bottoms, with permanent irrigated fields used exclusively for cultivating rice. The Thais live in huts raised on piles.

*The lowlands and plateaus of the centre and south.* Numerous small areas of lowland are scattered along the coast of central Vietnam; these silted plains receive heavy rainfall and become increasingly hot towards the south. Rice is grown on 1,225,000 acres, while secondary crops such as maize, sweet potatoes, manioc, groundnuts (peanuts) and sugar-cane occupy about 225,000 acres. The chief towns are Hue, the ancient capital of the Nguyen Tourane (Da Nang),

Half of the total population is under the age of twenty, which means that the working population is relatively small.

In spite of efforts to industrialise the country, and although the urban population has more than doubled in the last ten years, especially in the South, most of the people are still peasants. The rural population continues to be more than 75 per cent of the total, although internal migrations since 1954 have brought about some changes, for example the phenomenal growth of population in the Saigon area. The number of people engaged in commerce, transport, public and private administration and the professions has increased to 20 per cent, while secondary industry is still the least important activity, employing only 5 per cent of the total population.

The Vietnamese is closely attached to his land and to his village. Even the town-dweller, at least in the North, is proud of his native village. The distribution of the rural population is very uneven. The most densely populated areas are the rice-producing low-a small port of historical interest, and Nha Trang, a holiday resort. Fishing is very important everywhere along this coast.

The plateaus of the centre and south form a separate geographical region, with a distinctive climate, relief and population whose origins and traditions have nothing in common with those of the lowland peoples. This region of 22,000 square miles formed a separate administrative district attached to the kingdom of Annam, before the Republic of Vietnam was set up in 1956. Today, refugees from North Vietnam are settling in this area. Large tea and coffee plantations were established by the French and there is a rubber plantation north of Ban Me Thuot which marks the northern limit of cultivation of this crop in Vietnam. Market-gardening has developed considerably since 1950, and the produce is sold in Saigon. Large plantations of kenaf, whose fibre is a substitute for jute, have been started, as well as plantations of ramie.

Rice cultivation on large plantations characterises the lowlands of the South. In 1956 more than 5 million acres produced nearly 3 million tons of paddy. The expansion of rice cultivation here is relatively recent, and its development is due to the great schemes for water control. Secondary crops produced in the South include sugar-cane, fruits, manioc, vegetables, tobacco and rubber. In the South, unlike the North, large landowners and tennant farmers predominated until the beginning of agrarian reforms. Reforms are being carried out here, as in the north, but in a different way.

## ECONOMIC DEVELOPMENT

There was little change in the economy of Vietnam until modern times, which for Vietnam began a century ago. The ancient mountain economy has endured alongside changes that have been introduced. Most of the mountain-dwellers cultivate rice, using different methods according to whether they inhabit the hillsides or the valley bottoms. Some domestic animals are kept, and fishing and hunting supply sufficient food for the needs of the people. Industry is limited to small crafts which supply only local needs, such as the making of cooking-pots, earthenware jars and gongs.

Rice is the traditional basis of the lowland economy. Owing to the low population density, it can be grown extensively on the southern delta; but on the northern deltas, where the density is very high, cultivation has always been intensive and two crops are harvested each year. Other crops, such as maize, sweet potatoes and beans, are grown on the higher, drier areas above flood level. Besides food crops, lowland Vietnam produces raw silk and lacquer. Pigs and domestic fowl are kept and attempts are being made to encourage stock-raising, particularly of dairy cattle. Industry takes the form of specialised village crafts, using simple tools and supplying the local market. External trade is in the hands of the Chinese. In the eighteenth century Europeans attempted to establish trading posts, but they had no lasting effects.

THE MODERN ECONOMY. In the second half of the last century the Vietnamese began to grow rice by more up-to-date methods in order to export it. Their country was so well adapted to rice production that this is still the basis of the economy.

Agriculture supports 85 per cent of the population and by far the leading crop is rice. Differences between the rice cultivation of North and South have been accentuated by the different schemes adopted for controlling water supplies.

In the North, where cultivation was already intensive, modern irrigation works were carried out in the 1930's under the French to regulate the flow of water, by building dykes to control floods and barrages to conserve water when there is a shortage. The dykes have been raised higher, strengthened and protected, and the layout has been improved and completed. A campaign to encourage the use of manure and the selection of seed was also carried out. As a result of all these measures to improve output and raise average yields, the calculated increase in the North was more than 4,000 lb. per acre with two crops each year.

There have been similar improvements in rice

Vietnamese women at work in the paddy fields. Rice is the basis of both North and South Vietnam's economy. There is particularly intensive cultivation in the plains of North Vietnam. Here, improved methods of cultivation and intensive irrigation have been introduced in an attempt to raise yields.

production in the South, where physical and human conditions are different. In this area of extensive plantation cultivation the problem was not so much to increase the output of rice as to improve wasteland by extensive dredging operations. Work was first undertaken in 1866, and the area under cultivation increased from 1.3 million acres in 1880 to 5.5 million in 1937.

Before the Second World War the total output rose to 6 million tons, half of which was produced in the southern delta region. Vietnam exported 1,500,000 tons of rice through Saigon.

Maize is the most important of the other food crops, followed by vegetables such as beans and soya beans, sweet potatoes, manioc, market-garden produce, sugar-cane, tobacco, cinnamon, coffee and tea. A great variety of tropical fruits is also grown.

Changes in the traditional economy in the mountains, where the population is sparcer and less dynamic than in the plains, have been brought about with difficulty. Shifting cultivation has been controlled, and irrigation of the hillsides has been undertaken at Plei Eu. Market-gardening has been developed on the Dalat Plateau and the cultivation of tung trees, for tung oil, near Ban Me Thuot.

*Industrial crops.* Rubber is the most important industrial crop of Vietnam. It was introduced from Malaya at the end of the nineteenth century, and is cultivated on the red and grey soils of South Vietnam.

Red soils cover two plateau areas, the Lower Dong Nai region and the Lower Song Ba region. Grey soils, formed from ancient alluvium, granitic sands or marine clays, require heavy manuring These soils are nearer to Saigon and are cultivated by small planters or small companies. At the end of the nineteenth century tea and coffee plantations were started in Vietnam and, like the new coffee plantations, they were established mainly on the red soils of the high plateaus of Kontum and the Upper Dong Nai. Tea has been rather more successful than coffee.

Other industrial crops are cotton, which is grown in the Thanh Hoa and Phu Yen regions, kapok, widely grown before the war and now cultivated south of Hue, mulberry trees, for silkworms whose output is sufficient only for local industries, and lac, which is especially important in the Phu Tho region. Finally, the raw materials of the local craftsmen must be mentioned: bamboo, rattan, rushes and *cu-nao,* which provides a brown dye for cloth.

*Fishing.* Fish, together with rice, forms the staple diet of the Vietnamese. Coastal fishing is carried out in Along Bay in the North, off the coast of central Vietnam from Quang Ngai south to Cape Varella, and along the whole southern coast. A great variety of fish is caught, including shrimps and crayfish, which are widely consumed.

*Forests and savannas.* Today forest and savanna are found on the highlands of the interior. Forests cover nearly 5 million acres, of which 967,500 acres are in the north, 2,145,000 acres in the centre and 1,802,500 acres in the south. Open woodland is steadily replacing dense forest, which is found only on the more inaccessible slopes. Savannas are very extensive on the high plateaus of the south. The forests of Vietnam are an important asset so far little exploited, but valuable enough to be carefully conserved and developed.

*Mining.* Mining is most developed in North Vietnam, being limited in the south to a small coalfield near Da Nang with an annual production of 100,000 tons, a small goldmine, scattered deposits of molybdenum not so far exploited and important phosphate deposits on the Paracel Islands.

In the North, coal is the most important mineral. The richest coalfield is in Quang Yen province north of Haiphong, and extends for about 95 miles; the coal is good quality anthracite, hard and bright; east of Hongay it is mined in open-cast terraces. The production figure for 1963 was given as 3.2 million tons. Phosphates, apatite and salt are also mined; and tin, chromite ore, iron, zinc, tungsten, antimony and manganese are found as well. Some tin is smelted locally.

*Manufacturing industries.* Modern industries have developed on the deltas. Cement plastics and enamel ware are produced at Haiphong. There are large brick and tile works at Hanoi and at Long Buu in the South.

The glassworks at Hanoi built originally to make window panes (required for dwellings in the north of the country) and bottles, now specialises in the latter. Forest products are used in saw-milling, joinery, and the manufacture of matches and paper. Modern rice mills have been built at the ports, particularly at Cholon, the leading rice market of Vietnam. Some rice is manufactured into alcohol; the Vietnamese always use rice wine in ritual ceremonies. There is a large factory at Saigon.

Other important works in Vietnam are the modern sugar refineries in the South at Hiep Hoa and Khanh Hoi with an annual production of 61,000 tons, and smaller works at Tay Ninh, north of Saigon, and at Tuy Hoa; sugar production almost meets the requirements of the whole country; tobacco factories, vegetable oil refineries, soap works and breweries; spinning and weaving mills, mainly at Haiphong and Nam Dinh, and two large factories used exclusively for silk weaving, one at Phu Phong, the other at Nam Dinh; large modern printing works; engineering workshops; power stations, all thermal except three which are hydro-electric, at Cha Pa in the North, and at Ban Me Thuot and Ankroet on the Southern plateaus. A further hydro-electric project at Da Nhim in South Vietnam, paid for with Japanese war reparations, was completed in 1964 and can supply 850 million kWh annually.

*Communications.* Most of the railroads were built with the help of French capital. There are about 1,400 miles of track, but they run in short stretches and on the most important pre-war line, the Trans-Indochina Railroad linking Hanoi with Saigon, there is no through communication. North Vietnam has a line linking Haiphong with Kun Ming in China.

Before the war in Indochina, the road system of Vietnam was one of the best in the Far East. Today there are 3,875 miles of main roads and 10,625 miles of secondary roads in Vietnam.

Air transport, unlike road and rail traffic, has increased and is important both for international and internal communications.

*The ports and towns.* The ports of Saigon and Haiphong handle all the foreign trade of Vietnam.

Saigon did not begin to develop until the late eighteenth century, after the arrival of the French. The town has spread on to the sides of the plateau; the port, fifty miles from the sea, is easily accessible in spite of the winding river with its well-developed meanders. Its position at a meeting-place of international trade routes, its advantages as a port, and its situation in relation to its hinterland all account for its growth. The Chinese community at Cholon, an important and very wealthy commercial and industrial centre (weaving, rice-husking and soap-making), has also contributed to its development. Until 1955, the port was administered jointly by Cambodia, France, Laos and Vietnam. A great business centre, Saigon is now the capital of the Republic of Vietnam, and together with Cholon forms a conurbation of 1,600,000. Problems of urban development, such as traffic and the supply of water and electricity, have become acute, especially since 1955 but various efforts have been made to meet the increased demand.

Situated at the head of a gulf and away from the main sea routes, Haiphong is still the chief port of the

North and has a population of 369,000. It is about 12 miles from the sea on the right bank of the Cua Cam, one of the mouths of the Song Thai Binh. The main channel to the port has constantly to be dredged.

Hanoi, formerly the political capital of Vietnam and later the administrative capital of the Union of Indochina, is now the capital of the Democratic Republic of Vietnam. It is a fine city of broad, shady boulevards, with imposing buildings. Its importance as an educational and a scientific centre has assisted its growth and it now has a population of 644,000.

Hue, an ancient capital, was primarily a fortress, a closely guarded royal city with sumptuous temples and imperial palaces. The rather undistinguished modern town faces it across the Huong Giang River.

The other towns of Vietnam contain only a very small proportion of the population and have developed as commercial and administrative centres since the end of the last century, with the building of roads and railroads. Since 1955 the population of the southern towns has increased considerably; in the largest towns the buildings are being modernised and several factories have been built.

*Foreign trade.* Before the war the chief exports in tonnage and value were agricultural products. The most important was rice, and eastern Indochina, which included Cambodia, was one of the three leading world exporters of rice, together with Thailand and Burma. After rice came maize, then rubber as regards tonnage, but in inverse order as regards value. These three commodities accounted for nearly three-quarters of the total value of the exports. Coal and tin competed in value for fourth place, but coal and cement were the leading exports by weight.

The undeveloped state of Vietnam's economy is shown by the imports, which are mainly manufactured goods. Textiles are the most important with machinery and vehicles next in order of value. Petroleum products lead in tonnage, followed by chemicals.

Before Vietnam became independent, France was the main trading partner, being the chief buyer of rice, maize and rubber, and supplying more than half Vietnam's imports.

Since Hongkong and Singapore handle most of the goods in transit for Vietnam, it is impossible to determine the exact source of the country's imports or the destination of its exports; but apart from Singapore and Hongkong, Vietnam's three main customers in the Far East are China, Japan and India, all exporting small quantities of goods to Vietnam. THE POSTWAR ECONOMY. Since 1959 the economic development of Vietnam has been hindered by world events and its own internal problems. Until 1944 the country remained relatively stable, although cut off from France. The present economic situation is partly the result of the armistice agreement signed at Geneva in 1954, and partly due to subsequent measures taken by the North, supported by the Communist countries, or the South, supported by the West, especially the U.S.A.

Production and trade have been affected by large displacements of people within Vietnam since July 1954, by the differences between the economic systems of the North and South, by the events which have influenced the policies of the various countries of South-East Asia and the Far East during the last twenty years, and by internal strife in South Vietnam.

Consequently it is possible to give only a summary account of the temporary situation in this country, which is in process of reconstruction and at present still divided into two zones.

*Agricultural and industrial production and foreign trade.* Agriculture, especially rice and rubber production, is still the main activity in South Vietnam. In 1963, nearly 6½ million acres yielded well over 5 million tons of paddy. To ensure that production increases, measures are being taken to ease the pressure of population in the urban centres, to settle refugees from the North in the newly developed regions of Transbassac, the Jones Plain and the high plateaus, and also to move people from the overpopulated regions of central Vietnam on to the high plateaus in order to produce industrial crops. Such a scheme has led to the cultivation of kenaf and ramie at Plei Ku and Ban Me Thuot.

The most important industrial crop, especially for

Rubber processing in Vietnam. Rubber is the most important industrial crop in Vietnam. It was introduced from Malaya in the nineteenth century and is grown on the red and grey soils of the south.

The bicycle is widely used in
rural Vietnam, and water for
irrigation is much in evidence
even in the middle of the village.

Efforts to industrialise
Vietnam are continuing but,
although the urban population
has doubled in the last ten years,
the population is still essentially
rural. Mining is most developed
in North Vietnam with
deposits of coal, phosphates, gold
and molybdenum.

export, is still rubber. The proportion of young plantations (37 per cent are less than 20 years old) is greater
than that in Malaya (7 per cent), Indonesia (14 per
cent) or Ceylon (30 per cent), but the planted areas
are less extensive and consequently production is
lower. The following table for 1962 illustrates the
position:

| Malaya | 765,000 tons |
|---|---|
| Indonesia | 670,000 tons |
| Thailand | 194,000 tons |
| Ceylon | 104,000 tons |
| South Vietnam | 78,000 tons |

The staple food crops produced for home consumption are sugar-cane, fruits, coconuts, manioc,
vegetables, maize, soya beans, coffee and tea (some
of which is exported).

The most important industries are still those originally started with French or other foreign capital:
brewing, distilling, tobacco, soap and ice manufacturing, and weaving. There are also salt works and
sugar refineries, and a pharmaceutical industry is
being developed. A Franco-Vietnamese company was
established in 1959 for the manufacture and sale of
glassware. Power resources are small; but the output
of coal from Nong Son has risen to 100,000 tons.
Hydro-electric power projects involving the building
of dams on the Da Ninh and a power station at Dram
are completed. There has been little official response to
the new private foreign investments.

Foreign trade shows a deficit: in 1963, exports were
valued at 2,683 million piastres and imports at 10,016
million. The exports in order of value are rubber 60
per cent, rice 26 per cent, feathers, beer, scrap metal,
tobacco, salt, copra oil, matting and tea; the main
imports are textiles, vehicles, machinery, pharmaceuticals, iron and steel, petroleum products, yarn
and paper.

France is easily the chief customer of the Republic
of Vietnam, taking more than half the exports; the
United States and Japan come next. France also supplies nearly one-third of the imports, again followed
by the United States and Japan. Various economic
plans have been backed by financial support from the
U.S.A., and almost three-quarters of all imports are
made possible by funds from the same source.

As regards the Democratic Republic of Vietnam,
present information about production and trade is
more general. Rice remains the staple food crop and
the annual output is about 5.5 million tons following
the return to cultivation of the former rice fields.
Most of the peasants belonged to agricultural co-
operatives in 1963.

The former industries have started up again: coal
mining at Hongay, for, after rice, coal is North
Vietnam's most important product, cement-making at
Haiphong, textile manufacture at Nam Dinh, brewing
and ice-making at Hanoi, distilling at Hanoi and
Gia Lam, the production of thermal electric power
at Hanoi, Haiphong and other new power stations,
rice-husking at Hanoi, Haiphong, Nam Dinh and
Dap Cau (with Chinese aid), engineering at Hanoi
(with Russian aid), printing (with East German aid),
fish-preserving at Haiphong, the preparation of tea
at Phu Tho and Hanoi. There are power stations at
Thai Nguyen, Nam Dinh, Vinh and Thanh Hoa
and several under construction, three near Saigon.

Phosphates, apatite, iron, tin zinc and chrome are mined. Local crafts are still important.

Nevertheless, North Vietnam is still essentially an agricultural country. The total value of industrial production, both national and private, has risen to about 30 per cent of the total production. A three-year plan (1958-60) was followed by a five-year plan.

Foreign trade is entirely State-controlled and is mostly with China; exports are tending to increase and imports to decline. Coal from Hongay is the most important export.

THE FUTURE OF VIETNAM. During the first ten centuries A.D., and again at the beginning of the fifteenth century, the Vietnamese came under the influence of the Chinese, whose customs they learned to adapt. They were primarily interested in subsistence and there was little expansion beyond the lands which supplied their needs; methods of production and exchange were ingenious but simple. Law was mainly penal; social life was governed by family tradition, and administration by the mandarin hierarchy and the semi-independent village.

After the middle of the nineteenth century, a Western civilisation not only introduced an entirely new economy to this region, but also carried out social, scientific, cultural and medical work.

Present circumstances bring various problems to the fore. The problem is not whether the strong family traditions which inspire the people can be adapted to modern conditions and maintained; nor whether agricultural reforms undertaken at various places will bring about improvements beneficial to the whole country; nor whether development of education will help in the formation of an executive class which is necessary for industrial expansion; Vietnam is relatively rich in natural resources and its population is growing. Its future depends on the determined effort of all and on the energy of a leadership prepared to sacrifice political ends for the common good.

It is to be hoped that the independent spirit of these people will be asserted, and that Vietnam will be able to regain the prosperity it had achieved a short time ago.

The present frontiers of Vietnam are not natural ones; they were determined only after the first modern maps had been compiled.

But the history of Vietnam, influenced as it has been by Chinese civilisation, has set the country apart and made it unique among the other civilisations of the peninsula, which are predominantly Indian.

The Indochinese Peninsula, the scene of great migrations to which it owes its name, the meeting place of peoples of different origin who were at various stages of development, and who formerly fought one another, has produced states whose interests are basically similar and whose excellent natural resources, exploited by youthful energy, could make them among the most efficient in the world.

A Vietnam farmer drives his ox-cart in from the fields.

# THE ISLANDS
# OF SOUTH-EAST ASIA

# THE PHILIPPINES

Filipinos pride themselves on being the only Christian nation in the Far East, and are wont to claim that theirs is the third largest English-speaking country (27 million). Despite independence, their way of life is increasingly modelled on that of the United States of America. Their system of government is similar to that of the United States, and they follow closely American trends in education. The economic well-being of the republic depends on the American market. Nevertheless, Americanisation is still merely a veneer over an earlier Spanish colonial heritage, itself only a veneer on a solid foundation of Malayan culture. The typical rural dwelling is the nipa palm thatch and plaited bamboo house on stilts, often set in a banana clump.

The term Filipino indicates neither physical nor cultural characteristics, and is usually restricted to the Christian majority, whose way of life combines pre-Spanish, Spanish and American customs, in varying proportions. So far the Christian majority has failed to assimilate 1,300,000 *Moros* (Moslems) and 350,000 pagans, who have been little affected by Western ideas. The country remains predominantly agricultural, producing cash crops for export, and importing foodstuffs and manufactured goods, as it did in the colonial period.

## PHYSICAL ASPECTS

*The island communities.* The Philippines consists of an archipelago of more than 7,000 islands stretching for over 1,100 miles off the south-east coast of Asia. Most of this great cluster of islands are small, uninhabited and nameless. The eleven largest, each with an area of more than 1,200 square miles, are Luzon, Mindanao, Samar, Negros, Palawan, Panay, Mindoro, Leyte, Cebu, Bohol and Masbate; together they comprise 95 per cent of the total land area and have over 95 per cent of the total population. The two largest islands—Luzon and Mindanao—contain 67 per cent of the total area and have 49 per cent of the total population.

The islands are mountainous and volcanic, and form part of the great girdle of islands which circle the western 'rim' of the Pacific Ocean and which are the summits of ranges formed during the Alpine or Tertiary period of mountain building. Much of the surface rises to over 1,600 feet above sea level, and lowland occupies only a small proportion of the total land area. The principal lowlands — the central plain of Luzon and the Kotobato plain of Mindanao —are both inland plains; but there are many discontinuous small 'bay-head' plains along the highly indented coastline. In general, the mountain ranges lie parallel to the shorelines; their steep slopes are gashed by innumerable gullies, and landslides are common after heavy rain. Mount Kanláon—an active volcano in the north of Negros—rises to 12,700 feet above sea level, and is the highest peak.

*Climate and vegetation.* The archipelago stretches from about latitude 20° N. to latitude 5° N. and the climate, determined in the main by the monsoonal system of the Asian continent, is essentially humid tropical in type. Differences in altitude and aspect account for the many local climates. Temperature variations are largely due to differences in altitude. At Manila, the mean daily minimum never falls below the February figure of 20°C. (68°F.), and the mean maximum never exceeds the May maximum of 34°C. (94°F.), reached before the 'break' of the south-west monsoon. During the 'cool' season (December, January and February), waves of cold northerly air penetrate Luzon and reach somewhat to the south of Manila. Generally, throughout the archipelago, save in a few sheltered valleys, the mean annual rainfall exceeds 80 inches; and at many places it exceeds 120 inches. The heaviness of the rainfall is due partly to the monsoons and partly to the high incidence of typhoons (locally called *baguios*) which cross or pass near to the islands. On the eastward-facing shores, the wettest months are November, December and January, and there is no dry season. By contrast, nearly all the rain which falls on the westward-facing slopes is brought by the

About 200 miles by road from Manila, former capital of the Philippines, on Luzon Island, lies Legaspi City, overlooking the Albay Gulf. Behind it rises Mayon volcano (7,943 feet), a perfect volcanic cone.

south-west monsoon, which normally blows between May and October, and there is a well-marked dry season, January, February and March being the driest quarter.

Tropical rain forest still covers more than half the total land surface of the archipelago; adaptation to seasonal drought is marked in a great number of species by a seasonal fall of leaves. Commercially, the most important trees are the hardwoods of the *lauan* and *nara* groups, which are marketed abroad under the name Philippine mahogany. There are extensive areas of man-induced grassland, much of which is burned over once a year in order to renew the grass which, although poor, is used for pasture. The tropical grasses form a heavy turf.

## HISTORICAL DEVELOPMENT

The Philippines is situated at one of the cultural crossings of the world, where southward and northward migrants have met and mingled since time immemorial. It is uncertain at what date and from where the earliest immigrants came. Most of the eighty-seven languages and dialects spoken in the archipelago are of the Indo-Malay linguistic group and the 'Malay' physical strain is dominant in the present population. The most backward of the inhabitants are the Aëtas, who appear to be related to the Negritos of the Andaman Islands. They are of small stature and have remained at a primitive stage of cultural development, knowing nothing of tillage, weaving, pottery-making or metal-working; they survive in small groups in the mountains of Luzon, Mindanao and Mindoro.

*Pre-Spanish settlement.* Some two thousand years before the Christian era, Neolithic cultivators may have entered the archipelago both from the north and from the south-west. The builders of the spectacular flights of terraces in northern and western Luzon arrived before the beginning of the Christian era. They were cultivators who knew the value of irrigating their crops; they used bronze and gold; they built houses of bamboo and thatch; they had a complex social organisation for communal working of the land and for group control of the irrigation system. It is believed that they came from the China-Tonkin borderland. Their heirs today are the pagan peoples —the Bontocs, the Ifugaos, the Igorots and some of the Kalingas.

Later, between the eighth and fifteenth centuries A.D., the archipelago came under the influence firstly of the rich and powerful Indo-Malay Kingdom of Sri Vijaya, and secondly of the Javanese Kingdom of Majapahit, which reached its zenith about 1400. During the fifteenth century Moslem traders and pirates penetrated the archipelago and were already established in the Sulu Islands, Palawan and Mindanao when the Spaniards arrived in 1521. Moslem traders also reached Luzon, which came under the influence of the Chinese. The Philippines paid tribute to China in 1372, and during the first half of the fifteenth century it came under the direct rule of the Celestial Empire.

*The Spanish influence.* The Magellan expedition reached the Philippines in 1521, but more than forty years elapsed before Spain attempted to occupy the archipelago. In 1565, Lopez de Legaspi founded the city of Cebu on the island of the same name. In the same year Andres de Urdaneta discovered an eastward passage across the north Pacific to Mexico and thus made practicable the Spanish colonisation of the archipelago. His route, known subsequently as Urdaneta's Passage, was used by the Acapulco galleon—the annual ship between Manila and Mexico—until the end of the eighteenth century.

The Spanish occupation of the Philippines was both a military and a missionary enterprise. Those who carried it out were from Mexico, and the Philippines was linked only indirectly with Spain. The Spaniards easily achieved control over the greater part of the archipelago and established a regional administration similar to that which they introduced elsewhere in 'New' Spain. They replaced tribal organisation by an administrative pattern of *barrio* (local district), municipality and province; and replaced animism by the Catholic faith. They never succeeded in conquering the Moros of the southern islands, and their relations with them were as bitter as those between the mother country and the Moors in the western Mediterranean. They were also successfully resisted by the 'terrace' communities of Luzon.

The conversion of the Philippines to Catholicism was largely the work of the mendicant orders— Franciscans, Dominicans and Augustinians. The Roman Catholic Church in Spain looked on Manila, capital of the Philippines, as an advance base for the conversion of the Far East to the Catholic faith; Manila was made the seat of an archbishop in 1595. In 1960 there were 22,686,000 Roman Catholics in the Philippines.

The Spaniards introduced into the Philippines the *encomienda* land system which they had previously introduced into Central and South America. Large blocks of land together with the inhabitants were granted to the Roman Catholic Church, to the Missionary Orders and to Spanish and part-caste families. The *encomiendas* were cultivated by tenants, who tilled their lords' land in return for their own small holdings. The holding of land in the Philippines gave prestige, as in Spanish America, but an estate was valuable only when it was populated with natives to work it. A few families acquired substantial wealth which they increased when they were granted trading privileges with Mexico.

During the 333 years of Spanish rule, the population increased from about 500,000 inhabitants to over seven million, but the Spaniards controlled the granting of permission for entry into the archipelago. In this way a community of Chinese merchants was established in Manila, the chief port as well as the capital. Foreign trade remained a Spanish monopoly until the nineteenth century, when the principal ports were opened to international trade. The Spanish language, although widespread and the lingua franca, never became the common tongue of the Filipinos; and only a small minority of the Filipinos was entirely assimilated. The Spaniards raised the general standard of living; they introduced new plants, including maize and tobacco, and domestic animals.

In the nineteenth century, Spanish rule was increasingly resented by the educated Filipinos, some of whom had studied in Europe, and in 1896, during the Spanish-American War, they tried unsuccessfully to establish an independent republic. Two years later, Spain ceded the archipelago to the United States; but the patriots were not finally defeated until 1901. In that year a general amnesty was granted to all rebels and political prisoners who would take an oath of allegiance to the United States of America.

## THE AMERICAN PERIOD

The American 'colonial' government undertook three major reforms: a revision of the administrative system, the institution of universal education, and the establishment of free trade.

In the reorganisation of the administration the most important step was the separation of Church and State, which put an end to the long struggle between the Roman Catholics and the Moslems. A representative electoral system on American lines was introduced and the civil service was Filipinised. The Americans established a public primary school system, and legislated that all instruction was to be in English, though other languages could be spoken.

Free trade was never really achieved. The Philippine economy was released from domination by Spain only to become tied to the American economic system; 'free trade' developed only behind American tariff barriers, with limits on exports to the United States but with no restriction on American imports into the Philippines. This balance led to an increase in the production of export crops at the expense of food crops for home consumption, and the country ceased to be self-sufficient in food. Crop yields remained low and there was little mechanisation.

In 1902 the American colonial government undertook a programme of land reform, but the land laws introduced were ineffective in preventing the accumulation of large holdings. The American administration also abolished enforced labour, restrictions upon movement, and the head tax; it replaced the latter by a land tax on declared acreage. Despite good intentions, the American administrators failed to solve the land problem, largely because the more influential Filipinos opposed the measures taken.

The Americans failed to stimulate manufacturing industry in the Philippines largely because the import of American manufactures never balanced the export of Philippine raw materials and semi-processed products, such as abaca fibre, to the United States. Mining—especially of copper, gold, chromium, manganese and iron ore—was developed.

In 1934, the United States Government, with the agreement of the Philippine Legislature, inaugurated the so-called Commonwealth period, intended to last ten years, during which the Philippine Legislature would be responsible for home policy; at the end of the decade, complete independence was to have been automatically effective. The Commonwealth period was interrupted by the Japanese invasion and occupation of the islands in 1942, and full independence was not granted until July 1946. The official national language is based on Tagalog, a Malay dialect, but English and Spanish are widely used, especially in government and commerce. Quezon City, close to Manila, is the official capital.

## THE PRESENT ECONOMY

*Main food crops, stock-raising and fishing.* The Philippines is still a predominantly agrarian country, well over two-thirds of the labour force being employed in agriculture. Just under 20 per cent of the total land area of the republic is cultivated and another 8 per cent is reckoned to be potential crop land. The growing season is 365 days and a great variety of crops flourishes. Rice is the most important food crop and the staple diet of the majority of the inhabitants. Rice, maize (the staple food in the Visayan Islands) and yams occupy nearly two-thirds of the total cultivated area. The maize crop is sufficient for home consumption, but additional rice has often to be imported, in spite of a programme aiming at making the country self-sufficient. Further food crops include bananas, sweet potatoes, manioc, coconut and a wide range of other fruits and vegetables. Poultry and pigs are ubiquitous in the rural barrios and cattle, severely reduced during the Second World War, are increasing.

Fish is an important item of the Filipino's diet, but the total catch is insufficient for home consumption.

Copra harvest in the Philippines. Copra is an important cash crop on the islands. In 1962 over a million tons were produced.

There is little deep-water fishing, most of the catch coming from inshore fishing, swampy coastal lagoons and fishponds: every inland village is encouraged to have its own pond, and fish are being 'farmed'.

Many items of food are grown on smallholdings, and much fruit and vegetables come from small, garden-like plots. Filipino farmers are interested in mechanisation, but their holdings are mostly too small for effective use of agricultural machinery. Half of all the farms are less than 5 acres apiece and of these half are less than 2 acres each. Small-sized holdings are not the only impediment to the use of machinery in the Philippines. The exceedingly small working capital and the mechanical backwardness of the majority of farmers, the great number of landless agricultural workers, the high cost of imported machinery, the seasonal wetness of the paddy fields and the steep slopes of much of the cultivated area are other factors operating against mechanisation. Rice harvesting is usually primitive, with foot-threshing and wind-winnowing; in the remoter rural areas, rice is generally home-pounded. Most of the modern rice mills are in the intensive rice-growing areas, such as those situated in the central plain of Luzon.

*Commercial crops. Forestry.* The principal commercial crops are abaca (Manila hemp), sugar-cane and coconuts. Commercial forests are extensive and important, providing oils, gums and resins in addition to timber for building and furniture. Tobacco is now only of secondary importance — more tobacco being imported from the United States than is produced in the archipelago — and the production of pine-apples and of rubber is insignificant except in Mindanao. Abaca fibre was one of the country's earliest exports and was sought by Chinese traders long before the Spanish era. On the eve of the Second World War, production was largely in the hands of Japanese migrants concentrated in and around Davao. Production is now controlled by Filipinos and the whole of the annual crop is normally exported to the United States. Coconut products (copra, desiccated coconut, oil and fibre) form the country's chief export and are the greatest earner of

dollars. The unimportant position of rubber is a legacy of the American colonial period; the Americans discouraged plantation agriculture in the early 1900's, when rubber plantations were being extended in Indonesia and Malaya.

*Mining and manufacturing.* There is a great variety of minerals and metals, of which the most important is gold. Of the minerals, only chromite is of high quality; the manganese ores are of low quality and are scattered; there are important reserves of iron ore, estimated at 500 million tons, but no coking coal. The archipelago is deficient in power resources; the chief hydro-electric potential is in Mindanao, where the Maria Christina Falls have been harnessed to provide electricity.

Before independence, manufacturing mainly consisted of domestic handicrafts and the processing of agricultural products. Since 1946, the Government has looked on industry as a means of giving regular employment to the increasing labour force, and has encouraged industrialists to establish factories in all the cities.

*Communications. Trade.* Air services connect the principal islands and link the more distant provinces with Manila. There are also regular cargo flights, but the bulk of goods traffic is carried by inter-island steamers serving some two hundred small ports. The larger islands have regular road services.

The chief port is Manila, and ten other ports are open to international commerce. The country has trade with over seventy-five nations but that with the U.S.A. accounts for 70 to 90 per cent of the total, and there are special tariff arrangements between the two countries. The chief exports are copra, timber and sugar; the principal imports machinery and petroleum products. Foodstuffs account for about 17 per cent of all imports and comprise mainly rice (from Thailand and the U.S.A.) and wheat and dairy products (from the U.S.A.).

THE YOUNG REPUBLIC. Today the young Republic of the Philippines occupies a unique position in Asia. Mainly Christian, its citizens are neither wholly of Asia nor wholly alien to it. A double colonial experience has linked them with two mother countries—Spain and the U.S.A. Some two million or more have filial ties with China or Japan; and the Moros look to Mecca and have links with the inhabitants of Indonesia.

Since the end of the Spanish era, the population has nearly quadrupled, and it is still increasing. It is essentially a young population, over one-half being under 20 years of age. The nation is predominantly rural, though in the 1950's there was a marked drift to the cities, especially to Manila, where people hoped to find regular employment. Traditionally the country's wealth has been enjoyed by a privileged minority; there is still a gulf between this minority and an underprivileged majority—the so-called grass roots of the nation. Since independence, the latter have sought their share of the nation's wealth and privileges. Although primary education is free most Filipinos receive only three years of compulsory education, and the widespread illiteracy disfranchises the poorest sectors of the nation, among whom are the many landless farmers, thus preventing them from achieving the necessary political power to improve their status.

A cigar factory in Manila, Philippines.

# THE EAST INDIES

In this widest sense the term 'East Indies' includes all the islands between South-East Asia and Australia; that is about 10,000 islands stretching from Sumatra in the west to New Guinea in the east, and from Sumba in the south to the most northerly island, Batan, north of the Philippines. More than 130 million people live in some million square miles of land, scattered over a huge area larger than the United States and Canada together. It is difficult to study the islands as a whole, for there is too much variety among the peoples, their ways of life and their political organisations.

This is sometimes described as the Malay world, but it does not include Malaya itself nor, because of cultural differences, does it include New Guinea. There is also a structural division between the true islands and the parts of the Asiatic continent which have been separated from the mainland by a geologically recent rise in sea level, such as Sumatra and Borneo. Others define the East Indies as Indonesia; but though the term 'Indonesia' originally referred to a cultural sphere, it is used today for a political State which includes a part of the East Indies only, although the major part. In flora and fauna some of the islands are related to Asia and others have features similar to those of Australia.

Historically the western two-thirds of these islands have been subject to Hindu, Buddhist and Moslem influences that did not affect the eastern islands. Modern imperialism divided the East Indies without consideration of other regional groupings. Thus most breakdowns of this huge island world are rather arbitrary. It is customary not to include the Philippines in the East Indies, and we have accepted this exclusion.

Thus limited, the East Indies consist of some 3,000 islands, comprising 820,000 square miles of land area, with a population of 108 million. At the present time they are divided politically into different units: namely, Indonesia, East New Guinea, Portuguese Timor, and the territories of Sabah (formerly North Borneo),

Sarawak and Brunei. In 1963 Sabah and Sarawak joined with the Federation of Malaya and Singapore in forming the new state Malaysia.

## THE LAND AND ITS SETTLEMENT

*The variety of scenery.* Most of the islands of the East Indies consist of little more than a coastline surrounding a small area of coastal lowland. Some of the islands, however, are among the largest in the world. The interiors of New Guinea, Borneo, Sumatra, Sulawesi and Java, for example, are too large to be included in a description of the coastal regions. Until recently the people who lived along the coasts of Borneo and New Guinea were unable to venture inland without great difficulty; not until the Second World War did modern life affect the Stone Age civilisation of the interior of New Guinea.

All the East Indies are situated within the tropics. The temperature on the lowland varies from warm to hot. Inland the temperature decreases progressively with height; average temperatures are comparable with those of temperate latitudes, but without any marked range. On some of the high mountains the temperatures can be quite low, and the highest peak in New Guinea is always snow-covered; but in any case these mountain slopes are so rough and steep that men have not tried to use them.

In spite of a tropical position, the rainfall of the East Indies is not satisfactory everywhere. There are pronounced seasonal differences according to position and the orientation of the islands relative to the monsoons. From the north-east of Java to the Lesser Sunda Islands there is a marked dry season, and in many areas water supply is a major economic difficulty.

Sumatra, Java and Borneo have a flora and fauna very similar to that of South-East Asia. The number and variety of the forms of life decrease slowly eastwards. On the other hand New Guinea has vegetation and animals comparable to those of Australia; these disappear rapidly towards the west. What is known as the Wallace line marks the boundary of primarily Asiatic influence; it passes between Bali and Lombok,

Typical Sumatran homes with sweeping gables, thatched roofs and decorated walls.

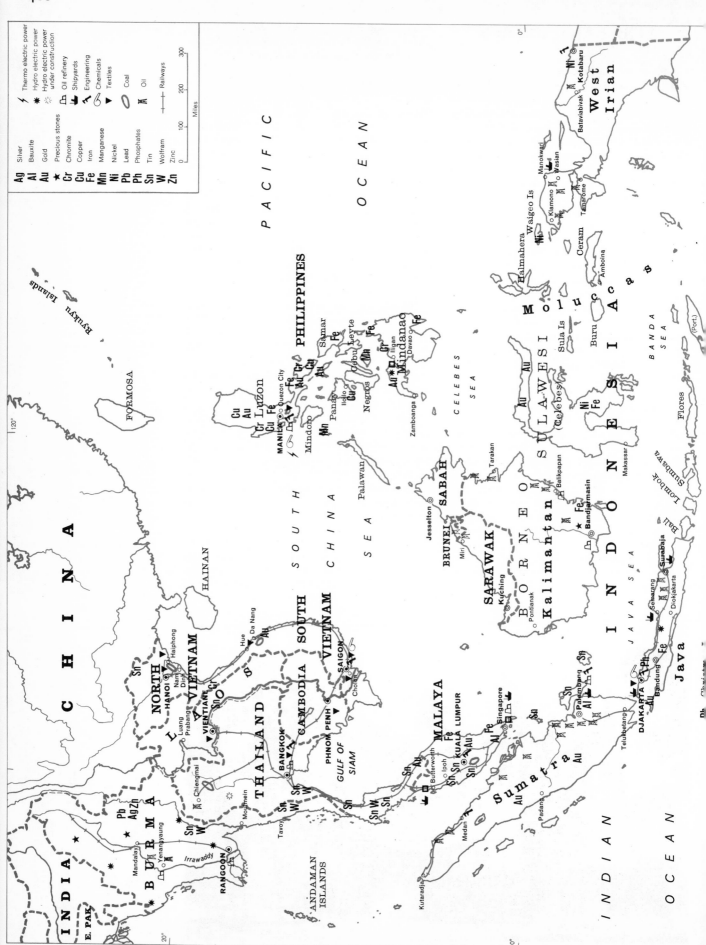

PACIFIC OCEAN

Ryūkyū Islands

FORMOSA

CHINA

120°

INDIA

E. PAK

BURMA

Pb
Ag Zn

Sn
W

Mandalay
Yenangyaung
Irrawaddy
RANGOON

Moulmein
Tavoy
Sn
W

THAILAND

Chiengmai

Sn W
W Sn

BANGKOK

GULF OF SIAM

Luang Prabang
L
VIENTIANE

NORTH
VIETNAM
HANOI
Nam Dinh
Haiphong
Sn

HAINAN

Hue
Da Nang
Au

CAMBODIA
PHNOM PENH
Cr

SOUTH
VIETNAM
SAIGON
Cholon

SOUTH CHINA SEA

ANDAMAN ISLANDS

MALAYA
Fe
Butterworth
Ipoh
Sn
Sn Sn
KUALA LUMPUR
Au
Sn W
Sn
Sn
Al
Fe
Singapore

Kutaradja
Medan
Padang
Au
Sumatra
Palembang
Sn
Al
Telukbetong

PHILIPPINES

Cu
Au
Cr Luzon
Cu Fe
MANILA
Quezon City
Mindoro
Mn

Samar
Fe
Cebu Leyte
Cr
Panay
Mn
Iloilo
Cu
Negros
Au Cr
Zamboanga

Iligan
Cr
Mindanao
Davao
Fe
Au

Palawan

CELEBES SEA

Jesselton
BRUNEI
Miri
SABAH
Tarakan

SARAWAK
Kuching
Pontianak

BORNEO
Kalimantan
Balikpapan
Cr
Bandjarmasin
Fe

JAVA SEA

Semarang
Djokjakarta
Surabaja
Fe
Bandung
DJAKARTA
Au
Java

INDONESIA

SULAWESI
(Celebes)
Au
Au
Ni Fe
Makassar

Halmahera
Waigeo Is
Ni Kotabaru
Bataviabivak
Manokwari
Klamono
Sasian
Tamarome

West Irian

Molu cca s
Buru
Sula Is
Amboina
Ceram
BANDA SEA
(Port.)

Flores
Lombok
Sumbawa
Bali

INDIAN OCEAN

0°

20°

Au

Pb Sn Ph

Fe

Au

Borneo and Sulawesi, Mindanao and Sulawesi. The Weber line, which marks the western extension of Australian flora, passes between Australia and Timor, Tanimbar and Aru, New Guinea and Ceram and then Halmaher. The transitional zone between the two lines is commonly known as 'Wallacea'. Only man has crossed these natural frontiers, adapting his food to the new biological conditions.

There is a great variety of coastlines: deep, calm estuaries and marsh that naturally became the haunts of fishermen and sailors; rocky shores with coral reefs and fast coastal currents, which are interrupted on some islands by rivers navigable for small boats or rafts; marshy coastal lowlands.

Inland, volcanic activity has had numerous effects. While active volcanoes threaten the fields and villages with periodic destruction, their old lava-flows provide rich agricultural land. The main areas of recent volcanic activity are Sumatra, Java, the Lesser Sunda Islands, Sulawesi, and Halmahera. In contrast, Borneo, the Mentawai Islands, Timor and New Guinea are primarily formed of old rocks, which have been weathered, leached and impoverished. It is these basic differences between the islands which are mainly responsible for the varying degree of economic development encountered here.

*An ethnic mosaic.* At present a large number of races are represented in the East Indies. The three main racial groups, Caucasian, Negroid and Mongoloid, are found in the islands, and they may have been here since the beginning of human colonisation. The Negritos, Negroids and Papuans form a large part of the populations in the eastern islands, while in the west they are a minority. The dominant people in the west are Malays, who are a product of much inter-racial breeding; they are often found along the coast, having driven the Negritos and Papuans inland. More recently groups came by sea from India or the Malay Peninsula and settled along the shore, living on, and from, their boats. Some of these settled in the East Indies, further complicating the racial pattern, while many continued to move farther east.

During the first centuries A.D. trade in this island world led to a varied influx of peoples in most islands, each group bringing its own social, religious, economic and agricultural customs with it. There were Indians, Arabs, Khmers, Annamites and Chinese, who all mixed with one another. The arrival of Portuguese, Dutch and British brought further cross-breeding. Indians, Arabs and Chinese continued to filter in, and their influence, like that of the Europeans, is much more marked in the west than in the east. In New Guinea Japanese influence was of short duration and European infiltration is less significant than in the western islands. Generally speaking, the interior of the islands contains purer racial types than the coastal areas, which were more easily accessible to migrant races.

In the western islands marriages between Dutchmen and the indigenous women, and even more between the Chinese and the local people, have added a new racial element to Java and Sumatra; this has increased the difference with the purer racial groups in the east.

Today, there are about 60 million people who may be called Malays; the Papuans and other allied groups

Bali, one of the smaller islands in the East Indies, is also one of the most beautiful. This view of central Bali shows a typical landscape, with palm trees and terraced cultivation.

number a little more than 1 million; there are 3 million Chinese, without counting the numerous half-castes. Some 250 languages and dialects are represented in the East Indies, the majority of which belong to the Malayan-Polynesian group. The lingua franca of many islands is common Malay, an adaptation and simplification of the Malay spoken along the Sumatra coast. The official language—Bahasa Indonesia— is a formalised version of it.

*Colonisation and economic development.* The Portuguese came to the East Indies to obtain spices. However, they encountered strong competition from the Moslem, Chinese and Malay merchants; with their trading posts scattered from India to Timor, they conducted a profitable business supported by the use of force. but never succeeded in monopolising the spice trade. Soon formidable rivals followed them. The Spanish concentrated their attention on the Philippines. In 1600 the English founded a company for trading with the East Indies, and in 1602 the Dutch merchants founded another. The Dutch organisation,

*Map opposite:*
Oil is important in Burma and Indonesia, rubber in Borneo and Malaya and tin in Malaya and in the Indonesian islands of Bangka and Billiton. Cement and bitumen are made at Singapore, where oil is also refined. Cambodia has good quality iron ore, as yet unexploited, some gold and precious stones; Vietnam has important phosphate deposits and a variety of other minerals in small quantities. Thailand, by contrast, is rich in mineral wealth which includes coal, copper, antimony, lead, rubies, sapphires, zinc and zircons and, most important of all, tin and wolfram.

which was more vigorous than the British, was not slow in asserting itself. The Dutch assumed a rôle similar to that which the Chinese had played until then; they took the place of the Chinese by making them their agents and representatives, and submitted to the demands of local potentates in a way that neither the British nor the Portuguese would have done.

The Dutch needed a large port as a control base in the western area, and an advance post in the eastern part, from which would come most of the spices. In order to avoid difficulty with the local rulers, they selected an undeveloped site on the north coast of Java, and with Chinese labour built the port of Batavia. Amboina became their easterly advance post, and with port after port they established their hold on the Indonesian coast. As early as 1700 the Portuguese had been driven from all the important ports, while skilful negotiations diverted the British.

Then the Dutch began to control the production of spices; they felled forests and orchards, depopulated the islands over which they were unable to exercise peaceful control, and fought illicit trade in an attempt to control the monopoly.

Although they were unable to establish a complete monopoly, they controlled both the economic and political life of the East Indies effectively. At the end of the eighteenth century the trading company failed, and was replaced by a government and administration to rule this great island empire of several million people.

The islands were changed considerably. Coffee, which had been introduced by the Europeans, had become very important, and its closely controlled production was much more valuable than that of any single spice. The local farmers had been encouraged to produce the goods required by the Dutch merchants.

The trade enriched the Indonesian chiefs and princes, but the small peasant often led a precarious existence, at the economic mercy of the local ruler and the Company. Many Dutch settled in the area, especially in Java. They built towns reminiscent of the Netherlands and married members of the upper class in Malay society. At first the Chinese were small traders and labourers in the Dutch service, but later they formed a powerful commercial minority.

At the beginning of the nineteenth century Britain gained control of Java and other islands, but in the end returned them to the Dutch and kept only Malaya. The Dutch colonial government was interested in making the development of the islands profitable for the mother country; only slowly were modern ideas of free trade and unrestricted production of agricultural products accepted.

Java was the main economic centre of the East Indies. Here the indigenous culture was most carefully maintained, the European plantations were largest and Chinese trade most active. During the three centuries of Dutch rule the population of Java grew spectacularly, while the other islands lagged far behind. So completely were they neglected that at the end of the nineteenth century the British were able to settle in north-west Borneo and south-east New Guinea without serious protest from the Netherlands. At the same time the Germans annexed

north-east New Guinea, which after the 1914-18 war came under British control, with a mandate from the League of Nations. The Portuguese never lost control of Timor.

The economic power of the East Indies remained centred in Java, and changes in the political organisation hardly altered the appearance of the islands. The Dutch introduced several changes in administration as nationalism began to develop among the Indonesians.

## THE PRESENT ECONOMY OF THE EAST INDIES

*Three types of traditional life.* Before European intervention, there were three main patterns of agriculture in the East Indies. On a large part of the north coast of Java, on Madura, Bali and some smaller islands, agriculture was carried on by settled villagers who grew irrigated rice, tended gardens and orchards and grew spices, especially pepper. The country was controlled by merchant-princes, settled in the ports, who organised the overseas trade and competed with each other for regional control.

The second type of agriculture was a shifting agriculture, such as is found under various names in all tropical lands and existed in most of the islands of the East Indies. Following a precise routine, the people moved their plots regularly throughout the jungle and forest. In the reclaimed clearings they grew unirrigated rice (in the western parts only), root crops such as yams, taro, sweet potatoes and other vegetables, and fruit. Banana trees, coconut palms and spice trees were planted in other parts, at first for local consumption and later for sale to one of the merchant-princes. The dispersed character of these products was one of the reasons for the development of coastal navigation. It favoured the expansion of the maritime Malay states; but it also encouraged the Portuguese to penetrate far into the East Indies and made the small farmers a prey to political and trade conquest.

The third way of life was based on sago and fishing; this was typical of the marshy areas of the west and south coasts of Borneo, the east coast of Sumatra and the shores of New Guinea. The sago palm or 'breadfruit tree' grows naturally in the swamps, and it can hardly be called an agricultural crop when compared with the diverse products obtained by the shifting type of agriculture. Fishing often played an important part. These unattractive swamps produced nothing of interest to the merchants, so they were largely neglected.

Apart from these three basic types, there were many other ways of life scattered throughout the islands. The interior of New Guinea, with its autonomous economy—which has been known only since the 1930's—is just one example of an area unaffected by the economic life of the great island world of the East Indies.

The arrival of the Europeans resulted in considerable changes in the traditional type of agriculture. Portuguese influence was very limited, but Britain and Germany introduced the plantation economy into their possessions. They tried coffee, cocoa, tobacco and coconuts. Only the coconut palm was successful in the non-Dutch parts, and it was not really profitable in New Guinea.

The Dutch tried a succession of different methods to stimulate and control the Indonesian economy: forced planting, fixed-quantity deliveries of selected crops, monopoly control, changes in land control and the plantation system. Each change left an indelible mark on some part of the East Indies; Java and Sumatra bore the brunt of this action.

When the Europeans arrived Java was exporting rice and other foodstuffs regularly. At present Java is no longer self-sufficient, not because of a decline in its agriculture but because of the very sharp increase in the number of agriculturally unproductive consumers.

The Chinese steadily acquired a more important place in the agricultural economy, without taking any part in political control. They probably started the sugar plantations, were the agents or sometimes the financiers of the Dutch and were interested in pepper, the Borneo diamond mines and fishing. They became so numerous that the Dutch and the Indonesians grew concerned at the part they played in the life of the community.

*Agriculture, stock-rearing and fishing.* The most important of the three main types of agriculture is the cultivation of permanent fields and gardens by settled villagers. This system has extended to cover nearly all of Java, much of Madura, Bali and Lombok, part of Sumatra, the coast of Borneo, part of Sulawesi, some of the Moluccas, and the shores of some other islands. Not all the peasants have animals or motor power available, and many use no implement more advanced than a hoe; but intensive cultivation often produces two or three crops a year. Cultivation is not only confined to subsistence crops; any surplus is sold in the great consumer market of Java. In the western areas irrigated rice is the main crop; in the east of Java and beyond, maize, yams, sweet potatoes and manioc replace rice as the basic product. Groundnuts (peanuts) and soya beans have recently become important. In Java, the gardens, orchards and fish ponds are often an integral part of the village.

Commercial crops are grown almost everywhere by small farmers, and the yields are quite high. The chief ones are sugar-cane, rubber, tea, coffee, cocoa, pepper and other spices, coconuts, kapok, sisal and other fibres, and tobacco. Each farmer does not grow all these products, but collectively their totals are much higher than those of the plantations.

Today this type of agriculture occupies a little more than half the cultivated area, or about 27 million acres, and is continually increasing with the progressive settlement of the shifting cultivators, and the division of old plantations into small farms with each new generation.

The second type of agriculture is the commercial cultivation introduced by the Europeans. The plantations which developed during the nineteenth century reached their maximum extent before the Second World War. They then covered about 6,400,000 acres, and produced about thirty different products. Quinine has always been a government monopoly; tea and coffee grow on the fairly high slopes, and do best on volcanic soil. Tobacco and the oil palm grow along the east side of Sumatra, sugar-cane in Java

Cutting hemp stalks on Sabah's largest manila hemp estate.

Inland fisheries in Indonesia. These fish 'fry' are specially bred in the flooded rice fields to restock the fisheries.

and coconuts in New Guinea. Rubber trees cover huge areas in northern Sumatra, and today Indonesia is the chief world producer of natural rubber. It is likely that plantation agriculture will steadily decrease in all parts of the East Indies because of the opposition of the small farmer, particularly in those areas where land pressure can be translated into legislation.

The third type of agriculture, shifting cultivation, has almost disappeared in Java, and is decreasing in Sumatra and along the shores of many islands where it used to be important. However, there are about 15 million acres of new forest clearings or recently abandoned lands where bananas, fruits, pepper or some other products are still harvested. Rice, maize, cassava or manioc, root crops and fruits are sold occasionally in the local markets.

Cattle and horses are commonly bred on Madura, Bali, Lombok and Sumbawa, and sold in Java and Sumatra. The economy based on sago has also been changed completely; it has become a crop on the western and southern coasts of Borneo and on some

Fishing and subsistence agriculture flourish all round the coasts of South-East Asia and Indonesia and agriculture on every available patch of land in the interior. Rice is the staple food, grown with irrigation where necessary; cereals and pulses, hemp and tobacco are also grown. Forests are very important — 60 per cent of the land area of Thailand is under forest — but generally not fully exploited due to lack of capital and machinery. Commercial crops include tea, sugar, coffee, bananas, pepper and spices. Cambodia has the greatest freshwater fish resources in South-East Asia.

of the eastern islands, Celebes and the Moluccas.

In an island world such as the East Indies, fish and the use of sea products are obviously important. There are no accurate statistics for the number of fishermen, or for the size of their catch, but the whole yield from both salt and fresh water is estimated at about 600,000 tons annually. Certain products, like turtle eggs and sea slugs, are sent in large quantities to China or to the Chinese in South-East Asia. The western part of the East Indies imports a great deal of fish for its large population. It is possible for the catch to be increased considerably, and attention is now being given to mechanisation.

*Mineral wealth and development.* For a long time diamonds have been mined in Borneo, gold in some of the islands and tin in the western islands; but the main development came with European operations in the nineteenth century. These included coal for bunkering from western Borneo, Sumatra and Java; tin from the islands of Bangka and Billiton; gold from Sumatra, Java, Borneo, northern Sulawesi and eastern New Guinea. Recent developments include the mining of bauxite, sulphur, phosphates, manganese, and nickel from southern Sulawesi.

Oil is, however, more important than all the other minerals. The East Indies have become the chief producer of oil in South-East Asia. The main deposits are found in southern Sumatra and, rather more scattered, along the coasts of Borneo. Java has a small output, and contrary to expectations output in West Irian is falling. Though mining is still of secondary importance in the economy of the islands, it is capable of considerable expansion.

*Industrial development.* In the East Indies there are all kinds of manufactured products which are typically Indonesian in style and method of manufacture. The best known are the ornamental goods, shawls, sarongs and other clothing, woven bark, wood carvings, and many other things of local interest. For centuries the East Indies have traded actively with mainland Asia, which provided them with many consumer goods; as a result handicrafts are less developed here than in other parts of the Far East. Java has for long been the main manufacturing centre, and the chief area for the import of Asiatic products.

The development of commercial contacts with Europe let in a flood of manufactured goods from the West. The Chinese played an important part in

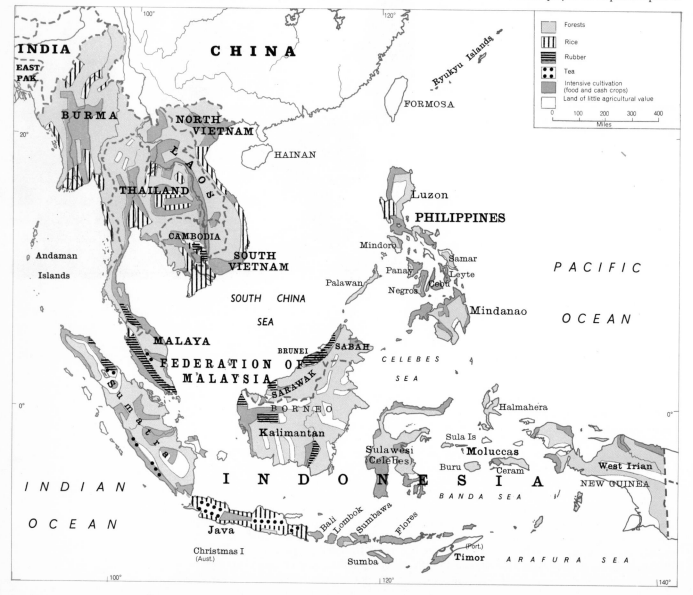

the distribution of these goods, and some of the European articles came into current use. This did not reduce the importance of the Java craftsmen, who still exported large quantities of goods to other lands in the East Indies.

The bustling trade along the coast contrasts with the scattered commerce of the interior, where the products are collected at hundreds of small local ports. A concentration of this trade is steadily taking place into the better equipped ports suitable for ships of larger tonnage. Roads and railroads run into the interior from these ports, which, therefore, attract trade at the expense of the smaller ports. Naturally Java and Sumatra have benefited most from the improvements in communications. The other large islands have not had comparable development, and communications are still designed to assist administration.

Although the development of trade and mining could be the basis of modern industry, most of the minerals are exported raw or only slightly processed. Textile manufacturers and engineering are well developed only in Java, and to a much lesser extent in Sumatra. At present there is a large oil refinery in Sabah (Malaysia), together with two important refineries in Sumatra and Java and four smaller ones in other parts of the Republic of Indonesia.

Until now industry has lacked encouragement by Governments. The nationalistic tendencies of the Republic of Indonesia are undoubtedly stimulating development of numerous industries, but it will be many years before there is a heavy industry of any importance. More and more manufactured goods are being imported in a complete or unassembled state, thus creating a local assembly industry; this applies particularly to factories assembling cars and electrical goods in Java and southern Sumatra, the centres of these modern industries; elsewhere such factories are almost non-existent.

The foundations of industrialisation are being laid with plans for the establishment of an iron and steel industry in Sumatra, Borneo and Java, great expansion of electricity supply and of cement production, the establishment of fertilizer plants, many new textile mills and chemical works. Care is being taken to spread industrial development over the different islands.

The East Indies have only just begun to recover from the serious damage caused by the Second World War. They have not regained their important pre-war position in world trade. Their main exports are rubber, petroleum, copra, tin, tobacco, and quinine; of secondary importance are palm oil, spices, sugar, kapok, coal and sago.

One of the main changes in trade during the last 75 years has been the decline of spice exports from the East Indies. Although spices are still widely grown on many islands, Java at present provides only a negligible share of world trade. The spice monopoly which once drew merchants to the East Indies has fallen into decline.

Among the imports, food is becoming more important with the growth of population. There is also the whole range of modern manufactured products, textiles, metals and machines. The exports of the Indies are primarily agricultural products and raw or almost unprocessed minerals. The Republic of Indo-nesia plays a large part in this trade, especially Java and Sumatra, where oil is important in providing employment and a source of revenue. The tin mines of Bangka and Billiton are worked partly by the Government and partly by private enterprise. The British Commonwealth territories export rubber, oil, tobacco and copra, but import hardly anything.

## THE EAST INDIES TODAY

THE REPUBLIC OF INDONESIA. Both during and after the Second World War there were many important changes: a rise in population, changes in agriculture, trade, industrialisation, and the Australian entry into the interior of eastern New Guinea. However, the greatest upheaval was political, resulting from the development of nationalism, encouraged by the brief stay of the Japanese. At the end of hostilities, a violent social and political explosion shook Java, Sumatra, and to a lesser extent the other islands. The Dutch tried political and military action, but they were unable to break the independence movement.

Reluctantly they had to yield. First the Netherlands East Indies were given internal political autonomy over an ill-defined Dutch-Indonesian empire, in which the Dutch kept a good part of the economic, political and military control. There followed a difficult period which ended with the formation of the present Republic of Indonesia in August 1950. Except for West Irian (Dutch New Guinea) the last link between the Netherlands and Indonesia was broken in 1954. The Dutch kept control over West Irian because of its oil deposits, about which they remained very secretive; but it was ceded to Indonesia in 1963 after the threat of armed hostilities.

The republic is divided into 24 provinces. Djakarta, formerly Batavia, is the capital and seat of government.

Oil plays an important part in Indonesian economy, being a major resource of revenue and providing employment for 50,000 workers. Anglo-Dutch and American oil companies now operate as government contractors; any new gas and oil exploitation will be handled by the Indonesian Government mining companies.

Independent Indonesia has been troubled by rebellion and civil war on more than one occasion. Sometimes the Government has been the target for semi-religious uprisings, particularly in Java; more usually, however, armed revolt has occurred in the Outer Islands, which are richer, less populated, and more important as sources of exports than Java, as a protest against the transfer of their resources to that island. Were it not for heavy aid — including arms aid — which Indonesia received from both the United States and Russia and still receives from Russia, it is doubtful whether the country could have retained its unity.

*Timor, Borneo, New Guinea and other islands.* The Portuguese part of Timor and the small neighbouring islands, long neglected, are beginning to benefit from a major economic and educational development programme launched in 1959 by Portugal. Tourism appears to be the most promising source of income. Of the former British East Indies, Sarawak and North Borneo became Crown Colonies and had special political systems established before the war; Brunei remained a protectorate, controlled by the local sultan. These three territories attained independent status in 1963 when North Borneo (as Sabah) and Sarawak joined with the Federation of Malaya and Singapore in Malaysia, an independent federation with the British Commonwealth. Brunei may join the federation later.

The eastern part of New Guinea appears as two areas on a political map: the North East and Papua. The North East is administered by Australia under the control of the United Nations; Papua is Australian territory. However, since 1950 the government of the two territories has been unified, with Port Moresby as the capital. This part of New Guinea is entirely Australian in its appearance, both culturally and economically.

Christmas Island, formerly incorporated with Singapore, was transferred to the Commonwealth of Australia in 1958. It is situated in the Indian Ocean about 220 miles south-west of Java. It is 64 square miles in area and has a population of about 3,000, including 2,000 Chinese and 725 Malayans. This densely forested island rises to a plateau 1,000 feet above sea level. Its deposits of phosphate of lime

are worked by the Christmas Island Phosphate Commission.

The Cocos or Keeling Islands, which passed from Singapore to Australian administration in 1955, are also situated in the Indian Ocean, about 1,720 miles north-west of Perth and 530 miles west of Christmas Island. There are twenty-seven small coral islands, with a total area of only five square miles, and about 600 inhabitants. Extensive coconut groves yield nuts, copra and coconut oil for export. The main settlements are on the islands of Home and Direction. There is an airstrip on West Island which played an important part in communications during the war with Japan, and is now controlled by the Australian Department of Civil Aviation as a stopping-place halfway between Australia and South Africa.

## OTHER IMPORTANT PROBLEMS

*The rapid growth of population.* One of the major problems of the East Indies is the increase in population. In 1961 the islands of Java and Madura contained 63 million inhabitants, i.e., a density of well over a thousand per square mile. All possible land is cultivated, almost down to the last acre, and the annual increase in population cannot be absorbed for long.

For several decades the Dutch resettled Javanese families in Sumatra, but the annual total moved did not equal the growth in population. Some of the Lesser Sunda Islands and the Moluccas are over-populated, but over the whole area the population pressure is much less than in Java. Recently there was a marked movement towards the towns of Java, so that Djakarta suddenly became one of the largest cities in the world, its population increasing to about 3 million. There are several other towns of about half a million, apart from Surabaja with more than a million inhabitants and Bandung with just under a million.

Though there are many parts of Indonesia which are not densely populated, today the Javanese does not wish to emigrate or leave his native soil, his rice fields or his gardens. Nevertheless the government

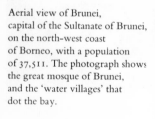

Aerial view of Brunei, capital of the Sultanate of Brunei, on the north-west coast of Borneo, with a population of 37,511. The photograph shows the great mosque of Brunei, and the 'water villages' that dot the bay.

A land redistribution commission in Sarawak: tribesmen are allotted their share of ground.

has put through a programme of transmigration to Sumatra and Borneo, with a total of 100,000 families by 1965. The movement towards the towns has made rapid industrialisation an essential programme of the Republic of Indonesia; but this will be difficult, for there is a shortage of capital and know-how.

*Trade and increasing competition. Cultural and economic changes.* The East Indies as a whole do not occupy the place in international trade that they held a century ago. Then, the monopolised tropical crops were much sought after by temperate countries; today many of these products are manufactured synthetically or are grown in other parts of the tropical world. Many of the goods for which the Dutch found easy markets, such as coffee, sugar, tea, fibres and rubber, are now faced with increasing competition. A hundred years ago exports provided a considerable revenue, which was more than enough for the small purchases by the Indonesians. Now, there are more Indonesian consumers and the scope of their foreign purchases has been widened. The Republic of Indonesia is even forced in difficult years to import food. As the value of exports could easily fall below that of imports, strict control of all foreign purchases and arrangements to encourage exports have been necessary. This is a new experience for Indonesia, and a society recently independent is unprepared for this measure.

In the other countries of the East Indies the problem is not so serious. In fact, Brunei, with a small area and population, and a simple way of life, is in the opposite position. Oil has brought this state so much revenue that the problem is to know how to use the money, for the unsophisticated population has no say in its distribution. Should the revenue be converted into dividends, reserved for the use of the Sultan of Brunei, or devoted to large public works (and if so, which)? The development of a modern city would help to raise the standard of living and the level of education of the people.

Important cultural and economic changes in New Guinea are planned through the steady infiltration of new ideas into the interior of the island, which will bring the ways of the modern world to the isolated groups in the central mountain ranges.

Finally, there is another important problem for Indonesia; this concerns the plantations in areas where the growing number of farmers need more land for their own subsistence. Plantation crops are tending to decline in area, and their share of the main agricultural products is also falling. Laws reducing the size of plantations were first introduced in Java, and they now apply to all the islands, though the only other island with serious population pressure is Madura.

THE FUTURE. The last problem concerns the surprising range of possible economic development within the islands. Borneo, Timor or the Fly plains of southern New Guinea are very poor lands in comparison with Java. Some of this difference is due to the skill of the people, for by careful cultivation some can get good crops from a poor environment. Only rich soils would allow the type of development which occurs in Java; the naturally infertile soils of the island of Bangka could never be developed like the rich lands of densely populated northern Sumatra.

These differences in fertility are due to the distribution of recent volcanic deposits in the East Indies. The islands which are widely covered with recent flows of basaltic lava are fertile; those whose surface is covered with decomposed granite or similar old igneous rocks are the infertile islands. The population has grown most on the rich soils: if Bali had not been a fertile island it would not be famous throughout the world for its cultural heritage, whereas if Timor, the island retained by the Portuguese, had been a fertile, volcanic island its economic development would not be so backward.

Throughout the East Indies, especially where the population density is high, agriculture can no longer remain almost the sole basis of the economy. New links must be forged between man and the land on which he lives in order to create new sources of wealth; the future of Java depends on this. The Republic of Indonesia must face this problem, especially in its Outer Islands, where mining and industry are unimportant. This will also tend to be increasingly necessary in the British Commonwealth lands as the standard of living rises.

# OCEANIA

# THE ARCHIPELAGOS OF OCEANIA

Oceania covers one-fifth of the world and is quite different from the rest. Asia, America, Africa and Europe are continents or part of continents; the seas and oceans which surround them are merely boundaries. Here it is the ocean, the great Pacific Ocean, which gives unity and name to the whole area. Oceania is a sea dotted with lands, not land bordered by seas.

Not all the islands in the Pacific Ocean form part of Oceania; the archipelagos close to the continents of Asia and America are an integral part of the neighbouring mainland. There can be no question of including the Japanese archipelago in Oceania, for these islands have an Asian people and civilisation. Their history and settlement, their continual struggle with the peoples of the mainland, all serve to make them part of the Far East. They have not the isolated way of life of these islands, scattered throughout the ocean. The same is true of the Philippines, the East Indies, the Aleutians and the coastal islands of Canada and Chile.

On the other hand Australia is part of Oceania. Though this small continent, three-quarters the size of Europe, is washed by the Indian Ocean in the west, and in the south faces the Southern Ocean, its eastern coast is bordered by the Pacific. Most of the habitable part of Australia faces this great ocean, and Australian history is linked to the European discoveries and settlement in Oceania. Australia and New Zealand are, however, treated separately, for their physical and human aspects to some extent set them apart from the rest of Oceania. Hawaii, a new state of the U.S.A., is described more fully on page 628.

*The Pacific Ocean.* The Pacific Ocean covers 68 million square miles, about one-third of the earth's surface. Over 10,000 miles divide the Philippines and Panama. In the north the Pacific has a narrow link with the Arctic Ocean through the Bering Strait; in the south it has no boundary, and the waters of the Pacific merge into the Southern Ocean.

The Pacific is not merely the largest ocean, it is also the oldest. Research shows that it has been permanent throughout geological time.

It is also, by far, the deepest of all the oceans, averaging 11,000 feet. The deepest trenches lie along the edges of the continents of Asia, America and their archipelagos, with the greatest depths occurring close to the highland edges of the continents. The deepest in the world is the Marianas trench (36,000 feet).

In the centre of the ocean the depth is relatively even, usually between 10,000 and 16,000 feet. Occasionally the ocean floor rises, sometimes above the surface of the sea, to form an island or a group of islands.

The archipelagos of Oceania, without including Australia, have only a very small area compared with the immensity of the sea — 150,000 square miles, of which more than two-thirds derive from the New Zealand archipelago.

The true Pacific islands are very numerous considering their total land area: there are at least 10,000, many of which are minute; to these should be added all the reefs which scarcely emerge above the ocean, and which form rocky hazards for ships.

## CONDITIONS OF LIFE

*The distribution of the islands.* The very small islands are most common in Micronesia. The Palau, Caroline, Mariana and Marshall groups are composed of 1,459 islands with a total area of only 830 square miles. Micronesia as its name implies, is a region of small islands, as distinct from Polynesia, the eastern part with many islands, and Melanesia, with islands of varying sizes. The term Melanesia is derived not from the physical characteristics of the islands, but from the black skin of the inhabitants (Greek *melas*, 'black').

Some of the islands stand out from this scattered collection because of their larger size. New Caledonia has an area of 6,465 square miles and is 250 miles

Oceania is a sea dotted with lands, rather than a land bordered by sea.

long. Hawaii and Viti Levu (Fiji) are each about 4,000 square miles in area.

These islands are not regularly spaced in the ocean but fall into groups separated by vast areas of water; the groups are usually aligned on submarine ridges, which in the south-west are arc-shaped. Fiji consists of 240 islands, Tuamotu of 80 atolls.

The northern, eastern and southern parts of the Pacific have very few islands; there are only four groups north of the Equator. Most of the groups are found in the south-west of the ocean, to the north of the Tropic of Capricorn.

*The high or volcanic islands.* The oceanic islands are classified by the Polynesians into two distinct types, the high or pointed islands and the low or flat islands. The high islands are volcanic, the low ones are built of coral.

Volcanic activity plays a vital part in Oceania. Hundreds of volcanoes have emerged from the sea, but there are thousands of others below the surface. They act as foundations for coral islands.

There are a great many active volcanoes, such as the impressive 13,675-foot Mauna Loa in the Hawaiian Islands, whose bubbling incandescent lava is a tourist attraction. Active volcanoes occur mainly on the edge of the ocean; the volcanoes in the Andes, North America, Japan and Indonesia are continued in the ocean by those of the Solomon Islands, New Hebrides, Tonga and New Zealand. Some have violent eruptions; in 1951, Mount Benbow suddenly erupted and devastated the island of Ambrym on which it stood. The 4,000 inhabitants of the island were forced to seek refuge on the neighbouring island of Epi in the New Hebrides. The 1946 eruption of Niuafoou on the island of the same name in the Tonga group killed no one but forced all the 1,300 inhabitants to leave the island.

Most of the volcanoes are, however, extinct or dormant. Vegetation has hardly had time to recover on some, and their features are surprisingly unchanged. Kao, in the Tonga group, is an almost perfect cone, 3,000 feet high; Mauna Haleakala on Maui, Hawaii, has an immense crater 21 miles in circumference.

Erosion on the oldest mountains has cut the lava-flows into narrow strips, eroded deep gorges and formed strange-looking isolated peaks. The jagged profile of Moorea is well known to Tahitians, and the series of domes and sugar-loaf mountains of the Korabasaga Range are a striking feature at Suva in Fiji. In spite of erosion many of the peaks remain high, as for example Orohena on Tahiti, whose 7,270-foot summit towers above the ocean.

Some of the islands in Melanesia are not formed completely of volcanic rocks. The highest peaks of New Caledonia are composed of sedimentary and folded metamorphic rocks; the older volcanic rocks are found only in the south. On Viti Levu, part of Fiji, the volcanic Korabasaga Range is not as high as the plateau of Nadrau, which is composed of Secondary rocks.

*The low coral islands and atolls.* The low coral islands are quite different from the volcanic and even better known. The atoll is the adventure island of the Pacific; it is a ring of land which hardly rises above the sea and is fringed by coconut palms. In the centre is the lagoon, with its calm, clear water.

Usually there are passages of varying depth which breach the coral and link the lagoon to the ocean. Ontong Java, north of the Solomon Islands, is the largest atoll, with a circumference of more than 125 miles, but the actual surface is broken up into some fifty small islands. More unusual are closed atolls such as Sikaiana in the Solomons, or Anaa in the Tuamotu group.

The atoll is often a desolate island without animals, fresh water or soil for vegetation. Many are only inhabited or visited to harvest the copra or to dive for pearls. The groups consisting entirely of atolls, such as the Tuamotu, Gilbert and Marshall Islands, beyond which is the small isolated Bikini-Eniwetok group, are some of the poorest parts of the Pacific Ocean, economically.

Coral reefs also border most of the volcanic islands, except in the New Hebrides and the Marquesas Islands. Fringing reefs are simply like stairs along the edge of the shore. The barrier reef is much larger, often hundreds of yards from the coast, from which

Tofua is one of several active volcanic islands in the Tonga archipelago. This picture taken from the outer rim of the crater which rises steeply from the sea to a height of some 2,600 feet, looks inland across a crater lake.

Lagoons and reef formations around the island of Bora-Bora, one of the Leeward Islands. The latter group, together with the Windward Islands, form the Society archipelago.

it is separated by a lagoon. There is a large barrier reef, 320 miles long, bordering New Caledonia.

These reefs and atolls have been created by many small animals, the coral polyps, which live in huge colonies and secrete calcium carbonate, forming cups to protect themselves. The unusual shapes vary according to the kind of polyp. An extraordinary variety of fish of all shapes and colours, who swim in this underwater labyrinth, enhances the range of colours in the masses of coral, which are often rather dull.

The coral polyp can live only in seas with a temperature of over 20°C. (68°F.) and at a depth of less than 200 to 260 feet; therefore fringing reefs cannot be formed around volcanic marine platforms (whether they reach the surface or not) except in areas of high temperature. Apart from New Zealand, however, all the island groups are in tropical areas.

*The tropical climate.* It is usual to praise the mild climate of the Pacific islands, the lands of eternal spring. Temperatures are in fact high, with only slight seasonal variations. The mean annual temperature at Papeete in Tahiti is 26.3°C. (80°F.). The heat is, however, made tolerable by the breezes from the trade winds, which blow for most of the year. The wind is refreshing, healthy and fairly dry. It blows from the east or the north-east in the northern hemisphere, and from the east or south-east in the southern hemisphere.

The trade winds bring rain only when their paths cross high land. Thus the atolls, being low, tend to be dry, while the volcanic islands have heavier rainfall, at least on their eastern or windward slopes, and these slopes experience little difference between the dry and wet seasons.

The wet season is usually much shorter than the dry season. For several months, from June to September in Hawaii, and November to February in Tahiti or New Caledonia, the trade winds fail and are replaced by large cloud systems which bring heavy rain—on the sea and on the low islands, as well as on the mountainous ones. This season is characterised by unpleasant humidity. In the islands closest to the Equator, such as the Solomons and New Hebrides, this wet season lasts for most of the year; farther from the Equator, the trade winds quickly sweep across the sky, leaving nothing but a train of cumulus clouds in their wake.

*The threat of hurricanes.* The greatest hazard of the climate in the islands is the hurricane, which occurs during the rainy season. After a few hours of strange calm, the wind suddenly rises and often blows at 125 m.p.h., uprooting coconut palms, blowing down dwellings, unleashing the sea and damaging the shores, while very heavy falls of rain swell the torrents, flooding the cultivated land.

These tropical storms occur at the northern and southern limits of the equatorial zone, and they describe a large arc towards the middle latitudes. In the Far East, where they are known as typhoons, hurricanes are well known; they regularly damage the islands of the south-west Pacific. On average there is one every seven years in the New Hebrides. Hurricanes become less common eastwards; in Hawaii they are very uncommon, and in Tahiti a true hurricane has not occurred since 1906.

The isolation of the islands and the fresh breeze of the trade winds have checked the spread of the usual tropical diseases. There is no yellow fever, and malaria affects only the most westerly island groups, those nearest to the Far East, the Solomons and New Hebrides. Elsewhere the mosquito exists but not the disease.

This does not mean that the islands have no diseases; dysentery, leprosy and elephantiasis are endemic. Further, the European settlement resulted in the spreading of deadly diseases, as will be discussed later.

Though healthy, the climate is, none the less, tropical: temperatures are always high and their equability is debilitating. The 'laziness' of local peoples can be partly blamed on the enervating climate.

*Vegetation and animal life.* These widespread and isolated islands have a distinctive vegetation. Altogether the variety of flora is small, and the number of plant species decreases away from Indonesia and towards the centre of the Pacific. In Malaya two hundred species of palm are found, on the Solomons eighteen and in Hawaii only three.

A New Caledonian landscape.

This dearth can be explained in some instances by their relatively recent formation. Some atolls are devoid of trees, like Canton and Johnston. Seeds were brought by the wind, sea and birds, and in some suitable bays a poor scrub has developed; but plant exchange with neighbouring regions has been limited by their distance from each other.

The vegetation is mainly endemic, that is particular to each group of islands. New Caledonia is remarkable in this respect, for eighty per cent of the indigenous vegetation is unknown in the rest of the world.

The same lack of variety is characteristic of the fauna of Oceania. Before the arrival of man the only mammal was the bat or flying fox. There are still crocodiles on the Solomons, but no poisonous reptiles on the islands. On Tahiti the main fauna consists of birds.

Man's settlement disturbed everything. The indigenous peoples brought all the cultivated plants with them on their migrations. Even the ubiquitous coconut palm did not sow itself on most of the atolls where

A Fijian holding a taro plant. The root of the taro, which belongs to the arum lily family is the staple food of many Pacific islanders. Many varieties are grown, some of which need water and thrive in creeks, and others (like this specimen) which flourish on comparatively dry hillsides.

in surviving on some islands; regeneration is difficult because of the long periods of drought, and many volcanic islands are disappointing because of their poor vegetation.

Tropical forest still grows in the centre of Viti Levu (Fiji) and Upolu (Samoa). Most of the Solomons, which are very wet, are covered with thick forest and a dense undergrowth of banana trees and tree ferns.

## THE PEOPLES OF OCEANIA

*The Melanesians.* It is customary to divide the Pacific islanders into three racial groups: the Melanesians of the western islands, the Micronesians of the north-west, and the Polynesians elsewhere, from Hawaii in the north to New Zealand in the south.

The Melanesians, who are also called Kanakas, are black-skinned or at least dark chocolate-coloured, and they live in the Solomons, New Hebrides, Fiji and New Caledonia. They settled in these islands a long time ago, but there is hardly any way of knowing the dates of the main migrations which led them there. The pre-history of Melanesia is absorbing, but its study has hardly begun.

The continual mixing of the different peoples has resulted in a dolichocephalic type with a broad fore-head, large flattened nose, deepset eyes and prominent brow ridges, square jaws, frizzy hair, good height, and strong build.

In some of the islands of Melanesia the original types appear; Bougainville in the Solomons there are true Pygmies; in the Solomons and New Hebrides types are sometimes seen with high-bridged noses and thin lips whose Papuan origin is obvious. The Poly-nesian type also appears in the Loyalty Islands, the Lau Islands (Fiji) and Ontong Java; some islands such as Rennell seem to be pure enclaves of Polynesians in Melanesia.

This mixing, whether old or new, shows in the extraordinary variety of dialects; in New Caledonia there are 23 languages, in the Solomons 40, and neighbouring tribes cannot understand one another. Diversity is also shown in certain ways of behaviour and ritual practices. This contrasts with the more uniform civilisation of the Polynesians and Micro-nesians.

*Polynesians and Micronesians.* The Polynesians or Maoris have much lighter skins than the Melanesians, often golden bronze in colour; they are brachyce-phalic, with brown eyes, sometimes slightly almond-shaped, a fairly broad flat nose, thick mouth, and black glossy hair which the women wear loose about their shoulders. They are tall (5 feet 7 inches is the average height for men), but usually they are short in the thigh, with thick ankles and feet with slightly fan-shaped toes.

There are slight variations from this general type according to the proportion of the three groups for-ming the Polynesian race, melanoid, mongoloid or yellow, caucasoid or white. On the Gilbert Islands the Melanesian characteristics seem to be very common. On the other hand, some noble Tahitians described by Cook and by Bougainville had almost white skins.

The Micronesians have no real racial originality;

it is found today; it was the Polynesians who brought it with them. All the animals reared by the indigenous peoples came from Indonesia, and as only small animals could be carried in a dug-out canoe, pigs, dogs, poultry and rats formed their livestock.

Europeans made considerable changes in the flora and fauna. From the very beginning attempts were made to acclimatise new plants in the islands. Cook and La Pérouse distributed plant seeds. Porter landed goats on the Marquesas Islands; a governor of New Caledonia released a pair of deer, and today there are 100,000, a great nuisance for farmers. The imported plant lantana now covers much of the volcanic slopes of Tahiti.

While the European was introducing new species of plants and animals, he also modified the vegetation by exploiting certain valuable species. Tulip-wood has almost disappeared from the islands of Melanesia, sandalwood has become rare, and the kauri is hidden in the most inaccessible mountains. The original forest has been badly spoilt, and it is having difficulty

they are similar to Polynesians, but shorter and with more pronounced mongoloid characteristics.

The Polynesian immigrants arrived relatively recently in most of the islands. The first Tahitians landed on their island about 150 years B.C. The Cook and Society Islands became important centres for dispersion much later. It was during the second century that the great voyages were undertaken to Hawaii, the fifth to Easter Island and the eleventh to New Zealand. The last expedition to New Zealand was in the fourteenth century.

We know about the last migrations, but not of the earlier ones which led the Polynesians right into the heart of the Pacific. There has been speculation as to whether they are of Asian or American origin. After considerable controversy most of the authorities agree that the Polynesians are of Malay origin.

The results of the famous Kon-Tiki expedition have often been misrepresented. They show that relations between America and Polynesia were quite possible with the primitive means available in former times, and contacts with Peru certainly existed; however, it is not likely that settlement really occurred from Peru. The Polynesian language has close similarities with Malay tongues and most of the features of the Polynesian civilisation are found in the Malay world, such as the animals reared (dogs, pigs, etc.), the plants cultivated (taro, yams), the tools, and above all the well-known outrigger canoe.

*Farming and the traditional way of life.* In spite of their important racial and physical differences, the Melanesians, Polynesians and Micronesians all have a similar way of life, which is described as the Pacific civilisation. This relative uniformity is mainly due to the geographical environment; all these islands are small and hot but with fresh breezes, and all the cultivated plants are tropical.

The coconut palm is one of the most useful products of the islands. It has a great variety of uses; the pulped flesh is eaten as a dessert, the milk is used for seasoning most of the dishes, and the juice is the only drink on the dry atolls; the trunks provide house frames, the large leaves are used for covering roofs, and the fibres are plaited into baskets, matting, and loincloths.

The coconut palm grows only along the shore in low-lying areas; it disappears on land over 1,000 to 1,300 feet above sea level. This peculiarity partly explains why most of the islanders live on the edge of the sea. The villages are dotted along the shore, and the interior of the mountainous islands in Polynesia, such as Bora Bora and Tahiti, is completely uninhabited.

In Melanesia the rôle of the coconut palm has been less important. In the New Hebrides certain tribes have preferred to forgo this tree and seek refuge in the isolated valleys of the interior, where they are able to grow root crops which are more important than the coconut. These species of potato, whose sweetness and flavour vary, include taro, yams and sweet potatoes, and form the basic food eaten by the people.

A patch of land is carefully prepared and often irrigated; the crop terraces of Hawaii, now abandoned, used to be very attractive. The islander plants with a digging stick, and then has only to survey his patch while waiting for the harvest. He digs up the vegetables for the day, as required. The diet is varied with breadfruit, pandanus, mango and banana (the poor man's vegetable). It should be stressed that rice is not a crop on the islands of Oceania, except in the Marianas.

Hunting is not important except for wild pig, and little meat is eaten. Domestic animals are rare: a few tough chickens fed on coconuts; dogs, which the Polynesians are very fond of; and, most important, pigs.

In New Hebrides pigs with curved tusks were, and still are for some tribes, sacred animals and a monetary standard. The wealth of a chief is measured by the number of pigs he possesses, and a young man can hardly get married without offering his future father-in-law some of these animals. A wife is usually worth between two and six pigs, according to the beauty of the latter.

The importance of pigs is partly explained by the relative unimportance of fishing, which provides the

rest of the food. The Melanesians are much more nervous than the Polynesians and do not like the sea. Also the shores of some islands, such as Bougainville, have few fish. The Polynesians keep to the edge of the sea, not simply for the coconut palms, but also because there is a lagoon in which they can fish. There are many varieties of fish and they are often very large; but fishing is more of a sport than an industry. The fisherman reaches the reef in his outrigger canoe, and using various methods he catches what he requires for the family meal. Sometimes he dives with a harpoon in his hand, to find a fish in its lair. The shark is a danger, but accidents are rare. It is usually the women who surround the shoals of small fish (ouma) along the shore.

On the whole, the peoples of the Pacific islands do not work very hard; nature is generous in supplying them with food. It is possible to be carefree, and on the islands only the enjoyment of the present is important. Long days are spent sleeping or talking over a bowl of kava, a stimulating beverage.

Bringing the catch ashore in Samoa. Once under the rule of the paramount chiefs of the royal families, Samoa is now divided into two parts — American Samoa, which consists of the islands of Tutuila and Manu'a; and Western Samoa, formerly a German protectorate, then under New Zealand administration, and since 1962 an independent sovereign state.

*Arts and crafts. Ritual ceremonies.* When the Europeans discovered the islands, local handicrafts were quite well developed. It is true that the islanders were still in the Stone Age, but there are no metallic ores on the islands except in New Caledonia. Pottery is found only in some parts of Melanesia; here again it did not spread among the Polynesians because of the scarcity of suitable clay in the volcanic and coral islands.

There was no written language, only some identification marks. Wood carvings were very carefully finished. There were decorated vases in the Solomons, carved war clubs in Samoa and wonderful canoes in the Solomons. The world's museums now contain superb painted skulls and head casts from the Solomons and New Hebrides; there are tattooed faces from the Marquesas, cork materials, attractive grass screens and the giant stone statues, the *tikis* of Easter Island.

Usually, ritual was responsible for the development of art. Magic played an important part in the life of the people, and witchcraft still dominates many peoples. Even the Tahitians who are good Christians are frightened of evil spirits.

There was never any political unity among the islanders. It was unusual to find a group of islands under the same authority. The 'kingdoms' such as that of Pomare in Tahiti were able to last only with European support. At the present time Tonga is administered by the United Kingdom through the Colonial Office.

Formerly there was regular fighting among the tribes, either by expeditions on land or by cleverly organised landings. War was an art, and the men spent many months preparing for it. Usually the aim was not the greatest possible slaughter, but to bring back a number of the enemy, preferably alive. Then a great festival began and the prisoners were cut up and eaten. In Polynesia cannibalism had a marked ritualistic character; in Melanesia cannibalism was a source of food and the shortage of meat and fish may help to account for the attraction of human flesh. Cannibalism may survive in some parts of the Solomons and in the New Hebrides, but generally it is no more than a distant memory of old men in the hills. When the Europeans penetrated into the Pacific islands, the destruction of all pagan ceremonies was one of their objectives.

## THE EUROPEAN ARRIVAL

*Discovery and settlement.* The discovery of the Pacific islands by Europeans occured very late. Magellan saw the Marianas only in 1521. His Spanish and Portuguese successors landed on the Carolines and Marquesas in 1595, and the New Hebrides in 1605. During the seventeenth century hardly any new lands were found: however, Tasman discovered Tasmania and New Zealand in 1642, and the Tonga and Fiji Islands.

It was the second half of the eighteenth century before the exploration of the Pacific intensified and before a real inventory of the archipelagos could begin. Geographers in London and Paris wanted to complete their maps, and this scientific activity added to the rivalry of the English and French at sea.

Captain Cook made the most important discoveries; he explored the archipelago which he called the 'Society Islands' and landed on the islands which bear his name. He sailed round the New Hebrides, saw New Caledonia, explored the coast of New Zealand and Australia and discovered the Hawaiian Islands, where he was killed. French explorers, including Bougainville and La Pérouse, also played an important part.

At this time, apart from the official navigators, there were many other ships sailing the Pacific. Traders, pirates, buccaneers and whalers landed on the islands and taught the inhabitants many of the vices of our society; there was often bitter fighting between them.

They came for fresh provisions, rest and women. The ships also tried to recruit for their own crews reduced by illness or desertion. Others came to the islands to collect valuable wood such as sandalwood, or to repair the masts of their ships. Some came to trade, but there was no gold or spices and commerce remained quite unimportant.

Missionaries settled on the islands, and after some initial difficulties succeeded in converting most of the islanders. Religious rivalry between French Roman Catholic missionaries and British Protestant missionaries was added to political contention. The annexation of the various archipelagos by France and Britain was usually made at the request of the missions, despite the lack of enthusiasm on the part of the governments, who wished to avoid diplomatic complications and responsibility for remote islands at the other end of the earth. France claimed Tahiti in 1843, New Caledonia in 1853 and Wallis Island; while Britain annexed New Zealand in 1840, Fiji in 1874, and the Cook and Tonga Islands.

*Spheres of influence.* In the second half of the nineteenth century, when economic interests were more important than religious ones, and the search for copra gave value to the coconut palms, German traders settled in Western Samoa (1856) and in the Solomons, Marianas and Carolines; the Americans claimed the Hawaiian Islands and Eastern Samoa. In 1919 the German possessions were divided between the British, Americans and Japanese.

In 1945, with the liquidation of the Japanese Empire, the great powers in the Pacific were reduced to only three: France, the United States and Great Britain.

France possesses New Caledonia and its dependencies, the Wallis and Futuna Islands, and French Polynesia, which includes the Society Islands, of which Tahiti is the most important, the Tuamotu and Gambier Islands, the Marquesas and Tubuai or Austral Islands. France administers the New Hebrides as a condominium with Great Britain.

The United States flag flies over the Hawaiian Islands, the Marshalls, the Carolines, the Marianas and, south of the Equator, the Phoenix Islands and Eastern Samoa.

The British Commonwealth administers Fiji, Tonga, the Cook Islands, the Solomons and the Gilbert and Ellice Islands. Easter Island belongs to Chile. Independence of Western Samoa was proclaimed in 1962, but the bonds with New Zealand remained closely tied.

*The rapid decline of the population.* The consequences of European settlement for the peoples of Oceania were at first disastrous, one of the first effects being a collapse in population. There were massacres and fighting between the islanders, now provided with destructive guns; on some islands, like the Marianas and Viti Levu in Fiji, fighting occurred between the inhabitants and the Europeans. The slave trade was also harmful: for a short time there was an important trade in slaves between the Solomons and New Hebrides and the plantations in Queensland and Fiji which required labour.

On Easter Island some, repatriated from Peru, carried smallpox back with them, and this devastated the population.

As this depopulation is so widespread, the main responsibility undoubtedly lies with disease brought in unwittingly by the Europeans. The indigenous peoples had their diseases—leprosy, elephantiasis and others—but they were endemic and did not threaten the future of the race. The population was decimated by epidemics of diseases such as influenza, whooping cough, measles, tuberculosis and syphilis to which the people had no immunity. In 1875 measles killed at least 40,000 people in the Fiji Islands alone. In addition, drinking alcohol helped to encourage illness and wearing clothes cold with the sweat of a tropical climate increased pulmonary disease.

The indirect consequences of the break up of the tribal system are more difficult to appreciate, but they were very important. The social structure and tribal discipline disintegrated.

Willing assistance has now been given for several decades to change this situation. The tragic decline in the population is only a bad memory now in most of the islands. This is the reward of long years of effort by missionaries, governors and doctors; hospitals, welfare centres and schools were established in the most backward islands. These efforts have provided a more favourable atmosphere for the introduction of other aspects of Western civilisation. The older people on the islands began to accept the new spiritual values brought by Christianity, and are now no longer opposed to it. At the same time a trading economy is growing up in the islands, and this is the way of life which is developing today.

*Towards 'civilisation'.* The most striking changes are often the most superficial, and here they are changes in the islanders' dress and dwellings.

Men and women are no longer naked or nearly so, except in the interior of the most isolated islands such as Big Namba in the New Hebrides and among certain small tribes in the Solomons. Elsewhere, as a result of persuasion by the missionaries, the people have adopted clothes, usually of brightly coloured cottons.

The dwelling has also changed. It is never a place of work as in many other rural communities; there are no agricultural implements. It simply consists of a hut to sleep in, with usually a hut for eating and a smaller one for cooking. There is great variety in the style of homes; in Fiji there are still huts made entirely from vegetation, looking from a distance like stacks of straw. The dwellings of the Fijians are usually very attractive, with huge roofs covered with the fronds of coconut palms or pandanus grass. They are built in rows on a large lawn, where children play and poultry wander about.

A tribesman of Papua in a dug-out canoe.

In Samoa the dwellings are built on piles or on large oval bases of stone. They do not have walls; between the posts of the framework matting is raised or lowered to take advantage of the evening breeze on a muggy night in the wet season.

There is a tendency in Oceania to abandon these rather fragile frame buildings, which require constant maintenance and much collective work. The British administration has taken measures to prevent their being replaced by 'modern' buildings. In French Polynesia the change has already been serious. The commonest dwellings in Tahiti are wooden huts with roofs of corrugated iron. During the day the roof becomes intolerably hot, and when it rains there is a deafening noise. Also, the boards of Oregon pine have to be bought, as well as the corrugated iron, which comes from Europe. However, there is no maintenance problem, for it will take at least twenty-five years for the roof to rust through or the boards to rot.

In New Caledonia there are no more of the very old types of dwelling, the round huts like beehives.

The huts were clustered into villages, each one occupying a position which was carefully allocated by ritual. The homes of the women were set back, while the attractive houses of the men, with carved roofs, occupied a place of honour at the end of the central avenue. Today the villages are composed of family houses made of mud, which are whitewashed and thatched. They give charm to the east coast, with their neat and tidy appearance, surrounded by flowers and coffee shrubs.

*A changing way of life.* The way of life itself is changing. Former products such as coconuts, root crops and fish still remain the basic food, but in order to pay for the products of European civilisation, the islanders have to earn money. They have developed the commodities which interested the traders yet required little effort from themselves. The main one is copra, the dried kernel of the coconut, from which valuable oil is obtained. All they have to do is open the nuts which have not been eaten by rats, and put the sun-dried copra into sacks. Most of the people of French

Nouméa, New Caledonia.

Polynesia, Samoa and many other islands live by producing copra.

Coconut palms are occasionally supplemented by banana trees, which grow without attention and are harvested when almost ripe, as a Chinese or European merchant comes by; they are important in Fiji and Tonga. The natives of New Caledonia rely largely on their coffee plantations. Yields are low, half those in other areas, largely owing to the damaging effect of irregular picking according to the price obtained in world markets.

Other sources of income include the troca oysters of New Caledonia, the Tuamotus and Palaus, vanilla in the Society Islands, kauri resin in Fiji, and oranges in Tahiti and the Cook Islands.

There is a very serious decline in local crafts; it is much easier to buy an old can than to make a wooden bowl. The Polynesians have abandoned their long sea voyages, and their famous outrigger canoes are no longer made. Fishing is in decline, yet every year tons of preserved fish are imported into the islands. The

Japanese organised very large fisheries in the Carolines, but the local population did not assist, being content to raid the reefs in the lagoons. When the Europeans wished to develop the islands, they had to do without local assistance and employ labour from Asia both in agriculture and mining.

## DEVELOPMENT BY EUROPEANS

*Agricultural development.* If account is taken only of the work done by the islanders, the archipelagos of Oceania would hardly have any importance in the economic world. However, the Europeans who have settled here have developed plantations of many tropical products for sale in world markets.

The discovery in 1868 of the production of vegetable oil from copra encouraged small-scale exploitation by the inhabitants of the islands and led to the establishment of plantations by Europeans. Most of the small planters using local labour eventually had their plantations absorbed into the large companies. The simple methods of drying in the sun or on a fire are being replaced by oven drying. Today copra is the most important product of the Pacific islands.

Among new crops, coffee has been introduced in New Caledonia by French small planters from Réunion. The Kanakas refuse to work on European plantations, so the labour force is chiefly Javanese.

Cotton had its period of prosperity when the American Civil War reduced the crop from the South, but it disappeared before the end of the nineteenth century, and its place was taken by sugar-cane. Copra has exercised a stabilising influence, for it produced only a slow evolution in the way of life. Sugar-cane, on the other hand, has caused great changes in the two archipelagos of Fiji and Hawaii, where it is grown over a vast area.

In the Fiji Islands the British settlers were fortunate because of the extensive alluvial plains suitable for sugar plantations, on Viti Levu and Vanua Levu. At first there were many small settlers, but they have been absorbed by an Australian company which today controls all the land with sugar-cane and the four sugar-mills. With the aid of abundant labour from India, production is continually increasing and has reached about 150,000 tons annually. The Fijians have taken little part in this economic activity, which has made their islands among the most prosperous in the Pacific.

In some places stock-farming has been established by Europeans. In New Caledonia there are 100,000 cattle grazing in the savanna, where they compete with about the same number of deer. The 81,000 cattle in Fiji are used mainly for work in the fields, and for rural transport.

*Mineral resources.* There are few mineral resources, for most of the islands are composed of recent volcanic rocks or coral. The deposits of guano on some islands were quickly exhausted.

There are also some phosphate deposits. These occur on old atolls which have been uplifted by earth movements, and are usually surrounded by inaccessible cliffs. The phosphates of Makatea, one of the Tuamotu Islands, are worked by a French company. Australia controls Nauru and Britain Ocean Island, which both have rich deposits. The extraction of phosphates from Palau Island has now been abandoned.

The island containing most mineral resources is undoubtedly New Caledonia, which is a huge mass of metal. The nickel output is increasing annually, and the island is the third world producer after Canada and the U.S.S.R. It is mined open-cast, mainly at Thio on the east coast. The ore, which has about a 3 per cent content, is sent by coasters to Nouméa for refining. Coal for the factory comes from Australia and elsewhere, including the United States.

The annual output of chrome ore from mines in the north of the island averages 40,000 tons; it is exported semi- or unrefined. Manganese has been mined only a few years; the reserves are very extensive. Production of iron ore is about 300,000 tons.

*Racial difficulties.* The plantations and mines could not have been developed without labour from the Far East, but the presence of the Asiatic peoples in the Pacific Islands has created serious problems. Cultivation of sugar-cane is laborious and did not interest the Fijians; so, from 1897 British settlers brought in Indian families. After the expiry of their contracts, many Indians asked to stay in Viti Levu, and although further immigration has been stopped since 1917, the people of Indian origin continued to increase very rapidly. Now there are 197,000 Indians, and only 167,000 Fjians.

Although almost all of them were born in the country, the Indians have retained the customs of their Asian civilisation. They have little contact with the Fijians in Viti Levu, and complain that the British administration favours the indigenous people and prevents Indians from buying almost uninhabited Fijian land, while they are forced to crowd on to the narrow coastal plain. They accuse the Australian-owned Colonial Sugar Company of exploiting them. The agitation is now taking a political turn.

In New Caledonia there are 8,000 Vietnamese and Indonesians. They do all the hard work in the mines and plantations. Many who settled freely in the country have become merchants, market-gardeners or craftsmen, while their wives have become servants in European families. The Government attempts to reduce their numbers so that they do not swamp the indigenous population. In order to reduce the number of new arrivals as much as possible, the manufacturers have bought powerful American machines; each of the three Lima scoops at the Thio mines now does the work of 300 labourers. Unskilled labour is replaced by the skilled specialist, who is very often European.

In nearly all of the other archipelagos there are Chinese merchants. The indigenous peoples of the South Pacific have so far shown themselves commercially incompetent, while the hard-working Chinese have become an almost essential intermediary between the Europeans and the islanders. Every village has one or more shops where the Chinese sell everything, and buy vanilla and copra cheaply as well as acting as moneylenders. In this way they have acquired a large part of the wealth of the islands. It has been estimated that two-thirds of the monetary wealth of French Polynesia at the present time is in their hands.

In the islands formerly under Japanese mandates, over 70,000 Japanese settled between 1915 and 1942.

Pineapple production in Hawaii: contour planting and terracing. This is part of a ten-year soil conservation programme, said to be the largest ever undertaken by a private enterprise. Hawaiian pineapple production is about 90 per cent of the world total.

They established sugar-cane plantations, developed the guano and phosphates, and organised important fisheries, in the Mariana, Caroline and Marshall Islands. After the Second World War they were all sent home and the islands have had difficulty in establishing a new economic equilibrium, even at a lower level.

EMERGENCE FROM ISOLATION. *The extension of air routes.* For some years now the development of this part of the world has speeded up very rapidly. Modern means of transport are bringing to an end the isolation of the Pacific islands.

The problem of communications with the interior hardly arises, for the main activity everywhere is along the coast. There are roads running more or less continuously along the shores of New Caledonia, Viti Levu and Tahiti. The only railways belong to the industries.

The opening of the Panama Canal and the rise in importance of California and Japan have resulted in an increase in the number of sea routes. But the most

Natives of Papua, New Guinea. In spite of their primitive way of life, about 62,000 Papuans are attending administration and mission schools, while the proportion of skilled and semi-skilled workers is increasing through expanding education in technical schools and apprenticeship courses.

important factor has been the great increase in the air routes across the Pacific; today all the centres of the large archipelagos can be reached quickly by air. Seaplanes serve the islands which have no airports. This expansion of air routes is assisting the development of the tourist industry in Oceania. Even so, the planes and steamers go only to the more important centres. Schooners and cutters have to be used to get to the small islands, and these are primarily cargo boats.

Some archipelagos are served by only one or two ships a year. An increase in the number of small seaplanes is therefore a necessity.

*Future development.* The war between Japan and the Allies had serious consequences for most of the islands: many were occupied by the Japanese; the coconut plantations on the Solomons were largely destroyed; other islands, like New Caledonia, became huge military bases. Since the end of hostilities, the atomic explosions of Bikini and Eniwetok and naval exercises have continued to stress the strategic value of the Pacific islands.

Many of the island people were stirred out of apathy by the presence of soldiers and the temporary withdrawal of the Allies; Japanese propaganda and the influx of dollars have also helped to rouse them. On some of the islands, including the Solomons, Samoa and Cook, some nationalistic agitation has occurred.

This nationalism is at present tempered by the local peoples' realisation that whatever modern services they have depend on the skill of the colonial or ex-colonial powers, and that their monetary economy is largely dependent on the markets in these countries. The French, Australian, New Zealand, British and American Governments are anxious to raise the standard of living in the islands and are seeking a better understanding of the problems involved.

In 1949 the South Pacific Commission was established in Nouméa, and this attempts to co-ordinate the work of the three great powers in the Pacific: the British Commonwealth, France and the United States. Australia and New Zealand are seeking to play an increasing part in the development of these islands, whose future is closely linked to their own.

# NEW ZEALAND

New Zealand is quite different from the other archipelagos of the Pacific; it is transitional between them and Australia. Its two main islands are much bigger than any of the other Pacific Islands proper and they are larger in total area then the British Isles. It is the only important archipelago situated in the middle latitudes, or temperate zone, south of the limit of the coconut palm. Its landscape is unlike that of the other islands.

There are 200,000 Maoris, who may have come from the Cook and Raiatea Islands, but the majority of the population (over two and a half million) is of British stock. New Zealand, like Australia, is a former colony which has become a Dominion of the Commonwealth.

## THE LAND AND ITS PEOPLES

SOUTH ISLAND. New Zealand is a beautiful country, with a wide variety of scenery. It is relatively narrow, aligned from north to south, and is close to an often stormy sea.

Both islands are mountainous, but the Southern Alps in South Island are the higher. These mountains, which dominate the west coast, include Mount Cook (12,349 feet). There are long glaciers which descend as far as the forest zone, long narrow lakes filling former glacier valleys, and in the south inaccessible, vertical-sided fiords.

The strong westerly winds bring incessant driving rain to the west of the mountains; in the south there are 200 to 240 inches per year. Below the glaciers there is forest; in the north this is warm, temperate rain forest with large conifers, and a humid undergrowth dominated by tall ferns many feet high.

In the south are forests of beech trees but they are different from the European beech, as they have small evergreen leaves. The whole forest is very wet and the mossy undergrowth has a musty smell. Virgin forest still covers large unexploited areas. This is the refuge of the surviving kiwis, once common in New Zealand.

In the east between the Alps and the sea lie the sheltered plains, the largest of which are the Canterbury Plains. Farther south, in Otago, there are mountain blocks between small faulted basins. In the east the climate is much drier, with less than 40 inches of rain, and sometimes barely 20 inches. The Alps form a barrier to the westerly winds, and a warm dry descending wind, similar to the föhn of the European Alps, sometimes blows. Natural vegetation is poor; the forest merges into scrub with tufts of the indigenous tussock grass, but the area is nevertheless cultivable.

NORTH ISLAND. New Zealand's North Island is in general lower than South Island, though the highest peak, Ruapehu, is 9,175 feet. However, much of the country consists of hills and small plains partly covered by sub-tropical forest. The climate is still damp, but the temperature becomes warmer; summer in Auckland is quite hot.

The unusual feature of this island is volcanic activity. The main peaks are extinct or active volcanoes; Ruapehu erupted last in 1945; Ngauruhoe is often crowned with a trail of smoke, and Mount Egmont has a cone as regular as Fujiyama. Magnificent lakes occupy former craters and valleys blocked by lavaflows. Other volcanic phenomena are geysers, hot springs, steam vents and deposits of sulphur on the central plateau around Rotorua. This thermal activity indicates that the area was the scene of enormous eruptions some thousands of years ago; and as late as 1886 Tarawera volcano overwhelmed a village.

New Zealand lies, in fact, in one of the most unstable parts of the earth's crust; it forms part of the 'fiery girdle' of the Pacific, and from time to time there are serious earthquakes.

*The decline and revival of the Maoris.* The 200,000 Maoris in New Zealand are descendants of the Polynesian navigators who once landed on the shores of North Island. Their exact origin is, however, the subject of debate. When each tribe arrived in its outrigger canoe, it kept its independence and settled in well-defined territory. The Maoris had difficulty in adapting to their new surroundings in a temperate land. The coconut palm would not grow in such a cool climate, and the yield of root crops such as taro and sweet potatoes was poor; bracken roots were often a keenly sought supplementary food. As there were no mammals, hunting was restricted to the moas that lived in the forests. The newcomers were left with only dogs to rear. Freshwater fishing in rivers and lakes was often a major source of food.

The Maoris had to dress more warmly and build houses with better protection against the cold. They retained the traditions of their ancestors: there were always inter-tribal war, cannibalism and various social and ritual activities. Art also developed with complex spiral tattooing, wooden sculptures on the houses, and small jade statuettes or *tikis*.

These fierce people reacted violently to the advance of the European. However, a busy trade was eventually established between the Maoris and the Europeans, and New Zealand became an important port of call for whalers. The islanders received alcohol and

Glentanner Sheep Station in Canterbury, New Zealand. Merinos at the foot of the 8,000 foot Ben Ohau Range. New Zealand flocks generally comprise about 1,000 sheep; but larger stations do exist.

rifles in exchange for their products, and the traditional wars became even more bitter. Missionaries settled here in 1814, and though the Maoris quickly adopted Protestant or Roman Catholicism, tribal warfare continued.

The temperate climate of New Zealand attracted British colonists who bought or simply took their lands. In 1840 the island was annexed by Great Britain. The encroachment by the settlers provoked violent Maori reaction.

However, instead of 150,000 at the beginning of the century, in 1896 there were only 42,000. At that time it was thought that they would soon become extinct.

Then suddenly there was a revival. The Maoris adapted themselves to the Western way of life; they dressed like Europeans and built wooden houses with corrugated-iron roofs. The population increased again with surprising rapidity; now there are more than 198,000 Maoris, nearly half of whom are under fifteen years old. They are not distributed evenly about the

An aerial view of Wellington city and harbour, looking south to Cook Strait. The political capital of New Zealand, it is a windswept, hilly city with a population of 158,700. While Auckland is the principal port for foreign trade, Wellington has all the traffic between the North and South Islands.

New Zealand's volcanic phenomena are numerous: active and extinct volcanoes, geysers, hot springs, steam vents and sulphur deposits. Practical use is made of nature's gift in geothermal power stations, such as this one at Wairakei.

country, being nearly all in the north, in the Province of Auckland. Most of them live in the country, but the number of urban Maoris in Auckland is increasing.

There is no longer a Maori problem in New Zealand. Intermarriage remains quite common, and the majority of Maoris have some European blood.

## THE PEOPLE AND THEIR WAY OF LIFE

'*The England of the Antipodes.*' In spite of the 165,000 Maoris, New Zealand is essentially a British country. Nearly two million English, Scots and Irish have firmly established the British way of life. No other Dominion is more traditional, more attached to the 'mother country', which is still called 'home'. The Dutch, Italian and other immigrants are only a handful, and they are soon absorbed into the Anglo-Saxon environment.

New Zealand is a land without want, where equality of wages is almost general. There is complete social security. Because of the standard of hygiene and the healthy climate, the death rate of 9.5 per 1,000 is one of the lowest in the world.

While 63 per cent of the population is urban there are no vast cities like Sydney and Melbourne. The four provincial capitals rival one another. Auckland, built on a narrow isthmus between two large bays, is the chief port for foreign trade. The city is dominated by small volcanic cones which have been made into parks. Wellington, the Dominion capital, is situated at the head of a wonderful bay off Cook Strait. It is a windswept city and its houses are built on steep hills. It is the most important port for coastal shipping, for it controls the traffic between the North and South islands.

Christchurch was founded to the singing of hymns, and its main roads are named after English bishops. From the spire of the cathedral the regular grid pattern of the streets stretches over this flat city of innumerable bicycles.

The smaller city of Dunedin is somewhat similar to Wellington but the accent of the people indicates that they are of Scottish descent.

The other New Zealanders live in smaller cities with populations under 50,000 in market towns, or in farms scattered throughout the countryside.

*Prosperous stock-farming.* New Zealand lives by its flocks and herds. In proportion to its population it is the most important stock-farming country in the world; there are 3 cattle and 20 sheep for every one of the population. Eighty per cent of the farm land is devoted to stock. Grass grows quickly and well all through the year, because of the humidity and the mildness of the climate. Also, most people are not interested in growing crops, although some wheat is grown on the rather dry Canterbury Plains, and fruit and vegetables are produced for home consumption.

Sheep-rearing is most important in New Zealand, and nearly half the total area of the country is devoted to it. Fine flocks cover all the hilly areas. In the dry parts of South Island merino sheep are reared for their fine quality wool. Everywhere else the sheep are crossbreds providing both wool and meat. The size of the average flock is about a thousand; large flocks are uncommon.

The development in cattle-rearing is more recent; it started at the turn of the century, when it was realised that refrigeration would allow the export of meat and milk products to England. The cattle are mainly reared on the plains of North Island where the grass grows vigorously. The rearing of beef cattle is not as important as dairy farming. New Zealand has become the leading world exporter of butter and the second for cheese; these products are mainly sold to Britain. The average size of a dairy farm is not very large — about 70 to 100 acres — and the farms are of a prosperous family type. The natural vegetation has been burnt and English grasses substituted. Aerial methods of crop sowing and fertilizing are increasingly used to improve the pastures. The stock-farmers have completely transformed the countryside; its European outlook is stressed by gorse, broom, willow, poplar and the coniferous reforestation. The milk is taken to a co-operative dairy, where it is made into butter, cheese or condensed milk and then sent to the ports.

A RICH COUNTRY. There is very little industry in

New Zealand. The mines are not very rich. There was a gold rush when prospectors searched the rivers in South Island, but today production is scarcely 4,000 lb. a year. There is little coal, but it is sufficient for the small needs of the country.

New Zealand has the advantage of large hydro-electric power resources. Most development has occurred in North Island but the reserves of South Island are enormous. The power is used in the textile and shoe factories, repair workshops and, most important, the agricultural processing industry. An oil refinery and an aluminium fabricating plant have been built and an iron and steel industry is planned.

The railroads bring the products to the ports, most of the goods then being transported by sea. New Zealand has a well-developed rail system including the longest tunnel in the southern hemisphere, but as the country is mountainous and rail travel slow, air travel is becoming more and more common. Auckland is the chief port for importing manufactured products, which come mainly from the United

# AUSTRALIA

Australia is one of the largest countries in the world. With an area of 2,971,081 square miles, it is comparable with the United States; yet the estimated population in June 1966 was only 11,540,764.

The Commonwealth of Australia was formed in 1901 with the federation of the six former colonies, New South Wales, Victoria, Queensland, South Australia, Western Australia and Tasmania. Each of the States has its own Parliament. The Federal Parliament and Supreme Court, established at Canberra, control affairs common to the whole country. Voting is compulsory. The Queen is represented by a governor General.

## PHYSICAL CHARACTERISTICS

*A hot, dry continent.* As Australia is situated either side of the Tropic of Capricorn. between latitude 10°41′S

Kingdom, for its part the chief purchaser of New Zealand's agricultural products.

Australia is now becoming a more important source of imports because of its proximity.

The New Zealand balance of payments is usually favourable, and the country is prosperous when world prices of agricultural products are sufficiently high. A sharp fall in the prices of wool and butter caused difficulties in 1957, and New Zealand fears the consequences that Britain's entry into the European Common Market would have for the mainstay of its economy, agricultural exports. The small size of the population allows a high standard of living, but checks further development. The country would benefit from more immigration, but the New Zealanders select very carefully; still, 365,000 permanent immigrants (i.e. who stayed at least a year) entered New Zealand between 1947 and 1963 and they were almost entirely British and Dutch. New Zealanders are less disturbed than the Australians at the growth of the Asian peoples.

and 43°39′S, it is in a comparable situation to the Sahara. The areas with adequate rainfall only form a narrow strip along the coast; in the centre of the country, under the influence of sub-tropical high pressure, rain is uncommon and the local winds are some times violent, and always drying. The temperature is burning by day and cold at night. At Alice Springs the absolute extremes of temperature are 47.2°C. (117°F,) and −5°C. (23°F.).

The climate is harsh with violent contrasts, made extreme by the great size of the country. More than one-third of Australia has an annual rainfall of less than 10 inches. The rains in the north come in summer (January) and in the south in winter (August).

In the southern hemisphere, the northern part of Australia is in the same latitude as the Sudan in the northern hemisphere. The climate is tropical, with a warm dry season followed by a hot wet 'summer'. From November to March heavy rain falls over the north-east.

The southern part of Australia is in a comparable

A windmill (Australian model) pumps underground supplies of water into a large ground tank on cattle country near the MacDonnell Range in the Alice Springs district. Due to the concentration of cattle at such watering points, pasturage is soon laid bare.

Cultivation from the air. A plane sprays hormone weed killer over hill country in New Zealand. Aircraft are increasingly employed to improve the quality of pasture land, to fertilize and sow large areas.

latitude to Algeria, Spain and California. Perth and Adelaide have hot dry summers and mild moist winters—in fact, a Mediterranean climate. Tasmania's climate depends primarily on the westerlies, which bring rain all the year round; the region around Melbourne comes under the same influence. The coast near Sydney also has abundant rainfall, mainly in summer. In fact, all along the east coast the highlands cool and condense the winds from the sea.

Thus the coastal districts have adequate rainfall although they are often threatened by drought. Dry and wet years occur in an unpredictable sequence, disastrous to the economic life of the country.

*A monotonous landscape.* There is no great variety of relief in this huge area.

The western section is an excessive plateau between 600 and 2,000 feet high, with some east-west ridges, like the Musgrave and Macdonnell Ranges. The rail route from Adelaide to Perth across the empty Nullarbor Plain has one straight stretch of 332 miles.

The Western Plateau is part of one of the oldest continents in the world, the Gondwana continent. At the beginning of the Primary era, Gondwana united the Deccan, Madagascar and South Africa. This crystalline mass was peneplaned during millions of centuries of erosion. The earth movements of the Tertiary era hardly affected it; there was some faulting and it was lifted slightly above the level of the sea.

Subsequent erosion has hardly worn this old mass of hard rocks, since there are no permanent rivers. Formerly, in a more humid period, some valleys were eroded. Large sand dunes now cover part of the plateau, but its most characteristic feature is extensive stony desert.

In eastern Australia is a large range of mountains, the eastern Highlands or the Great Dividing Range; its southern part is the Australian Alps. The 'Alps' are rounded and rise only to 7,328 feet. Kosciusko, the highest peak, can be ascended by car.

The Blue Mountains, which form a barrier west of the coastal plain near Sydney, resemble a plateau rather than mountains. Their dissected relief is unusual; great sandstone walls hang above the wooded valleys. The Australian Alps are in fact much older than the European Alps; they are Hercynian mountains uplifted in the Tertiary era. Tasmania has a sharper relief, for its mountains were dissected during the Quaternary glaciation.

Between the Western Plateau and the Eastern Highlands is a large lowland, the centre of which is below sea level. In the north it is an artesian basin, where the intermittent rivers lose themselves in large lakes, which are only vast stretches of mud encrusted with salt. Enormous quantities of water accumulated in the strata are tapped by artesian bores.

To the south, the Murray is of more recent origin. The Murray-Darling rivers are 2,542 miles long, but their usefulness is not proportional to their length. The Murray and its main tributaries are well supplied with water from the Australian Alps, but they flow across lowlands with little rainfall and are diverted by irrigation canals, so the flow becomes steadily smaller. In some years the Murray is unable to cross the sand bar which has been formed across its mouth. It is of little use for navigation.

*Vegetation and wild life.* The largest areas of the country are covered with grass or scrub and true forest covers less than 1 per cent of the country.

After a shower in the desert hundreds of grasses flower and ripen in a few days, then disappear for many months. In the former valleys, xerophytic shrubs seek the moisture of underground streams. The sandy desert has much more vegetation then the stony desert and is sometimes covered with spinifex.

In the areas with a little more rainfall there is scrub: spiny acacias known as *mulga*, and stunted eucalyptus or *mallee*; occasionally there are strange trees like the bottle-tree. Imperceptibly the vegetation changes to savanna; after the rains the Murray Basin and the interior of Queensland are covered with tall kangaroo grass. The trees increase in number to form an open forest of eucalyptus and acacias.

Dense forest is only found in the coastal areas. In the north-east, in Queensland, there is tropical rain forest of evergreen trees, lianas and tree ferns. Southwards it changes to temperate forest with less undergrowth, and dominated by magnificent eucalyptus, some of which are nearly 300 feet high.

This is the typical tree of Australia, usually providing hardwoods; there are more than 600 species. The only other genus which can compete is the acacia. The isolation of the Australian continent has allowed its flora to evolve virtually unaffected by outside influences.

Most of the animals are types which disappeared long ago on other continents. One difference from the Pacific islands is that Australia has many reptiles, including poisonous snakes and, in the north, crocodiles. It is the land of the *monotremata* and marsupials. The strangest of all is the duck-billed platypus: intermediate between bird and mammal, it lays eggs but suckles its young, and has a body covered with fur.

The young of the marsupials are born immaturely, and grow in the stomach pouch of the mother: such are the wallaby and kangaroo, and tree-dwellers like the opossum and the koala, a small, attractive bear.

The variety and beauty of the birds are exceptional. There are parrots of all colours, and members of the ostrich family such as the cassowary and emu, which cannot fly, although they can run at enormous speed.

All these animals are adapted to their geographical environment. The scarcity of water and vegetation forces them to cover considerable distances. The large kangaroos can travel at 20 m.p.h.

European settlement seriously disturbed the animal and plant life. The European has introduced his cultivated crops, fruit trees and conifers for reforestation. Cactus and prickly pear have spread with disquieting speed.

The native animals have suffered from the introduction of carnivorous animals and others competing for their food. Arable farming and stock-rearing have driven them into the driest areas. Rabbits eat their grass and rats destroy their eggs; new diseases cause heavy casualties. Man, too, by indiscriminate hunting of the kangaroo, koala, opossum and other fur-bearing animals has added to the toll in the past. Kangaroo hunting is now restricted, and many other native animals are protected.

## A RECENTLY SETTLED COUNTRY

*European exploration and settlement.* Australia's discovery by Europeans was quite recent. At the beginning of the seventeenth century some Dutch navigators sailed along the north-western shores, seeing nothing but arid land populated by savages.

In 1642 Tasman crossed the Indian Ocean, passed south of Australia and discovered the island which bears his name. He showed that Australia was a large island, not attached to the 'Terra Australis' or Southern Continent; his voyage was considered a failure, however, as he had not discovered any gold or spices.

During the second half of the eighteenth century, English and French navigators started to explore the Great Ocean. Cook surveyed the south-east coast of Australia, and his report to London led the Government to set up a colony of convicts in this distant land.

The first convicts, led by Captain Philip, arrived at Sydney in 1788. There were initial difficulties and often the threat of famine. Land was cleared and a little later Captain MacArthur received permission to rear merino sheep; thus began the leading activity of Australia. The Colony developed quite rapidly, the Blue Mountains were crossed and the Murray-Darling Lowlands explored.

In order to stave off possible French settlements, posts were established in Victoria and Tasmania, where the most difficult convicts were sent; later a free settlement was established in Western Australia. The convicts on the east coast were soon outnumbered by free settlers who came from England and Ireland. The convict settlements were not officially closed until 1868.

Pioneers and 'squatters' staked out land for themselves in the bush, and stock-rearing continued to grow; arable farming began in the Murray-Darling Lowlands. Explorers undertook the immense task of crossing the continent from east to west and from south to north. By 1875, in spite of lack of food and water, all the main geographical features were known. The discovery of gold in 1851 produced an unusual increase in the number of immigrants, both European and Asian. By 1889 the population had reached 3 million, and Australian wheat and wool were flooding the European market.

The economic crisis of 1929 brought home very sharply to the Australians how dependent they were on foreign purchases of their goods. The Second World War also brought home to them that they were too few to defend themselves against the Asian peoples.

*The aborigines.* In June 1961 (the last census) there was an estimated total of 40,801 full-blooded aborigines in Australia. They are dark-skinned, with small, long craniums, projecting faces, large flat noses and dark deep-set eyes; they usually have straight black hair, and are of average height. They probably originated in South-East Asia and crossed to Australia several thousand years ago. Hundreds of dialects illustrate the complexity of their origin.

In technique they have passed the stage of chipping stone; but they have no agriculture, partly due to the lack of vegetation in the country (it is noticeable that the European Australians have not cultivated any of the indigenous plants). With the exception of the wild dogs (dingos), the aborigines did not domesticate the native animals, and they depend, therefore, on hunting, using various kinds of spears and boomerangs—short curved sticks which return if they do not strike the target. The women gather seeds, roots and larvae. The aborigines are always nomadic, and their dwellings are merely shelters of branches or bark.

This apparently backward type of life does not prevent a very complicated social structure. A curious system of kinship exists in the organisation of the tribe. Art is mainly inspired by religion; it is confined to designs on bark and rocks, with contrasts of bright colours, of which ochre and red are important. The arrangement of colours on message sticks is a real language and often it is extremely beautiful, but there is no writing.

Unfortunately, European settlement was a disaster for the Australian aborigines. A peaceful and good-natured people, they understandably retaliated by

Punters and bookies at the races at Eagle Farm, Brisbane. Horse-racing has a tremendous following in Australia; over 11 million spectators attend the country's race-courses every year.

killing cattle and settlers alike when their hunting-grounds and sacred places were encroached upon. The Europeans cleared the land and the survivors were driven into the most arid parts of the country.

Barely one-third still live a fully tribalised life, and their resources are continually dwindling. Sometimes the Government has to leave supplies of food and blankets. Other aborigines have been settled in reserves controlled either by the government or by missionaries. More than a third work on the sheep farms and cattle stations, where they make excellent stockmen. Others have become 'Europeanised'; but in general they seem to find it much more difficult to adapt to Western ways than the Maoris of New Zealand. Those living on stations or missions receive some schooling and in 1958 an Aboriginal Scholarship scheme was established to provide for university education. Legislation also protects the aborigines' standards of health and economic well-being.

*A largely European continent.* There are no important racial minorities in Australia as there are in South Africa and the United States. In the late nineteenth century the European population feared that the result of the influx of Chinese immigrants (from 1851) and of Kanakas—Pacific islanders brought into Queensland to work on the sugar plantations—would be an overall lowering of wages and the standard of living. An immigration policy designed to limit the entry of coloured nationalities was therefore implemented; among European Australians there has been some protest against this, particularly during the last decade.

Australia is a European continent and principally a British continent. The country has a very small population for its size, and the density is about 3.6 per square mile. Every year there is an appreciable excess of births over deaths; the birthrate remains about average, but the deathrate is one of the lowest in the world—8.7 per 1,000.

*An urban population.* The majority of the people live on the east coast, in a crescent from Cairns to Adelaide, which is continued in a smaller strip in Western Australia. This crescent corresponds exactly with the arable land, and the population map closely coincides with the map of winter rainfall. However, even in this crescent, there are some large empty areas. In the rest of the country there is an average of one person for every 5 or 10 square miles. In fact, the bulk of the population (82 per cent) lives in the towns. Sydney has a population of 2,256,100, Melbourne of 2,003,100.

In each city the commercial centre contrasts with the huge residential suburbs. All the European styles of architecture are united: Renaissance banks and Gothic post offices can be found among imposing concrete and glass skyscrapers.

The streets are busy during the day, but at night everyone returns to his little house, often in a distant suburb. Suburban houses are usually bungalows of brick, stone or wood surrounded by a small garden; apartment houses are becoming more common. Much colonial architecture remains, particularly in Sydney and Melbourne, and is very attractive—of wood, with gabled roofs and wide shady verandas.

Saturday is devoted to games, such as cricket, rugby, swimming and tennis. Statistics show that every year 11 million spectators visit race-courses.

Sydney, with its fine harbour and great bridge, is the pride of its inhabitants. The city centre is rather cramped, with narrow, winding streets dating from early colonial days; factories have only been allowed to spoil certain areas, to the south at Botany Bay, and to the west at Parramatta. The centre of Melbourne is formed by a grid pattern of streets, often tree-lined; large parks help to avoid monotony. The northern shores of Port Philip Bay form its large harbour, and industries stretch round it south-west to Geelong. Brisbane has become the third city of Australia, and the wooden bungalows of the early days have been replaced almost entirely by imposing concrete buildings. Adelaide, founded by the Anglican Church, is more peaceful and traditionalist. Perth, though very isolated, is developing rapidly with many new industries; it has an excellent climate and pleasant streets which make it the most attractive city of Australia.

*Education.* Educational facilities are well developed The number of students attending primary and secondary schools in 1961-62, for instance, was over 2 million,

The bridge (the longest single-span bridge in the world), the harbour and part of the city of Sydney, capital of New South Wales. With more than two million inhabitants Sydney is one of the biggest cities in the southern hemisphere. It is Australia's principal port and an important industrial centre.

Melbourne, with the Yarra river flowing through its centre.

a much higher proportion of the population than in Great Britain. There are twelve universities, including one postgraduate university, which are attended by over 58,000 students. Total direct expenditure by State Governments on education amounted to £A154 million ($348 million) in 1961-62.

## AGRICULTURE, MINING AND INDUSTRY

Australia, nevertheless, remains an agricultural country and three-quarters of the exports are farm products. There are 15 sheep and 2 cattle per head of the population. To the fertile crescent should be added the stock-rearing areas inland which are becoming more and more developed.

*The world's leading sheep farming country.* In 1965 there were 170 million sheep in Australia, easily the largest number for any country in the world. The livestock numbers fluctuate astonishingly, due to the quantity of rain falling in the semi-arid parts of the country. In 1944, for instance, a terrible drought killed 22 million animals.

To safeguard himself against these uncertainties, the farmer has made dams, and sunk wells to utilise the accumulated waters of the Great Artesian Basin. Several thousand bores keep innumerable troughs supplied with water, as well as irrigating crops of green corn and lucerne. In times of drought the sheep die mainly of hunger rather than thirst. Artesian wells are bored along the tracks to allow the animals to make long journeys to the railheads.

Another danger which threatens the sheep is the competition of the rabbit, unfortunately introduced into Australia in 1862. Five rabbits eat as much as one sheep. It is very difficult to control them; huge enclosures have been made of wire fences, buried one foot underground; a virus similar to myxomatosis was spread and in 1950 between 200 and 300 million rabbits were destroyed in this way.

The fences also divide the farmers' lands into various pastures, the *paddocks*. The flocks are huge, and can consist of up to 100,000 sheep or more.

The farmhouse is called a homestead and usually comprises a large wooden house with a corrugated-iron roof, boarded huts where the hired hands sleep, garage, water tank, wind pump and shearing sheds. Wool production is still the main aim of Australian sheep-farming. Most of the sheep are merinos producing good quality wool. About a quarter are crossbred, giving both meat and wool.

The sheep belt runs from Queensland southwards to Victoria, parallel to the east coast but well inland. There is a second important region in the southern parts of Western Australia. New South Wales is the chief sheep-farming state, having more than twice as many head of sheep as its nearest rival Victoria. Queensland, Western Australia and South Australia also have considerable flocks. Merinos thrive best in dry, open plains on natural pastures, so the crossbreds are kept mainly in the damper agricultural districts.

The huge size of Australia, and the wide variations in climate that this involves, means that shearing occurs somewhere throughout the year, and this helps to keep the market steady.

Once the shearing is over, the bales of wool are

Scrubland in the Northern Territory of Australia. There are large areas providing excellent pasturage. In the dry south of the Territory some water is obtained from artesian basins.

Rounding up sheep in the Riverina district of southern New South Wales.

sent to the nearest railway station, often 60 miles away. Australia provides one-quarter of the wool sold on world markets. About three-quarters of the total clip is exported to Europe. Most of the mutton and lamb is consumed locally and so attempts are being made to improve the crossbred Corriedale sheep to provide more bulk together with high-grade wool.

*The importance of cattle.* There are about 19 million cattle. In the regions of adequate rainfall in the south-east, on the small coastal plains and along the Murray, cattle-farming is intensive. On the mixed farms where crops are also grown both milk and beef cattle are raised on rich pasture lands.

In contrast, in the north, the cattle stations are becoming even larger than those with sheep. The average size of a cattle station is between 1,000 and 2,000 square miles. In the Northern Territory two companies share 30,000 square miles. The cattle are left to roam over vast unfenced lands, the drovers only rounding them up for branding, or for the journey to the slaughterhouses.

The homesteads are even more isolated than those of the sheep-farmers; the radio-telephone and aircraft play an important part in communication with civili-sation. Children are taught by radio-telephone, and 'flying doctors' attend the sick. A service of 'flying veterinary surgeons' has also been organised.

Cattle ticks have done great harm, and frequent dipping in arsenical mixtures is necessary. However, drought still remains the greatest danger; in 1951, a very dry year in the north, thousands of cattle died of hunger, when a few miles away adequate grass was available. The cattle were too weak to reach these pastures, and there was no means of transporting them.

Although natural conditions in Australia favour the development of cattle stations, economic factors have inhibited their growth. The chief disadvantage is the country's isolation from suitable markets. The cattle are driven from the inland stations hundreds of miles to the railheads where they have to be refattened before being taken to the coast. Although the advent of refrigeration makes it possible, in theory, to export beef to Europe now, it has proved more profitable to use refrigeration for the export of dairy products. Consequently Australia consumes most of the total beef production herself, exporting the remainder to the United Kingdom, often in the form of tinned beef, and to South-East Asia.

Dairy-farming is an old-established industry in Australia, as its frequent and regular income during the intial stages made it attractive to the early settlers. The favourable climate means that housing for the cattle is unnecessary. The milk yields tend to be low, depending on the quality of the pasture, except where supplementary feeding is given. The chief

Agriculture and grazing predominate in the cultivable lands of New Zealand (two-thirds) and Australia (excluding the deserts of the interior). Primary products — meat, wool and dairy products — and their associated manufactures make up a large proportion of exports. Cereals, vegetables, vines, sugar cane and fruits, tropical in northern Queensland to temperate varieties in Tasmania, are widely grown. Coal, copper, lead and gold are mined in considerable quantities and there is some lead, iron, tungsten and zinc.

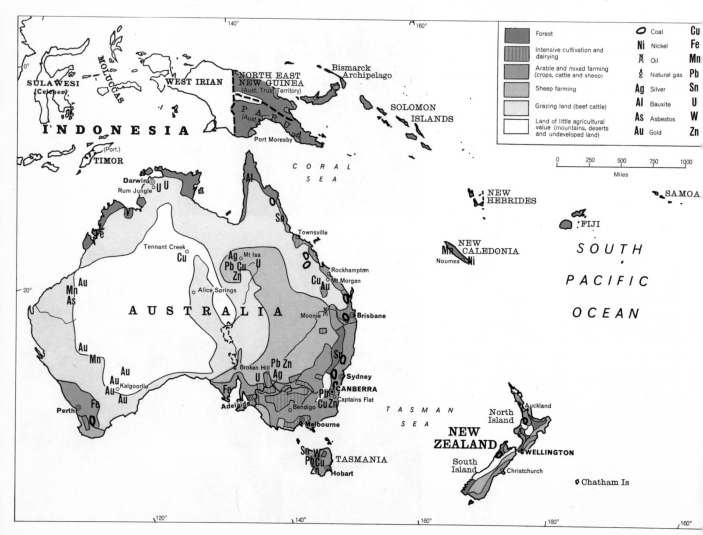

dairy-farming region is the south-east, particularly in Victoria, New South Wales and Queensland.

*The wheat crop.* The 'wheat belt' covers the Murray-Darling Plains close to the Eastern Highlands and the plateaus east of Perth in Western Australia.

Usually it is grown under an extensive type of monoculture, with dry farming. From an acreage of 16,469,000 the yield is 8,800,000 tons. Wheat has to face the competition of other wheat-producing countries, such as Argentina; in some areas, therefore, mixed arable and pastoral farming is developing. Mechanisation has nevertheless produced an increase in the wheat yield, and wheat exported in 1963-64 totalled over 6.8 million tons.

*Other crops.* With its great area and variety of climate, Australia can grow everything, from temperate fruits like the apples of Tasmania to tropical fruits like the pineapples of Queensland, vegetables, and raisin grapes on the irrigated lands along the Murray, or wine grapes on the hills around Adelaide.

However, until recently, there has been little development of tropical and sub-tropical products such as cotton, groundnuts (peanuts), millet or maize. This is, perhaps, because there is a shortage of labour, and a lack of interest among the European settlers in crops which they do not understand. The only important tropical crop is sugar-cane, grown on the coastal plains of Queensland. The yield is high: 1,750,000 tons are produced annually, and over half is exported. The main problem is that of labour; the Kanakas have been replaced by white workers and the cost of production is high, so that government subsidies are necessary.

Forestry is restricted to certain hardwood eucalypts. Fishing is adequate only for local consumption.

*Agricultural development.* There are over 2 million acres of irrigated land and although experiments in rain-making are continuing and large water-stores are being built, water resources are restricted. Australian agriculture has therefore developed by increasing yields rather than by farming new land; but farmers have been discouraged by the unreliability of the climate and price fluctuations.

The staple products are wool, meat and wheat, all of which are exported in large quantities. The amount varies, but in a good year such as 1962-63 wool production was 70 per cent, and other farm products about 66 per cent, above the pre-war average. Other valuable crops exported are apples, citrus fruits and grapes.

*Minerals and power resources.* Australia is rich in mineral wealth. In the 1850's the discovery of gold brought a rush of prospectors or 'diggers' from all over the world. The population of Victoria doubled in a few months. The main deposits were discovered north of Melbourne, at Ballarat and Bendigo.

The Victorian deposits were soon exhausted, but in 1885 gold was discovered in the desert at Kalgoorlie and later at Wiluna. Mining began in spite of the difficult geographical conditions, and is now a large industry. An aqueduct, 316 miles long, brings the water required for washing the crushed quartz veins. Gold production is now about 34 tons annually.

Australia produces silver and non-precious metals. At Mount Isa in Queensland, Broken Hill in the far south-west of New South Wales, and in Tasmania, there are rich deposits of zinc, lead, copper, tungsten and bauxite. Australia is the world's largest producer of lead. Reserves of iron ore estimated at 15,000

Coastal dairying country near Bega, in south-eastern New South Wales. Dairy products are important in Australia, both for home use and for export. In 1963, 206,000 tons of butter were produced and 59,000 tons of cheese.

million tons have been found in Western Australia. Limited amounts are also found at Iron Knob.

Huge sums of money have been spent on the search for oil, which was discovered in Western Australia in 1953 and later in Queensland. Production has not reached commercial quantities yet. Papua is also considered a possible source.

Annual coal production has reached nearly 25 million tons. The largest deposits occur in New South Wales, north of Sydney and around Newcastle. Some seams are opencast mined, elsewhere the mines are as much as 3,000 feet deep. The lignite of Yallourn in Victoria is obtained from large opencast workings; production amounts to over 18 million tons.

Sufficient coal is mined to export a small quantity to the Pacific islands; to New Caledonia. Electricity generation reached 30,636 million kWh in 1963-64. The largest thermal power stations are at Yallourn in Victoria (using lignite) and Bunnerong, New South Wales. Two more are planned.

Rich uranium deposits have been discovered at Rum

Mount Morgan Copper Mine, near Rockhampton, Queensland. Copper is one of the state's principal minerals; production for 1963 was 87,500 long tons. Copper refining is one of Queensland's largest industries.

Jungle and South Alligator river (near Darwin), at Mary Kathleen (Queensland) and at Radium Hill (South Australia); production began in 1954 and is now over 1,000 tons. Hydro-electric power stations are concentrated in the south-east, in the highlands. Present capacity is small, but potential has been estimated at 7 million kWh. A large programme known as the Snowy River Project is being carried out in the Alps, and it is planned to produce three million kilowatts by 1980. Eighty miles of tunnels are being driven through the mountains. This project will also irrigate two million acres of land. The heavy-water-moderated reactor at the nuclear research station at Lucas Heights (near Sydney) was opened in 1958; it has an output of 10,000 kW.

*The development of industry.* The number of workers employed in Australian factories in 1960 doubled the prewar figure, an indication of the spectacular growth of industry. Trade union organisation is very highly developed, there is an advanced system of industrial arbitration and a regularly adjusted basic wage. Home manufactured products are steadily increasing, making it possible to reduce the cost of imported finished goods. Difficulties facing the development of industry include the shortage of labour, high wages for moderately skilled work, strikes and the small size of the home market.

Annual steel production is now over 4.3 million tons, mainly from New South Wales at Port Kembla and Newcastle. Iron is brought by sea from South and Western Australia to Newcastle; coal is produced on the spot. Newcastle steel is therefore the cheapest in the world. During the Second World War iron works were built at Whyalla, close to the iron ore in South Australia. The Broken Hill Proprietory Company is building a steel works at Whyalla and an iron and steel works at Kwinana in Western Australia. The aluminium factory at Bell Bay in northern Tasmania opened in 1955; its annual capacity is being raised from 12,000 to 16,000 tons.

Another rapidly expanding industry is petro-chemicals; Australia now produces two-thirds of its own requirements.

The engineering industries are expanding, and produce machinery, jet aircraft, electrical products, engines, locomotives and cans. An automobile industry was started after the war.

The textile industry produces enough woollen cloth for home requirements, but there is a deficiency in cotton production. Synthetic fibres are developing and may be a threat to the woollen industry.

Nearly all the industries are concentrated in the ports, which are at the same time the main sources of demand and labour. Since the war, however, there has been some attempt at decentralisation. Sydney, Melbourne, and the other State capitals are also important export centres for Australian produce; wool, the principal export, is sent to Japan (the largest customer), England, France, and the U.S.A.; meat and butter are bought by Great Britain; wheat is sent to Europe and south-east Asia. Japan will buy about 300 million tons of iron ore during the 1970's.

A good rail network has been built to carry the agricultural products of the interior plains to the coast. Unfortunately each State started its railroads without consulting the others, and each uses a different gauge.

The Broken Hill company
at Newcastle, 104 miles north
of Sydney, is one of Australia's
most powerful
industrial concerns.
Established in 1916, it controls
coal mines, steel mills, iron-ore
smelters and shipyards,
and is Australia's largest single
employer of labour.
Its steelworks produce more than
a million tons of high-grade
steel annually.

The result is costly reloading at the change-over points. A programme for standardisation has met with serious financial difficulties, but most of the inter-city lines are now standardised.

Now rail is facing serious competition from road and air transport. There are 567,000 miles of roads, of which two-fifths are macadamised or bitumenised, and about one car for every five people. Civil aviation services are highly developed; in 1963-64 they carried over 3.25 million passengers on domestic services. Aircraft are also used in agriculture—for spreading seed or fertilizer, and for air freight. About ten international airlines serve Australia.

THE NEED FOR IMMIGRATION. Australia has economic potential and could play a more important part in the world than it does. The wide variety of climate could enable it to produce every kind of food necessary to feed a population of at least 35 million. Experiments have proved that the desert is fertile; the enormous cost of irrigating it is the drawback. But mineral resources are large and power potential is being rapidly developed. Industry has made rapid progress since the war.

However, the country is badly handicapped by its low population. The policy of controlling and limiting immigration has had disastrous effects. Shortage of manpower has checked the growth of agriculture and industry. High wages have raised the manufacturing costs of finished goods. The cost of maintenance of public services in a country so large is also a heavy burden for 10 million people. During the Second World War, the advance of the Japanese as far as New Guinea revealed Australia's vulnerability.

The attitude towards immigration has changed considerably. A Ministry of Immigration was established, and since 1945 more than 1.5 million immigrants have arrived in the country. Of these, 48 per cent were British, and over half benefited from assisted passages; Australia has concluded assisted migration agreements with the United Kingdom, Malta, the Netherlands, Italy and the Federal German Republic. In conjunction with the United Nations High Commissioner for Refugees, Australia has also settled European refugees and displaced persons. After the British, the largest group of immigrants are Italian, followed by the Dutch.

The absorption of these 'new Australians' has not been easy. As everywhere else, there were serious accommodation difficulties; immigrants had a long, enforced stay in camps. Also, agriculture requires labour, but the newcomers collected in the towns. Language difficulties often seemed almost insurmountable. However, the settlers have brought an energetic new spirit to what was formerly a somewhat isolated community. They have also proved willing to work hard, and have cornered certain food and catering industries.

Although there has been rapid economic growth, the increase in population has created a demand for more social services and more consumer goods. But prices for wool and wheat, dependent on fluctuations in the world market, have fallen at times, and Australia has not been able to balance its payments. Investment from abroad has helped to offset this, but there is still need for both increased population and productivity.

# LANDS AROUND THE PACIFIC

It has already been explained that in this encyclopedia traditional division into continents has been abandoned. The section that follows covers lands of Asia, the Americas and the two Poles. Grouped within it are regions which for long were separate worlds, almost without communications between each other or with the outside. Their civilisations evolved as separate entities and it is only during the past few centuries at most that these areas have been affected by the currents of international exchanges.

These long-isolated worlds lie around the most extensive of the earth's oceans—the Pacific. It is not only the largest ocean basin (it covers about half the surface of the earth), it is the primordial ocean, encircled with long strings of islands, areas of vulcanism and of especially violent seismic activity. Though its vastness still makes it first and foremost a barrier, it did not perhaps prove as insuperable an obstacle to early communications as the Atlantic, even though it is four times as wide from east to west; in fact population movements between Asia and America took place well before the arrival of Europeans in the New World. But early trans-Pacific voyages never allowed more than partial communication; they resulted in contacts and influences rather than in cultural fusion.

The second barrier to inter-communication was the northern Eurasian plains, the most extensive continental plains; they long formed the dividing line and barrier between the Far West and the Far East. The mountains bordering them are the highest in the world, their forests the most extensive, their tundras the most barren, and their infinite steppes often merging into desert. Here the scattered population remained so unstable and turbulent that for centruies it was viewed as a scourge by other communities, and this emphasised the effect of the physical barriers. Neither the Greeks, nor the Romans, nor the Chinese attempted to occupy these vast stretches of flat land; they merely skirted them and protected themselves with fortified frontiers and 'Great Walls' against nomad peoples beyond.

Later, a core of Slavs living in the shelter of forest clearings established a centre of resistance to the nomads. Soon, strengthened by their Byzantine Christianity. these Slavs ventured from the forests and won for agriculture the rich plains of black earth (chernozem) which until then had been given over to prairies and had been the domain of horsemen. They gradually spread towards the east, following the long corridor of fertile land stretching between forest and desert and, beyond the mountains in the east, as far as the Pacific shores and still beyond, into Alaska.

A barrier from time immemorial, the immense, empty plains of northern Asia remained inaccessible until our own day, and here the remarkable Soviet experiment is now being worked out.

The third area resistant to human population still remains: the Poles. The North Pole is simply an enclosed sea. Though arctic and frozen, it is little wider than the Mediterranean is long. In addition, the North Pole is fairly close to the most densely populated areas of the earth, for man is chiefly concentrated in the northern hemisphere, and particularly in temperate zones. Yet the Arctic Ocean has not played anything like the important rôle for which its central position surrounded by populous areas would seem to have marked it out. It is only within the last few years that those stretches of its sea without obstacles have begun to be used for transpolar services.

The Antarctic presents a totally different pattern; it is a continent larger than the sea surrounding the North Pole, and is encircled by a broad ocean. This is the only area of the earth in which a line of latitude runs full circle around the globe without crossing land. A wide band of pack ice often encloses the coast, making access difficult. Its isolation is thus complete. It is not even a barrier, for this continent lies outside all lines of communications and obstructs nothing. Antarctica is the largest continental area that is totally uninhabited.

Clearly, the contrasts that have evolved over the centuries in the various lands around the Pacific are almost as great as thosebetween different planets.

Perhaps most curious is the American continent, the 'New World'. A glance at a map shows at once the remarkable feature of this continent: its extent from north to south, which contrasts so markedly with Eurasia, and its slightly smaller compass from east to west. The American continent extends over 127 degrees of latitude (132 degrees counting the polar islands); that is, it covers 9,500 miles of the earth's 25,000-mile circumference. It is the continent that stretches farthest north—Ellesmere territory reaches the 82nd parallel north—and farthest south—Cape Horn lies beyond 50° south; beyond its southern tip the Antarctic islands link South America to Graham Land and the South Pole. The continent thus had contact with both the Arctic and the Antarctic, and is flanked by two great north-to-south oceans, the Pacific and the Atlantic.

Between these two stretches of sea extends first the great mountain ridge of the west, with the Rockies and the Andes together constituting the longest mountain range in the world; the ridge is broken only where it narrows in Central America. In the east of the continent, on the other hand, there are old mountains of the 'shield' type, more or less rejuvenated: in the north, the Canadian Shield; in the south, the Brazilian Shield. Between the western and the eastern upland areas is the broad central depression characteristic of both North and South America.

The band of deserts, so typical of the tropical regions in the Old World, where it forms a continuous zone across Eurasia from the African Sahara through Arabia and central Asia to Mongolia, is repeated in America on a smaller scale. The Caribbean Sea and the Gulf of Mexico, lying at latitudes where one would expect tropical deserts, have restricted the desert area to parts of Texas and of states westward to California.

In South America the band of deserts crosses the continent diagonally, from north-west to south-east. Starting at the coast of Ecuador, it crosses the mountains, runs through Argentina and ends in Patagonia on the Atlantic coast. This north-south direction, the distinguishing feature dominating the physical geography of the Americas, has been a determining factor in the history of its people, particularly of the original inhabitants.

The first Europeans to land in America were 'disorientated' by the disposition of the mountains; their first and almost sole attempt was to try to cross the whole width of the continent, but they encountered innumerable difficulties. On arrival they moved along the coast trying to get through the successive obstacles which faced them in the hinterland. When they had penetrated into the interior of the continent their chief aim was to push farther west, to the sea. This was particularly the case in North America, where the advance towards the Far West was a dominating feature of the first two centuries' history, and resulted in the formation of countries following broad east-to-west bands. Such are Canada, the United States and Mexico.

South America was not affected so strongly by this preoccupation with the West. Approaching the continent from the north and following the routes previously used by the Indians in their southward migrations, the Iberian newcomers advanced from Cartago to Lima, then followed the Andes towards Cordoba, and later towards Buenos Aires, thus creating the curious 'Camino del Peru', which crosses Latin America from north to south.

In both North and South America the Europeans arrived in the east, and the eastern seaboard soon became the most densely populated, the best developed and most civilised. There the 'new countries' were established: New England, New France, New Holland, New Spain, New Granada, New Scotland.

It was from the Atlantic seaboard that the New World's rapid evolution began. In less than four hundred years the population has increased from about 10 million to more than 300 million, of which about 30 million are Indians, 40 million Negroes and 2 million Asians. Even so, though it occupies 31 per cent of the total land above sea level, the American continent contains less than 13 per cent of the world's population.

The Far East — China, Japan and Korea — contains more than 985 million inhabitants: a third of the world's population or more than double that of the Far West on less than one twelfth of the land area. This population is settled farther south than that of the West, which is concentrated in the temperate areas; it inclines more towards the tropics and is associated with the climate of monsoons, where heat and humidity are closely linked and assure dense vegetation. It is, above all, a population inhabiting alluvial plains and even deltas. The basic food crop is rice, a plant which thrives in marshes. The rôle of domestic animals here is slight. There are no pasture lands and so no sheep; most of the cattle are oxen used for work in the paddy fields; pigs, poultry and fish, on the other hand, are of great importance, breaking the monotony of a diet which tends to be heavily vegetarian.

The growth of population is here the most rapid in the world. China's population alone rises by 12 million annually, more than half the total annual world increase. Japan sought the solution to its excess population problem by military expansion, but this brought only disaster. China, learning from experiments in demographic control made among the Soviet proletariat, adapted and applied them to its own, chiefly peasant, population, but doctrinal anomalies inherent in such control in a Marxist state made it hesitate in their use.

Variety, then, is the principal characteristic of the lands around the Pacific and here human effort and experiment can be observed in equal diversity.

FAR EASTERN ASIA

# JAPAN

Situated at the eastern edge of Asia, Japan is both a land's end and a crossroads. Confucianism and Taoism were introduced in the days of antiquity; Buddhism, as interpreted by China, found its way there in the Middle Ages, and the influence of Chinese civilisation reached its eastward boundary there. From prehistory onwards, through Korea and the Ryukyu, immigrant peoples brought with them the civilisations that were to give birth to that of Japan. Since the nineteenth century, under the economic influences of the West, the country has been the meeting-place of all the cultures of the world.

After a period of attempted expansion on the continental mainland and in the islands of the south, the present state of Japan (142,728 square miles) is now reduced to the original territory. The principal islands, from north to south, are Hokkaido, Honshu, Shikoku and Kyushu, surrounded by smaller islands including Sado, Awaji and the Goto archipelago. Barely a hundred years old in its modern form, this empire is sensitive to the smallest fluctuations in the international situation.

Japan's economic needs are largely dependent on her neighbours, and this helps in part to explain certain political events and reactions.

## PHYSICAL STRUCTURE AND FEATURES

*Old non-volcanic ranges.* The structure of Japan is the result of Alpo-Himalayan flexures rising at the edge of the ocean-deep of the Pacific, from the Malay archipelago to Taiwan (Formosa), from Taiwan to the Japanese archipelago and thence to the Kurils.

In mid-Palaeozoic time the old continental platform became folded, producing undulations in the form of arcs of more or less concentric circles, and the crests of the waves constituted the mountain ranges of China, Korea and Japan. These folds, submerged at the end of the Palaeozoic, faulted again during the Mesozoic and the Tertiary periods, compressing and dislocating the formations constituting the alternately exposed and submerged subsoil of present-day Japan. In the centre of this complex, transverse tectonic rifts furrow the island of Honshu near the meridian of Mount Fuji. Here the loftiest group of Japan's mountains is situated. At the edge of the folded ranges, weak zones have enabled volcanoes to pierce the earth's crust.

Lying in a northeast to south-west direction, and running from Kamchatka to South China, are the arc of the Kurils, the arc of Honshu and the arc of the Ryukyu. A central line of fracturing, running first along the east side of these ranges, then to the south of them and finally into the Inland Sea, has produced a series of narrow plains and minute basins.

*A ring of volcanoes.* These volcanoes seldom exceed 9,200 feet except in the middle of Honshu. The massif known as the Japanese Alps, however, contains the volcanoes Ontake (10,049 feet), Norikura (9,928 feet), Hodaka (10,465 feet) and Yari (10,433 feet); Mount Fuji (12,388 feet) rises on the fringe of the Tokyo plain, with Mount Asama (8,179 feet and

very active). Mount Fuji, which can be seen from Tokyo on a clear day, has a regular conical shape and the snows on its summit assume various hues—grey, horizon blue, mauve and gold. It has been quiescent since 1709, but a few volcanoes are still active.

Mountains and hills cover most of the country, but alluvial Quaternary plains near the sea offer favourable sites for urban centres. The largest of them, that of Tokyo, has an irregular surface and is approximately 3,860 square miles in extent. The cities of Hokkaido, Sendai, Nagoya, Osaka and Nagasaki are enclosed between low, steeply scarped mountain masses. In many places the lofty cliffs of the rias dip straight into the sea.

The narrowness of the plains allows the streams to flow unchecked, and they join the sea without attaining the breadth of a river. The Shinano, in Honshu, is 229 miles long, and the Tone 200 miles; the Ishikari, in Hokkaido, is 211 miles long.

In the mountain regions waters born of the rains

Showa Shinzan, an active volcano in Hokkaido. There are still fifty-eight active volcanoes in Japan. Showa Shinzan was formed suddenly in 1944.

Fishing for river-smelt with trained cormorants on the River Nagara (Gifu). This ancient form of fishing is practised by torchlight from May to October. Each boat is manned by a crew of four, with the master in the bows, in traditional dress, directing his four birds.

and melting snows rush from the summits in rapid torrents, breaking into superb cascades, or coming to rest in mountain-girt lakes such as Inawashiro (Honshu) and Biwa (north-east of Kyoto).

The still unstable land is subject to frequent shocks caused by landslides, eruptions, and earthquakes. The most violent earth movement of this century, that of 1923, which convulsed the regions of Tokyo and Yokohama, claimed 100,000 victims and destroyed 370,000 houses, partly by subsidence and partly by fire. In the face of these catastrophes, which are still almost unpredictable, man is powerless. In order to minimise, if not to prevent, the havoc the Japanese build small wooden houses that are light and flexible, and larger buildings are constructed of reinforced concrete which in the event of an earthquake shift position but do not collapse. Seismographic stations register on average 151 shocks a year at Kumamoto, 240 at Nagoya, and 516 at Gifu. Many of these pass unnoticed except by sensitive recording apparatus, but the remainder are more or less perceptible to the population.

*Monsoons and temperature.* Japan, extending from the 30th to the 45th parallel off the mainland of Asia, belongs partly to the subtropical, partly to the temperate, zone and is subject to monsoon influence.

A warm ocean current from the north equatorial current washes Taiwan and divides off Kyushu, one branch running along the east coast and mingling with the waters round the Kurils, the other flowing into the Sea of Japan, rejoining the first in summer by the Straits of La Pérouse and in winter by the Straits of Tsugari. A cold current flows south from Kamchatka; in winter the two meet at the 37th parallel.

From September onwards the monsoon, blowing from the north-west to the south-east, spreads cold air from the continent over the whole country, and precipitates rain in autumn and snow in winter. In Hokkaido and the north-west quarter of Honshu many villages lie under snow from December to March. In April the wind changes: the monsoon comes from the oceans — from the south in the Pacific, from the east in the Sea of Japan. This brings rain to the southern half of Japan and precipitation is also heavy along the Pacific coast.

Rainfall is lower in the regions beyond the mountains. On the side facing the Sea of Japan precipitation is greater in autumn and winter, while on the other side the land is flooded during the rainy season from mid-June to mid-July. Precipitation amounts to 61 inches at Tokyo (2 inches in January, 6 in June, 9 in September); Niigata, exposed to the sea of Japan, has 71 inches of rain annually (9 inches in December, 5 in June, 7 in September). Hokkaido is the driest of the islands: at Sapporo the average is little more than 39 inches a year. Rainfall is high in September because of the cyclonic depressions, which usually reach Japan by way of the south-east coast. The havoc they cause every year is extensive, sometimes endangering the crops of a whole region and ravaging the ricefields at harvest time.

Temperatures, too, vary under the influence of the monsoon. Tokyo, in the same latitude as Algiers, has a mean temperature of 3°C. (39°F.) in January. In the Japanese Alps, around Matsumoto, a minimum temperature of −24.8°C. (−12.6°F.) was recorded in 1900. In summer regional temperature differences are generally less marked, the wet monsoon's range of influence being considerably more extensive: in August, 25.7°C. (78°F.) is the mean at Tokyo, and 26.8°C. (81°F.) at Matsumoto.

*Richness of vegetation.* Vegetation is extraordinarily rich in these islands of diverse climates. In the extreme south it resembles that of the tropical zone; it is subtropical as far as the 37th parallel, and temperate as far as Hokkaido, where the boreal zone begins.

Twenty-eight species of trees have been identified in the Bay of Kagoshima, where sugar-cane — an annual crop elsewhere in Japan — is productive over a period of five years. The subtropical zone produces tall oaks with evergreen leaves, camellias over thirty feet high, orchids, wistarias climbing to 100 feet, conifers of every sort, bamboos and deciduous trees, including oak and hornbeam. The two last are also found in the temperate zone, along with other deciduous trees. Farther north firs and larch take over.

Forests cover 66 per cent of the land, a total area of over 64 million acres. The State forests (31 per cent), though difficult to exploit, constitute the most valuable reserve. Deforestation during the Second World War has produced some alarming after-effects, especially as the loss of southern Sakhalin deprived Japan of a very rich reserve of timber. A reforestation plan by the Government was carried out and privately. The vegetation is safeguarded by the humidity of the climate, which is subject alternately to tropical and continental influence.

Cotton is cultivated, but its total yield is very low; and so is that of sugar-cane, which is grown as far as the 35th parallel. There are no ricefields beyond the middle of Hokkaido. Rice, barley and potatoes are cultivated up to an altitude of 4,000 feet, and buckwheat up to 5,000 feet.

## THE JAPANESE PEOPLE

Some ethnologists believe the Ainu are the last representatives of the people who inhabited Japan before the Christian era. The Ainu now live in the island of Hokkaido, grouped by tribes. The men are hairy, and the women, dressed much like their husbands, tattoo moustaches on their upper lip. The ancestors of the Ainu were driven towards the north by conquering invaders.

Were these ancestors 'carriers' of Neolithic culture, thought to have been introduced here at the end of the third millennium before our era? Drawings engraved on types of bronze bells of the Yayoi culture represent houses built on piles — like those of Malaya — and Japanese boats of prehistory resemble those of Polynesia, so that in fact a mixture of cultures must have existed at a very early date. Communication with the continent through Korea was continuous. The archipelago was probably later invaded by tribes coming from the mainland of Asia and occupying the islands from the west. From the island of Kyushu and the western part of Honshu they may have advanced towards the east by way of the Inland Sea.

The origins of the Japanese language are no better known than those of its culture. Basically, the language is related to the Uralo-Altaic group; we can only suppose that it derived from the same mother-tongue as Korean, Mongol and even Turkish, with a contribution from Austronesian languages. In the sixth century A.D. the Japanese adopted the Chinese script.

*Brief history.* The recorded history of Japan begins with the introduction of Buddhism in A.D. 538. At that date an emperor had his residence in the neighbourhood of Nara, and a brilliant civilisation soon flourished under the impulse of the new faith.

In 794 the Emperor settled at Kyoto, which remained the capital for more than ten centuries. Japan had by that time become an autonomous country. Feudal authorities were established in the provinces, and in the twelfth century the effective government was set up at Kamakura, 31 miles from Tokyo. A sort of antagonism grew up between the eastern and western provinces. In the fourteenth century the administrative capital joined the imperial capital.

When, in the middle of the sixteenth century, the Spanish and Portuguese landed in Japan they found it in a state of feudal war. In the seventeenth century Tokugawa Ieyasu established himself at Yedo, now Tokyo, and founded a dynasty of governors which held sway for two and a half centuries and unified Japan. The port of Nagasaki alone remained open to foreign trade, and only Dutch and Chinese ships were allowed to enter it. From 1638 to 1853 Japan remained almost closed to the outside world, mainly for fear of the political intentions of Christian settlers.

In 1853 Commodore Perry, commissioned by the President of the United States, arrived to force the gates of the country. Men of learning set about widening their knowledge, and were not long in laying the foundation of modern science in Japan. The influx of foreign goods created a serious economic crisis, and modern industry became an urgent necessity. Finally, dissatisfaction with the rule of the Tokugawas ended in the revolt of the western provinces. In 1868 this drove the Emperor into Yedo, known from then on as Tokyo (capital of the East), and united the imperial and administrative capitals.

For nearly half a century Japan laboured to modernise itself. A constitution was promulgated; the Emperor was given the assistance of a cabinet and a parliament; railroads were built and factories began turning out highly finished machinery. Complete economic independence was the declared aim of military expansion.

In 1895 Japan triumphed over China, depriving the latter of Formosa. In 1905 it defeated Russia and acquired Kwantung, at the end of the Liaotung peninsula, and the southern half of Sakhalin. In 1910 it annexed Korea. Finally, in 1914, it entered the world conflict as an ally of the great economic powers, Great Britain, France and the United States. Important Pacific archipelagos were placed under Japanese mandate. Having made Manchuria a semi-colony, it engaged in war against China in 1937, and was led to ally herself with Germany and Italy in World War II. In the course of a few months it had occupied Hong Kong, Indochina, Malaya, Indonesia and the Philippines. From 1943 onwards it was forced to retreat and on the 6th August 1945 the first atomic bomb exploded over Hiroshima; the second, three

days later, over Nagasaki; and on August 15, 1945 Japan capitulated. The American occupation lasted seven years and a programme of radical social and political reform was initiated. In addition to a new constitution, the American administration showed enlightened benevolence in starting a programme of land reform and industrial organisation (including legalisation of trade unions) which enabled stability to be established. By the Treaty of San Francisco, Japan was dispossessed of all its colonies, and even of the islands of Bonin and Ryukyu and the Kuril Islands. Bonin and Ryukyu were placed under the administration of the United States; the Kuril Islands are now under the control of the Soviet Union.

Thus, after a phase of expansion, Japan is now smaller than it was in the middle of the nineteenth century, at the time of Commodore Perry's visit. At the present day it is faced with economic problems in a natural framework little different from the one it knew before it opened its gates to the West, though under very different conditions.

A farmer of typical Japanese stock. The origins of the Japanese people are obscure: some ethnologists think that the hairy Ainu tribe are the last representatives of the pre-Christian era people of Japan; but a mixture of cultures, and therefore of races, existed at a very early date.

*Over-population.* From the eighteenth century to the middle of the nineteenth, the Japanese population remained stable, with a total of about 39 million inhabitants. The introduction of modern hygiene and propaganda in favour of births helped to bring about a population increase, slow at first, then rapid, but lower since 1950. At the end of the Second World War, repatriation and demobilisation brought back soldiers and civilians who had served overseas. Further progress in hygiene, inspired by the American occupation, resulted in a decrease in infant mortality and an increase in the expectation of life. The average life span in Japan today is sixty-one years, as against forty-eight in 1935-36.

There are now over 98 million Japanese in the islands, and since the end of the Second World War the Government has been faced with the problems arising from over-population. Contraceptive methods introduced towards 1920 were much more readily adopted in 1945. The Government takes an active part in propaganda in favour of birth control, and abortion has become legal under certain specified conditions. The population increase has been reduced for the moment, but if the equally big drop in mortality is taken into account a general ageing of the population is to be feared.

At present the population density over the whole country is 668 per square mile. Over-population in times when industry was under-developed created a pattern of low wages and under-employment. The Japanese worker still tends to be concerned with job security, but with the recovery of the economy labour has become scarce and in the three years 1962-5 the level of wages rose by an average of 10 per cent.

## AGRICULTURAL AND ECONOMIC ACTIVITY

*A gardening agriculture.* Agriculture in Japan is classically regarded as a gardening job, a term that aptly reflects the minute subdivision of the fields and the maximum utilisation of every scrap of earth to which the Japanese farmer must resort in his struggle with the capricious climate, the irregularities of the ground and the scarcity of land.

The northern limit of rice cultivation lies in Hokkaido, where the soil produces only one crop a year. Winter crops cannot be grown in the extreme north of Honshu, but in the rest of the island two harvests can be reaped in each year, while three harvests are reaped annually in Kyushu and Shikoku.

A heavy total rainfall in the course of a year does not spare Japan from occasional drought. Reserves of water are laid on to meet this difficulty, and some 95 per cent of the ricefields are maintained by means of artificial ponds.

There is also a danger of flooding. The rainy season usually coincides with the transplanting of the seedling rice, and may hamper it. The typhoons occur during the harvest minth, in September, and sometimes cause serious damage. Apart from this usually very localised bad weather, the climate is favourable to agriculture, except in Hokkaido, where fog makes cultivation almost impossible on the Pacific coast and on the coast of the Sea of Okhotsk.

Immense quantities of natural and artificial fertilizers are required to prevent the soil from becoming exhausted. In addition, 18 per cent of the arable land is situated on slopes of more than 15 degrees, and the rain may carry away the manure from the tilled hillsides. The Japanese farmer is therefore obliged to dig drains and build terraces in order to prevent this. At the end of the spring the women, bare-foot in the water, start planting out the seedling rice, a delicate task demanding hours of exhausting work. Direct seeding is, however, being introduced.

*The problem of land allocation.* Despite the national rise the general increase in population chiefly affects the towns. The rural working population was 80 per cent of the total working population in 1870; at present it represents 25 per cent. The average size of families is higher in the country areas than in the towns.

The traditional type of farming is based on the family, and a farm may be run by three generations of workers. For this reason, when there is no longer room for them at home, the young people go off to the towns.

This migration effectively destroys the age balance in the structure of the rural population for there is little movement among the older people and 50 per cent of the men over sixty work in the fields. Only a few families employ agricultural labourers permanently, or hire them by the job or for a season.

The average size of the holdings cultivated by a single family has altered during the last 25 years. Before 1938, families owning 2½ to 5 acres were in the majority; from 1941 onwards the average size of holdings showed a continuous decrease. Today the average size holding in Japan is of less than 2½ acres, but farms of 20 acres are to be found in Hokkaido. The average area per farm is about a quarter of the average in Thailand, about one-sixth of that in Germany and about one-ninetieth of that in the United States.

Since the 1950 land reforms 62 per cent of the farming families own their farms, 5 per cent are tenants, and 33 per cent have part-owner, part-tenant status.

*Map opposite. Top:* Japan, showing the chief volcanoes, volcanic areas and the direction in which the chains are folded. *Bottom:* Agriculture and fishing in Japan. Rice is grown from Hokkaido to Kyushu, but the map shows how yields vary according to district. Fishing is carried on actively everywhere; but the distribution of areas where fish is locally consumed, exported, or imported can be seen to be determined by population distribution. *(see map page 510).*

Terraced ricefields. Only a small part of the Japanese soil is cultivable. This is a striking example of the stepped fields wrested from the mountainside.

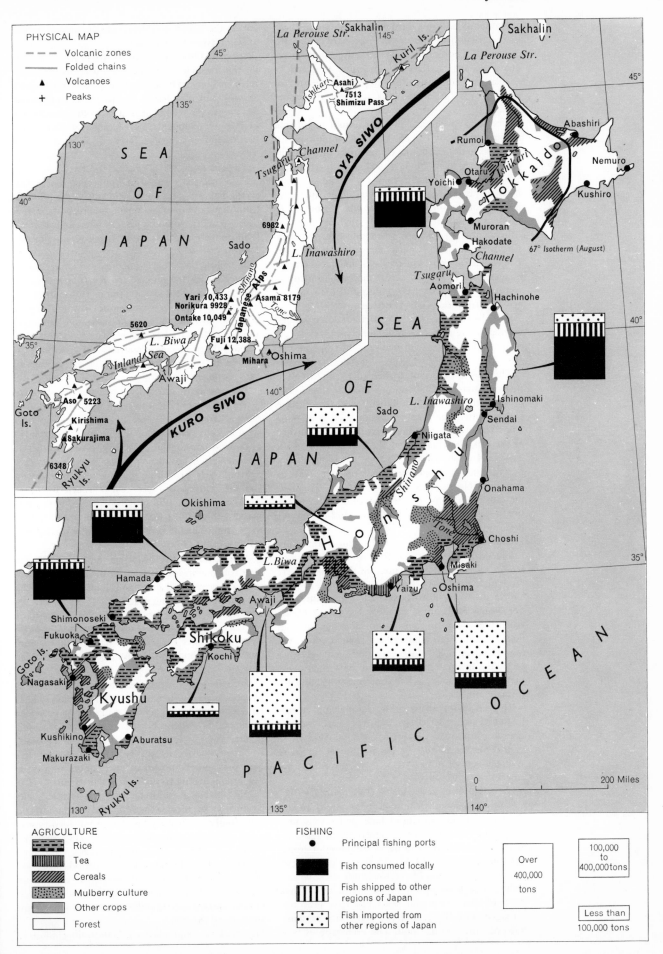

PHYSICAL MAP
- - - Volcanic zones
——— Folded chains
▲ Volcanoes
+ Peaks

SEA OF JAPAN

OYA SIWO

KURO SIWO

Sakhalin
La Perouse Str.
Kuril Is.

Ishikari
Asahi
7513
Shimizu Pass

6982▲

Sado

L. Inawashiro

Yari 10,433
Norikura 9928
Ontake 10,049
Japanese Alps
Asama 8179
Shinano
Tone
Fuji 12,388
Mihara

5620

L. Biwa
Inland Sea
Awaji

Aso 5223
Kirishima
Sakurajima

6348
Ryukyu Is.

Goto Is.

Oshima

Hokkaido
Rumoi
Abashiri
Otaru
Yoichi
Nemuro
Ishikari
Kushiro
Muroran
Hakodate
67° Isotherm (August)
Channel
Tsugaru
Aomori
Hachinohe

SEA

OF

JAPAN

L. Inawashiro
Ishinomaki
Sendai
Niigata
Shinano
Onahama
Tone
Choshi
Misaki
Yaizu
Oshima

Honshu

Okishima

L. Biwa

Hamada
Awaji

Shimonoseki
Fukuoka
Shikoku
Kochi
Goto Is.
Nagasaki
Kyushu
Kushikino
Aburatsu
Makurazaki

PACIFIC OCEAN

Ryukyu Is.

0 ——— 200 Miles

AGRICULTURE
▨ Rice
▥ Tea
▧ Cereals
▦ Mulberry culture
▩ Other crops
☐ Forest

FISHING
● Principal fishing ports
■ Fish consumed locally
▥ Fish shipped to other regions of Japan
⠿ Fish imported from other regions of Japan

Over 400,000 tons
100,000 to 400,000 tons
Less than 100,000 tons

Rather more than a third of the rural families keep their agricultural produce for their own use; the others sell a portion of their harvests. About three-quarters have at least one member engaged in ancillary or non-agricultural work—in forestry or fishing, or as an artisan—to augment the scanty resources.

The total revenue of the agricultural population amounts to about 13 per cent of the total national revenue, but with the development of industry the proportion is likely to decrease, especially as there is now little land left uncultivated.

*Importance of rice cultivation.* Arable land occupies 16.4 per cent of the surface of Japan, which amounts to about 14 million acres. It is obvious that the cultivated area could not be expanded in the same proportion as the steadily increasing population. Between 1922 and 1942 the land under cultivation increased to 14,826,500 acres; the establishment of factories and military bases reduced it to 12,264,650 acres in 1946, though it increased again later.

The Japanese have two agricultural techniques, corresponding to two radically different types of cultivation: that of rice plantations and that of rice fields.

There are three sorts of rice fields in Japan: 'dry' (the surface watered only by rain), which are found only in very small areas on hillsides, 'wet' (the surface always wetter than the surrounding soil), and 'semi-wet'. The water level differs according to the quality of the soil, the climate and the kind of seed used. The yield of the ricefields varies according to the mean regional temperature, but 10 per cent of those capable of yielding two harvests are used for only one. Some of the best land for growing rice is found in Niigata Prefecture and Yamagata Prefecture.

Crops are grown on a rotational system—commonly upland rice, wheat or barley, soya beans or rice wheat, sweet or white potatoes. In the cold districts crops such as pulses, buckwheat and millet are grown, and in the warm districts vegetables are cultivated. Sometimes fields are laid fallow for ten to fifteen years after three or four years' successive sowing. Fruit trees in large numbers are planted round the towns and in fields that cannot be used for other purposes. In contrast, cultivation near the towns may produce as many as five vegetable crops annually from the same field.

There is increased use of agricultural machinery. In 1960, 1,123,787 electric motors were used as against 956,100 in 1955; 1,698,985 oil engines as against 642,500 in 1950; 2,475,768 power threshers as against 828,000 in 1950; and 517,334 power tractors as against 13,240 in 1950.

Natural manure is still widely used. Chemical fertilizers most in demand are sulphate of ammonia, super-phosphate of lime, nitrate of lime, and soya waste. The Japanese Government is careful to encourage technical progress and the rational distrubution of crops, and during the Second World War it encouraged intensive cultivation of basic foodstuffs: rice, wheat, barley, soya beans, peas, broad beans, tubers and sweet potatoes. Fruit and vegetables have been encouraged since the end of the war. Rice remains, however, the essential food. The Prefecture of Nii-gata is the largest producer, with an annual harvest averaging over 800,000 tons.

*Other crops.* Other cereals are grown in winter, mostly in the ricefields. During the war the Government encouraged the cultivation of sweet potatoes for alcohol, and production was technically improved. Soya is grown in large quantities for the manufacture of various condiments, a food called *tofu* (fermented beans) and soya jelly. Soya fields now occupy 735,000 acres.

The chief vegetables of Japan are the *dikon, Colocasia antiquorum,* egg-plant, pumpkin, cucumber, carrot, hakusai, leek, onion, and salsify; the principal fruits mandarin oranges, apples, grapes, pears, grapefruit, peaches, plums, persimmons and loquats. Fruit and vegetable growing is encouraged in city suburbs.

Sericulture suffered from the food drive during the war. With an index of 100 for 1935 the figures for 1947 were: field area 30, number of workers 43, harvest of cocoons 17. However the Government gave help to farmers in re-establishing the industry, and today Japan takes second place only to China among silk producing countries of the world. Production of cocoons has risen from 53,478 tons in 1947 to 109,066 tons in 1962.

Tea, an important export before the war, declined sharply after it. The tea-growing area, halved during the war, rose from 75,000 acres in 1952 to 120,000 acres in 1963; production rose from 15,150 tons in 1952 to 81,000 tons in 1963. Exports are, however, considerably below their pre-war level. Ninety-five per cent of the processing of crude tea is mechanised and the remaining 5 per cent is rolled by hand. Tobacco production in 1963 was 157,000 tons, compared with the 1934-6 average annual production of 63,700 tons. The 1962 production of colza was 246,800 tons, as against 117,000 before the war.

Agricultural output fell after the Second World War reaching its lowest point in 1953-54. Since then it has recovered, and although still insufficient for the people's needs it is rising steadily.

*Development of stock-breeding.* The introduction of foreign breeds of cattle has greatly improved the quality of meat; since 1945, farmers have begun to combine cattle-farming with raising crops as a regular measure.

Since the beginning of the century, stock-breeding has been most highly developed in Hokkaido, which raises horses and cows, and is Japan's largest producer of cheese. Elsewhere, horses, oxen, cows, pigs and poultry are now bred, and meat from the region of Kobe is noted for its quality. Milk production has been reorganised and urban distribution improved. Egg production meets domestic requirements.

The demand for meat and milk is increasing, and production of meat and milk is expected to rise accordingly. In 1960 the number of milch cows was 1,002,000 as against 421,000 in 1955, and the number of pigs in 1962 was 3,994,000 as against 825,000 in 1955. During the same period, however, numbers of beef cattle and sheep fell: there were 2,320,000 beef cattle in 1962 as opposed to 2,636,000 in 1955, and the corresponding figures for sheep were 504,000 and 784,000.

*Importance of the fishing industry.* In the fishing industry, one of its most important resources, Japan met with serious obstacles after the end of the war. The international situation barred the country from the waters of the North Pacific, China, the Philippines and Indochina. As a result of agreements, however, it has now obtained a more extensive sphere of operation and has resumed its place as the greatest fishing country in the world. In 1963 it had nearly 400,000 fishing boats, many large, modern and efficient. Japan has ships engaged in whaling expeditions in the Antartic, and factory ships employed in packing crabs and other shellfish are in general use. Fishing technology and deep-sea fishing have been developed by big capital enterprises, which have also helped with capital and advice to develop fisheries in some countries of South-East Asia and South America.

As Japan is surrounded by two marine currents local fisheries supply a great variety of fish, but the Japanese fleet operates throughout the world: not only in the North and South Pacific, but also in the North Atlantic, the Indian Ocean, the Antarctic Ocean and, under regulations agreed with the Soviet Union, in restricted parts of the north-west Pacific.

Fish is the essential protein element in Japanese daily food, but fishermen make up barely 2 per cent of the working population; livestock is in short supply because grazing land is scarce and 20 per cent of domestic needs for agricultural produce must be imported. The Japanese look to industry for the development of foreign trade.

*Problem of energy. Labour situation.* Japan, albeit a great economic power since the First World War, lacks the mineral sources of energy needed to feed its industries. It is still prospecting for them, after the setback to territorial expansion, and trying above all to exploit hydraulic energy to the full.

Its untapped reserves of coal are estimated at 21,000 millions tons, but only a quarter of this is thought to be workable. The seams are generally scattered, thin and heavily faulted. The galleries in the mines are often steeply inclined and some are actully vertical. Rich coal measures are rare. Intensive rationalisation had reduced the number of mines from 850 to 337 by 1963. The large mines of Kyushu and Hokkaido are farther from the great industrial centres of Tokyo and Osaka than those of Honshu, north of the plain of Tokyo, and Yamaguchi in the extreme west of the island. Coal production in 1962 reached 54,399,000 tons, an increase over pre-war totals.

The cardinal problem in the coal industry is the marked rise in price (though power stations provide a ready market). Japanese coal is the dearest in the world market: the coal companies were in debt through having to satisfy the demands of the miners working in very difficult conditions. The closure of inefficient mines and increased mechanisation should solve the problem by 1967.

Reserves of mineral oil appear to be very small and home production reached only 898,000 kilolitres in 1963. Japan must therefore import petroleum. Refineries have been established near the ports, and handling and processing costs are being reduced to the minimum.

Great hopes are entertained of electric generating stations. Seasonal variation in the watercourses is very sudden and considerable, so that every hydro-electric generating station must be partnered by a steam generating station, to make up the fall in hydro-electric energy in the dry season. Technicians constantly draw attention to the fact that half the potential hydro-electric energy remains untapped, and the hopes of Japanese economists are now centred on the construction of new dams.

During the war the arms industry took precedence over all else, and at the same time many factories were destroyed. Since 1945 there has been a programme of rebuilding or readapting factories for peacetime industries, and production began to rise substantially from 1956.

Industrial works are grouped together in centres like Tokyo-Yokohama (the two cities are practically one, the first a centre of production and the second its port). This combination is repeated in the second largest city of Japan, Osaka-Kobe. Osaka, an immense business city of over 3 million inhabitants, is not unlike the industrial towns of the West. Nagoya, an old feudal city, is the third largest centre. Other

industrial towns crowd round the coal basins and electricity generating stations: Sapporo in Hokkaido, Niigata, Toyama, Kanazawa and Shimonoseki in Honshu, Nagasaki, Fukuoka and Kumamoto in Kyushu.

Out of a total of 96 million, Japan's working population in 1963 was 46 million, and of these only 12 million, or 26 per cent, were engaged in agriculture. Agriculture now accounts for only about 10 per cent of the gross national income. Many young people are therefore leaving agriculture for the cities and others, who stay, find side-jobs.

Increasingly industry is concentrated in large concerns which, at first with United States economic aid, have succeeded in building up since the war a highly sophisticated and efficient industry, which has been the chief contributor to the average annual increase of 9.6 per cent in the gross national product. Particularly important in this boom have been the heavy and chemical industries. With the rise in productivity wages have also risen, at first chiefly

Women in the flooded paddy fields transplant the rice seedlings. This is a delicate operation.

Grading coal at one of Japan's coal mines. Though theoretically reserves are quite large, few seams can be mined economically and those that are worked are generally thin and folded.

One of the many modern fishing ports along the Japanese shores. Japan is one of the great fishing nations of the world, for fish of all kinds from whales to shellfish abound in the nearby seas.
Many ships are fitted out as canning factories.

in the big industries and in centres like Tokyo and Osaka, but later also in medium and small enterprises. The workers' standard of living has also risen, in part because of fringe benefits, which may include housing, meals, transport, welfare and amusement facilities. Unemployment is negligible and in some industries a labour shortage is being felt, partly a result of increased mechanisation.

The workers' situation is thus in marked contrast to their condition before the war, and the trade union movement is far less militant than it was a decade ago, though union membership has risen to 35 per cent of the total working population.

*Industrial production; fluctuations.* Between the two World Wars, Japan succeeded in flooding the Asiatic market with her products. The second conflict brought fluctuations in maximum production, and after 1945 Japan had to overcome the depression that followed defeat, together with the loss of colonies—so important in the Asiatic world—and to satisfy the new demands of its workers. These problems were tackled

with great energy, assisted by economic aid from the United States.

Japan was quick to equip itself for heavy industry, but coal production is inadequate and Japanese iron ore is of bad quality, so that raw materials must be imported. Despite Japan's enormous success in the export field, exports amount to only 23 per cent of the gross national product (similar to the pre-war figure, but the home market has expanded greatly). In this situation productivity is obviously of the utmost importance and a modernisation plan was announced by the Government in 1950. The result was not only a rehabilitation of industries shattered by the war, but a complete modernisation and overhaul of practically all industrial plant.

Half the copper production depends on the recovery of used metal and imports of raw material. Production of non-ferrous metals is not large, and Japan is poor in precious metals. Zinc presents a mining problem peculiar to Japan, for the ore is usually mixed with cadmium, bismuth, and copper. But ways have been found to overcome this problem and by 1963 zinc production had risen to 282,000 tons.

Other metals produced in moderate quantity are lead, nickel, aluminium, tin, antimony, mercury, arsenic, cobalt, titanium, tungsten and molybdenum.

Japan is nearly self-sufficient in building stone, lime, dolomite, fire-clay, alabaster, silica, feldspar and gypsum. Kaolin, phosphorus, potash and bauxite must be imported.

Despite the high price of raw materials, the motor industry is making rapid strides, but cannot match the advance of shipbuilding. This is incontestably one of the most active and prosperous branches of Japanese production. The merchant fleet had increased to 9 million gross tons by 1964.

In the chemical industries, the production of fertilizers has increased substantially. Chemicals rank third after textiles and iron and steel. Fertilizers and printing ink are good export products.

Other important industries are cement —of which Japan furnishes 5.8 per cent of world production— dyes, gunpowder, paints, pharmaceutical products, and foodstuffs.

Production of chemical fibres also production of woollen goods is increasing. The sudden advance in textiles made of plastic materials is spectacular, but it must be remembered that before the war there was hardly any activity in this branch. Production in the cotton industry has not regained its pre-war level, owing to the loss of preferences in China. Competition from man-made fibres affects cotton as well as silk.

The silk industry ought to be the most highly developed of all, since Japan possesses all the raw material; but production, though rising, has not yet recovered since the war. Eighty-nine per cent of the silk output is exported raw, about half to the United States and the rest to Europe.

The current position of Japanese industry appears prosperous compared with that of 1945, and its expansion seems to be continuing. From 1961 to 1970 a doubling of the national income is foreseen.

*Survival of the artisan class.* Spinning mills, blast furnaces and factories look much the same in America, Europe and Asia; yet the Land of the Rising Sun still suggests miniature gardens, lacquered boxes, paper fans and dolls dressed in silk. Artisans still paint beautiful designs on silk; they still make wood carvings, and polish the eighteen coats of lacquer on the boxes that are a regional speciality.

The artisan class puts up a better resistance, perhaps, in Japan than in other countries of similar economic importance, owing to the simplicity of its daily life. For wear at home it will be long, no doubt, before the artisans give up their *getas*—the light wooden footwear held on by a strap of padded material; and the traditional furniture of paulownia or white sandalwood will continue to please their taste. After the war there was a revival in Japanese ceramics; the cups, dishes and vases of Seto and Kyoto are still the ornaments of Japanese homes, and they are finding a growing market in the United States and in many other parts of the world. The artisan class runs a risk of dying out slowly, in spite of the efforts being made by the exporters.

*Communications.* Lines of communication follow the coasts in general, because of the mountainous terrain.

Roads have been extensively improved of late, but most traffic still goes by the excellent rail system. Honshu and Kyushu are connected by an undersea tunnel and another is being built between Honshu and Hokkaido. The total length of the rail network amounts to about 17,450 miles, and more lines are electrified yearly. The majority of the lines is under State management; about 4,650 miles of the total belong to private companies.

Maritime transport is important, even in the interior. The Osaka-Kobe industrial centre depends on the transport system across the Inland Sea, which brings coal from Kyushu and Yamaguchi. Transport between Honshu and Hokkaido is also by water.

The two most important ports for all destinations are Yokohama and Kobe. On the Sea of Japan, Niigata has become a centre of the oil and natural gas industry and is developing as an industrial port, and industrial development at Tsuruga, where a second atomic power station is being built, affects all the surrounding area. Shimonoseki is about 75 miles from Korea, and Nagasaki, still playing the part it had in the sixteenth century, lies open to the seas of the south-west.

*Financial and commercial fluctuations.* Immediately after the Second World War the big family firms, known as *Zaibatsu*—financier castes—were dissolved. The three principal ones, Mitsubishi, Mitsui and Sumitomo, were reconstituted, but the old families were not allowed to buy up all the shares again. Japanese finances have now to seek a difficult balance between ineffectual dispersion and monopoly.

To avoid disaster, the Government froze banking accounts in 1946, and operated a forced exchange of spot cash by creating a 'new yen'. Deflationist procedures followed, to check the rise in monetary circulation, but as soon as industrial activity started again, inflation recommenced. Between 1946 and 1958 the national income rose from 361 to 8,449 billion yen, a nominal value nearly 24 times as great—but the actual value was only three times as great. The thorough rehabilitation of the Japanese economy, the extent of reinvestment and the increase in productivity showed clearly in the years 1959-62, when the average annual economic growth rate was 15.8 per cent; this brought a further rise in real income.

The Government hope that with the doubling of national income by 1970 average personal incomes will rise to the levels found in Western Europe.

Overseas trade is the key to Japan's future. Private transactions with foreign countries were authorised in 1947, and the 'Korean boom' brought a sudden improvement in foreign trade, which has steadily increased in volume ever since. With both imports and exports expanding, however, the problem has been to maintain a stable balance of payments. The situation deteriorated seriously in 1961, since when, under Government supervision, it has improved.

In 1964 Japan joined the OECD and accepted International Monetary Fund Article 8 nation status. Under the aegis of GATT Japan has also assumed the obligation to abolish import restrictions. Thus the problem confronting it now is how to push ahead with these commitments while maintaining a healthy balance of payments and preserving world confidence in the yen following the transfer to the open-system economy. Trade liberalisation brought a swift increase in

Shipyards at Nagasaki. Shipbuilding is one of the most vigorous and prosperous of the Japanese industries, and besides supplying the large home market accounts for a great proportion of the country's export revenue. Nagasaki is also a fishing and trading port.

imports in 1963, in response to a strong demand for consumer goods and foodstuffs, resulting from the rise in the standard of living. But while imports rose by 20 per cent, exports rose by only 11 per cent, which was near the average for the previous five years.

By far the most important trading partner is the United States. Imports from North American countries accounted in 1963 for 36 per cent of the total, followed by South-East Asian countries with 18 per cent, West Asian countries with 11 per cent and European countries with 9.9 per cent. There was a substantial increase in imports from non-industrial nations.

The principal imports are oil, raw cotton and raw wool, iron ore, lumber, coal, wheat, sugar and soybeans. The main exports are textiles, iron and steel, ships, clothes, fish and fish products, chemicals, light and heavy machinery and toys.

In the future, Japan hopes for increased access to the Chinese market, provided Peking does not insist on its rupture with Formosa. Finally, Japan has proposed the formation of a common market for South-East Asia, to facilitate transactions in the zone, but the scheme has not yet taken shape.

POLITICAL, CULTURAL AND RELIGIOUS LIFE. The notion of a Japan leading two separate lives, one traditional, the other modern, is out of date. The future history of Japan will be in line with the life of the rest of the world.

A new and improved Constitution drawn up on Western lines was introduced under the American occupation in 1946. The Emperor is now called 'Symbol of the Nation'. He receives a Parliamentary Allowance for the Imperial Household Expenses, and has no direct influence on the government.

The system of government is built around three bodies, on the American pattern. The Diet, representing the legislature, is composed of two chambers. The House of Representatives is elected by universal suffrage—women participating—with a mandate for four years. One half of the members of the House

of Councillors, elected for six years, is re-elected every three years. The functions of the Diet are the same as those of European parliaments. The executive is entrusted to a cabinet nominated by the Emperor at the designation of the Diet, the ministers being responsible to the chambers. The House of Representatives can demand their resignation by a vote of no confidence. There is one novelty in this Constitution: Japan has renounced the right to arm. It now possesses 'self-defence forces' composed of ground, marine and air forces.

Amendments to the Constitution are proposed by the Diet, and must be submitted to a referendum or approved at an election which is specially called by the Diet.

The highest juridical authority is vested in the Supreme Court, sitting in Tokyo, which consists of a president and fourteen judges. There are courts of appeal, regional courts, and 'family courts' to settle family disputes.

The administrative division of the country is very

Principal mines, industries, towns and rail routes in Japan. Some local sources of power, such as coal and oil, are inadequate and scattered, but numerous hydro-electric dams harness the watercourses, and large refineries have been established near ports. Note the areas of industrial concentration which coincide with the two major conurbations: Tokyo - Yokohama (over 11 million inhabitants) and Osaka - Kobe (over 4 million inhabitants).

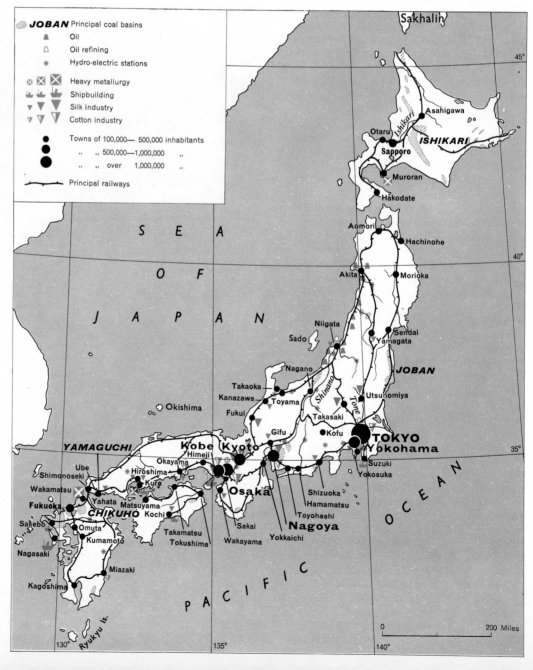

complex. Four regions have special treatment: Tokyo Prefecture, Kyoto, Osaka, and Hokkaido. Apart from these there are 46 prefectures. Within these prefectures there are certain cities, towns and villages considered as local entities.

For over twenty years the Japanese people, now sovereign for the first time, have been learning the ways of democracy. The population is kept well informed by big newspapers like the *Asahi*, the *Mainichi* and the *Yomiuri*, which have provincial editions. Japan has for many years had an exceptionally low illiteracy rate; peasants in the remotest regions read the newspapers daily, and most families have radio or television.

Yet the Japanese remains attached to his family tradition. Every little town celebrates the occasion of its annual temple festival. Everyday life is still very simple. As soon as he returns home, the worker sheds dungarees for kimono and eats his meal with wooden chopsticks.

However, the Japanese is sharply aware of scientific progress. Schooling is obligatory up to the age of fifteen and the Japanese usually shows great respect for knowledge in all spheres. Universities abound in the towns, but unlike those of Europe they do not represent any fixed level of education; the value of a diploma varies from one to another. The national universities enjoy the best reputation, together with certain privately owned ones like Waseda and Keio in Tokyo.

Buddhism is the major religion in Japan, with 55 million followers; but the Japanese lives in a sort of religious syncretism. He visits the Buddhist temple to commemorate the dead, and the Shintoist temple to get married; neither prevents him from celebrating Christmas. This medley is not the result of religious indifference; on the contrary, the most extravagant beliefs find the most enthusiastic response among the people.

After the war there was a considerable revival of Buddhism, which appears to be flourishing still. Shintoism, although undermined by nationalist propaganda during the war, is still practised by the masses. Protestant missions are making headway, but they are divided among themselves. The Roman Catholics, numerically weaker but with a centralised, hierarchical organisation, enjoy a more secure social position. Tokyo has been made an archbishopric and the number of native clergy has been increasing rapidly since 1945.

A SYNTHESIS OF CONTRADICTORY ELEMENTS. Japanese civilisation is based on a synthesis of opposing elements. The old life is still to be seen in the ancient templed city of Nara: the 'Pavilion of Dreams', recalling a regent of the seventh century; a statue of Maitreya in the Chugu-ji, one pensive hand touching a countenance of enigmatic serenity; and the gigantic Buddha of the Todai-ji. Yet Benedictine abbeys are perhaps just as untypical in our western civilisation as the Japanese temples, solitary retreats among the damp forests, mainly composed of giant Japanese cedars.

The wage-earner of Tokyo finds nothing incongruous in the contrast between the quiet of his suburban home and the noise of the business quarters. The capital's population increases enormously in the daytime, and during rush hours trains, trams, metropolitan railroads and buses are crowded like those of any Western city. Japanese office blocks are built in American style, and the Radio-Tokyo buildings are as much the pride of the people of Tokyo as the temple of Ueno or the Sojo-ji. The Imperial Palace, partly destroyed by fire during the war, and formerly the residence of the Tokugawas, is still surrounded by the moats of the feudal citadel, but the main bridge leading to it was built at the end of the nineteenth century to a design in European style. Tokyo has an area of 787 square miles; except in the business quarters the view is over low houses built of wood and plaster. But little by little these are being replaced by blocks of flats whose architects have combined Western methods with the traditional Japanese style.

This overall mixture is the result of the desire to be one of the great industrial nations, and of the innate capacity of assimilation, so typical of the Japanese people in general.

A bird's-eye view of the heart of Tokyo, showing the many tall buildings that have transformed the city. With a population of over ten million (one-tenth of the nation's total) Tokyo sprawls over an area of 787 square miles. It is the centre of the nation's politics, culture and communications.

Precision engineering is a booming sector of Japanese industry. Cameras and transistor radios have reached markets all over the world.

# KOREA

(See map page 515).
Agriculture, mining and industry in Korea. Cultivation is chiefly concentrated in the west; note the distribution of cotton and of the four principal cereals: rice, millet, barley and wheat. Relief and the harsh climate forbid the growing of rice in part of North Korea, which is more favourable to forests. Mineral resources are present in both North and South Korea but the mountainous areas of North Korea, with their many watercourses, have made it possible to install far more hydro-electric power stations than in South Korea. North and South Korea, separated by the 38th parallel, contrast sharply in their commercial traffic, that of the former being chiefly with China and the U.S.S.R. and that of South Korea being chiefly with Japan and the U.S.A.

Korea has lived in the orbit of China and Japan throughout its history and has been a bridge between the Asiatic continent and Japan. Its shores are flat and its estuaries deep on the western side: in the east the walls of its mountain ranges face Japan. It received the elements of its civilisation, its religion and its arts from China. It unsuccessfully resisted the Mongols in the thirteenth century and again the Japanese in the sixteenth. Until 1945 Korea remained a Japanese protectorate. Liberated by the outcome of the Second World War, it hoped at last to achieve independence. A line drawn at the 38th parallel between the zones of Russian and U.S. military occupation created instead two Koreas: North Korea (now the Democratic Republic of Korea) in September 1948, and South Korea (now called the Republic of Korea). In 1950 the South was attacked by the North. Not until 1953 after United Nations intervention was the boundary restored.

The distinction between the two does not correspond to a natural division of the country.

*A mountainous peninsula.* Dislocations occurred in Mesozoic times following on earlier foldings, and in the Tertiary and Quaternary eras, volcanic debris levelled the elevations and depressions towards the north, and formed the basaltic tablelands of the island of Cheju (Quelpart) in the south. Korea's mountain ranges run from south-west to north-east; the bordering islands are their outliers. Fractures and faults have indented them in a north-south direction. The north is dominated by the high Manchurian massif of the Changpai Shan, linked to the coastal chain of the Pukpollen by the Matollen. The peninsula itself is dominated by the Kimgan-san (Diamond Mountain).

From the heights of the Changpai Shan, forming the northern frontier of Korea, flow the Yalu and the Tyumen, one into the Yellow Sea, the other into the Sea of Japan, through the crystalline and basaltic soils of a cold, precipitous landscape. These rivers catch all the waters of the northern massif,

In this Korean village, the whole family helps with the silk-spinning. The cocoons are first boiled, then unwound. In North Korea, however, silk is giving way largely to artificial fibres.

and together have a high hydro-electric potential.

The western side of the peninsula contains three large plains. The Tae-dong waters the plain of Pyongyang. The Seoul Gap is the confluence of the Imjin and the Hang-gang. The third plain is that of the Kum-gang, between the massifs of the No-ren and the Cha-ren. These three 'plains' are broken by hills and escarpments; they form the demographic, agricultural and industrial centres of the country. In the south, the Naktong, the Am-gang, the Som-jin and the In-gang form basins in the coastal areas, and sheltered harbours like Pusan have been built.

*Monsoon influence.* In winter the continental mainland, which is colder than the ocean, brings the icy winds of the north-west. This winter monsoon, dry and cold, blows towards the sea and sweeps the whole country. The winds of the summer monsoon from the sea bring heat and humidity. This system is modified by cyclones caused when cold and warm waters meet off the southern tip of the peninsula. They are accompanied by violent rains, falling in spring and autumn. Typhoons, starting in the vicinity of the Marshall Islands, drive towards the continent along the line of the Equator, then curve round towards the north. At the end of the summer they assume hurricane force.

Although the annual average rainfall is 40 inches, the north, protected by the coastal range, receives only 27.5 inches a year. The south and south-east, on the other hand, exposed to the influence of the sea, enjoy a high annual precipitation falling mostly during the summer season which is very beneficial. However, the rains often bring devastating floods.

The coldest month is January, with a mean temperature of −21°C. (−6°F.) on the Upper Yalu and −2°C. (29°F.) at Pusan. In February and March the warmer weather brings the first cyclones. This is the peak of the snowy season in the north. Spring comes in April with the change in direction of the monsoons. Summer begins in June, and in July the true monsoon brings intense heat and humidity; rain, fog and mist spread over the country and grey clouds mask the mountains. In August, mean temperatures vary between 21°C. (70°F.) and 26°C. (79°F.). In September, violent storms herald the change of wind. The dry weather, of capital importance to the harvests, is broken by the autumn typhoons. At the beginning of October the winter monsoon brings dry weather again. In the south it may be still mild in December, when there is already snow in the extreme northern regions.

*Dense population.* The thirty-seven million inhabitants represent an average of about 435 persons to the square mile, but in the west and south, where half the population lives, density is about 800 to the square mile. Anthropologically, the Korean population has been homogeneous since the Neolithic Age, and belongs to the Koreano-Manchu Mongoloid group, part of the predominantly Austro-Asiatic family found from the archipelagos to Kamchatka. Shorter than the Chinese, with lighter eyes and skin, but thicker and softer hair, the Koreans are taller than the Japanese, with narrower noses, thinner lips and flatter faces.

There are sixty towns of more than 10,000 inhabitants, and only twelve cities of more than 100,000.

JAPAN: An industrial area of Tokyo

These—except for city-centres and some rebuilt towns in North Korea—are an untidy collection of little one-storey mud-houses with tiled or straw-thatched roofs held down by rope nets. Inside, an ingenious system of brick channels leads smoke from the hearth under the floor to escape through an outside vent. In this way, although lightly built, a Korean house resists extreme cold.

The largest cities are Pyongyang, the capital of North Korea; and in the South, Seoul the capital, Taegu, a great industrial centre, Pusan, the chief port, and Inchon. About 70 per cent of the people live in the country. The small urban population is mostly very poor, largely as a result of war.

The Korean language is thought to belong to the family of Altaic languages; the dialect of Seoul is the national language. Until the fifteenth century the Koreans used Chinese characters. In 1443 the present alphabetical script of twenty-four letters was adopted. *Richness of vegetation and fauna.* Korea has a very rich vegetation, due largely to the variety of its soil and climate.

North Korea exhibits the same type of landscape as north China. The mountains are covered with fir trees, often intermixed with birch, oak, aspen, and willow. Below the isotherm $-3°C.$ ($27°F.$), the forests are more like those of Japan, with evergreen broad-leaved oaks growing alongside camellias. Nearer the valleys bamboos grow to a height of thirty feet. In the plains the vegetation is ofetn subtropical or even tropical; crops include rice, kaoliang, maize and cotton, and large quantities of barley, wheat, millet, beans, potatoes and tobacco. The fruits most often grown are apples, pears, and peaches.

Large Manchurian tigers and smaller Korean tigers are still found on the northern frontier with Siberian leopards, black bears and wild boars. There are cranes everywhere, and storks, geese, and swans. Herons are found on the rice plantations, and the coasts swarm with gulls, cormorants, divers and auks. Korean waters provide a rich harvest of herring, cod, mackerel, anchovies, molluscs, crabs and shrimps. The fishermen often capture the fur seals of the Kurils, sea-lions and other seals, and whales.

*Mineral wealth and the problem of energy.* Mineral resources are chiefly found in North Korea. Iron deposits are evaluated at 1,000 million tons (at Musan, Chongchon and Hwangju). Mixed deposits contain zinc and lead, as well as silver, copper, platinum and arsenic. Copper is rather rare; but alumite reserves in the Pyongyang and Mokpo basins are estimated at about 70 million tons. Gold occurs in widely scattered deposits in both North and South Korea. Tungsten, molybdenum and nickel are extracted in the eastern and central regions. Magnesite constitutes a reserve of 33,500 million tons on the north-east coast. More than two-thirds of the coal reserves are located in North Korea. Hydro-electric power is also developed chiefly in the North.

Four-fifths of the electric energy produced in Korea is supplied by hydro-electric generating stations, giving 8 million kilowatts. There is still considerable undeveloped potential.

ECONOMIC ACTIVITY OF NORTH KOREA. There appears to be an industrial advantage in the North and an agricultural advantage in the South, but actually both

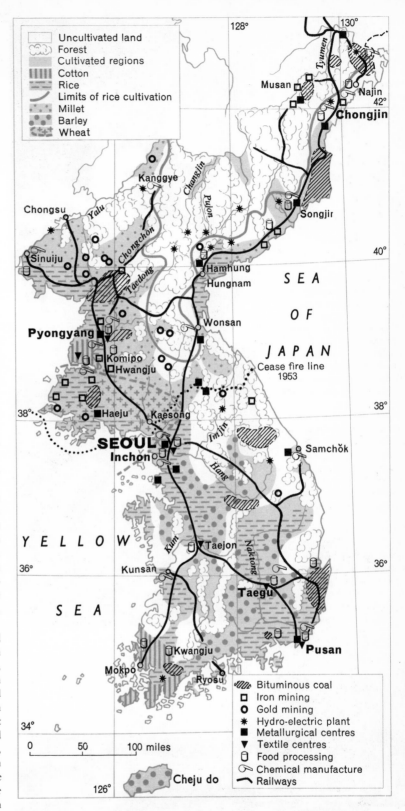

potentials are reduced by difficulties of exploitation, and of the two halves the South is decidedly the less favoured.

North Korea covers 56.5 per cent of Korea and has one-third of the population (about 200 inhabitants to the square mile). Cultivable zones are small, and less numerous than in the South—twenty-five per cent are allotted to rice, with a yield of 20 bushels an acre, against 27 bushels in the South. The figures

(See page 512.)

An old Korean dressed in the
traditional headgear and white
costume standing against
a typical landscape of rice fields.
Note the irrigation canal
bordered by a path and a few
trees, the hills rising abruptly
from the valley,
and the village at their foot.

*Opposite page:* A village in
South Korea. The land that
belonged to the Japanese
under the Empire has
been redistributed among
Korean families, with nearly
600,000 families allotted only 10
per cent of the cultivable land.
Irrigation difficulties, lack
of fertilizers, and storm damage
add to the difficulties
of farming, although the mild
climate makes for plentiful crops.

The Yungan chemical factory is
one of the many modern
industries which are rapidly
expanding in North Korea.
Industrial resources, notably iron
and other metals, coal and
hydro-electricity, are far richer
here than in South Korea.

New buildings in Pyongyang,
capital of North Korea, which
has been largely rebuilt since
the end of the Korean War.
Despite the dense population of
Korea there are relatively
few large cities and 70 per cent of
the people live in the countryside.

from Soviet authorities show an increase of 160,000
acres in cultivated land since the agrarian reform of
1946. Wheat is equally distributed in both zones, and
so are soya and buckwheat. The main crops grown
in the North are millet, oats, kaoliang, maize, beans,
potatoes and cotton. Almost all the fertilizer factories
started by the Japanese are here.

Collectivisation was begun in 1954. In spite of the
destruction wrought during the Korean War, farm
production is rising; half the fields were irrigated
and 95 per cent of ploughing mechanised by 1960; but
motive power on the farms has to be electricity rather
than fuel oil: North Korea has no known oil deposits.

North Korea produces 70 per cent of the country's
charcoal, has the only oil refinery, and possesses about
85 per cent of the total hydro-electric energy. It also
has a distinct advantage in industrial resources. Iron
and steel come from the North. Chemical industries
produce fertilizers, sulphate and phosphate of ammonia, superphosphate of lime, heavy oils and explosives. Seven out of eight cement works also
belong to this zone, and timber, paper and artificial
silk are additional assests.

The three-year development plan of 1953-56 and
the five-year plan of 1957-61 appear to have been
successful in the industrial as well as in the agricultural field. The 1961-67 plan gives priority to heavy
industry over agriculture. Mining, metal and chemical
industries are to be strengthened.

ECONOMIC LIFE OF SOUTH KOREA. South Korea has
an area of 38,452 square miles, or 45 per cent of the
country. Its population has risen from 15,870,000 to
26,300,000, giving a density of over 685 to the
square mile, largely due to an influx of about two
million refugees from North Korea and two million
Koreans repatriated from the former Japanese Empire.
The immigrants have flocked to the towns, creating
problems of food supply and hampering efforts to
raise the national standard of living.

After the agrarian reforms, the land that hitherto
belonged to the Japanese was distributed among
Korean families but, as a result, 587,974 families found
that they had been allotted only 10 per cent of the

# CHINA

cultivable land. Nearly three-quarters of the farms are less than 2½ acres in area. The milder climate makes the agricultural potential greater than that in the North. Rice can be harvested twice a year, and a good yield of oats, barley, sweet potatoes and American cotton is obtained. But farming is constantly threatened by irrigation difficulties, lack of fertilizers and damage by cyclones and typhoons. To relieve post-war destitution, American aid took the form of maize, rice and soya flour, which enabled agriculture to be restarted from 1945 onwards.

Mineral and industrial production is decidedly weaker in South Korea. There is little iron; a little coal is mined but only tungsten, gold and silver give a fair yield. The cutting of high-tension lines from the North has slowed down industrial activity, though by 1964 new hydro and thermal power plants were built to supply the current needed for the industrial centres already established. Production of machinery has dropped; that of textiles, footwear, metal goods, enamels, carbides, paper and soap is livelier.

Since the war great efforts have been made to broaden the base of the economy by increasing the production of minerals. Between 1954 and 1959, for instance, the output of anthracite coal increased fourfold; that of graphite increased sixfold; that of iron ore increased ninefold. Industries chiefly concerned with the production of consumer goods have expanded with American help, mainly in the form of industrial raw materials and equipment. South Korea, however, is still a debtor nation on a gigantic scale. In 1964 exports were equal to $120 million, while imports amounted to $404 million.

Communications are better than in the North, the rail centre of Seoul being on the south side of the 38th parallel. Maritime transport, although it has the advantage of good harbours, lacks ships

Trade exchanges are hampered by fluctuations in clearing prices, for the *won,* the monetary unit of Korea, is not accepted in the international market. Present data suggest, therefore, that the North could give Korea the economic balance of an independent state which she so badly needs.

The old Chinese geographers were content to think of China as the centre of the world; they called it 'Land of the Flowering Centre' (Chung-Hua). The Romans called it *Serica* (Land of Silk), and the people of the Middle Ages *Cathay* after a Chinese dynasty of Turkish origin. For a long time, Western geographers had no precise notion of its actual extent.

Modern China is one of the largest states in the world. From the northern frontier of Manchuria to the Gulf of Tonkin is as far as from Spain to Lapland; from the shores of the Pacific to the Pamirs is as far as from Paris to Moscow. With an area of nearly 4 million square miles, China is the most highly populated country in the world and, with more than 750 million inhabitants (excluding the population of Taiwan and the groups of Chinese that have emigrated to south-east Asia and the edges of the Pacific), has almost one-quarter of the world's population.

The People's Republic of China was proclaimed in October 1949. The various forms of political organisation that preceded it date back over thousands of years.

RELIEF, CLIMATE AND RIVERS. A rather sinuous line following the Great Khingan in the north-east, the edge of the Mongolian plateau east of the big loop of the Hwang-ho and the overhang of the Tibetan plateau above the Red Basin of Szechwan, ending with the Alpine ranges of western Yunnan at the end of the Himalayan undulations, separates two vast regional entities; their present appearance can easily be distinguished as the China of plains and hills, or East China, and the China of vast high-altitude tablelands, bordered or traversed by imposing mountain ranges. The China of interior ranges and tablelands is arid if not an actual desert, and very sparsely populated; the China of plains and hills, mostly well watered, is the traditional focus of concentration of the Chinese peasantry. The true Chinese (the Hans) are in the great majority in east and north-east China, whereas west China is chiefly inhabited by the peoples of the national minorities (Mongols, Tibetans, etc.).

*East China: plains and hills.* At the north-eastern extremity of the country (formerly Manchuria) lies a vast sedimentary basin, recently covered by fertile river deposits. It is drained towards the Amur by the Sungari and its tributaries, and towards the Gulf of Po-hai by the Laio. Surrounded by the Great Khingan to the west, the Little Khingan to the north, and by various ancient mountains to the east, it narrows in the south, and spreads out towards the north, which is its coldest part and the least favourable for traditional Chinese cultivation. In spite of their fertility, these 'black lands' of the province of Heilungkiang are only now being developed.

The greater part of north China consists of a vast alluvial plain built up by the Hwang-ho—a river characterised by its high silt content, violent seasonal fluctuations in volume and by recurrent and disastrous changes of course. In the south rises the Hwaiyang Shan and in the east the peninsula of Shantung, originally an island in the Yellow Sea, but now tied to the mainland by silt depositions from the Hwang.

Shangung itself, which reaches its highest point in the east in the sacred hill of Tai-Shan, includes several plains and basins.

The Great Plain is dominated in the west by a series of plateaus and stepped ranges (the plateaus of Shensi and Shansi, and the ranges of Utai Shan and Taihang Shan), covered with loess, which varies from 100 to 1,000 feet in thickness, in basins like that of the Hwai, and of Taiyuan. To the south is the long, massive chain of the Tsinlings, an extension of the immense Kunlun range.

Beyond the Yangtze-kiang, east China is still characterised by a succession of plains, hills and low mountains, less distinctly systematised than in the north. Three large basins, that of the lower Yangtze-kiang, the Red Basin in Szechwan, and the Si-kiang basin round Canton, are separated by complex networks of low hills. In the south-west, calcareous plateaus forming karst landscapes alternate with the groups of steep chains in Yunnan.

*West China: plateaus and high mountains.* These vast

A recently constructed canal in South China, built by members of a People's Commune. Good communications are sorely needed in China, one of the largest states in the world, with an area of nearly 4 million square miles and nearly one quarter of the world's population.

ranges and plateaus, thousands of miles long, are the result of slow geological transformations still at work; but the old, arid erosion has produced stony and sandy deserts in the depressed areas and extreme denudation of the mountains.

The tableland of Tibet rises to over 12,000 feet almost consistently. It is a mountainous zone with massive chains stretching fairly regularly from west to east; the principal chains are the Kunlun and the Altyn-Tagh, which bound Tibet in the north, and the Trans-Himalaya and Karakoram, which border it in the south. The ranges enclose a number of valleys and lakes. The largest of the valleys is occupied by the Upper Indus and the Upper Brahmaputra (or Tsangpo), and is the only region at all hospitable. The Tibetan ranges are turned towards the south at their eastern end by the insular shelf of south China; here, in western Yunnan and in Szechwan, a serried cluster of sharp peaks rises, separated by deep valleys (the difference in levels amounting sometimes to 10,000 feet), which form the upper course of the

great rivers of south-east Asia, the Irrawaddy, Salween, Mekong and Yangtze-kiang.

Lower plateaus lie to the north and east of Tibet. In Sinkiang they from two hollows separated by the Tien Shan: Dzungaria, the northern hollow, occupied by the Tarim and its tributaries, is asymmetrical. The Tarim follows the foot of the Tien Shan almost all the way. The arid climate creates the desert of Takla Makan. The Tien Shan (average height 15,000 feet) is very old, with massive outlines; it is terminated in the west by divergent secondary chains enclosing depressions like that of Turfan (900 feet below sea level).

China occupies only the eastern and southern edges of the Mongolian plateau or Gobi Desert. These sandy expanses, 3,000 to 6,000 feet high, are bordered to the south by the end of the Kunlun, here called Nan Shan, in the south-west by the Yinshan chain, which has forced the Hwang-ho to turn south at the top of its great loop, and in the east by the Great Khingan. The Ordos Plateau, surrounded on three sides by the loop of the Hwang-ho, joins the Gobi plateau and the loess plateaus of east China.

*A climate of contrasts.* From November to February the Siberian-Mongolian anticyclone extends towards the south-east and cold air (the winter monsoon) flows in this direction. From March to May, while the tropical Pacific anticyclone recedes, the Siberian anticyclone continues to influence north China. Depressions pass along the 'front' of Siberian polar air, producing rain in the basin of the Yangtze-kiang and in south China. From June to October the continental high pressures die out except in the south-west and in Tibet. The tropical air of the southern hemisphere is diverted, first towards the north, then towards the north-west, and brings the summer monsoon in north China; it flows towards east China and on meeting the cold front produces cyclonic rain. In September, winter conditions are re-established with great rapidity.

This complex situation explains the variations in rainfall and temperature. North China gets rain only in summer, and the arid zone (less than 10 inches a year) begins in Shensi and Jehol; south China is better and more regularly watered. Temperatures remain uniform in summer, from north to south, through the whole of east China; but in winter they are much lower in the north than in the south. The south-east side is the only region to be almost free from frost.

Climate regions are easily defined in central China. From the Trans-Himalaya onwards, where 19 inches are recorded, rainfall decreases very rapidly towards the north. In the hollows of Sinkiang the winters are very cold and the summers very hot; the dryness is extreme, and except on the mountain ranges rainfall is less than 4 inches a year.

In east China rainfall decreases not only from south to north, but from coast to interior; the winter is cold except on the southern fringe and on the plateaus of the south-west; the agricultural season lasts six months in the north-east, seven months on the loess plateaus, eight months in the valley of the Yangtze-kiang, eleven in Szechwan, and is continuous everywhere else.

This diversity is still more striking if its variations

over a period of time are considered. Peking has an average rainfall of 24 inches a year, but in sixty-six years the city has had four years with averages of over 39 inches, and four more with averages of less than 12 inches. In much of China agriculture is necessarily marginal, at the mercy of annual fluctuations in rainfall and temperature.

The extreme luxuriance of the natural vegetation is explained by the diversity of the climate. The mixture of species is particularly varied in the mountains. There is the same wealth of cultivated plants. The Chinese soil suits cold climate cereals (spring wheat, millet, Kaoliang—a sort of sorghum) and those of temperate regions (maize and winter wheat); it is even favourable to crops as diverse as soya beans and tobacco, sugar-cane and cotton, tea and apples.

*Flood and drought: three giant rivers.* The varied relief and the extremely irregular rainfall make the distribution of running water very unequal. In some parts there are enormous hydrographic basins like those of the Hwang-ho, the Yangtze-kiang and the Si-kiang. In others there are only relatively restricted hill systems, like those of the Hai-ho and the Hwai in the Great Plain, or of the little rivers of Chekiang, Fukien and Kwangtung. Sometimes, because the frontiers often abandon the line of the watersheds, rivers rising in China may join the fluvial basins of neighbouring countries. This is the case with the Tibetan Tsangpo, the upper arm of the Brahmaputra, and the upper valleys of the Irrawaddy, the Salween and the Mekong. In north-west China, shortage of water may prevent the formation of drainage areas large enough to reach the sea, so that there are temporary watercourses lost in the sands or the salt lagoons. There may even be no running water at all, as in many parts of Sinkiang and Mongolia.

Of all these waterways, the 'three giants' (Hwang-ho, Yangtze-kiang and Si-kiang) have the strongest influence on human activities in China. They both feed and threaten crops, they provide a means of internal transport, and they offer a particularly useful hydro-electric capacity.

The Hwang-ho is 3,162 miles long, and occupies a basin more than twice the size of France or four times the size of Colorado, U.S.A.; from Tibet it gathers enough water to cross the steppes and deserts of Inner Mongolia, making a big loop towards the north; it has a flow of 3,250 cubic metres per second at its mouth, and at Lanchow, where it leaves the Tibetan plateau, 4,000 cubic metres per second. The Yangtze-kiang, only a little longer, drains a much larger area (772,200 square miles), having collected a number of tributaries from the plain of Szechwan, the hills of the south-east and the Tsinling Mountains, whereas the Hwang-ho flows alone over most of its course. The Yangtze-kiang has a flow of 29,000 cubic metres per second at its mouth. It is the second largest river in the world, after the Amazon. The Si-kiang is 1,304 miles long. Its basin is 154,000 square miles and its average flow 8,700 cubic metres per second. It has a volume therefore more than twice that of the Hwang-ho.

These huge rivers are fed by the abundant but irregular rainfall of east China. Hence the unreliability of their flow and the frequent occurrence of floods and freshets. The Si-kiang is a tropical river; its waters are

at their lowest in winter, when the weather is still warm and the scanty rainfall evaporates very quickly; it reaches its highest level in summer, and its freshets are sometimes as much as 59,000 cubic metres per second.

The average maximum flow of the Yangtze-kiang is of the same order (60,000 cubic metres per second) and also occurs in the summer, during the heaviest rains. Its lowest level is in January and February, but even then its flow is never less than 3,600 cubic metres per second. The Tung Ting and Poyang lakes, to the south of the river, act as regulators in its periods of spate. They reach their highest level in the spring— earlier, that is, than the Yangtze-kiang — and have begun to go down when the Yangtze-kiang is rising, so that they can absorb a certain amount of the overflow. The freshets of the Yangtze-kiang, which always occur between July and September, are nevertheless dangerous: those of 1931 and 1935 were caused by heavy cyclonic downpours, and the flow at Wuhan reached 75,000 cubic metres in 1931 and 80,000 cubic

A boat being hauled and pushed up rapids in the Yangtze gorge. A series of gorges and rapids above Ichang forms an obstacle to steamers on the Yangtze, but smaller boats can travel as far as the plains of Szechwan. The great rivers of central and southern China such as the Yangtze, Si-kiang and their tributaries, form an important transport network, whereas in the north the Hwang-ho and other rivers are uncertain transport routes owing to the irregularity of their flow.

Peasants in Shantung Province
building a small reservoir.
This project was part of China's
irrigation campaign, which
lasted from October 1957
to January 1958. During these
four months nearly 100 million
people engaged in building
small water conservancy works
throughout the country and
about 19,450,000 acres of
farm-land were freshly provided
with irrigation and
drainage facilities.

metres in 1935, when floods inundated 121,500 square
miles and left more than three million dead.

The freshets of the Hwang-ho can bring floods as
catastrophic as those of the Yangtze-kiang or the Si-
kiang in August-September (the period of the heaviest
rainfall), in autumn (secondary rainfall) or in the
spring (when the snow starts to melt in Tibet and
Mongolia).
On the other hand its waters may fall much lower
than those of the great rivers (down to 140 cubic
metres in February), leaving the lands it usually irrigates completely dry. The situation is further aggravated by the enormous mass of loess it carries down.
In a normal year, this mass (whose colour gives the
Yellow River its name) amounts to a thousand
million cubic metres at 75lb. to a cubic metre of
water. It is deposited in the plain and raises the bed of
the river, so that the latter flows above the level of its
valley, with a levee on either side. When the levees
bursts, an immense area is left at the mercy of the
waters. If flooding is very heavy, the Hwang-ho may
even make a new bed. In 1853 the embankments gave
way near Kaifeng, and the river abandoned its eight-
hundred-year-old course to the sea its old mouth
south of Shantung in favour of the present course
500 miles farther north.
The same irregular flow and constant threat of
floods characterise the other hill rivers of north China;
the Hwai, which drains the south of the Great Plain,
and the numerous little rivers which meet at Tientsin
to form the Hai-ho.
The navigability of Chinese rivers depends on the
flow and the shape of the beds. Ease of navigation is
the chief difference between the rivers of the centre
and south (Yangtze-kiang, Si-kiang and their tributaries) and the Hwang-ho and other rivers of north
China. The Si-kiang is accessible as far inland as Wu-
chow for ships drawing 12 feet of water and even as far
as Nan-ning for small steamers. The Yangtze-kiang
will take sea-going ships as far as Wuhan, and big
steamers as far as Ichang; here the river is broken by
gorges and rapids which make it difficult but still
possible to reach the plains of Szechwan, where navigation becomes easy again. The Tung Ting and Poyang

lakes, and the rivers feeding them, the Kan-kiang and
Siang-kiang, have formed excellent waterways. The
Hwang-ho, on the contrary, with its heavy deposition,
unstable bed, and low winter waters, makes a very
unreliable waterway in its natural state.

Better use and better regulation of the waterways is
one of the oldest problems that the Chinese have had
to solve. The sound repair of the embankments,
reservoirs and channels was for many centuries the
criterion of good administration and of the Empire's
prosperity. But the magnitude of catastrophes such as
that of 1931 proved that China had not completely
mastered her waterways.

A POPULATION OF 750 MILLION. The oldest known
centre of population in east Asia was in north China.
Archaeological excavations carried out near Peking, at
Chu-ku-tien, led to the discovery of *Sinanthropus* or
Peking Man, who already possessed a certain technical
skill, judging by remains of fires and chipped quartz
found among his bones.

Towards 4000-3000 B.C. there existed a fairly
advanced Chinese civilisation in the middle valley of
the Hwang-ho, cultivating millet, breeding dogs and
pigs and fashioning pottery and tools of polished
rock. To these technical accomplishments were added,
in the course of thousands of years, sheep, goats and
horse-breeding, wheat cultivation and the manufacture
of bronze. In the fertile plains of loess and river
deposits of the Middle Hwang-ho, the Fen-ho and the
Wei-ho, the need for a strong political authority to
organise methodical distribution of water and super-
vise the embankment made itself; in this region
the first Chinese states made their appearance, under
the ancient dynasties of the Shangs and Chous towards
the end of the second millennium B.C. The Chinese
people already looked much as they do today: of
medium height, with slender limbs, narrow eyes and
stiff black hair; they had their own cultural traditions,
and a singular ideographic script.

From these primitive homes in the loess plains the
Chinese people expanded progressively, by military
conquest and by emigration. They reached the
Yangtze-kiang in the first millennium, and had spread
over the whole of south China at the time of the
Han dynasty (between the second century B.C. and
the second century A.D.). Chinese colonists settled in
the plateaus of central Asia after the first centuries
A.D. although Manchuria was not effectively taken
until the twentieth century.
*Ethnic diversity*. Throughout the Great Plain of north
China, in the whole of the Middle Yangtze-kiang
region, in the loess plateaus of Shansi and in Shantung,
the Chinese proper—the Hans—form a homogeneous unit, in terms of language, customs and
physical type.

In the entire region to the south-east of the Yangtze-
kiang, the strains of non-Chinese populations are still
apparent—in physical type, for instance, which is
decidedly smaller, more fragile, and more strongly
pigmented, and in language, which takes the form of
a multitude of varying dialects unintelligible to the
people of the north, and retaining traces of the ancient
regional languages.

In the forest regions of the south-west (Yunnan,
Szechwan, Kweichow and Kwangsi) the process of
'sinisation' of the original populations is still less

advanced. The Hans are to be found only in the best of the valleys, along the roads and in the towns. Most of the area is occupied by the many non-Han ethnic groups; there are twenty minorities, differing enormously in language, social organisation, religion, customs, dress and agricultural methods. Few belong to any homogeneous unit, owing partly to their nomadic habits and partly to Chinese military expeditions which broke them up into a number of groups, each with its own name.

The regions of the west and north-west were not finally absorbed in the Chinese state until the seventeenth and eighteenth centuries. The original populations form more stable and homogeneous groups than in the south-west, and some have reached a higher degree of political organisation and cultural activity, particularly the Tibetans and Mongols, followers of Buddhism-Lamaism, and the Turkish Uighurs, who are Moslems. These minority peoples are most numerous in Sinkiang, where Uighurs, Mongols, Kazakhs, Kirghz, and half-a-dozen other nationalities live side by side. The Hweis are group apart; ethnically very near to the Hans, and speaking the same language, they differ from them in their religion—Mohammedanism. There are many Moslem Chinese in the Yunnan, and still more in Shansi, Shensi and Kansu.

North-east China is the cradle of the Manchurian people, who conquered the Chinese Empire in the seventeenth century and installed the Manchu dynasty of the Ts'ins in Peking, the last dynasty of Chinese imperial history. Up to the end of the nineteenth century the Imperial Government strictly forbade Chinese immigration into the ancestral territories, an interdict that was not raised until the beginning of Tsarist penetration into the region in 1896. In less than half a century a demographic 'rush' brought to Manchuria nearly forty million Chinese peasants turned farmers, miners, labourers and railwaymen. Today the Manchus represent less than 5 per cent of China's population. The north-east also includes an important Korean minority in the Kirin region, to the north of the Korean border.

This complex ethnic geography has two main features. Firstly, these national minorities occupy an immense arc made up of forest massifs (Great and Little Khingan), steppes (Mongolia and Sinkiang), cold deserts (Tibet), mountains (Szechwan, Yunnan) and high plateaus (Kweichow, Yunnan and Kwangsi). Secondly, they surround the plains, basins and low hills of central and east China which, easily irrigated and cultivated, have been the favourite zone of Han farmers for thousands of years.

In the course of history therefore, relations between the Huns and the minority peoples have not always been of the best. The local Chinese authorities burdened the minorities with taxes and requisitions; they tolerated, and even organised, the seizure of the best land which was often collective tribal property; they allowed Chinese merchants to sell textiles, tea, salt and indispensable tools at exorbitant prices and to buy local products—furs, wool, skins and valuable forest produce—at low rates. The minority peoples were administered exclusively by officials of Han nationality, who were often ignorant of the local language and forbade its use in administrative and

judicial affairs. The minorities, on the other hand, suffered Chinese domination with impatience and were in constant revolt.

*The demographic problem.* However, these national minorities amount to only thirty-five million, little more than 5 per cent of the total. The average figure of 200 inhabitants to the square mile for the whole of China is correct only in theory. North of a diagonal line from Harbin to Kunming there are fewer than 3 inhabitants to the square mile, whereas in the south and east there are vast zones in which the density reaches 400 to 550 to the square mile (the Great Plain of China, the Red Basin in Szechwan and the region of the Middle Yangtze-kiang), and in many coastal plains of the south-east the figure even exceeds 1,200 per square mile.

About 85 per cent of the population is still rural, and extreme inequality in population distribution emphasises great inequality in agricultural development. Agriculture is impossible in certain regions of the west, and only marginal in many others; but in

A Tibetan. In south-west China, as in north-west China certain populations form homogeneous ethnic groups. The Tibetans are held together by their faith, Buddhism-Lamaism.

A Moslem woman of north-west China. Her hooded veil is an adaptation of the traditional veil. In west and north-west China and especially in Sinkiang many different ethnic groups have resisted complete assimilation, and their survival is encouraged by an Institute of National Minorities in Peking, which attempts to provide them with an alphabet if they have no written language and ensures their political assimilation. by forming local associations for learning Chinese.

Chinese children in Shantung.
Forty-two per cent of China's
population are under eighteen

*Map opposite:* Principal
mineral and power resources in
China. China has proved to be
very rich in various minerals.
These have long been exploited in
the north and north-east of
China, but today many new
mining centres have been
opened. Rivers are being
systematically harnessed for
hydro-electricity in conjunction
with a plan for improving
navigation facilities and
irrigation projects. A
comprehensive plan for the
Hwang-ho (Yellow River)
basin is now being carried out;
numerous power stations are
already in service on the
chief rivers. China's largest
hydro-electric installation at
present is on the Middle Sungari.
In addition to other sources of
energy, China now has
atomic energy.

zones where wheat and rice have been intensively
grown for centuries, there are population densities, on
cultivated land, of 2,100 in Shantung, 2,600 in parts
of the Red Basin and the island of Tsungming, and
3,100 in Kwangtung.

The results of the 1953 census were a surprise to
most Western experts. According to estimates, the
population of China was 400 million, or at the most
500 million. It was generally accepted that because of
epidemics, famine and low standards of hygiene the
deathrate was high and the birthrate relatively low,
so that the body of the population must be almost
stable. However, though the deathrate was high, the
birthrate had also remained very high, which explained the increase in population of more than 200
million, or more than 50 per cent, since 1909-11, the
date of the most recent reliable census. The birthrate
has today risen to 37 per thousand, and the absence of
famine, and improvements in hygiene had brought
the deathrate down as low as 11 per thousand in 1960.
The Chinese population is probably increasing by
more than 12 million a year; 42 per cent of the population are under eighteen, and 16 per cent under four
years old. The estimated population in mid-1965 was
750 million.

In the younger generation the sexes are more or
less equal in number, whereas the proportion of

women is definitely lower among the older generations, so that the general total still shows a slight
preponderance of men. In old China—and not so
long ago—women occupied an inferior place in
society; the 'feminist' tendency of the new Chinese
government's reforms since 1949, and the measures
taken to ensure the effective emancipation and equality
of women have already produced appreciable results
in the demographic sphere.

At the present rate of increase it would probably
take only eight years for China to reach a total of a
thousand million inhabitants. A policy of birth control on a large scale was implemented in 1956 and
permitted sterilisation and abortion on the slightest
pretext. This policy was suddenly abandoned at the
end of 1958, and birth control was permissible only
on a doctor's recommendation. An explanation of
the sudden policy reversal may be that orthodox
Marxists believe that a socialist economy should be
able to eliminate the threat of famine and unemployment through the development of agriculture
and industry. After a series of poor harvests, however,
the birth control campaign was re-introduced in
August 1962.

*The Chinese State.* The People's Republic of China
was proclaimed in October 1949 before the Tien-
an-men, the largest gate of Peking. The Chinese
Communist Party thus ended a long series of revolutionary struggles which since the nineteenth century
has been waged with two main objects: the conquest of the land by the peasants and the restoration
of China to the rank of a fully sovereign power.
The Constitution adopted in September 1954 is highly
centralised; all powers are entrusted to the People's
National Assembly, elected for four years by indirect
suffrage.

There are twenty-two provinces, and these still
correspond, for the most part, to the administrative
organisation that was in force under the Kuomintang
and under the Empire; there are also five autonomous
regions; and two 'municipal zones' — Peking and
Shanghai — are directly affiliated to the Central
Government.

The provinces are subdivided into rural counties
(*hsien*), as distinct from the 'municipalities' or large
cities of more than 50,000 inhabitants (about 2,150
counties and 162 municipalities). The rural counties
themselves are made up of 'People's Communes',
small- and medium-sized centres thriving principally on commerce and industry (some 220,000
rural districts and 5,000 cities divided into 26,578
communes).

In each of these units local affairs are managed by
Popular Assemblies whose decisions are implemented
by local Popular Committees. There is a tendency at
each level, to confer a special status on urban centres;
this is a novel feature of Chinese administrative
organisation, explained no doubt by the differences
in the economic and political development of town
and country, and the need to treat town problems
separately.

The larger regions inhabited by national minorities
controlled directly by the Central Government,
on an equal footing with provinces and municipal
zones; this is the case with the autonomous region
of the Uighurs (formerly the province of Sinkiang),

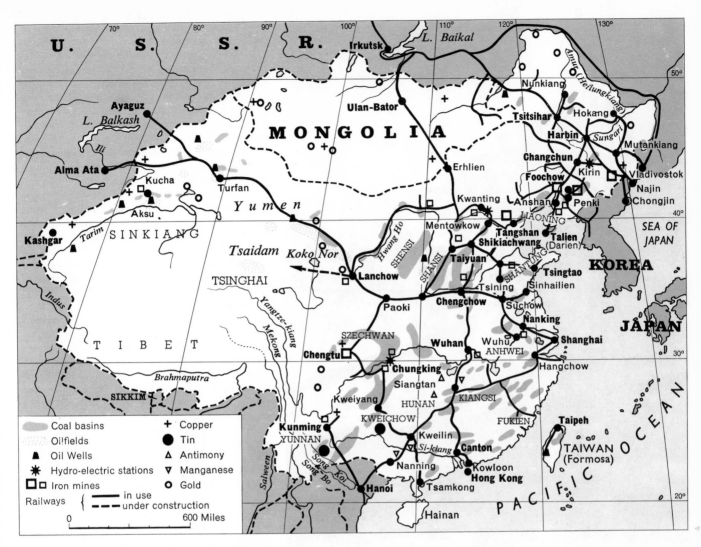

*Map legend:*

Coal basins
Oilfields
Oil Wells
Hydro-electric stations
Iron mines

+ Copper
● Tin
▲ Antimony
▽ Manganese
○ Gold

Railways { —— in use / --- under construction }

0          600 Miles

the autonomous region of the Chuangs (former province of Kwangsi), Ningsia-Hui and Inner Mongolia. Smaller minority zones are organised within the framework of the province of the country in which they are found.

Tibet, ruled by the ecclesiastical feudality of the Buddhist-Lamaist monasteries and by the Dalai Lama and his court, has been part of the Chinese Empire for centuries though preserving its own institutions and customs. After Chinese military occupation of Tibet in 1951 an agreement between Peking and Lhasa authorities recognised the latter as 'local authorities' of Tibet. The ensuing condition of brutal repression precipitated a revolution in 1959. This was ruthlessly crushed by the Chinese authorities and the Dalai Lama fled to India with many friends and followers. In September 1965 Tibet became an autonomous region with the same administrative status as Inner Mongolia. In 1964 the population was 1,321,000. At least 100,000 Tibetans live in exile in India.

INDUSTRIALISATION AND PLANNING. *Economic activity and five-year plans.* Industrial development in China, by any standards, was still in its infancy in the early 1950's. Immediate establishment of social ownership (collective or State) of agricultural, industrial and commercial undertakings, was considered impossible, though this was the ultimate objective. To this end a series of five-year plans for industry was inaugurated

in 1953, to be supplemented by a special ten-year programme for agriculture which, though covering the years 1956–67 was not implemented until April 1960. The particular task of the People's Republic is to co-ordinate under its direction and control, three very different forms of economic activity: the State

A People's Court in a Chinese village. The Government tries to involve the community in changing some of its old ways, such as the fondness for smoking opium.

A bridge over the Taitzu River in the city of Penki, Liaoning Province, the iron and coal centre of north-east China. The six rail and road bridges across the river are the main communication links in the city. The size of the northern rivers varies enormously according to season, and bridges have to be built long to allow for sudden rises in volume (this photograph was taken in October). An important project completed in 1957 was the construction of the 3,750-foot Yangtze River Bridge for road and rail traffic at Wuhan, central China. This has provided a through route from Canton to Peking where before it was necessary to cross the river by ferry.

undertakings, chiefly concerned with the sectors of heavy industry, wholesale trade and transport, but very rarely with agriculture; mixed undertakings, where capital is shared between the State and private interests, predominant in light industry and playing a large part in small and medium trade; and the introduction of co-operatives, of special interest to the artisan class, which have made very rapid progress in agriculture since the autumn of 1955. Private undertakings have practically disappeared, and the first phase of the 'transition period' towards complete social ownership has ended. The small craftsmen and tradesmen have all been absorbed into the co-operatives. Until 1962 the former owners and shareholders were paid a fixed share of the profits of their former factories as dividends. Thereafter the intention was that they should act as directors of the mixed undertakings and in the State's various economic organisations.

Four years of rehabilitation and reconstruction helped to repair the disasters of the long years of civil and foreign war, and to raise industrial and agricultural production levels. Essential communications were restored and the basic mechanisms for economic control and expansion were introduced, inflation halted and State banking and State trading companies established. By 1953 rehabilitation had reached a stage where planned development could be undertaken and,

with the end of hostilities in Korea, the way was clear for the introduction of the first five-year plan (1953-57). This plan was energetically pursued and visitors returning from China in 1954 and 1955 reported impressive results. It emphasised the development of heavy industry at the expense of light industry and consumer goods. It also provided for a system of hydro-electric schemes on the Hwang-ho, Yangtze-kiang and other rivers, only part of which, however, was completed in the course of the five years. Agricultural production rose mainly through co-operative effort and consequent better yields.

A ten-year plan (1956-67) reaffirmed the rapid development of heavy industry and production assets, regional decentralisation of industry, and progress in agriculture and transport. In 1960, however, the government acknowledged that the plan had fallen behind the intended level of economic and industrial growth. The widespread failure of harvests in 1960 and 1961 was partly responsible, as was the withdrawal of Soviet financial and technological aid. Certainly many large projects have had to be abandoned or curtailed and sights considerably lowered because of differences between Moscow and Peking government. Food rationing was introduced, considerable reorientation of manpower and resources becoming necessary to minimise the hardship and unrest which ensued. By these methods greater economic self-sufficiency was achieved.

By 1961 long term planning gave way to annual plans directed towards increasing agricultural production. Industrial plans were consolidated and priority given to those serving agriculture. Moderate success led to the commencement of another five-year plan in 1966.

*A future industrial power.* Before 1949 Chinese industry was hampered by inadequate use of natural resources, poor technical equipment, and ill-balanced regional distribution of existing industries.

The industrialisation of China thus presented the problem first and foremost of finding capital to realise this ambitious programme. The State furnished a good deal of the capital, but private and mixed undertakings were called upon to play an important financial part. Today the revenue from State undertakings (industry, transport and commerce) supplies more than two-thirds of the funds required to finance the economic programme; most of the remainder is provided by urban and rural taxes. China has concluded agreements with the Soviet Union and other socialist countries for exchanging equipment goods for agricultural and mineral products. Of the great industrial undertakings outlined in the first five-year plan 141 were established with the help of Soviet capital and technicians. The first Chinese factory to make generating turbines was completed in 1955 with help from Czechoslovakia; a large-scale modern sugar refinery was put into service during the same year at Paotow (Inner Mongolia) with equipment and technicians provided under the auspices of the German Democratic Republic.

*Problems of power, raw materials and labour.* China is rich in coal, like all countries where the original rocks lie near the surface of the soil over wide areas. The resources available in Shansi and Shensi alone, consisting mainly of rich coal, are estimated at a thousand

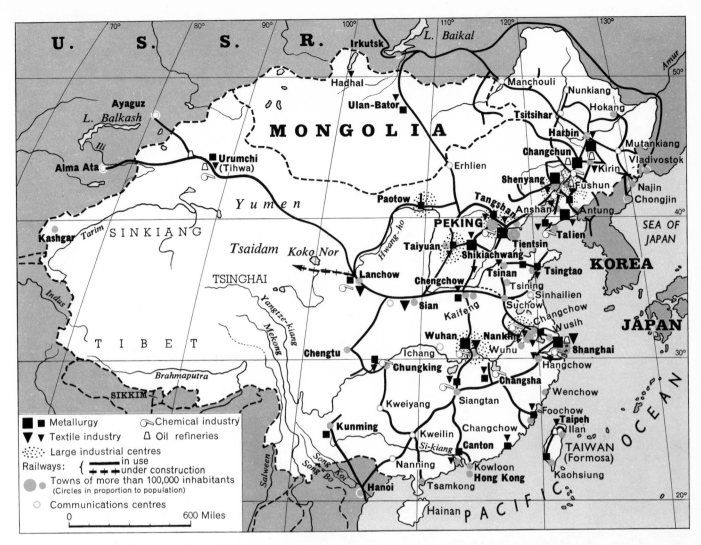

Principal industries and rail routes in China. The north-east, formerly Manchuria, and the former free ports continue to be the most important industrial centres. But a new pattern is being superimposed on these old features of China's industrial geography; industrial centres have been set up in the interior; in areas where previously there was nothing but agriculture and crafts. The creation of new communication routes — roads, a rail system, bridges (notably the big bridge over the Yangtze-kiang) — has aided the economic development of the barren regions; most of the rail routes built since the first five-year plan (1953) have been in the north-west and south-west, which altogether occupy more than half the area of the country but until recently covered only 500 miles.

million tons. The other large coalfields being fully exploited are in the north-east (Fushun, Penki, near Shenyang, and Hokang in Heilungkiang); in the north (Mentowkow and Tangshan, near Peking); in Shantung and in Hunan. The new mining centres, little known and hardly exploited until 1949, are now productive, among them those of Kweichow, Szechwan and Singkiang. The first five-year plan doubled coal output (124 million tons in 1957 against 63 million in 1952). By 1961 estimated production of coal and lignite had risen to 350,000 metric tons.

Oil extraction has been practically confined to a few wells in the region of Yumen (West Kansu), and there are many more neglected opportunities to be developed here than in coal-mining. Prospecting is still going on in Shensi, Szechwan and Singkiang, and known potential resources are already several times greater than those discovered before 1949. Distillation of oil shale mixed with the coal of Fushun also seems to offer certain possibilities. The total output of oil is relatively small, a problem which must be solved, especially as road transport is bound to expand enormously to meet the requirements of industry, which is also expanding. Production in 1963 was 7 million tons.

A rapid increase in electrical output is also imperative. The potential capacity of 1,598 principal rivers has been evaluated at 300,000 million kilowatt-hours, but before 1949 the only serious attempt to exploit

this has been made by the Japanese on the Sungari. But major irrigating, draining and damming works now undertaken all over the country, especially in the basins of the Hwang-ho and the Hwai, will make it possible to feed a number of generating stations with only a low head-fall, as well as the rivers harnessed direct. The Kwantung reservoir, built in the north of the Great Plain to regulate the Yungting river, is already producing electric power. Output rose to 18,000 million kWh in 1957, and 41,500 million in 1959. It was 58,000 million kWh in 1960 and continues to rise.

By 1949 the iron deposits of Liaoning, Hunan and Anhwei had been prospected and partially worked, and so had the copper mines of the north-east, the antimony and manganese mines of Hunan, the tin mines of Yunnan and the gold of Heilungkiang. There was no output of aluminium, and that of iron was well below the estimated figure. By 1963, however, aluminium extraction had reached 110,000 tons, and in 1962 the production of pig-iron was claimed to be 19,700,000 tons. Mineral prospecting has been most actively pursued in the new lands of the north-west (Sinkiang, Tsinghai), often in conjunction with new road construction which, in Tibet, for instance, has resulted in some valuable discoveries in the region of Tsinghai.

China is rich in natural textile fibres (cotton, silk,

and ramie); home wool demand will no doubt increase with the rise in the standard of living, and this will make fresh demands on the sheep-farmers in the steppes of the north-west. Agriculture also provides the country with an abundance of oil seeds and tobacco, besides timber and other forest produce.

Extremely badly paid, with no technical experience, the Chinese worker used to be little better than a peasant driven from his fields by poverty and transplanted to the town. Although the skill of the Chinese artisan is legendary, the degree of skill in industrial labour and its effective output was necessarily low. A number of measures have been adopted to remedy this situation: higher wages, holidays with pay, medical attention, accident insurance, improvement in workers' housing conditions, and technical courses. The workers' own initiative has been called upon for the constant improvement of working techniques and processes; technicians sent by the Soviet Union, Poland and Czechoslovakia have also helped to improve the quality of industrial work. In addition, rural labour

A small blast furnace in Szechwan Province. Exploitation of coal established in the north and north-east China, and it is in these regions that industry was first established. Now active prospecting has resulted in the opening of new mines in Sinkiang Szechwan and Kweichow and hydro-electric dams are also being constructed.

set free by the increase in agricultural co-operation has been tapped. The urban population, formerly very small compared with that of the country as a whole, is growing fast, and today forms about 15 per cent of the total.

*Old and new urban industries.* The manufacture of machinery and other production tools is already extensive. The principal centre was established in Shanghai, with two other centres in Tientsin and Shenyang (Mukden). China now produces generators, heavy drilling-machines, pile-drivers and shaping-machines, as well as precision tools and textile machinery. Iron-smelting and heavy metallurgy are represented by the old-established centres of Anshan and Wuhan, where the works have been rebuilt and enlarged, and by a third metallurgical combine under construction at Paotow (Inner Mongolia). In the sphere of constructional engineering there is a truck factory at Changchun, and elsewhere in the north and north-east there are works manufacturing electric plant and rail plant. Much attention is given to chemical

industries, agricultural machinery and civil engineering plant.

Besides these new elements in Chinese industrial life, older branches are still being developed: spinning mills, and silk, cotton and wool weaving; matches and tobacco; paper mills and printing works (which increase with the fight against illiteracy); glassworks, china factories and food industries. As the demand for consumer goods constantly increases, the old artisan class, now organised almost everywhere in co-operatives, will continue to play an indispensible part, with their hand-weaving industries, rice-paper mills, porcelain and china, bamboo and basketwork, and lacquered articles. Handicraft production still accounts for approximately 20 per cent of China's industrial production.

*Old and new industrial centres.* The location of Chinese industry before 1949 corresponded fundamentally to the extent of foreign economic control over the country. The first five-year plan was designed to integrate Manchuria and the four great 'treaty ports' into the national economy. The north-east, rich in mineral resources, remains one of the principal industrial centres. It includes the Anshan combine with its gigantic blast furnaces, rolling mills, and seamless-tube factories; the machinery works of Shenyang; rail plant at Harbin; truck works at Changchun, and textile and chemical industries, flour mills, and sugar and oil refineries. In the old free ports there are textile, match and tobacco industries (Tientsin and Tsingtao), textiles and machinery (Shanghai), metallurgy and textiles (Wuhan and Hankow). Controlled distribution takes into account the geographical source of raw materials, the condition of internal communications and the extent of regional needs. The first plan anticipated that out of 694 large industrial units to be created, more than two-thirds would be situated in regions of the interior previously little or not at all industrialised. In north China, Taiyuan near the coal measures of Shansi, Chengchow at the junction of the two biggest railroutes in China, Shihkiachwang in the middle of the Great Plain, and Peking itself — which must participate if it is to retain its place as capital — are on the way to becoming great industrial centres, and so are Canton (Kwangchow), Changsha, Chungking — which has to supply the fifty million consumers of Szechwan — and Kunming (Yunnan-fu) in central and south China. In the north-west there is the metallurgical combine of Paotow, the extraction of petroleum and non-ferrous metals, and the textile factories fed from the cotton fields of the Fen-ho valley, and the sheep flocks of the steppes.

*The peasant in industrialisation.* The industrial capacity of the peasantry has been the object of an experiment without precedent in other socialist countries: since 1958 it has been industrialised without being urbanised.

In all the rural districts, especially those within the framework of the 'People's Communes', quite small industrial units have been established. These are distinguished by their small output, low technical level and high consumption of labour, and also by their very low equipment and transport costs (location is closely connected with that of the raw materials). This experiment is being followed with interest, especially by under-developed countries, poor in capital but rich in labour and raw materials.

AGRICULTURAL PRODUCTION AND CO-OPERATION. On the eve of agrarian reforms in 1947 and 1950, it was estimated that 10 per cent of the rural Chinese population owned from 70 to 80 per cent of the land. Even small farmers who were nominal owners of their farms were bound to landlords by loans at exorbitant rates of interest or by various compulsory tolls. Landless peasants and day labourers formed an enormous mass without even the relative economic stability of the farmers.

*Agrarian reform, co-operatives and communes.* Peasant discontent throughout Chinese history has therefore assumed the acute forms of agrarian agitation and armed uprising, and in the course of the recent civil wars, land ownership has played a chief part. The Chinese Communist Party, of which the poor peasants were one of the principal supports, carried out reforms which dispossessed the landed proprietors without compensation, and 300 million peasants benefited by the redistribution of land totalling 247 million acres.

Chinese agriculture then found itself faced with fresh problems. Expanding industry required more raw materials and a rapid increase in food production to feed an increasing urban population. In return, it made possible various schemes to improve rural equipment and to carry out a programme of major hydro-electric works, measures without which the necessary advance in agricultural production could not be realised.

But individual small farming was not in a position to make use of the new opportunities. The Chinese leaders therefore tried to set the peasantry on the road to agricultural co-operation. By the end of the first five-year plan the whole rural population had been grouped into co-operative systems. In this initial phase, three types of co-operatives existed side by side: 'mutual assistance teams', which enabled a certain number of tasks to be carried out jointly, while preserving freedom of management for each undertaking; 'semi-socialist co-operatives', in which the land was owned in common and each worker was rewarded in proportion to his work and to his original contribution of land; and 'collective farms' proper.

In 1958, first as an experiment in the vast wheatlands of Honan, the 'People's Commune' appeared. Formed by the fusion of several rural co-operatives and roughly equivalent to the former rural district (hsiang), it is a unit of agricultural and industrial production. As a substitute for the rural cantons, it forms the basic cell of the administrative system and of the military hierarchy; it has its own schools, canteens, laundries and day nurseries, thus assuming a certain number of the peasant family's responsibilities — like the Israeli *kibbutzim*.

*Large-scale works.* Chinese agricultural production stands to benefit, not only by the expansion of the co-operative movement, but by the policy of large-scale undertakings pursued since 1949. These works have four main agricultural objects: river control to protect the land from floods; irrigation of arid land; belts of woodland to give protection against the desert winds and the typhoons coming from the Yellow Sea; clearance of uncultivated land for immediate development.

River control work is distributed over four principal sectors: the tributaries of the Hai-ho, the Hwai, the Hwang-ho and neighbouring small rivers, and the Yangtze-kiang. In 1954 the Hwai scheme proved its worth during freshets which would have caused floods even more catastrophic than those of 1931. On the Yangtze-kiang dykes at Wuhan stood a similar strain that summer. Although at one stage the river level had risen to 95 feet (against 91 feet in 1931), 41,000 square miles were flooded in the Yangtze-kiang basin (against 122,000 in 1931), and there was no loss of human life. The extensive control works on the Hwang-ho are designed to turn the river into a 'staircase', unable to overflow, by means of forty-two dams and four main hydro-electric stations, each of which, as 'multi-purpose works', will feed the generating stations, build up reserves of water in case of drought, and permanently irrigate the neighbouring regions. The whole course of the Hwang-ho will become navigable. At the same time, work has been started on a scheme which it is hoped will reduce soil erosion considerably throughout the entire basin.

Reforestation will play in important part here, providing a screen against winds harmful to agriculture. The principal forest belts have been planted on the Great Khingan, along the Middle Hwang-ho and on the coasts of the Liaotung and Shantung peninsulas.

Large-scale developments are aimed at protecting the cultivated zones and extending their area by means of irrigation (by repairing old canal systems, sinking wells, installing motor pumps and increasing the number of small storage basins). The irrigated area has increased as a result: over 51 million acres in 1949, 126 million in 1958. In addition to all this, methodical survey has shown that there are vast untilled areas in which agriculture is climatically possible, especially in Inner Mongolia, in Heilungkiang, Sinkiang and Kansu.

Chinese agriculture has always been marked by its intensity. The farmer's methods, in maintaining soil fertility and in multiple cropping, if primitive, have proved remarkably effective. On the other hand, the finer arts of agronomy — seed selection, animal

In order to feed a population running into hundreds of millions China is making an effort in every direction. In addition to increasing yields, the Government is taking measures to increase actual acreage. Methods include irrigation and soil conservation, both by the building of terraces and by reforestation. Scientific progress and vigorous campaigns by the Government have helped to raise crop yields. Here commune members in Szechwan Province are shown applying fertile soil to the roots of young wheat plants.

Gathering the first silkworm cocoons of spring, in Shuanteh County in Kwangtung, where seven or eight crops are harvested each year. The five traditional sericultural provinces are Kwangtung, Shantung, Hupeh, Chekiang and Szechwan.

Maize harvest in Shantung Province, north-east China, the country's major maize-growing area. Other principal crops in the north-east are soya, wheat, tobacco, cotton and sugar-beet. On the plateaus, wheat and millet are grown, with cotton fruit, vegetables and rice in the sheltered basins; on the Great Plain, kaoling and winter wheat; while rice is the main crop in the south.

husbandry and the fight against pests and disease, are only now becoming generally known. In spite, therefore, of its reputedly high development, only moderate returns have been achieved. The 2,000 State farms and 8,000 State agricultural stations are designed to remedy this weakness. In 1958 a number of new methods were generally adopted: dense planting, deep ploughing, generous application of manures, and campaigns against birds and parasites.

*Agricultural production and stock-breeding.* Until recently, cereals formed the major part of agricultural production, a natural state of affairs in an under-industrialised country where the population, being very poor, must be content with a monotonous diet. But increased production since 1952 indicates that the irrigation schemes, co-operation and crop improvement plans have been successful. By 1958 total grain crops were officially stated to have reached 254 million tons, and 275 million tons by 1959. From 1960 to 1965, however, wheat had to be imported, and a further three-year wheat purchase was agreed with Canada in 1965. This was attributed to natural disasters including droughts, floods, typhoons and insect pests,

which was thought to have affected more than half China's cultivated area.

Spring wheat is still the main crop on the fringe of the steppes in Kansu and Inner Mongolia; millet on the loess plateau; kaoliang in the north-east and in the Great Plain; and winter wheat on the loess plateaus, the Great Plain, in the north-east, and also on the Lower and Middle Yangtze-kiang; rice throughout the south. But the progress in husbandry has already begun to alter the classical distribution of cereals in China; rice is spreading towards the north and to the extreme north-east; double-cropping rice is beginning to penetrate the Yangtze-kiang, while wheat is spreading towards the south and west in the semi-arid regions where a type of dry farming is called for.

The increase in other food crops points to a rise in the rural standard of living and an increase in the urban population, whose diet is usually more varied. Sugar-beet and sugar-cane are the two crops for which the highest rates of increase have been planned. Tea plantations suffered heavily during the civil wars, and are naturally slow in building up the same yields as previously. Fruit trees are being planted everywhere. The variety of the Chinese climate favours the cultivation of a large number of oil-yielding plants — some of them traditional, like mustard, cotton and sesame, others more recent, like soya.

Stock-breeding remains far behind the times, owing to the extreme and long-standing poverty of the Chinese peasantry, the intensive occupation of the land, especially in the rice-bearing regions, and the cheapness of labour, which made it hardly worth while to maintain draught animals. The solution is being sought in rational development of the north-west steppe regions. Now that the development of internal communications affords them an outlet to the whole of the Chinese market, Sinkiang, Tibet and Mongolia are capable of producing an exportable surplus of meat far greater than in the past. By 1959 the number of sheep and goats for the whole of China had risen to 113 million, cattle to 65 million, and pigs to 180 million.

Cotton-growing is increasing in traditional centres (Kansu, Hopei, Hupei, southern Shensi), as well as in new regions, particularly in the Uighur autonomous region (Sinkiang). Yields are being increased by the introduction of long-fibred varieties, vernalisation of the seed and the use of insecticides. The tobacco crop has more than doubled over the same period. Efforts are being made to improve the quality in the five traditional mulberry-growing and silkworm-breeding centres of Shantung, Hupeh, Chekiang, Szechwan and Kwangtung.

Since before 1949 the increase in soya cultivation has brought expansion in the industrial oil industry; cotton-seed has been developed extensively along similar lines.

*Six major agricultural regions.* Of the six great agricultural regions, four are very old; the Great Plain, the loess plateaus, the plains and basins of the Middle Yangtze-kiang, and the Red Basin in Szechwan. The fifth region, that of the tropical plains and basins of the south coast, has been cultivated for nearly two thousand years. The sixth, the north-east plain, has been intensively exploited only since the end of the nineteenth century; before this Chinese immigration was artificially impeded for political reasons.

The plateaus of Shensi and Shansi are given over to intensive cultivation of spring and winter wheat and millet, while cotton, fruit, vegetables and rice can be grown in the sheltered basins. In the immense, monotonous expanse of the Great Plain, covered with loess and alluvium, kaoliang and winter wheat are grown, with soya, maize, sweet potatoes, groundnuts and cotton; rice is grown mostly in the southern part (Hwai region). In the north-east, the principal crops used to be those commanding the best foreign (especially Japanese) markets — chiefly soya, with maize, wheat and tobacco, and enough kaoliang for the needs of the Chinese farmers. Cotton is now grown in addition, with sugar-beet and tobacco. The development of the virgin lands of Heilungkiang will provide a better food supply for the big industrial centres of the region.

The plains of the Middle and Lower Yangtze-kiang proper are exceptionally rich; wheat is grown in winter, rice once or twice a year, the mulberry is cultivated for silkworms, and tea grows on the hills. There are also tobacco, oil-seeds and cotton, for this is the chief cotton-producing region in China. The Red Basin in Szechwan has a large rural population, and enjoys the benefit of a hot, moist climate, raising crops of rice, tobacco, wheat, colza, fruit and vegetables in the plain itself and on its numerous terraced slopes. The terraces are also a characteristic feature of the Si-kiang delta and the other hill basins of Kwangtung and Fukien, where rice, sugar-cane, mulberry, tea, citrus and tropical fruits, and even the coconut palm are intensively cultivated.

*China as an agricultural unit.* Agricultural yields in China until very recently were comparable to those of European agriculture in the fourteenth and fifteenth centuries. The leeway to be made up is therefore considerable. Important experiments to remedy this situation and to modernise agriculture have been begun, some undertaken locally and some by the central ministry of agriculture. New and expanding colleges of agriculture are adding their quota to this effort, and increased numbers of students are graduating to serve in agriculture and related fields. It is hoped that greater yield and greater output per man hour, together with improvements in marketing facilities and provision of capital, will assist the Chinese farmer and improve his lot.

Progress is already reported: cereal production in 1959 reached 275 million tons. The cotton harvest, from a pre-war maximum of 848,000 tons, was claimed to be well over 2,400,000 tons in 1959, and today China is one of the most important cotton producers in the world.

These advances have made it possible to reduce the arable land and to divide it into three: one-third for crops, one-third for pasturage and artificial fodder, one-third for forest, a distribution that must obviously take into account the particular nature of each region and its suitability to pastoral agricultural or forestry purposes.

TRANSPORT AND COMMERCIAL ACTIVITY. *The new pattern of internal transport.* A fairly well developed natural network of communications leaves only a few regions, such as Yunnan and Tibet, isolated. The Great Plain communicates easily with the north-east, with Mongolia, and with Sinkiang. The Hwang-ho links the last two routes from Paotow to Lanchow, while the cols of the Tsinlings connect Shensi with the plains of Szechwan. In central China the Yangtze-kiang forms an excellent link with Szechwan; the high valleys of its southern tributaries are separated from the Peh-kiang by low, easily crossed ridges.

In the old days China took the greatest possible advantage of these natural traffic routes, by land in the north, by porterage and caravan along the 'Silk Route' from Sian and Lanchow, or along the 'Tea Road' from Kalgan or by boat on the southern rivers. Wooden chutes established on the cols made it easy to link the rivers serving Wuhan in the centre and Canton in the south. But the rail system was organised from the free ports, where foreign interests were mainly centred. Manchuria was the sole exception, for the Japanese and, before 1914, Tsarist Russia actually built a whole closely woven network in the north-east.

Shanghai, the most populous city in China. The photograph shows Soochow Creek, one of the arms of the Wong-ku River. There are numerous sampans used as homes in the city; as in many Chinese cities, the town has invaded the river, and these floating quarters are lifted up and down by the tides and the wake of the steamers.

A tea plantation in Chimen County, Anhwei Province. Chimen Black Tea has been famous for over eighty years. During the past ten years measures have been taken to boost fallen production; these included the restoration of abandoned plantations, the opening of new ones, and scientific management.

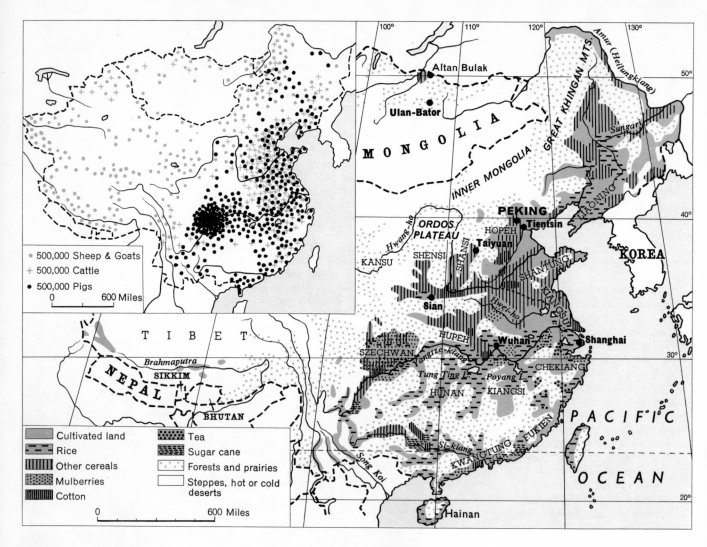

- 500,000 Sheep & Goats
- 500,000 Cattle
- 500,000 Pigs

0          600 Miles

Cultivated land     Tea
Rice     Sugar cane
Other cereals     Mulberries     Forests and prairies
Cotton     Steppes, hot or cold deserts

0          600 Miles

Distribution of stock-breeding and chief crops in China and Outer Mongolia. Sheep are most numerous in the prairies and steppelands, while the cattle are concentrated in the east and pigs are bred mostly in Szechwan. But the traditional aspect of China's agriculture is undergoing profound changes. Formerly there was a contrast between the wheat and sorghum lands of the north and the rice lands of the south; today the cultivation of rice is steadily spreading towards the north, while other cereals, especially wheat, are being grown increasingly towards the south and west.

The road system was limited (about 62,000 miles). The Burma Road and the North-West Road, connecting Kunming with Mandalay, and Lanchow with Alma-Ata, were exceptions brought about by the circumstances of war and Japanese occupation. The target of the first plan for communications — 6,200 miles of new roads — was exceeded before 1957, and in 1960 the total was claimed to be 250,000 miles.

River traffic remains largely dependent on natural seasonal conditions. River conservancy is a recent development: the Grand Canal, built by the emperors in the old days to link Nanking to Peking and to provide the capital with rice, was practically silted up and derelict. The five-year plan provided for technical improvement of the system and for concentration on river navigation in the south and west, which had been most neglected during the earlier period.

The new policy in transport is clearly visible in the new railroutes: an immense internal artery runs from Kunming to Paotow, linking Yunnan, Szechwan, Shensi and Inner Mongolia. It has branches communicating with the Yangtze-kiang region and with the Great Plain; it also forms the starting-point of the great westward lines (from Lanchow to Kansu and Sinkiang, along the old Silk Road, and the Trans-Mongolian from Tsining to Ulan Bator and Irkutsk) and of the great routes to Tibet.

But roads, quicker and less expensive to build and better adapted to hilly ground, play the most important part in opening up the south-west. Most of the thousands of miles of newly built roads are in Kwei-chow, Yunnan, Szechwan, Tsing Hai and Tibet. The planning of air communications shows the same concern to rescue the south and west from their isolation.

The transformation of the waterway system is necessarily slower to achieve since it is bound up with the completion of 'multi-purpose' works like those of the Hwang-ho and the Hwai. But already traffic on the Yangtze-kiang between Ichang and Chung-king has been improved by the removal of sills and by a system of navigation beacons at night.

*Progress in home markets.* There is now a Chinese National Market. The lines of communication just described have acquired special importance since its establishment. Wholesale trade is in the hands of State companies which plan the exchanges, organise transport and fix purchase prices paid to producers. These companies run a few retail shops which serve to regulate re-sale prices. The development of the national market has had a marked influence on planning agricultural production. In a poor province like Kwangsi, for instance, ordinary food crops are being replaced by plantations of pineapples, which now have become a trade commodity throughout the country.

The national minority regions derive special benefit from this commercial expansion. The State companies

offer good prices for their produce, and provide them with cheap tea, cigarettes, textiles and so on. This has led to the revival of ancient fairs long in abeyance, like that of Tali in Yunnan, of Lanchow on the Upper Hwang-ho, and those of Inner Mongolia.

*Rural villages and houses.* Chinese villages still look much the same as they must have done to Marco Polo in the thirteenth century. Nearly always huddled together, built of natural materials found locally, they offer the peasant labourer only the most primitive of living conditions, and improvements in this sphere must take second place to major industrial developments.

Group habitation is the general pattern. This is sometimes attributed to the insecurity of the Chinese countryside for so many centuries, but one must also take into account, especially in South China, the ties of family solidarity which bound most of the villagers to a single clan, honouring a common ancestor, and — even today — often bearing the same surname. But grouped rural habitation is probably a legacy of Chinese agricultural organisation in the past. The importance of irrigation, and the magnitude of the struggle against drought and flood made it necessary to keep the houses situated close together in the centre of the village.

In Kansu, Shensi and Shansi there are troglodyte villages hacked out of the flanks of the loess cliffs. In the Great Plain of the North, rural houses are mostly built of bricks of dried earth. The thatch roofs, resting on wooden pillars, not on the walls, consist mostly of kaoliang straw, which is rigid and damp-proof. In the south, the abundance of palm trees, bamboos and reeds of all kinds allows greater variety; baked bricks with a bluish tinge imparted by a special firing process are used as well as wood; even woven basketwork is employed where the climate is suitable. In the mountains of south-west China the villages of the national minorities often betray the Indonesian affinities of the population; sometimes they are built on piles — especially the granaries — and their boldly shaped roofs form a contrast to the low houses of the Chinese.

But everywhere the houses indicate the hardness of the peasants' lot. As a general rule they consist of a single floor, with two or three rooms and a yard, but no garden or paddock. Furniture is rudimentary, almost non-existent, and the whole structure affords the inmates little protection from the weather. Even where winters are cold, the sole means of heating is the *kang,* a wide bench of dried earth, heated from inside with straw, or rubbish — or coal if it can be had locally; on this bench the whole family lives and sleeps — unhygienically — in winter. In strong contrast were the luxurious dwellings of the big landowners of the village.

The face of the villages is changing slightly. The manor house now provides the administrative centre for the People's Commune, the co-operatives and the village cultural activities. There is already more comfort inside the houses; baked bricks and tiles, now industrially manufactured, take the place of thatch and dried earth. There are new elements; agricultural implement stores, communal granaries, branch shops of State commercial companies, and in most advanced regions, the first electric installations.

*Different 'generations' of towns.* One of the first types of town, of very ancient origin, consisted of a nucleus of dwellings surrounded by walls. These towns were called *cheng.* Closely connected with the old rural economy, they protected the dwellings of the big landowners not resident in the villages, their servants, and craftsmen. Here, too, lived usurers and merchants, and the mandarins in their offices or *yamen,* representing the interests of the State and the big landowners. Another type was the rural market, or *che,* to which the peasants came to barter necessities.

These ancient towns preserve their old quarters, the little streets with their many-coloured streamers, their booths, and their craftsmen's shops. But the modest towns of the *hsien* and the big cities like Canton, Lanchow, Sian and Chengtu, have a completely new look today. State services of every sort have been introduced: public health, husbandry, irrigation, commerce, education. Such towns are also financial centres, distributing loans to artisan and peasant co-operatives, and supplying the surrounding country with provisions. Industrial quarters are developing, and in the towns of the Great Plain and the Yangtze-kiang, as well as the big centres of the interior — Sian, Lanchow, Canton and Chengtu — factories grow up alongside modern-style workers' houses, nursery schools, workmen's clubs and trade union offices.

The old 'treaty ports' were of very different origin. Whether situated inland like Shenyang (Mukden), Hankow or Chungking, or on the ocean bays and estuaries, like Tientsin, Tsingtao or Shanghai, they had developed in less than a century, after the Western Powers and Japan had established privileged 'concessions' in the form of banks, commercial and navigation companies and factories. The *Bund,* or business quarter — a row of imposing Western-style buildings, generally situated round the harbour — was the distinguishing feature of all these towns born of the then dependent Chinese economy. On the outskirts lay the workers' quarters. These towns still fulfil their original function, but great efforts have been made to harmonise their activities and also to rid them of their slums.

A third 'generation' of towns is that of the built-up areas that have grown up as a direct result of industrial development, tentative still between the years 1925-35 but on a much larger scale since 1949. These purely industrial cities are situated mainly in the north and north-east, among them Anshan (mines and heavy metallurgy), Fushun (coal and chemical industry), Tangshan (coal, cement and spinning mills). Towns of this type are already springing up in other parts of China. The extension of the railroads also induces the growth of urban centres.

Peking, the capital, is typical of the multiple aspects of Chinese urban life today. The centre of the town, within its quadrilateral of medieval walls, preserves its traditional appearance: the sumptuous palaces of the old 'Forbidden City', artificial lakes, monumental gates, wide avenues, the grandiose Temples of Heaven and Temple of Agriculture, the little streets where the old fur, jade and silk trades are carried on. But these old quarters are already undergoing transformation: the Imperial palaces and gardens have become public parks, kindergartens, or the site of State departments. New buildings for government services, ministries

Industrial development in China has led to the springing up of built-up areas such as this one, especially since 1949.

These purely industrial cities are situated mainly in the north and north-east, but are also beginning to appear in other parts of China.

Pastures in the Pamirs. The narrowness of the Pamir range has allowed progressive erosion to drain the whole plateau; the valleys are parallel and deeply hollowed out by the rivers. Great quantities of Chinese tea, rice, porcelains, silks and other manufactured goods are traded against Tibetan furs, sheepskins, musk and gold. This thousand-year-old track, formerly the great Silk Route, connects India and China by the Mintoka Pass.

and hotels are being rapidly erected, decorated and roofed to harmonise with the ancient city. Peking is now overflowing its old boundaries. To the west and north, towards the hills, lies the academic quarter of the city, with the Tsinghua University, the People's University, the Central Academy for National Minorities, agricultural and industrial institutes of all kinds, and a school of music. To the east, in the same way, modern industrial quarters are developing.

INTERNATIONAL RELATIONS. *China and its neighbours.* Its land and sea frontiers have never prevented China from taking an active part in international life. The coastal corridor bordering China and Korea in the south has been used for centuries. Between the Little Khingan and the mountains of Kirin is the wide gap of the Sungari river, through which north-east China communicates easily with the Soviet Far East, itself in the full swing of development.

The Sino-Mongolian frontier abandons the Gobi Desert only to follow the steep ranges of the Mongolian Altai. But even in this unfavourable region

communications have been established for centuries.

The ease of communications between Sinkiang and central Asia has been of considerable historical importance. It was by these roads that silk and doubtless gunpowder and many other Chinese inventions must have reached the Mediterranean basin early in history. Along them Mohammedanism and Nestorian Christianity penetrated into China, and wheat, and perhaps bronze, earlier still.

The China-Afghanistan border is only twelve miles long. The frontier between India and China is perhaps the only region in which the term is to some extent justified, since it is formed by the Himalayas, prolonged to the west by the ranges of the Karakoram. Even here, however, there are passes. China is completely isolated from the Himalayan States of Nepal and Bhutan, whose only outlet is to the Indo-Gangetic Plain. The roads from China into India, especially those of Kashmir, were busy thoroughfares in the Middle Ages.

With Burma, Laos and Vietnam, at the end of the long list of countries bordering on China, communications are again very easy, because of the orientation of the great rivers that flow down to the deltas of south-east Asia: the Irrawaddy and its many tributaries, the Salween, the Mekong, the Black River (Song-Bo) and the Red River (Song-Koi). These constitute a series of routes, early adopted by the caravans which carried the intellectual and political influence of China abroad in the Middle Ages.

The continental character of Chinese territory should not obscure the fact that, after the U.S.S.R., China possesses the longest stretch of coast on the western side of the Pacific. While the north coast is low and muddy, except for the two rocky peninsulas of Liaotung and Shantung, the south coast is dotted with islets, bays, creeks and sheltered estuaries.

The ports of south China were visited by Arab merchants in the Middle Ages (a quarter of the town was even set apart for them) and by Japanese and Indians. It was the regularity of the monsoon in this region which, from the days of sail onwards, made it possible to establish regular maritime relations between China and her neighbours on the shores of the Indian Ocean and western Pacific.

*Trade relations resumed.* In 1949, China's principal trade partners were those industrialised countries (Western countries and Japan) which had established financial and political control over the country. In the old days only craftsmen's products and a few rare agricultural and forest products (lacquer, silk, tea) were exported. Imports consisted chiefly of Western industrial products and food products. As there was no unified Chinese national market, it was not unusual to find one port exporting some commodity produced in large quantities by its hinterland, while some other port was importing the same commodity from abroad, for which it had a local market.

The profound transformation effected since 1949 has tended principally to balance China's international trade. The country established close relations with the Soviet Union, North Korea, the Mongolian People's Republic and North Vietnam, importing from them mainly equipment needed for its industrialisation programme. In exchange, China supplied oilseeds, silk, tea and ores. Ideological disputes have led

to a 75 per cent fall in trade with the U.S.S.R. since 1960, and a rift with Mongolia.

China maintains almost equally close relations with former dependent and colonial countries of Asia, including those of Pakistan, Burma, Ceylon, Malaya —and with Arab countries like Egypt and Syria. It buys cotton, rubber, wood and oil from them in exchange for its own traditional exports.

What will be the future of the economic relations between the new China and the Western Powers? For there is no doubt that China's needs, especially of equipment, exceed what the Communist countries can supply. A new development was the purchase in 1961 of 28 million bushels of wheat and over 12 million bushels of barley from Canada. In 1962 Canada, Australia, France and Argentina provided some 10 million tons of grain. Canada contracted to ship 3-5 million tons of grains (185 million bushels of wheat) over the years 1963-6, and 223,800,000 bushels of wheat in 1966-9.

CHINA AND THE CHINAS. *Regional units and autonomy.* Administratively the old division between 'China of the eighteen provinces' and the 'Chinese dependencies' (Manchuria, Mongolia, Sinkiang and Tibet), has completely broken down. We have seen how the five-year plans and the modernisation of transport, to say nothing of the administration itself, are affecting these allegedly separate Chinas in identical fashion.

The provinces are so many little homelands, rich in traditional dress, food, folklore and individual character. Must they eventually give place to a more rational partition, based both on their physical and economic structure? The question is important and figured in the list of eleven scientific problems of which the 'Academia Sinica' decided to make an organised study. Other problems were concerned with the development of atomic energy, with highly polymeric organic compounds, oil prospecting, and the laws and problems of a transitional economy.

Recent economic evolution has accelerated the formation of strictly economic regional units; their development is the sign of regional economic specialisation dictated solely by a new, planned organisation of the national economy, which demands from each region what it can best produce and offers in exchange everything else the region needs.

The ethnic and linguistic diversity of China has set the government a difficult problem. Relations between the Hans and the national minorities have been transformed by a very flexible policy of local autonomy and by the changed conditions of home trade, and also by the plan's large investments in industry, health and education for the benefit of the minorities. It will take a long time, however, to soothe age-old antagonisms between the peoples of the steppes and mountains and the Hans. The number of dialect groups is partly responsible for the long survival of the Chinese ideographic script, the only direct means of communication between people unable to understand one another by word of mouth. It is known that the People's Government has decided not to abolish ideographic characters, but to supplement them with an alphabetic (latin) script, scientific vocabulary, and so on. This will be concurrent with the unification of the various spoken languages in favour of the dialect of Peking.

*The Chinese outside China.* The diversity of the Chinese world is further complicated by the existence of groups of Chinese emigrants outside China. Some of these groups have been settled for centuries: at Cholon in Vietnam for instance, and in the Philippines. In general the exodus coincided with periods of rural unrest at home. Today Chinese colonies are found all over south-east Asia, on the fringes of the Pacific and in countries bordering the Indian Ocean. These groups of emigrants traditionally remained in close touch with their homeland, and often sent some of their savings to the family at home.

Today movements of population continue in two main spheres: the first is the large-scale internal redistribution of population. Improved internal communications, the development of a vast national labour market and the ever-increasing demand for agricultural as well as for industrial goods, will ensure the continuation of this vital redistribution for some time to come.

At the same time, there is continued evidence of unrest and oppression in the steady stream of refugees and fugitives who make their way across the border, and who have recently created a problem of some magnitude in Hong Kong.

*The unity of China.* Age and permanence give Chinese history its distinctive character. Even at a time when Chinese economy still preserved the strictly local character it had had for centuries, there existed a single China, held together by its solid mandarin system, by its classical Confucian writings, its peasant traditions and its special forms of musical and theatrical expression. These things were strong enough to survive civil wars and barbarian invasions, and even to absorb Turkish, Mongol and Manchu conquerors. But until 1949 Chinese unity was still a fragile thing. It is now, slowly, being consolidated, and the revival of the centre, the south and west is a fundamental feature of the new China.

# TAIWAN (FORMOSA)

The island of Formosa (13,924 square miles) lies to the south-east of continental China. It is about 248 miles long, and varies from eight miles to eighty in width. Its population in 1962 was 11,375,000.

The rich soil of the mountain fields at Pulo, in Formosa, supports four harvests a year, two vegetable and two rice crops. Primitive ploughs drawn by buffaloes are still much in use, but climate and soil favour agriculture, which is Formosa's principal economic activity.

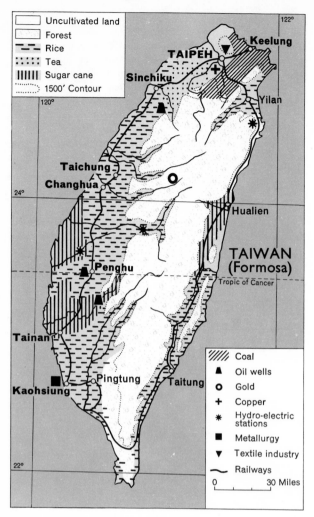

Uncultivated land
Forest
Rice
Tea
Sugar cane
1500' Contour

TAIWAN
(Formosa)

Coal
Oil wells
Gold
Copper
Hydro-electric stations
Metallurgy
Textile industry
Railways

0          30 Miles

Taiwan (Formosa), showing rural life, agriculture, industries and railroutes. The towns and cultivated areas which produce rice, tea and other tropical plants are mostly in the north and west, while the centre consists of a huge area of mountains and forests.

A main mountain chain, with saw-toothed crests, rises gradually from south to north (from 6,500 feet to 11,000 feet) and gives the island two opposing slopes. The eastern one, intersected by narrow, dense-ly wooded valleys, drops steeply towards the Pacific, the western side descends to the Formosa Strait, flattening out into a very fertile plain along the coast. The climatic zones vary with the altitude from tropical to temperate. The island is subject to monsoons.

*The island's history.* Until the end of the fourteenth century Formosa, peopled by aborigines of Malay-Polynesian origin, remained isolated. In 1621 the Dutch gained a footing in the Pescadores and later in Formosa. In 1682 the Manchu dynasty conquered Formosa and incorporated it in the province of Fukien; all foreign trade was forbidden until 1858, when the influx of Chinese immigrants enabled agriculture to be developed rapidly. In 1895 the island was ceded to Japan by the treaty of Shimonoseki, and in 1945 it surrendered to Chiang-kai-shek, who established the Chinese Nationalist Government there in 1949.

According to the Constitution of December 1946, Formosa is a republic, with a president and a vice-president nominated by the National Assembly and assisted by five councils.

Except for the 150,000 aborigines, who live in the mountains of the interior, the inhabitants are Chinese immigrants. In fifteen years the urban population has more than doubled.

*A land of agricultural economy.* Before the Second World War, Formosa supplied her own agricultural needs and exported rice, sugar and fruit to Japan. Agricultural production suffered badly during the War, but various government measures have brought it back to its previous prosperity. Seventy per cent of the farmers now own the land they cultivate, and interest-free or low interest loans have helped them to improve their equipment. Large quantities of fertilizers have been distributed, and irrigation has increased the cultivable area.

Rice, sweet potatoes, groundnuts (peanuts) and soya beans can be harvested twice a year. Spring wheat, recently introduced, appears to be successful; sugar-cane supplies a large industry; tea, bananas, pineapples and various tropical fruits are among the exports.

The area of the ricefields and the yield per acre rose substantially after 1955. Sugar-cane is harvested from November to May. The sugar industry is concentrated in a single enterprise, the Taiwan Sugar Corporation, whose production is regulated by the export quotas fixed by the International Sugar Conference.

Jute fibres harvested locally are used to make the sacks required for packing rice and sugar. Cotton, recently introduced, does not yet yield enough to supply the industry; raw cotton has to be imported.

Cross-breeding with bulls brought in from India has been gradually improving the quality of the local cattle. The breed of pig has also been improved.

The forests, very rich in a number of species, including camphor-laurels (there is a State-mono-polised camphor industry), were denuded in the War, but a programme of reforestation is being carried out. *Industrial and commercial activities.* Industry proper employs rather more than 300,000 workers. Mining and the manufacture of building materials are the most important branches. Coal mining (80 per cent of all mining) produced 4,720,000 tons in 1963, part of which was exported to Japan and North Korea. Treatment of various ores produces a small amount of gold, silver and copper. These is also a petroleum industry, and numerous minor industries, including handicrafts, sugar refining and cement works.

Formosa is obliged to import both raw materials and manufactured goods, and obtains the necessary currency by exporting foodstuffs. Its chief customer and supplier is Japan, followed by the United States. Recent trade agreements concluded with various countries of Asia have opened new markets.

Commercial transport is carried on mainly through two ports, Keelung and Kaohsiung. There is a good airport at Sungshan. Railroads tend to be confined, as do roads, to the western plain and the north-east of the island.

A first four-year plan, which came to an end in 1956, succeeded in stabilising the internal economy. In the course of the second plan (1956-60), large-scale irrigation works enabled more than 247,000 acres to be put under cultivation, and electric generating sta-tions, both hydro-electric and hydraulic and thermal, to be developed. It also provided for increased pro-duction of fertilizers and improvement of internal transport. A third four-year plan (1961-64) helped to develop food-processing industries. The 1965-8 plan envisages a 7 per cent annual economic growth rate. This should bring Formosa nearer to self-sufficiency.

# MACAO

This little Portuguese territory (6 square miles) is a rocky peninsula situated on the west side of the estuary of the Pearl River or Canton River. It is linked in the north to the island of Chungshan by a narrow sandy bar.

In 1559 the Portuguese obtained permission from the Ming dynasty to build a few trading centres. But it was not till 1887 that Macao was recognised by the Chinese government as a Portuguese possession. Ninety-seven per cent of the population is Chinese; the remainder is composed of Europeans, half-breeds, Indians and Negroes.

The peninsula and the two small adjacent islands (Tiapa and Colôane) are administered by a Governor and enjoy considerable financial autonomy. Macao is an important gambling centre in the Far East, and gambling licences constitute a major source of local revenue.

Until the cession of Hong Kong to Great Britain, Macao was the only port in China open to foreign trade. Harbour installations have spread to the west, and are frequented by sea-going vessels as well as by local junks; the transit trade in goods is run entirely by the Chinese.

# HONG KONG

*A British Crown Colony.* This colony (391 square miles) comprises, firstly, a rocky island (granite, schist, basalt) with an area of 32 square miles, situated to the west of the Pearl River, and secondly, on the continent opposite, the peninsula of Kowloon and a mountainous hinterland of low fertility, fringed by a number of islands and known as the 'New Territories'. The mile-wide strait which separates the island from the continent forms a very fine harbour. The island was ceded by China to Great Britain in January 1841, and the Treaty of Nanking of August 1842 confirmed the cession.

The size of the population has varied a great deal. Consisting, before the British occupation, of about 4,000 Chinese fishermen, it had already risen to 20,000 in 1842. Increased in 1949-50 by many refugees from continental China, the population in 1963 was estimated at 3,642,500. There has been great difficulty in finding accommodation for all the newcomers, and in 1960 a large building programme was planned to resettle about 100,000 people annually during the ensuing five years. Nearly two-thirds of the non-Chinese population is of British or Commonwealth origin.

The colony is administered by a Governor, assisted by an executive council and a legislative council.

Victoria, the capital, extends for more than five miles along the north coast of the island, backed by the central mountain (1,823 feet) on whose slopes villas rise in tiers. Excellent roads, streetcars and funicular railways offer good communications.

*Agriculture, fishing, industry.* The cultivation of food crops is being developed in the New Territories by means of irrigation. Nine-tenths of the rice, the basic food of the Chinese, has, however, to be imported from Thailand, continental China and Burma. Fishing is thriving and the fishing fleet is being modernised.

Cotton is the principal industry, with the clothing industry second; and a wide range of light industries has been developed since the end of the Second World War. The shipbuilding yards are in full production, both for repairs and new construction.

THE WAREHOUSE OF SOUTH-EAST ASIA. Hong Kong is a major business centre and a free port levying duty only on tobacco, alcohol, pharmaceutical products and perfumes. Re-exports represent 76 per cent of exports; goods of local manufacture sent abroad consist mainly of cotton materials, rubber goods, and clothing; iron and lead ores are also exported. There is also a considerable amount of local trade carried on by junks.

Kaitak airport serves fourteen international airlines. The railroad from Kowloon to the Chinese frontier (23½ miles) connects with the Chinese lines to Canton, Shanghai and beyond. Since 1949 there has been no direct passenger service.

The western part of Macao, with the Pearl River and the Chinese foothills in the background. The port was founded by the Portuguese in the sixteenth century; it is used by ocean-going vessels as well as junks.

Junks, sampans and a modern ship in the fine harbour of Hong Kong. In the background is the city of Victoria, commonly known as Hong Kong, the name of the island on which it stands. It is a key post in the Far East for Britain, and an international market of Asia.

# MONGOLIA

Mongolian landscape in the region of Bulgan. This high plateau (3,500 feet) and the heights surrounding it are drained by the rivers of the Selenga basin, but the appearance of the landscape is mainly due to detrition. The rocks split as a result of variations in temperature and the particles are carried away by the violent winds that sweep the region. Such conditions encourage the growing urbanisation of Mongolia's 1,019,000 population. Overall density is only 1.7 per square mile.

In Mongolia, horses are used for transport and for tending the flocks. The women are as good riders as the men.

The Mongolian People's Republic, established as an independent state since 1921, corresponds to the old 'Outer Mongolia'. 'Inner Mongolia', on the other side of the Gobi Desert, is now an autonomous state within the People's Republic of China. On the southeast border of the Republic, the great monotonous plateaus of the Gobi Desert rise from 3,000 feet to 4,500 feet, an unbroken desert on the Chinese frontier, and covered with barren steppes in the interior. There is little or no rainfall, but a marked difference between winter and summer temperatures. The remaining two-thirds of Mongolia contains the Mongolian Altai and Khangai, both over 13,000 feet, and the forest-clad Hentein Nuru, joining the Siberian ranges of the Lake Baikal region; fairly well watered valleys and plains separate them. The whole region is rich pastureland, with important reserves of fur-bearing animals (marmot, otter, squirrel). In these rugged

surroundings, the intrepid Mongol horesmen were bred seven centuries ago.

The whole of the northern half of the country is drained by great rivers like the Kerulen (a tributary of the Amur), and the Selenga, with its tributary the Orkhon, which empty into Lake Baikal. The lakes of the north-west form enclosed basins into which the torrents flowing from the Altai and the Khangai converge.

*Nomadic stock-breeders.* For centuries the Mongolians derived their food, the materials for their clothing and their dwellings (the *yurt* made of felt), even their fuel (dried dung), almost exclusively from intensive nomadic stock-breeding. Even today, although there is a modern currency (the *tughrik* equivalent to a rouble), wealth is still evaluated in *bodos*, a very old unit corresponding either to an ox or yak, a horse, half a camel, seven sheep, or fourteen goats.

Until the twentieth century the *arats*, or common stock-breeders, were organised under the quasi-feudal authority of their princes. Stock-breeding is still the predominant activity today, and the main endeavour has been directed at its modernisation. The production of hay, non-existent until 1921, reached a million tons in 1955 after the creation of a network of mechanised haymaking stations. Veterinary services have been established in the chief centres, and 40,000 new wells have been dug. Total livestock amounted to 25 million head in 1963, including 14 million sheep.

*Birth of agriculture and industry.* It was only very slowly, and in small numbers, that the nomadic *arats* took up agriculture and industry. The twenty-nine big State farms and a large number of co-operatives are mostly distributed over the northern part of the country and barely meet Mongolia's cereal needs.

In the industrial sphere, priority has been given to exportable products (tinned meats, woollen goods) and to activities meeting the demands of current consumption (coal-mines in Nalaikha, a generating station at Ulan Bator, leatherwork, felt-mills, saw-mills). Many of these industries derive from stock-breeding. The principal factories are grouped round Ulan Bator (formerly Urga) and Choibalsan (Bayan Tumen) on the Kerulen, near the eastern frontier.

Industrial undertakings (three-quarters belong to the State, the remainder are co-operatives) supply only about half the needs of the country. Other necessities come from Russia and until recently from China, in exchange for wool, furs, and so on. The 'Railway of the Three Nations', completed in 1955, which links Ulan Bator with Irkutsk (U.S.S.R.) in the north and with Peking in the south, played an essential part in the development of international trade. Now trade must use the long Siberian routes rather than the Chinese route. In the rest of the country the only modern means of transport is the tracked motor vehicle.

Mongolia is a country of contrasts: the yurt remains the most usual type of dwelling, but it may now boast a gramophone and many other accessories of modern life; in the towns, still few and far between, the most modern buildings rub shoulders with the yurts, and trucks with camels and yaks. Slowly economic regions are emerging (the industrial regions of the north; the hay region of the north-west), and are acquiring distinct individual characteristics.

THE EURASIAN PLAINS

# UNION
# OF SOVIET
# SOCIALIST REPUBLICS

With 8,599,000 square miles of territory, the Soviet Union is by far the largest state in the world, nearly forty times the size of France, three times as big as the United States, and twice the area of China. From north to south it measures more than 2,750 miles, from west to east more than 5,500 miles—almost a quarter of the earth's circumference. Its southernmost township, Kushka, lies in the same latitude as Crete (35° North), while Moscow and Leningrad are respectively 456 miles and 870 miles farther north than Paris.

## PHYSICAL FEATURES
## AND NATURAL VEGETATION

*Structure and relief.* A wide plain bordered along more than half its circumference by enormous mountain ranges and sloping gradually towards the Arctic Ocean forms the 'Soviet amphitheatre'. A substratum of very ancient rocks extends under almost the whole country, with occasional outcrops, especially in Karelia, on the Lower Dnieper and the Donets, near the northern Urals and in Central Siberia (the Siberian Shield). Heavy folding created the Ukrainian massif, the Valdai plateau, the heights of the Volga region, the Sayan Mountains, and the chains of Transbaikalia. The Hercynian flexures produced, *inter alia*, the Urals, the Altai and the Great Khingan. Later still, the sea formed deposits of very varied age and character. Alpine folding on the periphery of the Russian platform formed high reliefs from Kamchatka to the Carpathians, via the Stanovoi range, the Sayan, the Altai, the Tien Shan, the Trans-Alai, the Pamirs, the Elburz, the Caucasus and the Crimean Mountains. Depressions were numerous round all these faults, especially in Central Siberia. Later, the Quanternary era witnessed the great glacial invasion with its successive fluctuations: an enormous proportion of the territory is covered with glacial or fluvio-glacial topsoils.

At present the surface relief displays two main elements: the Russo-Siberian tableland and the bold relief surrounding it. The Russo-Siberian platform is low but far from flat; its relief is the product of erosion. In strong contrast is the rugged periphery with its powerful mountain ranges. The Soviet Far East is folded, faulted, and shaped by volcanic action, and between the U.S.S.R. and the rest of Asia rise majestic ranges with lofty summits, immense glaciers and deep valleys: the Altai (14,783 feet), the Tien Shan (over 22,950 feet), the Pamirs (24,600 feet) and the Caucasus (18,477 feet).

*Climate and rivers.* Russia's coastline is relatively short (37,300 miles); it is mostly low and swampy, affording little reliable shelter and almost always bordering on enclosed seas or seas that are frozen for long periods. Except on the Murmansk coast the Arctic seaboard is intensely cold, especially is East Siberia. The Pacific coast, also cold, is notorious for its fogs. The Caspian Sea, completely land-locked, has flat coasts bordering arid steppes. The seaboards of the Black Sea and the Sea of Azov are silted up at several points, and sometimes frozen. Finally, the Baltic coast is shallow, low in salt content and easily frozen, and fog makes navigation dangerous.

The weakness of maritime influence explains the eminently continental character of the climate. Except in small areas (the south coast of Crimea has a Mediterranean climate, Transcaucasia is subtropical, hot and damp, and the Far East has a harsh climate but is watered by heavy monsoon rains), the whole country is dominated in the winter by intense cold with very high presssures (the 'Siberian anticyclone'), and less marked low pressures in the summer. Sheets of icy air alternate with burning winds and the country is poorly watered. Summers are hot everywhere, even north of the Arctic Circle, and winters long and severe. Frosts lasts for three or four months in the west and south, and for eight or ten in the far north of Siberia, where mimum temperatures of $-20°C.$ ($-4°F.$ to $-30°C.$ ($-22°F.$) are normal, and $-40°C.$ ($-40°F.$) to $-50°C.$ ($-58°F.$) not exceptional.

The climate is milder from east to west and from north to south and increasingly arid from north-west to south-east. The dry lands of the Lower Volga mark the transition to Soviet Central Asia, the northern part of which has a climate like that of east Russia, but still drier and more extreme. Farther south, the Aral-Caspian region may fairly be described as a desert.

Most of the rivers of European Russia have enormous basins, gentle gradients, and tremendous length. Both European Russian and Siberian rivers freeze for several months of the year; precipitation is light, and flow is therefore relatively small. The rivers are adequate, however, because their basins are wide and evaporation over most of the year is slight. Quite apart from their wealth in fish, they have always been valuable waterways.

*Four types of natural vegetation.* The soils of the *tundra*, in the extreme north, are exceedingly poor, perpetually frozen below a certain depth. Immense stretches in the south are covered with poor greyish podzols. Farther south, the humus content increases; farther south still are the black soils (chernozem), particularly rich in humus in their upper layer and in calcium carbonate underneath.

Round the Caspian Sea, the Aral Sea and Lake Balkhash there are soils of a light chestnut colour, more saline but extremely poor in humus. This region is succeeded by a desert area whose soils are usually richer in salt than humus. Fortunately, at the foot of the mountains of Central Asia there is a tract of loess covered with typical grey soil of good quality.

There are four main types of natural vegetation: tundra, forest or taiga, steppe, and desert. On the tundra there are no trees, only creeping low shrubs and sparse brushwood, peat-bogs and immense expanses of moss and lichen, alternating with the clayey or rocky nudity of 'rocky' tundra, or with grassy spaces where polar flowers strike a brilliant note here and there. There are many birds, rodents, and carnivores. Reindeer are the most numerous of all.

The tundra is succeeded by the forest zone, corresponding roughly to the belt of podzol soils and

covering about half the territory. In Siberia and
northern European Russia it is known as the taiga, and
consists mostly of conifers, with a number of peat-bogs
and marshes. In European Russia, south of the line
Leningrad-Kostroma-Kirov-Sverdlovsk, the 'mixed
forest' has deciduous trees and resinous trees. The
forest is decidedly richer in game than the tundra.
Southwards, the wooded steppe, with mostly grey
soils, is a transition area between the true forest and
the steppe.

The rest of the Union, apart from the Aral-Caspian
deserts, forms the steppe proper, completely treeless.
On the brown soils from the shores of the Black Sea
to northern Kazakhstan and the Siberian steppes,
perennial bulbous plants and low scrub gradually give
way to grasses and salt-loving plants. Towards the
south-east lies the grey steppe, where artemisias predominate. This is succeeded by the white steppe with
its bushy or creeping vegetation, and its many salt-
loving species. Finally there is the desert.

The desert, covering the Aral-Caspian region, can
support only a zerophilous flora. There are green
meadows, however, in valleys subject to floods.
THE GREAT NATURAL REGIONS. The U.S.S.R. can be
divided into a few great natural regions, characterised
less by their relief than by their climate, the nature of
their topsoil and vegetation and, recently, by man's
influence on his environment.

*Tundra and forest.* The tundra lands form the northern
extremity of the continent, extended by the Arctic
islands. Even where altitude is low, topography is
rugged. Harshness and aridity and the extreme poverty
of soil and vegetation used to allow the very few
inhabitants (Nentsy, Komis, Khants, Chuchkis, Hel-
mens) only a precarious nomadic existence, based on
hunting, fishing and reindeer-breeding. Now, coal,
petroleum, various ores and some rare metals have
been discovered, and apatite mining in the Khibiny
Hills has fostered a vigorous mining and chemical
industry, aided by the hydro-electric power of the
Murman Mountains. A polar agriculture has sprung
up, supplying fresh vegetables to the workers in the
Kola Peninsula and on the Lower Yenisei. Towns, too,
like Kirovsk in the Kola Peninsula, and Novilisk, the
largest industrial centre of the region, with 100,000
inhabitants, have also grown up.

South of the tundras, the great Russo-Siberian
forests, or taiga, stretch from the Baltic to the Pacific,
from the White Sea to the Black Lands. The taiga is
dense and difficult to travel through but rich in game
and fur-bearing animals, especially in Siberia, where
forest industries are an important economic resource.
Agriculture, based on denshering (grubbing and burning weeds) and fallowing, yields modest harvests of
rye, oats, barley, potatoes, flax and hemp. Coal, petroleum, graphite and Iceland spar have been little
exploited so far, except for the coals of the Pechora,
gold in the Aldan and Kolyma regions, and diamonds.
Arkhangelsk, on the White Sea, is a busy port with
thriving industries. The population is mostly Asiatic,
of low density and governed by a Russian minority;
urban centres are mostly very small except for Vologda
in European Russia and Yakutsk in Siberia. Round
the forest fringe lie districts which are much more
civilised.

*South-east Siberia.* South-east Siberia includes the

Derricks on the Caspian Sea
at Baku (Azerbaijan).

An inhabitant of the taiga,
dressed in fur cap and padded
jacket, fishing through the ice
on one of the taiga rivers.

On the edge of the tundra,
in Chukotsk National Region,
reindeer dig under the
snow for moss and lichen
The trees are stunted in these
Arctic regions; farther
north they disappear altogether.

Baikal region, the eastern end of the Sayan Mountains and the Tunkin range, and to the north a complex of huge rift valleys like that of Lake Baikal (fifty times the size of Lake Geneva and considerably larger than Lake Erie), and bold gorges like that of the Angara. Then there is Transbaikalia, with little relief. Finally, bordering the indented coast of the Tartary Strait, there is Primorskaya. Much drier inland than on the coast, the climate is everywhere harsh and cold. Agriculture, struggling against the poverty of the soil, the dryness of the interior and the excessive humidity, gives low yields (buckwheat, oats, maize, wheat, soya, sunflower and fruit); stock-breeding is more successful (horses, cattle and sheep, the last predominating). There was little to attract Russian colonists to the region except its mineral resources—graphite and silver in the old days, and now copper, tin, zinc, precious stones and gold, as well as iron and coal in the Bureya Mountains. The growth of Krasnoyarsk, Irkutsk, Khaborovsk, Blagoveshchensk, Komsomolsk and the Pacific ports of Vladivostok and Nakhodka prove the success of attempts to 'colonise' this region by cultivating it and developing its industries and communications.

*The Baltic. The Great Lakes. White Russia.* Primary rocks here seldom break through a thick layer of glacial detritus. Altitudes are modest but local relief is often fairly rugged. The rivers follow irregular courses, and drainage is poor. The winter is severe; the summer is not very hot, but damp. The chequered history of the region, where very old-established populations (Estonians, Letts and Lithuanians) have been fought over by Swedes, Russians and Germans, explains the existence of numerous ethnic minorities and the curiously mixed character of the few towns. Although timber is still a major resource, cereals, artificial fodder, beet potatoes and flax have an important place. Dairy-farming is becoming the main investment. Industry is developing: Riga, Tallinn and Vilnius are important centres for mechanical engineering. Most of the large towns are ports: Kaliningrad, Klaipeda in Lithuania, Riga in Latvia, second only to Leningrad among Baltic seaports; and Tallinn in Estonia.

To the north-east of the Baltic countries lie the great Russian lakes: Ilmen, Peipus and Beloye—all three formed by morainic dams—and Onega and Ladoga, two immense lakes whose beds were fashioned by glacial erosion. The region is low-lying; harsh, damp and foggy, especially in winter; the climate and infertile soil have favoured forest growth. As a nexus of communications with the Russian seas and a great national outlet to the Baltic, the region benefited by the creation of the new capital of Leningrad, a city of more than three million inhabitants. It is also one of the largest Soviet ports, a powerful industrial centre, and one of the important intellectual centres.

Farther south, the western part of the Union (corresponding more or less to White Russia) is infertile. Its low relief is chiefly the result of glacial accumulation, and its morainic soil is mostly poor sand and clays. Badly drained, with a relatively damp climate, the country abounds in pools and marshes, but it has forests too. As a frontier zone, it has undergone innumerable devastations. The population is mixed (Byelo-Russians, Ukrainians, Poles, Lithuanians, Jews) but scanty. There are only a few large towns. Wheat, flax, vegetables and dairy-farming are increasing, but forestry remains the chief resource.

*Concentrated industry in Muscovy and the Ural region.* This is the geographical centre of European Russia and the most active and populous district of the whole Soviet Union. The Moscow basin, where low-lying plains alternate with ridges and low peaks, has a northern part, with podzol soil and a relatively damp climate, and a drier southern part, where the chernozem makes its first appearance. Agriculture (cereals, market-gardening, fruit-growing, potatoes and flax) benefits from an extensive market. There is now a greater variety of industries here than in any other Soviet region, expanding not only because of local resources in coal and raw materials but also because of the abundant supply of labour, the number of roads and railroads converging on Moscow, government protection and the re-transfer of the capital to this traditional centre of Russian life.

The textile industry, originally dependent on local crops of flax and hemp, has now turned over to wool and cotton. Metallurgy (mechanical engineering, arms and cutlery, agricultural machinery, rolling-stock, engines and cars) has now outstripped textiles in importance. The chemical industry is progressing rapidly. Muscovy, with its population of nearly 25 million, is naturally highly urbanised. Moscow is an attractive city; with eight million inhabitants, it is one of the largest cities of the world and is still growing at a rapid rate.

An asymmetrical range, with a fairly steep eastern side and a wide, gently undulationg western side, the Urals have undergone no folding since the end of the Primary era, and are completely denuded. The climate is rigorous and the soil poor. The wealth of furs, ores and timber, and the use of the Middle Urals as a passage to Siberia brought occupation to the whole range.

The Middle Urals, rich in platinum, copper, manganese, iron and a certain amount of coal, are today the seat of a busy metallurgical industry (blast furnaces, rolling-stock, machine-tools, electrical equipment). The western side has only one big metallurgical centre, Zlatoust; but the eastern side, enormously abundant in iron and containing the famous Magnet Mountain, has become one of the leading industrial regions of the Union. The growth of industry is shown in the extraordinary development of Chelyabinsk and Magnitogorsk — the latter a comtemporary creation out of nothing. There are now more than ten million inhabitants.

The borderlands of the Ural country, the basins of the Kama and the Upper Samara, form an industrial fringe of the Urals proper. The coniferous forest here gives way to the salt vegetation of the semi-desert. There is a basic Asian population with a later addition of Russians. The rapid growth of the towns in this region has followed the progress of industry and commerce under the influence of the neighbouring Urals.

*Carpathian Ukraine and Russian Carpathians.* The greater part of the Carpathian Ukraine is devoted to the cultivation of maize, oats, wheat, potatoes, hemp, beans and vines, and the remainder is given over to cattle. Except for sawmills there is little industry as yet; the towns are hardly more than market towns. The mass of the population, consisting of Ukrainian peasants formerly oppressed by large landowners, traders or usurers, was until lately among the most backward and poverty-stricken of Europe. Hungarian up to 1919, Czechoslovakian from 1919 to 1938, the country is now politically united to the Ukrainian ethnic group.

The U.S.S.R. has thus spread to the Danubian basin, partly owing to the ease with which the beskids (Russian Carpathians) can be crossed. Owing to their high humidity these mountains are covered thickly with forest except near the summits, where grassy slopes afford pasture for flocks and herds. Petroleum is almost the only industry.

*The Chernozem belt.* The country of the steppes — wooded steppes to begin with, bare steppes later — begins south of the forest zone. Its northern part is much wetter than the south, and contains the famous chernozem soil, a wide belt linking the Union from the Carpathians to the Altai, passing through the Ukraine, the Middle Volga and, beyond the Urals, through south-west Siberia.

The region of the west corresponds more or less to the Ukraine. The high fertility of the soil and the continental climate early attracted a large mixed population. Enormous expanses are given up to wheat, and sugar-beet, hemp, tobacco and sunflowers; vegetable gardens and orchards are common; horses and cattle are bred, and so are poultry and bees. Until lately the only thriving industries were those directly connected with agriculture (tanning, milling and sugar-refining); but recently coal, oil and particularly iron have been added. Fairs are an old institution in many places. There are a few large industrial centres: Poltava, Kharkov, Zhitomir, and Kiev, the powerful regional capital, with over a million inhabitants.

The Volga plateau is less favoured. The left bank of the river, remarkably low and flat, contrasts with the high cliffs of the right bank (the Zhiguli Hills). The soils are mostly excellent (chernozem and grey podzols) and the vegetation is much the same as that of the Ukraine. But the continental climate often brings catastrophic droughts. The Russian settlement, with a large admixture of foreigners, has superimposed itself on an Asian population. The most important industry was once flour-milling, but the emphasis has now shifted to oil. The Volga plateau has great timber resources in the north, and produces large crops of cereals and flax. The Trans-Volgan steppes are famous for livestock and are admirably suited to wheat-growing. The urban population has settled along the Volga, because in addition to fishing and farming the valley offers opportunities for trade. It has proved an excellent channel of penetration and colonisation, first military, then civil, In recent years industry has promoted the development of Kazan, Ulyanovsk (Simbirsk), Kuibyshev (Samara), Syzran and Saratov. Mass production of hydro-electric power and exploitation of adjacent Uralian oilfields has hastened this. Drought is combated by several irrigation schemes.

On the other side of the Urals the low-lying wooded steppe of West Siberia, with a continental climate of extremes, has been cleared, In addition to a very large production of rye, barley, oats and wheat, potatoes and flax, stock-breeding is now thriving, and the population is consequently relatively dense. A few towns have grown up, encouraged first by the passage of the Trans-Siberian Railway, and by industrial growth. The most important of these are Omsk, Novosibirsk, Tomsk and Barnaul. The Kuzbass (Kuznets basin) has also been largely industrialised. At the foot of the Altai a great many Russian settlers, as well as Tatars and Kalmucks, are engaged in stock-breeding and wheat-growing, thanks to the clearance of virgin soil, and in leather-working. Great mineral wealth has been discovered (a rich coal deposit, copper, and silver-bearing lead and gold). The iron of the Urals has turned Kuzbass into a gigantic metallurgical workshop, with locomotive works, chemical factories, cement works, tanneries, flour mills, refineries, textile factories, all employing hundreds of thousands of workers.

*The steppe regions.* The zone of the steppes suffers from poor soil and a very dry climate, so that its development has been difficult and progress rather slow.

The western region, formerly called New Russia, is the best part. Its monotonous relief includes first the Donets valley, leading from the Dnieper to the Don; then the old denuded plateaus of the Dneiper and the Donets; finally the coastal region of the Black Sea and the Sea of Azov, in which the low, broken plain of Bessarabia leads to a practically horizontal plain reaching the sea opposite the Crimean Peninsula.

Of the valley of the Donets and the plain that connects it with the Dnieper, the western part is the richest, producing wheat, vegetables, and a little rice; on the poor plateaus of the Dnieper and the Donets, scanty wheat, maize, water-melons, and fruit trees are offset to some extent by the prosperity of some kinds of stock-breeding: in the steppes bordering on the Black Sea, agriculture is fairly successful (cereals and orchards, and further east, wheat, vines, and fruit; flowers and fruit in southern Crimea). Stock-breeding is an important resource.

Industry, however, is the major concern, especially in the ports (shipbuilding yards at Nikolayev, iron-works at Kerch, Rostov-on-Don, Taganrog and Kherson, food industries at Odessa), and in some large towns of the interior (flour mills, cloth mills, mechanical engineering in Kharkov); it is supported mainly by the electrical supply from the Dnieper, the rich iron ore deposits of Krivoi Rog, and the Donets coal basin. The chief centres of this congested industrial region are Dneprodzerzhinsk, Dnepropetrovsk, Zaporozhye and Krivoi Rog; and in the Donbass, Makeyevka, Gorlovka, Kramatorsk, Lugansk and Donetsk, the heart of the Ukrainian 'black country'. The busiest Black Sea ports are Odessa, Kherson and Sevastopol.

The White steppe includes the Caspian plain, much of which is below sea level, and the valleys of the Lower Ural and Lower Volga. The soil is generally poor or useless, and the climate, burning hot in summer, very cold in winter, is too arid for cultivation. The steppes of the north, with fairly good grey soils that can be cultivated without irrigation, grow wheat. The population, mainly Asian, is chiefly engaged in stock-breeding—horses, camels, sheep and goats. The

Government has encouraged the settlement of nomads. Thousands of them are now engaged in agriculture — a trend that was hastened by the irrigation of the trans-Volgan steppes. Fishing and the exploitation of salt deposits are further valuable resources. The Ural valley is only sparsely populated; the valley of the Lower Volga alone enjoys a certain prosperity, with exceptionally thriving fisheries, flourishing market-gardens and orchards, and a long-established river and rail traffic was greatly facilitated by the opening of the Volga-Don Canal. The population is dense and the cities are increasing in size, among them Astrakhan, a great Caspian trade and fishing port, with large canning factories, and Volgograd, a river port, rail junction and also an important industrial centre.

Farther east lie the eroded steppes of Kazakhstan. Here the soil is poor; many of the rivers die in mid-course, and the largest lakes, like Lake Balkhash, are quite shallow. There are vast expanses without water at all. Until recently the only sectors of any value were colonised by the Russians — the Emba valley and the Siberian borders, with urban centres like Akmolinsk, Aktyubinsk, Semipalatinsk and Ayaguz (Serghiopol) where there were fisheries, cereals, market-gardening and cattle-raising. For thousands of years the rest of the region was a camping-ground for nomads breeding stock and fishing. Today many of the less arid 'strips' (especially in the north) are being cultivated. There has been remarkable industrial progress in north Kazakhstan. The coal measures of Karaganda, and rock salt and petroleum on the lower Emba are exploited; Dzheskazgan is the most important source of copper in the U.S.S.R.; huge iron ore deposits are worked in the Kustanay region; gold and silver are mined near the Altai, and elsewhere there are lead, zinc, nickel, phosphates. New towns engaged in the chemical industry are springing up, and old towns are expanding. The population is increasing with the fresh demands for labour.

*The Aralo-Caspian deserts.* The rest of Soviet Central Asia is chiefly occupied by the immense, almost flat plain of the Aralo-Caspian deserts. The Aral Sea (nearly three times as large as Lake Erie) is shallow, buts its fauna, both freshwater and saltwater, is fairly rich and the few dwellers on its shores live by fishing. The Caspian (245,440 square miles) is the biggest lake in the world; shallow, low in salinity, it has a fauna of surprising richness, and on its eastern shores there are some considerable deposits of salt, petroleum and ozocerite.

To the west of the deserts, rising 650 feet above the Caspian, lies the bare Ust Urt plateau. The Kazakh steppes lead to the Kizil Kum, an arid region lying between the arms of the Syr Darya. The Kara Kum region, south of the Amu Darya, is even worse. Besides the pastoral nomadism of the Kazakhs and Turkmens there is a systematic policy of irrigation, including a search for underground water and utilisation of the Syr Darya. Considerable stretches are today cultivated by former nomads now settled on the land. Potash has been found in the Ust Urt, and in the heights of Kazakhstan there are very rich deposits of copper ore.

*A majestic mountain barrier.* The steppe and deserts are bounded to the south and east by an enormous mountain barrier. Of Primary foldings worn almost level by ceaseless erosion, these ranges were 'recovered' and rejuvenated by Alpine folding, and upthrusting appears still to be going on. Erosion has been the chief agent in creating the present relief.

The Alai valley, 372 miles long and 6 to 9 miles wide, separates two rather different regions. In the north is the Tien Shan, including massifs over 13,000 feet high and to the east the great mountain cluster of the Khan Tengri (23,620 feet) containing the 37-mile Inyltchek glacier. In the upper zone of these mountains vast coniferous forests grow alongside sub-alpine and alpine meadows; the extent of the wooded areas and the quality of the pastures indicate a humidity line above which crops cannot be raised or human dwellings established.

The second region, the southern sector, includes the Trans-Alai (Lenin Peak, 22,373 feet, Peak of

The port of Odessa on the Black Sea. In addition to being the traditional outlet for the wheatlands of the Ukraine, Odessa has important oil refining and chemical plants and exports oil and petroleum products.

Gunib, a town of Inner Dagestan, eastern Caucasia. Note the upthrust syncline (part of a fold that was once concave but, disengaged by erosion, has become a crest). The aridity of the slopes, flat roofed houses and cypress trees emphasise the southern situation of Dagestan.

the Union, 24,382 feet, and Fedchenko glacier, 44 miles long, and the enormous plateau of the Pamiers (13,000 to 16,000 feet high).

South of the plains of central Asia, corresponding more or less to old Russian Turkestan, the Kopet Dagh (Turkmen Hills) are little over 8,000 feet high but the burning, arid climate deprives them of true forests and of many vegetable and pastoral resources. Habitation is possible at higher altitudes than in the north.

All these mountains have natural resources of some kind: fish (especially in Lake Issyk Kul), game, even crops in the lower valleys of the Tien Shan and the western Pamirs, and fruit trees at the foot of the Kopet Dagh. There is seasonal grazing on the hills and in the valleys for camels, cattle, sheep and goats, and at high altitudes for yaks — these animals supply the mountain-dwellers with meat, milk, cheese and leather. In the Pamirs prospecting for precious ores, lead, zinc and sulphur continues, and in the Tien Shan for arsenical ores. Construction of hydro-electric installations and a road system has begun. Some nomads have been settled in the Tien Shan, and are combining crop-raising with stock-breeding. In the Pamirs, wheat and potato fields have recently been planted at heights over 9,600 feet. In Alpine meadow areas a great effort is being made towards rational development of stock-breeding, which has a great future here. But perhaps the mountains' greatest value to date is the water they supply to the lands below. *Oases of Central Asia and Kazakhstan.* Until recently, the belt of loess at the foot of the ranges, and the valleys of the great rivers, constituted the only culti-vable lands of these regions. The *tongai* (zones subject to floods) are covered with fertile, moist alluvia, and the loess is wonderfully fertile when it has been irrigated.

In the extreme north, on the Siberian borders, the Dzhety-Su (or Semirechye), with excellent cherno-zem soil and loess, has been colonised by Russian peasants, who have built a number of irrigation *aryks,* and grow wheat, rye, vegetables and fruit. Alma Ata (Verni), Siberian, oriental and rapidly expanding, is the capital of Kazakhstan.

In contrast, the former Turkmenistan, so pros-perous in the days of the Seleucids, Sassanids and Seljuks, was ruined by war and neglect. The Trans-Caspian Railway and the efforts of the Govern-ment have begun to revive the region. In the Ash-khabad district, the Tedzhen delta and around Murgab, cotton, cereals, peas, melons and fodder are being cultivated with increasing success. Ashkhabad is de-veloping various industries: textiles, carpets, canned goods and soap.

Over 1,780 miles long, the valley of the Syr Darya and its approaches form one of the richest regions of Soviet Central Asia. The river shrinks as it crosses the desert towards the Aral Sea, but the soil is good and irrigation easy. Even upstream, the region of the Chirchik and the Arys is rich in wheat, rice, cotton and sheep. Recently the discovery of copper, lead and zinc has turned Chimkent into an important indus-trial city; while Tashkent is a junction of roads and railroads, the home of many different industries, an intellectual centre, and it also serves as the capital of Uzbekistan.

The Fergana basin is even richer. Its loess bears fine cornfields, vineyards and orchards; stock-breeding and silkworm-rearing flourish; gold, sulphur, lead, coal and petroleum are exploited, and modern indus-try is growing up alongside the old handicrafts: food-stuffs, electro-chemistry, electro-metallurgy and espe-cially textiles. Cotton has become more and more the essential product, furnishing raw material for large ginning, spinning and weaving works. Farther west, the middle and lower valleys have fewer natural advantages and are hardly developed. But south of the Syr Darya, the Zeravshan, before petering out in the desert, feeds a number of fine oases (such as Samarkand and Bukhara), in what was formerly Sog-diana. Here wheat, vines, fruit trees and cotton are grown.

Still farther south, beyond more fruit and cotton growing oases, including that of Dyushambe, capital of Tadzhikistan, is the Amu Darya; it measures 1,560 miles from its source in the Pamirs to the Aral Sea. Full-flowing but with a very slight gradient, heavy silting and a constantly changing course, it cannot easily be utilised, and its valley is mainly an unhealthy *tongai*, with reedy jungles. Its most prosperous region at present is the oasis of Khiva, where cotton, maize, rice, lucerne (alfalfa), melons and other fruits are grown. Sheep are bred, but the market has almost no industries, and the lower valley, depopulated and covered with ruins, is difficult to develop.

*Ciscaucasia and the Caucasus.* South of the arid rift-valley of the Manuch, which used to link the Sea of Azov to the Caspian, lies Ciscaucasia, the region leading to the Caucasus. Its bedrock and Tertiary formations have been largely covered by detritus carried down from the mountain chain. A low ridge running down from the Elbrus separates the basin of the Kuban from that of the Kuma and the Terek. The first, inland from a low, muddy coast, is a plain with a good chernozem soil, a continental but damp climate, and a vegetation like that of the steppes but richer than in south Russia. Mass colonisation in the nineteenth century russified the country. Horse, cattle and sheep breeding have prospered here, and so has agriculture. Industry, for long represented only by flour mills, canning factories and oil works, is now diversified and there is abundant petroleum. Maikop, Stravropol and Armavir are large cities, and Novorossisk is the outlet for petroleum.

Eastern Ciscaucasia has a dry climate and a much poorer soil. Its steppes and deserts are feeding-grounds for the camels and sheep of the Nogai Tatars, though in the valleys of the Kuma and the Terek Russian settlers grow wheat, barley, vines, fruit and vegetables. At the foot of the Caucasus the fairly well watered basin of the Ordzhonikidze (Vladikavkaz) has a good road system and produces rich crops. The region possesses hot springs, deposits of silver-bearing lead and zinc, and an oilfield at Grozny with large refineries.

The rest of Caucasia is a good deal less Russian and, with one or two exceptions, much less advanced economically. The Caucasus, 800 miles long and 60 miles to 140 miles wide, is an obstacle crossed with difficulty by cols over 8,000 feet high.

The western Caucasus, 250 miles long from the Sea of Azov to Elbrus, rises from 9,500 feet to 13,000 feet, with almost impassable cols. The high humidity extends the glaciers and produces extraordinarily dense forests. The Central Caucasus, from Elbrus to Kazbek, is only about 120 miles long, but also very difficult to cross. Much drier, at least on the north side, its vegetation is much less dense, and, except in the south, grassy slopes often take the place of forest land. The northern crest reaches 18,480 feet in Elbrus, and 16,552, in Kazbek; the southern crest, less broken but lower, forms the watershed. The eastern Caucasus, which begins at the Darial Pass, is characterised in the Khevsury Alps by soft schists, largely worn away by erosion; in arid Dagestan by a gently undulating stony plateau in which a few recent valleys touch 13,000 feet; in the Caspian range (14,700 feet) by the presence of a considerable amount of scree formed by lack of moisture and the intense mechanical disintegration of the rock.

In the western Caucasus the only favoured parts are the coast and the borders of western Ciscaucasia, peopled by Russian settlers; the interior, deserted by its Circassian or Abkhasian inhabitants at the time of the Russian conquest, is almost empty. Considering its altitude, the central Caucasus is sparsely inhabited, except in the basins of the north side. In the eastern Caucasus the population of the Khevsury Alps is also thinly scattered; in the Dagestan only the lower valleys are inhabited, though fairly densely, and the Caspian range has a few villages.

Game and fur-bearing animals abound, and the centre and the west have some fine forests. Extensive 'meadow forests' and subalpine and alpine grazing land give plenty of pasturage for livestock. Nowadays some of the meadows are sown for hay crops to feed livestock. Some valleys, those of Dagestan in particular, produce cereal crops, vegetables and fruit, but the outliers on the north side of the western Caucasus are a green, well watered zone.

*Transcaucasia and Soviet Armenia.* Transcaucasia comprises three natural divisions. In the west the lowland of Colchis is an alluvial plain with a very wet climate, a luxuriant forest vegetation, turbid rivers, a flat, muddy coast and a soil that is often swampy except on the hillsides and in the upper valleys. The latter are well favoured. Further east, Georgia proper forms a mountain frontier between the Black Sea and the Caspian, and a dividing line between two climates and two types of vegetation. This region of humps and hollows is like a dry steppe, but fertile, with irrigable districts where agriculture is successful. Still farther east lies a great sunken plain whose alluvial soil is the product of the Kura and its tributary the Araks; its central part, the Shirvan, and its southern extension, the Mugan — drier even than Georgia — form a sterile steppe in which only the valleys are cultivated. Kakhetia, in the north, has some fine forests, meadows, fields and vineyards, and so has the Nukha region. In the south the Kirovabad district, at the foot of the Armenian heights, is irrigated and well cultivated, and in the extreme east the Talish forests have been replaced by fields and gardens.

Transcaucasia has therefore many fine resources. Fishing is active in the Caspian and on the Lower Kura; the authorities are increasing vegetable crops and orchards throughout the country in an attempt to create a 'new Florida'. Sheep-breeding is the great resource of the steppes, with cattle in the cooler valleys and buffaloes in the wet lands. Industrial resources include rich deposits of manganese and coal, water power and the oilfields of the Apsheron peninsula. Alongside the old handicraft industries there are new ones: coal-mining, hydro-electric plants, spinning mills and cotton and silk weaving, hosiery and — most important — petroleum. However, the towns are slow in developing, except for Tbilisi (Tiflis) in the heart of Georgia, and Baku, capital of Azerbaijan and fourth city of the Union, with a population of 1,147,000 in 1965.

Soviet Armenia has far fewer natural advantages than the other parts of Transcaucasia. Beyond the mountainous region sometimes called the Little Caucasus, of which the Karabakh (8,166 feet) is the most noted sector, lie monotonous volcanic plateaus. The climate is dry and arid steppe far exceeds forest.

The soil is often of good quality; in the river basin and in the damp or irrigable valleys there are cereals, orchards and luxuriant vineyards, and cotton-growing and dairy-farming are on the increase. Armenian handicrafts are now partnered by large-scale industry, favoured by the country's wealth of waterfalls, stone quarries and ore deposits. Although there are only two important towns, Leninakan (Alexandrepol) and Yerevan, capital of the Armenian Republic, the country supports nearly 100 people to the square mile.

## MAIN FEATURES OF THE POPULATION

*High birthrate.* As a general pattern, population density in the U.S.S.R. decreases from west to east. Colonisation is still following the same direction.

The Russian population has increased rapidly and constantly. A high deathrate, especially among the poorer classes, was the result of the low standard of living, unhygienic housing, insufficient protection against the rigorous climate and inadequate medical care. There was considerable infant mortality. But the birthrate was higher still. The excess of births over deaths used to be well over a million a year, and the figure had nearly doubled by 1914. An increase of such magnitude set difficult problems.

The regime of the village community, with its periodical redistribution of land, was bound to bring a sharp reduction in everyone's portion if the population increased heavily; and big industry, slow to develop, offered an inadequate outlet for the increase in population. Emigration was the only remedy.

*Population movements.* Certain over-populated districts had long had recourse to temporary emigration; the north supplied mostly workmen (carpenters, stone-masons, tanners, brickmakers); the south, agricultural labourers. But permanent emigration was essential. After 1861 numbers of former serfs went to the towns and were taken on as factory workers; many more settled on the lands of the chernozem. In the second half of the nineteenth century the Russian population of the Middle and Lower Volga made an immense advance. Beginning in the 'nineties, many Russian subjects, especially those of foreign descent, left for the United States and Canada. But permanent emigration was predominantly directed towards Russia in Asia.

Russian emigration to the Caucasus colonised only the steppes of the Kuban area. Settlers in Central Asia were confronted not only by climatic difficulties, which could be overcome, but by the need to adopt new methods (such as irrigation) and by the hostility of the numerous local populations settled in the oases. Tens of thousands of Russian colonists settled in Turkestan in the trans-Caspian oases, along the Zeravshan, the Amu Darya and the Syr Darya. They flocked to the Fergana and increased the population of large towns like Tashkent, Andizhan and Samarkand. But many more immigrants went to the Kazakh steppes, where irrigation was not absolutely necessary. Driven from home by the famine of 1890, or by the agrarian crises, and attracted to Kazakhstan by land hunger, by relatively high wages and by the construction of the Trans-Aralian railroad, in 1908 they numbered 140,000 in the province of Akmolinsk alone. But the great majority of the inhabitants of Central Asia were still indigenous.

Attention had long been excited by Siberia's wealth of furs and precious metals. and the opportunities offered by its trade with China. It was invaded not only by Cossack peasants and soldiers sent by the government, but by serfs, free peasants, unofficial colonists and, more numerous still, by political and criminal deportees who were often men of ability able to perform useful services to the country of their adoption.

With the abolition of serfdom, the regime of the *mir* forced innumerable poverty-stricken peasants to go to try their luck in Siberia, only to be decimated by disease and death. The State then decided to organise colonisation itself. By planning land portions, transporting emigrants and 'scouts' at cheap rates, and finally by building the Trans-Siberian Railway, the Government gave the movement a vigorous fillip. After the Russo-Japanese War and the revolution of 1905, still greater efforts were made. Reorganised, concentrated, and furnished with a rich budget, the Board of Peasant Emigration was offered the Altai (almost the size of Spain) by the Tsar. The result was excellent: in 1914 the population of Siberia included 9,500,000 Russians.

*Mixed populations.* In three and a half centuries more than thirty-five million Russians had streamed over and beyond the frontiers reached by Ivan the Terrible. However, the populations existing before the arrival of these colonists had not been destroyed or submerged.

This was particularly true of Caucasia, which had served as a refuge for an incredible variety of peoples. There were the Georgians, with a very old civilisation, and the Armenians, whose aptitude for trade gave them great influence but exposed them to jealous hatred, increased by the fact that their Christianity represented a foreign element in a mainly Mohammedan country.

In Central Asia, the agricultural, industrial and commercial aptitudes of the Tadzhiks and their intelligence made them some of the most interesting inhabitants. The Uzbeks had great influence through numbers and dogged industry.

The ethnographic map of Siberia reveals enormous areas as non-Russian and sparsely inhabited. In the tundra only hunters and fishers really counted: the Ghiliaks of Sakhalin; the Koriaks of the coast of Okhotsk, the Ostiaks of the Uralian borders and Obdorsk, and the Chukchi, related to the Eskimos. In the taiga, the Tunguses were less important than the Yakuts, who were skilled stock-breeders, artisans and traders. In the steppe the native peoples held their ground better; the Buriat Mongols of Baikal and Transbaikalia and the Tatars (sometimes called Kirghiz) were skilled nomadic stock-breeders. Under Russian influence many of them became traders and even farmers.

In Russia, therefore, when the old regime collapsed, there existed besides the ruling population a group of supressed peoples and a group of immigrant peoples not yet wholly absorbed. The latter included about 200,000 Greeks in the Black Sea regions, 1,500,000 Germans scattered in the towns but numerous in the south-west and on the Middle Volga, where they found large agricultural colonies, and some 2,000,000 Jews, placed by Imperial policy in Russian Poland and in the towns of the west and south-west.

In Caucasia the aliens were overwhelmingly in the

Turkmens, living on the banks of
Amu Darya (Turkmenistan).
They belong to the group of
Turkish peoples in Central Asia.
The man is wearing the *chugurmah*,
a head-dress made of casracul fur.

majority except in the north-west; in central Asia
they formed five-sixths of the population. In Siberia
they formed probably no more than 10 per cent of
the population, and in Russia the Slav element was
absolute. Outside Russian Poland, where they constituted almost the entire population, Poles formed
scattered pockets in the west and south-west regions
once subject to their own country.

Historical, economic, social and geographical factors have played some part in determining this inequality. Climate was a major influencing factor: too
dry in the south, too cold in the north, better in the
centre and the south-west. The quality of the soil,
the nature of the vegetation (steppes and clearings
being far more easily cultivated than forest land) and
the presence of water also played a part.

Some towns rose in the shadow of a *kreml* — a
combination of citadel, arsenal and sanctuary; others
were ports, or the sites of great fairs like Nizhni-
Novgorod (Gorki). The industrial towns of the nineteenth and twentieth centuries (the mining district of
the Urals, the Moscow region, the Donets basin)
were dull and monotonous.

In town houses, double windows sealed with wax
in winter, powerful heating installations and enormous stoves kept out the cold. They were built of
the same material as rural houses. Except in the
Crimea and the region of the Great Lakes, stone was
reserved for monuments and the dwellings of a few
rich people. In the southern provinces brick had been
increasingly employed for several decades. Despite
the danger of fire, wood was practically the only
building material known to the north.

In the semi-desert Caspian steppes Tatar and Kal-
muck nomads live under the *kibitka,* a tent of felt
on a framework of trellis, and travelled about in
horse-drawn carts; in the frozen lands of the extreme
North, Lapp, Samoyed and Ostiak nomads lived in
canvas or skin tents and used sledges in their migrations. But the vast majority of Russians were peasants
or, more precisely, village people.

Rural housing in Russia has attracted little study.
The great estates probably encouraged the growth of
large villages, because in the absence of the landlord
the bailiffs found them easier to look after, or because
factories started up on the nobles' own lands. The
inhabitants of the steppes gathered in groups as a
defence against pillagers. Security has often encouraged
the inhabitants of big villages to spread out, and the
landlords to establish new farms. Rural housing was
much more concentrated in the south than in the
centre and the north.

*Villages and peasant houses.* The villages of Great Russia
were strung out along a single street, with vegetable
plots and walled yards behind them. Those of Little
Russia, surrounded by road and thornbush fencing,
allowed free rein to everyone's personal taste, and
instead of a modest wooden chapel there was a
brightly painted church.

In Ukraine and South Russia the *khata* was the
most usual dwelling: its basic structure of skilfully
interwoven branches was plastered inside and out
with a thick coat of mud, or covered with long
strips of dried turf, reinforced with further beams
and branches, also turfed; when dry, the whole was
plastered with clay; the roof was invariably thatched;
sometimes the walls were painted with whitewash on
the outside.

In Great Russia the *isba*, almost always low and
square in shape, was made of tree trunks; the inter-
stices were stopped up with hempen tow, and a mixture of earth, straw and reed plastered over the walls;
the roof, with widely projecting eaves, was usually
made of wood. Unlike the khata, whose outbuildings

Inhabitants of Khabarovsk
Territory, in the far east of
Siberia, working in their
village library.

The Empire itself comprised three elements. The
purest ethnically, but the poorest and fewest, were
the White Russians of the west (Upper Dnieper,
Upper Neman, Duna or Don and Pripet). Five or six
times more numerous, the Little Russians (or Ukrainians) of the south-west were the 'southerners' of
Russia. The large majority belonged to the Great
Russian group, which finally imposed its authority
over the whole of Russia, and with it the language
which has become classic Russian.

*Urban population; rural population.* One of the most
striking features of the population was its unequal
distribution and concentration.

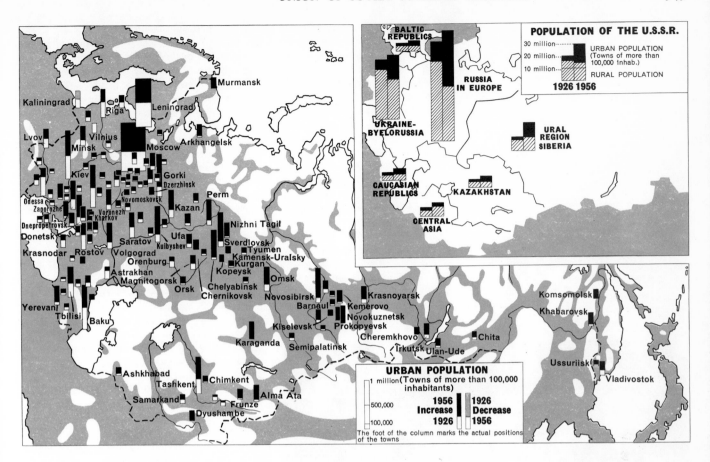

(cattle-stall, cart-shed, barn) were scattered round an

(cattle-stall, cart-shed, barn) were scattered round an enclosed yard, the isba had everything under one roof. The stove, made of several thicknesses of brick, was used for cooking, heating and as a bed. But isba and khata were alike in that they had only a few narrow openings, little light, little ventilation, and contempt for cleanliness. Epidemics were violent and recurrent and there was a high rate of infant mortality.

*Houses in Siberia, Central Asia and Caucasia.* Siberian villages looked gayer and more inviting and their streets were better kept. As a general rule the taiga zone had villages of wooden isbas, and the steppe had villages of khatas built of cob. The towns — old fortified posts standing on high river banks, or trade centres — were distinguished by their size and the geometrical layout of their newer quarters, and by the scarcity of churches and convents compared with their counterparts in Russia.

The northern regions of Central Asia had Russian villages built of wood and some of cob, and the large towns each had their Russian quarter, with brick-built houses, large administrative and scientific buildings, and wide tree-lined streets laid out geometrically. The general appearance of the towns was, nevertheless, oriental, with tortuous, narrow and dirty streets, houses with blind walls facing the street, covered markets and bazaars. The native villages of the oases were built of hardened loess, sometimes mixed with conglomerates. Immense expanses of steppe and desert had no dwellings except the nomad tent.

In Caucasia housing was rarely of Russian type. The need for defence was shown in the Georgian houses half buried in the ground, and the frequent occurrence of fortified towers and villages.

*Political and social regime up to 1917.* Government intention was to Russify the native peoples entirely in course of time, and by 1917 this had been accomplished in the case of many Tatars, Buriats and Yukats. It proved more difficult with the Mohammedans of Central Asia, and the Finns and Poles in Europe. Serfdom had only been abolished in 1861, and since then there had been no serious attempt at political or social reform. Russia was a bureaucratic state in which the Tsar endorsed the decisions of the ruling bureaucracy. Stolypin's reform of 1910 had distributed millions of acres, but these had been taken out of communal estates and the lands of the nobles were left as before. The peasants lived in ignorance and poverty aggravated by ever-increasing taxes. Russia was still a quasi-feudal state, in which murmurs of revolt could be heard.

## THE PATTERN OF RUSSIA'S EVOLUTION

*A backward state.* To endow the country with modern transport and factories, large capital investments were needed, and the meagre yields of agriculture and of a budding industry could not furnish these. Russia had therefore to seek engineers and money from abroad, and in 1914 only 53 per cent of the funds invested in Russian industry was of national origin.

Russian trade was that of a new country whose economy was still hardly developed. The volume of exports rose rapidly because industry was unable to make use of certain resources (oil, manganese, flax, etc.), and others (wheat, sugar, butter) had little home consumption.

*Reorganisation by the Soviet regime.* The Revolution of

Population growth of cities in the U.S.S.R. from 1926 to 1956. In the inset panel a comparison of the first and second columns reveals the extent to which the proportion of rural to urban population changed in thirty years. Urbanisation has been marked and rapid. The main map shows the growth of population in the chief cities of the Soviet Union during the same period: some towns have sprung from nothing since 1926, usually in connection with the industrialisation of certain areas Kalingrad (formerly Königsberg) is the only city whose population has dropped over these three decades. It is interesting to compare this map with the map showing urban growth in the United States. (*See* page 593).

1917 abolished the old governmental machinery, and in December 1922 the Union of Soviet Socialist Republics was organised, by those constructive pact Russia, the Ukraine, White Russia and Transcaucasia were united in a Confederation. Russification was rejected by the Soviets, as the cultivation of national individuality was held to be just and wise.

The Union of Soviet Socialist Republics (U.S.S.R.) is now a federation of fifteen states to which recent legislation concedes a degree of autonomy. The states are the Russian Soviet Federative Socialist Republic (R.S.F.S.R.) (capital, Moscow) and the Ukrainian (Kiev), Estonian (Tallinn), Latvian (Riga), Lithuanian (Vilnius), White Russian or Byelo-Russian (Minsk), Moldavian (Kishinev), Armenian (Yerevan), Kazakh (Alma Ata), Georgian (Tbilisi, formerly Tiflis), Azerbaijanian (Baku), Tadzik (Dyushambe, once Stalinabad), Kirghiz (Frunze), Turkmen (Ashkhabad), Uzbek (Tashkent), Soviet Socialist Republics. The names Kazakhstan, Tadzikistan, Kighizia, Turkmenistan and Uzbekistan are also used. The term 'Soviet Central Asia' usually refers to these last four.

A group of Muscovites crowding round a news-stand during a session of the Supreme Soviet.

The republics are divided into territories, regions, autonomous regions, national administrative districts, and a certain number of Autonomous Soviet Socialist Republics (A.S.S.R.). The R.S.F.S.R. has fifteen A.S.S.R.s: the Karelian (capital, Petrozavodsk), Chuvash (Cheboksary), Tatar (Kazan), Mordovian (Saransk), Kabardino-Balkar (Nalchik), North Ossetia (Ordzhonikidze), Bashkir (Ufa), Udmurt (Izhevsk), Buriat (Ulan Ude), Yakut (Yakutsk), Dagestan (Mahachkala), and the A.S.S.R.s of the Komis (Syktyvkar), the Maris (Yoshkar-Ola), the Kalmucks (Elista) and the Checheno-Ingushes (Grosny).

*The first three five-year plans.* For some years after the 1917 Revolution the economic situation proved difficult: transport was more or less at a standstill, many mines closed down, industrial production foundered, agricultural production was tragically reduced, and there was an acute dearth of produce.

'Planned production' was the objective of the five-year plans; the U.S.S.R. was to be endowed with a powerful heavy industry supported by an enormous mining output; light industry was to be developed, the cultivated area considerably enlarged, crops and stock-breeding diversified and increased in yield, and the transport system extended to meet national needs.

The State, which owned all natural resources and was directed by commissars with almost dictatorial powers, was in a position to enforce its will in economic as well as political matters. It did not shrink from the most Draconian measures, even when these included the transfer of human beings thousands of miles from their homes, a form of transplantation that proved costly in terms of human lives. A first five-year plan was put into force from 1928 to 1933.

The Government sought the aid of science and subsidised extensive research; it also applied itself to the rational organisation of labour. Combines made their appearance — groups of factories employing methods of concentration in both a horizontal and a vertical direction.

Where direct loans were not obtainable, long-term credits were negotiated abroad. The Government borrowed from the population of the Union; above all, in order to pay for its foreign purchases by mass exportation, it levied an enormous proportion of the harvests at very low prices. Forty per cent of the natural revenue was devoted to the needs of the plan. This brought a great decline in the general standards of living.

To increase the output of industry, night work was resumed, with piece-work and assembly-line production. The collectivisation of landed property did not always work smoothly; stock-breeding met with disaster, industrial prices remained high and quality poor, foreign trade was much reduced — but the first plan attained a good many of its objectives. The kulak class (the small minority of wealthier peasants) was suppressed, collectivisation of the land advanced widely, industrial production more than doubled, the working population was increased, various large-scale works were completed, there was a marked drop in illiteracy, and military power was strengthened.

A second five-year plan began in 1933. Despite the need to give pride of place to the development of heavy industry in view of the pressing threat of war, the plan succeeded in doubling the production of consumer goods and increasing that of agriculture. Then, on the eve of the Second World War, a third plan was put into operation, concentrating above all on the chemical industry, for the problem of fuel and power was a vital one.

THE EVOLUTION OF SOVIET ECONOMY 1928-39. *Agriculture modernised.* Natural conditions, as we have seen, are not all favourable throughout Russia. There are some good soils in the territory, some moderately good, and many that are impossibly poor. The climate is often unfavourable; the snowfall is usually too slight to afford any protection to delicate vegetation and drought is also a constant fear. In a country in which long winter idleness forces the peasant to earn enough in a few summer months to keep him for the rest of the year, a good harvest can be expected in only 5 per cent of the territory. Human conditions, in contrast, lend themselves to planned improvement.

Collectivisation was practically completed during the second five-year period during which 93 per cent of all undertakings were collectivised. Between 1928 and 1941 about 4,000 sovkhozes were also created, immense State farms usually of 75,000 to 150,000 acres or more. These were committed by government orders to specialised production. However, hasty organisation in the sovkhozes, poor management and lack of qualified personnel often brought financial difficulties.

The new Russian agriculture was founded chiefly on the kolkhozes (collective farms). The peasants formed agricultural co-operatives or collective farms by pooling their lands, cattle, farm implements and stocks of seed. In practise, the kolkhoznik retained a small individual holding consisting of his cottage, the garden adjoining it (from half to three-quarters of an acre), and a paddock for his own livestock. He was a paid labourer in the kolkhoz. It took some years for this system to become finally established against the open or convert resistance of the peasants.

In addition to co-operative efforts the mechanisation of agriculture was undertaken in the hope that it would lead to a big increase in the area of tilled land, and that hope was fulfilled. With persistent effort and at enormous expense a polar agriculture took shape around Igarka, in particular, and in the Kola Peninsula, an enormous areas were won for cultivation in the Urals, in Kazakhstan, Central Siberia and the Far East.

*The world's largest cereal production.* Between the two wars a persistent effort was made to give production a rational and industrial character. At the end of 1940 the rural population appears still to have constituted some 67 per cent of the Soviet total; the variety of agricultural produce was no less impressive than its volume.

The rotation of crops was still based on cereals, together with beet, potatoes and a certain textile plants. Sown lands, in full yield, occupied more than 240 million acres in 1939, and the harvest of wheat, rye, oats and barley represented a good third of world production.

Cereals, then, had advanced, but at the same time other crops were eating into the corn-lands as a part of the crop rotation system. The potato harvest in 1939 provided a quarter of world production. The yields were small, but the acreage was constantly increased. In 1939 the Union provided a quarter of the world beet harvest. Hemp and flax production had also risen considerably. Cotton, introduced with striking success into Transcaucasia and the oases of Turkestan under the Tsarist regime, was revived and vigorously encouraged by the Communist regime, which adopted as its slogan in Central Asia 'Water for Cotton'. The area devoted to cotton more than doubled between 1928 and 1940, and the harvest quadrupled; only the United States and India surpassed the U.S.S.R. yield. Other industrial crops, such as tobacco and oil-yielding plants, were much smaller by comparison, and the percentage of areas devoted to nurseries, fruit-farms and market-gardens was minute, pointing conclusively to an insufficiently developed agriculture.

The new regime gave fodder its due place in the rotation of crops by increasing sevenfold the area it had covered in 1913; the problem of the rotation of crops, however, had not been wholly solved at the outbreak of war in 1939.

*Crisis in stock-breeding.* The contempt in which stock-breeding had almost always been held in old Russia was evident in the niggardly space allotted to fodder crops and in consequent malnutrition of the animals. Early attempts at collectivisation, however, had had disastrous effects. Rather than abolish their beasts to a kolkhoz, many kulaks preferred to slaughter them. The 'collective' care of the stock also had a ruinous effect on the animals' health and their yield. Permission had to be given to the kolkhozniks to keep a few head of stock on their own smallholdings, which did much to reconstitute the national livestock.

The cultivation of some kinds of smaller stock showed some promise — silkworm-breeding, for instance, in Transcaucasia and Fergana, though the authorities did little to encourage this. Bee-keeping was far more extensive. Poultry-farming provided quite a substantial resource in the provinces of central Russia, the Urals and West Siberia.

Mechanisation of agriculture was increasing but transport draught animals were still bred locally. Dogs

Women share in the task of harvesting wheat in the Ukraine.

were bred for draught purposes in the polar regions, and reindeer were indispensable in the frozen lands of the north.

The poor quality of most of the cattle reflected the lack of good pasturage. The stock of horses had only partly recovered its strength by 1939.

Sheep-breeding suffered a similar crisis although natural advantages were offered by the grazing grounds in the steppes of the Black Sea, the Caspian, Central Asia and even Siberia. A serious effort had to be made towards better selection and better feeding. The settlement of nomadic sheep-breeders was encouraged and the area of sheep-breeding extended, especially in Turkmenistan and Kazakhstan, but by 1938 there were still 30 million too few.

Only pig-breeding — traditionally prosperous — was wholly successful. Collectivisation had reduced its strength by about two-thirds, but so energetic was the effort to revive it that by the end of the second five-year plan the 1928 figure had been exceeded.

To sum up, what Soviet agriculture had so far

An open-pit coal mine in eastern Uzbekistan. The Fergana valley contains one of the numerous newly developed mining centres in the Soviet Union.

As it also has water-power, oil and uranium resources it is an important supplier of energy. The U.S.S.R. is extremely rich in mineral resources. They are widely distributed and by no means fully exploited: vast deposits are believed to exist in Siberia, but the basins have not yet been fully explored. The Government has encouraged the growth of local industries near the source of raw materials or of power, for transport is difficult and expensive.

accomplished was impressive: though it was still insufficient, prodigious transformation had at least provided the basis for systematic industrialisation of the U.S.S.R.

*The rise of industry.* Russia's wealth in sources of energy and raw materials are all being tapped. A line of rich deposits stretches along Primary massifs continued from those of central Europe: the Donbass or Donets basin, whose yield increased sixfold between 1913 and 1940; the Kuzbass or Siberian basin of the Kuznetsk; and the Karaganda basin in Kazakhstan, estimated to have reserves of thousands of millions of tons of coal. The U.S.S.R. possesses several other coal deposits, and many beds of lignite and peat. Russian Asia is well endowed with enormous coal wealth. Soviet output went up from 19 million tons in 1913 to 191 million in 1941, and national deposits were evaluated at one-fifth of the world's coal capital.

After the collapse following the Revolution, a successful attempt was made to increase oil production. Mechanisation of agriculture, among other things, made it a necessity. The Caucasus continued to be the chief supplier, with the oilfields of Gronzy, Maikop and Baku; and the exploitation of the Emba and Sakhalin fields was greatly increased. Meanwhile, concentrated prospecting led to the discovery of oil in many places. Output reached 38 million tons in 1941, compared with 9,200,000 tons in 1913. Russia-in-Europe alone was found to have about fifteen deposits of natural gas.

The U.S.S.R. has many good low and medium

heads of water power, including the rapids of the Dnieper and those of the Svir-Volkhov system, the tributaries of the Kama, the Syr Darya and the Amu Darya, and the great Siberian rivers. But most of this is only 'summer horsepower', made useless in winter by freezing. With few exceptions, the regions really rich in water power are those near the mountainous borders of the country, far from the densely populated and highly industrialised districts most in need of energy. In 1940, of the 40,000 million kilowatt-hours output, only one-eighth was produced by high falls, and the U.S.S.R. was mainly using power from low-head sources with a big output.

Water power alone could not solve the problem of electrification. A number of thermal stations had to be built, some run on oil (Caucasus), some on low-grade coal (Urals, Moscow), others on natural gas, and a great many on peat (Gorki, Leningrad). With an output approaching 40,000 million kilowatt-hours, the U.S.S.R. had attained third rank in the world by 1939, whereas in 1913 it had ranked fifteenth. Electrification of the railroads had been started, and both public and domestic lighting was increasing in towns.

*Wealth of raw materials.* Throughout its northern half the Union has enormous timber resources covering 2,000 million acres (a third of its territory and nearly a fifth of the forests of the world). In 1939 forest land provided annually over 6,000 million cubic feet of timber—oak, walnut, cedar, birch, lime, elm, hornbeam, and a large quantity of pine and fir. From the start of the five-year plans a great effort was made to extend the centres of exploitation towards the north-east, and to organise and equip them on more modern lines.

In addition to timber, the forests produced a wealth of furs, especially of valuable kinds. The Caucasus still possesses a varied fauna (marten, otter, fox, lynx, bear, panther), and so does Central Asia (tiger, leopard, panther, bear, wild boar, fox); while in Siberia, in the Altai, the Krasnoyarsk territory, Yakutsk, Kamchatka and the Far Eastern Ussuri region, the forests teem with sable, ermine, marten, otter, squirrel, silver fox, lynx, cheetah, wild boar, bear, panther and tiger. Lest the Siberian forest, like the Russian forest, should become impoverished as a result of greedy exploitation, the Soviet government collectivised hunting and brought it under strict control. Reserves were established over a total area of several million acres. This measure aims at safeguarding native species and acclimatising foreign ones, including muskrats and North American skunks.

The Soviet régime soon began reorganising both river and sea fishing. At the beginning of World War II, 142,000 fishermen had been grouped in 810 freshwater and 830 saltwater fishing kolkhozes; annual catches amounted to about 160,000 tons, of which 30,000 to 40,000 was freshwater fish. Fish, always a large part of the Russian diet, is now the basis for a very big canning industry.

With its wealth of wheat, oats, barley, beet, potatoes and oil-yielding crops, the U.S.S.R. was able to start a number of flour mills, breweries, sugar factories, refineries, distilleries, potato-starch works and oil works. Stock-breeding, though still inadequate, helped to supply a fairly extensive milk, butter and

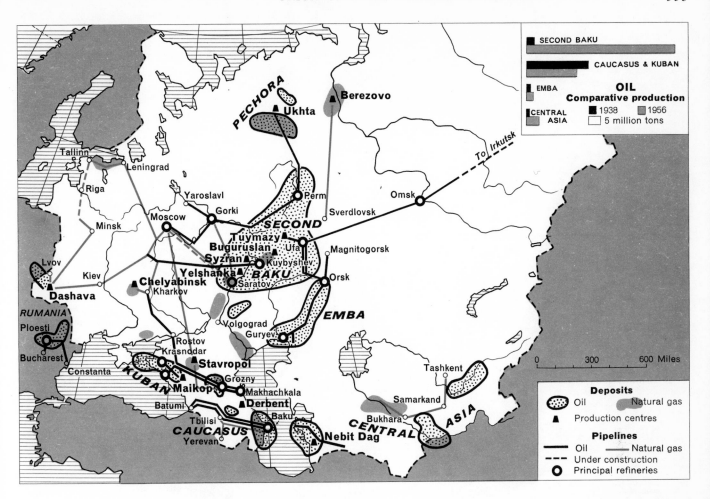

Chief oil and natural gas deposits in the U.S.S.R. The traditional oil-bearing regions are Caucasia (Baku, Grozny, Kuban and the Black Sea and the Maicop region) and Emba, in Kazakhstan. These have now been surpassed in importance by the second Baku field, situated between the Urals and the Volga. This field is the most important in the Soviet Union and supplies the eastern regions by pipelines. Natural gas, which is found either together with oil or separately, is also distributed to the large cities by pipelines of as much as 550 miles in length.

cheese industry, and sausage and tinned meat factories. In the rubber industry, the yield of latex plants had hardly progressed beyond the stage of promise. The textile industries also had the benefit of substantial native supples.

The Urals are rich in precious stones (diamonds, rubies, sapphires, emeralds, opals, topazes, amethysts, jade) and in tungsten, chromium, molybdenum, titanium, palladium and osmium—in short, all the rare metals required for the manufacture of special steels. These metals are also found abundantly in the Far East, Karelia and the Kola Peninsula. The mines of Chiature in Georgia and those of Nikopol in the Ukraine allowed the U.S.S.R. to supply 40 per cent of the world's manganese production in 1941.

The Union was no great producer of silver; but from 1938 onwards Soviet platinum seemed in a position to recover first place in world output. Even under the old régime the various gold mines had together produced a total of about sixty tons a year. The search for gold was actively and energetically pursued, regardless of the enormous expense. In 1929 only 23 goldfields were known; in 1940 Kazakhstan alone had 360 reefs, and many others had been discovered in the Kola Peninsula, in Svanetia, Baikalia, Primorskaya and Yakutia. The exact output was not revealed, but it seems certain that towards 1939 it was nearly 300 tons a year, and that the Soviet untapped gold reserve was among the world's largest.

The Union possessed nearly all the useful minerals, often in vast quantities: potash and soda, phosphates,

salts of various kinds, the fossil mineral known as ozokerite, graphite, asbestos, bauxite, mercury, tin, zinc and lead. Copper was plentiful, but supplies were much smaller than those of America. The U.S.S.R. was beginning to regain its superiority in iron ore, and deposits of manetite and haematite had been discovered, amounting to thousands of millions of tons. It was established that the famous Kursk Magnetic Anomaly discovered in 1783 was caused by the presence of an enormous deposit of iron ore. This must be one of the largest metalliferous basins in the world. The U.S.S.R.'s output of iron for 1942 had been forecast as 40 million tons.

*Progress in industry.* The textile industry, most prosperous of all under the old regime, had been least developed by 1939. The fur industry, which now prepared the skins at home instead of exporting them unprocessed, was in better case; but the leather industry, particularly boot and shoe manufacture, remained backward.

Before 1917 there were few branches of the food industry that were not found in Russia, specialised according to the agricultural produce of the different regions. Although tinned fruit and vegetables did not at once assume much importance, in 1939 tinned meats were in mass production and there were as many fish-canning factories as there were fishing kolkhozes.

The chemical industry was the creation of the Soviet regime, for in 1917 it was practically non-existent. even in the ports of the west. The metallurgical

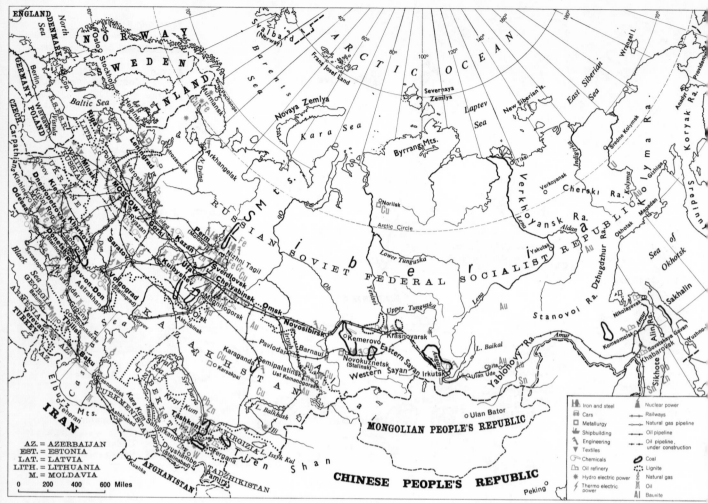

The Soviet Union is rich in mineral deposits. It has been claimed that the Union contains more than 50 per cent of the world's resources in manganese, iron ore, potassium salts, and apatite, and nearly one-third of its phosphate. In addition, the Soviet Union extracts substantial quantities of copper, zinc, lead, aluminium, cadmium, tungsten, graphite, gold and silver. Coal production is increasing and is almost completely mechanised. Oil, originally exploited only around Baku on the Caspian Sea, has been found and developed more recently in the Southern Urals and the Volga basin. Uranium deposits are worked in Taboshar, Adizhan, Slyndianka and on the Kolyma River. Efforts to establish major industries east of the Urals, in Siberia and in the Soviet Far East have met with some success.

industry was originally concentrated on three main points: the Ukraine (Krivoi Rog), the Urals (Magnitogorsk) and the Kuzbass (Novokuznetsk). These three have been joined by those of Leningrad, Muscovy, Transcaucasia, and Bureya in the Soviet Far East.

The advance in heavy metallurgy facilitated the rise of constructional engineering. It produced chiefly rolling-stock, tractors, automobiles and ships.

The birth and progress of numerous ancillary industries must also be noted, including the manufacture of watches, scientific apparatus, cameras, radios, and musical instruments. The building industry attained enormous prosperity.

Soviet industry had shifted its centre of gravity eastwards. Formerly mere reservoirs of raw material and commercial outlets for Russia-in-Europe, the *okrainy* (literally 'extremity') had industry mushrooming everywhere. The old-established industrial regions—Leiningrad, Muscovy, the Central and Southern Urals, South-East Ukraine—retained their preponderant importance; others were created, mainly on the northern border of the Altai, on the Middle Volga, in the Kola Peninsula, on the Pechora, in Transcaucasia, the Far East and Kazakhstan.

Industry had its failings: costs were high and quality often poor, and any attempt to compete with other nations for foreign markets would have been bound to fail. Either because the country had first to be given the means of equipping itself, or because of the pressing threat of war, heavy industry had advanced

far more rapidly than light industry, which was not yet able to supply sufficient consumer goods.

The Government, aware of the gravity of the problem, made every effort to solve it.

*Roads.* One of the greatest problems was to construct roads. The second five-year plan had provided a fresh and determined effort for the benefit of the western part of the Union, and also of Siberia, Central Asia and Caucasia (one road, 435 miles long, climbed to 15,400 feet to cross the Pamirs; another, joining the Caspian to the valley of the Amu Darya, crossed the desert of Kara Kum), and in 1938 the Union possessed almost 148,000 miles of roads open to motor traffic in all seasons. But of the theoretical 850,000 miles of total road system, 712,000 miles were no better than miserable tracks, so that this system could not possibly suffice for increased needs. The third plan (aimed at trebling the number of motor vehicles, building new roads and improving the existing ones) was difficult to carry out, hampered by climatic conditions, sparseness of population, the remoteness of the villages and the financial burdens entailed.

*Importance of waterways.* With the five-year plans a great effort had been made to restore the waterways which had been totally disrupted by the Revolution and the Civil War. Improvements were carried out at the principal river ports; plant was renovated, many rivers were canalised and, more important still, many canals were dug. The two principal ones were the Stalin Canal or Baltic-White Sea Canal (140 miles long and connecting the two seas by way of the Neva, Lake Ladoga, the Svir and Lake Onega, with a succession of eighteen locks) and the 75-mile Moskva-Volga Canal which, with its huge reservoir basin of 7,800 million cubic feet and a five-stage lock could accommodate ships of 10,000 tons displacement and 13 feet draught. In addition, the Mariinsky system and the old Berezina Canal were renovated to improve connections between the Baltic, the Volga and the Dnieper. The lower reaches of the Dnieper were opened to regular navigation by the famous 'Dnieproges' dam, a preliminary of the great plan to connect the Arctic, White, Baltic, Black, and Caspian seas, one of the main features of which was the digging of the Volga-Don Canal; this to be combined with the harnessing of the Volga itself and the irrigation of the Volga steppes. Good progress was made: in 1939 inland navigation traffic had almost trebled in seven years, but it still represented only 8 per cent of the total volume of traffic operating in the country at that time.

*Inadequacy of the rail system.* The rail network, incomplete, inadequate, with a layout that betrayed the Tsarist intention of subordinating the interests of the okrainy to those of the mother country, was one of the first victims of the revolutionaries. At least a quarter of the track had to be repaired, and two-thirds of the locomotives had been rendered useless. From 1928 to 1938 only 4,350 miles of new track were laid; the main effort was to be for the benefit of the backward okrainy. The Akmolinsk-Karaganda line was built, and the famous Turksib, which was 894 miles long, formed an economic connection between Turkestan and Siberia, enabling the former to specialise in the production of fruit, vegetables and cotton, and the latter to supply cereals, fodder, timber, hides and metals.

Even this achievement was inadequate, and the whole of economic life was seriously hampered by the lack of rail communications. The second plan increased personnel, increased and improved rolling-stock, doubled several important lines, electrified many more, and built new ones.

This was still not enough, and the third plan provided for yet more new lines, several of which were ready for use in the first months of the war.

By 1940 the system covered 65,900 miles (including 19,000 miles of double track, more than 1,200 electrified, and 10 per cent provided with automatic signalling apparatus). Constantly extending, in the okrainy even more than in the centre, it was able to provide 94 per cent of passenger transport and 90 per cent of goods transport. It was still incomplete (little over 7 miles per thousand square miles), and its rolling-stock, of different gauges to start with, was dangerously overworked and worn out. It is now known that Hitler relied heavily on the inadequacy of the rail system for his victory over the Soviet Union, and his calculations came remarkably close to being correct.

*Air transport.* In so vast a country air transport was an absolute necessity. Only this and radio could enable the central power to retain permanent control over certain outlying territories, particularly in the Far North. Speeds were low, time-tables unreliable, but in 1939, 200,000 passengers and 50,000 tons of freight

(chiefly postal freight) were carried; activity was increasing yearly, and there could be no doubt that commercial aviation had a great future.

*The problem of maritime traffic.* The prospects of maritime traffic, less favourable in this country of under-developed and mostly inhospitable coasts, slowly improved. By 1939 the 1928 tonnage had more than quadrupled, and some of the greatly modernised ports had become very busy. Such were the timber ports of Arkhangelsk, Murmansk and Leningrad. The Black

Sea ports also expanded; traditional exporters of wheat, they now exported petroleum and finished or semi-finished goods.

Recovery was undeniable; in 1938 nine-tenths of the Union's foreign trade was sea trade. From 1931 onwards the Government began investigating the possibilities of a northern sea route. Repeated air reconnaissances were carried out; polar stations were established, small ports equipped, including Novy Port and Salekhard (Obdorsk) at the mouth of the Ob, and Igarka at the mouth of the Yenisei. Crossing the eastern end, the coldest and most dangerous part of the route, remained a difficult operation to attempt. But a firm connection was established between north Russia and the mouth of the Yenisei and a regular flow of trade was assured.

THE RESUMPTION OF FIVE-YEAR PLANS. The ruins left by the war were beyond description; the official total estimate was twenty times that of the damage suffered by France and Belgium in 1914-18. In all, 1,710 towns and villages had been razed by fire and transport had been badly disrupted; 70,000 villages and hamlets had been destroyed (about 6 million buildings) and 98,000 kolkhozes and 1,876 sovkhozes devastated; 175 million acres (twice the cultivated area of France) had been reduced to 'scorched earth'; 47 per cent of the sown lands—often the best—was lost to Soviet production. The cereal harvest was reduced by 38 per cent, and that of sugar-beet by 84 per cent.

But worst of all was the appalling loss of life, especially in the western provinces of the Union. Leningrad had 600,000 dead and a million missing;

Logs floating down a river to the sawmills. Wood is one of the Soviet Union's great natural resources, for forests cover over a third of its total area. The U.S.S.R. occupies first place in the world for the volume of timber felling and for the output of sawn timber. Excluding collective farm production, output in 1964 was 260 million cubic metres.

White Russia lost a third of its inhabitants. In all, the U.S.S.R. lost 17 million people, of whom about half were civilians.

*Demographic recovery.* With impressive social ardour, men and women laboured strenuously to rebuild the ruins. Measures were adopted to give more security and assistance to families. These, together with a rise in the birthrate that is usual after war, ensured a rapid increase in the population. Inevitably, large capital investments were involved. The housing crisis was still acute, and after 1947 it appeared less necessary to encourage population growth. Today the population of the U.S.S.R. is over 229 million inhabitants.

The devastated regions were repeopled and regions previously neglected were developed. When hostilities ended there was an immediate mass return to the west by the refugees who had sought escape from invasion in the eastern provinces. This movement ended in 1946 and economic necessity prompted the redistribution of the population.

The new regions, even the north, were fast becoming industrialised, and the workers often came

A bird's-eye view of Volgograd, formerly Stalingrad. Volgograd is a river port linking the Volga to the Don and the Donbass. It was the scene of one of the biggest battles of World War II; reduced to a heap of rubble in 1944, it is a symbol of reconstruction today. It has a population of over 590,000.

from rural areas. As before the war there was an exodus towards the urban centres and again the growth of urbanisation was rapid.

*The fourth five-year plan.* The intense war effort had paved the way for economic expansion as well as military victories. To make up for the temporary loss of the harvest yields of west, south and central Russia, immense territories had been won for cultivation in Siberia and Central Asia; in all, in 1942, nearly 5 million more acres were sown than in 1941. Machinery and technicians in the industrial regions threatened by invasion had been transferred to the Urals and Siberia. National safety now demanded an intense effort towards streamlining production, increased output, and the greatest possible utilisation of all local resources, in order to reduce the transport of raw materials and fuel. Several new mines were opened, as well as thermo-electric and hydro-electric generating stations and industrial works of all kinds, among them the new blast furnaces of Magnitogorsk.

Even so, the industrial output of 1945 was barely

three-fifths of the 1940 figures, and the output of agriculture was smaller still. The fourth five-year plan (1946-50) had therefore to be chiefly a plan of reconstruction. By mobilising four million workers, who increased output from 15 to 20 per cent, it aimed to increase coal and petroleum production beyond pre-war figures; to develop equipment industries (especially foundries, steelworks, sulphuric acid works and automobile works), to restore the whole of the destroyed rail system and add new lines; and to electrify about 3,700 miles of line.

In 1950 transport was still highly inefficient and provoked endless criticism. Hydro-electric output was still below the country's potential; the ores of some kinds of non-ferrous metals were being mined in too small quantities, thus causing bottlenecks in the equipment industries; the backwardness of industries producing consumer goods was notorious, and the housing shortage was still acute.

*The fifth five-year plan.* The aim of the fifth plan was to increase national revenue by 60 per cent and the total output of industry by 70 per cent by speeding up development of sources of energy and the basic industries, and to stimulate the production of industrial and agricultural consumer goods (including houses).

While the plan launched several vast undertakings and effected economic advance, about one-third of its aims could not be accomplished in the time. Consequently a sixth plan (1956-60) was drawn up. In 1957 schemes for decentralising industry and agriculture necessitated the adoption of a seven-year plan (1959-65). As a measure of its success industrial output in 1965 was 84% above that of 1959.

The aims of the twenty-year plan (1960-80) are to increase production as follows: electric power, ninefold; oil, fivefold; coal, double; grain, double; milk, treble; meat, fourfold. Two new iron and steel centres are to be developed in Kazakhstan and in Kursk region. A thirty-five hour working week is expected by 1970, and housing, water, gas, heating, public urban transport and school meals are to be free by 1980. Such is the measure of economic and social recovery.

*Regrouping of kolkhozes. 'Agro-towns'.* Collectivisation of farms was still in force, and had even been increased. But it was impossible to cultivate the often minute kolkhoz units scientifically and employ costly mechanical equipment to advantage. If the number of kolkhozes was greatly reduced by regrouping in large units, output would improve and thereby increase production, besides freeing more kolkhozniks for industrial tasks and reducing redundant personnel.

The reform came into force in 1949; the average farming unit was increased to at least 2,900 acres, and the number of kolkhozes reduced by about 60 per cent.

Uniting several kolkhozes led to concentrating their populations in one large community of, perhaps, 9,000 to 10,000 inhabitants, where living conditions might be established approaching those enjoyed by workers in the towns. Some of the planners wanted to go further still, and advocated the foundation of *agrogorody* ('agro-towns'), each of about 10,000 inhabitants. This appears to have been set aside.

*The fight against drought.* Other changes included the harnessing of the Volga. The Moskva-Volga Canal had been opened in 1938, and regular artificial seas had been created behind the dams. But farther down-stream the Middle Volga was unable to take ships of more than 10,000 tons, and work on this stretch could not be resumed until 1950. About that date, important constructions were completed in Asia, including the Przhevalsk line, east of Lake Issyk Kul and the line from Dyushambe (Stalinabad) to Kurgan-Tyube and Pyandzh, to allow exploitation of the cotton-growing valley of the Vakhsh.

Drought attacks the steppes once in four years, and the Volga plain once in three. Besides burning up the crops, it lays the soil open to furrowing by rainstorms and denudation by wind action. At the end of the last century, experiments in the stony steppe between the Volga and the Don showed that the creation of forest belts reduced the drying effect of the *sukhovei*, blowing from the east. It was therefore decided to carry out a fifteen-year plan (1951-65) to transform the steppe into a wooded region with many large clearings.

Irrigating large areas of the steppe entailed building powerful dams and digging canals. These irrigation schemes were usually linked with hydro-electric generating stations, since the need for irrigation was usually associated with need for electricity.

Among the large-scale undertakings the Dnieper dam is one of the most important. The harnessing of the Middle and Lower Volga, an even more grandiose scheme, had a triple aim: improvement of navigability, production of power, and irrigation of extensive land areas. Work was resumed in conjunction with the construction of the Volga-Don Canal.

The Asiatic provinces were also scheduled for numerous schemes of this nature. In the region of Kuban, for instance, south of the Manuch Depression, and the Georgian steppe of Samgora, to the east of Tbilisi (Tiflis), agriculture has recovered since the opening of canals irrigating nearly 200,000 acres of field and meadow, and in the desert of Kara Kum, whose soil seems to be very fertile in itself and only in need of water.

The U.S.S.R. hoped to reclaim by irrigation works a total of about 70 million acres, either for cultivation or for stock-breeding, through the extension of permanent pasture and the increase in artificial feeds. The unprecedented size of the undertaking demanded exceptionally powerful technical equipment, almost total mechanisation of work, and machines with stupendous output.

*Increase in sources of energy.* Soviet industry has many post-war successes to its credit in the sphere of energy. So far it had exploited very little of the national water-power potential. In fifteen years coal-mining more than doubled. The rapid repair of the Donbass undoubtedly contributed to this spectacular recovery, as well as extensive mechanisation in the mines and the adoption of new techniques such as hydraulic working and underground carbonisation, and the recruitment of a younger and more efficient labour force. The main reason, however, for increased coal production was the opening up of the Asiatic basins.

Immediately after the war it seemed unlikely that the oilfields could recover. But the crisis had been surmounted by 1951; remarkable technical progress and the recovery of oil from prematurely abandoned

wells put the industry on its feet again. New fields were exploited. Though Baku continued to keep the lead, the resources of the Emba, the northern Caucasus, Central Asia and the Far East had now been supplemented by those of the Pechora (Ukhta) and of the 'Second Baku'. The U.S.S.R. developed its refining and cracking capacity by establishing oil refineries near the places of consumption or the oil-fields themselves. It is difficult to estimate the U.S.S.R.'s uranium reserves; there are few countries in which research and achievement relating to atomic industry have aroused so much interest.

*Increase in metal production.* In the absence of precise statistical data it is impossible to make a close estimate of the progress in gold-mining, still less of the Union's gold resources. They are enormous, and of late their wealth has been continually confirmed. The Selenga basin in the Far East, and the reefs in Kazakhstan, the Urals, Transbaikalia, the Aldan, the Yenisei, the Lena, and the rich placers of the Kolyma Range represent an inestimable capital.

The Lenin hydro-electric generating plant, a vast undertaking completed in 1951, whose capacity is 2,500,000 kW. Its construction was part of a project to provide hydro-electricity and irrigation.
Despite great progress made in the construction of dams, most electricity is still produced thermally.

The great irrigation schemes undertaken during the thirties increased the area under cultivation and yields, especially in Central Asia and Caucasia. Cotton was one of the crops most concentrated upon and production has risen steadily. Here, cotton is being packed on a farm in Azerbaijan.

A gradual increase in Russian iron ore output and a severe reduction in United States output in 1958 and 1959 put the U.S.S.R. in first place in world production. Flooded and pillaged during the war, the mines of Krivoi Rog have been repaired. They account for one-half of the national production, the rest coming chiefly from the Urals (from Magnitogorsk) and in smaller quantities from the mines of Ayat. But for some years now, to save lengthy rail transport, new deposits have been mined, in West Siberia, in Kazakhstan, and in the Kola Peninsula.

Two alloy metals have become very important: chromium, which has replaced nickel in many iron alloys, and manganese. The output of manganese is about five times the pre-war figure, and represents almost one-half of total world production. The output of copper, lead, zinc, tin and bauxite is definitely increasing.

In these circumstances the great basic industries have naturally progressed. The iron industry is indisputably the second in the world, ahead of Great Britain and the German Federal Republic, and steel production is constantly rising. The Ukraine, with Krivoi Rog, the Lower Dnieper and the Donbass, remains the major iron-smelting region of the Union, but the Urals supply nearly a third of Soviet cast iron and steel. A serious attempt is being made to decentralise this industry and distribute it more satisfactorily by assigning a larger rôle to the Kuzbass and by developing the iron industry of the Volga regions and of Transcaucasia and north Russia.

*Other important industries.* In recent years aluminium production has been second or third in the world.

The scattered character of the industry is economically advantageous. Besides aluminium works in the west, there are four in the Urals, and Siberia has recently acquired well-equipped centres in Baikalia, the Kuzbass and the west.

Works that were transferred from the west to Siberia stayed there after the war, and the enormous workshops of Russia-in-Europe have been restored, with increased production capacity.

The production of superphosphates is now important in the Kola Peninsula, in the Leningrad region, in central Russia, in the region bordering the Urals, in the Ukraine and in Central Asia. Nitrogenous fertilizers, of which Soviet agriculture has enormous need, are also being abundantly produced. The establishment of the hydro-electric generating stations of the Volga and the rivers of Central Asia will greatly stimulate the manufacture of synthetic ammonia and nitrates. The tonnage of potash fertilizers, soda and sulphuric acid has increased to a remarkable degree in recent years, and so has the manufacture of plastics.

Production tonnage is not known, but there is no doubt that the inadequate yields of latex plants and the absence of Parà rubber are in part made up for by the manufacture of a considerable amount of synthetic rubber.

Invasion served only to increase the eastward shift of the industrial centre of gravity and today a good half of the Soviet factories are in the Urals or even farther east. A number of new industrial regions have appeared: the Middle Volga, Central and Southern Urals, Kazakhstan, Kuzbass and Primorskaya, besides centres scattered about Siberia. The attempt to industrialise the whole national territory, for political and strategic reasons as much as for economic ones, has been indisputably successful. A typical case is that of the industrial complex of Magnitogorsk. Included in the first plan, completed in 1937, its production was almost doubled when the Ukrainian iron industry was temporarily lost. The fourth five-year plan increased its metallurgical potential, but added mechanical engineering, synthetic rubber manufacture, atomic industry and chemical industry.

In 1941 the central Urals also became a place of refuge for the industries of the west, which at once made it necessary to develop the regional coal-mines, to create more thermo-electric generating stations, harness water power and increase the production of iron ores. All this led to the rise of further industrial complexes: Chelyabinsk on the eastern side, Kyshtym, in which mechanical industries predominate, and Sverdlovsk, which combines mechanical engineering with iron-smelting, aluminium-working and the manufacture of electrical equipment, and includes the important 'Ural-Mashzavod' industrial equipment factories, the largest in the U.S.S.R.

*Agricultural progress.* To avoid heavy transport costs and serious delays in supply, it was necessary for each industrial region to have an agricultural centre on which to draw. The percentage of cultivated land therefore had to be increased, and the yields of stock-breeding and agriculture raised. The Government provided the additional cultivated areas with means of irrigation, it introduced dry farming, vernalisation of seed, and new, cold-resistant varieties of wheat,

Heavy industry has been the field of the most intense efforts by the Soviet Government. These industries are increasingly dispersed throughout the country, not only in the Urals, but also in the middle Volga region, Kazakhstan, the Kuzbass, and areas of Siberia.

barley, oats and rice, which extended the limit of their cultivation. Large areas were reclaimed, especially in West and Central Siberia, in the Far North and in Kazakhstan, and with the adoption of fresh crops (wheat, rice potatoes, etc.) the rotation was accelerated and yields were greatly increased.

Soviet agriculture is now more varied and extensive than ever before. Cereals alone cover more than three-quarters of the sown land. The chernozem districts, the clearance of virgin lands and the irrigation of the southern regions have played a large part in the U.S.S.R.'s leading place in world wheat production. The Union is in the first rank too with the rye and oats of the north-west, while rice now thrives in the irrigated lands of southern Ukraine, Kuban, Kazakhstan and the Far East.

Industrial crops now occupy about 13 per cent of the cultivated area. Silkworm-breeding is still little developed; but half the world's supply of hemp is of Soviet origin, and Soviet flax represents over half. Cotton production is still increasing. Sugar-beet, grown alternately with wheat on chernozem soil, has now spread to the plains of Georgia and the Far East, but the sunflower, as an oil-yielding plant, has had to compete with the steady increase of soya products on the new Russian farmlands. Potato-growing, formerly found chiefly in the western part of the Union, has spread further, and its production is still by far the largest in the world. The areas devoted to vegetable and fruit crops have been much slower to develop.

The difficulty of reviving stock-breeding after the war led the authorities to introduce a three-year plan of rehabilitation in 1949. Fresh regions had to be acquired for the stock, and average yields increased; the stud farms were encouraged to produce better breeds for the benefit of the kolkhozes.

*Improvement of transport.* The need to improve transport was pressing. The roads still presented the most difficulty. By 1950 the U.S.S.R. had four times more motor vehicles in use than in 1940 (without counting farm tractors), and regional traffic, which had been neglected in favour of inter-regional communciations, had now to be taken in hand. Trunk roads were built and hundreds of thousands of miles of carriageway were opened to motor traffic. In the Urals and the frontier zones old roads were rebuilt and new ones put under construction.

An all-out effort was made to make better use of the Siberian rivers, especially for the export of agricultural products, timber, wood fibre and wood pulp —all products for which there is an ever-growing world demand.

It was in the western regions of the U.S.SR., however, that substantial improvements were first made in water-borne traffic. The Volga, with its great tributary the Nama, was altered to carry barges of 4,000 to 6,000 tons and tankers of 12,000 tons. The completion of the Volga-Don Canal was a tremendous economic victory. By giving the great Russian river an outlet into the Black Sea as well as the Caspian, it remedied its only serious natural deficiency, and made its valley an important link between Moscow and the Mediterranean regions.

But the Government's efforts to improve transport were directed first and foremost towards the rail

Russia is traditionally a farming country and there are nearly 500 million acres under cultivation. The area has been increased by the ploughing up of 103 million acres of virgin land, and a further 49 million acres will be brought into use in the next 20 years by irrigation schemes in the Central Asian desert. There has been a great increase in mechanisation in the past 10 years and there is a mounting demand for chemical fertilizers. Forests cover 2,000 million acres of the U.S.S.R., mainly in the Asiatic part, along the northern seaboard and in the Urals. There is a steady planting of forests as crop-protection belts. By far the most important agricultural product is grain. which is grown chiefly in the rich chernozem belt. There are smaller crops of sugar-beet, textile fibres, sunflower, vegetables and fruit of all kinds including vines. There are 140 million head of sheep, found mainly in vast herds on the steppes, and about half as many cattle and pigs. Goats, camels and yaks are kept in the more desolate regions.

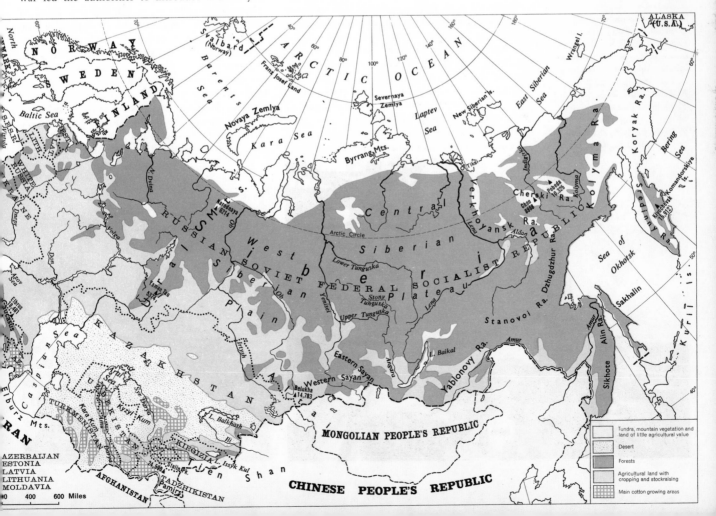

system. West of the Urals a large proportion of it was equipped with a heavier superstructure and stronger rails, and an extensive scheme of electrification is being carried out. In Soviet Asia the trans-Mongolian line prolongs the Ulan Ude-Ulan Bator lines towards Tsining and Peking; a branch line on the trans-Caspian line, following the left bank of the Amu Darya, establishes a connection between the piedmont of Central Asia and the new cotton fields and pastoral zones of Turkmenistan and Uzbekistan. The 'Second Trans-Siberian' was successfully completed, and its contribution to the development of the lands of Kazakhstan and West Siberia cannot be over-estimated.

For reasons military, political (unifying the Soviet complex) and economic (developing isolated and not easily accessible regions), the post-war period has witnessed a great drive to extend the network of domestic and international air services. Soviet aircraft now have new functions: transport of goods and passengers; the service of agriculture (sowing, spraying chemicals and fertilizers, fighting parasites, protection of forests against fire); and as an auxiliary of the health service (transport of patients, doctors and medicines, destruction of disease-carrying rodents during epidemics and of mosquito larvae in the marshes).

The development of modern transport has been particularly striking. So is that of the lines connecting Moscow with the spas and resorts of the Crimea and the Caucasus. Large modern airports have been built near Leningrad, Riga, Kharkov, Sverdlovsk, Krasnoyarsk, Chita and Khabarovsk.

Neglected by the first five-year plans, the merchant fleet has since increased considerably in tonnage; the idea of the 'sea route of the Soviet North' (Glavsemorput) was never far from mind. Every autumn the Arctic ports of Arkhangelsk and Murmansk saw the arrival of cargoes of timber, furs, salt, provisions and foreign war material (in which last respect the Arctic seas played a prominent part in provisioning the U.S.S.R.). After the war ended, the Glavsemorput authorities possesed a wealth of oceanographic information, the fruit of close co-operation between

icebreakers, observer aircraft and scientific stations strung out along the coast.

The merchant service has also been strengthened by annexations resulting from victory. The U.S.S.R.'s window on the Baltic is now larger than ever; Riga is Russian again, and Königsberg (now Kaliningrad) until lately an East Prussian town, is Russian also. The Soviet Union has a wide front on the Black Sea, though access to it—by the Straits of the Bosporus, the Dardanelles and the Sea of Marmara—is under Turkish control. At the Pacific end of the U.S.S.R., Russia has now regained the whole area of Sakhalin.

These economic developments have had far-reaching consequences, one of the most striking being the constant reduction of the distance between the okrainy and Russia proper. Reconstruction is proceeding fast, the national revenue is increasing, and the standard of living, sadly low in 1945, is incontestably rising.

*Economic weaknesses.* The economy has its weaknesses, however, and one has only to study the Soviet press and analyse industrial reports to realise the extent of certain deficiencies.

The transport system as a whole is still not equal to its task. The waterways, in spite of their natural advantages, are not only unusable during the whole of the winter, but their courses, especially those of the Siberian rivers, do not always serve the needs of the population. In many parts of the U.S.S.R. motor vehicles are useless for six months of the year. The merchant fleet is still below strength. Air transport, in general, gives less cause for complaint.

Some basic industries are still deficient. To begin with, there are bottlenecks in the supply of raw materials to certain industries. Rubber production from latex plants, for example, has not fulfilled expectations, and in spite of the Union's extensive manufacture of synthetic rubber, it is still obliged to import large quantities of Far Eastern natural rubber through Hong Kong and China. An analysis of the fifth five-year plan showed serious deficiencies in the manufacture of cast-iron and inadequate production of non-ferrous metals. There was also a very large

Harvesting the sunflower crop in the Bereznov district of the Ukraine. Oil is made from the seeds and the plants are stored in silos to be used for fodder.

Kazan, an important port on the Volga, whose freight turnover is constantly increasing.
The Soviet Union's system of inland waterways, including rivers and canals, forms a useful network. The ultimate intention is to link up 'the five Russion seas' (Baltic, Black, Caspian Aral and White Seas).
This scheme is linked with the harnessing of rivers for hydro-electric generation and irrigation of surrounding lands.

deficiency in electric power and coal production.

On the other hand, increase in quantity has often been dearly paid for by loss in quality.

There are complaints of insufficient production of consumer goods—in the building industry (timber and cement), and still more in the textile industry. Flax and wool output fail to meet demands.

*The agricultural crisis.* According to Soviet experts, rural labour, as a rule, is not yet properly trained. Mechanisation, in spite of progress made, is not yet sufficiently extensive. Better techniques, better developed and more extensive mechanisation, prevention of soil erosion, increased irrigation and dry farming, more intensive use of chemical fertilizers and other products (especially weed-killers) would considerably increase the average productivity of the cultivator.

Agriculture has suffered from bad management, too rigid planning, and excessively high targets demanded by the State. Soviet agricultural production is remarkably abundant and varied, but its increase has not kept pace with the rapid increase in urban population, and consequently with the number of consumers.

Despite great efforts, the Soviet economy did not achive all the results anticipated by the fifth five-year plan. It became clear that a fresh approach would have to be made.

## A NEW ECONOMIC POLICY

*Reforms and improvements.* In 1953 the authorities, besides trying to improve the transport system announced a great drive in favour of neglected light industry. The population was badly clothed; the textile industry must therefore be vigorously encouraged, and so must the production of 'cultural goods' such as bicycles, motor-cycles, sewing machines, refrigerators, radio and television sets and watches. The improvement was substantial, although the Government was obliged to reduce its military budget and to appeal for help to the armament industries. The ministries of the defence and aircraft industries were called upon, the first to produce some of the bicycles and refrigerators required, and the second some of the aluminium utensils and metal bedsteads.

But the main sphere of effort was to be in the recuperation of agriculture. The Machinery and Tractor Stations were improved, their personnel increased and reinforced by a multitude of technical experts, the number of tractors was considerably raised and supplies of chemical fertilizers to the kolkhozes increased. But it had become obvious that the interest of the individual must be appealed to. The property tax was reduced by half, or abolished altogether in certain cases, while the levy of supplies to the State was considerably lightened, and arrears not yet delivered were wiped out. These fiscal reliefs were accompanied by incentives to private stock-breeding. At the same time kolkhoz farming was assisted by advance payments to the kolkhozniks before their respective shares had been worked out, by a reduction in obligatory deliveries to the State, and above all by a substantial increase in the prices paid for these by the Government. Provision was made for simplifying the agricultural administrative services; a reaction

against the disastrous officialdom that pressed too heavily on the development of Russian farming.

However, to improve agricultural conditions to the desired degree, enormous capital investments would be needed, and the already huge Soviet budget could not bear such a burden unless equally enormous savings could be made elsewhere. There were two ways of doing this. Firstly came the temporary shelving of the scheme for regrouping the rural population in 'agro-towns' which would mean enormous expense in uprooting and rebuilding innumerable villages, organising the new centres on quasi-urban lines making new roads, altering the layout of fields.

Secondly, there was modification of the over-ambitious plans for altering the face of nature, which had multiplied during the last years of Stalin's rule. Work on the North Crimea Canal, the Ural-Volga Canal and the famous Turkmenistan Canal, supposed to be well advanced, was held up. Afforestation of the steppe may be proceeding according to plan, but the major undertakings of Stalin's regime seem to have been suspended. Nevertheless vast projects were pursued, such as the damming of the Upper Vakhsh in Tadzhikistan to provide a 2,700,000 kW power station by 1971.

*The sixth five-year plan.* The sixth five-year plan (1956-60) was still essentially concerned to increase the output of energy, and of heavy and light industry, and to improve the quantity and quality of the productions of agriculture and stock-breeding. The emphasis, as before, was on the economic development of Siberia and Central Asia.

Whilst coal-mining was intensified in the deep mines of the Donbass, the open-cast mines of the east were more actively exploited. Oil production in the Second Baku continued to increase. Electric power stations collected the energy potential of the rivers of Soviet Asia. Railroads and rolling-stock were the object of a 15-year improvement scheme which will ultimately electrify many tracks. Nuclear research and experiments were vigorously pursued.

The operation 'Virgin Lands', which in the space of two years succeeded in bringing more than 81 million acres of waste land under cultivation (some

A flock of sheep on the transhumance pastures of a state farm in Azerbaijan. In this region stock-breeding is the traditional activity, but it has been developed and breeds have been improved.

7 million in the European part of the U.S.S.R. and 74 million in Asia), was still pursing a vast programme which demanded the recruitment of many workers.

Like its predecessor, the sixth plan was concerned to improve the standard of living.

Towards the end of 1956, it was decided that detailed economic planning should be decentralised and vested in 104 regional Economic Councils (reduced to 47 by 1963 and by 1965 divested of some of their powers). Following these reforms even those areas whose industry and farming had been little developed in the past, were granted new prerogatives to give better organisation of labour, better planning, and higher production figures in all industries.

A furthur reform that came of this plan was the decision to turn the tractor stations into technical repair stations, and to sell the machinery stored in them to the kolkhozes, where these had increased in area, production and revenue. But in regions where the kolkhozes were unable to acquire tractors the Stations were to retain their function.

*The seven-year plan.* The seven-year plan of 1959-65 provided for a further great advance in agriculture, reorganisation of the power supply to industry, wide developments in heavy metallurgy, a fresh distribution of production centres, expansion of the chemical industry, and a heavy increase in textile production.

The development of virgin soil and waste land north of the Caucasus, in the Urals, North Kazakhstan and South Siberia, has brought considerable increase in wheat production. Soviet agriculture can now be devoted to two main tasks; the increase of food and industrial crops (potatoes, sugar-beet and maize), and the development of stock-breeding.

By 1963 potato production had risen by 70 per cent. The area under sugar-beet is being increased in Ukraine, Moldavia and all the chernozem regions, in Siberia, the Urals, the Middle Volga region and Byelorussia (White Russia). Sugar production was to be doubled per head of population, and an attempt was made to popularise maize and extend its cultivation farther northwards by introducing new varieties. Results here are closely linked with the development of stock-breeding, especially in regions less suited to crop cultivation.

Production of fodder reached in the eastern regions, the north-west and the centre has allowed increased cattle-breeding. To raise meat production, an important place was allotted to pig-breeding, and sheep-breeding was extended in the northern Caucasus and in Kazakhstan.

Production of woollen material reached 472 million square metres in 1964, against 300 million in 1958. But interest is chiefly centred on the production of artificial fibres, a feature of the modernisation and expansion of the chemical industry which now plays a vital economic rôle.

Expansion in petro-chemistry has been remarkable. Here, attention is chiefly focused on the production of plastics, artificial fibres and synthetic rubber from petroleum derivatives. This accounts for most of the new factories, planned or already in production, in the Middle Volga, the Urals, the Tatar (Kazan) and Bashkir (Ufa) A.S.S.R.'s and in the Kuibyshev region. The construction of machinery for the chemical and petroleum industries was the principal task of the mechanical engineering industry, together with the supply of equipment for purposes of heavy industry.

*The twenty-year development plan (1960-1980).* The new development in heavy metallurgy is extremely important and has brought a new geographical distribution of the great bases of the iron industry. New centres are being created. In Russia-in-Europe the exploitation of the Magnetic Anomaly of Kursk involve sinking a huge mine destined to feed the blast furnaces of Lipetsk, where the ironworks have been enlarged. For the development of the iron industry of the Ukraine, it is proposed to exploit the ores of Kremenchug in the Middle Dnieper region. The ironworks of Cherepovets, sited on the shores of Lake Rybinsk, is designed to furnish the rest of the metal required for the metallurgy of the north-western districts, including Leningrad.

In the Urals, the three principal combines have been enlarged. New mines have been sunk to further

The administrative buildings, warehouses, bakery, shops, canteen, and so forth, of a collective farm in newly developed land in Kazakhstan. In the foreground is the main thrashing floor, where the grain is dried and winnowed. It is then delivered to the state elevators about twenty miles away.

Virgin lands being brought under cultivation in the Altai. This vast area is being planted as an orchard.

the exploitation of the famous Magnet Mountain near Magnitogorsk. A combine for the enrichment of ores has been put into service at Sokolovsk-Sarbai.

Lastly, in the Asiatic part of the Union, three great new complexes will constitute the third metallurgical base: Taishet-Bratsk, between the Yenisei and Lake Baikal, using the coal from the Cheremkhovo basin, Achinsk-Krasnoyarsk, and Karaganda in Kazakhstan. This will allow coal-mining to be developed in the coal basins of Karaganda, Kuzbass and Cheremkhovo at a far lower cost than in the Donets and Tula basins. The founding of a great industry in the eastern regions will draw on the Siberian rivers for power.

The balance of sources of energy is likely to be altered by the increased output of petroleum and natural gas. The main objects of the twenty-year period apart from massive increases in electric power, machinery and fertilizers, are advances in steel, oil, cement, meat, textiles and milk production, creation of a deep-water inland waterway system and accelerated development of Asian areas through diversion of northern rivers for irrigation.

NEW FEATURE IN RUSSIA'S HUMAN GEOGRAPHY. Many physical, historical and psychological factors remain necessarily unalterable; but by 1941 the face of Tsarist Russia was hardly recognisable under its new Soviet features.

Many ways of life have been completely transformed. Some nomad populations have settled down and taken to agriculture, and some have been drawn into industry.

*Towns, urbanism and industrialisation.* In towns, houses have been demolished to make way for new streets, vistas have been opened, and imposing boulevards laid out. Schools, institutes, libraries, museums have been erected. Stone, rarely used in building Russian cities, has been replaced by reinforced concrete, largely used in the construction of bigger buildings. The Soviet town, especially if it has had a long commercial history, still functions as an exchange centre, or 'centre of organised redistribution'; but with the socialisation of the means of production, the paramount rôle of the town is administrative and industrial.

*A new geography of population and production.* There are exceptions, of course, but from the start of the first three five-year plans a tremendous urban growth took place which must be accounted one of the ruling factors in Russian history of that time.

Today, 175 cities have populations of over 100,000; there were 31 in 1926. Twenty-eight cities have more than 500,000 (3 in 1926); eight cities have exceeded the million mark.

'Mushroom' cities have sprung up by the dozen in uninhabited surroundings, especially since 1930: Magnitogorsk (Urals) has 333,000 inhabitants; Karaganda (Kazakhstan) 477,000; Zaporozhye (Ukraine) 529,000; in the Kuzbass, Novokuznetsk (Stalinsk), Leninsk-Kuznetsk, Prokopyevsk and Kemerovo total more than a million.

The U.S.S.R. now has an urban population of about 115 million (26 million in 1926). The overall increase in population from 1939 to 1959 was 9.5 per cent, and during that time the population of West Siberia increased by 24 per cent, the Urals by 32 per cent, Central Asia and Kazakhstan by 38 per cent, and the Soviet Far East by 70 per cent.

*Three main-currents of foreign trade.* Today, Russian trade is a state monopoly. It is distributed over three sectors: the other socialist countries (People's Democracies of Eastern Europe, China, Mongolia, North Korea and North Vietnam); the economically underdeveloped countries (India, Burma, Pakistan, Cambodia, the United Arab Republic, Afghanistan, Iran, the Lebanon, Yemen and Turkey); and, lastly, the technically advanced countries.

Trade with the socialist sector represents about three-quarters of the total. It is to an increasing extent a system of direct exchanges, the U.S.S.R. and some of these countries having set up a joint council of economic assistance. A number of agreements, involving substantial long-term credits at low interest, have been signed with underdeveloped countries producing mainly raw materials and foodstuffs but with no or few basic and manufacturing industries. The U.S.S.R. buys their surplus products and sells them in exchange for tools and whole plant. This sort of trade has increased more than fivefold since 1952. Exchanges with the Western world are also in course

Night view of Red Square in winter. On the right are the Kremlin Walls and, at their foot, the Lenin Mausoleum. At the far end of the square is the sixteenth century St. Basil's Cathedral with its colourful onion-shaped domes, characteristic of Byzantine architecture. Behind it is the Moscow University building, opened in 1953.

of development, especially now that certain export restrictions to the U.S.S.R. have been eased or removed. The chief customers and suppliers are Finland and Great Britain, followed by the Netherlands, Belgium, Sweden, Italy, France, Switzerland, West Germany, the United States and Latin America. In exchange for machines, equipment, food products and textiles, the U.S.S.R. sells timber, cellulose paper, cereals, cotton, coal, manganese and other nonferrous metals, chemical products, food products and textiles.

On the whole, consumer goods represent about the same proportion of imports as in 1913, but the development of the country's natural riches is reflected in a reduced demand for foreign raw materials. Industrialisation still calls for an increase in machinery and equipment. The U.S.S.R. has made a radical departure from the economy that characterised Russia at the beginning of the twentieth century.

# THE NORTH POLE
# AND GREENLAND

# THE ARCTIC REGIONS

The Arctic region is that area of land and sea lying round the North Pole where polar climate prevails. The Arctic Circle follows the 60°30′ N. line of latitude, but the northern limit of the tree-line is probably a better indication of the lands that can be called Arctic: Greenland, Spitsbergen, the northern parts of Iceland, Labrador's coast, Northern Siberia, Alaska and Canada, and the fringe of Europe's Arctic coast. The North Pole is the meeting-point of the U.S.S.R., the United States, Canada and the Scandinavian countries. The resulting political situation has profoundly altered the rôle and significance of the Arctic regions.

Briefly, the north polar zone is divided into two areas: the 'Euro-Asian' and the American.

*Sea routes: The North-West and North-East Passages.* When the passages to the north-west and north-east were navigated, the former in 1906, the latter as early as 1879, the Western world no longer needed the northern routes to reach the Far East. These routes were only of interest to the coastlands of the Arctic Ocean. The North-West Passage had long been recognised as commercially useless, in spite of the possibilities offered by icebreakers. The colonisation of North America had taken place from the Atlantic towards the Pacific; the Arctic region of America was not included in the economy of the continent and was generally believed to be of little value.

The North-East Passage was quite different for Russia. With the extension of the Gulf Stream and the existence of *polynias* (ice-free channels), the geographical conditions, at least in the western sector of the north-east route, are better than those of the North-West Passage. As early as the sixteenth century, enterprises such as the Kara Sea Expedition (for furs) had been highly profitable. Interest in the Arctic coast was also encouraged by the advance of the pioneer front beyond the Urals, the routes formed by the courses of the great northward-flowing Siberian rivers, and the discovery of minerals.

It is important to take account of economic and human factors in appreciating the part played in the life of modern Russia by the northern sea route, which developed from the North-East Passage. This route, which today allows a return journey between Murmansk and the Pacific during the same season, has opened up the Siberian hinterland and orientated it northwards. Arctic Russia is now a zone of convergence and attraction, while Arctic America, until recent years, was a marginal and forbidding region.

Now changes are taking place. Inclusion of Alaska in the American Federation, like the political and administrative reorganisation of the North-West Territories of Canada, clearly shows a desire to integrate the Far North with the rest of the continent. Again, the starting of a vast system of communications (the Alaska Highway, the Mackenzie Highway, the Great Bear Lake route, the Hudson Bay railroad, the network of the Canadian Pacific airlines, and so on) is a prelude to the exploitation of rich natural resources and increased population. Finally, more advanced technical developments, particularly in atomic sub-

Husky dogs are a valuable means of transport in the Arctic: their great strength, stamina and resistance to cold makes them entirely suitable as transport animals

marines, make it possible to reconsider the problem of sea communications along the northern shores of America.

*The exploitation of the Far North.* Today, the settlements both of the Soviet Far North and of the American Arctic islands are expanding. Bases have been established, not only on the mainland and islands, but on the polar ice itself (T1, T2 and T3 are islands of ice used for setting up drifting American bases: the Soviet Union also uses floating stations, such as North Pole 1, 2, 3, 4, etc.). In the present state of international affairs the polar region of the earth is particularly sensitive. The industrial regions in the Urals or Siberia, like their American and Canadian counterparts, feel less protected by the Arctic Ocean than by the Atlantic. Moreover, the meteorological stations in the Arctic are becoming indispensable in the life of these countries; the data they provide can influence agriculture, communications and fishing, over large and even distant regions.

The polar region plays a particularly important

*Map opposite:* The Arctic, showing the extent of pack-ice in different seasons and the general direction in which the ice drifts. This drifting, discovered and confirmed by successive expeditions, is relatively fast: the Russian station North Pole 4 set up on the ice in April 1954, north of Wrangel Island, was found a year later (after being subjected to the Polar nights and temperatures of –50°F.) to have drifted 1,500 miles (325 miles as the crow flies). The North-East and North-West Passages, navigated respectively in 1879 and 1906, are now opened by powerful ice-breakers of which the most recent are nuclear-powered, like the American submarine *Nautilus*, the first to have crossed the Arctic under the polar ice-cap.

part in determining the weather in temperate latitudes, since it is situated between the low pressure systems of the Atlantic-Pacific and the high pressure systems of America-Eurasia. It is therefore an observation post of the greatest importance, and scientific data collected from the permanent stations (Russian, Canadian and American) and by the reconnaissance aircraft which fly daily to the Pole is already considerable.

Developments are of two kinds: bases for observation or defence, and bases for lines of communication. It is important to realise that these are technical developments and require a specialist population There is therefore no question of a pioneer frontier, as in regions of colonisation. The frozen soil requires special techniques in constructing buildings or airfields; the extreme cold and, still more, the wind, necessitate special types of architecture and the use of glass wool insulation and triple walls.

The supply lines appear on the map like an immense spider's web. Along the Russian coast, the G.U.S.M.P. (Control of Northern Sea Route) has at its disposal a fleet of icebreakers, some able to cross pack-ice 16 feet thick. Canada, with the second most extensive polar territories, had only one modern ice-breaker until 1950. Since then this significant defi-

hand, twilight is a handicap, because observation of sun or stars is impossible, and because it can last throughout the entire flight of the aircraft. The magnetic compass cannot be used within a zone where the horizontal magnetic field is below 0.05 gauss (the limit of sensitivity of the instrument); assistance by radio-control from stations on the ground is precarious, for radio can be jammed by magnetic or radio-electric phenomena; ground location is still unreliable in all zones where maps are inaccurate or incomplete; and finally, the convergence of the meridians towards the geographical North Pole makes normal methods of navigation impossible. To overcome the difficulties, navigation based on a grid system and using a directional gyroscope has been developed.

Although polar communications are now technically possible, political considerations make it difficult to use them extensively and regularly. The Arctic Ocean will be the 'Mediterranean of the modern world' only when the unrestricted exchange of travellers, goods and ideas is well established from shore to shore across the ice.

# GREENLAND

Greenland is the largest island in the world, with an area of 840,000 square miles (nearly nine times the size of the United Kingdom, or over three times the size of Texas), and about five-sixths of it is covered by a great ice sheet. It owes its political and strategic importance to its position on the air routes of the northern hemisphere, rather than to its natural resources. It has a population of 33,140 (1960), of whom about 2,760 (1960) are of European extraction.

Under the present policy of Denmark, of which it was a colony until 1953, when it became an integral part of the realm, Greenland is experiencing unusual economic and social changes.

*Five-sixths ice cap.* Greenland lies north of the 10°C. (50°F.) isotherm for July (warmest month), and covers 24° of latitude. In parts of the island the ice is 10,000 feet thick; it rests on bedrock which is depressed in the centre and elevated at the edges.

Composed chiefly of Archaean gneiss and granite, the Greenland massif was isolated from the Canadian Shield after pre-Cambrian times. After having experienced a variety of climates (it was tropical in Tertiary times), the region was extensively frozen in Quanternary times. The coastal belt, at present free from ice over a width of about 20 to 120 miles, is generally rugged and high. The ice cap reaches its highest point (about 10,000 feet) approximately 60 miles to the north-west of a point situated at 70°54′5″ N. and 40°38′ W. The ice front of the Humboldt glacier is 60 miles wide. The ice cap is receding in some places and advancing in others. It is moving towards the 'yderland' (the coastland which is ice-free) at the rate of three feet a year in the neighbourhood of Egedesminde, Disko Bay (1912-49). The melting of the ice cap would produce an increase of 23 feet in sea level spread over the waters of the globe.

The present climate of Greenland is always cold. At Thule, the most northerly Eskimo settlement in

An Eskimo woman of the Kazan tribe in her igloo home in the North-West Territories. There is no heating in the igloo and she is sitting on a platform made of ice and covered with pelts. Her thick clothing made of caribou skins protects her from the rigours of the cold. The trunk and the few thing on it are her only possessions.

ciency has been remedied. The United States became interested in fitting out polar ships only after signing the Canadian-American agreement of Ogdensburg in 1940, which inaugurated American collaboration in the polar zone of Canada and Greenland. Today the Americans have several ships comparable with the Russian icebreakers, but aircraft are mainly relied on to carry vital supply loads.

Flying conditions in high latitudes present certain special problems, but neither the extreme cold nor the polar winters are serious obstacles; the latter, in fact, allows navigation by the stars. On the other

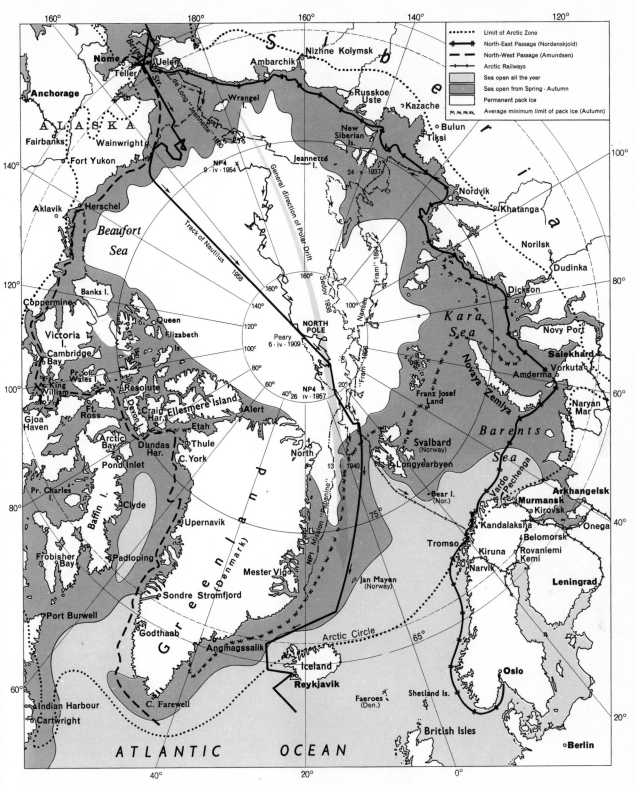

the Arctic (76°32′ N.), the mean temperature is −9.7°C. (14.5°F.) (1947–49), the precipitation 2.6 inches (1948–49), and the polar night lasts for four months. However, at Ivigtut, in the extreme south, the mean annual temperature is 0.6°C. (33°F.), annual precipitation reaches 46 inches and the polar night lasts only a few weeks each year. In the centre of the ice-sheet, extreme temperatures recorded (1949–50) are −64.8°C. (−85°F.) (minimum) and 0.7°C. (33°F.) (maximum). Precipitation is always in the form of snow and ice-crystals. Finally, Greenland experiences

a marked difference in climate at the same latitude: the west coast is warmed by a branch of the Gulf Stream as far as Umanak, north of Disko, while the east coast is isolated and cooled by a cold current flowing directly from the polar sea.

The great coastal plateaus are deeply eroded by the work of ice and the planing action of the glaciers. They are covered with morainic deposits and thousands of lakes, and marked by a great network of valleys and fiords, as much as 200 miles long. In the southern part of the island, these plateaus are carpeted

Drying fish on the west coast of
Greenland. The fish are hung
up to dry during the brief but
warm summer. This west coast
also benefits from a moderation of
the extremes of Arctic cold
owing to the influence of a
branch current of the Gulf Stream.
The photograph shows some
of the increasingly common
permanent wooden houses which
the Eskimos are building.

A Greenland glacier in a fiord.
Composed chiefly of Archean
gneiss and granite, the Greenland
massif was isolated from the
Canadian Shield after
pre-Cambrian times.
The region was
extensively frozen in Quaternary
times. The ice has now melted
along the coastal belt, over
a width of about 20 to 120 miles.

with tufted grasses and dwarf birches, mountain ash
and willows which reach a height of between 3 feet
and 6 feet. The total number of sheep varies between
15,000 and 20,000, depending on the fodder harvest.
There are about sixty cows and about 150 Icelandic
horses. Herds of musk ox and reindeer, foxes, hares
and occasional wolves still roam over the wild, arid
plateaus of the extreme north, which are covered with
stretches of moss, saxifrage and lichen.

*The men of the harpoon.* Small groups of people of
Eskimo origin, whose lives are closely controlled by
their physical environment, have been settled on the
coast for a long time. The Eskimo, who probably
originated in Asia, is small, with Mongoloid features.
His village is a collection of igloos (to be precise,
dwellings not made of snow are called igloos, or
igdlous, while houses made of snow are called igloo-
iaks or igdlou-eaks).

'Village' is too grand a name for these confused
collections of mounds of turf and stone, or wooden
huts, whose importance is judged by the height of
the pile of refuse which accumulates in front of each
door. A primitive igloo has a single room, entered
through a passage one or two yards long. The bed is
set at the far end of the room, and along the sides
are the oil lamps and various utensils in daily use.
The walls are hung with sealskins or newspapers.
An airhole or *krignak* (nose) provides ventilation.
Igloos are becoming relatively rare, except in the
extreme north-west; in such towns as Godthaab and
Julianehaab on the south-west coast, the houses are
constructed of timber imported from Denmark. They
may contain several rooms, which are sometimes lit
by electricity, and they are decorated with pans and
religious prints. The Greenlanders are for the most
part Protestants.

Once, the inhabitants were clothed entirely with
the skins of animals: jackets of reindeer or sealskin,
trousers of polar bear or sealskin and sealskin boots.
The seal was the main resource: it supplied man with
his daily food, its oil provided heating and lighting,
its skin was fashioned into clothes, boots, tents and
kayaks. In addition, the occasional sale of skins gave
the hunter money to buy tobacco and the gun he
needed. Hunting for birds, walrus, bears and, in particular, foxes used to give the hunters an appreciable
surplus. For example, from 1930 to 1939 the average
number of foxes killed annually in the single district
of Thule was 455 per hundred inhabitants. Greenland
was largely self-sufficient.

This economic regime was possible only for a small
population—as long as there were enough animals.
But the pressure of population in the nineteenth century, following colonisation, which is itself explained
by an appreciable improvement in living conditions,
necessitated a complete change in the simple economic
structure. At the same time, a rise in the sea temperature of about 4°C. (7°F.) hastened the departure of
the seals, and made a new economic and social policy
even more urgent.

*Origin of the people, and their future.* Archaeological
discoveries seem to confirm that for at least a thousand years these desolate shores were occupied by
people of the Eskimo race. The question of their origin
has been much disputed. It is, however, very likely that
they came from the mainland of North America. In the

fourteenth and fifteenth centuries, after living in isolation during the Dark Ages, they came into contact with Viking colonies which they ultimately destroyed.

The south-west colonies were converted to Protestantism in 1721. They came under Danish administration with the dispatch of the first governor in 1728, and with the administrative arrangements of 1774. Very soon more than four-fifths of the entire population of the country were settled in West Greenland (30,109 inhabitants in 1960), as well as the major part of the Danish community. Since the 5th June 1953, the Greenlander has enjoyed full Danish citizenship. The population of the three territories of the North, East and West (Koloni, Udsted, Boplads), is distributed in 185 settlements, of which seven have over 500 inhabitants. Originally, the population was scattered because it lived by hunting, but it is becoming more concentrated.

Before Europeans explored the east coast, the population was dispersed from Cape Farewell to Peary Land, but now there are only two settlements: Angmagssalik and Scoresbysund.

For two centuries there have been intermarriages between Eskimo women and Danish government administrators and workers, and the development of a new Nordic people is taking place. There is an important and steady increase in the population. In 1958 the birthrate was 47.0 per 1,000.

*The new economy.* With this rapid and appreciable increase in population the traditional food resources soon became insufficient.

It is clear that in a primitive society the standard of living must be improved before the people can improve their cultural standards. Before Denmark took over this large island, the Eskimos literally used to die from hunger when hunting failed. It is possible to foresee the time when the present population will have doubled without the risk of an unbalanced economy. The purchasing power of the population has more than trebled since 1939. In the northern region of Thule, and in the scattered villages, gay little houses painted in the Scandinavian style cling to the rocky slopes. The grouping of the widely dispersed population into five or six large towns is under consideration, in order to organise the fishing industry more efficiently, and to cut down the expenses incurred in the running of hospital and school services. Since the Second World War, extensive military air bases have been established by America; these have no economic influence on the life of the country.

POLITICAL DEVELOPMENT AND FUTURE PROBLEMS. It has been the unchanging policy of the Ministry for Greenland in Copenhagen to promote and encourage political and cultural development on Danish lines, while preserving local traditions. The Greenland Landsraad with thirteen deputies is elected by universal suffrage. Apart from this, two Greenland deputies represent the island at Copenhagen.

An underdeveloped country whose progress is hampered by its position, its cold climate and the absence of any large or diverse resources, Greenland does not seem to have built up a balanced modern economy, and certain aspects give cause for concern. With the steady increase in population, the improvement in living standards, and the fact that the Greenlanders

cannot support themselves by seal-hunting and fishing, the island has not been self-sufficient for several decades. The strong demand for imported consumer goods and equipment should, in theory, be balanced by an increase in exports. However, exports are still deficient, and the considerable difference between imports and exports is being met by subsidies from the Danish government.

Increasing Greenland's exports is all the more difficult because the economy lacks variety and the level of productivity is low; transport is difficult; mineral resources, except for cryolite, lead and zinc, are small, and there is a possibility that the trade in cod will not always be profitable. It is significant that Danish private investment in the area remains small. Private investment is not attracted to countries with weak economic structures, where capital is scarce and geographical conditions unfavourable. Despite this, the economic development of the country seems to be progressing at a fairly satisfactory rate at the present time, despite the difficulties.

Greenland in summer. Note the U-shaped glacial erosion of the mountainside, the barrenness of the wide valley and the morainic debris which litters it. The ponies were used as pack animals on an inland expedition.

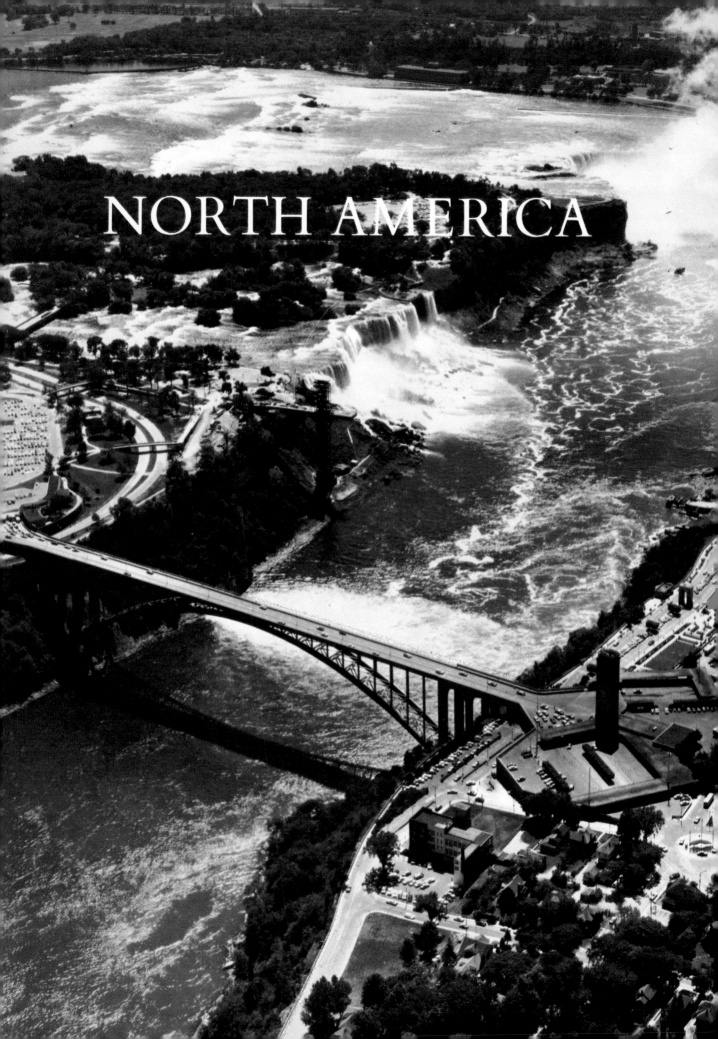

NORTH AMERICA

# ALASKA

For many years after the United States purchased Alaska from Russia in 1867 it was regarded as a remote land of snow and ice, inhospitable to all but Eskimos. Although gold was discovered, furs trapped, and the offshore seas were known to be teeming with seals and fish, Alaska remained a neglected step-child. Today, on the contrary, it is a favourite son, considered to be the last great undeveloped and potentially rich area in the United States. And it stands at the crossroads of an air-minded world which is coming to look upon the Arctic Sea as a polar Mediterranean, the shortest route between most of the centres of population and power in the northern hemisphere. By the great-circle route Fairbanks is more than 200 miles closer to Berlin than is Chicago, and more than 500 miles closer to Moscow. Further-more, at no other point on the globe are Soviet and United States territories so nearly contiguous: Bering Strait is less than 75 miles wide.

In 1959, when Alaska achieved statehood in the United States, it became by far the largest state in the Union, having an area of 571,065 square miles (more than twice that of Texas, and six times that of the United Kingdom) and the smallest population of any state (226,000 in 1960). As might be expected in such a vast land, relief, climate, and ways of life vary considerably from place to place.

*The south-eastern region: the Panhandle.* The region of the south-east, confined between the Pacific shore and the nearby Canadian border, and shaped like a pan-handle, is nearly 630 miles long and barely 12 miles wide in places, with a maze of deep fiords and irregular islands of which the main ones form the Alexander Archipelago. The highlands, an extension of those in British Columbia, are composed chiefly of Primary and Secondary blocks smoothed by glacial erosion, and their average height is 5,000 feet on the mainland, and 2,600 feet on the islands. The climate is mild for such high latitudes, the average temperatures at Sitka being 0°C. (32°F.) in February, and 14°C. (57°F.) in August. Thanks to an abundant rainfall, between 80 inches and 160 inches a year, falling mainly from September to January, the mountains are covered with dense coniferous forests up to a height of about 2,500 feet. Above this is the permanent snowline. The forests are inhabited by deer, bears, wolves, mink, white squirrels and mountain goats. Colonies of beaver and otter live close to the rivers, and birds are plentiful. The coastal waters abound with herring, halibut and, above all, salmon. The ice-free bays and fiords are dotted with fishing villages, and most of the larger towns — Ketchikan, Petersburg, Wrangell, Sitka, and Juneau, the capital — are primarily fishing centres. Although the catch has declined in recent years, prob-ably because of overfishing during World War II, fish, mostly salmon, is the basis of Alaska's biggest industry, currently bringing in an annual revenue of about $90,000,000.

Among the state's most promising natural resources are the forests of the Panhandle and other coasts. It has been estimated that it would be possible to cut one thousand million board-feet of hemlock, Sitka spruce, and western red cedar every year on a sustained-yield basis. This timber, close enough to ice-free tidewater for profitable exploitation, is ideally suited for pulp, and since Government restrictions on cutting have been eased, huge multi-million-dollar pulp plants have been built at Ketchikan and Sitka, and others are planned for Juneau and Wrangell. Fortunately, in the many nearby streams there is plenty of potential hydro-electric power for these and various other industries.

*The Gulf of Alaska region.* Beyond the Lynn Canal, the mountains rise sharply to greater heights in the St Elias Range, culminating in Mount St Elias (18,008 feet) in Alaska territory and Mount Logan (19,850 feet) on the Canadian side of the border. Why the sudden change in appearance — all the more surpris-ing since it does not extend far, and since along the Gulf of Alaska the more moderate heights of 6,000 feet soon reappear? It is due to the violent earth movements of the area. These are illustrated by the huge structural depression of the Copper River to the

north-west of the St Elias Range; this basin is sur-rounded to the east by the volcanic mass of the Wrangell Mountains, rising to more than 16,000 feet, and to the west by a typical horst, the Talkeetna Mountains. The irregular coastline demonstrates the complicated general structure, with precipitous and jagged headlands alternating with deep irregular bays.

Around the Gulf of Alaska the tourist can enjoy some of the most exciting scenery in the whole of the territory: high snow-covered mountains, fiords and glaciers, including the huge Malaspina glacier which covers an area of 1,500 square miles.

The temperature falls to –18°C. (0°F.) in winter, while in summer it hovers around 16°C. (60°F.). The sky is nearly always overcast; near the coast there are almost 150 inches of rain a year. The variety of both flora and fauna here is rather limited. Only the large mammals thrive, such as the powerful brown bear and the grizzly bear, which have almost exterminated the caribou and white mountain-sheep. The large elk has survived much better in the Kenai Peninsula.

Main Street in a small town in Alaska. When it was purchased by the U.S. from Russia in 1867, Alaska was thought to be remote and inhospitable, in spite of its reserves of gold, furs and fish. In 1959 it achieved statehood in the U.S., becoming by far the largest State of the Union, and is now looked upon as a promised land of vast undeveloped resources.

Niagara Falls. Goat Island divides the cararact into the falls that belong to the United States (to the left) from the more curved Horseshoe Falls in the background, which belong to Canada. In the foreground is the Rainbow International Bridge.

The white population has mainly settled at sites controlling access into the interior, such as Cordova, Seward, and especially Anchorage, at the head of Cook Inlet. With a population of 44,000, Anchorage is the largest city in Alaska and contains splendid new schools and new housing developments, fine shops and luxury hotels, several radio and TV stations, and an international airport. Its main activities are fishing and fish preserving, and mining. Since the discovery of an oilfield in the Kenai Peninsula in 1957, with reserves estimated at 1,000 million barrels, half a dozen major oil companies have spent several million dollars on further exploration and drilling here and elsewhere in the state. There is talk of building a refinery, which would in its turn attract other industries.

According to present estimates, Alaska's chief untapped mineral resources are coal, iron ore, tin and copper. The only one of these currently mined to any degree is coal, mainly from a mine north-east of Anchorage and another about midway between Anchorage and Fairbanks, which together produce some 600,000 tons a year.

Anchorage is also the major farming centre, as it is the outlet for the nearby Matanuska valley and Kenai Peninsula agricultural settlements where, making the most of the long, sunny, summer days and a three- or four-month growing season, large-scale cultivation of potatoes, hardy vegetables, oats, barley, and even wheat has been attempted with notable success, and where poultry and dairy and beef cattle are raised.

More than half the population of Alaska is grouped round about a dozen centres scattered along a narrow coastal strip between Ketchikan, in the extreme south of the Panhandle, and Anchorage.

*The Alaska peninsula and range.* Beyond Cook Inlet the Pacific coast of Alaska continues in the wide sweep of the Alaska Peninsula. This is extended towards the south-west by the equally concave line of the Aleutian Islands, and towards the north-east by the Alaska Range. The high peaks of this range, Mount McKinley (20,320 feet), Mount Hayes (13,740 feet) and the Nutzotin Mountains (over 10,000 feet), dominate and form a great arc around the depression of the Susitna and Copper Rivers.

The intensity of earth movements here is proved by numerous features. There is, for example, a marine trench more than 23,000 feet deep, and marked volcanic activity. The volcanoes are dormant in some places and active elsewhere. There is also the large anticline of Primary and Secondary rocks which has been highly folded, even more faulted, and recently uplifted; and there are the high ranges with sheer slopes, particularly on the northern side. It would seem that formation of the relief is not yet complete.

The winter remains temperate, but temperatures hardly ever exceed 10°C. (50°F.) even in midsummer. This is one of the foggiest places in the world, for here the icy waters of the Bering Sea meet the warm Japan current of the North Pacific. Because of the Arctic winds that sweep over the northern slopes of the mountains, the forest here is confined to the lower slopes. The chief resource of the coast, if not the only one, is fish. The Aleutian people, who are closely related to the Eskimos, live entirely by fishing. They used to hunt whales and fur seals. Now, the whale has almost disappeared. To prevent the disappearance of the fur seal, an international agreement established a reserve on the Pribilof Islands, a little to the south of the winter ice in the Bering Sea, and just on the boundary of American and Russian territory. The agreement allows a catch of 25,000 seals a year.

*The interior plateaus.* The centre of Alaska, situated between the mountains of the Pacific Ocean in the south and those of the Arctic Sea in the north, is composed of plateaus continued from British Columbia, and extending clear across the state to the Bering Sea in the west, gradually falling from 4,000 feet to 1,700 feet.

This huge area is a region of structual folding, the whole of it peneplaned and hollowed into inland depressions which determine the courses of the rivers, especially the Yukon, the upper quarter of which flows in Canada. It enters Alaska shortly after the confluence with the Klondike at Dawson City, and flows from east to west, more or less equidistant from the Arctic Sea in the north and the Pacific in the south. Its tributaries are the Porcupine and the Koyukuk on the right bank and the Tanana on the left bank.

This region has a decidedly continental climate, characterised by very long and cold winters with temperatures often as low as –29°C. (–20°F.) and –40°C. (–40°F.) or even –50°C. (–58°F.), and warm summers, averaging between 16°C. (61°F.) and 18°C. (64°F.) in July at Fairbanks. However, precipitation is light (about 12 inches), which helps to make the cold bearable.

At about 1,700 feet to 2,000 feet forests give way to alpine pastures dotted with clumps of poplars, aspen, and birch. Black pines grow in the swamps. The scarcity of human settlement has allowed the natural fauna, the caribou, the white sheep, and moose, to survive here better than elsewhere.

The Yukon and its left-bank tributary, the Tanana, have an abundant and regular supply of water from the meltwaters of the glaciers of the Wrangell Mountains and the Alaska Range, so, in summer, the Yukon is navigable the length of its course in Alaska.

This is the land of the Eskimos, in turn fishermen and hunters according to the season. In summer the soil thaws, at least near the surface, but the climate is dry and cold and not exactly ideal for farming. It was the mines that attracted the white man to this area towards the end of the nineteenth century, to the rich gold placer deposits of the Upper Yukon, the Seward Peninsula near the Bering Strait, and the Fairbanks region. Their output grew until 1906, when the best deposits were exhausted. Circle, on the Upper Yukon, and Nome, on the Bering Sea, are mere shadows of their former selves. However, gold is still mined near Fairbanks and on the Seward Peninsula, and Alaska's annual income from gold runs to nearly $6 million.

Fairbanks, with about 13,300 inhabitants, is Alaska's second largest town. Today it is a growing town, proud of its fine university, modern hospital, banks, and radio and TV stations, and it is still an important trading and gold mining and smelting centre. Increasingly, it is obtaining its milk, butter, meat, eggs and vegetables from the expanding agricultural settlement in the nearby Tanana valley.

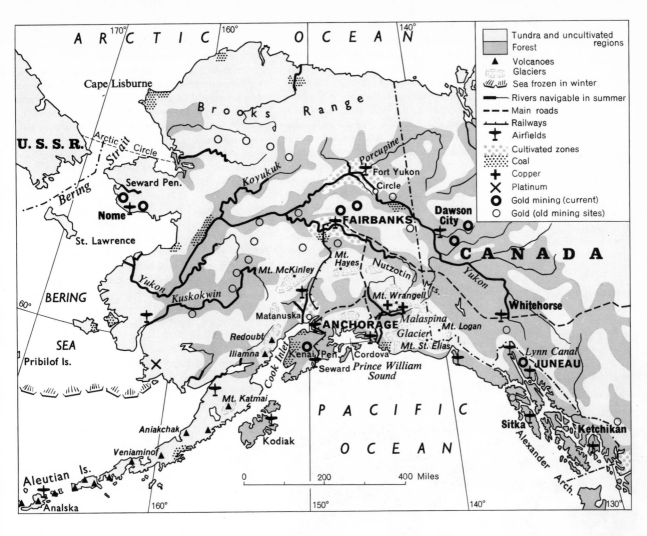

*The Arctic region.* The Arctic region includes between one-quarter and one-fifth of Alaska. It can be divided into three east-to-west belts. In the south is the Brooks Range, about 600 miles long and 120 miles wide, which reaches 9,000 feet in the centre, and onwards the west falls to about 2,000 feet near Cape Lisburne. Then comes the zone of Jurassic folds, dissected by river erosion into ridges of hard rock which gradually level out towards the north, finally merging into a broad plateau.

On the coast the winter lasts for ten months, and the temperature in January and February is usually below –29°C. (–20°F.) and may drop to –50°C. (–58°F.). The sea remains completely frozen until the month of August, when the few weeks of summer begin. The frozen sea withdraws, leaving a narrow and dangerous channel for steamboats. The surface of the land thaws, the mosses and lichens become a mass of flowers, the Arctic foxes appear and the domesticated reindeer move towards the sea. The Eskimos make all haste to catch fish to store for the rapidly approaching winter.

Here, too, some white people have been attracted by mining prospects. The subsoil is apparently rich in coal, and near Cape Lisburne it seems to be of good enough quality to warrant working. The American Navy controls a huge concession of about 14,000 square miles in area, where exploratory drilling for petroleum was carried on for several years. Point Barrow is the most northerly port in the state, as well as being the smallest and longest icebound. The Point Barrow Arctic Research Laboratory, besides studying local plants and fossils, earth magnetism, and seismographic tremors, tracks earth satellites.

*The present situation and future prospects.* Between 1890 and 1900, following the discovery of gold deposits, Alaska's population nearly doubled, from 32,000 inhabitants in 1890 to 63,000 in 1900. It remained more or less stable until 1920, after which a slight increase occurred.

There was a new period of growth between 1940 and 1950, when the civilian population increased from 72,000 to 128,000. This growth has continued until the present day, and is due mainly to substantial white immigration; the Eskimos have increased very slowly, and the Aleutians have definitely declined in numbers. There has been a decided increase in the white proportion, which was about 55 per cent of the total civil population in 1940, 72 per cent in 1950, and 80 per cent in 1959. There are about 186 males to every 100 females.

The increasing importance of the military population has accentuated this disequilibrium. When Japan threatened the western United States during World War II, air bases were established, and thousands of military and civilian personnel were brought in. Alaska is a key outpost to the defence of the United States, and its radar stations are part of the distant

Alaska, the forty-ninth state of the U.S.A. and a huge pioneer outpost on the Arctic Circle. Alaska is strongly characterised by certain physical features such as high relief, volcanoes, frozen seas, glaciers, tundras, rivers that are useless for a great part of the year. Today new roads, airfields, radar stations, mines and growing cities are transforming it.

early warning line encircling northern Canada and Alaska to warn of the approach of enemy planes.

Such large military expenditures have been a prime stimulus to the recent development of Alaska. And so, too, has been the building of roads between the bigger towns and an international highway, open all year round, linking the American West with Fairbanks via Canadian territory. For a long time the only means of moving men and goods in Alaska was by water; today, this is still the only way of reaching some places, but dozens of local air routes have been established between towns and isolated communities, carrying machinery, mail, fresh food, medicines, and people. However, isolation is still a major problem over vast areas.

Another problem is the seasonal nature of the fishing industry. Great numbers of workers are needed during the four-month active period; during the rest of the year, unless they migrate elsewhere, they find it hard to make a living. There is also the problem of distance from large markets, and the high cost of transportation to them. Nevertheless, fishing is likely to remain the key industry, together with the exploitation of forests and mines.

Attempts are being made to develop further the agricultural potential in all climatically suitable areas. At present Alaska produces only about 15 per cent of its own food requirements. From the rest of the United States it receives butter, eggs, poultry, meat, vegetables and fruits. Some experts estimate that in time the state should be able to produce 80 per cent or even 90 per cent of its food. Others are less optimistic, because of the short growing season, the lack of rain in inland areas, the acidity of the soils in many places and their poorly developed structure, and the permanently frozen subsoil which results in low soil temperatures and consequently slow plant growth. New methods being used to overcome such difficulties include spreading coal dust so that the dark surfaces will absorb the available heat, the development of hardy vegetables and cereals, and the use of solar radiators and reflectors.

Finally, the tourist industry is expanding. To attract the visitor there is the spectacular beauty of the landscape, good hunting and fishing, and interesting wild life. However, distance and the shortness of the summer season are discouraging factors.

For about ten years Alaska sought admission as a state of the American Union. The application was more or less bound up with a similar application of the Hawaiian Islands, which were also Federal Territory, and was delayed for a long time by political considerations. Now that it has achieved statehood, Alaska is undoubtedly going to attract the necessary capital to develop its own economic resources more and more. Meanwhile its strategic position, of vital importance to the whole of the United States, will encourage the supply of helpful loans and support.

Fairbanks, Alaska's second largest city. Unlike most Alaskan cities, which are on or close to the coast, Fairbanks is situated far inland, near the geographical centre of the state. Despite its northerly latitude, it enjoys three months of summer at temperatures that often reach 32°C. (90°F.).

Aerial view of the great Brooks Range of Alaska.

# CANADA

Canada is a large country, the second largest in the world, after the Soviet Union, having an area of nearly four million square miles, a million more than its neighbour to the south, the United States.

Vastness in itself, of course, is not necessarily an advantage, and may even be a disadvantage. At the moment, huge sections of Canada are too inaccessible to be of much economic value. The only well-populated part of the country is a narrow zone along the 4,000-mile United States border, which includes less than one-eighth of the total area, and this zone, a few hundred miles wide at the most, is not even continuous. At no point does it extend across the whole country. It consists in fact of four separate regions, four successive Canadas: the Atlantic Provinces (Newfoundland, Nova Scotia, New Brunswick, and Prince Edward Island); the St Lawrence lowland (southern Quebec and Ontario); the Prairies (including Manitoba, Saskatchewan, and most of Alberta); and the Rockies and the Pacific Coast (western Alberta and British Columbia).

A fifth region, the Far North, the land of taiga, tundra and permanent ice, is largely uninhabited and unproductive.

*Atlantic gateway to North America: the St Lawrence.*
North America's principal physical landmarks — the
Rocky Mountains, the central lowlands, and the Appalachian Mountains — extend from north to south,
and the great river systems, the Mississippi, Mackenzie and Yukon, have the same north-south trend.
The one major exception is the St Lawrence River,
which flows north-eastwards into the Atlantic Ocean
along a transverse valley between ancient rocks, and
enters the sea through one of the widest estuaries in
the world.

The extent of this river basin is enormous, almost
a million square miles (about five times the area of
the United Kingdom or a third of that of the United
States), and approximately a third of it is covered by
waterways and lakes. Lake Superior, at the head of
the river system, is the world's largest freshwater
lake. Since it is only about 600 feet above sea level,
the seasonal régime is just as remarkable: maximum
flow in early summer is only twice minimum flow in
autumn. This ratio is in striking contrast to other
large rivers such as the Mississippi, which varies in
the ratio of 25 to 1, or the Columbia River at Grand
Coulee Dam with a ratio of 35 to 1. The explanation
is that the Great Lakes act as a series of regulators,
and surface evaporation compensates largely for the
higher flow of summer. Such regularity is of course
an enormouse advantage for the production of hydro-
electricity and has facilitated the development of the
Great Lakes as a navigable waterway.

It was Scandinavian sailors in search of whales and
cod who first came to know the coasts of Newfoundland and Nova Scotia and probably the great
estuary of the St Lawrence, all of which were exceptionally rich in fish. This was about the year 1000,
long before the time of Christopher Colombus. These
were lonely and unfriendly lands, lands that 'God
reserved for Cain' as Jaques Cartier later described
them. John Cabot is usually credited with their
discovery in 1497; he was followed by other explorers looking for a route to the Far East by way of
the western hemisphere, notably Cartier, who planted
a cross on the Gaspé Peninsula in 1534. Far Eastern
spices were in great demand in Europe, and the
Mongols and Turks had cut off overland trade routes.
Hopefully, Cartier even went so far as to call the falls
above Montreal on the St Lawrence the La Chine
(China) Rapids.

Although it did not lead to the Far East, the
St Lawrence became a great French route to the West,
to the heart of the North American continent. Thanks
to it, the explorers advanced with remarkable speed,
and by 1611 they had reached the western end of
Lake Superior. In 1672 Jolliet and Marquette discovered the Mississippi, and in 1682 La Salle reached
the mouth of the river near the present site of New
Orleans, having travelled there from Canada. It is
not surprising that central North America has many
French place names.

The banks of the St Lawrence provided good sites
for the early colonists, and for a long time the population kept entirely to them. In this forested and
roadless land the river was the easiest transportation
route. Later, with the discovery of the great wealth
of the interior, first furs and pelts, then timber, coal,
iron, and many other minerals in the west, the river

was used to develop a system of inland waterways
that is today probably the greatest in the world. To
overcome the many obstacles, such as rapids and falls,
canals were built, notably the Welland Canal by-
passing the famed Niagara Falls. However, it was not
until 1959 that the shipping bottleneck created by the
International Rapids above Montreal was eliminated
by a series of spectacular engineering works, undertaken jointly by the Canadian and United States
Governments, and all channels were dredged to a
depth of 27 feet, thus permitting ocean-going vessels
to sail directly from the Atlantic Ocean to the Great
Lakes ports. Since then cargoes on the Seaway have
steadily increased, reaching 39 million tons in 1964,
27 per cent more than the previous year. The chief
cargoes carried are wheat and other grains from
the Prairies downstream, and iron ore from Labrador
upstream. Optimists are predicting that a St Lawrence
River port will one day rival New York as the gateway
to North America, and they may not be far wrong.
Already two-thirds of the Canadian population and

a high proportion of its industry are concentrated in
the Laurentian Basin, which now enjoys the benefit
of large quantities of additional hydro-electricity
provided by the Seaway's new power plants.

*Severe winters.* The two sides of the North Atlantic,
the European and North American, so alike in their
coastal features, have completely different climates.
While Western Europe is affected by the warm
waters of the Gulf Stream, the Canadian side is not.
Quebec, in the same latitude as La Rochelle, on the
Bay of Biscay, is as cold as the Russian port of Murmansk. The difference between the temperatures of
the two coasts is about 20°C. (36°F.).

It is particularly in winter that these two continental coastlands are contrasted. In Europe, the 0°C.
(32°F.) January isotherm lies north of the North Cape
in Norway, while in North America it lies near
St Louis in the United States, which is in the same
latitude as Sicily. Atlantic Canada is like the eastward-facing regions of Kamchatka or the island
of Sakhalin, both affected by cold currents. Canada

One of Canada's many pulp
mills. Pulp and paper are of
prime importance in Canadian
industrial growth.

Every year in March icebreakers begin to clear a passage through the frozen St Lawrence at Montreal. Though Montreal is at the same latitude as Bordeaux, and the estuary of the St Lawrence corresponds in latitude to the northern part of the Bay of Biscay, the winter climate on the western littoral of the Atlantic is infinitely more severe, the difference in temperature being about 20°C. (36°F.).

includes that part of the American continent which adjoins the Arctic Sea, and these lands are penetrated by a maze of gulfs and arms of the sea which make them particularly susceptible to Arctic influences. One of these gulfs is Hudson Bay, almost an inland sea, and one of the coldest in the world, although it extends as far south as the latitude of London.

The lakes and seas provide evidence of the fundamental difference in winter conditions. Ice does not exist along the Norwegian coasts, while the Gulf of St Lawrence is often closed by winter pack ice. Freshwater conditions are even worse. The St Lawrence River, in the same latitude as the Seine, is frozen for more than four months each year, and the greater part of the surface of the Great Lakes, which extend nearly as far south as the latitude of Naples, is covered with thin sheets of ice for three months.

Canadian winters are so much more severe than those of Western Europe that it is hard to realise that these areas correspond in latitude. Parts of Canada are in the same latitude as London, Bordeaux, and Genoa. However, winter temperatures obviously vary greatly over such a vast country. In Montreal January temperatures average −4°C. (25°F.). On the Arctic islands in the Far North, the average is 37°C. (−35°F.). Winnipeg, in the interior, averages about −18°C. (0°F.); Victoria, on the Pacific coast, because of the moderating effect of the warm oceanic air masses moving in from the west, averages nearly 4°C. (40°F.) in January.

In summer, too, there are great differences, as indicated by averages of 21°C. (70°F.) in July in Montreal, 2°C. (35°F.) in the Far North, 20°C. (68°F.) in Winnipeg, and 16°C. (60°F.) in Victoria. Summer usually comes suddenly, except on the Pacific coast. In April the ground may still be snow-covered, while in May, after the thaw, the vegetation begins to grow rapidly and within a few days the trees are in full leaf. When winter is over, summer has arrived, and this season of abundance is prolonged by an autumn of comfortable temperatures and generally clear skies, when the landscape is aflame with the scarlets, reds, oranges and golds of turning leaves.

As one season gives way to another the landscape is completely changed. There is no longer the same rhythm of life. The hectic activity of summer is followed by the silent numbness of winter. Land and water alike disappear beneath several layers of snow and ice.

Most of northern and interior Canada gets less than 20 inches of precipitation a year, and the Prairies sometimes less than 12 inches, whereas parts of the west coast receive as much as 100 inches. Over much of the country precipitation is the result of the meeting of cold, dry polar air from the north and warm, moist tropical air from the Gulf of Mexico or Atlantic Ocean. These air masses move out through eastern Canada and particularly through the St Lawrence valley, which consequently averages from 40 to 60 inches of precipitation, much of it in the form of snow.

Laurentian Canada has one of the highest snow averages in the world. Montreal can expect a snowfall of more than 9 feet in an average year, and Quebec frequently gets 10 feet. On the Prairies, on the contrary, the snowfall is often less than 3 feet, and even in the depth of winter large islands of bare soil can be seen amidst the white countryside. Where the snow cover is thinner, the soil is frozen to a greater depth. In the St Lawrence region the depth of freezing is generally slight and can be measured in inches. On the Prairies the soil is sometimes frozen to a depth of 6 feet, and conditions are similar in the Far North where only the surface soil thaws in summer.

*Adapting to winter.* The winter season has marked biological consequences; there is a general slowing down of life. Nothing grows during these months and even animal life undergoes great changes. The great army of summer mosquitoes disappears. Enormous migrations take place. For birds, the finest breeding-grounds extend along the Canadian coasts, which are rich in fish, and huge flocks of wild geese, bustards, cranes and quail fly north from Louisiana and Florida each spring and south again in the autumn. Certain herbivorous animals also migrate. The caribou leave the tundra where they graze on lichen and moss during the summer, and return to the fringes of the sub-Arctic forest in the winter. Unfortunately they are now dying out. The Prairie buffalo (or bison) used to travel great distances, along routes which took them to the borders of Alaska and the shores of the Gulf of Mexico. These were almost completely destroyed by white settlers, in the late nineteenth century, and now buffalo can be found only in the National Parks.

Men as well as animals are affected by the harshness of the cold season. This is a land where it is necessary to know how to overcome the problems of extreme cold, and it was in Canada that Western Europeans, and particularly the French, first learned to deal scientifically with such winters.

The first problem was housing. The old French type of stone house was found to be damp and cold. What was needed was a wooden house whose relative lightness allowed it to be raised off the ground to avoid the dangers of thaw. Wooden boards replaced slate and tile for roofing, because they resisted the snow more effectively. A system of closed fires was adopted, and this made it necessary to store large quantities of fuel and to conserve for each settlement sufficient forest land to provide wood for the long winter.

Then there was the problem of clothing. Wool was the ideal choice, but sheep were scarce in this land of bears and wolves. Also, cloth was very expensive and had to be used economically. Rags were used to make coarse coverings called *catalognes*. Special items of clothing were introduced: coarse coloured shirts, mittens and other garments. Naturally skins and furs were also widely used.

Above all, diets had to change. For a long time winter mortality was the result of scurvy rather than of cold. Plans for the winter food supply had to be made early, meats and vegetables had to be preserved whenever they became available. Foresight and thrift were followed by festivals and feasting in November if the season had been a good one. The winter months came to an end with the making of maple syrup.

Occupations also had to be adapted to the season. Fishing was restricted or interrupted during the winter, and much other work came to a standstill. The principal winter job was felling timber in the forests, for it was easier to transport logs over snow than rough earth, and in the spring they could be floated down the swollen streams for milling or marketing.

Finally, there was the problem of winter transport. From the Eskimos and Indians, the early European settlers learned the art of making special shoes, such as moccasins and various kinds of snowshoes; an amazing variety of sledges took the place of wheeled vehicles. Gradually the settlers came to realise that snow was an advantage for some kinds of transport, especially of bulky and heavy materials like timber and stone.

Today as much wheeled traffic as possible is kept on the move throughout the winter by snow ploughs. On the rivers, powerful icebreakers carry on the struggle against the ice. The St Lawrence is now kept free from ice until the end of December and navigation begins again after April. The period when the river is ice-bound is becoming progressively shorter.

All in all, the Canadian people seem to have overcome the problems of winter with inventiveness, adaptability and foresight.

*The vast forests.* To the city-dweller, or one accustomed to the woodlands of western Europe or the eastern United States, it is difficult to appreciate the immensity of the Canadian forests. They cover more than 1,600,000 square miles, roughly 40 per cent of the country's total area, or 17 times that of the United Kingdom. According to present estimates, three-fifths of this forested land has potentially marketable timber; some 720,000 square miles are currently accessible for commercial exploitation.

The northern limit of the forests is the 'tree-line', extending in an arc from the coast of Labrador along the south shore of Hudson Bay, and thence north-west to the mouth of the Mackenzie River. Beyond this line, the vegetation is low-growing, and consists mainly of grasses, mosses, and a profusion of flowers in the short summer season. Southward, the forests extend as far as the United States border, except in the drier western interior lowlands known as the Prairies.

Although there is some intermixture, three types of forest predominate: softwoods (coniferous), chiefly

spruce, pine and cedar, in the north; hardwoods, (deciduous), chiefly birch, maple, ash, elm, oak, hickory and beech, in the south; and in the warmer, wetter Pacific coastal region, Douglas fir, Sitka spruce, red cedar, western hemlock, red alder and broad-leaved maple. The Pacific forests, thanks to the propitious climate, reach tremendous size. In southern British Columbia, for instance, Douglas firs attain a height of 300 feet and a circumference of more than 50 feet.

In the relatively drier Laurentian region the forests are generally smaller. Also they have been decimated by indiscriminate cutting, insect pests and fires. The most dangerous season for fires is May and June, when foliage is still sparse and the atmosphere is dry after the snow. From May to October guards live in the watch-towers erected throughout these forests, and on dry and windy days aircrcraft carry out reconnaissance flights to spot danger signals.

In the eighteenth century, when timber was beginning to be scarce in Europe, America became a useful forest reserve. Shipbuilding centres were established in the New World by various European countries: by Portugal, for instance, in Brazil; by France in Canada; and by England in New England. This exploitation robbed the Laurentian forests of a great number of the finest trees. However, towards 1870, a new industry appeared, which required not sawn timber but pulpwood, and pulpwood could be made from smaller trees, such as spruce. Therefore the wood pulp industry moved to the more northerly regions where spruce was plentiful. In the lands north of the St Lawrence, towards Labrador, new towns like Forestville grew up around huge pulp mills. Today, Quebec province is the leading Canadian producer of pulp and paper; British Columbia ranks first in the production of lumber.

The value of the Canadian wood products and paper products industries has increased enormously in the last few years, from approximately $1,700 million in 1947 to very nearly $3,500 million in 1959. Logging, lumbering, some 8,000 sawmills, and over 125 pulp and paper mills provide work for about 1,500,000 people. Canada is in fact the world's leading producer

Forests in Newfoundland. The immense Canadian forests cover more than 1,600,000 square miles — roughly 40 per cent of the country's area. Three-fifths of this expanse has potentially marketable timber, of which only 720,000 square miles are at present available for exploitation.

of wood products, and supplies more than half of its newsprint.

*The first rural settlements.* The early settlers who arrived via the St Lawrence established riverside homesteads, *fronteaux* as they were called, and rarely ventured inland, mainly because the river was then the best means of transportation. There were no roads and for a long time no vehicles; both were unknown to the native Indians. Roads were slow to develop; the first, between Montreal and Quebec, was not constructed until 1734, more than a century and a half after settlement began.

In addition, the alluvial lands along the shore were fertile, and in places there were small areas of meadow land free from forest, especially where it was sandy. These were the only natural pastures which could provide hay for the animals, at a time when the land was completely forested and the clearing of a field was a long and laborious task.

So at first the population spread along the waterways and every settlement was closely connected with a river. A waterside civilisation grew up. By the end of the period of French settlement, a traveller could have seen almost all the houses of Canada by canoeing along the St Lawrence and Richelieu Rivers and their tributaries. Waterfront was at this period synonymous with inhabited region. The properties bordering the river, 'river lots', were arranged lengthwise in strips. The typical holding was a narrow strip of land adjoining the river.

By the end of the eighteenth century, the frontages along the main waterways were all occupied. As families multiplied and new immigrants arrived, they founded settlements farther inland. These new properties had no access to the rivers; they needed roads, and from this time on roads began to compete with the rivers as transport routes, and soon surpassed them in importance. The supremacy of the road brought about a change in the pattern of settlement. At first the houses were all set on one side of the road, at the edge of the forest. When the second tier of settlements developed, houses were built opposite one another in a double row and gradually the roads were extended.

The system of building in rows or 'ranges' and the type of settlement which thus developed, with houses spaced out along roads, reconciled two usually conflicting advantages. The dwellings remained independent on their respective estates, and yet were quite near one another. As a result there was a solidarity between neighbours, a feature that was appreciated in a new country full of dangers.

This range type of settlement was quite different from the rectangular-shaped districts characteristic of the British townships of Ontario and the Prairies.

## THE MAJOR REGIONS

THE ST LAWRENCE REGION. The whole of eastern Canada, which borders the Atlantic, is composed of rocks which are among the oldest in the world. Geologically, this area is part of the so-called Canadian Shield. During several cycles of erosion it was peneplaned, and during the last of these a great ice sheet covered eastern Canada — until some tens of thousands of years ago. What emerged when it receded was a typical glaciated land, dotted with thousands of lakes, rounded hills and moraines.

The broad trough of the St Lawrence valley crosses the Canadian Shield diagonally from south-west to north-east, and separates two high massifs, the Appalachians to the south-east and the Laurentian Plateau to the north-west. The most productive lands of eastern Canada are concentrated in this valley, which extends for more than 600 miles from Newfoundland to the Great Lakes, with an estuary of sorts at each end. The mouth of the river on the Atlantic coast, an estuary larger than the English Channel, forms a small sea, the Gulf of St Lawrence, almost enclosed by the Strait of Belle Isle and Cabot Strait flanking the island of Newfoundland. In the south-west, the river leaves the Great Lakes system through a broad outlet, known as the Thousand Islands because of the more than 1,500 islands that split the waters of Lake Ontario into as many channels as they find their way into the river. It was along this valley corridor that the French settlers, many of them sturdy men from Normandy, Brittany and the Vendée, created what is today French Canada, the province of Quebec. Other groups came to Canada later, mainly from the Atlantic coast of America, farther south, penetrating the interior by an overland route. These were the British, who created British Canada in the province of Ontatio.

*The province of Quebec.* Most of Quebec, Canada's largest province, larger than any state in the United States and six times the size of Great Britain, is cold in winter and rugged. Most of the people are concentrated in the rather small pockets of rolling or flat fertile soil. Only about one-eighth of the province is settled; about half is commercially valuable forest; the rest is unproductive forest, tundra, wasteland, and water. Nevertheless, Quebec has tremendous resources, besides its forests, namely its farms, rivers, mines and people, and of course it shares in the benefits derived from the great St Lawrence Seaway including transportation facilities and hydro-electric power supplies.

The most productive farming region is the St Lawrence lowlands, where the growing season is from 150 to 200 days a year. A variety of crops is raised here, including tobacco, sugar-beet, excellent grapes, peaches, apples, strawberries, blueberries, raspberries, vegetables of all sorts, potatoes, and some grains such as wheat, barley and rye. This is also maple syrup country, hog country, and dairy country. Quebec produces more milk than any other province, and large quantities of butter and cheese.

Quebec also produces more hydro-electric power than any other province, thanks to ninety-odd power plants along the St Lawrence, Ottawa, Saguenay, and St Maurice Rivers and their tributaries—in all nearly 50 per cent of Canada's total installed capacity of 20,000,000 kilowatts, which is the second largest in the world, after the United States.

Such abundant and cheap power has attracted a variety of industries, notably the making of aluminium at Arvida on the Saguenay, using bauxite imported from the Caribbean area. Other large industries include pulp and paper, butter and cheese making, meatpacking, metal smelting and refining, petroleum products, electrical apparatus, textiles, clothing, tobacco products, railroad equipment and aircraft. Some of these are based on imported raw materials, and some use local ones, notably iron ore, copper, lead, zinc, gold and asbestos. Incidentally, Canada is the world's leading producer of asbestos.

Of the 5,624,000 people who live in the province of Quebec, four-fifths are of French origin and speak French as their first language. Montreal, with 2,260,000 inhabitants, is the nation's major industrial city and port, its largest city, and the second largest French city in the world, after Paris. This is a cosmopolitan metropolis, where French and English (about a quarter of the total) live together in a more or less amicable 'marriage of convenience', a booming, roaring city, which nevertheless has great charm, beautiful cathedrals and museums, and two of Canada's outstanding educational institutions, McGill University and the University of Montreal.

Quebec City, another important manufacturing centre, is generally considered the most picturesque of Canada's cities, the one with the most European flavour and the most imbued with a sense of history. It was founded in 1608 by Samuel de Champlain, and the old city is still circled by walls.

*The province of Ontario.* One-third of the nation's twenty million people live in the province of Ontario, but, like Quebec, vast sections of it, especially in the north, are virtually uninhabited. However, it is the forests of northern Ontario which supply more than one-quarter of the paper made in Canada, and its Sudbury basin mines are the source of two-fifths of the country's copper and nearly three-quarters of the world's output of nickel. Platinum, cobalt, gold, iron and uranium have also been found in commercial quantities. Around such mines and along the waterways several towns have grown up and become industrial centres, making pulp and paper, steel, transportation equipment, and flour, notably Sudbury, Fort William, Port Arthur, North Bay, and Sault Ste Marie. This last is located on the St Mary's River between Lake Huron and Lake Superior on the most westerly channel of the St Lawrence Seaway, and it is claimed that its locks, with those on the American side, handle more traffic than the Panama and Suez Canals together.

Densely populated southern Ontario, especially the Great Lakes and St Lawrence lowlands, is one of the most productive farming areas in Canada, the principal crops being tobacco, cherries, peaches, grapes, corn, soya beans and a variety of vegetables such as lettuce, celery, onions, carrots and potatoes. Less fertile sections are occupied by pastures for dairy cattle.

Although southern Ontario is not as rich in minerals as some other parts of Canada, it nevertheless has abundant salt, limestone, sand, gravel, gypsum, cement and quartz. Such building materials have been a distinct advantage in the current urban and industrial growth, as have the large thermo-electric stations using United States coal from south of the Great Lakes and numerous hydro-electric plants on the Niagara, St Lawrence and Ottawa Rivers.

Canada is today one of the world's leading manufacturers—probably the sixth largest. About 30 per cent of the national income is derived from manufacturing, and Ontario is the most industrialised

province, followed by Quebec. The gross value of manufactured products in the two provinces together amounts to some $19,284 million out of a national total of $24,243 million. One or the other province produces the great bulk of the nation's gasoline and fuel oils, chemicals, non-ferrous metal products, iron and steel goods, textiles, tobacco products, canned and frozen foods, beverages, and printing and publishing. Ontario alone produces 99 per cent of Canada's motor vehicles, 79 per cent of its heavy electrical machinery, 80 per cent of its primary iron and steel, 82 per cent of its rubber goods, 70 per cent of its electrical appliances, and from 50 to 75 per cent of its sheet metal products, aircraft and parts, industrial and farm machinery, and furniture.

Several thousand of these manufacturing establishments are in Toronto (population 1,989,000), another of Canada's rapidly growing cities, now the second biggest, which is also a financial, commercial, cultural and educational centre. Other industries are centred in Hamilton (iron and steel), which has been likened to Cleveland in the United States; Windsor, facing Detroit on Lake Erie and similarly occupied with the making of automobiles; and such cities as London, Kitchener, St Catherines, Kingston and Sarnia. Ottawa, capital of Canada and quieter than Toronto, is considered one of the country's most attractive cities.

In all, 12,292,000 people live in Quebec and Ontario, nearly two-thirds of the total population. Only two other provinces have more than one million inhabitants each—an indication of the vast extent of unused land. Economists, looking to the future, to a fuller development of the natural resources and industry, would like to see a sizable increase in population, and such additional manpower will probably have to come from immigration, since the domestic rate of population growth is rather low.

THE ATLANTIC PROVINCES. Although Jacques Cartier failed to find a route to the Far East during his voyage in 1534 along the shores of Newfoundland, New Brunswick and Prince Edward Island, he brought back reports of abundant furs and fish, which spurred adventurous Europeans to come there to hunt and fish. Seventy years later, in 1604, two Frenchmen, Poutrincourt and Champlain, established the first real colony in the Atlantic Provinces, near what is now Annapolis Royal in Nova Scotia. The earliest English settlement was founded by John Guy six years later near Bay Roberts in Newfoundland. During the following decades various other groups arrived, both French and English, establishing fishing villages at good harbour sites and small farms and lumber camps. In 1749 the British founded Halifax, primarily as a naval and military base, from which they hoped to weaken their long-time rivals in the New World, the French. And indeed, six years later, they did expel the Acadians (French), and opened their lands to settlers from England and New England. In the 1770's some Scots and Irish came. Then, between 1782 and 1784, about 25,000 people who remained loyal to the British Crown and were unwilling to live in an independent United States arrived, settling principally along the Atlantic coast of Nova Scotia and in the St John River valley in the adjoining province of New Brunswick.

Today three-quarters of the 1,984,000 inhabitants of the Atlantic Provinces are of Anglo-Saxon descent; the rest are mainly French (about 300,000), Germans, Poles, Czechoslovakians, Russians, Italians, Danes or Dutch.

Although settled early, the Atlantic Provinces have not prospered as well as the other regions of Canada. Unfortunately the wet cool climate is not favourable to many crops, and much of the land consists of rough hills or uplands with thin stony soils. The only good agricultural areas are the lowlands of Prince Edward Island, parts of Nova Scotia along the Bay of Fundy and the Northumberland Strait, the St John valley of New Brunswick, and small pockets in Newfoundland.

The gently rolling surface of Prince Edward Island, often called 'The Garden of the Gulf', is dotted with neat, well-fenced, attractive farms. The soils are not naturally very fertile, but they become highly so with the application of fertilizers and lime, and a greater proportion of the land is under cultivation than in

any other Canadian province. The chief cash crop is potatoes, grown for the table and especially for seed: half of the nation's best-quality seed potatoes come from the island, which also sells seeds to Maine, long known as the top potato producer in the United States. Most farmers also grow hay, oats, and some vegetables and fruits, raise hogs and poultry, and engage in part-time fishing, mainly for lobsters. Lush meadows provide excellent pasture for dairy and beef cattle.

Lowland Nova Scotia also is a dairy and beef cattle and poultry region; here the main crops are oats, hay, silage and apples. One of the most productive apple-growing areas in Canada is the Annapolis valley, which is blessed with a longer growing season—134 days a year—than is usual in the Atlantic Provinces. It is protected by North and South Mountains from chilling winds that might damage the trees, and in the spring the cool Bay of Fundy prevents the buds from opening too soon, before the danger of frost has passed; and in the autumn the same bay, now warmer, delays the first frost, thus allowing a sufficient period of time to elapse in which the apples can be picked.

The main sources of farm income in New Brunswick are the potatoes, hay, fruits, especially apples, and dairy herds on the river terraces of the St John valley, which is largely responsible for New Brunswick's first place in agricultural income among the Atlantic Provinces. Other than this, the principal farm activities are the raising of hogs, chickens, strawberries and cranberries, the picking of blueberries, and the making of maple syrup.

In most of Newfoundland farming is hampered by poor soils, dampness, and summer coolness caused by winds from the Labrador Current, which is often ice-laden even in July. Potatoes and turnips are the chief crops, and vegetables from a few market-gardens near the city of St John's.

*Forests, mines and fisheries.* After the American Revolution, Great Britain, finding itself short of timber, much of which had come from the Thirteen Colonies, turned to Canada, and the forests of the Atlantic Province became the basis for a flourishing business and transatlantic trade. St John in New Brunswick grew into a great timber port, and eventually Nova Scotia's famed Bluenose schooners, originally built to carry timber to Britain, carried wares across the seven seas—until the advent of steam navigation and iron vessels in the 1880's.

Today, in spite of serious depletion, forests still cover four-fifths of New Brunswick, three-quarters of Nova Scotia, and half of Newfoundland, and even on Prince Edward Island almost every farm has a woodlot used for fuel or making pit props, railway ties, and pulpwood. Conifers, especially spruces, predominate; they are the most valuable commercial trees, and the raw material for the most important forest industries, the manufacture of wood pulp and paper, much of which is shipped out to the United Kingdom and the United States.

Mining is another principal source of income and employment in all the Atlantic Provinces except Prince Edward Island. There are coal deposits in the Minto area of New Brunswick, and some of the largest in the nation along the Atlantic shores of Cape

Fine grade paper being produced at a mill in Ontario. Newsprint is a leading export. In fact Canada's output of newsprint is more than three times that of any other country and provides about 45 per cent of the world's newsprint needs.

Montreal, the largest city in Canada. This rapidly expanding city has at present, with its suburbs, a population of over 2,000,000, more than two-thirds of whom speak French; it may therefore be called the second largest French-speaking city of the world, after Paris. In the early 1600's it was a centre for fur-trading; then, in the latter half of the nineteenth century, though over 1,000 miles from the Atlantic, it developed its river frontage into a port for ocean-going vessels. Its industrial activity has expanded steadily and the opening of the St Lawrence Seaway has further stimulated it.

Breton Island in Nova Scotia. Unfortunately much of the Nova Scotia coal is obtained from submarine seams far from the pitheads, thereby making exploitation difficult and costly. This, plus the distance from large markets, has led to a steady decline in output. It is currently cheaper for factories in southern Ontario, for instance, to buy coal from the United States than from Nova Scotia. Railroads, steamships, thermal electric stations, and iron and steel plant at Sydney, one of the largest in Canada, are the main users of this coal.

About 90 per cent of Canada's gypsum comes from quarries in Nova Scotia; most of it is shipped out via Halifax to plants making wallboard and wall plaster on the east coast of the United States.

Mineral production, the most valuable primary industry in Newfoundland, brings in about $121 million each a year, mainly from iron (70 per cent), lead, zinc, copper and silver. Some three million tons of iron ore are being taken annually from underwater deposits off Bell Island, for use in Sydney or export to the United Kingdom and West Germany. Many millions more are coming from the huge iron deposits in northern Labrador along the Newfoundland-Quebec border.

For four centuries the shallow seas south-east of Nova Scotia and Newfoundland, the most extensive and famous fishing waters in the world, have been the economic mainstay of the Atlantic Provinces. Here the 100-fathom contour line marking the edge of the continental shelf lies more than 24 miles offshore, and the warm waters of the Gulf Stream meet the cold Labrador current, creating ideal conditions for the proliferation of plankton.

Toward the end of March each year fleets of trawlers and draggers, equipped with trawling lines and nets, set out for the Grand Banks and remain at sea for several weeks, except for periodic trips to port to unload the catch and take on bait and ice. Inshore fishing, generally within six or eight miles of the coast, starts in June and lasts through September. In this short season vast quantities of cod, haddock, herring, halibut, tuna, salmon, sardines and lobsters are brought in for sale fresh or for freezing, filleting, smoking, drying, canning, or processing into fishmeal, fish liver oil, and fish glue. These processes give employment to well over 50,000 people. Although the fleet and processing plants are generally not as modern and well equipped as those on the Pacific coast, the value of fishery products (approximately $128 million) is nearly as great. Efforts are now being made, particularly in Newfoundland, to increase efficiency by concentrating the fishing industry in larger towns, where productivity can be improved and costs can be cut, and where housing, medical services and educational opportunities are better than in the small isolated villages, as is the supply of available labour.

Several industries, based on local or imported raw materials, other than pulp and paper, iron and steel, and fishing, have developed in the Atlantic Provinces. In Halifax, a city with a fine harbour, oil-refining, sugar-refining, flour-milling, and shipbuilding are the principal industries; in St John's in Newfoundland clothing, beverages, food processing, shipbuilding and repairing and woodworking. Charlottetown on

A cod fisherman mending his nets on the east coast of Canada. The seas south-east of Nova Scotia and Newfoundland have for centuries been the economic mainstay of the Atlantic Provinces, and are the most extensive and famous fishing waters in the world.

Prince Edward Island specialises in highly prized butter and cheeses. St John, the largest city in New Brunswick, refines sugar, builds and repairs ships, and makes railway rolling-stock. Moncton, second city in the province, is a rail centre, also concerned with oil-refining, meat-packing, making wood and metal products, and textiles. But industrial growth, and in fact almost every aspect of the economy in the Atlantic Provinces, has suffered from isolation, distance from markets, and the high cost of transportation.

Tourism appears to be the most vigorous new industry, and is becoming a valuable supplementary source of income. The principal attractions are the forests, the sea, the marvellously indented shores dotted with picturesque villages, the sandy beaches, the 60-foot tides of the Bay of Fundy, the famous Reversing Falls on the St John River, and the tidal bore on the Petitcodiac River. Another attraction of Atlantic Canada is the Gaspé Peninsula, part of Quebec province, famed for its wild, rocky, cliff-lined shores.

THE PRAIRIES: REALM OF WHEAT. Between the St Lawrence valley and the Prairies the forest extends for more than 600 miles. In the old days, settlers tended

Mechanical potato-lifting on a farm in New Denmark, a district of New Brunswick. In the Maritime Provinces the oceanic climate favours mixed farming.

to avoid it, travelling by canoe via the Great Lakes. Today one can cross it by car over a paved road traversing the entire continent. This road, the Trans-Canada Highway, is an engineering feat opened in 1962. There are also two transcontinental railroads. But these are the only overland links between the valley and the Prairies, and it takes twenty-four hours or more to get from Montreal or Toronto to Winnipeg. The area of uninhabited forest is, however, gradually being reduced. New centres of agriculture and industry are being established which may eventually eliminate at least the wildest part of this wilderness.

Beyond Winnipeg, in the Prairies, there are no more forests or ancient rocks, no falls or deeply incised valleys, and the rivers are generally smaller and slower-moving. Huge areas are sedimentary rocks, the soil is deep, changing from black earth to yellow sand, the landscape is flat or gently rolling, and the grass is long, the famous pasture of the millions of buffalo which once grazed here. As mentioned earlier, precipitation is scanty and the winter cold intense. Nevertheless, grazing is possible almost throughout the winter, for the snow cover is periodically melted by the Chinooks, warm winds from the west and south-west whose arrival may bring a 40-degree rise in temperature in a few hours.

The first Europeans to penetrate this hunting ground of the Indians were French, and they left behind many French names along their routes. The first settlements were those of half-breed Franco-Indians, who took part in uprisings against British colonisation during the nineteenth century. Real settlement only began with the construction of the railroad in 1885, and the discovery that this was excellent land for crops: land, moreover, that did not first have to be cleared of trees. Three-quarters of all Canada's cultivable land is in the Prairies.

The problem was, what to grow. Wheat could not survive the winter in soil which had only a thin covering of snow and was frozen to a depth of several feet, at least not the type of winter wheat which was sown before the snows in eastern Canada. A special variety was therefore developed, a spring wheat which could be sown in May, soon after the thaw, and which could be harvested in September, just before the autumn frosts. This is Manitoba wheat (also called 90-day wheat because it requires only three months to reach maturity).

In the wheat-growing rush that followed, the harvests were found to be excellent year after year, without fertilizer or rotation. Teams of land surveyors appeared on the scene; huge tracts of new land were divided into sections of equal size, 6 miles by 6 miles, taking as a base line the United States border, the 49th parallel. These sections were called townships and were further divided into 36 plots of one square mile. This regular rectangular pattern was adopted everywhere—very different from the ranges, the linear pattern of the riverside settlements in French Canada. Maps showing numbered squares permitted the formal purchase of plots of equal size to people who had never even seen them. The first plots were sold off at the remarkably low price of ten dollars a section.

The chief problem in the settlement of this new area was that of labour. At first, armies of workers came from the east to help with the harvest, but it was not long before machinery was introduced. Today enormous combines are used, which, operated by two men, can do the work of thirty men and fifteen horses. As these machines require a large capital outlay, they are often owned by companies rather than individual farmers. The work is done more and more under contract, the farmer engaging one of the syndicates to undertake the whole harvesting operation. The director surveys the crop from the air and supervises the movement of the combines from south to north as the wheat ripens. Spring sowing operations after the thaw are carried out in the same way. This is a highly scientific but somewhat wasteful method of cultivation: yields are low, and the soil is rapidly exhausted. Also, it does not tend to increase the region's population. Nevertheless such methods have brought Canada to third place among the world's producers of wheat, after the Soviet Union and the United States, and have given it a huge surplus each year and an acute storage problem. The problem was eased slightly in 1961 by the sale of 244,600,000 bushels of wheat to mainland China, 7,400,000 to the Soviet Union, 11,000,000 to Czechoslovakia, and 7,300,000 to Poland. Further sales have been made to these markets in every year since 1961.

A typical Prairie farm consists of a cottage-type building, made of wooden boards. The grain is stored in small sheds, or granaries, on the wheat field, or is taken directly to elevators on a rail route. In this tree-less land, the farmhouse is often sheltered by a hedge of willows which forms a windbreak against violent gales. Wind, in fact, proves a great danger in this country. Where cultivation has removed the protective covering of grass, the soil is easily eroded; in places dunes even encroach on the fields. In the drier zones, it has been found advisable to abandon wheat in favour of ranching. Today, ranching on a very large scale, especially the raising of beef cattle, has replaced cultivation, particularly in southern Alberta and southern Saskatchewan. The crop land tends to be localised in a broad fertile crescent curving north-ward between Winnipeg and the Rockies and enclosing the pastoral prairie that lies in the south and south-west.

The animals withstand the cold weather well. They remain out of doors almost all winter and when the grass is buried beneath a thin covering of snow they can easily remove it with their hoofs. When it is very cold they take shelter in the stacks of hay provided on the pasture land. They obtain drinking water by breaking the ice on the ponds.

*The melting-pot of the Prairies.* The population of these more recently settled regions has not the same homogeneity as that of the St Lawrence region, which is almost entirely French and British. The original agricultural settlements were established mainly by Anglo-Americans and Scots; there followed an invasion of French-Canadians, who gathered in certain districts, such as St Boniface near Winnipeg; then people of all nationalities came in. These included Ukrainians who found there black soils similar to those in southern Russia; Hungarians, who made settlements chiefly in the region of Edmonton; a large number of Icelanders, who settled round the big lakes to the north of Winnipeg and took up fishing; plus Italians, Jews, Negroes and others. There is as yet little unity among these widely scattered peoples. They live independently and preserve in this new land many of the customs of their former country. The principal focal points are the rail stations, dominated by the high outlines of the grain elevators.

Settlement is still unstable in the drier wheat areas where droughts periodically cause crop failures. Also, the land is easily abandoned, since the farm buildings are of little value. Deserted properties are therefore exceptionally numerous. The most stable agricultural economy of the Prairies is in the so-called Park Belt, north of the wheat lands. Here the black soils are among the most fertile in the world, there is no moisture problem, and crop failures are almost unknown. Actually, in recent years the Park Belt has surpassed the agricultural productivity of the wheat and grazing lands. About half of the land is planted in wheat, the other half in barley, oats, vegetables and flax. Because of the availability of feed, pigs are raised, and cattle are brought up from the ranching zone to be fattened. Around the urban communities, dairy cows and poultry are also raised.

*Mineral wealth of the Prairies.* The discovery of rich mineral resources in the Prairies is further diversifying the region's economy. Already the income derived from mining is more than half that obtained from agriculture. Vast coal deposits, almost at the surface, have been found on the edge of the Rockies, the highest grade of bituminous being in the broad foothill section between Edmonton and Calgary. Exploitation of this coal has not increased as much as might be expected, in view of the enormous quantity there for the taking. The explanation is, once again, isolation, the high cost of shipping the coal out to markets; and, also, the discovery of huge deposits of oil and natural gas. Since the fabulous Leduc oilfield was disocvered in 1947, exploration and drilling have brought to light other equally fabulous finds, notably at Redwater, Golden Spike, and Pembina, and elsewhere in western and south-eastern Saskatchewan, in south-western Manitoba, and along the Athabasca River in Alberta.

Oil and natural gas from the Prairies now reach Vancouver on the Pacific and as far east as Montreal through some of the longest pipelines in the world, which in turn are linked with sections of the United States network. Canada, with its cold winters and growing industries, is fortunate to have some of the world's largest oil deposits.

Beneath the Prairie soils are also some of the biggest known deposits of potash, used to make fertilizer, and valuable deposits of salt and gypsum. There is sand, gravel, building stone, cement and clay. Nearly all the requirements in hydro-electric power are supplied by two large dams on the Saskatchewan River system, which will provide water to irrigate at least 500,000 acres of dry farmland.

*Industry grows in the Prairies.* The three Prairie Provinces, Manitoba (capital Winnipeg), Saskatchewan (capital Regina), and Alberta (capital Edmonton), have only 3,312,000 inhabitants, in an area of more than 750,000 square miles, and most of them are concentrated in the southern third and in the rapidly growing cities.

The largest city is Winnipeg, starting-point for the waves of settlers who brought the Prairies under the plough sixty-odd years ago, and today a city of over 487,000, with immense grain elevators, the biggest railroad yards in Canada (both transcontinental rail routes pass through it), and all sorts of industries — meat-packing, oil-refining, flour-milling, the making of iron and steel products, clothing, rolling-stock and paper products. Regina is much smaller and is primarily a distributing centre for farm implements. Edmonton, in the heart of the new oil lands, is Canada's fastest-growing city, and the road, rail, and air gateway to the north-west; the chief industries here are petro-chemicals, slaughtering, meat-packing, and the processing of dairy products. Calgary, another fast-growing industrial town, which has recently acquired a huge new petro-chemical plant, is known throughout Canada and the world for its colourful annual Stampede.

For all its wealth, agricultural, mineral and industrial, and its dense local network of railroads, a basic

The trans-continental railroad here passes through the Fraser Canyon, near Lytton in British Columbia. After emerging from the Rockies, the Fraser River empties into the Pacific at Vancouver. Its low valley made relatively easy passage for the railroad, whose terminus became Vancouver.

In the Prairie wheat-belt the fields are almost completely flat. Each one is very extensive, and they stretch as far as the eye can see, interspersed with farm buildings. The dairy barns in the foreground of the picture are typical of this prosperous area near Moose Jaw, Saskatchewan. Mechanisation, involving the use of huge machines, is an essential feature of agriculture on the Prairies.

Vancouver, British Columbia, occupies a magnificent site on the Pacific coast. It has nearly 828,000 inhabitants and is a port for wood and grain. Business, industry and cultural activities have made it the key city of the Pacific coast of Canada. Mountains with immense forests rise from the very edge of the city.

problem of central Canada has been distance and the high cost of transportation to outside markets. There are no easy communications by water here, as in the east. However, the western end of Lake Superior, now connected directly with the Atlantic by the St Lawrence Seaway, is not too far from the Prairies: Port Arthur and Fort William are the main centres for the shipment of wheat and livestock. And towards the west there are three rail routes, two terminating at Vancouver and the other at Prince Rupert.

THE ROCKY MOUNTAINS AND PACIFIC REGION. Westward, beyond the vast Prairies, looms a giant snow-covered wall, which can be seen from a great distance. It rises to a height of over 11,500 feet, and is crossed only by a few difficult passes. This Rocky Mountain system, composed of a series of north-south folds, is one of the most extensive in the world.

West of it a remarkably straight flat valley, the Rocky Mountain Trench, 2,000 to 3,000 feet above sea level, more than 1,000 miles long and 2 to 10 miles wide, extends all the way from the Yukon into the United States. Beyond the Trench, still farther westward, are the Columbia Mountains in the south, and between these and the Coast Mountains lies an undulating interior plateau of basaltic lavas dissected by valleys and deep lakes. The Coast Mountains are composed of rows of jagged peaks, many of them over 9,000 feet high (13,260 feet at Mount Wadding-

ton), towering above the coastal fiords. Off the coast is another, partly submerged, range, the peaks of which form Vancouver Island, the Queen Charlotte Islands, and a dozen others.

The whole of this mountain zone has been shaped by glaciation. Ancient glaciers have left behind magnificent lakes, U-shaped valleys, and deep fiords Some lakes, such as Lake Kootenay and Lake Okanagan, are more than 60 miles long. They are very different from the shallow irregular lakes of eastern Canada. Here the ice accumulated in the interior of the mountain ranges, able to flow only to the sea through a few outlets, which served as drainage channels for the enormous glacial discharge. The chief of these glacial outlets is today followed by the lower course of the Fraser River, which enters the sea at Vancouver, the vital western gateway of Canada and comparable with the Hudson valley serving New York on the eastern coast of the United States.

The innumerable ice-excavated coastal fiords, which penetrate far inland, have precipitous sides cut by hanging valleys with magnificent waterfalls. Since the ice retreated relatively recently, the fiords have as yet been little affected by silting. However, one delta, at the mouth of the Fraser River, has become a fertile coastal plain, the best farming area in the region. This provides Vancouver with a rich immediate hinterland.

Naturally, a mountain barrier of such size acts as a climatic divide. The warm, humid oceanic climate, which in Western Europe, for instance, penetrates far inland, is here confined to a narrow coastal strip. The southern part of Vancouver Island, though farther north than Quebec, which is frozen for five months, is well known for its winter warmth and fogs. Enormous hydrangeas remain in bloom almost throughout the year. Towards the north the coastal climate is similar to that of Norway, and the pack ice that so often blocks the Gulf of St Lawrence is unknown. It is this warm humidity of the Pacific coast that has produced the magnificent forests of this area.

The interior plateau, on the contrary, is dry and parts are almost semi-desert. This is a land of grassy steppe, sage brush, and even cactus. Thus in western Canada humid and arid lands, forest and near-desert are found side by side, in marked contrast with the other Canadian regions, which are rather uniform in climate and vegetation.

As there was little land suitable for farming, the early inhabitants concentrated on the sea, particularly the area round Puget Sound, whose sheltered fiords and warm and cold waters mixed by powerful tides offered excellent conditions for marine life. They discovered here one of the world's richest spawning grounds, swarming with salmon, halibut, cod, herring and lobster.

The Indians based a flourishing economy on fishing; so did the Spaniards, who came from the south, from Mexico via California, and the Russians, who came from the north, from Alaska. The English appeared only about 1850, when they came to realise the importance of Puget Sound, and established a naval base at Esquimalt, west of Victoria, now the Pacific base of the Royal Canadian Navy.

Pacific Coast salmon, famed for their high quality,

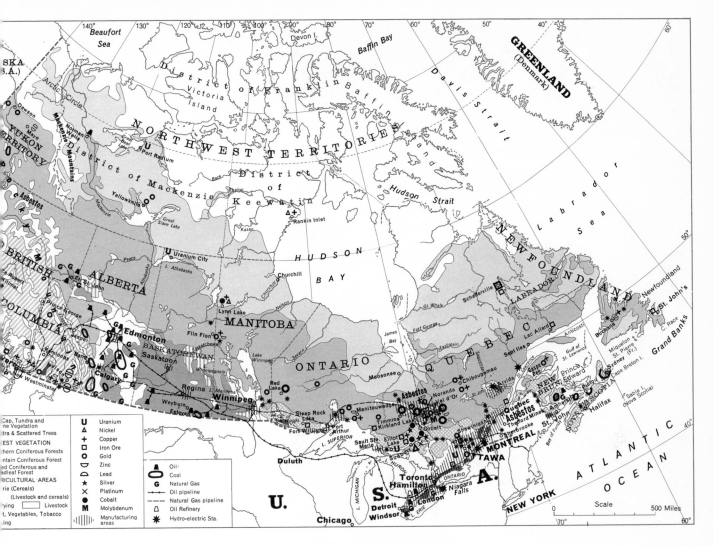

Economic map of Canada showing mineral resources and vegetation.

Legend:

|  |  |
|---|---|
| U | Uranium |
| △ | Nickel |
| + | Copper |
| □ | Iron Ore |
| ○ | Gold |
| ▽ | Zinc |
| ◁ | Lead |
| ★ | Silver |
| ✕ | Platinum |
| ● | Cobalt |
| M | Molybdenum |
| ⫿⫿⫿ | Manufacturing areas |

|  |  |
|---|---|
| ▲ | Oil |
| ⬭ | Coal |
| G | Natural Gas |
| — | Oil pipeline |
| --- | Natural Gas pipeline |
| ⬠ | Oil Refinery |
| ✳ | Hydro-electric Sta. |

Ice Cap, Tundra and Alpine Vegetation
Tundra & Scattered Trees
FOREST VEGETATION
Northern Coniferous Forests
Mountain Coniferous Forest
Mixed Coniferous and Broadleaf Forest
AGRICULTURAL AREAS
Prairie (Cereals)
Dairying (Livestock and cereals)
Livestock
Fruit, Vegetables, Tobacco
Wheat (Livestock and cereals)

and sold throughout the world, bring in an annual income of over $30 million and have brought in even more in the past. To prevent over-fishing, which has been widespread, Canada and the United States have set up an international Salmon Fisheries Commission to regulate fishing methods and fix open seasons.

Productive forests cover three-fifths of British Columbia, and forest industries contribute nearly half of the province's income. No other part of the world yields so many cubic feet of timber from its forested area, and timber mills are numerous, including the largest ones in the world at New Westminster at the mouth of the Fraser River. Huge quantities of pulp and newsprint also come from these forests. Here, too, excessive exploitation has been the pattern, but the provincial government has now initiated a policy of conservation, reforestation and fire control.

*The rapid growth of Vancouver.* The coming of the transcontinental railroad and the discovery of minerals marked the beginning of real settlement on the Pacific coast. The city of Vancouver, ideally located on Burrard Inlet, the most southerly of the British Columbian fiords, and at the railroad's terminus, grew with astonishing rapidity: from 29,000 in 1901 to more than 828,000 including suburbs in 1964. It is now second only to Montreal among the nation's ports, exporting British Columbian lumber, pulp and paper,

minerals and fish; and wheat, livestock, and minerals from the Prairies. Vancouver is also famed for its magnificent setting between wooded mountains and the sea, and for its public park in which some gigantic trees have been preserved.

In the fertile hinterland, the alluvial valley of the Lower Fraser, a variety of crops is grown: fruits, vegetables, bulbs, seeds and hops; dairy cows and poultry are raised too. Besides this, other notably good farming areas are in the Okanagan valley (especially famed for its Mackintosh apples, and the Kootenay and Peace River valleys, which are particularly valuable, as they are some of the most northerly cultivated lands in Canada. Beyond this, the land becomes too wet and cold and there are few cultivated valleys. At Prince Rupert foodstuffs are among the most expensive in Canada.

*The rôle of minerals and power.* As early as 1858, gold placer deposits were discovered in the valleys of the Upper Fraser and its tributary, the Thompson; then followed the rush to the north, to the Klondike through Alaskan ports. The famous Premier gold mine was opened near Portland Canal; copper was mined not far away at Anyox on Observatory Inlet. In the mountains an increasing number of mineral deposits were found, which necessitated the construction of branch rail lines, especially to the rich Gold Range near the United States border where copper

The Kitimat aluminium smelter in British Columbia, which is situated at the head of a fiord on the Pacific coast and about 150 miles inland. The plant is one of the largest in the world, and makes use of power generated by a waterfall fed by the glaciers of the nearby mountains.

Sorting and grading apples in the Okanagan Valley, British Columbia. The orchards of British Columbia supply fruit to other parts of Canada and much is exported to Britain.

and gold mines were opened at Rossland, Trail, and Fernie. Towards the north the gold mines were linked by the difficult line from Squamish to Quesnel. Uncommon minerals like cadmium and palladium were found near the Sullivan mine, which is the leading producer of lead and zinc in Canada. Several coal fields, at Nanaimo and on Vancouver Island, for instance, facilitated the establishment of industry, though now these mines face serious competition from petroleum which comes in from Edmonton and the abundant water power from the glaciated valleys, which have the largest reserves of hydro-electricity in Canada. The power station at Cheakamus, sixty miles north of Vancouver, is considered the largest in the world to be entirely operated by remote control.

British Columbia at present ranks fourth among the Canadian provinces in value of mineral production, the leading minerals being lead, zinc, asbestos, gold, silver and copper.

The exceptional wealth in power resources has attracted various industries which are large consumers

of electricity, in spite of the scarcity of labour. A huge aluminium plant has been built at the head of an inlet at Kitimat, which now produces more than the very large plant at Arvida, built below Lake St John in eastern Canada.

A tourist industry has also developed in these spectacularly beautiful lands, and famous national parks have been established, like those of Banff, Jasper, and Glacier, which are visited each year by thousands of tourists. The lakes attract thousands of enthusiastic fishermen and yachtsmen too. All in all, the Rocky Mountain region is overcoming its isolation and lack of population.

THE FAR NORTH AND ITS PIONEER FRONTIER. Beyond the more or less densely populated 300-mile-wide belt of Canada lies the vast, almost empty Northland, which consists of four sub-regions: the northern part of the Canadian Shield, the Mackenzie lowlands, the Cordilleran zone in the Yukon, and the Arctic islands. The polar archipelago, which includes the most northerly lands in the world, is permanently frozen and covered with snow almost throughout the year. Farther south the endless tundras, the 'barren grounds', begin, and these are succeeded by poor forest of birch and spruce, with snow and ice in winter and mosquitoes and marshes in summer. It is difficult to decide which is the less unpleasant of these two seasons.

Among a total of 39,000 inhabitants of the Northland are about 11,500 Eskimos, who depend for their livelihood mainly on fishing, sealing, trapping fur animals, and hunting. Unfortunately, artificial fur fabrics have slashed the demand for natural furs, and hunting is declining, as the herds of caribou have almost disappeared. However, things are changing. Aircraft today carry hunters to their trapping zones; doctors, businessmen and police make their rounds by air. Frozen lakes make excellent natural airfields, and numerous landing grounds have been built, the biggest of which are Goose Bay, Gander, Fort Chimo, and Frobisher Bay. Military air bases have also increased in number since the North Pole has become a frontier of observation between the Soviet and American worlds. Furthermore, air travel is making it possible to carry out extensive prospecting for mineral reserves, which are apparently numerous.

The most valuable mineral deposits are the great iron fields extending south from Ungava Bay along the Quebec-Labrador border, which are becoming particularly important to the industries of Pittsburgh as the ores of Lake Superior approach exhaustion. These reserves of iron ore, which contain from 40 to 59 per cent iron, are estimated to reach 1,500 million tons. Not far away there are also considerable deposits of titanium. A railroad 360 miles long has been built across Labrador, to carry the iron to the port of Sept Iles on the St Lawrence estuary, whence it is shipped via the Seaway to the Great Lakes ports. It was the prospect of such traffic that led to the joint Canadian-United States agreement to improve navigation on the river above Montreal. An entirely new town called Schefferville is being built on the Burnt Creek field in Labrador, and the port of Sept Iles is becoming a vital economic centre on the St Lawrence estuary.

Farther west, north of the Prairies, a wealth of other minerals has been discovered. Copper, zinc and silver are being mined near Lynn Lake and at Flin Flon in northern Manitoba; uranium is being mined on the northern shores of Lake Athabasca; large reserves of oil and natural gas have been found near Peace River in northern Alberta; and the tar sands along the Athabasca River are believed to contain 100,000 million barrels of oil. Two deposits of asbestos and one of silver have been discovered in the Yukon Territory. From Yellowknife on Great Slave Lake comes gold, and from Port Radium still farther north, on Great Bear Lake, comes uranium, which is flown out by air.

Although air transport is the pioneer method of communication, railroads are obviously more practical for many purposes. Besides the Labrador line already mentioned, there are two that reach Hudson Bay, one from Ontario running to the southern coast of James Bay, and the other linking Saskatchewan with Churchill, a grain-exporting centre. In the Prairies, lines stretch north to the Mackenzie basin as far as the head of navigation on both the Athabasca and Peace Rivers, and other lines are under construction.

Roads are also being built. In Quebec province, there is a road from Lake St John to Lake Mistassini (where there are copper deposits). Even more enterprising was the Alaska Highway built during the Second World War along the edge of the Rockies, from the Prairies and through the Yukon to Fairbanks, Alaska.

The pioneer frontier in the north is constantly advancing, but unevenly, in a series of outposts or even islands, some of them established for fishing or hunting, some for mining, and a few for farming. The oldest and most important of the isolated agricultural regions is that at Lake St John, which is cut off from the populated zone of the St Lawrence by an expanse of Laurentian forest. Today it has a population of more than 200,000. Farther west is another agricultural island, which has developed more recently, at Abitibi. This continues to expand eastward and northward on the border of Quebec and Ontario. The boldest of these centres of colonisation is the Peace River region in northern Alberta, where the duration of the growing season is less than a hundred days a year.

In the most northerly parts of the tundra the problem of food supply cannot be solved by agriculture, but there may perhaps be pastoral possibilities. The herds of caribou that once supported tribes of Indians are now reduced to a few thousand animals. It is proposed to replace them with domesticated reindeer imported from Lapland or Siberia. Reindeer-breeding in Alaska has already yielded excellent results. The herds are spreading eastward as far as Labrador, and possibly one day the great wastes of the north will become important for the production of livestock. The revolution in the Far North has scarcely begun; it undoubtedly holds many surprises. In fact in the whole of Canada, with the possible exception of the Atlantic Provinces, tremendous changes will undoubtedly take place.

This is a nation that is forging ahead economically. Already it has become one of the world's leading producers of many valuable commodities, including wheat, forest products, fish, asbestos, nickel, zinc, petroleum and aluminium. About thirty per cent of its national income is derived from manufacturing, mainly pulp and paper, non-ferrous metal smelting and refining, petroleum products, food processing, and saw-milling, based on local raw materials; other manufacturers are machinery, motor vehicles, aircraft, rubber, textiles and clothing, and electrical equipment, based chiefly on imported raw and semi-manufactured materials. Only about a third of its hydro-electric potential has so far been tapped, and the as yet unexploited storehouse of minerals offers equal promise for the future. Despite a harsh environment, a high standard of living has been achieved.

Very real problems are, however, created by underpopulation and by the uneven distribution of the existing population, to which reference has already been made. A solution to these problems would encourage the development of raw materials and manufacturing industries; and with the fuller use of natural resources the standard of living, already high, would almost certainly rise higher still.

There are 11,500 Eskimos living on the Arctic rim of Canada. Some still follow their traditional habits and customs, wandering in search of the animals that are the base of their economy. During the brief Arctic summer they live in tents, like this one at the north-west end of Baffin Island. However, most of the Eskimos have been or are being absorbed into the modern stream of life.

Furs are important in the north not only for local use but as a trading commodity. At the trading station at Eskimo Point, Northwest Territories, the furs are taken out of the warehouse several times during the winter to be aired in the sun and wind.

# THE UNITED STATES

The United States is often said to be the richest nation on earth, and it probably is. The most obvious signs of this are its myriads of automobiles, telephones, television sets, household appliances, palatial homes, privately owned aircraft and motor boats; its stupendous factories, dams, and bridges; its far-flung transportation network; its soaring skyscrapers; and even the fantastically high salaries paid to its idols of the entertainment world. What is not so often stressed is the ingenuity that has helped to create this wealth, an ingenuity stimulated by a social system where the individual has had an opportunity to make a profit out of his technical abilities and invest the profit advantageously.

The products of this ingenuity have revolutionised every realm of the American economy — lumbering, farming, mining, transportation, industry — and have profoundly affected the ordinary daily life of every citizen, primarily by reducing the amount of time and labour he needs to expend to provide himself with adequate food, shelter, clothes and transportation, and with a surplus for luxuries that in other days were reserved for kings.

Ingenuity alone, of course, cannot create such wealth. But the United States has had the enormous advantage of abundant and varied natural resources and great size. Bounded by the Atlantic to the east, Canada to the north, the Pacific to the west and Mexico to the south, the conterminous United States, a huge quadrilateral, extends 3,000 miles from ocean to ocean and more than 1,200 miles from the Great Lakes to the Gulf of Mexico. With the newly created states of Alaska and Hawaii, rather detached outposts, one in the Far North the other in the middle of the Pacific, the total area of the fifty states comes to 3,552,198 square miles.

Such size, apart from placing it among the world's largest nations, along with the U.S.S.R., the Chinese People's Republic, Canada and Brazil, has facilitated large-scale operations of all sorts, and has prompted an attitude of mind quite unlike that of peoples hemmed in by close national boundaries. There is a sense of space — space to live in, space to cultivate, space on which to raise cattle or build factories. For generations the adventurous and self-reliant could go westward for more space, beyond the horizon, beyond the frontier of settlement. It is not surprising, therefore, that the American is accustomed to the large scale and the feeling of space, perhaps one of the reasons for his confidence in the future.

Another reason for these generally admitted national characteristics is undoubtedly ancestry. The great majority of the 35 million immigrants who have arrived in the United States came because they were seeking to escape privations and vested power and privilege, and believed this to be a land of economic opportunity and freedom, a land where the ordinary man could 'start out with nothing and reach the top'. And more often than not this quest for the good material things of life has been reasonably successful.

Optimism and confidence in the future are also the result of being free from devastating foreign invasions and of an ingrained faith in the democratic idea. If the American wishes to escape from his family's particular ethnic group, social level, faith, or community, it is within his power to do so, and if he disapproves of the actions of the Government he feels he can express his views through his vote.

## THE ENVIRONMENT
## THE MAIN NATURAL DIVISIONS

The physical features of this giant country are of massive proportions. The Atlantic coast down to and including Chesapeake Bay has many indentations, but south of this and along the Gulf of Mexico the shore is smoother. The more mountainous Pacific coast is even less incised. With the exception of Puget Sound and the estuary of the Columbia River in the north, and San Francisco Bay in the centre, the coastline is relatively straight.

While nature has appeared to enjoy fashioning the relief of Western and Central Europe into a variety of land forms, in the New World it seems to have been content with a more rudimentary result. The main alignment of relief is from north to south. Beyond the Atlantic coastal plain, there are two immense mountain systems, the Appalachians in the east extending from north-east to south-west, and in the west the Rocky Mountains which run almost exactly from north to south. Between these two are the vast interior lowlands and plains, drained by the Mississippi and its tributaries. Between the Rocky Mountains and the Pacific coast ranges is a huge basin, known as the Great Basin, flanked by the Columbia Plateau in the north and the Colorado Plateau in the south. The coastal mountains consist of the Cascades in the north, the Sierra Nevada in the south, and in the centre, nearest the shore, the Coast Ranges.

The tide of population was mainly from east to west; the first waves of settlers, groups from the Atlantic plain, reached the foot of the Appalachians. Others went beyond and reached in turn the Ohio, the Great Lakes, the Mississippi, the Missouri, the Great Plains, the Rocky Mountains, the Columbia River, and finally the Pacific. Thus settlement did not develop everywhere at the same time in the same physical conditions, nor did it take the same form from one end of the country to the other. To each major physical region there correspond, in greater or lesser degree, social and economic differences which are still noticeable today.

*The structure of the country: the Canadian Shield.* Between the Appalachians and the Rockies the nearly level plains cover an immense area of Archaean bedrock with what is often quite a thin layer of sedimentary rocks. The bedrock had been folded in a distant era, and had already been worn down before the end of the Pre-Cambrian times. This vast complex of schists, granites and gneiss outcrops over more than half of Canada, and this suggested the term 'Canadian Shield'. Geologists have used the term to describe this old base, discovering about the same time other 'shields' which are more or less comparable — the Baltic Shield, for example. These Archaean rocks occur in the United States in several places. Between the St Lawrence and Hudson Rivers they form the Adirondack Mountains, which are sometimes incorrectly related to the Appalachians. They also occur to the west and south-west of Lake Superior, but the extensions here soon disappear under the more recent horizontal deposits. The Shield reappears near the city of Austin in southern Texas; and its old rocks are also found, covered with sedimentary strata, at the bottom of the gorges of the Colorado River. This is the oldest and almost immutable foundation of the structure of the continent. It was against ·this unyielding mass that the sedimentary rocks were folded, giving rise to the Appalachian Mountains in the Primary Era, and the Rockies in the Secondary and Tertiary.

*The Appalachians and the Atlantic coastal plain.* The Appalachians, running parallel to the Atlantic coast, are very similar to the Hercynian system of Western and Central Europe. They were folded at about the same time, towards the end of the Primary Era; both have been worn down by several cycles of erosion, and rejuvenated by general distortion and changes in sea level. Erosion had already peneplaned the first mountain ranges by the beginning of the Secondary Era; as a result of the unequal resistance of the rocks, large longitudinal valleys had been eroded from the long and narrow outcrops of limestone, marl and clay, while similarly elongated outcrops of sandstones and conglomerates were thrown into relief, forming an equal number of parallel ridges. Thus the Appalachians may be compared with a recently folded mountain system, such as the French Jura; the two have similar hills and ridges, combes and valleys, all aligned, more or less continuously, from north-east to south-west. The Great Valley forms an almost straight line in the centre of the mountains, from the valley of the Hudson to the valleys of the Tennessee and Alabama Rivers. Communications are relatively easy in the direction of the old folding, but much less so in the transverse direction, from south-east to north-west. To cross from one valley to another, the route must zig-zag taking advantage of the gaps, some of which still contain rivers (water gaps), while others (wind gaps) are dry. By linking longitudinal and transverse valleys and occasionally making use of suitable passes, the pioneers at the end of the eighteenth century found a way of getting beyond the mountains into the Ohio valley.

The coastal plain lying between the Atlantic and the Appalachians varies greatly in width. It virtually does not exist east of the Hudson, where the old crystalline rocks often reach the sea. To the south, as a result of fairly recent land elevation, belts of sand and clay become broader. Still more recently, a movement in the opposite direction caused submergence, which changed the lower valleys into long, broad estuaries, such as those of the Delaware and Chesapeake, which are really arms of the sea, penetrating from 120 to 200 miles into the interior of the plain.

South of the Potomac the coastal plain steadily widens. The offshore bars which joined to form Cape Hatteras have turned the bays into brackish lagoons. Farther south and along the Gulf of Mexico the weak wave action no longer succeeds in sweeping away or accumulating in bars the silt brought

Rockefeller Center, New York.

Giant sequoias, or redwoods, in Yosemite National Park in California. In certain sheltered valleys in both the United States and Canada, on the western slopes of the Rockies and the Sierra Nevada, conifers grow to an extraordinary size. Some sequoias reach a height of 360 feet.

down by the rivers, and low-lying islands form, relatively unstable until mangrove succeeds in fixing them. Behind this swampy landscape, the winding, sluggish lower courses of the rivers are bordered with marsh. Then, on a higher terrace, begins the area of pine forest, which covers the sandy soils.

Florida, which projects from this coast, extends towards Cuba in a string of coral islands. It is composed of a limestone platform, dry and fissured in the higher parts, elsewhere saturated with tropical rainfall. It is bordered by huge swamps in the east, west and particularly in the south, where the Everglades cover an area of more than 5,000 square miles with a network of shallow waterways, forests, and tropical creepers.

*The central plains.* The central part of the great Mississippi basin consists of Primary sedimentary rocks, while to the west there are Cretaceous beds, and still farther west outcrops of Tertiary rocks; the northern half, the area of the Great Lakes, the Ohio and Missouri, was covered during the Quaternary glaciation. At times the advance was relatively restricted, at others more widespread, and the result of these advances and retreats was to leave behind a mass of ground moraines, sometimes in groups of oval hills, as well as terminal moraines in more distant ridges. There is also a zone of loess, fine soil picked up by the winds and redeposited in front of the ice. The appearance of this vast area with its rivers and innumerable lakes, and its resources, has been determined by the successive advance and retreat of the ice. Farther south the rivers have carried and distributed still more of these sandy, clayey deposits during their annual floods. The Mississippi is continually working towards the recession and eventual silting up of the Gulf of Mexico.

This cover remains superficial, and between the Missouri and the Arkansas the old Primary rocks appear in the Ozark Mountains, a limestone plateau from 1,300 to 2,600 feet high, which is forested. Between the Arkansas and Red Rivers the Ouachita Mountains briefly reintroduce the old rocks of the Appalachians, and the Wichita Mountains those of the Canadian Shield.

*The mountainous West.* The Rockies rarely exceed 14,000 feet and are in many ways less dramatic than the Swiss Alps. The horizontal surfaces of the plateaus and the basins of subsidence are more dominant than the isolated peaks of the volcanic mountains. Geologists maintain that there are in this complex three periods of folding, spaced out between Jurassic times and the end of the Tertiary Era, and separated by periods of inactivity and erosion. Each new movement affected the eroded materials of the earlier ones. Shaken and distributed, the old rocks reacted with a lack of stability; faulting resulted in subsidence here and elevation there; elsewhere flexing and warping occurred. In the north-west of the mountain region vertical faulting led to volcanic outpourings which covered vast areas with thick lava flows. During the course of this long history, there has been continuous erosion. In order to maintain their courses during the process of uplifting the rivers have incised themselves into a succession of rocks; this is spectacularly illustrated by the enormous Grand Canyon cut by the Colorado River. Glaciers have also played their part, though rather less than might have been expected, for the greater part of this region is essentially arid. It is only in the neighbourhood of the Pacific that glaciated valleys and serrated peaks are found.

In sum, moving from east to west, first the Rockies themselves stand out, forming a barrier that is particularly high in the centre, where the Colorado massif has several dozen peaks close to 14,000 feet high. Next, the tabular areas predominate, with the Wyoming basin and the Colorado Plateau, reaching as far as the next line of peaks, the Wasatch Mountains close to the Great Salt Lake. These are composed of old but recently elevated rocks, and were not produced by recent folding. The plateaus then continue, more extensive than ever; they are fairly level and have more rainfall in the north, in the Columbia-Snake basin, than farther south, in Utah and especially Nevada, where they are much drier and are divided into narrow strips of desert by faults aligned from north to south, each a wilderness of burning heat in summer and freezing cold in winter.

Then, with the Cascade Range in the north, an old

The Badlands, a spectacular area of erosion in South Dakota, chiefly the result of action by running water and wind. The name is also applied to similar areas in North Dakota, Nebraska and several other western states.

Barges passing through the open bridge span on the Mississippi River at Hannibal, upstream from St Louis. The Mississippi flows right through the United States, from Minnesota in the north to the Gulf of Mexico in the south, draining an immense basin — the third largest in the world, after the Amazon and Congo basins.

peneplain submerged under huge volcanic eruptions, the high mountains reappear; in the south, the Sierra Nevada includes the highest point in the United States (excluding Alaska), Mount Whitney, 14,495 feet, not far from the trough of Death Valley which descends to below sea level. Then follows a series of depressions, the largest of which is the elongated oval of the Central Valley of California. Westward again is found the last mountain barrier, the Coast Ranges, which are fairly low but quite recent in formation.

THE VARIETY OF CLIMATES. For anyone coming from Western Europe the outstanding characteristics of the weather in the United States are well marked contrasts and frequent and often violent changes. There are rarely any of the subtle variations in weather or the uncertain play of sun and wind so familiar in Great Britain or on the Atlantic coast of France. Over much of the country the summers are hot and sultry, the winters long and rigorous. In the interior particularly, heat waves and cold waves bring sudden changes, making the thermometer rise and fall visibly.

Moisture-laden winds from the Pacific are cooled as they move up over the Coast Ranges and again over the higher Cascade and Sierra Ranges, and hence the coastal areas, at least in the north, have an average rainfall of 60 or more inches a year. Most of the area between these ranges and the Rockies lies below the level of the mountains to the west, and therefore is very dry — less than 10 inches of rain — and parts of it, just to the east of the higher ranges, are true desert. The Rocky Mountains get between 20 and 40 inches of rain a year, the northern Rockies because here the Pacific ranges are less of a barrier than those farther south, and the southern Rockies because they are much higher than the Sierras. Beyond the Rocky Mountains, on the Great Plains, the average rainfall drops to between 10 and 20 inches.

In the eastern half of the country, roughly east of the 100° line of longitude, moisture comes from the Gulf coast and Atlantic winds — the Appalachians, much less high than the Rockies, do not act as a serious barrier to the Atlantic currents. A broad belt from the Great Lakes to the Gulf of Mexico has an average of from 20 to 40 inches of rain annually, as does interior New England; the rest of the east gets between 40 and 60 inches, and parts of the south-east can expect well over 60 inches. Over all the eastern half of the country the rainfall is fairly evenly distributed over the year, though generally somewhat more occurs between May 1 and October 1; westward, droughts are frequent and sometimes prolonged except on the well-watered Pacific coast. Snowstorms and blizzards are naturally more frequent and severe in the higher mountains and in the Far North near the Canadian border; here annual snowfalls of 80 to 100 inches are not uncommon. In the south, by contrast, from Virginia on down the Atlantic coast and westward along the Gulf states, through Texas, New Mexico, Arizona and California, snows are rare. This part of the United States and coastal Washington and Oregon enjoy a frost-free season of two hundred or more days a year, with average January temperatures of 10°C. (50°F.) or more, whereas in the north, especially on the Great Plains, it is more likely to be 100 days, with mean January temperatures below –10°C. (14°F.). All over the interior and the south summer temperatures are high, ranging from 21°C. (70°F.) to 35°C. (95°F.); the coolest places are in Maine, around the Great Lakes, in the far north-west, along the Pacific coast, and in the mountains.

In the spring and early summer, tornadoes occur, particularly in the interior lowlands, when cold dry winds from the north meet warm humid air masses from the south. These tornadoes move at speeds of from 20 to 40 miles an hour, and winds near the centre may reach 200 miles an hour. They often cause an immense amount of damage in their path, but the path is generally not more than a quarter of a mile wide and 20 to 30 miles long. Hailstorms are another hazard in this region. On the Atlantic and Gulf coasts, tropical cyclones or hurricanes periodically endanger property and lives. However, destruction and loss of life from such storms have been very considerably reduced in the last few years thanks to advance warnings on radio and television.

The McIntyre Range in the Adirondack Mountains. The original dense forest still covers vast areas — even in New York State.

The Arizona Desert. Such deserts are a constant reminder of the astonishing diversity of the American landscape.

GREAT VARIETY OF NATURAL VEGETATION. The distribution of natural vegetation is, obviously, determined by various combinations of temperature and rainfall. The south-east, which is both the hottest and wettest section, is covered with a huge forest, which near the Gulf of Mexico is clearly subtropical, with mangrove along the coast; farther inland there are evergreen oaks, walnuts, cypress and poplars, hidden under mosses. The long-leafed pine grows in the drier areas, and the oak and red pine on the lower slopes. Northwards the forest changes to the Atlantic type and stretches as far as the sea, the Great Lakes, and the middle course of the Mississippi; pines and firs are dominant in the north and on higher ground, with birch, beech, oak and chestnut in the south and in the valleys. The tall grasses of the Prairie take over west of the Mississippi. Here flowers of every hue bring a riot of colour each spring, and in autumn the grasses wither, enriching the soil with dark humus. Near the 100° line of longitude the flowers are paler and the grasses become shorter, tougher, and coarser, leaving the soil exposed between tufts. These are the Great Plains, where the wind raises dust storms several hundred feet high. The Rockies, being better watered, are fairly well wooded, but the parched lands of the basins and plateaus westward support little but sage brush and cactus. The mountain ranges near the Pacific are covered in the north with magnificent coniferous trees, and there are patches of giant Sequoias; farther south a type of vegetation known as chaparral, similar to the maquis of Mediterranean lands, is dominant, with stunted evergreen oaks and wild lilac.

Within the territory of the United States are to be found nearly all the different physical characteristics of the Old World. There are the steppes and deserts of Asia, and the luxuriant coastlands of tropical Africa. There are the rounded summits of ancient mountains, and the bold outlines of recently folded ranges. There are the well-watered lands of northern Europe and the dry brilliance of the Sahara. Blizzards and tropical storms alternate. Such variety is in itself a natural resource of immense value.

## THE GROWTH OF POPULATION

*The American Indians*. At first the white colonists called the people they found in America 'Indians'; later, mistaking for a natural colouring the red that they sometimes put on their bodies, they called them 'Redskins'. Though equally incorrect, both expressions have persisted. Ethnographers have recently been trying to substitute the term 'Amerindians' to describe these first inhabitants of the New World, but there is some doubt about the aptness of the term, for it incorrectly implies that these people are of American origin. In fact they came from Asia. However, they quickly lost all contact with their land of origin, and so became a distinct people. Some of these groups developed relatively advanced civilisations on the plateaus of Yucatan in Mexico and in Peru. Those occupying the present territory of the United States remained more primitive, and at the same time developed distinct cultures. Certain tribes, such as the Pueblos of the arid south-west, were

sedentary and practised agriculture with the aid of irrigation. Most of them were nomadic or semi-nomadic and their chief means of livelihood were hunting wild animals, fishing, and raising here and there a few crops of potatoes and maize. They practised such crafts as spinning and weaving wool, tanning, basketry, and making shell necklaces; these gave rise to fairly active exchanges between neighbouring and even remote tribes.

The European administrators appreciated the right of the American Indians to retain at least part of their territory, and the missionaries and sometimes the governments endeavoured to respect this right, but the average colonist tended to disregard it. In the drive to the west, the Indians were gradually pushed back, by guile or force, to the grasslands and mountains and deserts beyond the Mississippi. Later, with the building of transcontinental railroads, even here their territory came more and more into dispute. Undermined by wars and illness, they steadily declined in numbers, from somewhere around a million when the Europeans first arrived to approximately 237,000 in 1900.

During the 1890's the United States Government became aware of a moral responsibility to prevent the extinction of the last Indian tribes. A Bureau for Indian Affairs had existed for many years, and from this time on it intervened more effectively to protect the Indians and seek their welfare. In Oklahoma and Utah petroleum was discovered in the middle of the Indian reservations, and here some of the tribes became wealthy. In many reservations, as a result of better hygiene in their daily lives, the number of Indains ceased to decline. During the prosperous years between 1920 and 1930 the total Indian population even increased, to 332,000, and since then it has continued to rise, reaching 470,000 in 1960 (exclusive of Alaska and Hawaii).

An important minority of the Indians still speaks a dialect, practises a traditional form of worship, and is happiest when driving its herds in the few lonely places left to it. Some folklore is preserved for the benefit of tourists. But the Government and other agencies are endeavouring to educate an increasing number of young Indians and train them to take their place in American society and participate actively in the national economy.

Today, Indians, half-breed and full-blooded, make up only 0.2 per cent of the population of the United States; they live chiefly in Arizona, New Mexico and California.

*The arrival of the white man: the Pilgrim Fathers*. The Spanish, who were the first white people to explore America, were searching above all for goldmines and a sea passage to India. They realised quite soon that there was nothing to interest them north of Florida and Mexico.

The French, coming in by way of the St Lawrence valley, found a route toward the west, but it did not lead to the Far East as they hoped; it resulted only in furs being sent to Paris via Quebec.

In the first third of the seventeenth century, English traders, adventurers and religious refugees, sometimes in separate groups, more often a mixed company, began to settle along the Atlantic coast between Canada and Florida, especially in Virginia and

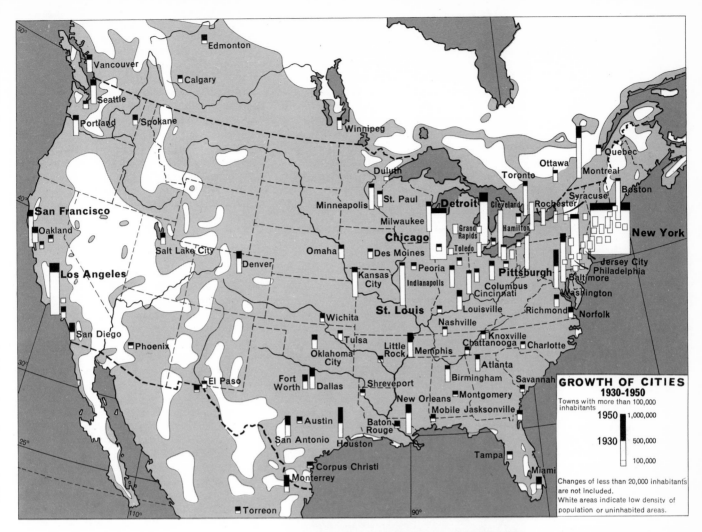

GROWTH OF CITIES
**1930-1950**
Towns with more than 100,000 inhabitants

1950    ■ 1,000,000

1930    □ 500,000

         100,000

Changes of less than 20,000 inhabitants
are not included.
White areas indicate low density of
population or uninhabited areas.

Massachusetts; the Pilgrim Fathers who landed from the Mayflower in 1620 and their descendants were the chief upholders of the moral and democratic traditions which have so deeply influenced the nation's history.

However, from the seventeenth century onwards the English were not the only ones to settle on this coast. Scots, who were staunch Protestants and determined to prosper, and Irish escaping Cromwell's persecution, both came to seek their fortune. The Swedes who came did little more than proceed up the Delaware estuary, but the Dutch made several settlements, including New Amsterdam at the mouth of the Hudson River, which in 1664 became New York under British rule. Soon afterwards German peasants, victims of religious intolerance or the poverty of their fatherland, settled in Pennsylvania. Some of these immigrants came as indentured servants, who received their passage money in return for their agreement to work on a farm or tobacco plantation for a few years. Once their time of service was up, they left to start farms of their own. As the market for tobacco was expanding rapidly, Virginia planters began to import Negro slaves as labour in the tobacco fields.

In 1783, when the thirteen colonies achieved independence from Britain, they had a total of about four million inhabitants, the great majority of whom were Protestant and English-speaking.

Population growth of cities in the U.S.A. and Canada. Most of the large cities of the United States already had high populations in 1930, the tendency towards urbanisation having made itself felt as early as the beginning of the century (compare this map with that of the U.S.S.R. p. 549). The urban population of the United States is about 130 million (out of a total of 192 million).

An Indian girl from Oklahoma. Indians form no more than 0.2 per cent of the total population of the United States today. They live chiefly on reservations, where they are encouraged to preserve their culture, and where tourist come to buy their handicrafts. Today, however, Government policy favours gradual assimilation.

*The great invasion of immigrants.* The young republic at this time had just begun to nibble at the edge of the vast wilderness stretching westward across the continent. But the great epic was about to begin. Restless and curious, bold, independent, and in love with freedom, the American pioneer little by little pushed the frontier at the limit of cultivated land ever westward, from the Appalachians to the great interior lowlands, to the Rockies, and on beyond to the Pacific, until toward the end of the nineteenth century few areas remained to be opened up.

During this century of national and industrial crises in Europe, many thousands of refugees and unemployed workers, lured by a desire to improve their lot and achieve freedom from oppression of all sorts, arrived in successive waves, increasing and modifying unceasingly the cosmopolitan character of the American population.

Until 1840 the English and Scots were most numerous, then it was the turn of the Irish, stricken by famine in 1846; after them came German patriots crushed in 1848, and Scandinavians who found they lacked room to expand between their glaciers and fiords. Until 1880, the working population of the towns and countryside remained North European by a large majority, and spoke English or German.

About 1890 a different type of immigrant began to arrive, from Central and Eastern Europe, and the shores of the Mediterranean: southern Italians and Sicilians, people from Austro-Hungary (Czechs, Slovaks, Croats, Slovenes, Rumanians and Serbs), Poles, Jews from the ghettoes of the Carpathians and of Tsarist Russia, and Greeks and Armenians. Every year until 1914, whole shiploads of such immigrants came in. Most of them did not known a word of English and many could not read or write.

The older Americans, proud of their Anglo-Saxon traditions and culture, became uneasy at these invasions; for example, there were 1,285,000 immigrants in 1907, and of these more than three-quarters came from the borders of the Mediterranean, the Danube, or Vistula. These Latin and Eastern masses appeared to threaten the standard of living of the worker, the

authority of the pastor, the standards of taste and behaviour, and even democracy itself. The First World War solved the problem momentarily, as immigration to the United States fell to nothing; but peace had hardly been re-established before it resumed, with 560,000 immigrants in 1920, and 805,000 in 1921, of whom again three-quarters came from the Mediterranean lands or Eastern Europe. Both the trade unions and the nationalists became alarmed enough to clamour for protection measures.

*Controlled immigration.* Between 1921 and 1929 immigration regulations became progressively more stringent. At first the total number of immigrants was limited to a maximum of 360,000 annually, and finally to 153,714. The regulations also sought to eliminate as far as possible the 'undesirable' elements by a quota system, which varied from nation to nation. The British, Germans and Irish, who unquestionably dominated settlement up to 1890, were assured of the lion's share, and the flood of Mediterranean peoples, Jews and Slavs was reduced to a small trickle. The economic crisis of 1929 put a stop to immigration; in fact, between 1931 and 1935 emigrants exceeded immigrants by 172,347. Just before and during the Second World War, a number of victims of war and persecution were given refuge in the United States.

Since 1946 immigration has been resumed on a small scale. The law controlling it until 1965 was passed in 1952, though it did little more than simplify the provisions of earlier legislation. Of the 154,887 people to be admitted annually under the quota system, more than 80 per cent were to come from Northern and Western Europe, and only 24,502 from Southern and Eastern Europe, 2,990 from Asia, 1,700 from Africa, and 600 from Oceania. In 1953, a special law concerning refugees and expellees authorised the entry of an additional 214,000 persons of German, Italian, Greek, or Far Eastern origin, or from Communist-dominated countries. But for more than thirty years immigration has played a secondary rôle in the growth of the population of the United States.

*The Negroes.* The Negroes who were brought in as slaves were put to work mainly in mines and on plantations, though some worked in factories and as domestic servants. There were never many slaves in the colonies of the Northeast, where the climate was less propitious for agriculture and a more democratic outlook prevailed. On the other hand, from early times they were numerous south of the Mason-Dixon line, which separates Pennsylvania from Maryland, and even more numerous south of the Potomac, from Virginia to Florida, in the cotton-growing belt. From the beginning of the nineteenth century cotton occupied a position of major importance in the economic life of the South, and even in that of the Federation as a whole.

At about the same time the states in the north began to suppress slavery at home and oppose its extension elsewhere. This was the origin of the long dispute which led to the bloody, bitter Civil War and the abolition of slavery in 1863. Henceforth the freed slaves became officially the equals of the white people. Even today in the southern states this legal equality is only gradually becoming a reality despite the many measures taken to ensure it.

Negroes form an important minority in the United States. In recent years they have been taking an increasingly active part in American public life and have made important contributions to American culture, particularly through their music. The photograph shows the Student Council, responsible for many aspects of school discipline, at a High School in New York City. It is presided over by a Negro girl student.

In 1790 the Negro population constituted a little less than one-fifth of the total population of the Federation, and it was confined mainly to the area south of the Mason-Dixon line. Since then its relative importance, numerically, has declined. For the last fifty years it has been stable at about 10 per cent of the total. The birthrate has stayed definitely higher than that of the while population, but so has the deathrate. The fluctuations in these proportions depend on the relative changes in the two rates, but in any case the changes represent a small proportion of the total. Thus there are no firm grounds for the assertion that the higher birthrate among the Negroes will result, if not in their numerical superiority, at least in a continuous increase in their percentage of the total population.

What has changed is the distribution of the Negroes. After the Civil War the southern planters worked out a rather unsatisfactory arrangement known as share-cropping. Negroes still worked in the cotton fields, but they received a share of the crop which enabled them to buy their food, clothing, and so on. They were free to leave the plantation if they wished, but few of them did, for there were few opportunities for them to improve their situation elsewhere. It was not until the First World War, when immigration from Europe almost stopped and manufacturers in the northern cities began to suffer from shortages of unskilled labour, that large numbers of Negroes tried their luck north of the Mason-Dixon line. This out-migration has continued, and today about half of the Negroes in the country live outside the South, mainly in the industrial suburbs of New York, Philadelphia, Chicago, Cleveland, Detroit, and Los Angeles, in fact in all the large industrial centres. Here they find, if not always a warm welcome, at least better opportunities for earning a living, bringing up their children, and attaining a higher material standard. The number of Negroes in the South has increased only slightly since 1930; it has fallen relatively, and even in certain cases absolutely, as in the state of Mississippi, which was the only state where, in 1930, the Negroes were in the majority. By 1940 this situation no longer prevailed, and the proportion of Negroes, though higher in the South than anywhere else in the nation, has continued to decline.

Finally, it should be observed that, for statistical purposes, the term Negro includes all those who have any Negro blood, no matter how little. Half-castes make up at least half of the coloured population. In any case the Negroes are an important minority in the United States, which has made undeniable economic and cultural contributions. The remaining differences in standards between the races continue to create many problems, which can only be solved gradually by goodwill on all sides. Otherwise a racial explosion is possible.

*The people of Asian and Polynesian origin.* When gold was discovered in California in 1849, thousands of treasure hunters arrived from all over the United States and indeed the world. Among them were some Chinese and Japanese, who came primarily to dig gold and stayed to farm or practise certain trades. They were prepared to work so hard for so little reward that they incurred the hostility of Americans with whom they competed, and after 1880 Asian immigration was practically forbidden.

Well over half of the 260,800 Japanese immigrants in the United States have settled in California; elsewhere they do not form a significant group except in Washington and in Illinois around Chicago. The 200,000 Chinese living in the United States can be divided into two almost equal halves, one living in California, the other scattered over the remainder of the country, the only community of any size being in New York City. There are also about 107,300 Filipinos, two-thirds of whom live in California.

Statistical information does not distinguish the other peoples, such as Koreans, Asian Indians, Indonesians and Polynesians, but merely supplies a total of some 104,000, exclusive of Hawaii and Alaska. The Asian communities on American territory are certainly tourist attractions, particularly the Chinatowns of San Francisco and New York, but they do not raise any social problems.

*Mexicans and Puerto Ricans.* The inhabitants of Mexican origin escape enumeration in two ways: in the census they are included with those of European origin, although the majority of them have an obvious proportion of American Indian blood; and many of them avoid official control by entering the country without permission from either their own Government or from Washington. This may be accomplished by crossing the Rio Grande River, which marks the border between the two countries, hence the name 'wetbacks' which is often given them. Those looking for work, and this is the principal object of the immigration, generally find it as seasonal labourers on the farms of Texas and California. If recognised as wetbacks, they are conducted back to their own country. Many of them shuttle back and forth across the border in this manner year after year.

The inhabitants of Puerto Rico have all the rights of American citizenship and are therefore free to settle in the country. In the last few years more than 700,000 of them have flocked in, mainly to New York City, creating housing, labour and social problems similar to those of former mass immigrations. Attempts are being made to limit this invasion by administrative measures, and also by assisting the development of industries in Puerto Rico which can increase opportunities for regular employment at home.

THE DISTRIBUTION AND GROWTH OF POPULATION. When the Europeans landed on the Atlantic shore, it seems likely that there were more Indians to the east than to the west of the Mississippi, for the resources of the coastal plain and Appalachian forests were superior to those of the grasslands and mountains of the West. The arrival of the Europeans accentuated still further this uneven population distribution. In 1790 nearly all the people of the young republic lived on a strip of land of varying width along the Atlantic shore from Maine to Georgia, and in a few prongs pushing into the interior up the main river valleys; few pioneers had been bold enough to reach the foot of the Appalachians, and even fewer bold enough to cross these mountains.

The drive to the West resulted in the settlement of millions of people in the great area stretching from the Appalachians to the Pacific Ocean; however, the cities and industries of the Atlantic coastlands and the Great Lakes region also grew simultaneously, and it is this part of the country, east of the Mississippi, barely a quarter of the territory, which still has a far greater population than the area to the west of the Mississippi.

However, during the decade between 1950 and 1960, the greatest rates of population increase occurred very definitely in the South and the West. Florida, which has become a playground for the rest of the country and a favourite place for retirement, had a population increase of 76 per cent; Louisiana and Texas grew by over 20 per cent. Farther west, New Mexico, Colorado and Utah's rates of growth were 39, 32 and 29 per cent respectively, while those of Arizona, Nevada and California were 72, 77 and 46 per cent. No states in the Midwest, except Ohio and Michigan, increased by more than 20 per cent, and many showed increases as low as 10 per cent or less. Three states—West Virginia, Mississippi and Arkansas—actually declined in population. As an illustration of this westward trend, in 1900 California was the twenty-first state in order of population, in 1920 the eighth, in 1940 the fifth, and it is now second only to New York.

The outstanding growth of Southern and Western states should not be allowed to obscure the fact that the East is still the most densely populated part of the United States, and is likely to remain so for a long time to come. Only two large areas have a population density exceeding 100 per square mile (which is low compared with the densities of Western Europe): the northern part of the Atlantic coast between Boston and Washington, and the south shore of the Great Lakes from Buffalo to Milwaukee. Elsewhere, comparable densities occur only in scattered areas such as the middle section of the Ohio, near the edges of the Appalachians, and the immediate neighbourhood of Los Angeles, San Francisco and Seattle. Almost all the region between the foothills of the Rockies and the Atlantic has a population density of at least 25 per square mile; so have most of the Pacific coastlands. In the great upland section of the West, on the other hand, the density rarely exceeds 8 per square mile and in places falls below 1. These examples are sufficient to show that the average population density for the United States — 52 per square mile—is misleading, as average national densities usually are. What is more significant is that there are marked contrasts from region to region, from state to state, and even within the same state; in California, for instance, almost empty deserts occur near crowded residential or industrial suburbs.

An unusual characteristic of the people of the United States is their mobility—in search of a better farm, a better job, a better home, a better school for the children, they are prepared to move often and sometimes long distances, perhaps a trait inherited from their mobile ancestors. It has been calculated that more than one-fifth of the population moves from one house to another each year. Most of these are moves within the same county. But some six million people change their state annually. Much of this internal migration is to the South and West. The centre of gravity of the population is moving slowly westwards following the 39th parallel fairly closely. It took fifty years for the centre to cross the state of Indiana, reaching Illinois by 1950. With the addition of Alaska and Hawaii to the Union, and with the continued rapid growth of the Western states, the centre in 1960 had reached Centralia, Illinois, about 60 miles east of the Mississippi River.

*The rural population.* While the distribution of population between East and West is changing slowly, the movement of people from the country to the towns has been much more noticeable; there has virtually been a revolution. In 1790 the urban population, which is defined as that living in settlements of more than 2,500 inhabitants, hardly exceeded 5 per cent of the total. Half a century later, in 1840, it had only doubled its relative importance; but after this the trend became very marked. By 1900 the urban population was 40 per cent of the total; today it is over 70 per cent.

In the country the population is rarely concentrated in villages, except in the older areas of settlement—in New England and New York, in particular—where in the early days concentration was needed for defence against the Indians and the French, and the inhabitants gathered around the church and the fur trader's store. But concentration here was also due to the lack of fertile land, and the early development of fishing, seafaring and trading, all of which required proximity and co-operation with others. Account should also be taken of the importance these small communities attached to their children's religious and educational welfare. There was then a combination of practical and religious reasons for not leaving the community.

Elsewhere conditions were different. South of the Potomac, the unit of settlement and work was the plantation, in the centre of which lived the owner surrounded by his share-croppers and slaves. Along the ever-moving frontier there was no shortage of space, and each pioneer took possession of as much land as possible. The concessions of land were usually rectangular plots a quarter of a square mile in area, so the farmers acquired the habit of living isolated from their neighbours. At a crossroads a few shops would form the nucleus of a village; today this is still typical of the greater part of the vast rural areas of the United States.

*The small towns.* The whole world is familiar with the names of the great American cities, but few foreigners appreciate the part played by the small towns and cities of some 10,000 to 50,000 inhabitants, although American poets have sung their praises, sociologists have made them the subject of monographs and theses, and parents and grandparents have described their intimate charm to their offspring. Whether sited at a crossroads or a railway junction, round a factory or a quayside, a pit-head or local market, they continue the comradeship of former times, the legendary days of the squatter and pioneer, when everyone had to help his neighbour in order to survive. Rivalry between communities is common, in a desire to win the confidence of speculators and industrialists, transporters, and distributors of manufactured products and attract new inhabitants and increase employment opportunities. But within each community a real sense of comradeship often

exists, in spite of differences in wealth, social standing, and the like. Such differences, as a matter of fact, are not too obvious; everyone follows a more or less similar way of life, sends his children to the same schools, and takes part in the same recreations and the same civic activities.

It is difficult to be precise about the percentage of the country's total population living in these towns and cities, but statistics confirm that they are growing at the expense of the rural areas and are increasing in size and population at about the same rate as the larger cities.

*Regional centres and capitals.* In 1790 there was no city in the United States with a population of 50,000; today there are 130 with over 100,000 inhabitants: sixteen of these have more than 500,000, and five have more than a million—an indication of the enormous growth of conurbations.

It should not be forgotten that the United States, because of its size and traditions, is a decentralised country, economically and politically, and this despite the undoubted progress of the forces of centralisation. There are thirty urban centres with populations of from 250,000 to 500,000 which dominate the affairs of a whole region without necessarily attaining national importance.

On the other hand, there are several large cities whose activities influence the whole nation. Washington, D.C., the capital, for example, is the political centre of the country, and New York is the commercial, financial and cultural centre. Detroit supplies the nation with automobiles, Akron with tyres, Los Angeles with films. Two other very big cities, Chicago with more than 3.5 million, and Philadelphia with 2 million, should be viewed as the nerve centres of large industrial areas rather than as capitals on a national scale.

To the European, the external apperance of American cities is often a surprise. Although each has its own individuality, there is a high degree of standardisation, with the buildings fitted into a geometrical framework, except in Washington, D.C., and in the old districts of the earliest cities, such as Boston and New York. Most cities are dominated by skyscrapers, and are divided into areas according to function: commercial, residential, industrial, and so on. However, in the last few decades a more dispersed pattern has been superimposed on the traditional one. Faced with long journeys to the city centre, the people of the more distant suburbs have developed their own neighbourhoods which are almost independent of the city centre. Each has its banks, films, drugstores, shops, markets, schools and churches. Los Angeles, for example, resembles a continuously expanding planetary system rather than a single planet, and much the same pattern is appearing in many other large cities as they develop. The danger is that such cities may become vast urban sprawls.

*The growth of population.* The population of the United States increased for some time at the rate of about three million people annually; on 1 April 1950 there were 151 million inhabitants; by 1 April 1955 the figure was 164. Excess of immigrants over emigrants during the same period was probably over two million. The balance was thus due to the excess of births over deaths. Never, in fact, has the deathrate been

so low or the birthrate so high as it has been during the last forty years.

The lowest point in the decline of the birthrate coincided, not surprisingly, with the worst of the economic depression in 1933. Recovery then brought a fairly regular rise, apart from a slight fall during the war years 1944 and 1945, when many Americans were fighting abroad, and a sharp rise in 1946 and 1947, when millions of young people returned, and many married. The birthrate showed a distinct decline for the next three years up to and inluding 1950. Then in 1951 it rose to 24.5 births per 1,000, as against 23.6 in 1950. Since then it has risen and fallen again, being 25.3 per 1,000 in 1957, 24.3 in 1959, and 20.0 in 1965. The explanation of the general increase over the last thirty years is not clear, but neither is there a clear explanation of the worldwide rapid increase taking place.

Small-town storekeepers: typical figures of the United States. The small towns and cities, with 10,000 to 50,000 inhabitants, play a great part in the American way of life. Poets have immortalised them, sociologists have analysed them, and their residents have idealised them; but they do continue a tradition of neighbourliness and self-reliance.

Chicago, largest city of the midwest, lies on the west shore of Lake Michigan. Traditionally the great outlet for the meat and grain of the American midwest, it is today a thriving city challenging those of the East Coast, for it has a unique position as a commercial and communications centre, especially since the opening of the St Lawrence Seaway.

As for the deathrate, it has been falling almost continuously for the last fifty years, until it is now almost half what it was in 1900. Infant mortality shows the most marked decline; it is five to six times lower than at the beginning of the century. Medical advances have considerably reduced the incidence of tuberculosis, pneumonia, intestinal and venereal diseases, while deaths from typhoid fever, diphtheria and dysentery are rare. However, cancer, circulatory and heart diseases have increased. The total deathrate figure is noticeably higher than in the Netherlands or New Zealand, the countries with the longest expectation of life.

The male deathrate at all ages is higher than the female deathrate, a disparity between the sexes which seems to be common to the whole human race.

The variations in the number of marriages are not exactly the same as those for births. Both reached a minimum at about the same time during the Great Depression, and a maximum at the end of the Second World War. Subsequently, when the marriage-rate began a steady decline the birthrate fell slightly and then increased again. The number of families has not tended to increase for several years, which suggests that the number of children per family is gradually becoming larger.

There is a trend in the United States, as elsewhere in the world, towards earlier marriage. The average age at marriage is about $21\frac{1}{2}$ for women and a little less than 24 for men.

The ratio of divorces to marriages has increased continuously and rapidly since 1900. In that year there was one divorce for about twelve marriages in the United States, in 1915 it was one for ten, and in 1940 one for six. The maximum rate, two divorces to seven marriages, occurred at the end of the Second World War in 1945. The ratio has declined for several years, to one divorce in four marriages, but this is still enough to give the United States the highest divorce rate in the world.

RELIGIOUS ASPECTS. The various European nationalities who came to populate the New World brought with them their own religious faiths, and established their own churches with their own clergy. The separation of Church and State, which has been the official policy, and the absolute equality of all forms of worship before the law, has fostered friendly co-operation between the religious bodies and political organisations. The proportion of the population of America enrolled as members of a church has grown continuously throughout the life of the Union, and today it has risen to 62 per cent; declared atheists are few in number.

Roman Catholics are by far the most numerous and observant religious group, with about 42 million members, or a fifth of the population. The Protestants form several groups, which taken together include nearly two-thirds of all religious believers, and they represent the dominant sentiment of public opinion. The Roman Catholics are proportionally most numerous in the large cities of the East and Midwest, where most of the immigrants from Ireland, Italy, southern Germany, Poland and French Canada concentrate. There are relatively few in the rural areas, especially in the South, where the white settlers provided the first waves of colonisation, and where,

except in Louisiana, the Negroes are Protestant by a large majority.

The numerical order of importance of the Protestant church is as follows: the Baptists have a membership of about 21 million; the Methodists, about 12 million; the Lutherans, about 8 million; Episcopalians, 3 million; and Presbyterians, 4 million. These different faiths are further divided into a large number of sects which have special names. The Eastern Christian churches, which are separate from the Holy See, have 2.7 million members, and there are also over 5 million Jews.

NATIONAL UNITY. One of the interesting facets of American life is the creation of a distinctive culture out of a medley of peoples with differing cultural backgrounds. In no other large country have so many diverse peoples come to live together as a nation. Each group of immigrants originally had a natural tendency to collect in the same sectors of the towns and in the same parts of the country, and obviously each was separated from the others by linguistic differences and by special prejudices — national, religious, social, and economic. Marriages between people of different nationality and religion were not common. Marriages between Negroes and whites were forbidden in most Southern states, and were very uncommon indeed elsewhere.

Nevertheless, many forces have been continually at work strengthening and increasing national unity. One has been the mobility of the people, which prevented the formation of rigid castes. Another has been the common English language, spoken by all second-generation Americans. Another has been the potent influence of the democratic ideal, which tends to make each man feel he is as good as the next, and can fraternise with him. This has inculcated in the young the firm belief that all men have the right to life, liberty, and the pursuit of happiness, regardless of their origins. Still another welding force has been the feeling common to all Americans that their standard of living and political and social systems are superior to any other. In recent decades, such mass means of communication as the press, films, radio and television have intensified this trend towards national unity. The transport network has also assisted this process.

TRANSPORTATION. In so large a country, where there is such a variety of soil and climate, peoples and resources, the problem of transportation quickly became of extreme importance. Transportation influenced the development of settlement, and often determined the supremacy of rival cities and regions. The Indians had already established a network of tracks and navigable water routes for travel and trade, and they showed the white man the best portages between river basins, which were frequently cleared to facilitate carrying canoes from one river to another. In those days rivers were the principal routes inland; the rough paths were more suited to the horseman than to vehicles.

With the drive towards the West and the development of the territory beyond the Appalachians, a variety of means was used to link the ever-changing frontier with the Atlantic seaboard. The waterways, roads and railways spread, often in competition with each other.

*Navigation on lakes and waterways.* One of the most important functions of the waterways was to link the Great Lakes, sometimes called the 'American Mediterranean', with the Atlantic and so make inland cities into ports.

The Great Lakes stretch from north-west to south-east, and then from south-west to north-east, forming an inland sea 95,000 square miles in area, or slightly smaller than the United Kingdom. It is divided into three levels by rapids and waterfalls: Lake Superior, so called because it is the highest, at an altitude of 602 feet; Lakes Michigan, Huron and Erie, some 20 to 30 feet lower; and finally, Lake Ontario, separated from Lake Erie by a drop of 326 feet, half of which is the spectacular Niagara Falls. Lake Ontario is connected with the Atlantic by the St Lawrence River, which is also interrupted by a series of rapids above Montreal, so that large-scale construction has been necessary for the full development of the waterway. Rivalry among American interests and between American and Canadian interests was the chief cause of the many delays and obstacles to the construction of a route between Montreal and Lake Ontario navigable by ocean-going vessels. It was not until the 1950's that the two governments got together and completed the task, thus creating a thruway into the heart of the continent, one of the greatest waterways in the world. Although ice impedes navigation on the St Lawrence Seaway for three or four months during the winter, the volume of traffic is rising by leaps and bounds, new industries are established in the vicinity of the huge new hydro-electric power stations, and the ports all along its route are looking forward to increased business of all kinds.

From the beginning of the nineteenth century the two big ports of the Atlantic coast, New York and Philadelphia, vied with each other in establishing the best routes into the hinterland on the other side of the Appalachians. New York won the upper hand in 1825, when it built the Erie Canal linking Buffalo on Lake Erie with the Hudson River and thus New York. Philadelphia tried to build a canal, called the Union Canal, right through the mountains to Pittsburgh on the Ohio River, from which another canal led to Lake Erie, but the many locks made the journey excessively slow and costly. The Erie Canal played a large part in the opening up and development of the Middle West. It carried vast numbers of immigrants and manufactured goods westwards to Ohio, Illinois and Michigan, and vast quantities of lumber and wheat and later iron ore eastwards.

Another main outlet for the wealth of this hinterland was New Orleans, on the delta of the Mississippi which juts out into the Gulf of Mexico. From its source near the Canadian border to its mouth, the Mississippi drains with its tributaries the immense central plain of the United States. Commercial activity has decreased considerably as a result of competition from more rapid means of transport, but the Mississippi is still important as a route for bulk items. For a long time its constantly changing channel and meanders hindered navigation, but a nine-foot channel is now maintained as far north as St Paul and Minneapolis. The Missouri has a similar channel as far as Kansas City, and so does the Ohio for its entire length. The course and flow of the Tennessee, as all the world knows, has been completely transformed thanks to the famed government project undertaken by the Tennessee Valley Authority. Another vital waterway is the Columbia River in the Pacific Northwest, which has also been transformed from a menace to an asset by huge projects.

*Roads, railroads and air transport.* From the beginning of the eighteenth century roads began to supplement waterways where these were slow or non-existent. The oldest, and for a long time the most important, was that linking the Atlantic ports from Boston to Charleston, but it was never very suitable for wheeled vehicles. Later, when traffic increased across the Appalachians, the state of Pennsylvania built a proper road through the mountains, from Philadelphia to Pittsburgh. The road network had scarcely been started and the central government was only just beginning to take an interest in the first National Road from the Potomac to the Ohio and beyond to the Mississippi, when the railroads made their appearance. These quickly replaced the roads in the conquest of the West. It was not until after 1920 that public interest in the development and improvement of the road system revived, as a result of the mass production of inexpensive automobiles. Today, roads and highways reach every community of any size throughout the country.

For thirty years or so the railroads have been struggling against road and air competition. Their great period of supremacy occurred at the end of the nineteenth century and the beginning of the twentieth, when they dominated the economic and political life of the country. Today they are still trying to regain their former importance, or at least to halt their slow decline, and some efforts are being made to modernise methods and services. Passenger trains are faster and more comfortable, while freight services are attempting to combine operational flexibility with reliability.

The railroads are owned by private companies, and on most routes there is a choice between two or more lines. A Government commission is responsible for ensuring that identical charges are made. On at least five main lines it is possible to cross, in about three days, the 3,000 miles between the Atlantic and Pacific shores. Similarly, there are at least five main lines providing north-south transport from the Canadian border to Mexico and the Gulf Coast states. Chicago is the greatest railroad centre in the country, and it is in direct communication with almost all the other large cities, often by several lines. Distinct evidence of over-extension in railroad capacity and duplication in routes is currently leading to a series of mergers between the large rail lines, particularly in the area east of the Mississippi where the rail network is very dense; it is much less so west of the river, where both the population and resources are far more scattered.

Statistics show that the number of railroad companies has declined by more than a half since 1925, and that the length of track in use has been reduced by 10 per cent over the same period. The less profitable routes are being abandoned to road competition—a common occurrence in Europe, too. The number of passengers carried, after a large increase during the war because of troop movements, service leaves,

The San Bernardino-Santa Ana
Freeway near Los Angeles.
Magnificent highways
are becoming more numerous
everywhere, especially in the East
and the Far West, and
flyovers are common outside
the largest cities.
The road network everywhere
in the United States
is being constantly improved.

and migrating workers, has fallen again to the 1935
level, but the average length of each journey has
increased by 50 per cent. There is much less goods
traffic today than twenty years ago. Coal and coke
form about 30 per cent of the rail freight, and these
are followed by manufactured goods and mineral
products. These three classes of freight constitute more
than 80 per cent of the total traffic. Thus the products
of agriculture, forestry and livestock play a relatively
minor part in rail transport.

The obvious increase in the use of roads for the
transport of goods is borne out by statistics; the
number of trucks (or lorries) has almost trebled since
1936, and they operate not only over short distances
but over medium and very long distances. Motor-
coach services and some 60 million private cars carry
more people than the trains and more cheaply.

The road network is being constantly improved.
The main roads built or subsidised by the Federal
Government are four times as long today as they
were in 1925, while unpaved rural roads have
decreased by a half in the same period. Magnificent
highways are becoming more numerous everywhere,
and especially in the East and the Far West; there are
fast roads, without intersections, and they by-pass
busy town centres. Construction and maintenance
costs are met by federal, state, or municipal funds,

and by tolls levied on the road-users. The ordinary
roads are being made wider and more durable.
Within one generation of almost continuous effort, a
road system of about 3 million miles has been constructed, and of a quality unequalled anywhere else
in the world.

The overall pattern of the roads, particularly the
main roads, is rather similar to that of the railroads,
except that roads are more common in the mountainous areas. The road network reflects the uneven
distribution of population and wealth.

The great distances to be covered and the national
devotion to speed account for the importance assumed
by air transport during the last years, for both
passenger and goods traffic, nationally and internationally. The private companies compete in terms
of speed and comfort as well as price. Now the most
distant cities can be reached in a few hours; one can
travel by jet airliner from New York to San Francisco,
for example, in less than six hours of actual flying
time. Flowers, early fruit and vegetables, live lobsters
and other luxury and semi-luxury produce come
fresh to the consumer over vast distances. And flying
makes short work of even the highest mountain
ranges, though atmospheric instability causes frequent
changes in the routes. Thanks to air travel the United
States has assumed manageable proportions and has
today become a unit as closely knit as many a smaller
nation.

THE TRANSMISSION OF IDEAS. The numerous means of
rapidly transmitting ideas, sounds and pictures have
also contributed to the unity of the country. Gone
are the days of Indian smoke signals, and messages
carried on foot or on horseback. The telegraph,
films, radio and television reign supreme. Statistics
confirm the impressions of a traveller: for a population of 192 million there are 168 million radio sets,
as against 150 million in the rest of the world, 84
million telephones, with 87 million elsewhere, and
53 million television sets, as compared with 33
million. Radio stations may be counted in the thousands, television stations in the hundreds; all are
operated by private companies.

Although newspapers are more widely circulated
than in most other countries in proportion to the
population, they appear as the poor relations of radio
and television. All such means of transmitting ideas,
plus the nationwide distribution of books and magazines, help to bring together the land and peoples
of this very large republic. And yet, distinct human
and economic regions still exist. Variations of relief
and climate, rivers and seas, the resources of the
land, and the character of the people, are fundamental factors which even the inventions of this
century have not been able to obscure, in the United
States or elsewhere.

## REGIONAL LIFE

The different regions have taken shape as a result
of man's infinitely varying ways of adapting to and
using nature's diversity. Their changing features and
their boundaries may be discussed, but it is impossible
to doubt their existence. Whether the past or the
present is considered, or the mode of life or the

mental outlook of the people, it seems reasonable to distinguish five main regions in the United States. The Northeast, relatively old, highly industrialised and densely populated, is bounded by Canada to the north, the Atlantic to the east, the southern borders of Delaware, Maryland and West Virginia to the south, and a line running from the upper Ohio River to Lake Erie to the west. The immense South, also old, for a long time primarily agricultural, is bounded by the Atlantic, the Gulf of Mexico, approximately the 100° line of longitude to the west, and the northern borders of Oklahoma, Arkansas, Kentucky and Virginia to the north. The Middle West, with its huge agricultural and industrial production, covers the area between the Northeast, the South, the 100° meridian, and Canada. Farther west lie the Great Plains, wheat and livestock country, roughly between the 100° line and the Rocky Mountains. And finally, between the Rockies and the Pacific, is a region often called the West, comprising several large sub-regions such as the Northwest, the Southwest, the Pacific Coastlands. All such divisions, of course, imply transitional zones, and their boundaries as here defined should not be taken literally.

THE NORTHEAST. *New England, Boston and its neighbouring towns.* Between Canada, the Atlantic and the Hudson valley, lies the region settled mainly by the Pilgrim Fathers and called New England. This is one of the two oldest parts of the United States (the other is Virginia), and is most like Western Europe, with old forest-covered mountains, many grassy valleys, coasts fringed with rocks and beaches, villages clustered round their churches with pointed spires, and schools, colleges and universities in profusion. But it is essentially American. It played a large part in the drive towards the West, and its cultural tradition and ideals have influenced the whole country. Also it has contributed more than its share of inventors, statesmen, authors and philosophers.

Rural New England, one aspect of the region, has changed its nature: dairy-farming and such specialised crops as potatoes, tobacco, cranberries, and blueberries long ago replaced cereal crops. The stony ground, infertile soils and short growing season have never offered farmers much encouragement here, and in some places land has been laid to fallow. Forest covers more than half of New England, and though much of it is second growth and rather poor in quality, it nevertheless supports numerous sawmills and paper and pulp mills, particularly in Maine.

In the early days fish was the first staple of trade. Sold in the West Indies and Europe, it enabled the colonists to buy raw materials which became the basis of manufactures. Fishing is still an important source of income, especially in Gloucester and Boston, which supply the nation with large quantities of cod, herring, mackerel, haddock, halibut and lobster, both fresh and frozen.

Mining in New England has been confined mainly to the quarrying of high-quality building stone — granite, marble and slate — in Vermont and Maine. Vermont is also the chief producer of asbestos in the United States, from deposits in the northern Green Mountains. Maine has a flourishing paper industry.

Tourism is another big source of income, the attractions being the indented coast, rocky headlands, forested coves, picturesque fishing villages, the relatively cool summers, mountain ski resorts, and the Old World charm of the houses and customs.

Industry has grown up everywhere, originally taking advantage of the waterfalls, the proximity of the sea, and the skilled labour of the people. Later, manufacturing expanded, using coal from Pennsylvania. Paper mills, sugar refineries, breweries, foundries, textile mills and machine shops were among the principal industrial enterprises. It was here that the manufacture of wool and cotton textiles began at the end of the eighteenth century, and expanded to a point where New England led the nation for

The small village of East Corinth, in Vermont. With their surrounding hills and woods, such villages — each grouped round its church — are reminiscent of certain rural areas of western Europe. The six states of New England were among the first to be settled, and they have retained to some extent the aspect and traditions of the old world.

many decades. Then came shipbuilding, especially the famous Yankee Clippers, the sleekest, fastest sailing ships afloat, which established trade with China.

Despite the fact that New England lacks coal, oil and metallic minerals, it continues to contribute a great deal to the nation's industrial output, largely because of the skill of its workers, the initiative of its employers, and the research of its technicians. It specialises in goods of high quality, based on imported raw materials and power — high-quality woollen goods, the finest cotton fabrics, finely worked boots and shoes, delicate clocks and watches. It also makes electronic equipment, machine tools, instruments, sewing machines, typewriters, chemicals and rubber goods. Foreign competition, however, is a problem, and the relative economic importance of New England is declining, but only very slowly.

Boston is the financial and intellectual centre of New England, and proud of the independent spirit of its old families. The city still keeps in its downtown area the irregular pattern of its streets, marked out, so tradition has it, by the leisurely return of the cattle to their stables from the communal pasture or 'Common'. Although the suburbs are inhabited mainly by Catholics, the economic and moral control of the city still belongs to the Puritan families descended from the Pilgrim Fathers. At Harvard, freedom of thought is combined with the care for tradition appropriate to a university founded more than three centuries ago. Not far away, the Massachusetts Institute of Technology attracts the most promising research scientists. The professors and students of these two great seats of learning, and many neighbouring ones, maintain New England's intellectual prestige all over the United States and in fact throughout the world.

Boston and its numerous satellites, Cambridge, Lawrence, Lowell, Lynn, Brockton, and others, have nearly 2,500,000 inhabitants; a third of these work in the docks or in the offices close to the Common, or in the suburban workshops. South of Massachusetts lies the very small state of Rhode Island, which since the beginning of its history has been the refuge of non-conformity; it is now mainly composed of a collection of industrial towns around the port of Providence, and a great naval station at Newport. Connecticut stretches along the shore in the direction of New York, and its western extremity is beginning

Aerial view of Wilmington, an industrial town specialising in chemicals on the Delaware River. Like the majority of American cities, Wilmington has developed on a fairly strict geometric plan.
A few towering office buildings stand out in the central district, but this serves only to accentuate the uniform pattern elsewhere. Functional town-planning is one of the most original features of the American scene.

to merge into the suburbs of the great metropolis, upon which its market-gardens and specialised industries closely depend. The independent spirit of New England is ever-present in New Haven at Yale University, the age-old rival of Harvard. Connecticut, still country-like and within commuting distance of New York, has become a favourite retreat of the big-city dweller.

*Concentrated urban and industrial development.* Between the Hudson, the Atlantic and the Potomac, and to the north-west of Lakes Erie and Ontario, there lies a region almost twice the size of New England, with three times the population, and which from New York City to Washington dominates the economic and political life of the country.

Here the coastal plain gradually widens, and the coast becomes straighter and sandier, but it is breached by wide estuaries where shipping activites developed at an early date. First there is the estuary of the Hudson with New York, then comes that of the Delaware with Philadelphia and Wilmington; finally there is

Chesapeake Bay, an old glacial valley in the process of regrading, but deep enough to have brought prosperity to Baltimore, and into which flows the Potomac from Washington. Between these long bays the ocean forms the sand into dunes and offshore bars, and along these is a whole string of resorts for the millions of neighbouring townsfolk. On a hot summer weekend in Atlantic City, for instance, easily accessible from both New York and Philadelphia, it may be difficult to find a patch of sand to lie on or a spot of sea in which to bathe; but there are many smaller seaside resorts frequented by those who prefer to sun themselves and swim and boat and fish in relative peace.

The hinterland behind a zone of gentle, fairly fertile hills between the Delaware and the Susquehanna, consists of the old Appalachian Mountains with their parallel ridges formed by erosion, their deep valleys, forests and heath-land. In earlier days it was more convenient to go round this complex area by way of the almost level Hudson valley and its tributary the Mohawk to reach Lakes Ontario and Erie than it was to proceed direct from Philadelphia, Baltimore or Washington. This is one of the main reasons for the decisive lead that New York took over its rivals as early as the first half of the nineteenth century.

The exploitation of the forests and their clearings was not for long the only source of wealth to attract the pioneers and settlers into the heart of the mountains. Quite early on, extensive deposits of anthracite and high-grade bituminous coal, iron ore, and limestone were discovered on the slopes of the Appalachians—in fact, all that was needed not only to build and heat houses, but also to produce iron, steel and cement. It was also in Pennsylvania that for the first time, in 1859, petroleum gushed from American soil, and for more than thirty years the area remained the chief producer.

These factors stimulated an intense urban and industrial development, chiefly in the east near the Atlantic and in the west in the region of the Ohio and the Great Lakes, though a little occurred everywhere. To feed these millions of miners and factory workers, the farmers specialised more and more in market-garden produce—potatoes, sweet potatoes, cauliflower, cabbage, sweet corn, peas, beans, lettuce, asparagus, onions and tomatoes, especially in New York, New Jersey, and Delaware near the ocast. They also specialised in dairy-farming and poultry-raising, and the cultivation of the vine and fruit trees in central New York and near Lakes Erie and Ontario. The bulk production of cereals and meat was left to the vast areas farther west. The mountains, particularly the Catskills and Adirondacks, with lonely woodlands, scores of lakes, playing fields and ski runs, have become resorts for people escaping from the great urban centres.

In this middle Atlantic region well over 40 million people are crowded together in an area smaller than that of the United Kingdom, giving the highest density of population in the New World. Nine-tenths of these people live in urban centres, and the life of the innumerable suburbanites and small-town dwellers revolves to a large extent around these centres. By far the most important is New York, which in its conurbation has approximately 16 million people—a population slightly smaller than that of Canada—concentrated into an area not much larger than a medium-sized English county.

*New York.* For the European visitor and for the American tourist, New York means above all Manhattan. This small block of granite is an elongated island shaped like a ship ready to put to sea, its bows turned towards the ocean, its sides washed by the Hudson River on the west and the East River on the east, its stern being separated from the mainland by the Harlem River. This unique site, which Verrazano glimpsed in 1524 and Hudson explored in 1609, was bought by the Dutch from the Indians in 1626 and called New Amsterdam, until it was renamed New York, after the Duke of York, when it came into British hands in 1664. But it was not until 1825, when the glacial valley of the Hudson was linked to Lake Erie by canal, that this port triumphed over its Atlantic rivals, Boston, Philadelphia and Baltimore, and over New Orleans, to become the nation's chief point of entry and departure for both goods and passengers, by sea, land, and eventually air.

Capital and financial transactions became concentrated here, as well as industry. Until the First World War, Wall Street was sometimes restrained, sometimes assisted, by the City of London and even the Bank of France, but afterwards it became the most important financial centre in the world. At the same time the port of New York, blessed with a superb deep-water harbour, surpassed all its European rivals in volume, by loading and discharging almost as much cargo as the 'great four' of the North Sea, London, Hamburg, Antwerp and Rotterdam, put together; some 130 million tons equally divided between coastal and foreign trade. The 1929 crash depressed it only momentarily, and since the Second World War New York's port has been second only to Rotterdam's.

Lack of space on this small island for so vast a volume of commerce and business inspired the development of the skyscrapers whose slender pinnacles tower above the city—the famed Manhattan skyline. The oldest skyscrapers can be seen in the southern, older, part of the city near Wall Street. They have now been overtopped by those in midtown, between 34th Street, the Empire State Building, and 50th Street, Rockefeller Center. New ones, not as high as these giants but still thirty or forty storeys high or more, are going up every month in the biggest building boom New York has experienced for several decades. For the most part the skyscrapers accommodate offices, but they also contain hotels, restaurants, apartments, and even hospitals.

Huge residential and industrial areas have grown up, some in Manhattan itself but most of them beyond it. With Manhattan, the Bronx (north of the Harlem River), Queens and Brooklyn (to the east and southeast of the East River, on Long Island), and Richmond (on Staten Island), the city of New York proper has a population of nearly 8 million. The conurbation of New York spreads out in all directions: towards the north it includes the wealthy and open districts of Westchester County; in the east it overflows into the state of Connecticut and out over Long Island; it extends to the west beyond the Hudson, where it includes several towns in the state of New

Jersey, from Newark to Jersey City—a collection of large communities which in most countries would be counted as large cities. It is difficult to find a boundary to this heavy settlement area; it lies perhaps where the power of attraction of the metropolis weakens and tends to be replaced by that of another centre.

All the peoples of the world are represented in New York's population. The Chinese form a small Chinatown. There are nearly 700,000 Negroes, mainly in Harlem, the largest Negro centre in the world. Similarly there are many more Jews, Italians, Irish and Puerto Ricans in New York than in any single city in their native lands. Germans, Poles, Russians and Czechs also form groups of several hundred thousand each. These various peoples tended to congregate, especially in former days, in certain quarters of the city, and it is easy to recognise the dominant nationality of such districts by the accent or features of the passers-by, by the language of its newspapers, advertisements, and film titles. A glance in the markets and

The skyline of New York City looking north, with the East River on the right. Up to the eighteenth century this southern tip of Manhattan Island, which is now the financial section, was inhabited by only a small hamlet of settlers. It is now the commercial hub of the city and to a large extent of the United States. Ocean-going liners can dock almost at the foot of the skyscrapers, thus giving New York unique advantages. There is a total water frontage of 650 miles.

food stores is equally instructive. In New York it is possible to tour the gastronomic world in less than eighty minutes.

To feed, clothe, shelter, transport, inform and amuse this huge collection of people, a fantastic number of industries have grown up in New York: industries that now supply much of the United States with cotton goods, and women's and men's clothing of all kinds, hats and furs, machines and tools, chemicals, domestic and commerical equipment, books, magazines, art products and furniture. Almost all of the larger corporations in the nation maintain offices in the city, where far-reaching policy decisions are made, affecting the lives and livelihood of many millions of people throughout the country. Every day an average of at least 200,000 tourists or visitors in transit are received, fed, and entertained. While it is the nation's leading financial, commercial, industrial and transportation centre, it is also the intellectual and artistic capital, whose universities, schools, art museums, concerts, opera, ballet and theatre rank among the finest in the world.

The people of the rest of the United States often claim that New York is not American, and it is indeed unlike any other city in the United States, a heterogeneous mixture of America and Europe, with some contributions from Africa and even Asia—a city predestined, one might say, to become the seat of the United Nations. It is a city of the world, without arrogance or affectation, a dynamic city, energetic and ever-changing, indifferent and good-natured, colossal yet friendly, a young giant of a city, more typical perhaps of our times than of a particular country.

*Other large cities of the Northeast.* Philadelphia, the 'city of brotherly love', founded by William Penn and his Quakers at the head of the long Delaware estuary, has retained a strong sense of tradition. It has great pride in its famed citizen Benjamin Franklin, one of the most acute, creative and broad-minded thinkers of his time, and in its own rôle in the creation of a great nation.

It was here that the colonial representatives met after the Boston Tea Party and the closing of that port by the British in 1774, and adopted the Declaration of Rights and the Articles of Association. In May 1775, the Second Continental Congress met here, and on 4 July 1776 adopted the final draft of the Declaration of Independence drawn up by Thomas Jefferson, John Adams, Benjamin Franklin, Robert Livingston and Roger Sherman. On July 8 it was publicly read in the State House yard, an event that marked the beginning of the end of British rule in the American colonies. After the Revolution, Philadelphia became the capital of the new nation and remained so (except for one year, 1789) until 1800, growing meanwhile into the country's biggest city and, after the discovery of coal inland, its greatest coal port. Although it was outstripped by New York after the opening of the Erie Canal, it continued to grow; today it is the fourth largest city in the United States, a great industrial centre, refining oil, building ships, making chemicals, locomotives, electrical supplies, machinery, tools, and all sorts of consumer goods. The port handles large quantities of oil, coal, grain, flour, textiles and railroad equipment going out, and

oil, coal, iron, manganese, sulphur, nitrates and sugar coming in. Not far to the north-east is Morrisville, with an immense integrated steel plant, which occupies six square miles. To it come shiploads of iron ore from Venezuela, coal from Pennsylvania and West Virginia, and limestone from Pennsylvania.

The original Quakers who settled in Philadelphia and elsewhere in Pennsylvania were soon joined by Germans, who came to clear land and establish farms. Later, the development of the mines in the western part of the state attracted large numbers of other immigrants, especially Italians and Poles, who form a high proportion of the population of Pittsburgh, the chief city of the iron and steel industry, and of the neighbouring industrial centres. Coal, however, is being replaced more and more by petroleum and electricity as sources of energy, and some coal-mining towns, such as Scranton, lost more than 10 per cent of their inhabitants during the 1950–60 decade. Pittsburgh itself, with 2,500,000 in its metropolitan area, is much smaller than Philadelphia (4,300,000 in the metropolitan area), which has had the advantages of being closer to the large market in the cities along the seaboard, of having a much greater variety of industries, and a broad well-protected harbour.

To the south of Philadelphia and also sited on the estuary of the Delaware, is Wilmington, the chief city of the multifarious chemical industries of the firm of Du Pont which makes every conceivable chemical product from high explosives to synthetic textiles.

It is only a short distance from the Delaware to Chesapeake Bay, near the head of which lies Baltimore, a city of 940,000 inhabitants (with dependent areas, 1,700,000 inhabitants). This is another great commercial and industrial centre, making iron and steel (particularly at nearby Sparrows Point), smelting copper brought in from the western states and Chile, building ships, and refining oil. Being relatively close to the immense coalfields of Pennsylvania and West Virginia, it is one of the largest coal ports in the country. The importance of the Negro district in this city confirms the feeling that one has crossed the traditional line between North and South. Here the rhythm of life begins to slacken a little.

At the head of navigation on the Potomac, more than sixty miles from Chesapeake Bay, Washington, the Federal capital, was built to house the government and central administration. For more than a century Washington was a quiet, drowsy, spacious provincial town, built in a star-shaped plan centred on the Capitol. Today it is very different, a city of more than 760,000 inhabitants or 2 million with its surrounding towns. Politics and administration are the chief activities, and as the United States has played an increasing rôle in international affairs, these activities have multiplied and diversified, requiring teams of specialists and technicians of all sorts. About thirty large buildings, generally in neo-classical style, are none too many to house officials and documents. It has been impossible to retain the original plan for the city, although it still looks like a planned city. The diagonals of the intersecting avenues and the squares, laid out by a French major, Pierre L'Enfant, are in pleasing contrast to the usual block pattern of American cities. There are splendid trees in the public parks and private gardens, and the winters are short and the summers sub-tropical. Skyscrapers and factory chimneys have been avoided.

The eastern cities of Boston, New York, Philadelphia, Baltimore and Washington, and Pittsburgh farther inland, dominate the life of the Northeast; but more modest centres should not be ignored. The chief ones are aligned along the old route to the West, the Hudson River and Erie Canal. They are Albany, capital of New York State, its neighbour, Schenectady, headquarters of an important electricity company, and Troy, with a big hosiery industry; then comes Rochester, the chief centre of the photographic industry; and finally, at the outlet of the Erie Canal into the lake of the same name, Buffalo, which until the St Lawrence Seaway was opened in 1959 was in effect the head of navigation on the Great Lakes. Quantities of wheat from the American and Canadian West are unloaded in Buffalo to feed the largest concentration of flour mills in the United States. Other huge industries are steel, chemicals, and electrical goods. The Niagara Falls nearby not only attract tourists from all over the world, but are a powerful source of energy for these and other manufacturing plants.

*Farms and mines in the Appalachians.* From central New York, through Pennsylvania, and on into West Virginia, uplands predominate. These are part of the Appalachians, the long parallel series of features consisting of, from east to west: the Piedmont; the Blue Ridge Mountains; the so-called ridge and valley area, the chief valley being the Great Valley, one of the longest mountain valleys in the world; and beyond this, the Appalachian Plateau. Although the Piedmont areas of Pennsylvania and West Virginia are small, they have the best farmlands in these states. Lancaster County, in Pennsylvania, is especially favoured: the growing season is about 200 days a year, and an average rainfall of 40 inches is well distributed through the year. It was settled by Germans who during the last 200 years have made it one of the richest farming areas in the United States. Wheat and tobacco are the main cash crops. Corn is another major crop, most of which is fed to large herds of dairy and beef cattle and to poultry. Hay and potatoes are grown everywhere. Several of the long narrow valleys of the ridge and valley area in Pennsylvania are also fertile, and produce corn, oats, wheat and hay, generally cultivated in strips, but the growing season here is no more than 170 days a year. Dairy-farming and the raising of cattle and hogs are other principal sources of income in these valleys.

Probably no other area in the world of comparable size has produced as much coal as the ridge and valley and plateau country of Pennsylvania and West Virginia, and yet astronomical reserves remain. In all, the United States is believed to have now more than a third of the world's coal reserves. Until 1958 it led the world in coal production—the Soviet Union took first place in that year.

THE SOUTH. The South is one of the most distinctive regions in the United States, from the point of view of climate, culture, tradition and landscape, and it is often labelled the 'most colourful' part of the country. Torrential summer rains, heat and humidity

make it a tropical or semi-tropical land. It is rich in trees and fruits, and crops of many kinds grow exuberantly. Droughts do occur sometimes, especially in the west, where the average rainfall falls to as little as 30 or even 20 inches a year near the margin of the Great Plains; but most of the South gets between 40 and 60 inches, and is on the whole better watered than most other parts of the United States. Also the rain is fairly evenly distributed through the year, a distinct advantage for the farmers. Snow is rare in most places, except in the Appalachian and Ozark uplands and, again except in the uplands, the growing season is 200 or more days a year; in southern Florida it is frequently 365 days. Summer temperatures of 32°C. (90°F.) are common even in the mountains and along the coasts.

Agriculture long played a much more important part in the South than industry, but in the last few decades a revolution has been taking place, fundamentally changing the character of the economy. The farm population has been declining steadily since

The Capitol Building, Washington, D.C., which houses Congress, the national legislative body. The first Congresses of the United States wished to avoid choosing as capital any existing city and so in 1790 decided to build a new city in the marshy woodland on the banks of the Potomac which they named after George Washington, the first President, whose home was nearby.

about 1920. Almost all the rural counties have lost population, both white and Negro, whereas the urban population has increased by more than one-third, a clear indication that this is no longer a 'colonial' type of society, producing raw materials for export, but is rapidly acquiring a diversified economy in which industrial activities and services give employment to half or more than half of the working population. Another striking change taking place in the South is the exodus of the Negroes: whereas they constituted nearly 40 per cent of the South's population a hundred years ago, they now constitute less than 20 per cent of it.

This huge region, extending from the Atlantic to

After special storage tobacco is shipped to warehouses to be sold. This highly profitable crop is grown in increasing quantities in the southern states, pushing the traditional cotton farther west.

the Great Plains and from the northern borders of Oklahoma, Arkansas, Kentucky and Virginia to the Gulf of Mexico, covers approximately one-quarter of the United States, and is inhabited by a similar proportion of the total population. It consists of several sub-regions which may be roughly defined as: the Atlantic Coastal Plain and the Piedmont; the Appalachian and Ozark-Ouachita Uplands; the Cotton Belt; Florida; and the Gulf Coast.

*The Atlantic Plain and the Piedmont.* The English set foot on the American continent in 1607, south of the Potomac on the James River, in the territory named Virginia in honour of Queen Elizabeth I. It was Elizabeth's richest colony and afterwards became and long remained an influential state in the Federation. Together with the states to the south of it, it constitutes the 'Old South', which in 1861 preferred to secede rather than abolish Negro slavery, and for four years waged unequal and desperate war. After its defeat the Old South went through a long period of rebuilding and suffered from acute economic stagnation, from which it has only recently emerged.

Cotton is no longer supreme. Many other crops are grown, including all sorts of vegetables which are shipped to northern markets in the early spring: corn, peanuts and soya beans in the Piedmont, and all these together with tobacco on the Coastal Plain. In Georgia and elsewhere some beef and diary cattle are now

grazing land that was formerly in cotton, thus rehabilitating much land that was eroded and depleted by both cotton and tobacco. In the Piedmont section of Virginia most of the tobacco grown is of the dark type used in pipes; in North Carolina, the major tobacco-producing region in the States, it is the lighter flue-cured type exported and used in the millions of cigarettes made in North Carolina, Virginia and Kentucky. More tobacco is consumed per person in the United States than in any other country—about 11.5 pounds a year.

Industry long ago developed at the foot of the Appalachians, taking advantage of the Fall Line, which extends from Washington, D.C., south to Atlanta, Georgia; along this line the rivers fall sharply, in a steep gradient, to the coastal plain. More recently the centre of industrial development has shifted somewhat to the higher Appalachians in Tennessee and North Carolina. Here the rivers are steeper and fed by a rainfall of 80 or more inches a year. In all, nearly one-fifth of the total hydro-electric output of the United States is produced in the Piedmont. It is in the Piedmont that more than two-thirds of the nation's cotton goods are manufactured, as well as nylon and rayon and other synthetic textiles, chemicals, fertilizers, and pulp and paper. On the other side of the mountains, the coals and iron ore of the Birmingham region are the basis for an important metallurgical industry, which is exceeded in size and importance only by that of Pittsburgh and the region of the Great Lakes.

Thus a 'New South' has been created, commercial and utilitarian, whose capitals, like Atlanta in Georgia with a population of nearly 500,000, and Birmingham in Alabama with 341,000, have not the languid charm of the older cities, such as Richmond, the capital of Virginia, once the centre of the tobacco industry, or the colonial port of Charleston in South Carolina with its magnificent gardens of camellias, azaleas and magnolias. In sixty years Charleston's population has increased by only 15 per cent, a unique example of slow growth in the United States. Norfolk, in Virginia, although it is an 'old' town, is among the rapidly growing cities, a great naval station and port and shipbuilding centre.

*The Uplands.* The Uplands, the Appalachians in the east and the Ozarks and Ouachitas in the west, account for the greater variety of the states of Kentucky and Tennessee on one side of the Mississippi, and of Arkansas on the other. In the more isolated deep mountain valleys and coves in the Appalachians resources are limited, people still live much as the pioneers did, and prefer to do so. They grow or make nearly everything they need and have little desire to buy or sell anything. On the forested slopes, however, lumbering and the making of pulp and paper are growing industries, and in the ridge and valley section winter wheat, corn, hay and large quantities of apples are raised, along with some beef and dairy cattle. Coal mined in eastern Kentucky and Tennessee and northern Alabama provides fuel for several large thermo-electric plants.

The great projects undertaken in 1933 in the Tennessee valley by the Federal Government have brought new life to this state and its neighbours. Floods had been causing nearly $2 million worth of damage a

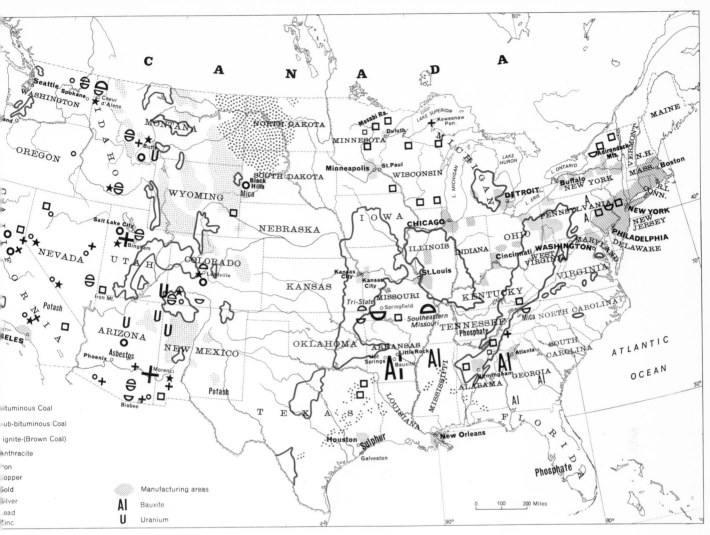

Bituminous Coal
Sub-bituminous Coal
Lignite-(Brown Coal)
Anthracite
Iron
Copper
Gold
Silver
Lead
Zinc

Manufacturing areas
Al Bauxite
U Uranium

0 100 200 Miles

year, and nearly a quarter of the acreage in the valley was rapidly being destroyed by erosion. Crop yields were decreasing, incomes were low and uncertain, taxes were high. In short, the valley's main natural resources were being either abused or destroyed.

The Tennessee Valley Authority undertook an immense multi-purpose project aimed at controlling floods, developing navigation, generating electric power, and reforestation. Some thirty dams were built on the Tennessee River and its tributaries, electric power plants and transmission lines were built, at first to carry electricity to farms in the area, 90 per cent of which had been without it, and to markets outside the area, and then to an increasing number of new local industries. Much-needed fertilizer was one of the first items manufactured, and the visible results in higher crop yields soon led to its widespread use throughout the valley. Other industries, attracted by the cheap and abundant power, joined the TVA project, notably those concerned with processing copper, steel, manganese, phosphate and zinc; with manufacturing aluminium, sulphuric acid, caustic soda, explosives, aircraft and rayon; and, at Oak Ridge, with nuclear research and atomic bomb manufacture. In fact, this region where the English of Shakespeare and the folklore of Elizabethan times have been preserved is now the forefront of scientific and social experiments. Louisville, capital of Kentucky, how-

ever, continues to take pride in its bourbon whiskey made from local corn, in its cigarettes made from local tobacco, and in the horses raised on the famous tree-shaded, lush Bluegrass farms around Lexington.

In the more remote parts of the Ozark-Ouachita highlands farming is of the subsistence type, whereas in the Arkansas River valley and several other valleys cotton and tomatoes are raised as cash crops. There is some lumbering and mining. In fact, the district on the Missouri-Arkansas border and another close to the Oklahoma-Kansas-Arkansas border are the leading producers of lead and zinc in the United States.

*The Cotton Belt.* The present area of the Cotton Belt coincides in part with the traditional cotton empire of old but extends much farther west, into the Mississippi valley and far beyond into Texas, up to about the 20-inch rainfall line. Its northern boundary is approximately the northern boundary of the area where 200 frost-free days a year can be expected, and its southern and eastern edges are the wetter, more sandy Atlantic and Gulf coastal plains. In each of the major producing areas cotton is the predominant crop, but by no means the only one. In North Carolina it is associated with tobacco; in South Carolina and Georgia, with peanuts and corn; in Alabama, soya beans and corn are second crops; in the Mississippi valley (eastern Arkansas and western Mississippi), one of the very richest and most prosperous cotton

The United States has been fortunate in possessing rich mineral deposits, although the high industrial development has led to exhaustion of some resources. Almost 40 per cent of the world's coal is found in America, and there is the additional advantage that most of it lies in horizontal seams, near the surface. The chief coalfield is the Appalachian field. The other major deposits are the Interior and the Rocky Mountain coalfields. In some areas coal production is uneconomic because of competition from oil. This comes chiefly from the centre and south of the U.S.A. and thousands of pipelines carry the oil to the urban centres of the east coast. Deposits are found in 26 states, but Texas, Oklahoma and California supply over half the total output. America also possesses rich deposits of iron, copper, zinc and molybdenum, besides gold and silver.

areas, soya beans and rice are also grown; in Texas, corn and peanuts in the central part of the state, and grains and hay in the north-western sections are associated crops.

Although cotton had been raised in the South since the earliest days, it was not until 1793, when Eli Whitney invented the cotton gin, and new machines for spinning and weaving were invented in England and then in New England, that cultivation was undertaken on a vast scale. At the time of the Civil War, in the 1860's, the South was supplying more than three-quarters of the world's cotton. The destruction of plantations in the east during the Civil War was a major factor in the migration of cotton westward to drier areas. Another was the boll weevil, which prefers a humid climate. This pest lays its eggs in cotton bolls. The grubs feed on the boll when hatched, thus causing it to dry up and fall off. After crossing the Mexican border in 1892, the boll weevil damaged in some years nearly half the cotton crop. It has now been brought more or less under control by spraying, but continues to thrive better in the eastern part of the South than in the western part. Such spraying is often done by planes flying low over the fields. As everywhere else in the United States, mechanical equipment does most of the work on cotton farms — tractors, seeders, weeders, combines, pickers and so on. The mechanical cotton picker can pick as much as a thousand pounds of cotton a day; but it does not eliminate leaves and stems as thoroughly as a skilled human picker, and higher-grade cottons are still hand-picked. Although cotton today provides only half of the farm income in the big producing areas, the South nevertheless is a major contributor to United States cotton production, which amounts each year to about one-quarter of the world's supply.

Cotton is the basic raw material for a host of other industries besides the making of cotton textiles and cotton clothing. From its fibres cellulose is made, and paper, rayon, plastics and cellophane. Cottonseed oil is made into salad oil, margarine, soap, and meal for cattle feeding. Soya beans are also made into oil. Other

major industries in the Cotton Belt are lumbering, the manufacture of paper and pulp and furniture, the extraction of some iron and bauxite, and above all of oil. The largest oilfields in North America are in eastern Texas in the Cotton Belt. Texas as a whole provides some 40 to 50 per cent of the nation's petroleum.

The state of Texas, larger then France, Switzerland, Holland, Belgium and Luxembourg put together, is justly proud of its wealth of resources — oil, natural gas, cotton, cattle, sheep, citrus fruits and poultry. It is also proud of its size. It is the second largest state in the Union since the recent addition of Alaska, which is more than twice as big, but it is twice the size of California, the third largest state. It is proud, too, of the range of its climate, from torrential downpours on the Gulf Coast to almost desert-like aridity on its western border. It is proud of the past, of the ten years of independence between leaving Mexico and joining the United States. It prides itself, as well, on the present, and on what it hopes will be the future; and the immense fortunes which have been made here sometimes encourage it to dream of competing with the East in financial, political and intellectual affairs.

But this is not all. The cities of Texas are growing rapidly; many have almost doubled their population in the last twenty years. Houston, with 938,000 inhabitants, is the chief centre for petroleum, commerce and industry; Dallas, with 680,000 inhabitants, is the centre for cotton and more recently for aircraft production; Fort Worth is concerned with stock-raising and the meat industry. These cities are mainly commercial centres, competitors in business; but they are also competitors now in beautifying their appearance, and in their encouragement of the plastic arts, the theatre and education. Austin, the state capital and a university town, and San Antonio, with a population of nearly 600,000, owe much of their charm to the buildings, which are a lingering reminder of their Spanish past.

Like Texas, Oklahoma, the old Indian reserve which was opened to settlers in 1889, has prospered by the extension of the cotton-growing lands and above all by the discovery and exploitation of oil right in the middle of the state capital, Oklahoma City, which had 4,000 inhabitants in 1890 and today has more than 300,000. The growth of Tulsa, the headquarters of the petroleum companies, is even more spectacular: in 1890 it did not exist, in 1900 it had 1,300 inhabitants, in 1950 it had 182,740, and today it has 262,000. An abundant and continuous stream of crude petroleum flows in a thousand pipelines from Texas and Oklahoma to industrial centres across the nation.

*Florida.* In Florida the amphibious character of the landscape, the huge swamps and nearly 30,000 lakes, the alligators, the palm trees, are still unchanged. But there is a modern Florida represented by the great beaches lined with hotels and villas to suit every pocket, resorts such as popular Miami Beach, fashionable Palm Beach, Tampa and its neighbour St Petersburgh, which have been invaded by an increasing number of vacationers and retired people eager to enjoy the mild climate. It is largely thanks to them that Florida's population is increasing by leaps and bounds, much faster than that of California, its rival in

Mechanised harvesters are increasingly replacing handpicking on the cotton plantations, especially in the new cotton-growing areas of California, Arizona, Oklahoma and Texas, and many of these machines are bought by the farmers co-operatively. Though the Negro population of the old cotton belt of the south-east has diminished through migration to the industrial north, it remains more than a third of the total.

golden fruit, sunshine and charm. Between 1950 and 1960 the population of Florida jumped from 2,771,000 to 4,900,000.

Besides the tourist industry there are other sources of wealth which are considerable. One is the forests of Southern pine which cover more than 30,000 square miles, and keep a dozen large pulp and paper mills busy. Another is the citrus fruit industry, which brings in nearly half the farm revenue.

The annual value of the United States citrus crop, including lemons, grapefruit and oranges, runs to over $5 million. Four-fifths of the crop is oranges, and the total orange crop amounts to about one-third of all the oranges grown in the world — surely one of the reasons why Americans are so addicted to the large morning glass of orange juice. The first oranges were planted by Spaniards near St Augustine in Florida in 1579, and until the late 1800's the industry developed mainly in this vicinity. A series of devastating frosts eventually led the orange-growers to migrate farther south, to the central part of the state where the danger of frost is less. Nevertheless, frost remains a hazard. Most growers now keep some seventy stoves per acre ready to be fired if a frost is forecast. The harvesting, packing and marketing of the citrus crop are highly organised operations, regulated to ensure the quality of the fruit and packaging according to size. More than half of the Florida orange crop is processed into juice or concentrated form in some fifty plants.

The second most valuable source of farm income in the state is the growing of sixty vegetables or so, especially tomatoes, celery, beans, sweet corn, peppers, radishes, potatoes, lettuce, squashes and cabbage. These reach northern markets during the winter and early spring, long before they become available from local fields. Some cotton is also grown, with peanuts, soya beans, tung oil, tobacco and, since imports from Cuba have stopped, increasing quantities of sugar-cane. As in other parts of the South, cattle-raising has become in recent years another profitable farm activity, with a total of 1,735,000 head of cattle in 1965.

Although Florida has no big industrial centres such as those of the Northeast, it manufactures considerable quantities of pulp and paper, processes its agricultural produce, and manufactures chemicals and plastics. Fertilizers and insecticides are made from phosphate mined in the central part of the state; the mines here produce three-quarters of North America's supply of phosphate.

*The Gulf Coast and New Orleans.* From its confluence with the Ohio to the Gulf of Mexico, the Mississippi flows slowly, raising its bed of recent alluvium above the sediments already laid down and continually accumulated at its mouth at the expense of the sea. It meanders freely, and in former days frequently flooded the surrounding country. Its lowest tributaries, the Arkansas and Red Rivers, which come from the Rockies, still occasionally flood their lower valleys. The Lower Mississippi flood plain is a confusion of swamp and forests, lakes and backwaters and shifting meanders which man has not entirely succeeded in subduing. However, the main river stream is now embanked, the floods are controlled, and most of the alluvial plain has been drained and is in use.

In the Gulf Coast section of the river valley, rice and sugar-cane are grown extensively. Both were introduced by the Acadians who migrated here when Canada came under British rule, and the fields are as long and narrow as they are in the French sections of Canada. After the ploughing, harrowing and flooding of the fields, low-flying aircraft plant the rice. The use of such machinery has made it possible for one man to tend some eighty acres of growing rice, as compared with three or four acres in, for instance, India, where everything is done by hand. The growing of sugar-cane, too, is a highly mechanised operation, and here, as in Florida and for the same reason, the acreage planted is increasing. The average individual in the United States eats annually nearly a hundred pounds of sugar, more than in any other country, and sugar is one of the nation's principal imports.

In the Lower Rio Grande valley crops are much more diversified, including grapefruit, oranges, early potatoes, onions, tomatoes, carrots and beets.

Almost all of North America's sulphur comes from the Gulf Coast; and beneath the swamps and the floor of the Gulf of Mexico are tremendous oilfields which currently produce some 2 million barrels of oil a day, much of it by means of wells constructed in offshore waters.

The refining of oil began in the early 1900's, but it is only since the Second World War that the Gulf Coast has become the leading refining area in the United States. The four main centres are Houston-Texas City, Beaumont-Port Arthur, Lake Charles, and Baton Rouge. Abundant oil and natural gas and other raw materials, plus excellent transport facilities by sea, by natural and man-made inland channels, and by road, have fostered a spectacular growth of other industries since the early 1950's — chemicals in the Houston-Texas City district, at Port Neches, Corpus Christi, Orange, and Deer Park in Texas, and at Baton Rouge, Lake Charles, and New Orleans in Louisiana; the smelting of tin at Texas City, using tin imported from Bolivia and South-East Asia; the manufacture of aluminium at Port Lavara in Texas, and magnesium at Freeport, Texas.

A mammoth shovel used in extracting natural phosphate rock from Florida's marine beds. Here, as elsewhere, American engineers have responded impressively to the growing need for output of minerals.

New Orleans, for long the principal outlet for the wealth of the Mississippi basin, is still today a giant port, handling more than 20 million tons of commercial goods a year. Nearly 200 deep-draught vessels can berth simultaneously at its waterfront docks, which stretch out over twelve miles, the main imports being sugar, molasses, burlap bags, jute and sisal, and the main exports cotton, corn, flour, soya beans, petroleum and chemicals. In the city and along the river upstream are hundreds of industrial plants, a great many of them new, turning out aluminium, chemicals, petroleum products, and so forth. New Orleans has a reputation for charm and colour enjoyed by few other American cities, and tourism is a big industry. Visitors come from all over the country to hear good jazz, relish the excellent cuisine, wander through the old Spanish and French quarters, and visit the columned mansions nearby.

One other industry of the Gulf Coast, and for that matter of the other coastal parts of the South, is fishing — oysters from Chesapeake Bay and the Atlantic off Virginia and Louisiana, and shrimps, mullet, red snapper, Spanish mackerel and bluefish from the Gulf.

THE MIDDLE WEST. The Mississippi, which rises in the Middle West, divides the United States into two distinct parts. To the east, the land is generally well watered and was originally covered with fine forests

Pittsburgh, Pennsylvania, the world capital of the steel industry, is situated at the confluence of the Allegheny and the Monongahela where they join to form the Ohio River. Heavy-metal industries have developed chiefly between the Ohio and Lake Erie. The Great Lakes make it relatively cheap to transport iron ore from Minnesota, Wisconsin and Michigan to coalfields in the Ohio valley.

of white pine, beech and birch; it has more people, more industries, and better means of communication. West of the river, rainfall decreases and extremes of temperature are increasingly greater towards the foot of the Rocky Mountains. Forest is succeeded by grassland which changes imperceptibly into the steppeland of the Great Plains. It was in this transition zone between forest and steppe that the large-scale cultivation of cereals developed — corn in the Middle West, spring wheat and winter wheat in the Great Plains — and in the more arid sections, the large-scale raising of cattle and sheep.

The Middle West was brought under cultivation during the first half of the nineteenth century, and

became the most productive industrial belt in the world in the second half. It is well endowed with fertile soils, fuels, minerals, navigable waterways, railways and roads, and is a great producer of cereals, meat, milk, butter, cheese, preserved foods, coal, petroleum, copper, iron ore, pig iron, steel, and a host of other manufactures. It has a more balanced economy than any other region in North America, and has one-third of the continent's population. Three of its cities have more than one million inhabitants, six others more than 500,000, and twelve others more than 200,000.

This region perhaps more than any other has been the melting-pot of the diverse peoples of Europe, out of which a common outlook and nationality were cast. Between 1820 and 1914, several million immigrants came in, mainly by way of the Ohio River, the National Road, and the Hudson and Erie Canal. Until about 1880 they were predominantly English, Irish, German and Scandinavian; after that were added Canadians, Russians, Italians and people from Central Europe. By 1890, 79 per cent of the inhabitants of Minnesota were foreign-born, in two other Middle Western states the proportion was 50 per cent or more, and in others it ranged from 30 to 50.

The Middle West includes two fairly distinctive farming regions: a dairy-farming area, and the famous Corn Belt. The Great Lakes dairy zone consists mainly of Michigan, Wisconsin and Minnesota. Near the lakes the climate is less severe than farther inland: in autumn the cold air masses coming down from Canada are tempered considerably by the great expanse of relatively warm water — Lakes Superior, Huron and Michigan together cover an area of 77,220 square miles — so that winter does not set in as early as in the interior. In the spring the cooler lakes retard the advent of warm weather. The main crops are potatoes, corn, oats, hay, tomatoes and sugar-beet. Chickens and pigs are reared and a variety of fruits grown, notably apples, peaches, pears, cherries and grapes. But this is above all dairy country. About two-fifths of the nation's dairy farms are in these states, producing vast quantities of milk, butter and cheese; Wisconsin cheeses are prized throughout the entire country.

The best dairy breeds are selected with care and the animals are submitted to strict veterinary control; the most modern and scientific methods are applied to milking, preservation, transport, and milk manufactures. Nearly one-quarter of the capital on an average farm is in machinery and equipment. However, the dairy industry is suffering somewhat from the competition of Europe and Australia which can sell produce more cheaply, and the butter manufacturers are suffering from competition from margarine. The Federal Government buys stocks, and disposes of any surplus milk products.

*The Corn Belt.* To a visitor from Western Europe, used to a great variety within a short distance, a drive through the corn empire of Ohio, Indiana, Illinois and Iowa may seem somewhat monotonous. The landscape is level or rolling, and in summer, for most of these 1,000 miles, a wall of corn taller than a car lines the way. A break in the wall is a welcome change. It is likely to reveal a perfect picture of agricultural prosperity — big, brand-new farm buildings, barns, silos, pig and cattle feeders, farm machinery, sheds, a spacious, comfortable house, and perhaps a row of trees serving as a wind shelter. Before it was settled, this area was divided into 'sections', one mile square, and straight roads today follow these section lines, making a checkerboard pattern particularly apparent from the air. Occasionally one comes to a wooded valley, and there are of course the big cities of Cleveland, Columbus, Cincinnati, Detroit, Indianapolis, Chicago, and so on.

The hybrid corn of the Middle West was born of an accidental cross between two types and then further strains were developed by scientific experimentation. They are taller and have sturdier stalks and much larger ears of corn than the Indian maize. Yields average some 55 bushels per acre and may reach 100 bushels or more. Corn is the largest and most valuable crop raised in the United States, and although it is grown all over the country, the biggest crop comes from the fertile prairie soils of the Corn Belt; these soils are dark in colour, some so dark as to be almost black, and high in organic matter and nitrogen.

Some of the corn is canned or frozen for human consumption; most of it is used to raise pigs and cattle and fatten cattle brought in from ranches farther west. In addition to corn, cattle and pigs, the average farmer also raises wheat, oats, hay, soya beans, and a few dairy cows. Thanks to the machine, corn can be grown and harvested at a cost of as little as four man-hours per acre. By pushing buttons or other devices in his barn, the farmer can feed some 500 cattle and 500 hogs in about fifteen minutes. Ground corn arrives from one silo, silage from another, shelled corn from another; vitamins, minerals, antibiotics and hormones are shot into the feed, which is then propelled into a channel over the animals' feed troughs and released into the stall of each individual animal. Mechanisation has also helped to control erosion, weeds and diseases, and increase the use of fertilizers. But it has also helped to create in the United States a major problem — over-production of basic crops. To prevent prices of farm produce from dropping to a point where few farmers would stay in business, the Federal Government guarantees prices on many crops, and stores the surplus, at a cost to the American taxpayer of some $3,500 million a year. The problem has no easy solution. Sale abroad of the surplus at cost or even below brings complaints from other exporting countries and from the American taxpayer who is footing the staggering bill.

*The industrial centres.* Industries in the Middle West include lumbering, fishing, food processing, brewing, and the mining of vast quantities of iron ore, copper and limestone. The high-grade iron ore (50 per cent or more iron content) of the Mesabi Range in Minnesota and other ranges in Minnesota, Michigan and

Over 53 million acres of land are under cultivation in America and a further quarter of the total land area under forest. Wheat is one of the most important crops, grown east of the Rocky Mountains. Cotton production is moving from its traditional place in the South to the lands west of the Mississippi River. Tobacco is the chief crop of Carolina, Kentucky, Virginia, Tennessee and Georgia. Beans, flax, rice and vegetables are also important, and California is famous for its citrus fruit orchards. Among livestock, cattle are by far the most important. Out of approximately 100 million head, nearly 80 per cent are beef cattle. Pigs are the second largest elements, followed by sheep. Since 1960 the number of horses and mules has fallen so low that records are no longer kept.

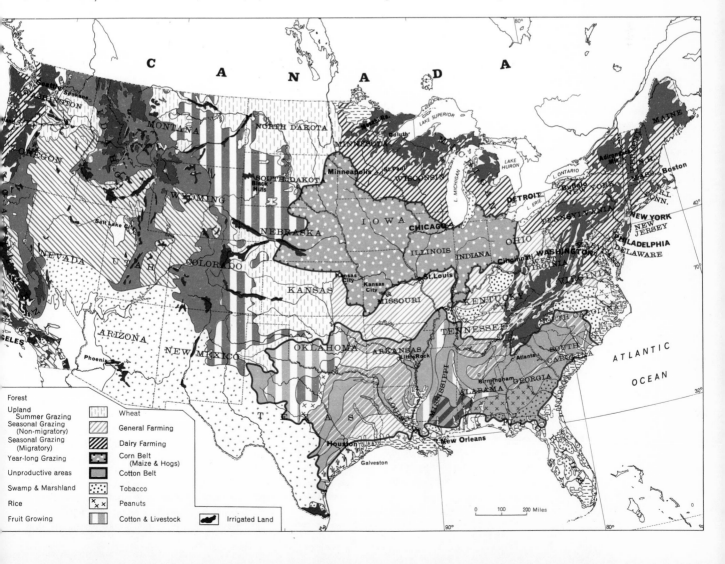

Forest
Upland
  Summer Grazing
Seasonal Grazing
  (Non-migratory)
Seasonal Grazing
  (Migratory)
Year-long Grazing
Unproductive areas
Swamp & Marshland
Rice
Fruit Growing

Wheat
General Farming
Dairy Farming
Corn Belt
  (Maize & Hogs)
Cotton Belt
Tobacco
Peanuts
Cotton & Livestock
Irrigated Land

0    100    200 Miles

Wisconsin, located near enough to the Great Lakes for easy shipment out, have been for the last fifty years a prime factor in the growth of the United States iron and steel industry, the growth of the Middle West, and the growth of the nation as a whole. Until very recently this region supplied 85 per cent of the nation's iron ore. The higher-grade ores are now approaching exhaustion, but lower-grade ore, called taconite, is being mined, and iron ore is being imported from Labrador in Canada via the St Lawrence Seaway.

Pittsburgh, using coal from the Appalachians and iron from the Mesabi, became the first great iron and steel centre. The same combination, plus the coal deposits of Ohio, Illinois, Indiana, Kansas and Iowa, explains the enormous development of the heavy iron and steel industry in the lake ports of Cleveland, Toledo and Detroit, and at the inland cities of Akron, Youngstown and Hamilton. Blast furnaces are just as numerous on the southern shore of Lake Michigan at Chicago and Gary.

The availability of vast quantities of finished steel, plus a huge market and excellent transportation facilities, were major facts in the development of the second most important industry in the Middle West — the making of automobiles and trucks. Although Detroit is the big centre, largely because it was here that Henry Ford developed mass production methods, a dozen other cities in the area either manufacture or assemble automobiles, notably Flint, Pontiac, Lansing, Cleveland, Toledo and Milwaukee. Extreme subdivision of labour, assembly-line techniques, improved road networks, the high wages of the average employee in the United States and a plentiful supply of petroleum have all contributed to the phenomenal growth of the motor industry — from something like 180,000 cars and 6,000 trucks in 1910, to 7,000,000 cars and 1,200,000 trucks in 1960. This in turn has stimulated a host of other industries making not only iron and steel but upholstery materials, copper, lead, aluminium, rubber tyres, wire, and all the other components that go into a car or truck. One out of every seven people in the United States makes his living from the motor industry or one of its related manufacturing industries.

It would be difficult to exaggerate the influence of the automobile on American ways of life. Farmers far from railroads and rivers take their produce to market by truck. People who live in rural areas drive fifty or sixty miles to the nearest city to shop or lunch with friends. Children in isolated communities are picked up by buses and brought home by buses and can thus attend bigger and better schools. Families can travel long distances for a vacation far more cheaply than by rail or air. Those who dislike the big city atmosphere, but have to work there, can live in quiet suburbs and drive into town and out again each day — thereby creating frustrating traffic problems at rush hours in and around all major cities in the nation, despite myriads of intricately interlaced six and eight lane parkways and thruways. With nearly 90,000,000 cars and trucks for a population of about 192 million, it is obvious that the American is the most mobile creature on earth (in all the rest of the world there are only some 40 million cars and trucks).

Other major industries in the Middle West include the manufacture of machinery, especially electrical and agricultural; machine tools; meat-packing; flour-milling; electrical equipment; chemical products; and petroleum-refining. Although the oil deposits of Ohio, Indiana, Illinois, and Michigan are not among the nation's major fields, they are far from unimportant. In short, the Middle West is superior to any other in the United States for the volume and variety of its industrial production.

Not surprisingly, urban centres are numerous here, and some are more impressive for the extent of their factories and workers' suburbs than for their public buildings or the charm of their town planning. However, in the last decade several cities, notably Pittsburgh and Detroit, have initiated long-term planning schemes, which include replacing dark tenement apartments with airy tall ones surrounded by parks and malls, broadening streets, erecting skyscrapers overlooking lakes and rivers, and building civic centres of ultra-modern design. Commercial firms, such as General Motors and Ford, are responsible for several of the most interesting and most beautiful new structures.

*Chicago*. The main city of the Middle West is Chicago, the nation's third-ranking metropolitan area in population and industrial production; the chief railway terminus in the country, with twenty-seven routes of twenty companies; the nation's largest slaughterhouse of cattle and pigs; a great producer of flour, meat, and beer, iron and steel, machinery, ploughs and tractors, furniture, canned foods and fertilizers. It stretches along the shore of Lake Michigan for more than thirty miles, and its 3,500,000 inhabitants, or more than 6,200,000 in the metropolitan area, are a typical American mixture of peoples: descendants of English, Germans and Scandinavians living mainly near the lake in the more prosperous areas; Negroes in the southern section; and between them Irish, Southern Europeans, Jews and Slavs. A line of skyscrapers faces the lake and many others tower over the city — Chicago, like New York though on a less extensive scale, is engaged in a building spree, and is erecting several interesting modern-style buildings, of which it is very proud. It also takes pride in its art museum, concerts and universities. It was at the University of Chicago that Enrico Fermi and his associates achieved the first controlled nuclear chain reaction of atomic energy in 1942.

Chicago has often dreamed of overtaking and replacing New York as a city and port, and now that the Great Lakes are open to ocean navigation it may become the nerve centre of the continent, as it is already its centre of gravity. The port of Chicago now handles about 22 million tons of goods a year, a sizable share of which comes from or is destined for the markets of European and other overseas countries.

Other important cities in the Middle West include Minneapolis, in Minnesota, with large flour mills, and St Paul, its twin and rival, concentrating on slaughtering and meat-preserving. Farther south is St Louis, located at the point where the Missouri River joins the Mississippi, which grew up as a fur-trading post and jumping-off spot for those bound farther west. After the railroads came, it continued to grow and compete with Chicago for agricultural

MEXICO: Market scene

produce from both the Middle West and the Great
Plains. With its suburbs it has a population of nearly
2 million. Kansas City, at the confluence of the Missouri and its tributary the Kansas River, also depends
on the surrounding rich agricultural lands, and is a
major meat-packing and flour-milling centre.

Undoubtedly the whole of the Middle West has
been increasingly influenced by the opening of the
St Lawrence Seaway. Even the most cautious are
expecting bigger increases in trade on this 'fourth sea-
coast'; larger docks and warehouses are being built
in a number of ports, and missions are being sent
inland and abroad to Europe to seek new markets
and sources of raw materials.

*The Great Plains.* Industry gives way to agriculture in
the Great Plains, which stretch at an altitude of between 1,500 and 4,000 feet clear across the country,
from the Canadian border to the Gulf of Mexico
between the Middle West, the South and the Rocky
Mountains. The skyline stretches to the horizon. Here,
indeed, one has a sense of space—the farms are more
widely spaced, the straight and lonely roads seem to
lead nowhere, you can drive for a hundred miles
without seeing a filling station, or even a man or a
horse. Eventually the approach to the Rockies is indicated by rocky peaks or true mountain masses like
the wooded Black hills of South Dakota. Everywhere farming is closely dependent on the rainfall,
which averages only some 10 to 20 inches a year and
is unreliable. The mountain barrier to the west creates
a rainshadow, and the moist tropical air masses from
the Gulf of Mexico that come up the Mississippi
valley swerve eastward toward the Atlantic except
during the spring and early summer. At this time of
year, rains often occur in sudden violent storms.
Drought, hail, and in the north frost and snow are
other problems facing the Prairie farmer. Ground
water has been tapped increasingly for irrigation and
cattle-watering holes, in places to a point where the
withdrawal of water exceeds the annual replenishment,
a serious situation, particularly in the Texas Great
Plains.

The cattle era on the Great Plains, in the nineteenth
century, has been celebrated in so many books and
radio and television plays that it has made the American cowboy a legend throughout the world. He was
indeed an intrepid individual, living a lonely, dangerous life, especially in the early days of hostile
Indians and unfenced open ranges, and even as late
as the 1870's and 1880's, when he took his great herds
over the long treks from Texas to Dodge City and
Abilene for slaughter or shipment eastward on the
newly built transcontinental railways. The arrival of
swarms of farmers, the use of barbed-wire to limit
rangelands and control breeding, overgrazing and
overstocking, bitter disputes between sheepmen,
farmers and cattlemen, plus a disastrous blizzard
were all factors which conspired against the traditional
cowboy.

Today, ranching is the principal activity in the
western higher margins of the Great Plains: sheep
producing high-quality wool and meat in the hilly
areas where rainfall is lowest and grass cover thinner,
and beef in the better-watered, more grassy parts of
Texas, Nebraska and Montana. Careful breeding, improved grasses, controlled grazing, the aid of trailer

A cattle market in Omaha.
The Prairie farmer
has many problems:
he is closely dependent on an
unreliable rainfall,
and had also to cope with
drought, hail, frost and snow.
However, ranching is the
principal activity in this region,
and in all, some 25 million cattle
are slaughtered every year
in the U.S.

trucks and all sorts of other machinery, and the shipping of animals to the Corn Belt for fattening, are
all typical of most ranches in the Great Plains, even
of the very large ones in Texas—and many are
very large by any standards. The King Ranch is bigger
than the state of Rhode Island. Another, the Matador
Ranch, covers 800,000 acres. In all, in the United
States, some 25 million cattle are slaughtered each
year—an indication of the high protein content of
the average American's diet.

The amount of wheat grown in the Great Plains is
equally impressive: spring wheat in the north, mainly
in the Dakotas, which have long severe winters;
winter wheat in Nebraska, Kansas, eastern Colorado,
Oklahoma and northern Texas. Of these, North
Dakota leads in the output of spring wheat, Kansas
in that of winter wheat. By ploughing the fertile
chestnut or brown soils after every shower so that
the moisture sinks in, by alternating cultivating and
fallow periods, by using machines on a large scale,
the Great Plains wheat farmers manage to grow nearly
three-quarters of the nation's wheat. They do not
attempt to achieve high yields per acre. Rather they
try to reduce as much as possible the amount of
labour per acre, and in this they have been extraordinarily successful, the average now being, for
ploughing, planting, and harvesting an acre of wheat,
only 2 hours of man labour and $1\frac{1}{2}$ hours of tractor
labour.

In the northern part of the Great Plains, the rivers
swollen by melting snow permit irrigated cultivation
of alfalfa and sugar-beet. In the south, drought-
resistant sorghum, used as a winter feed for cattle,
and some irrigated cotton are grown.

It is in the semi-arid Great Plains, relatively humid
for a few years and then struck by prolonged droughts,
that the American farmer has encountered disaster
again and again. Over-optimistic, he has ploughed
thousands of acres that should have been left in grass,
and grazed too closely thousands of other acres.

EXICO: Donkeys used as beasts of burden near Oaxaca.          Lush vegetation outside Acapulco.

Exhausted soil has become sand and blown away in enormous duststorms. In this way whole counties have been changed to near-desert. The most serious and widespread droughts occurred in the 1930's and, coinciding with low grain prices and high farm indebtedness, resulted in a mass emigration. Again between 1950 and 1958 prolonged droughts occurred, especially in the central and southern parts of the area.

However, in the meantime a full programme of soil conservation has been undertaken by the Federal Government: much land has been returned to pasture, and conservation measures have been initiated. Nevertheless discouraged farmers are leaving the Great Plains. The population fluctuates from year to year, and is not increasing anything like as fast as in some other parts of the country. There is a general decrease in the number of farms, an increase in their size, and an appreciable migration from farms to towns. These are mostly small centres that grew up as farm markets, in which slaughtering, canning and flour-milling are the chief industries.

THE WEST. In the Rocky Mountain foothills begins the highest, the most rugged, and driest region of the United States. It was the last to be explored and settled, and is by far the least populated. For a long time mining was the chief attraction in these awesome lands, which the pioneers crossed as quickly as possible to reach the better-watered, more hospitable Pacific coast.

*The eastern border.* The boundaries of the four large states of Montana, Wyoming, Colorado and New Mexico, astride the Rocky Mountains, are almost everywhere formed by the lines of latitude and longitude, as they are in many Western states. Montana, adjoining Canada, experiences winters of blizzard and bitter cold, worthy of eastern Siberia, whereas New Mexico in the south is extremely hot and dry. All four states have scanty and unreliable rainfall, so that crops cannot be cultivated regularly unless they are irrigated, and the sheep and cattle ranches have to be very extensive because of the poor quality and scarceness of the grass.

More copper has probably been taken from the deposits at Butte in Montana than from any other deposit in the world, and a great deal of silver, zinc, lead and gold has come from this district. Deposits of oil and bituminous coal have been discovered and exploited. In fact this state has experienced a succession of booms and declines as new mines have been discovered or old ones exhausted. Wyoming would probably be almost empty were it not for the extension of these coal and oil deposits, but its most obvious natural resource is the beauty and strangeness of its volcanic scenery, the most remarkable examples of which can be seen in Yellowstone National Park. Here, in a setting of high snow-covered mountains, in an area of 3,400 square miles, more than twice the size of the English county of Kent, is as wonderful a collection of geysers, hot springs, mudlakes, canyons, waterfalls, living and petrified forests, and wild animals as could be imagined.

Yellowstone is only one of a dozen National Parks in the West. Others equally fascinating and awe-inspiring are Glacier in northern Montana; Rocky Mountain and Mesa Verde in Colorado; the Carlsbad Caverns in southern New Mexico; the Grand Canyon in Arizona; Bryce and Zion in Utah; Kings Canyon, Yosemite and Lassen Volcanic in California; Crater Lake in Oregon; and Olympic and Mount Rainier in Washington. These parks have been set aside to preserve some of the most remarkable natural features of this remarkably varied and spectacular landscape.

Colorado has the highest mountains in the Rockies; several dozen of them rise to between 13,000 and 14,500 feet above sea level. It also has dense forests, and the largest supplies of water for irrigation, which is used to cultivate various crops, such as wheat, fodder crops, potatoes and sugar-beet. A great variety of minerals has been discovered here, and in earlier days the state experienced several mining 'rushes'. Today the principal minerals extracted are gold at Cripple Creek, lead and zinc at Leadville, and molybdenum at Climax, said to be the largest molybdenum mine in the world. Big deposits of carnotite ores, which are rich in uranium, have been found on the Colorado Plateau (western Colorado, eastern Utah, north-eastern Arizona, and north-western New Mexico). In the 1940's the sudden demand for uranium set off here one of the most feverish metal rushes in history, by thousands of professional prospectors and many thousands of eager amateurs.

Mining and sugar-refining stimulated the growth of Denver, which has 494,000 inhabitants; other contributing factors have been its central position at the approaches to the Rockies, and its sunny climate, cool in summer, provides excellent ski-ing conditions in the winter.

New Mexico owes its distinctiveness to the successful development of a Spanish-Indian civilisation, relics of which can be seen in the centuries-old pueblos, such as those near Santa Fe. Santa Fe is a beautifully located city on a high, wide plateau surrounded by higher ranges, where the clear atmosphere produces dramatic lighting effects on the rose-coloured mesas. The state's economy is based mainly on the agricultural lands of its irrigated valleys its sheep and cattle ranches, mammoth deposits of low-grade copper, and the tourist trade.

*The heart of the uplands.* The four states of Idaho, Utah, Nevada and Arizona, situated west of the highest Rocky Mountains, occupy a complex region of plateaus and canyons, isolated ranges and depressions, lava flows and enclosed basins, which make up the largest and most desolate mountain mass in the United States. The most characteristic features of this territory are a sparse population and aridity and barrenness everywhere except on the higher land and the irrigated lowlands. Scrub vegetation covers large areas with coarse tufted grass.

On the mountain slopes of Idaho there are fine forests, and on the irrigated lands potatoes, sugar-beet and vegetables are cultivated. It is mining, however, particularly of zinc, lead and silver at Coeur d'Alene that has attracted most people to the state. Utah is equally important for lead and zinc, and more important for copper, found in Bingham Canyon. The presence of coal and iron ore has fostered an iron and steel industry which sends its products out to western markets. The skill, hard work and enthusiasm of the Mormons has turned the area around

Salt Lake City into a huge irrigated oasis of fields of vegetables, sugar-beet, hay and alfalfa, as well as orchards and pastures. Salt Lake City is an important financial and commercial as well as a religious and political centre, and Great Salt Lake, which gave it its name, is a remnant of huge, ancient Lake Bonneville; it covers now an area of 1,500 square miles, making it the largest body of water west of the Mississippi. Salt has been extracted from it from the earliest days: the water has a salinity of 25 per cent, or eight times that of the ocean.

Nevada is the most sparsely populated state in the Union, with only 285,000 people dispersed in some fifty settlements over an area larger than the United Kingdom. There are some extensive cattle and sheep ranches and a few irrigated patches around Reno, but drought is an ever-present problem. The empty spaces, consisting mainly of sand dunes and salt pans, are, however, being used to some extent today—as atomic testing grounds. The gold and silver mines are still productive, but their heyday is over. Laws favourable to quick divorces have brought notoriety and some wealth to Reno, while Las Vegas, where gambling of all kinds is unrestricted and every motel has a swimming pool, attracts pleasure-seekers from southern California.

On the boundary between Nevada and Arizona lies one of the largest hydro-electric and flood control projects in the United States, Hoover Dam on the Colorado River, and farther downstream are three other dams: Davies, Parker and Imperial. Together these dams have transformed the once unruly and dangerous river into an economic resource of the first order. In all, some 900,000 acres of once empty, dry, useless land in southern Arizona and southern California are now being irrigated and producing two or more crops a year of cotton, alfalfa, vegetables, citrus fruits, dates and sugar-beet. Water from the Colorado and hydro-electric power from the Hoover and Parker Dams are even being carried by aqueducts and transmission lines as far as Los Angeles, California, which has for many years been engaged in an uphill struggle to keep pace with its ever-growing need for both.

Arizona is considered one of the most attractive of the Western states, known for the grandeur of its landscape, especially the Grand Canyon of the Colorado River, for the invigorating healthiness of its dry, sunny climate, its spectacular sunsets, its fascinating ancient Spanish mission churches, and its thirty Indian tribes. The Gila River Project, of which Yuma is the centre, and the Salt River Project near Phoenix, have created extensive irrigated areas where, with plenty of sushine and a year-round growing season, citrus fruits, vegetables, cotton and alfalfa are produced. Mining, especially of copper, is a big source of revenue (Arizona produces about half of the country's total copper output). Tucson, Phoenix, and several other cities in Arizona are growing rapidly, as are several in Nevada. Both of these states are experiencing a boom in population, which is seriously depleting the supply of underground water.

*The Pacific coastlands. Seattle and Portland.* In the last half-century the Pacific region has developed more rapidly than any other part of the United States, both in the size of its population and in economic activity.

When the three states of Washington, Oregon and California are considered together, they show a population density lower than the average for the country. But thirty years ago their total population was only one-twentieth of that of the Union; today it is more than one-tenth. Their importance in the nation's economic life has increased even more.

The prevailing winds from the Pacific bring to the coastal parts of Washington and Oregon a gentle persistent rain reminiscent of Scotland or Ireland. Farther south, in California, the rainfall decreases and there is a well-defined dry period in summer; the summers are hotter and the winters warmer. The temperate climate of San Francisco gives way in Los Angeles and San Diego to the Mediterranean, or rather Moroccan, type of climate, with very low humidity and perennially clear skies.

Marked differences in relief cause many variations in local climates. Sea influence is soon restricted by the relatively low Coast Range, which receives heavy rainfall and is densely forested. Inland, behind this

The Hoover Dam on the Colorado River, on the Nevada-Arizona border, is one of many vast constructions for harnessing the natural resources of North America. It is 726 feet high, the total capacity of its reservoir, Lake Mead, is just over 30 million acre-feet and its generating capacity is 1,345,000 kW. Farther east, the Tennessee Valley Authority features similar construction, providing electricity for vast areas in surrounding states.

range, three long valleys divided by volcanic intrusions extend from the Canadian border to Mexico. The northern section, the Puget-Willamette lowland, has abundant rainfall and is linked to the Pacific by Puget Sound, an arm of the sea, and by the estuary of the Columbia River. The central section, called the Central Valley, easily the largest, has only one outlet to the Pacific—the Golden Gate, which opens into San Fransico Bay—and the southern portion of this valley gets so little rain that crops cannot be grown without irrigation. The third section, the Imperial Valley, is near the border and extends into Mexico, and was a desert until water from the Colorado River was brought in. Death Valley, north of the Imperial Valley, is one of the hottest and driest and most desolate places on earth.

These discontinuous lowlands are overshadowed by high mountains, old rejuvenated massifs above which rise volcanic outcrops or recent folds such as the Cascade Range in the north and the Sierra Nevada in the south, which present a barrier more than 13,000 feet high to the moisture-laden winds from the ocean. The heavy rain and snowfall on these ranges produce magnificent forests, mostly coniferous, and including some giant Sequoias, and in California feed the multitude of streams and irrigation canals without which most of the state would be completely arid and uncultivable.

Farther east, beyond these ranges, there is practically no rain, except in the Columbia River valley of Washington, which is less cut off from the ocean. Elsewhere the finest forests in the world suddenly give way to thorn bushes and soon to the barren lands characteristic of Nevada. At least half of southern California shares the desert conditions of Arizona. The eastern half of Oregon is little better provided for than the thirsty lands of Idaho. The Pacific coastlands are narrow, ending in the line of high ranges which form a divide between water and near-desert, between crops and bare soil, between abundance of all kinds and parched desolation.

In coastal Washington and Oregon, the most valuable of nature's gifts is the soft, steady rain during the mild winters and cool summers, rain which waters a Japanese type of landscape round the shore of Puget Sound. Snow-covered volcanic heights, like Mount Rainier, 14,408 feet high, tower above the dense forests of Douglas fir, western hemlock, Sitka spruce and western red cedar, while lower down is a maze of islands, peninsulas, channels, and bays, and, in the Willamette valley, orchards, fields of hay and oats, poultry farms, and meadows full of dairy cattle. It was in this beautiful and imposing setting that a small lumbering settlement became the outfitting port for the miners who set out to seek gold in Alaska and the Yukon, and in a little over half a century developed into a major port and commercial centre. This was Seattle, now a busy port which trades with Alaska, Hawaii, Japan, South America and the Atlantic coast of the United States, exporting wheat from the interior plateaus, notably the Columbia, usually referred to as the Columbia basin, quantities of timber from the surrounding mountains, and apples and other fruits from the orchards, and importing furs, silks, petroleum and salmon. Seattle is also an industrial city, building ships and making aircraft

chemicals, pulp and paper and furniture, and canning fish.

Portland on the Columbia River, the chief port and city of Oregon, also depends on the export of wheat, timber, fruit and salmon: it specialises in trade with the Far East and through the Panama Canal with New York. One of its chief attractions is Mount Hood, an extinct snow-capped volcano nearby.

The Columbia basin, which extends into Idaho along the Snake River, is one of the major dry-farming areas in the United States, the main crop being wheat; and its irrigated lowlands, producing alfalfa, hay, sugar-beet, beans, and the famed Idaho potato, are among the most extensive in North America. Irrigation has been made possible here thanks to the Columbia Basin Project, particularly Grand Coulee Dam and Lake Roosevelt, which now water some 600,000 acres and will eventually irrigate 1,200,000 acres. In addition, Grand Coulee and the other dams built on the river together possess a hydro-electric capacity of 5,562,000 kWh, and four new dams are planned or are under construction.

*San Francisco and Los Angeles.* The Sacramento and San Joaquin Rivers, which flow across the Central Valley of California in opposite directions, join together to enter San Francisco Bay, forming a natural outlet for the wealth of all the lands they irrigate, lands producing fruit, vegetables, meat, cotton and rice, and some of the best wines made in the United States. San Francisco is a great port exporting canned fish, cotton, rice, iron and steel goods, and petroleum products, and importing petroleum, manufactured articles, coffee, tea, cacao, raw sugar, pineapples, bananas, wool, Manila hemp, newsprint and rubber; it is also a big manufacturing centre for iron and steel, chemicals, electronic equipment, automobiles and machine tools.

The city, perched on the hills which lie between the ocean and the bay, was founded in 1776 as a Spanish mission, one of nearly twenty established in California during the 1700's. In 1848, when gold was discovered nearby, setting off the biggest Gold Rush in history, San Francisco still had fewer than a thousand inhabitants. Two years later it had 35,000; and by 1870, 150,000. Today it has more than 740,000 inhabitants and if the numerous cities on the bay which come within its orbit are included (the industrial community of Oakland, the university town of Berkeley, the fruit-canning centre of San Jose, and many others), the total population is nearly 4 million, roughly one-quarter of the state's population. For many decades San Francisco was the undisputed capital of the West, often called 'Queen of the Pacific', being first in finance, commerce, industry and cultural activities. Although its rate of growth has now slowed, it is likely to remain a queen, a city which takes great pleasure in its opera, theatres, concerts, museums of art, universities, and superlative setting; a city of great charm with a cosmopolitan atmosphere rare in the United States with the exception, of course, of New York City.

In 1960, the population of the city of Los Angeles was 2,479,015; Los Angeles County had 5,979,203 inhabitants, and the metropolitan area (Los Angeles and Orange Counties) had 6,683,563. Sixty out of every hundred Californians are grouped around these two large cities, San Francisco and Los Angeles, and if San Diego, a naval and commercial port near the Mexican border, is added, then two out of three Californians live in or near the three main centres and ports in the state. The importance and intensity of this fast urban growth is both a result and a cause of the rapid rise in the political and economic power of California.

Los Angeles, a small Spanish market town founded in 1781, was neglected in the Gold Rush, but suddenly began to come to life in 1876, when the Southern Pacific Railroad completed a line linking it with San Francisco, thus providing a roundabout route for shipping oranges and other produce to eastern markets. The city experienced its first boom in the middle 1880's, when the Santa Fe Railroad reached it. In the 1890's oil was discovered nearby and the California Fruit Growers' Exchange organised nationwide distribution of Californian citrus fruit. In the first two decades of the 1900's, the population of Los Angeles quadrupled, largely as a result of the rising output of oranges and petroleum and the migration from New York of the motion picture industry. A breakwater was constructed in San Pedro Bay to form a harbour, and an inter-urban transportation system was established to link the city with the surrounding agricultural land.

When water from the Los Angeles, San Gabriel and Santa Ana Rivers became inadequate for city and irrigation needs, a 338-mile aqueduct was built to bring in Owens River water from the eastern face of the Sierra Nevada. During the 1920's, the motion picture and allied industries and those making oil-well machinery continued to grow; new oilfields were discovered; and several water-deficient communities joined the city in order to obtain more water. The most extraordinary growth in the city, however, has taken place since the 1940's.

With 800,000 employed in manufacturing, metropolitan Los Angeles is becoming the nation's second industrial centre. Older industries such as food processing, car assembly, shipbuilding and the making of rubber goods have expanded tremendously, as have those manufacturing steel, machinery, petroleum products, soap, petro-chemicals and plastics. The production of motion pictures, radio and television shows has in turn stimulated the industries making clothing, cosmetics and jewellery. Many aircraft plants that were built during or just after the war have converted to rockets and missiles, and associated with missiles has been the growth of the electronics industry and research and development firms. Thousands of new factories are turning out consumer goods to satisfy the rapidly growing local market, which includes a large number of elderly retired people who have come from all over the country to settle and enjoy the ideal conditions — clear skies and consistently mild temperatures.

As the city has grown into a sprawling metropolis including a hundred or more agglomerations, its water and power problems have again and again become acute, in spite of a second 300-mile aqueduct built to tap water from the Colorado River at Parker Dam, and transmission lines built from the Owens River and Hoover Dams, 260 and 266 miles long respectively, to bring in hydro-electricity. The California

Bayshore Freeway, San Franscisco.

Row crop irrigation in the western United States. The Sacramento and San Joaquin rivers flow across California in opposite directions, irrigating immense tracts of land that produce fruit, vegetables, cotton, rice and wines.

Water Plan of 1957, still under development, will bring in water from as far away as the western slopes of the northern Sierra Nevada, and construction of several new dams, including one on the Feather River, has begun.

Water has been a major problem, too, throughout the southern part of the Central Valley, a flat valley blessed with fertile alluvial soils and a mild climate, which has become one of the greatest agricultural regions in the world. The problem is how to conserve water derived from the heavy snowfalls in the Sierra Nevada Mountains and fed into the many tributaries of the Sacramento River in the north for use in the very dry southern summer. The main purpose of a huge project, known as the Central Valley Project, has been to bring surplus water from the northern half of the valley to the deficient southern half. Five large dams constructed on the Sacramento and San Joaquin Rivers or their tributaries, and an impressive system of canals, pumping stations, hydro-electric stations, and distribution channels hundreds of miles

A farmer in Ohio examines wheat to decide whether it is time to harvest. Extensive cultivation is the general rule in the midwest, mechanisation is highly developed, and the farms widely separated.

California has a wide range of crops, for its climate varies considerably from north to south. It is known for the quality of its citrus fruit, which is exported all over America and to Europe.
Cultivation is largely mechanised and some orange plantations cover 2,000 acres.
The photograph shows an orange grove in southern California. The smudge pots or oil burners between the rows are lit at night to protect the fruit from frost.

long, now provide irrigation water during the dry summer season. It is the 8 million acres, thus brought under irrigation that make California the leading state in the Union in the variety and value of farm produce. Among the chief crops in the Sacramento section of the valley are sugar-beet, asparagus, tomatoes and other vegetables, rice, wheat, barley, olives, alfalfa and clover for beef and dairy cattle, and grapes for wine or for sale dried or fresh. Vineyards are also a typical feature of the farmland in the San Joaquin section. But even more typical here are citrus fruits, figs, olives, peaches, plums, nuts, avocados, all sorts of vegetables, dairy and poultry farms, and cotton. California has become the leading cotton-producing state outside the Cotton Belt. Besides farming there are several other industries in the Central Valley, notably the extraction of oil and natural gas.

A great deal of cotton is also raised in the Imperial and Coachella valleys, which are south of Death Valley and the Mojave Desert, two of the driest and

hottest spots on earth. Sixty years ago the Imperial and Coachella valleys were uninhabited; today, the Colorado River water irrigates thousands of acres of cotton, truck crops, citrus fruits, dates, flax and sugar-beet.

## ECONOMY OF THE UNITED STATES

AGRICULTURAL LIFE: THE DECLINE IN FARM POPULATION. At the time of the First World War, 32 million Americans, nearly one-third of the population, lived off the land by cultivation or stock-raising; today there are not more than 22 million living on farms, of whom only 14 million are actually farmers, or only 8 per cent of the total population; and concurrently the proportion of land in farms of one thousand acres or more has increased from 25 to nearly 50 per cent. The value of agricultural production, which represented one-tenth of the national income in 1929, is barely one-twentieth today. And yet the country is suffering chronically from agricultural surpluses.

A fundamental principle has been the reduction of costs through labour-saving machinery. The aim has been to seek from the land, of which there is plenty, not the highest yield but the greatest possible profit. For example, on the relatively new lands of the West, it is more profitable to be satisfied with a rather modest yield per acre, and even to leave half the cultivated land fallow each year and so economise on labour and fertilizers. The yield per acre is about two-thirds to one-half as large as in Great Britain or France, but on average at one-third the cost; on balance, the result is a considerable profit to the American farmer.

Extensive farming of this type is the usual practice on the corn and spring- and winter- wheat farms in the Middle West and Great Plains, where land is plentiful. A degree of mechanisation and specialisation has been achieved here that is almost industrial. In the older rural parts of the South, properties are much more split up, and they are cultivated by farmers and Negro share-croppers of small means, using more traditional methods. In California and the Northeast, the dairy, market-gardening and fruit-growing farms are generally fairly small and methods are more intensive.

*A more rational use of the land.* For a long time the use of the land was left entirely to the individual. It was not until towards the end of the nineteenth century, when farmers were moving into the semi-arid lands of the West, that the Federal Government began to show concern about land use. And it was not until the 1930's that the Government sounded a serious warning about hurried exploitation without fertilizers or proper care, under which the most fertile loams were in danger of being turned to sand and picked up by the wind and rivers and carried away, leaving behind a bare and unproductive soil for future generations.

At the present time there are a number of official agencies devoted to the development of irrigation in the dry lands of the West, the drainage of swampy areas, especially those of the Mississippi valley, the struggle against soil erosion by regularising the flow of rivers and practising a suitable crop rotation, the

provision of cheap fertilizers, and the dissemination of technical advice to farmers.

President Roosevelt's administration was notably enterprising in this respect. It was responsible for the economic redevelopment of the Tennessee valley by means of the giant TVA Project, which was so successful that it became well known throughout the world as an example of what could be achieved by large-scale planning and development over an area of many thousands of square miles. Between 1933, when the project began its work, and 1961, the income per head in the valley increased over nine times, while the average income per head for the country as a whole increased less than six times.

For more than thirty years official and private agencies have also been fighting against excessive specialisation, which is harmful to the conservation of the soil and obviously in the long run harmful to the interests of the farmer, who must depend on often severe and unforseeable fluctuations in the world price of his one and only crop. There has consequently been persistent and largely successful encouragement of diversification of crops. Flax, formerly almost unknown in the United States, made its appearance in rotation with spring-wheat about 1935, and within five years its acreage had doubled. Sugar-beet is being grown more and more with oats, in California and especially Colorado. Soya beans have been introduced into the Corn Belt, with a 50 per cent increase in acreage between 1948 and 1958, and peanuts are widely grown in the Cotton Belt, thus providing new sources of vegetable oil. Cattle-raising has increased steadily in the Cotton Belt. The volume of production of the traditional crops, corn, wheat and cotton, is stable or even declining slightly in favour of other crops which are capable of yielding equally good profits.

*The main crops and stock-farming.* The United States nevertheless remains easily the leading producer of corn, with about half of the world's crop; it produces one-quarter of the world's crop of cotton, the cultivation of which is becoming more and more important in Texas and California under irrigation, and is decreasing in the Old South; it produces nearly 30 per cent of the world's tobacco crop, which comes mainly from North Carolina and Kentucky. Its wheat production, which varies considerably from year to year, is second only to that of the U.S.S.R., and it still produces on average almost as much as the next two countries combined, China and Canada. The rice and sugar-cane raised on the tropical lands bordering the Gulf of Mexico, however, are far from satisfying home consumption. On the other hand, the production of vegetables and fruits is adequate for the most varied and extensive demands. California is by far the leading state for grapes (especially dessert grapes), lemons and peaches, and Florida for oranges. In all, the United States has enough to eat its fill and quench its thirst, producing almost all its requirements apart from certain tropical products such as cane sugar, coffee, tea and cocoa. Coffee, which is drunk in large quantities, forms with sugar the largest food import.

Dairy-farming tends to predominate near the great urban centres of the Atlantic coast and the Great Lakes, which are heavy consumers of milk and milk products, though butter consumption has fallen by a

half during the last twenty years, to the benefit of margarine and other fats of vegetable origin. On the other hand, the consumption of meat has increased by 20 per cent compared with pre-war days. The meat-producing animals, cattle and pigs especially, are reared mainly in the Corn Belt and the surrounding country, and large numbers of cattle reared on the Great Plains of the semi-arid West are sent there for fattening. The huge flocks of sheep on the Great Plains and in the Rockies are reared for their excellent wool and meat. Poultry and eggs are important in the American diet, and here again the Corn Belt is the chief source. Horses are still used as beasts of burden in the Middle West and the West, and mules in the South, but they are disappearing in the face of increased mechanisation. In 1920 there were 22 million horses and 250,000 tractors; today more tractors than horses are used—over 4.5 million compared with less than 3.6 million.

The United States has far more pigs (56 million) than any other country in the world, with the single

Contour ploughing such as is practised in the eastern states and in Oklahoma, where the relatively high rainfall and undulating countryside make it necessary to combat soil erosion by ploughing along the contour lines. The varied landscape contrasts with that of the great midwest plains, and with its groups of farms and clumps of trees is reminiscent of certain rural landscapes in Europe.

exception of China, and is first in numbers of beef and milk cattle; it is only eighth in the world list, however, for the numbers of sheep. A whole army of experts is engaged in applying the latest scientific techniques in stock-raising and in arable farming in order to obtain the highest possible return.

The most difficult problem is to ensure the sale of agricultural produce, both regularly and at an adequate price for the farmers. The latter complain that their interests are frequently sacrificed for the benefit of the industrial workers and people of the towns, who are anxious to obtain their food at the lowest possible prices; while the people on the land have to buy manufactured products which become more and more expensive as the workmen's wages increase. This complaint is a familiar one and has been heard since the days of early Rome, but it is a fact that the rural population benefits less from American prosperity than the urban population.

The fisheries and forests, the first resources to be developed by the Indians and white pioneers, continue to be large sources of revenue. Here again the early attitude was to make unrestricted profit from these supposedly inexhaustible resources. However, for more than half a century now steps have been taken to conserve, replace and improve them. The finest forests and their best commercial development are to be seen in the humid sections of the Northwest, in the states of Washington and Oregon. The chief fishing grounds lie, as they always did, off the shores of New England and farther south between New York and Chesapeake Bay, in the Gulf of Mexico, and in the Pacific Ocean round Puget Sound and off San Francisco. The United States does not produce enough wood products and fish for its own requirements, and imports considerable quantities, chiefly from Canada.

INDUSTRIAL TECHNIQUES. Though a great agricultural producer, the United States is an even greater industrial power, one of the most important industrial powers of today.

It owes this importance to its abundance of fuels, minerals, and other raw materials, and to American ingenuity. Since the times of the early pioneers, labour has always been expensive and in short supply relative to the needs of development. The main problem of industry, even more acute than in agriculture, has been to make maximum use of manpower by providing it with increasingly efficient machinery, and by so organising production that all loss of time and energy is avoided. This concern gave rise to the famous Taylor system, a system of scientific management for reducing manufacturing costs initiated by Frederick Taylor, an American efficiency engineer. For half a century the system has constantly been improved and elaborated, notably by Henry Ford and a host of other industrialists. It is applied in nearly all industries and especially in engineering. It gives very high returns, and consequently relatively low manufacturing costs.

These persistent efforts towards economy have also resulted in mass production with a limited number of models, as this helps to keep down overhead costs; it has led, too, to the formation of large firms able to undertake continual research into new and more efficient methods. Although Trusts, consisting of a number of similar firms under unified control, were condemned by public opinion and the law towards the end of the nineteenth century, some continue to exist in different form, and today they are more often looked upon as useful organisations for industrial progress.

The trade unions, which are wealthy and powerful, have become almost middle class. Differences are often settled by a compromise acceptable to all parties, rather than by strikes. Nevertheless, some strikes have lasted for several months, as in the steel industry in 1959, which shows that fundamental differences did exist.

A new class has developed between the owners and the workers; this consists of directors and experts concerned above all with the continuity and growth of national production; they are opposed to strikes as well as to inflation and unemployment. These men from all social backgrounds are trained to understand human relations just as much as financial and technical problems. They are an important new element in the American economy and are playing an increasing rôle in the formulation of social and economic policies.

*Sources of power.* The United States is the world's largest producer of petroleum, natural gas and electricity, and the second largest producer of coal.

Plentiful though it is, coal is rather more representative of the past than the future: in 1920 it provided 78 per cent of all American power, today it provides 26 per cent. Its use and production are decreasing, especially the anthracite of Pennsylvania. However, the United States remains a chief world producer, slightly behind the U.S.S.R., and produces some 25 per cent of world output. The chief fields are on the western slopes of the Appalachians, from Pennsylvania to Alabama and including Ohio, West Virginia (the largest producer) and Kentucky. Exports account for nearly one-tenth of production, and they are sent mainly from Hampton Roads in Virginia, which specialises in this trade, to Canada, South America and Europe.

At present, petroleum is the main source of American power; it provided 13 per cent in 1920 and provides 42 per cent today. Natural gas with which it is associated yielded 4 per cent of the power in 1920 and yields 29 per cent today. The bulk of these two products comes from the states in the southern half of the Mississippi lowland: Kansas, Oklahoma, Louisiana, and especially Texas, which alone produces 40 per cent of the natural gas and 40 to 45 per cent of the petroleum of the whole country. Californian petroleum production is barely a third of that of Texas, and it is a long way behind it for natural gas. The United States almost has a monopoly of the world's natural gas production, with 88 per cent of the total. Its share of world petroleum production has fallen from 66 per cent in 1945 to 35 per cent now; this quantity, though enormous, is still insufficient to meet requirements, and nearly one-eighth of the total consumption is imported from Venezuela and the Middle East. As for reserves, at the current rate of consumption they will be exhausted in about twenty years; but wells are being drilled deeper and deeper, and exploitation of the offshore deposits in the Gulf of Mexico and the Pacific has hardly begun;

besides, in twenty years' time there may be new sources of power. Whatever the future, today thousands of miles of pipeline distribute crude oil, refined products and natural gas to all the large industrial centres in the country.

Electricity is important now and will certainly remain so in the future, for its applications are continually being increased, not only for the myriads of household appliances used by the average family, but for a variety of industries. There is no doubt as to how it will be produced. At present thermal power stations are responsible for more than two-thirds of the total production. Nevertheless the importance of hydro-electric power is increasing constantly, as witness the great projects either completed or planned in regions such as the Appalachians (Tennessee Valley), the Middle West (the dams of Niagara and along the St Lawrence Seaway), and more especially in the West (Hoover Dam and others on the Colorado, and the dams of the Columbia River Project). Electricity from nuclear power has made a promising start. Since the opening of the first commercial atomic power station at Shippingport, Pennsylvania, near Pittsburgh, eleven more have been opened in various parts of the country. In 1965 six more were under construction and a further eight or nine were planned. But even without full development of the programme for atomic power stations, the United States is likely to remain for a long time one of the foremost producers of electrical power in the world.

Whatever may be the rate of nuclear power development, the United States appears to be better situated than any other country to take advantage of it, because of its research in this field and its own wealth of uranium from Colorado and Utah.

*Abundance of mineral wealth.* The United States is amply provided with all kinds of minerals, with the exception of tin, chromium, manganese, nickel and bauxite.

We have already considered the large quantities of iron ore in the vicinity of Lake Superior, where 80 per cent of the total is produced, and the existence of the excellent system of transportation to the Appalachian coal mines. Iron is also found in Alabama, near Birmingham, and in the Rockies. On the whole the reserves seem considerable, but far-seeing industrialists have already begun to import foreign ore, and to acquire substantial interests in foreign developments, notably in Canada, Brazil, Venezuela and Liberia.

The country no longer seems to be threatened with a shortage of copper; for while the rich deposits of Lake Michigan are beginning to be exhausted, and those of Montana, near Butte, are becoming secondary, the recently opened mines of Arizona, Utah and New Mexico, with a consistent output, are producing more than three-quarters of the national total. American companies, with an eye on the future, also control important mines in Chile, Mexico and Canada. Home output is one-quarter of world production.

Similarly, the United States is well ahead in the production of lead, with 10 per cent of the world's total coming from Missouri, Idaho and Utah; but as a precaution large quantities are imported. The same applies, or nearly so, to zinc, with 13 per cent of

Sheep-herding in Montana.
In the American West,
broad pasture lands lie between the mountains,
though in Montana, near the Canadian border, a more rugged northern aspect is seen in the coniferous forests.

An oil refinery in Texas.
Every kind of mineral is found in quantity in the United States, with the exception of tin, chromium, manganese, nickel and bauxite.

The open-pit copper mine at Bingham, Utah, the largest in North America.
Utah is the second largest copper-producing state (Arizona is first), and its share of the national total is 18 per cent.

world production, and imports equal to more than one-and-a-half times this quantity. The chief producing areas are in the Rockies (Montana, Idaho, Colorado), the Ozarks (Oklahoma) and the Appalachians (Tennessee).

The production of bauxite was relatively small before the Second World War, when France was the chief producer; it doubled during the war and has increased four times since then. Now the United States is the fifth largest world producer. Arkansas supplies 96 per cent of the domestic output, but most of the bauxite used in the industry comes in from Jamaica, British Guiana and Guinea. The United States aluminium industry has become the largest in the world, producing about one half of the world total.

As regards the rare metals, the United States is most fortunate in its supply of molybdenum, with 72 per cent of the world output (from Colorado), sufficient to allow one-sixth of it to be exported. It is less rich in titanium, with 33 per cent of world production (exclusive of the U.S.S.R.), and barium, with 30 per cent. It is also an important producer of tungsten and vanadium. The precious metals are now of only secondary importance in the American economy; 4 per cent of the world's gold production comes from South Dakota, Utah and California; and similar proportions of platinum and silver from Idaho, Utah, Montana and Arizona.

The United States again takes the lead with the minerals needed by the chemical industry. It is the most important producer of phosphates, with over 40 per cent of world output, from Florida, Tennessee and the Carolinas; there are also extensive reserves in Utah and Idaho. Approximately 27 per cent of the world production of potash comes from New Mexico, California, Utah and Michigan, where there are still large reserves; 69 per cent of the world's sulphur comes from Louisiana and Texas; and 28 per cent of its salt from the rock salt of Michigan, New York State, Ohio and Kansas, and the salt pans of Texas, Louisiana and California.

*Iron and steel, engineering, and the chemical industry.* Favoured by a wealth of coal, iron ore, and transport facilities to link them, the American iron and steel industry is by far the most important in the world, producing more than one-quarter of the total world output of iron and steel. The blast furnaces, open furnaces and steel works are generally grouped together, especially between Pittsburgh on the Ohio and Cleveland on Lake Erie, in the two states of Pennsylvania and Ohio, which produce nearly a half of the nation's total. Another group lies on the shores of Lake Michigan, close to Chicago, around the boundary of Illinois and Indiana (at Gary). Alabama (Birmingham) is also a big producer, as are several states in the west, such as California, Utah and Colorado.

Being so well endowed with iron and other metals, the United States is an important producer in all branches of the engineering industry. This ranges from locomotives and other railway stock to typewriters and the most delicate machines for computing, recording, and translating foreign languages. There are shipbuilding yards on both coasts, a wide variety of agricultural, industrial and domestic equipment manufacturers, and of course the two largest steel consumers, the building and automobile industries. Approximately 70 per cent of the world's vehicles are made in or around Detroit, while Akron in Ohio makes all the necessary tyres. The other engineering industries are generally less concentrated; Chicago is the leader in agricultural machinery, New York and Boston in office equipment, Philadelphia in locomotives. The tendency is towards increased dispersal, so that industries are nearer their raw materials, market, or labour supply.

The size and variety of the chemical industry again make the United States the world's chief bulk producer of sulphuric acid, soda, fertilizers, dyes, and the largest manufacturer of finished products, such as paper (consumption for newspapers, magazines and packaging is staggering), photographic films, many plastic products, and innumerable products such as synthetic rubber and artificial textiles, including rayon, nylon, orlon and dacron. The heavy industries are to be found near their raw materials, for example, sulphuric acid in Texas and Louisiana and phosphates in the Carolinas, while the light industries are near the large consuming centres.

Coils of cold-rolled sheet steel at the Lackawanna, New York, plant of the Bethlehem Steel Corporation give some idea of the scale of American industrial economy.

The plant of the Monsanto Chemical Company at St Louis, Missouri. Situated at the confluence of the great Mississippi and Missouri Rivers, St Louis is a key city for all types of manufacturing and processing industries.

*The textile and food industries.* The textile industries, though less prosperous than the others, still play a vital rôle in the American economy, and are more or less sufficient for the country's requirements. Boston and its associated towns in New England, Lawrence, Lowell and Providence, have to a certain degree kept in the lead in the woollen industry, and they are responsible for two-thirds of its production. Much of the cotton produced now comes from factories in the Piedmont, in the Carolinas, Georgia and Alabama, which have the advantage of proximity to the raw material, abundant electric power, and a relatively cheap and abundant supply of labour. Natural and artificial silk is produced around New York City and Philadelphia.

When one considers the vast development of the food-processing industries, one should keep in mind the national desire to simplify work in the kitchen, a desire prompted by the scarcity and high cost of servants, and also the fact that perishable produce must be processed to be able to withstand transport over long distances and long storage periods. The preserving industry developed early in America, and soon grew rapidly, becoming both specialised and standardised. The industry first developed with meat, around Chicago in particular, then followed milk and milk products, notably in Wisconsin, and fruit and vegetables, mainly in California and on the Atlantic coast from New England to Florida. Three-quarters of the fish eaten is preserved: it is prepared and canned not far from the chief fishing ports of Puget Sound and New England. One of the biggest food industries, besides flour-milling, which is located mainly around the Great Lakes and in the central lowlands, is sugar-refining with all its associated products, such as sweets and chewing gum; the raw materials are cane-sugar, much of it imported, and sugar-beet, mainly from the Western states, or, on a much smaller scale, maple-sugar from New England. In all, the food industries employ nearly 10 per cent of the American workers and account for 17 per cent of the total industrial production.

THE RELATIVELY MINOR RÔLE OF FOREIGN TRADE. The home market consumes about 90 per cent of all American production, and, therefore, foreign trade is not of major importance to the economy. Nevertheless it is by no means negligible. The major exports are wheat and fruit and other foodstuffs, some raw materials, such as cotton, coal, and petroleum and its products, and above all manufactured articles, which represent 30 per cent of the total exports; machinery alone forms about 20 per cent of the total, and automobiles also a large proportion.

Imports, which are always smaller than exports, consist of the following: manufactured products, including paper, fertilizers and petroleum products, almost 40 per cent; raw materials, including rubber, wool and non-ferrous metals, 30 per cent; the rest is foodstuffs, of which coffee alone constitutes 14 per cent of total imports and sugar 4 per cent.

Western Europe buys more from the United States than it sells to it—though this situation shows signs of changing since the emergence of the European Economic Community. Asia, despite its rubber and tin, buys more than it sells. Canada and South America almost balance their trade with the United States.

Commerce with the Communist countries is small.

The enormous volume of domestic commerce in the United States is perhaps understandable if one remembers the variety of landscapes, climates and soils; the distribution across the nation of crops, forests, minerals and industries; the distribution of population; and the rapid means of transporting goods — all of which stimulate exchanges from region to region, exchanges unhindered by tariffs between states. Large-scale, intensive advertising, designed to make the population want and buy more and better things, has also stimulated business. And so has the extension of credit which makes it possible for the average person to buy expensive items by instalments.

Even though the volume of foreign trade is a rather small part of the national commerce, it is still essential for maintaining the equilibrium of the economy. Commercial circles are constantly on the watch for new markets and new sources of raw materials, and the Government, directly and indirectly, supports their efforts. The more informed businessmen appreciate the need for harmonious co-operation between the United States and the rest of the world.

A PEACEFUL, INDUSTRIOUS, DEMOCRATIC NATION. Where in other civilisations the élite has sought wisdom, military glory or political power, in the United States it has sought business. The corporate empires, which have replaced the railroad, oil and steel barons of the nineteenth century, limit their political adventures primarily to maintaining their commercial position, which can best be preserved in a peaceful world. They are also strong advocates of a stable government, which creates a climate conducive to large-scale, long-term business ventures. The Puritan influence itself, which combines concern for eternal salvation with a vigorous concern for the practical enterprise here and now, helps to explain the American's attitude towards business. And the New England tradition, making a virtue out of hard work, helps to account for the industriousness of the average American. The vigour characteristic of the immigrant, who was willing to leave home in search of a higher standard of living, is still visible in the almost universal drive among Americans to improve their economic status. Although the 'frontier' has disappeared in a physical sense, the tradition of a frontier inviting exploration has fostered a spirit of individual resourcefulness and inventiveness which has stimulated innovations in business and also in industry.

Undoubtedly the mixture of peoples has also played a part. Each immigrant group contributed something from its heritage and in turn absorbed something from the others, creating an American tradition out of an amalgam of many traditions, a concept rooted in the democratic ideal of freedom and justice under the law. Universal education has certainly been a factor, and so has the abundance of trained technicians. But, in the final analysis, the United States could not have achieved such a high standard of living for its citizens had it not been endowed with advantages of size, variety in landscapes and climates and a wealth of raw materials and energy; the fullest use of these has been made through the high productivity of its workers, technological ingenuity, good transportation facilities, a large home market, and abundant capital.

# HAWAII

Compared with the massive mainland of the United States, the twenty-odd islands and many islets of the state of Hawaii appear as mere specks, flung across some 1,600 miles of the immense Pacific Ocean. And indeed they are small, covering in all an area of only 6,407 square miles, slightly more than that of Connecticut and Rhode Island combined. Of the eight main islands, the largest is Hawaii, known as the 'Big Island', which covers just over 4,000 square miles. The other seven, in order of size, are Maui, Oahu, Kauai, Molokai, Lanai, Niihau, and Kahoolawe, the last of which has an area of only 45 square miles; it is uninhabited and is used for military target practise. Beyond Niihau the still smaller islands and islets stretch out in a slight north-west to south-east arc as far as Midway.

The oldest of the Hawaiian islands are these smaller ones, formerly high volcanoes, now eroded to near sea level. The youngest is Hawaii, which is currently in a stage of upbuilding and active vulcanism; its two 13,000-foot volcanic peaks, Mauna Loa and Mauna Kea, standing some 26,000 feet above the ocean floor, are the highest volcanoes in the world. The other seven main islands are extinct volcanoes, now in the process of being worn down by erosion. Apart from lava, the only other kind of bedrock in the islands is coral limestone, which forms submerged reefs offshore and several fairly extensive lowlands around the coasts and in the central part of Oahu north-west of Pearl Harbor. More than half of the 735,000 inhabitants of Hawaii are of Oriental ancestry, mainly Japanese and Filipino, plus a few Chinese and Koreans. About one-fifth of the population are part-Hawiian, and the remainder are white people (chiefly from the mainland United States and Northern Europe) and people of mixed ancestry. It is thus clear that this newest state in the Union (Hawaii became a state in 1959) is as much of a melting-pot as the older ones, if not more so. Many of the immigrants came in towards the end of the nineteenth century and the beginning of the twentieth to work in the expanding sugar and pineapple fields. Being unmarried for the most part, far removed from their homelands, and living on plantations or in small villages in close proximity to other groups and native Hawaiians, they quickly intermixed to a point where sociologists are predicting the emergence of an 'Hawaiian' people.

Although only eight per cent of the state's surface is considered cultivable — the rest is forest or pasture or too rugged to be of any use — the growing of sugar-cane and pineapples was for long the mainstay of the economy, and these crops are still two of the four major sources of revenue. Both are well suited to the mild temperatures, that rarely go below 21°C. (70°F.) or above 25°C. (77°F.), except of course in the higher mountains, which are cooler. The cane is raised mainly in the wetter windward locations or on lower leeward ground where it can be irrigated; the chief pineapple plantations are on higher slopes and are unirrigated. Since it is the north-east trade winds which bring most of the rain, the north-eastern slopes are wetter, the south-western slopes drier; the windward side of Mount Waialeale on Kauai, for instance, has 450 inches of rain a year, and has had as much as 600, whereas in some leeward, lowland places the average drops to eight inches. At sea level on the windward side of the islands, the average rainfall is 40 inches.

Sugar was growing in Hawaii when Captain Cook landed in 1779, but as an industry it dates from 1835. Today cane occupies nearly 225,000 acres in 28 plantations and a few small farms, all on the islands of Kauai, Maui, Hawaii and Oahu. Present production by 26 companies is about 1,200,000 tons a year. The rapid extension of pineapple plantations dates from 1876, when the United States and the Kingdom of Hawaii signed a trade agreement which provided for duty-free imports of sugar to the mainland. Production from 77,000 acres in 17 plantations and several small individual farms on Kauai, Oahu, Molokai, Lanai and Maui averages about 28,000,000 cases of fruit and juice a year. Other than these crops, the main agricultural products include tropical fruits and vegetables, poultry, cows and beef cattle, and additionally of macadamia nuts, flowers and coffee. More than 75 per cent of the agricultural land is in pasture in some 400 ranches, half of them on the island of Hawaii, and the slaughtering of beef cattle is a big industry in Honolulu.

The state owes its large source of income to its strategic location in the Pacific; in some years revenue derived from United States military installations and associated construction and other industries, chiefly on the island of Oahu, has exceeded that derived from all other sources except sugar. However, efforts are being made to diversify the economy, principally by developing industry. Manufacturing now consists primarily of food processing; the maintenance and repair of ships; the making of clothing and furniture, of machinery for the plantations, of wares for sale to tourists, and of steel, based on imported scrap, in a mill opened in 1959; and the refining of oil for use in the factories and electric-generating plants.

The port and city of Honolulu, the capital of Hawaii, the largest island in the State of Hawaii.

Tourism, the fourth mainstay of the economy, is Hawaii's most rapidly growing industry. During the last decade the number of visitors has increased more than tenfold, to 200,000 a year, bringing in an annual income of some $95 million. New hotels, restaurants, shops, and other facilities are going up everywhere, but especially on the famed Waikiki Beach, a part of Honolulu two miles long and three to five blocks wide, which is on the leeward side, where waves are not too dangerous for surf-riding and other water sports. Other tourist attractions are the year-round mild climate, the blue sky, the spectacular volcanoes, the black-lava fields, the coral-sand coves between rocky headlands, the multitude of orchids, the palms, the tropical fruits — mangoes, papayas, avocados, bananas, and naturally, pineapples — the colourful festivals and pageants, the invariably charming welcome, and a standard of living comparable to that on the mainland United States. Now that one can fly from California to Hawaii by jet in four-and-a-half hours, there is every likelihood that the tourist industry will continue to grow.

# MEXICO

Mexico is by far the largest of the countries that separates the United States from the continent of South America. With an area of 760,335 square miles, it is about eight times as large as the United Kingdom, or nearly three times as large as the state of Texas. Though considered to form part of the North American continent, its southern area at least, south of the Isthmus of Tehuantepec, belongs to Central America, and it would be more correctly described as transitional between the two regions. Its northern boundary with the United States extends from coast to coast for about 1,800 miles, the major eastern part following the course of the Rio Bravo (Rio Grande). In contrast to the powerful and influential neighbour to the north. Mexico's neighbours along the relatively short southern boundary are Guatemala and British Honduras. To the west Mexico faces the vast expanse of the Pacific Ocean, to the east the Caribbean Sea and the Gulf of Mexico, where a near neighbour is the island republic of Cuba.

Today Mexico is a Federal Republic of twenty-nine states, two territories (Baja California Sur and Quintana Roo) and the Federal District of Mexico City with twelve surrounding villages. The story of the country's political development may be divided into four parts. First came the era of the Indian empire, which lasted until the Spanish conquest early in the sixteenth century. Then for three centuries the country remained the Spanish colony or viceroyalty of New Spain, gaining independence in 1821 as the Empire of Mexico. There followed, during the third phase, half a century of political instability, turbulence and nation-wide poverty, during which power changed hands between two regencies, two emperors, a number of dictators, and over seventy different governments. In 1876, after one of the traditional army revolts, Porfirio Díaz assumed power and was installed as president in the following year. Apart from a single brief period (1880-84), Díaz remained in office until 1910. He imposed stability on the country, encouraged foreign investment, developed the railways and the mining industries, and brought about a ninefold increase in the value of Mexico's foreign trade. He also ruthlessly suppressed all opposition and ignored the grinding poverty of the masses. He contributed to their misery, in fact, by expropriating the village *ejidos* or common lands to the benefit of the landed aristocracy; by the end of his term over 95 per cent of the heads of rural families owned no land. The revolution that broke out in 1910 and inaugurated the modern, fourth period in Mexican history was a spontaneous armed rebellion against the Diaz dictatorship. It was the beginning of a period of reform which was marked by the new constitution of 1917 and the progressive administration of 1934-40.

With merciless autocracy and revolution in the immediate past, it is not surprising that recent Mexican governments have experienced enormous difficulties in their attempts to achieve national unity. Their struggle has not been made easier by the many diversities in the land and in its people. Mexico is a mainly mountainous country, but it varies in altitude from snow-capped volcanoes such as Orizaba or Citlaltepetl (18,700 feet) to areas below sea level in Baja California. There are extensive areas of open land on the central plateau, but there are also steep, rugged mountain ranges around its edges and, beyond these, narrow coastal plains. Along the south-east coast, facing the Gulf of Mexico, the heavy rainfall, exceeding 80 inches annually in parts of Veracruz and Tabasco, supports tropical rain forests, but arid deserts are found in the north-west. The urban areas surrounding Mexico City and a handful of other towns are densely populated, but most of the population is very thinly distributed throughout the rural areas. Probably the most noticeable contrast in Mexico is the wealth of a small minority of European descent living in the main cities compared with the abject poverty and ignorance of the Indians in outlying villages.

The Cereus variety of cactus, near Mitla, in the state of Oaxaca, Mexico; its stiff thorny columns grow to a height of 20 to 25 feet.

## LAND, CLIMATES, VEGETATION

*The natural divisions.* Well over half of the country stands at an altitude of 3,000 feet or more above sea level. The major feature of surface relief is the high central plateau, which extends from the northern boundary to the Isthmus of Tehuantepec and also covers the greater part of the country's width. Along its seaward sides the plateau is flanked by two chains of mountains known as the Sierra Madre Occidental and the Sierra Madre Oriental, which are extensions of ranges in the southern United States. In the extreme south-east there are further uplands, the Chiapas Highlands, which extend into Guatemala and form part of the Central American plateau. The Mexican lowlands are merely narrow fringes between the mountains and the sea, broadening out in the south-east, however, into the extensive peninsula of Yucatan. Finally, there is the long peninsula of Baja California (Lower California), with its mountainous core extending from the ranges of southern California, again bordered by narrow coastal plains.

*The central plateau.* The central plateau slopes generally upwards from north to south. Its surface is far from uniform, the *bolsons* or basin-like depressions in the northern section, standing mainly at 3,000 to 4,000 feet, being surmounted by ranges of block mountains, about 3,000 feet above them, which have a general alignment from north-west to south-east. One of the most conspicuous of these depressions is the Bolson de Mapimi, which occupies the adjoining areas of Chihuahua, Coahuila and Durango and has an altitude of a little over 3,000 feet. The only large rivers are the Rio Bravo and its tributary the Rio Conchos, so that most of this northern part of the central plateau has no drainage to the sea. To the south is the extensive Bolson de Mayran, which has an altitude of about 3,600 feet at its lowest point. The southern section of the central plateau stretches from this depression as far as the valley of the Rio Balsas. Here the intermontane basins, unlike the *bolsons* of the northern section, are cut off from one another by mountains, and stand at considerably higher altitudes, varying between 5,000 and 8,000 feet. The Basin or Valley of Mexico, in which the capital Mexico City is situated, for example, at its lowest is more than 7,400 feet above sea level. Above the intermontane basins tower many magnificent volcanic peaks, including Orizaba or Citlaltepetl, the highest (18,700 feet), Popocatepetl (17,887 feet), Ixtaccihuatl (17,342 feet), Naucampatepetl or Cofre de Perote (14,048 feet), and the now well-known Paricutin (9,100 feet), which first erupted in 1943. Volcanoes abound through Mexico almost from the northern to the southern boundary, but especially across the highest part of the central plateau from Cape Corrientes on the Pacific coast east-south-east towards the southern coast of the Gulf of Campeche — one of the world's outstanding regions of volcanic activity, owing to the insecurity of the basic structure of the isthmus.

In this part of the central plateau drainage has been hampered not by aridity, as in the north, but by volcanic activity, and there are numerous shallow lakes and swamps in the intermontane basins. The largest Mexican lake, about 80 miles long and 35 miles wide, is Lake Chapala, which lies in the lowest part of the Basin of Jalisco. Into this lake empties the Rio Lerma, while from it flows the Rio Santiago, descending more than five thousand feet over falls and rapids to the Pacific Ocean. Other rivers that rise on the plateau also drain a number of the basins, both on the Pacific and the Gulf side, notably the Rio Panuco, which reaches the sea at the port of Tampico. Lake Texcoco lies in the Basin of Mexico, along with a number of other small lakes, its surface being only a few feet below the level of Mexico City. At one time a much larger sheet of water, it has been drained during the present century into the Rio Moctezuma, a tributary of the Rio Panuco.

*Mountains and lowlands.* The mountainous western flank of the plateau, the Sierra Madre Occidental, rises, like the plateau itself, from north to south. It presents a formidable barrier to communications between the plateau and the Pacific coast, being 100 miles or more in width and in its highest summits reaching over 10,000 feet above sea level. It is dissected by many rivers, which have cut deep longitudinal valleys, occasionally breaking through the intervening steep-sided ridges to form narrow gorges or *barrancas*. In the south an eastern extension of the Sierra crosses the plateau, while a western branch, the Sierra Madre del Sur, continues more or less parallel to the coast. In this region, too, the streams have cut so many deep valleys that little of the surface is level, and the highland region terminates suddenly with a steep escarpment at the low-lying Isthmus of Tehuantepec. The Rio Balsas has cut its valley far back into the highland region, isolating the Sierra Madre del Sur from the mountains and plateau to the north. Beyond the isthmus the land again rises abruptly with the Chiapas Highlands. East of the plateau the Sierra Madre Oriental is also difficult to penetrate, but, being both narrower and lower than the Sierra Madre Occidental, except in the south, is generally less forbidding. It attains its greatest heights in the volcanic peaks Orizaba and Naucampatepetl.

The lowlands along the Gulf of Mexico, which in the north are merely a continuation of the coastal plains of Texas, are narrowed southwards by various

The volcano Paricutin was formed suddenly in a field in 1943. It quickly reached a height of several thousand feet and devastated the surrounding country within a radius of 60 miles, including the small market town of Parangaricutiro.

outliers of the Sierra Madre Oriental and isolated volcanic cones. Their coast is low, sandy, and fringed by shallow lagoons, while the mouths of the rivers are obstructed by bars, with the result that there are no good natural harbours. Mexico's two leading ports, Veracruz and Tampico, are both on this coast, but they are largely artificial. On the Isthmus of Tehuantepec the lowlands broaden out again, and, apart from scattered hills, the entire Yucatan peninsula is a plain. The northern and western coasts of Yucatan are low, sandy and regular; the eastern coast is indented with bays and flanked by a number of islands, one of the largest, Cozumel, being where Cortes made his first landing in Mexico. Yucatan consists almost wholly of a limestone platform of recent geological age, drainage is underground, and sink-holes or *cenotes* are characteristic features of this rugged, karst-like landscape.

The Pacific coast of Mexico is much longer and more indented than the Gulf coast, but is cut off from the interior by the steep slopes of the Sierra Madre Occidental. In the north-west the Sonora Desert, adjoining Arizona, is another region of mountains and *bolsons*. The Gulf of California separates this desert from the peninsula of Baja California, sometimes termed 'the fleshless arm of Mexico', which is dominated for almost its entire length by a chain of rugged mountains. At one point only, in the Sierra San Pedro Martir in the north, do these mountains rise above 10,000 feet. They lie nearer the Gulf of California than the Pacific Ocean, descending abruptly to the arid, extremely narrow eastern coastal plain. To the west they fall more gradually by a series of plateaus and terraces which are cut by numerous *arroyos*, dry river beds that contain surface water only after rainfall.

*The climates.* Mexico has a considerable longitudinal extent, stretching approximately from 15°N. to 32°30′N. latitude, and this is one of the reasons why its climate is so varied. Another reason is that there are such great differences in altitude, with the major part of the country consisting of a high plateau. As the latitudinal limits indicate, the Tropic of Cancer runs practically through the centre of the country, but it would be wrong to conclude that the southern part of Mexico enjoys a uniformly tropical climate: so much of the land stands on the plateau some thousands of feet above sea level. The north-west comes within the desert zone, as exemplified in the Sonora Desert and the Vizcaino Desert of Baja California; the former, in fact, resembles the Mojave Desert of California. Southern Mexico lies in the region of the north-east trade winds, and the eastern coastal plains as far as the Yucatan peninsula have a hot climate with heavy summer rainfall. On the other hand, the plateau is separated from maritime influence by the enclosing sierras, and is strikingly dissimilar in climate from the hot dry north-west and the hot wet south-east.

It is because the greater part of the country stands on the high plateau that any attempt at the usual simple climatic division of the country would be misleading. Often the Mexican in his mountainous terrain thinks of directions as being either 'up' or 'down', rather than north or south, east or west: his particular regional climate, too, is determined more by altitude than by latitude. It is usual, therefore, to divide the country climatically into three vertical zones, known as the *tierra caliente*, the *tierra templada* and the *tierra fria*.

The *tierra caliente*, or 'hot land', is the zone from sea level to about 3,000 feet, and includes all the coastal plains, the Yucatan peninsula and the Isthmus of Tehuantepec. Within this zone the mean annual temperature is 24°-27°C. (75°-80°F.), and in the low-lying parts of the desert regions there are many days when the thermometer registers well above 38°C. (100°F.), or higher than anywhere else in Central America. At the same time the range of temperatures between the warmest and coldest months is relatively small. In the *tierra templada*, or 'temperate land', which extends from about 3,000 to 6,000 feet above sea level, the mean annual temperature is 18°-24°C. (65°-75°F.). This is the most favourable of the three types of climate from the human standpoint. Above the *tierra templada* is the *tierra fria*, or 'cold land', extending from about 6,000 to 9,000 feet, where the mean annual temperature varies between 13° and 18°C. (55° and 65°F.). The winter is not cold, though there are slight frosts at night fairly frequently, and the summer is never hot.

Along the extreme eastern borders of Mexico all three zones are affected at times, chiefly during the winter, by a cold northerly wind known as the *norte*, which is an extension of the 'norther' of the southern United States: the temperature suddenly falls by several degrees, causing discomfort to human beings and sometimes damaging the crops. To complete the vertical climatic picture of Mexico, one might add a fourth zone, the *tierra helada* or 'frozen land', above 9,000 feet: the highest and coldest of all, a zone of bare rock and snow-capped summits and virtually uninhabited.

It has been estimated that only about one-eighth of Mexico receives adequate all-year rainfall, one-half is permanently deficient, and the remainder is deficient either in summer or in winter, mainly the latter. As we have seen, rainfall is heaviest on the coastal plains, and lower mountain slopes of Veracruz, Tabasco and Campeche, where in places the annual rainfall is 80 inches or more. Rainfall is particularly deficient in the north-west, while the northern part of the central plateau is also arid, the rainfall in both these areas being less than 15 inches annually. Throughout the country the year is divisible into two parts, the rainy season and the dry season. In the extreme north-west the small amount of rain comes in winter, and summer is a time of drought, as in neighbouring California. Elsewhere the rainy season is summer, between the months of June and September. The onset of cloudy wet weather in June is so marked that temperatures are highest during May, not July, in most of southern Mexico, in places as far apart as Mexico City and Merida, San Luis Potosi and Oaxaca.

*Natural vegetation.* Such diversity of climates gives rise to a rich variety in natural vegetation, from the desert plants of the north-west and north to the tropical rain forests of the south-east. Rainfall and altitude are the principal factors determining the type of vegetation. In the arid regions, especially in the north-west and north, the characteristic plants are the yucca trees, numerous species of cactus, and many types of agave bush. Agaves are economically the most important, one species yielding the liquid from which the fermented drink *pulque* is made, while from the leaves of another species henequen fibre is obtained. In complete contrast to the xerophytic vegetation of the arid regions, the dense forests of the wetter parts of the *tierra caliente* contain scores of species of tropical trees, including mahogany, rosewood and logwood, lianas being interlaced with their trunks and branches and innumerable palms and ferns growing around their feet.

Ascending from the *tierra caliente* to the *tierra templada,* we find that the trees typical of the tropical forests are gradually replaced by many varieties of oaks and other broad-leaved trees. Oaks are still predominant in the lower levels of the *tierra fria,* but in the upper parts conifers mingle with them, while at still greater altitudes as far as the timberline — the upper limit of trees, at about 13,000 feet — the forests consist almost entirely of pines and firs. Between the timberline and the snowline, or limit of permanent snow, which on Orizaba, for example, is at about 14,600 feet, there are small areas of alpine grassland.

The Mexican population is predominantly Indian rather than European in origin, with 55 per cent Mestizo, 29 per cent pure Indian, 15 per cent pure European, and less than 1 per cent Negro. The mestizo, or half-caste, race has a greater number of Indians in its ancestry. This is the part of the population that is increasing proportionally more than any other.

for the relative decline in the Indian population are that they live in the poorest conditions and are the most ignorant and least adaptable section of the population. In the early days of Spanish colonisation only the men emigrated to Mexico, and, on settling, intermarried with the local women; moreover, neither during the later colonial period nor after the war of independence was there more than a trickle of Europeans into the country. This explains the small but unmistakable decline in the proportion of pure whites in the population. Over 30,000 Negroes had been brought into Mexico during the early colonial period to work as slaves on the *haciendas,* or large estates, but by the end of the war of independence many had been absorbed or had bought their freedom and left. Descendants of mixed Negro and Indian blood were known as *zambos,* those of mixed Negro and white blood as *mulattos.*

In colonial times by far the most influential people in Mexico were the small minority of European-born Spaniards, known to the rest of the population as *gachupins,* or wearers of shoes, who had most of the power and wealth of the country. Today racial discrimination does not exist, but it would be a mistake to conclude that all sections of the population have been welded into a homogeneous Mexican nation: there is a wide gulf in outlook, culture and development, for instance, between the mestizo living in an urban community and the pure Indian in a remote village. The mountainous nature of the country has helped to maintain racial and cultural differences by hampering communications. Generally speaking, the north and west of the country are occupied chiefly by mestizos and whites; this is the more productive area both in agriculture and mining. The inhabitants of the south and east are mainly mestizos and Indians, winning a livelihood by subsistence farming and possessing little personal economic wealth.

The majority of Mexicans at least have a common language—Spanish—but at the last census about fifty other languages had to be used; over a million Indians still speak only their native tongue and do not even understand Spanish. On the other hand, several of the aboriginal languages have died out in recent years. In religion there is a slightly greater uniformity, for 97 per cent of the population are members of the Roman Catholic Church. A peculiarly Mexican feature of their faith is their veneration for the Virgin of Guadalupe, whose shrine stands near Mexico City and is visited by thousands of pilgrims each year. By the constitution of 1857 the Church was separated from the State, and during the present century the political influence of the Church has been still further curtailed. The constitution of 1917 declared that the property of the Church belonged to the State. Otherwise the Church appears to flourish: the most impressive building in every town and village is the church, and shrines may be seen throughout the countryside.

## PEOPLES AND CULTURES

*Racial composition.* A significant fact about the people of Mexico is that they are predominantly Indian rather than European in origin. Recent estimates of the composition of the population indicate that 55 per cent are mestizo or mixed Indian and European, 29 per cent are pure Indian, 15 per cent are of pure European descent, and less than one per cent Negroes. Even these figures, showing that the mestizos form the majority, conceal the fact that they are individually more Indian than white, for there was a greater number of Indians than of Europeans in their ancestry. During the last 150 years an interesting change has taken place in the composition of the population. At the beginning of that time the mestizos formed 41 per cent of the population, the Indians 40 per cent and the pure Europeans 19 per cent: it is evident that the proportion of mestizos is increasing at the expense of those of unmixed origin. The main reasons

*The Indians.* Today the Indians live in village communities and represent more than half the rural population of Mexico. Each community is responsible for its own laws and customs, its members have few daily needs and seldom attempt to produce more than they can consume, and they are usually illiterate.

Even here, among the short, black-haired, copper-skinned inhabitants of these essentially Indian villages are some with paler skin and brown hair, indicating the infiltration of the mestizo. In the villages, too, the influence of sixteenth-century Spain may still be seen in the dress, ornaments and dances of the Indians. The basis of their agriculture is now, as it has been since earliest times, the cultivation of maize (corn); many of the customs associated with maize cultivation, such as methods of preparing the food and types of cooking utensil, have been handed down since the days of the Spanish conquest. Dwellings vary according to the environment, from the open house of wood roofed with palm leaves in the hot, humid *tierra caliente,* to the flat-roofed hut of adobe of sun-dried bricks on the drier plateau. There is little furniture in the Indian home beyond a few stools and a wooden chest or two, a millstone for grinding the maize, and some pottery.

It is usual to classify the Indian population according to language. The largest number speak the language known as Mexican, or Aztec, a dialect of the Nahau language. This was the language of the Toltecs, who came from the arid north to conquer the Mayas and reached the peak of their development about A.D. 900. Two centuries later the Toltecs were in decline, and about A.D. 1300 they were conquered by another Nahua-speaking people from the north, the warlike Aztecs, who also established their capital in the Basin of Mexico and whose wealth inspired the Spaniards to ideas of conquest in the New World. In numerical strength the Maya is the second most important language group today. The Mayas, who developed a high degree of culture, were established in Yucatan and neighbouring parts of Guatemala, and this is the area where their descendants now mainly live. Other Indian language groups included the Zapotec and Mixtec of southern Mexico and the Otomi of central Mexico.

*The population problem.* The steady diminution of the Indian section of the population, revealed by successive linguistic censuses, is more than outweighed by the rapid expansion of the remainder. At present the population is over 34 million, of whom 55 per cent are rural and 45 per cent urban, with a tendency for the latter to increase at the expense of the former. The census for 1960 showed an increase of more than 34 per cent over 1950, representing an annual rate of growth of 3.43 per cent, one of the highest in the world. At 45.5 per thousand in 1960 the birthrate has remained very high, but the deathrate has fallen dramatically, from 26.1 per thousand in 1932 to 11.7 in 1960, chiefly owing to improvements in hygiene and medical services. The most striking feature of the change has been the improvement in the health of young children: in the 1920's the infant mortality rate was over 200 per thousand, with diarrhoea, enteritis, pneumonia and malaria the main scourges; but this figure had fallen to 123 by 1939 and to 74 per thousand by 1960 and has continued to decrease steadily.

A result of the rapid growth in population has been the temporary migration of Mexican workers to the southern United States, where the farmers need extra manpower at certain seasons. There were probably as many as 800,000 of these *braceros,* until the U.S. Government curtailed their free entry in 1964, most crossing the Rio Bravo illegally. Mexican farmers, in fact, have complained that there are not enough workers to harvest their own crops, and have requested the Government to stem the continual flow of *braceros* to the United States. The solution is to create some hundreds of thousands of new jobs in Mexico through the expansion of agriculture and the development of industry.

The increase in population has created a critical problem in education, for every year the school population is swollen by 50,000 more children. Mexico is desperately short of classroom accommodation as well as teachers, and, although primary education is theoretically compulsory, only six in every ten children between six and fourteen years of age can actually attend school, while one Mexican in every two can neither read nor write.

## ECONOMIC DEVELOPMENT

*Agriculture: the main occupation.* When the Spaniards came to Mexico, they introduced a system of private

Women and girls sorting coffee beans. The hand labour essential for the operation is plentiful in Mexico.

ownership of land in the shape of the *hacienda* or large feudal estate. They settled mainly on the central plateau, their *haciendas* being devoted to agriculture in the centre and stock-rearing in the north, while the hot lowlands were left amost undeveloped. After the revolution which began in 1910, and particularly during the Cardenas presidency of 1934-40, the *hacienda* lands were expropriated and converted into *ejidos* or in some cases into private farms of limited acreage. The *ejidos* consist of rural communities of several families, each of which works its own farm; they are organised politically, and receive technical help and credit from the Federal Government.

Throughout Mexico the basic food crop is maize, which occupies over half of the cultivated land. Owing to backward methods of production, however, yields are scarcely one-third of those in the United States, and even an output of about 6.4 million tons per year, more than twice that of twenty years ago, is insufficient for domestic consumption. Beans, with a production of 8,000 tons in 1963, are also an important food crop, while wheat, which is being increasingly consumed, is significant in the temperate areas: again, the output of wheat, 1,8000,000 tons in 1963, has been quadrupled since 1940. More rice is also being eaten, especially in the towns, and its cultivation is being developed on reclaimed land in the humid tropical areas: the record crop of 266,000 tons in 1963 was slightly greater than domestic requirements. Sugar-cane is the main crop in some of the hot coastlands and certain valleys in the south; not only are several refineries in the producing areas supplied, but there is also a surplus available for export.

Cotton, one of the two chief export crops, is grown mainly on irrigated lands in the north. Production in the Mexicali area, for example, increased ten times

A mining zone in the mountainous state of Chihuahua. This northern state produces lead and silver, both important sources of foreign revenue In colonial days silver accounted for 80 per cent of Mexico's exports to Europe. Production still amounts to over a fifth of the world total.

between 1929 and 1957, till the region was producing one-third of the national output. Coffee, the second export crop, is mainly cultivated in the *tierra templada* of Veracruz and Chiapas. On the Yucatan peninsula about nine-tenths of the world supply of henequen, a fibre similar to sisal, is produced. Other important crops include oranges, tomatoes, bananas and tobacco, illustrating again the great variety of Mexico's agricultural products.

Stock-rearing is the principal occupation on the sparsely populated grasslands and scrub of the north and the coastland. Cattle, introduced by the Spaniards, were of poor quality, but the herds have been improved of late by artificial insemination.

*Mining and industry.* With respect to certain metals Mexico is one of the richest countries in the world. During the four centuries after the Spanish conquest the country produced about two-thirds of the world output of silver, and during the colonial period Mexico's economy depended on silver-mining. This metal, in fact, once represented the major part of Mexico's exports, but, while still important, output being over one-fifth of the world total, it has now been overtaken by lead, copper, zinc and petroleum. These metals, lead, copper, zinc and silver, are important sources of foreign currency, but petroleum is

more significant to the country's economy and its relative value is increasing.

Mexico has coal resources, including high-grade coking coal at Sabinas in Coahuila; the output fluctuates, but it reached 2,070,000 tons in 1959; petroleum is therefore an invaluable source of power. The mining industry had, however, been developed almost entirely by foreign interests, chiefly of British and American origin. In 1938 the foreign companies which had discovered and developed the oilfields were expropriated by the Mexican Government, and since then Pemex (Petróleos Mexicanos), the nationalised petroleum company, has controlled the oil industry. The main producing areas lie along the Gulf coast from Tampico to the Isthmus of Tehuantepec. In 1901 the first successful well was drilled west of Tampico, and in 1908 another important field was discovered inland from Tuxpan. Production rose to a peak in 1921, when Mexican oil amounted to about one-quarter of the world output, but then production and exports in general declined until nationalisation. Pemex ahd great difficulty in maintaining production even at reduced levels, and only succeeded by fully exploiting the new Poza Rica oilfield near Tuxpan. With technical and financial help from abroad, the company raised the output from 1945 onwards, till in 1961 this amounted to 18,900,000 tons, more than four times the lowest annual output (in 1942), and Mexico continues to occupy tenth place among world oil producers. Despite the possession of 14 refineries, Mexico is still compelled to export crude oil and fuel oil at relatively low prices and to import refined products such as petrol and kerosene at higher prices.

Some iron ore is mined, and the iron and steel industry at Monterrey and Monclava has been expanded in recent years, using coking coal from Sabinas, iron ore from Durango, and local limestone; production has increased almost fivefold since 1945. and an annual output of nearly 2 million tons of steel ingots is maintained. Apart from the food and drink industries, such as sugar-refining, distilling, brewing and canning, however, the textile industry (chiefly cotton) is the largest, being located mainly in Mexico City, Puebla, Guadalajara and Orizaba. More recent industries include the manufacture of electrical appliances, which at present have a very limited market, or fertilizers and other chemicals, and the assembly of automobiles. The expansion of the building and allied industries has been most apparent in the capital, Mexico City, with its tall modern buildings up to 44 storeys high.

*Towns and transport.* In Mexico City there is much to remind the inhabitants of their country's past and also much to point the way to the future. Symbolic of the past is the great cathedral, near the site of the Aztec temple destroyed by Cortes in 1521; the foundations were laid in 1573 and the building was completed about 1811. The pattern of the future may be seen in the skyscrapers, the airport, the new roads, factories and residential suburbs. Mexico City, with textile, food-processing and a variety of other types of manufacture, is the country's principal industrial centre. Its population rose from about 300,000 at the beginning of the century to 1,029,000 in 1930, has since risen to well over 3 million, and is still increasing.

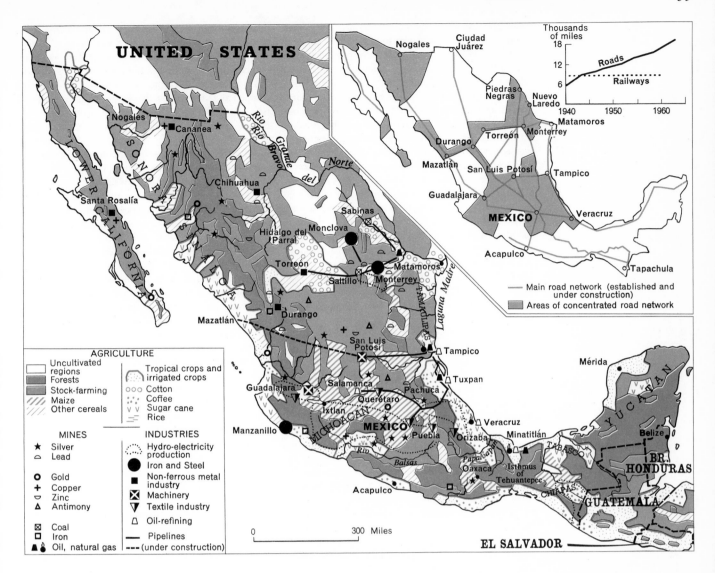

UNITED STATES

Nogales · Cananea ★
Santa Rosalía
Chihuahua
Hidalgo del Parral
Torreón
Saltillo · Monterrey · Matamoros
Durango
Mazatlán
San Luis Potosí
Guadalajara
Manzanillo
Salamanca · Pachuca
Querétaro · Tampico · Tuxpan
Ixtlan
MÉXICO · Puebla · Veracruz
Acapulco · Oaxaca · Minatitlán · Orizaba
Mérida
YUCATAN
Belize
BR. HONDURAS
GUATEMALA
EL SALVADOR
SONORA · SINALOA · LOWER CALIFORNIA
Rio Grande del Norte · Rio Bravo
Laguna Madre · TAMAULIPAS
Sierra Madre
MICHOACAN · Rio Balsas · Papaloapan · Isthmus of Tehuantepec · TABASCO · CHIAPAS
Sabinas · Monclova
300 Miles
0

**AGRICULTURE**

- Uncultivated regions
- Forests
- Stock-farming
- Maize
- Other cereals
- Tropical crops and irrigated crops
- ○○○ Cotton
- Coffee
- v v Sugar cane
- Rice

**MINES**

- ★ Silver
- ⌂ Lead
- ○ Gold
- + Copper
- ▽ Zinc
- △ Antimony
- ⊠ Coal
- □ Iron
- ▲ Oil, natural gas

**INDUSTRIES**

- Hydro-electricity production
- ● Iron and Steel
- ■ Non-ferrous metal industry
- ⊠ Machinery
- ▽ Textile industry
- △ Oil-refining
- — Pipelines
- --- (under construction)

Inset map:
Thousands of miles
18
12
6
1940   1950   1960
Roads
Railways

Nogales · Ciudad Juárez
Piedras Negras · Nuevo Laredo
Durango · Torreón · Monterrey · Matamoros
Mazatlán · San Luis Potosí · Tampico
Guadalajara · Veracruz
MEXICO
Acapulco · Tapachula

— Main road network (established and under construction)
Areas of concentrated road network

It has to contend with two serious problems. The first is the gradual sinking of the ground—the marshy bed of Lake Texcoco: the *Palacio de Bellas Artes,* for example, completed in 1935, has already subsided more than five feet. A second problem is the instability of the earth's crust in this region, a fault-line running through the underlying rocks near the city: in 1957 there was a severe earthquake, killing over a hundred people and necessitating the demolition or reconstruction of many major buildings.

Guadalajara, Mexico's second city, became an important settlement in early colonial days, being the centre of a relatively densely populated agricultural area, and more recently has acquired textile and other manufacturers. Between 1940 and 1963 its population rose from 229,000 to 90,000. Monterrey, the third city and undisputed capital of the north-east, now has a population of 729,000, and is the only other town with more than half a million inhabitants. Besides its steel mills, it has breweries, cigarette and glass factories, cement works and other plants, and is the chief centre of lead-smelting. The city expanded rapidly after the building of the railroad and became the focal point of the railroad system of north-east Mexico. It developed further with the construction of the Pan-American Highway from Laredo, Texas, through Monterrey and on to Mexico City, which brought ever-increasing numbers of American tourists into Mexico, and led to the building of air-conditioned hotels, motels, tourist camps, petrol (gas) stations and other amenities of the automobile civilisation.

Road construction, in fact, has been one of Mexico's outstanding post-war achievements, and has contributed substantially to the tourist industry becoming the largest single source of dollar income. In 1939 Mexico had 5,660 miles of highways, but in 1964 there were 29,000 miles of hard-surface roads. During twenty-five years the number of motor vehicles in the country had risen from 139,000 to 1,042,000, which included 353,000 trucks; more than half the goods transported within Mexico now travel by truck. In conjunction with the rail network, the roads also help to link the highlands at different levels with the lowlands, and encourage former subsistence farmers to increase production by enabling them to market surplus crops outside their own locality. The roads also have far-reaching social effects, breaking down the isolation of village communities and fostering a sense of national unity.

PRESENT PROBLEMS AND FUTURE DEVELOPMENTS. As we have already remarked, one of Mexico's greatest needs is an increase in agricultural production, firstly in

Principal agricultural, mining and industrial resources of Mexico.
*Inset map,* the road network. Crops are varied in this country where there are contrasts in relief, climate and in coasts — Atlantic and Pacific. Cultivated areas are spreading increasingly into the lowlands that are being drained and made healthy: this 'march towards the sea' is bringing new settlement to the coastal areas. The road network is being systematically developed as part of the project to exploit fully all the considerable resources of Mexico.

order to raise the general standard of living and secondly to provide sufficient food for the million or so new citizens who are born into the republic every year. How much has been achieved to this end? After a preliminary decline due to the carrying out of the *ejido* programme, there has been a continual rise in agricultural production over the last three decades: the area under cultivation and the average production per acre have both increased. The latter was achieved by supplying farmers with mechanised equipment to replace the ox-drawn wooden plough and the hoe, better seeds, superior breeds of livestock, fertilizers to enrich the soil and insecticides to protect the crops. There has also been a greater diversity of crops, exemplified by the increased acreage devoted to wheat and rice, while the increased per capita consumption of these cereals is at least a small indication of rising living standards. These changes have been effected in spite of a general decrease of man-power in agriculture, including a considerable decrease in the number of farmers practising subsistence agriculture.

In the dry lands of the north and north-west the acreage of cultivated land can only be increased by irrigation. Several large irrigation plans were initiated in 1926, during the Calles presidency, and over the subsequent twenty years 2 million acres of land were irrigated; since 1946 this rate of land reclamation by irrigation has been considerably accelerated, and by 1963 the area under irrigation amounted to nearly six million acres. It has been estimated, however, that the irrigated area must reach 17 million acres before the country can become self-supporting in agricultural products. Throughout central Mexico further large areas have been brought under cultivation by planting the *maguey*, the species of agave that yields a sweet liquid known as *agua miel* from which *pulque*, the popular alcoholic drink, is made. The *maguey* plant thrives on poor, thin soils on which other crops cannot be cultivated.

Another part of the comprehensive plan for economic development is the so-called 'March to the Sea' programme, for which the Mexican Government decided to allocate 250 million pesos in 1954. The object of the scheme was to move and resettle millions of people from the more densely populated central plateau to the undeveloped but potentially productive lowlands along the Pacific and Gulf coasts, and the funds were to be used in the first place to improve communications and develop port facilities. Within two years more than the allocated sum had been spent on this first phase of the programme, and the Government announced that a similar sum would be expended on the second phase, the development of several small harbours along the two coasts.

One of the most difficult problems in agricultural development is to teach modern farming methods to a backward and often illiterate peasantry, but a beginning has been made with the practice of soil conservation by contour ploughing, terracing, and crop rotation. The exploitation of the forests is also associated with soil conservation. Mexico is believed to have about 50 million acres of commercially valuable timber lands, including pine and spruce among the softwoods and mahogany, logwood and rosewood among the tropical hardwoods. Too much reckless and unplanned cutting had destroyed many of the best timber stands, leading to spring floods, reduced water supplies in summer, and soil erosion. Reforestation was commenced, over 2 million trees being planted in 1947-8, and in 1951 the Government temporarily stopped all cutting in 22 states, permitting a resumption only under supervision. Nearly 4 million acres of timber lands are now held in forest reserves and national park forests.

A danger in modernising agriculture, particularly with the greater use of machinery, is that it may lead to a reduction in the number of farm workers—and unemployment. Fortunately, economic development in Mexico has been balanced between agriculture and industry, and industrial production has increased simultaneously with agricultural production, creating new jobs, especially in the manufacture of machinery, cement, glass and steel. The extended use of electric power has formed part of the plan for industrial expansion, and production has more than doubled in ten years. In 1960 the Government again developed their plan by taking control of the Mexican Light and Power Company, formerly owned by foreign interests, and at the same time reminded the nation of the continuing progress of the Revolution with the slogan '1915 — La Tierra, 1938 — El Petroleo, 1960—La Electricidad'.

Mexico's economic development during the last half-century is reflected to some extent in its foreign trade. Before the Revolution and even in the 1930's the chief exports were minerals, whereas today two agricultural products, cotton and coffee, occupy the leading places, followed by lead, copper, zinc and petroleum. Prior to 1910 the main imports were basic foods and railroad equipment, but today they are motor vehicles and machinery. Hoping to become self-sufficient in food crops, Mexico has succeeded in reducing its purchases of basic foods—but some maize and other various foodstuffs still have to be imported.

With agricultural and industrial development, the general standard of living has risen more quickly in Mexico than in most Latin American countries. Yet this standard is still very low by Western criteria: outside the large towns the daily wage of a manual worker varies, according to the region, between 4 and 13 pesos—from 2s 6d to 7s 6d, or 32 cents to 1.04 U.S. dollars. In some rural areas, and especially in the more remote Indian villages, there is still malnutrition and acute poverty. It is in these areas that educational and health services are also sorely needed.

Schemes which would bring about such economic and social improvements require capital investment on a large scale. A great deal of money is required, for instance, for the river basin and electric power development now proceeding in the Papaloapan valley, the first phase of which has been completed; for the building of more dams and irrigation works in the arid north; for the 'March to the Sea' programme; and for the construction of more motor highways. The Mexican Government has raised considerable funds for these development projects by taxation, and more than once has devalued the currency in order to encourage exports, local industries and tourism, and to discourage non-essential imports; in 1954 President Cortines imposed 100 per cent duties on automobiles and television sets, and heavy duties on cigarettes, jewellery, clothing and other so-called luxury imports. Unhappily, such measures cause special suffering to those living on fixed incomes, and the attendant rise in the cost of living penalises workers in the lowest income range—the very people whose conditions the Government is striving to improve.

The provision of capital from public and private sources within Mexico has been inadequate, and the country has been obliged to borrow foreign capital; since the end of World War II, in fact, there has been a considerable influx of money from abroad, especially from the United States. In 1959 it was estimated that 80 per cent of foreign investments in Mexico were of United States origin. The bonds that link Mexico's economy with the United States are further illustrated by the fact that two-thirds of her foreign trade is with her northern neighbour—73 per cent of her imports come from the United States, 58 per cent of her exports go to the United States.

Mexico is aware of the present need for foreign investments, and there is no inconsistency in this awareness in a country which expropriated the foreign oil companies in 1938. In the past, foreign interests frequently took their profits from Mexico without consideration for the country's economic development; today the Mexican Government insists on the reinvestment of a large proportion of such profits in Mexican enterprises. Given political stability in Mexico, there is no reason why investment should not still be favourable to the foreigner; equally, there is no reason why Mexico, having achieved much in a short time, should not achieve much more by the wise use of all available funds.

# THE BRITISH AND FRENCH ISLANDS OF THE WESTERN ATLANTIC

## SAINT-PIERRE AND MIQUELON

This small archipelago of eight islands, a French possession covering an area of 93 square miles, is situated on both sides of the 47°N. line of latitude and within sight of the southern coast of Newfoundland. The group is partly composed of Primary rocks and belongs to the ancient Appalachian system. There is ample evidence of Quaternary glaciation. The relief nowhere exceeds 800 feet, but there are steep hills and wild inhospitable coasts.

Saint-Pierre is made up of hills, once wooded but now almost completely denuded by the inhabitants. Langlade is a plateau of peat-bogs bounded by a precipitous and indented coastline; it is dissected by narrow incised valleys where the only remaining coniferous forests in the archipelago grow. A fine natural causeway, built up by the sea and covered with grass and dunes, links it with Miquelon. This island has rocky ridges, marshy plains, a low-lying coast with lagoons. The accumulation of pebble deposits in the north has formed an alluvial plain which joins the

long rocky promontory protecting the Miquelon roadstead to the rest of the island.

Although it is in the same latitude as Tacoma, Washington, U.S.A., the Saint-Pierre and Miquelon archipelago has a wet climate with strong winds and fairly low temperatures; the mean temperature is 6°C. (43°F.).

There is a population of about 5,000. Originally the inhabitants were Basques, Normans and Bretons, but today more than half the population is of British origin, the descendants of Newfoundlanders.

Fishing apart, the resources of the archipelago are insignificant. It is possible to grow some food crops for local needs, but agriculture is more and more neglected. The breeding of fur-bearing animals was once popular, but this has almost been abandoned. There is some trade in wines and luxury goods, which are imported from France and re-sold to the Canadians. However, if it were not for a large French subsidy the economy of these islands would collapse.

## BERMUDA

The Bermudan archipelago, situated in latitude 32° 28′ N. and longitude 67° 5′ W., rises up in the middle of the Atlantic Ocean from depths of 15,000 to 16,000 feet, about 600 miles from Cape Hatteras, the nearest point of North America.

The total area of the 360 islands and islets of this archipelago, which is composed of coral, is about 21 square miles, but only about twenty of the islands are inhabited.

The islands were discovered at the beginning of the sixteenth century by a Spanish navigator, Juan de Bermudez, and were at that time uninhabited. In 1609 the survivors of an English schooner wrecked on the reefs while on its way to Virginia found refuge there: the Virginia Company founded the first capital, St George, in the north. In 1620 a Parliament met, and in 1684 the Crown took over the government.

Today there are over 48,040 inhabitants, excluding the personnel of the American military and naval bases, which cover an area of 2.3 square miles, and tourists and other temporary residents. The climate is healthy, with warm equable temperatures averaging 21°C. (70°F.). The extensive beaches, well protected by reefs and surrounded by trees, and the clear waters, make Bermuda an ideal resort. Six airlines serve the archipelago. In order to preserve a peaceful atmosphere for the inhabitants, motor traffic is permitted only subject to certain restrictions.

The population is concentrated in the principal island, Great Bermuda, where Hamilton (3,000 inhabitants) has been the capital since 1815; its deep-water harbour can accommodate large ships. St George has retained its colonial character.

The soil of Great Bermuda is fertile, but the 3,000 acres of land under cultivation cannot meet the needs of the population; most of the necessary foodstuffs come from America. The island also imports petroleum products, clothing, building materials, and wines and spirits. The tourist industry earns a very important income for the islands. In 1961, for example, there were 170,000 tourists—well over three times the total permanent population of the islands.

# THE CARIBBEAN LANDS

# THE WEST INDIES

From the entrance to the Gulf of Mexico to the shores of Venezuela, the arc of West Indian islands forms a discontinuous bridge between the two Americas. Boldly outlined in the northern part, the chain dwindles on the eastern and southern borders; the Greater Antilles, aligned from west to east, fringing the seven hundred islands of the Bahamas, are succeeded by the southern chain of the Lesser Antilles which continue in the Leeward and Windward Islands to Trinidad, beyond which they extend as far as Lake Maracaibo.

The West Indian parabola spreads out for three thousand miles from Cape San Antonio, the most westerly point in Cuba, to the small island of Aruba, where the southern arm of the arc ends. The islands are spaced over a distance of nearly one thousand miles between latitudes 10°N. and 23°N., and for 1,250 miles from longitude 60°W. to 85°W., but their total area is only 87,000 square miles, which is rather more than nine-tenths of the area of the United Kingdom, or one-third of Texas.

From the seventeenth to the nineteenth centuries, the Spaniards, English, French and Dutch disputed ownership of the islands. Later the United States intervened. Today there is a gradual movement towards independence among the larger islands of the West Indies, though much of the archipelago is still connected with Great Britain, France, the Netherlands and the United States.

*A mosaic of islands.* The wide range of racial types, of land use and of methods of cultivation corresponds to a great variety of relief and natural vegetation.

The differences in the size of the islands is one reason for their diversity. Of the four Greater Antilles, the largest is Cuba, 44,000 square miles, and the smallest, Puerto Rico, with 3,423 square miles. Even if the Bahamas (4,404 square miles) are included with the Lesser Antilles, their total area is barely 9,650 square miles. Montserrat is only 33 square miles, and Saba only 5 square miles in area. The Grenadines consist of 600 scattered islands, some of which are insignificant in size.

The geologist Suess drew attention to the existence of three quite distinct concentric arcs; an outer arc composed of recent limestones, a central zone of older rocks which rises up to form bold mountain ranges in the Greater Antilles, and an inner arc of young volcanic rocks represented by the lesser Antilles. Recent research has established that the structure of the West Indies is more complex than was imagined. Geophysical research has shown the existence of an area to the east of the West Indies, where the gravity values are below normal and this partly corresponds to deep marine trenches. Associated with this is a very marked tendency of the land to rise, accompanied by earthquakes and volcanic eruptions. The West Indies is a cordillera in process of formation.

The low limestone islands like Grande-Terre, Marie Galante, and Barbados, can be contrasted with the young volcanic islands which, from Saba to Grenada through Guadeloupe, Dominica, Martinique, St Lucia and St Vincent, have rugged relief features with solfataras and mountain peaks. Elsewhere volcanic hills or *mornes* which have been worn down by erosion, as in St Martin or St Barthélemy, divide up the Tertiary limestone plateaus. However, it is in the Greater Antilles that the combination of plains and mountain ranges, old volcanic rocks and marine sediments is most remarkable. The Sierra Maestra of Cuba, the Blue Mountains of Jamaica, the ranges of Hispaniola (Haiti and the Dominican Republic) and Puerto Rico are sometimes over 9,000 feet. Remarkable structural troughs like that occupied by Lake Saumâtre in Haiti and Lake Enriquillo in the Dominican Republic are evidence of powerful earth movements.

The latitude of the islands is the cause of climatic differences. The low rainfall of the cool season is much more marked in the northern parts of the Greater Antilles than in the Lesser Antilles, except in the Leeward Islands, near the Venezuelan coast, which are almost semi-desert. Exposure and altitude accentuate regional variations. Exposed to the wet trade winds, the windward slopes receive heavy rainfall; the coastal plains have an annual rainfall of 80 inches, and this increases to a total rainfall of 300 inches on the high volcanic slopes of Guadeloupe, Dominica and Martinique. On the leeward side the rainfall rapidly decreases, falling to less than 60 inches on the coast. Where the land is not high enough to cause condensation drought is severe, as in the low limestone islands of the outer arc and in the small low-lying volcanic islands. On the sides of the volcanic islands of the Lesser Antilles, and even more on the high mountain ranges of the Greater Antilles, altitude makes it possible to escape from the humid heat of the lowlands, and here there are numerous 'hill stations'.

As a result, within a few hours it is possible to travel through dense, almost equatorial forest, thorn bush and cactus-covered semi-desert. In Martinique there is a marked contrast between the great forests, with lianas, epiphytes and tree ferns on the slopes of Carbet, and the stony almost desert-like savanna; a similar contrast exists between the dense forests of Dominica or Guadeloupe and the poor scrub of St Barthélemy, Les Saintes or Désirade. In Haiti, the lower slopes of the La Selle massif are well-watered and wooded, while round Lake Saumâtre the land resembles the Mexican desert, with cereus cactus (torch thistle) and prickly pear. In the Central Cordillera in the Dominican Republic, or on the southern slopes of the Sierra Maestra in Cuba, there are large pine forests which are not typical of tropical areas.

*Racial mixture.* The West Indies are noted for their heterogeneous population. The Arawaks and Caribs, who inhabited the islands before their discovery by Europeans, disappeared and were replaced by a white population, which in turn was overwhelmed by the influx of Africans brought to the islands by the slave-traders. Widespread inter-breeding produced the race of coloured people who today form the main part of the West Indian population. The abolition of slavery resulted in the desertion of the estates by the Negroes, and the planters employed workers from Asia who were brought in by contract.

The racial mixture varies from one island to another, and sometimes between neighbouring districts in the same island. The old Spanish colonies had fewer slaves than the French and British islands. At the end of the eighteenth century there were 35,000 white people in the Spanish part of Hispaniola and 30,000 in the French part; on the other hand, while there were only 30,000 slaves in the Spanish territory, there were 465,000 in the area under French control. Today there is a striking contrast between the Negro state of Haiti and the Dominican Republic, two-thirds of whose population consists of mulattos and mestizos. According to the latest estimates, the populations of Cuba and Puerto Rico are respectively 71 per cent and 73 per cent white and only 15 per cent and 20 per cent Negro. Trinidad is distinguished by the outstanding importance of the East Indian element, which is becoming the largest racial group in the island.

*The variety of agriculture.* Equally marked contrasts exist in agricultural landscapes, methods of cultivation and land use. The red clay soils of the gentle windward slopes and the brown soils of the alluvial plains and limestone plateaus provide the factories with sugar-cane. Bananas are sometimes grown together with coffee trees in plantations; there are sisal plantations in the Greater Antilles and cocoa plantations on the wet lowlands of Hispaniola and Trinidad. On the food-producing lands there is mixed cultivation of coffee, cocoa, bananas, mangoes, oranges and breadfruit, and underneath these, the large leaves of the taros, whose roots are used for food. Maize, manioc, sweet potatoes, yams and Angola peas are grown on the same plot of land. In spite of forest regulations illicit 'gardens' creep in along the edges or in the interior of the State forests. In the dry regions there are savanna grasslands used for stock-rearing, and cotton fields scattered among extensive areas of scrubland.

The traditional agriculture of the small farmer who grows his crops according to the methods used by the Caribs has nothing in common with the large sugar estates where, over thousands of acres and under the supervision of agricultural overseers, farming operations are constantly improved and modernised in order to profit from the latest techniques. The variety of soils and situations, the ease of access to the islands

and the employment of slave labour were the foundations of a successful plantation economy. In spite of serious economic crises since the seventeenth century, sugar-cane has ensured the prosperity of the West Indies. The list of important West Indian crops has now lengthened considerably: coffee, cocoa, bananas, citrus fruit, pineapples, tobacco. Mixed cultivation of food crops is carried on alongside plantation cultivation almost everywhere, and this explains the extraordinary resilience of the West Indies to the economic and social crises which affected them, as well as the possibility of abnormally high densities of population, and also the great variety in economy resulting from the differing policies of the colonial or independent local governments.

There are numerous types of settlement: swarms of huts scattered over the food-growing areas, hamlets where settlers and agricultural workers are grouped together in those regions where sugar-cane only is grown, small sleepy market towns, towns built in the old colonial style and capital cities with marked American influences. Again, there is variation in the value of the mineral resources and consequently, from island to island, there are marked differences in the degree of industrial development.

*West Indian unity.* In spite of these contrasts there is a unity throughout the West Indian islands, and paradoxically its chief factor is diversity. The distinctive geographical character is the continual change from mountain to plain, from forest to savanna, and the great variety of racial groups and ways of life.

Insularity is also a strong unifying factor and everywhere the sea forms the horizon. The sea helps to provide a livelihood for many of the people on the dry islands, and it makes a substantial contribution to the diet of the coastal peoples. The sea is also the means of inter-island communications, and trade was one of the main factors in the success of the tropical plantations which made the islands famous in the seventeenth and eighteenth centuries.

But certain disadvantages result from this island situation. The facts of environment, history and the direction of trade have all had the same effect, that of separating the islands from one another. Links between colonies and their mother countries have overshadowed those between one island and another. Today, only industrialists, technicians and politicians are aware of West Indian unity, thanks to air transport and the international organisations of the Caribbean area. Although there is some movement of population between the islands, for example the seasonal movement of labour and temporary and permanent emigration from the underdeveloped islands to those where wages are higher, this hardly affects the basic feature of isolation. The inconvenience of travel by steamer, the high cost of air transport, monetary and customs formalities, language difficulties, and the absence of commercial links between islands producing the same commodities, have resulted in an insular outlook, which leads the West Indians to think of many problems purely from their own point of view.

The West Indies are all tropical islands, so that there are marked similarities between them. The climate on the lowlands is always hot and wet with a mean annual temperature of about 26°C. (78°F.) - 27°C.

St Lucia: one of the Pitons, great rocks at the southern end of the island.
Such 'sugar-loaf' formations are characteristic features of the area, being the remains of volcanic cones.
Dense vegetation grows right down to the shore.

(80°F.), the sky is often cloudy, humidity is high, and trade winds blow regularly except during the 'winter' season, when heavy rains make the climate more unpleasant. During the hot season devastating hurricanes also occur. Throughout the whole archipelago the same great families of plants recur, and mangroves fringe the coastal marshes everywhere.

The West Indies are often described as nature's paradise; however, hurricanes, volcanic eruptions and earthquakes, the poverty and instability of some of the soils, and the enervating climate which makes physical labour arduous, must not be discounted. The observer is struck by the wretchedness of the poor, whether among the white population of Les Saintes and St Barthélemy, or among the Negroes of Haiti and Jamaica. Those in charge of production generally complain of absenteeism and the low output of the workers, which is partly due to the co-existence of a modern trading economy with the mixed cultivation of tropical food crops that reduce the necessity for hard work. Dwellings are often poor; simple huts made of boards or thin slats are roofed with straw or corrugated iron. A high birthrate, together with an appreciable decline in mortality, which is the result of improvements in hygiene and tropical medicine, sets formidable problems concerning future over-population.

The same way of life can be found throughout the West Indies. It is both carefree and gracious, with a passion for politics and discussion, for religion and superstition, and for freedom in styles of dancing and music. The harmony which is so characteristic of life in the 'Islands' can be found in all the regional groups which are now to be discussed.

## THREE INDEPENDENT REPUBLICS

Three States freed themselves from the guardianship of France and Spain and declared their political independence: Haiti in 1804, the Dominican Republic in 1843, and Cuba in 1898. French has remained the official language in Haiti, and Spanish in Cuba and the Dominican Republic. The past is evident everywhere, and along with Puerto Rico the two large islands of Cuba and Hispaniola form outposts of Latin civilisation close to the United States, while after the Spanish-American war of 1898 which brought independence to Cuba, the military and economic influence of this neighbouring great power was asserted.

On several occasions the United States has intervened to restore order in Haiti and the Dominican Republic. Haiti is linked to the dollar area, buys 63 per cent of its imports, and sells 48 per cent of its exports to the United States. The Dominican peso is equal in value to the dollar, and the capital which is chiefly invested in the sugar refineries is largely of American origin.

CUBA, THE SECOND LARGEST WORLD PRODUCER OF SUGAR. Cuba is the largest and most densely populated of the Caribbean islands, with an area of 44,000 square miles and a population of about 7,000,000. The central part is mainly lowland; to the west, in the province of Pinar del Rio, is the Sierra de Los Organos. The highest mountains, the Sierra Maestra,

are in the south-east. The structure of the island is limestone with karst features.

Agriculture employs nearly half the working population, and together with the trade and industry which result from it provides the livelihood of 90 per cent of the population. Sugar and its products alone provide nearly nine-tenths of the value of the island's exports. The provinces of Camagüey and Oriente, which have large mills, are more important than the central provinces.

The tobacco-producing regions are in the centre and west of the island, and about 40,000 tons are produced annually. After tobacco in order of importance come fruit (pineapples, bananas and avocado pears), rice, coffee and animal products. Agricultural reforms are being undertaken. All land was nationalised in 1959, and by the following year 764 co-operative farms had been established.

There are ten towns with more than 50,000 inhabitants, and Havana, the capital, has a population of 1,000,000. As yet there is no problem of over-

The West Indies consists of a mosaic of islands containing a wide range of racial types, methods of cultivation and land use.
The racial mixture varies from one island to another and even between neighbouring districts on the same island; while agriculture covers numerous crops ranging from coffee to cotton.
The photograph shows workers returning from the sugar-cane fields.

Aerial view of Santo Domingo, capital of the Dominican Republic. The city has been redeveloped since it was completely destroyed by a hurricane in 1930. In the foreground is the new harbour, which can accommodate large liners.

population, for 25 per cent of the cultivable land remains undeveloped. There are some mineral resources, including iron ore, manganese, chromium, nickel and copper. In addition to sugar mills, Cuba has textile factories, cement works, flour mills, and oil refineries. The island has one of the best systems of communications in the West Indies, and the tourist industry has been widely developed.

After the revolution of 1959 the Cuban Government set about nationalising major industries and redistributing land. The economy had formerly been directly or indirectly controlled by United States financial interests. However, in January 1961 the United States broke off diplomatic relations with Cuba, which proceeded with a policy of political and

A Puerto Rican pineapple cannery. Pineapples are the third most important crop in Puerto Rico (after sugar and tobacco).
Its cultivation is a year-round activity employing about 5,000 people, for it requires great care. Over 80 per cent of the crop is canned, the rest being shipped fresh to the United States.

economic rapprochement with the Communist countries; 80 per cent of Cuban exports went to the U.S.S.R. Both the U.S.S.R. and China agreed to buy Cuban sugar and to extend credit for industrial development. The U.S.S.R. supplied Cuba with petroleum and armaments including ballistic missiles; the United States as a result established an arms blockade of the island in October 1962 and the ballistic missiles were returned to the U.S.S.R.

HAITI, THE FRENCH-SPEAKING NEGRO REPUBLIC. The Negro Republic of Haiti is very different from Cuba. Its 10,700 square miles support a population estimated in 1964 to be about 4 million, the majority being Negroes, with an important mulatto minority.

Haiti occupies the western third of Hispaniola. The southern mountain range overlooks the Cul de Sac lowland and Lake Saumâtre. In the north there is a series of parallel ranges separated by the Artibonite valley and the Hinche plateau. The mountains in the north-west project to form a peninsula south of which is the Gulf of Gonaives. These relief divisions give a great variety of landscape and vegetation.

Agriculture, almost the only occupation, is mainly concerned with the mixed cultivation of food crops, such as bananas, yams, manioc, rice, Caribbean cabbages, maize, millet and fruit trees. The dwellings are very primitive; without any doubt the population

remains one of the poorest in the West Indies, and it is increasing. Density is about 320 per square mile. Reforestation, the fight against erosion, the provision of water for agricultural purposes, and international aid should lead to better economic development in the island. Coffee, cultivated on the hills by small farmers, is the leading export. Other main crops are sugar, cocoa and tobacco. Sisal cultivation is developing rapidly. Molasses, cotton, beans and timber are of secondary importance. Rum and other spirits are distilled and cattle and horse breeding are encouraged.

THE DOMINICAN REPUBLIC. Beyond the land frontier of Haiti lies the Dominican Republic, covering the eastern two-thirds of Hispaniola. In 1964 there was a population of 3,452,000 in this country of 18,800 square miles, giving a density of 182 people to the square mile. This state is the Spanish part of the island, which was not greatly developed during the colonial period; slaves were never very numerous here.

The highest mountains in the West Indies are to be found in Hispaniola. The Cibao or Pico Duarte is 10,440 feet high and many peaks in the Central Cordillera are nearly 10,000 feet high. Between the ranges there are large plains, such as the well-known Vega Real, the Azua Plain and the Constanza valley.

Although recent attempts have been made to develop the land, only 9,900 square miles are cultivable and 12 per cent is in rich pasture. Large areas are still covered with forests, rich in rare species, which could be developed in the future. Official encouragement is given to those who want to develop unoccupied regions, and the State supports a policy of European immigration. The cultivation of sugar-cane is still the basis of the agriculture, but coffee, cocoa, rice, maize, tobacco, bananas and oranges are also exported. Stock-rearing is sufficiently important for some meat to be exported.

For some years there have consistently been favourable balances of trade, a reflection of the expanding economy. A large-scale effort has been made to increase industrialisation. There are already 3,000 miles of good roads in the Dominican Republic, and the construction of new routes continues. The capital, Santo Domingo (for 23 years called Ciudad Trujillo), is a large town with a population of 529,000, and has the advantage of a modern deep-water port. It is proud of the fact that it possesses the tomb of Christopher Columbus, which lies in what is commonly claimed to be the first cathedral built in the Americas by the Spaniards (in 1512).

## THE AMERICAN WEST INDIES

PUERTO RICO, A SPANISH-SPEAKING, OVERPOPULATED AMERICAN ISLAND. According to the terms of the Puerto Rican Constitution of 1952, Puerto Rico, the most easterly island of the Greater Antilles, is 'a Commonwealth in close association with the United States, but with autonomy in its internal affairs'. The island did not become American territory until 1898, and the population remains mainly Spanish-speaking.

Puerto Rico is 3,423 square miles in area. A central mountain region, with Cerro Punta rising to 4,392 feet, extends right to the western coast, but there are

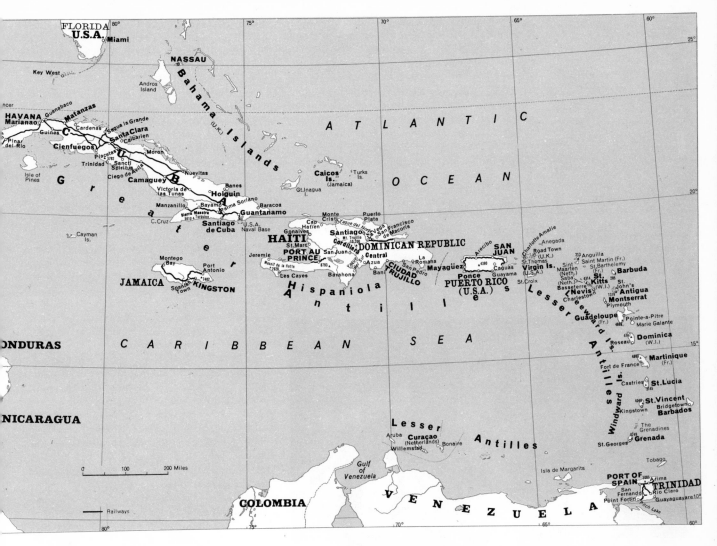

coastal plains along the northern, eastern and southern shores. There is a region of very fine karst scenery in the north-west of the island. The southern coast on the leeward side is semi-arid.

The population figures for July 1964 totalled 2,584,000. The birthrate is 31.5 per 1,000. Emigration of Puerto Ricans to the United States is insufficient to relieve overcrowding. The overpopulation has resulted in the Land Authority taking over large estates and re-distributing land. Tax exemption and a favourable loan policy encourage the establishment of new industries, which are intended to employ tens of thousands of workers and to reduce the volume of imports.

The most important products are sugar (about 1,266,000 tons produced annually), molasses, rum and alcohol. Tobacco, coffee, pineapples, coconuts, vanilla and lemons come next in order of value. Imports exceed exports, indicating that the country is in the process of capital development. The capital, San Juan, is a large town of over half a million inhabitants. There is a well-organised tourist industry. THE AMERICAN VIRGIN ISLANDS. Three small dependencies of Puerto Rico, the islands of Viques, Mona and Culebra, are the forerunners of the Lesser Antilles. The Virgin Islands, which continue them towards the east, belong to Great Britain and the United States.

The American Virgin Islands are about 132 square miles in area and have nearly 32,000 inhabitants grouped in the three main islands of St Thomas, St John and St Croix.

The population, which declined steadily for a century, has recovered in recent years, and there was an increase of nearly 20 per cent between 1950 and 1960. The capital of St Thomas, Charlotte Amalie, contains about four-fifths of the island's population. The United States is far more interested in the strategic value of the Virgin islands than in the sugar products from St Croix and the rum and bay rum from St Thomas and St John.

## THE NETHERLANDS WEST INDIES

Aruba, Bonaire and Curaçao, not far from the Gulf of Maracaibo, are by far the most important of these Dutch territories in the Caribbean region. The others, less important, are part of the Leeward islands; they are St Eustatius (8 square miles), Saba (5 square miles) and the southern part of St Martin (13 square miles). These three islands have a total population of barely 3,700, most of them English-speaking Negroes.

The three islands near the Venezuelan coast are much more important. They have a semi-arid climate and are small in area; Aruba has 70 square miles, Bonaire,

There is a great deal of variety in the West Indian islands: in size, altitude, climate, ethnic composition (people from every corner of the globe), in language (every language spoken in the New World except Portuguese, and in addition Dutch and Danish), and in political regime (from colonies to independent states). Unity is, however, conferred to a great extent by the setting of the Caribbean Sea and similarities in economic activities. Political unity such as that attempted by the Federation of the West Indies, which came into being in 1958 and comprised all the British Caribbean dependencies except the Virgin Islands, has encountered difficulties: in 1961 Jamaica decided to secede from the Federation, and it finally broke up with the departure of Trinidad and Tobago in 1962.

The Trinidad Pitch Lake.
A worker shows the consistency
of the natural asphalt.
About 150,000 tons are exported
annually. The island also
possesses oil reserves and has
refineries both for its own
and for Venezuelan oil.
As a result Trinidad is far more
prosperous than most
of the East Indies.

Packing green bananas in a fruit
shed at Montego Bay, Jamaica.
Almost all of them are exported
to Britain and Western Europe.
They are shipped green and
not allowed to ripen until they
reach their destination.
Bananas are among the most
important of the immense variety
of West Indian crops.

III square miles, and Curaçao 172 square miles. Agriculture is not important. However, the Royal Dutch Oil Company has established refineries on Curaçao and Standard Oil has its own on Aruba. These installations refine Venezuelan petroleum, and this industry is the mainstay of most of the population. Curaçao had 127,840 inhabitants in 1960. Aruba 58,868, and Bonaire, which is chiefly agricultural, only 5,755. The installation of large refineries in Venezuela is a serious threat to the economic future of these islands. International tourism is developing.

## THE BRITISH WEST INDIES

The British West Indies Federation, formed in 1957, included Jamaica, St Kitts, Nevis, Antigua, Montserrat, Dominica, St Lucia, St Vincent, Barbados, Grenada, Tobago and Trinidad. The independence of Jamaica in 1961 and Trinidad and Tobago in 1962 led to the dissolution of the Federation of the West Indies.

Barbados achieved independence in November 1966. The remaining territories comprising the West Indies Associated States have internal self-government, while the British government controls defence and external affairs.

Jamaica is 4,411 square miles in area. It is very mountainous, the Blue Mountains reaching a height of 7,400 feet. The population is increasing rapidly and today amounts to 1,706,000 with a density of more than 365 to the square mile. Sugar-cane occupies 150,000 acres and about 450,000 tons of sugar are produced annually. Sugar and bananas are the leading export crops, and cocoa, coffee, maize and citrus fruits are also quite important. Jamaica is the leading world producer of bauxite, and alumina and bauxite together are by far the most valuable export. Industries are being introduced. Kingston, the capital, is the largest town.

The Bahamas are a group of seven hundred small islands with a total area of 4,404 square miles. About twenty are inhabited; there are altogether 131,000 inhabitants, of whom 50,000 live in the island of New Providence where the capital, Nassau, is situated. There is some agriculture, but the archipelago depends mainly on the tourist industry.

The Leeward Islands form the northern group of the Lesser Antilles. In addition to the British Virgin Islands, they include on the one hand, Anguilla, Barbuda and Antigua, small islands which are low and arid and whose principal sources of income are stock-rearing, the cultivation of cotton and sugar-cane, fishing and shipping; and on the other hand, the volcanic islands of St Kitts, Nevis, Redonda and Montserrat. The islands have an area of 400 square miles and a population of 130,500.

The Windward Islands cover 826 square miles, and are more densely populated with 314,295 inhabitants. They include Dominica, St Lucia, St Vincent, Grenada and the Grenadines. Apart from the coral reefs or *cays* of the Grenadines, these islands are mountainous and bristle with volcanic peaks. There is a small amount of agriculture. Dominica is the last refuge of the original Carib people. St Lucia and St Vincent are of very little importance economically, and Grenada and the Grenadines are concerned almost exclusively with food crops and fishing.

Barbados is prosperous, with 240,000 inhabitants in an area of 166 square miles, giving a density of almost 1,450 people to the square mile. Sugar-cane plantations occupy about 51,000 acres, and annual sugar production exceeds 160,000 tons.

Trinidad and Tobago are island outposts of the South American continent. Tobago is not very important, with an area of 116 square miles and a population of 40,000. Trinidad has an area of 1,864 square miles and a population of 900,500. Sugar and its by-products are the main resources, and 226,000 tions occupy about 51,000 acres, and annual sugar plantations provide about 8,000 tons of cocoa beans for export per year. Coffee, citrus fruits and coconuts supply both home and foreign markets. Pitch Lake, a curious natural feature of the island, produces about 150,000 tons of asphalt annually. More than 7,000,000 tons of oil are produced, and Venezuelan oil is refined. The island is economically prosperous, but a very important East Indian minority may raise serious political problems for the future.

## THE FRENCH WEST INDIES

In 1946, Martinique and Guadeloupe were promoted to the status of French Departments. Martinique has an area of 425 square miles and a population of 292,000. The Guadeloupe archipelago is 688 square miles in area and its population numbers 283,000.

Martinique is mainly mountainous and volcanic. Mount Pelée erupted in 1902 and 1929. The island of Guadeloupe proper is also volcanic, with rugged relief, and Mount Soufrière still has solfataras. The small archipelago of Les Saintes is also composed of volcanic rocks, but Grande-Terre, adjoining Guadeloupe, Marie Galante and Désirade are sedimentary islands composed of Tertiary limestones, with gentle relief. The distant dependencies in the north, St Barthélemy and St Martin, are composed of rounded volcanic hills or *mornes,* limestone plateaus and broad alluvial lowlands.

Bananas and sugar-cane are the main sources of wealth in Martinique and Guadeloupe. The latter island produces about 163,000 tons of bananas and 172,000 tons of sugar annually, while Martinique has a much smaller output of both commodities. Other agricultural products are coffee, cocoa and vanilla. Agriculture is of little importance in the arid dependencies of Guadeloupe. Fishing is important.

The population of Martinique and Guadeloupe is essentially a mixed one. There are many East Indians, but they are being assimilated. The population of St Barthélemy is entirely white, and both Les Saintes and Désirade have mainly white populations.

Fort-de-France, with 85,000 inhabitants, and Point-à-Pitre, with 26,000 inhabitants, are busy ports. Basse-Terre, the capital of Guadeloupe, is a small administrative town. The rest are only large villages.

# CENTRAL AMERICA

Central America comprises, from north-west to south-east, the republics of Guatemala, Honduras, El Salvador, Nicaragua, Costa Rica and Panama, and the British colony of Honduras. The respective capitals are Guatemala, Tegucigalpa, San Salvador, Managua, San José, Panama and Belize.

*Geographical unity: isthmus and structure.* From the isthmus of Tehuantepec to Panama, with only a narrow depression in Nicaragua, occupied by a large lake, the backbone of Central America is formed by a mountain chain topped by jagged peaks rising to over 13,000 feet, enclosing populous *mesas* (plateaus) which have a pleasant climate and fertile soil. A series of about 250 volcanoes — some now active, such as Fuego in Guatemala, Izalco in El Salvador, Momotomba in Nicaragua — form a line separated from the Atlantic by a strip of land enriched with volcanic alluvia. Across the chain flows a profusion of streams, yellowish and swollen during the rains, but disappearing in the dry season. The population is densest in the north-west and most settlements are between 2,000 and 5,000 feet up.

On the Atlantic slope, from Yucatan in Mezico to Colombia, there are low stretches of coast, marshy and damp, sprinkled with lagoons; the mosquito-infested bays form an almost unbroken sequence. Bananas grow in ideal conditions. But the climate is somewhat trying, and the population very sparse.

From Tehuantepec to Panama, on the Pacific coast, the rainy season (May to October) alternates with the dry season (November to April), whereas on the Atlantic coast the prevailing north-east winds bring rain all the year round. On the Pacific coast the driest part of the year is the period January to March, with less than three inches of rain.

*Ethnic unity: the Indian of Central America.* Everywhere there are found Indian populations which are predominantly of Maya ancestry. In many places Indian and white cultures exist side by side, as in Costa Rica. Elsewhere thare are half-breeds of Indian and Negro, the *zambos,* or of Indian and Spaniard, the *ladinos*; everywhere their ancestors have left ruins behind them, sometimes imposing, yet always expressing the spirit of the aboriginal race.

The Indian is small, with an open countenance, attractive, bright eyes and rather a childish expression, clad in gaily coloured materials. Trotting along the roads, laden with scores of earthenware pots filled with fruits and other produce to be sold or bartered in a market that may be over thirty miles away from his home, and followed by women with their young families, he is the soul of Central America.

Spanish domination, after the conquest, set its seal on these territories, imprinting them with the Catholic religion, the language, the customs, the monuments.

*Economic unity: essentially agricultural countries.* The economy of Central America is based almost entirely on agriculture: 85 per cent of the inhabitants spend their life in the fields; 90 per cent of the exports are agricultural. Just before the rains, the Indians burn the grasses, and often the forests; the ashes and other residua are used as fertilizers. On the modern farms chemical fertilizer is extensively used.

San Juan de los Morros, a pass which lies between the depression of Lake Valencia and the Llanos. It forms part of the irregular chain of the Inner Cordillera.

Everywhere agriculture falls into two well differentiated categories. The first, which is capitalist in type and frequently in the hands of foreigners, produces coffee, cotton, bananas and cacao for export, with the use of very modern plant and local labour. The second is domestic, without technical aids; crops include maize, beans, and in smaller quantities rice, the basis of the local diet. Wheat, yams, manioc, sorghums and vegetables are also grown.

The United States is the chief customer for agricultural products and the chief supplier of manufactured products.

Industry includes food processing (coffee and sugar), cotton gins, tanneries and sawmills; but electric power is almost entirely lacking and roads are underdeveloped.

Life in the European manner is very costly everywhere, and extreme poverty exists side by side with extravagant luxury.

*Diversity of Central America.* There are considerable differences between the various countries. The central mountain spine spreads out in Guatemala, which has a delightful climate in most of its territory, and in Eastern Honduras, the Switzerland of Central America. On the other side, where the mountains are drawn to one side, as in Nicaragua, there are majestic plains penetrated by long rivers. In Panama the climate almost everywhere is tropical, hot and damp; in the mountainous parts of Costa Rica it is cool all the year round.

There is ethnological diversity, too: 'Indian' is a word that covers very different racial characteristics. The Mayas, by nature gentle and peaceable, and their descendants, the Lencas, make up a group with very well-defined physical features and qualities. The Toltecs and related tribes, on the contrary, were warlike in temperament, and their descendants have often retained the aggressive spirit. The Negroes, who live on the Atlantic coasts, are peace-loving, gentle and good-natured. Lastly, there is a whole gamut of half-breeds. The population of a city like Panama, the outcome of every permutation of interbreeding, is keenly aware of its political and economic ambitions, with a consciousness still lacking in the Indian of Honduras or of Guatemala.

The Spaniards settled wherever there were gold and silver mines. Panama and Nicaragua show only a tinge of Spanish influence, whereas its effects on El Salvador and Costa Rica are in much greater evidence.

Finally, there are countries of Indians, such as El Salvador, where 98 per cent of the population is composed of mestizos (Spanish/Portuguese and Indian half-breeds) and Indians; or Guatemala, whose population is 54 per cent pure Indian; and countries of white people, such as Costa Rica, where 85 per cent of the population is of Spanish origin.

The contrasts stand out also in the varying degrees of development: while in El Salvador or Costa Rica the most modern agricultural systems in the world are encountered, in Honduras and in Nicaragua agriculture is still primitive.

The question now is whether an inter-nations organisation can emerge. Unity was first revealed at the beginning of the nineteenth century when the federation of the United Provinces of Central America

was established. The Charter of the present-day Organisation of American States was adopted in 1948. There are 21 members, all of equal status: Argentina, Bolivia, Brazil, Chile, Colombia, Costa Rica, Cuba, Dominican Republic, Ecuador, El Salvador, Guatemala, Haiti, Honduras, Mexico, Nicaragua, Panama, Paraguay, Peru, U.S.A., Uruguay and Venezuela.

Construction of a road from the Mexican-United States border through Mexico, Guatemala, El Salvador, Honduras, Nicaragua, Costa Rica, Panama, Colombia, Ecuador and Peru to Chile has been completed. The section in Central America was completed in 1962 in spite of difficult tropical conditions. The total cost over the past twenty-five years has been 140 million U.S. dollars of which the United States supplied 80 million.

# GUATEMALA

With an area of only 42,000 square miles, Guatemala has about 4,278,000 inhabitants, and is thus the most densely populated state in Central America. With its rugged volcanic peaks, some rising to over 13,000 feet, and its delightful lakes, this is one of the most fascinating countries in the world.

*Importance of volcanic activity.* The central crest is formed by an imposing chain of mountains, an extension of the Mexican Sierra Madre. There are over thirty volcanoes here; some, such as Tajumulco, the highest peak in Central America (13,812 feet), are still active.

In this imposing central massif with its agreeable climate thousands of villages lie in irregularly shaped valleys. For the most part these villages practise a system of animal husbandry; the inhabitants, amiable and artistic in temperament, remain almost entirely untouched by 'Western civilisation'. The capital, Guatemala, situated on the plain of Las Vacas (at 4,850 feet), has 573,000 inhabitants. Less than an hour's journey away are the magnificent ruins of Antigua, with the volcanoes Fuego and Acatenango towering above. In the sixteenth century it was the real capital of the whole of Central America; it was completely destroyed by an earthquake in 1773.

Passing from this Cordillera towards the Pacific we meet Los Altos — plateaus which in the clearness of their air and in their vegetation closely resemble the Mexican plateau. The descent from Los Altos to the coast offers a range of every possible type in climate and vegetation. The strip of flat land separating sea from mountains varies between 15 and 40 miles in width. It is a hot and unhealthy region, the natural continuation of the lowlands of Honduras and Mexico.

On the descent from the Central Cordillera towards the Atlantic the climate becomes tropical, with unhealthy marshes and impenetrable forests infested with insects. Yucatan, British Honduras, Peten and Honduras present a homogeneous unit. This entire zone — subject to severe flooding from the rains that come from the Gulf of Mexico, and barely fit for habitation — was the centre of the ancient Maya civilisation. Today, the nomadic Pokonchis and the Kekchis roam the forest.

Guatemala is watered by many swift rivers. Those

emptying into the Pacific are generally short, rising in mountains which overhang the coast. On the Atlantic slope the watercourses are longer and larger: the Motagua (330 miles), the Dulce, which is navigable and flows into Lake Izabal, and the Usumacinta, which forms part of the frontier with Mexico.

Lake Izabal, about 36 miles long, is the largest lake, but the most beautiful is Lake Atitlan, whose waters reflect the volcanoes Atitlan and San Pedro. Another is Lake Amatitlan, 7,700 feet above sea level.

*Guatemala, country of the Mayas.* The Indian populations are the heirs of highly developed civilisations. The most important among them was that of the Mayas, who left behind some imposing ruins, especially in the Peten region, whence they migrated to Yucatan. Their political power and civilisation was at its zenith about 400 B.C. The chiefs were hereditary, with the nobles forming a body in attendance, and the priests a class apart. The Mayas were extremely advanced in their culture, especially in exact sciences (mathematics and astronomy), and they left behind them impressive achievements in the realms of architecture, sculpture and paintings. They were skilled in ceramics, weaving, gold and silver working. Their present-day descendants, now on the road to extinction, subsist in small groups in the forest, dependent for their livelihood on hunting and fishing.

The Quichés, who live on the high central plateaus, had an ancient capital at Xelaju, hidden away in the rich valley of the Rio Samala. The Cakchiquels are found chiefly in the region of Chimaltenango, the Zutuhils near Lake Atitlan and the Pokonchis mainly in the eastern part of the country. These Indians, as a rule friendly in their ways, by nature vivacious, easy-going and artistic in temperament, have a fine physique. Deeply attached to their traditions and superstitions, they cultivate only the produce essential for their family consumption, for their wants are few.

Spanish conquerors mingled with these autochthonous elements in the sixteenth century. Santiago de los Caballeros, founded in 1524, was destroyed in 1541 by an earthquake. The conquered territory was declared a *capitania general,* and in 1570 the *Audencia de Guatemala* (Guatemala Court of Justice) was created. Guatemala became an independent republic in April 1839.

*Inadequate economic development. Future prospects.* Guatemala has an agriculture of the Central American standard type: a capitalist agriculture with great modern plantations. producing goods for export, and native husbandry which supplies, frequently by archaic methods, produce necessary for domestic consumption.

In the vast plantations coffee of exceptional quality is grown, which represents 70 to 85 per cent of the total value of exports. The most important belts of production are on the slopes facing the Pacific, the areas around Ocos, in the Costa Cuca, in Coban, on the lower Polochic and to the south of Lake Izabal. Bananas, much less important, take second place. Owned mainly by the United Fruit Company, the estates stretch across the whole width of the country and are connected by rail from Puerto Barrios on the Atlantic to San José on the Pacific, these being the two chief ports for the export trade. In addition to

its trading activities, the United Fruit Company has built railroads, ports, schools, and hospitals.

Cotton exports doubled between 1954 and 1956. The Indians make wonderful multi-coloured fabrics from cotton. Rubber is cultivated in Peten and exported via Puerto Barrios. Valuable timbers are grown, especially mahogany in Peten, and cedar.

Ninety per cent of the population is rural, devoted to stock-rearing and growing produce for home consumption. Maize takes up 63 per cent of the land under cultivation. After that come rice, potatoes, oats, wheat and beans.

Cattle and pig breeding, of some importance in the centre and north-west, supply hides and skins for export.

There is no industry in the strict sense of the term, only small factories meeting local demand. Minerals exist in certain places and could form the basis of industrial activity: gold at Las Quebradas; silver, vigorously exploited by the Spaniards, particularly at Huehuetenango and in Chiquimula; copper lead and manganese.

Guatemala's economy is still that of a poor country, but it possesses important resources still unexploited and a rapidly increasing population, whose younger elements are preparing themselves, in the university centres, to develop the country's economy. Road construction programmes are well advanced, and the tourist industry, already active, cannot but increase in a land of such natural wealth and fine scenery. The government has undertaken a courageous campaign for the education of the masses and for raising the average standard of living.

Guatemala's economy retains many traditional features, although it possesses important resources still unexploited — among them minerals, which could form the basis of a flourishing industry. The youger elements of Guatemala's rapidly increasing population are receiving a university education that will equip them to develop their country's future.

# BRITISH HONDURAS

With the Atlantic as its eastern border, Guatemala to the south and west and Mexico to the north, British Honduras forms a small, very thinly populated enclave of 8,867 square miles with 105,000 inhabitants. The Turneffe Islands are included in its area.

The region is flat and marshy, with a hot, damp,

unhealthy climate. The Cockscomb or Maya mountains do not rise above about 3,300 feet.

The territory of Belize was ceded to Great Britain in 1859, and Guatemalan governments have been unceasing in their claims for its restitution ever since. At present British Honduras is under the rule of a Governor assisted by an executive council.

This region was once inhabited by the same aboriginal groups that populated Yucatan, Guatemala and Honduras. The population is mainly agricultural. Sugar figures highly in the economy, output being increased from 35,000 tons in 1965 to 60,000 tons in the following year. The forests of mahogany, rosewood and logwood are an important source of revenue and citrus fruits come close in economic importance.

# HONDURAS

*The Indians. The Spanish conquest. Independence.* Coming from Guatemala at the beginning of the Christian era, the Mayas occupied the northern and western portions of the country. They left a legacy of impressive ruins, in particular at Copan, where a city covered an area of 8 square miles. Other ruins are to be found at Tenampua, at Comayagua and on the Bay Islands, providing ample evidence of a high degree of knowledge and artistic sense.

On the plateaus and in the surrounding valleys live the descendants of the Mayas. They are few in number and have never mingled with the other inhabitants. In eastern Honduras, too, there are Indians who are free of cross-breeding, but rather primitive, descendants of one of the groups that succeeded the Mayas. Other Indians, usually with a Negro strain, live on or not far from the Atlantic coast, in the Mosquitia region. Industrious and bellicose, they all put up a fierce resistance to the Spanish conquerors.

Pedro de Alvarado, by putting down the last revolt headed by the famous Indian chief Lempira, restored peace in 1536 and founded the city of Villa (today San Pedro Sula). Honduras was then united with the *Capitania General de Guatemala.* It rose in revolt against Spain with the other Spanish provinces of America in September 1821, and later joined the federation of the United Provinces of Central America. In 1838 it was declared an independent state, and it became a republic. The history of independent Hoduras is made up of a succession of revolutions, wars and risings.

*A rich country, sparsely populated and undeveloped.* The area of Honduras is 43,227 square miles, and its population (about 2,163,011) is 87 per cent mestizos.

It is hot on the coasts — 31°C. (88°F.) mean temperature — temperate in the plains and valleys, and cool on the hills — 23°C. (73.5°F.). In the capital the temperature reaches its maximum in May with 31°C. (88°F.) and its minimum in December with 10°C. (50°F.). Very copious rain falls from May to October in the interior and the south, and from October to March in the north; many parts of the country are rainy all the year round.

Honduras is a mountainous country, thinly populated, which holds vast agricultural promise in the wide areas of cultivable land in the temperate zone, and in its wealth of mines: both these resources are poorly developed. The country may be divided into four parts: the central core, the Pacific zone, the Atlantic slopes, the islands and archipelagos.

The central core is an imposing volcanic massif aligned east to west, cut through by a deep fissure from the Caribbean Sea to the Gulf of Fonseca on the Pacific. In this depression are the two rivers: the Goascoran flowing from Rancho Chiquito to the Pacific, and the Humuya which empties into the Atlantic, the whole gap forming an excellent natural line for inter-oceanic communications.

In the centre of this core, at an altitude of 3,200 feet, stands the capital Tegucigalpa, its population numbering 167,000. Thirty per cent of the population lives in this region, attracted by climate and natural resources. The Spaniards took a very special interest in this area because of its mineral wealth (especially gold and silver).

Honduras has only a very small Pacific coast, between El Salvador and Nicaragua. At present its population density is highest in the Pacific region, especially in the valley of Choluteca. This region produces maize, cotton, sugar-cane and coffee. It maintains large numbers of cattle. There is only one harbour, Amapala, but it is an excellent one, in the shelter of the fine Gulf of Fonseca. The thirty islands of the Fonseca archipelago are situated around this area.

The Atlantic slope is sparsely populated and insufficiently exploited, despite its great resources in forests and mines. It is an agricultural region producing an abundance of bananas, coffee and sugar. Along the coast lies the finest bay in Central America, Bahia Cortes, over eight miles wide, where Cortes founded Puerto Navidad, now Puerto Cortes. An archipelago of over twenty-five islands including Roatan, Utila, Guanaja, Barnereta and the Swan Islands lies along the coast.

There are no active volcanoes in Honduras. However, some lakes, such as Yojoa (fresh water), and Caratasca (salt water) are of volcanic origin.

*Honduras, country of the banana.* Honduras is above

Tapping chicle in the forests of British Honduras. Chicle is a white resinous latex, and is tapped like rubber; it is the basis of chewing gum. Most of the population are half-breeds, generally illiterate, who live on agriculture and fishing.

WEST INDIES: Local Saturday market in Dominica, the last refuge of the Carib peop

all else the country of the banana, and the finest domain of the United Fruit Company, which owns about 250,000 acres, 380 miles of railway and several harbours. The Standard Fruit and Steamship Company, too, owns very fine plantations, 300 miles of railway and a few harbours. An average of 11,000,000 stems is exported annually to the United States. Sixteen per cent of the ground under cultivation is devoted to coffee. Far behind these two great export products come sugar-cane, tobacco, rubber and cotton (seeds). Maize, which takes up 43 per cent of the cultivated areas, remains the staple food of the Indians, who also eat beans, potatoes and oranges. Cacao, coconut, rice and kapok are also produced; coconuts are gathered and mahogany, cedar, pine, rosewood, sandalwood, laurel, orangewood and balsam are an important source of wealth.

Stock-rearing, which dates from the earliest days of colonisation, is one of the main resources.

The mines, rich and numerous, especially in gold and silver, are in general poorly exploited. In 1962 2,803 troy oz. of gold, 2,686 tons of silver and 8,573 metric tons of lead were exported. Zinc is also mined.

Industry in the strict sence of the term is still undeveloped and only represents 10 per cent of the national revenue, but during the last ten years there has been successful advance in this direction. Spinning mills, sawmills and flour mills, factories manufacturing powdered milk, canned goods, soap and cigarettes have been established.

*Development programme.* Honduras, one of the Central American republics where potentialities for economic expansion are greatest, is also one of the least developed. The government has instituted a five-year plan for rational exploitation of agriculture, stock-rearing, mines, industry and road construction. An important hydro-electric plant is under construction at Rio Lindo.

To cope with the problem of illiteracy a vast programme of school building has been introduced. Honduras, anxious to link itself with modern states, is also making an attempt to preserve two pure native nuclei: a few families of Xicaques and Mosquito Indians who are dying out.

# EL SALVADOR

El Salvador, the smallest of the Central American republics (8,260 square miles), has an irregular, four-sided shape; 27 per cent of its area is under cultivation, a further 35 per cent is pasture land and it is spanned by numerous roads and railways.

Ninety per cent of the soil belongs to El Salvador nationals, small landowners who produce principally coffee and cotton, often by very up-to-date methods, in fenced plantations. The population, with a density of over 300 to the square mile, has reached a total of 2,878,000.

Variations in the temperate climate are explained by differences of altitude. On the coast and in the low-lying regions it is hot and damp; in the hills it becomes colder. The year is divided climatically into a dry season and a rainy season, the latter continuing from April to October.

*Beauty and diversity of the landscape.* As varied as it is

picturesque, El Salvador consists of a central plateau, with an average altitude of nearly 2,000 feet, intersected by many valleys and fringed on the north and the south by two mountain chains running from east to west. This sheltered volcanic plateau, with an agreeable climate and fertile soil, produces one of the best coffees in the world and is densely populated. The Southern Cordillera, parallel with the Pacific, is formed by a series of volcanoes ending beyond Aconcagua and Conchagua in two volcanic islands. Between the Cordillera and the Pacific is a flat strip 6 to 12 miles wide, an extension of the Guatemala strip.

Izalco, which first appeared in 1770, is an almost constantly active volcano. It is only one component of a group of hundreds of other volcanoes. Their alarming subterranean activity has often been revealed in destructive earthquakes.

The strangest of the lakes is Coatepeque, hidden in the crater of a volcano; the finest are Ilopango, in the middle of which two islands emerged in 1880, and Guija, on the Guatemalan frontier. The only river fit for navigation and the longest (37 miles), is the Lempa, which rises in Guatemala, touches Honduras and finally empties into the Pacific.

*From the Spanish conquest to independence.* El Salvador

A schoolteacher in El Salvador distributes vitamins and antibiotics to schoolchildren.

Banana stems being brought by mules to the collecting station at the edge of a plantation in Honduras. Honduras is above all a banana-producing country: an average of 11 million stems are exported to the United States annually.

was probably inhabited before the era of the Mayas, who occupied the country from the third to the ninth century A.D. The Toltecs, who followed them, came from the Mexican plateau and settled first around Lake Guija. Several other groups of Indians occupied the country. Some were nomads, but many cultivated maize and cacao. They were divided into castes, made sacrifices to the gods and worshipped the stars. Interesting remains of these civilisations have been preserved in the ruins of Tazumal, Cihuatan and Tehuacan.

Setting out from Guatemala in 1524, Pedro de Alvarado quickly reached Acajutla, which he occupied, then Cuzcatlan, which put up a fierce resistance. During the whole period of Spanish rule the territory of the present republic was under the domination of the *Capitania General de Guantemala*.

The provinces of Guatemala, to which San Salvador and Sonsonate were attached, proclaimed their independence after Mexico did so, on 15th September 1821, and entered the Mexican empire of Iturbide in January 1822. After the collapse of that empire the provinces of Central America combined in a congress which established the federation of the United Provinces of Central America. Civil wars broke out, and ultimately El Salvador declared itself an independent republic on 2nd Februrary 1841. For a century its history was marked by revolutions, coups d'état and wars with other countries.

*Land of 'ladinos'.* The population of El Salvador is composed of 92 per cent half-breed Indians, called *ladinos*, only 5.6 per cent pure Indians and 2.1 per cent white people. This is the effect of its geographical position (the country has no outlet to the Atlantic) and also of political unrest, which tends to deter immigration.

The half-breeds are generally the owners of small plots of land cultivated under favourable conditions. There are some estates, including coffee plantations. The land cannot absorb all the available manpower; there are considerable waves of migration to Honduras, Panama, Guatemala and Costa Rica.

*El Salvador, third in world coffee production.* After the Spanish conquest, the Indians, having devoted themselves mainly to the cultivation of maize, cacao and a few vegetables, began to trade tobacco, indigo and balsam (resin from certain trees). But the transformation of the economy dates from the introduction of coffee in the nineteenth century. With a harvest lasting from November to January, El Salvador now ranks third among world producers. Thanks to the fertility of the volcanic slopes and to a favourable climate, yields are high and quality exceptional. Coffee represents up to 76 per cent of the total value of exports, most going to Germany and the United States. Since the beginning of this century El Salvador has practically lived on the coffee crop; the cultivation of cotton is a more recent addition. The country's economy is thus at the mercy of the price variations and demands of the international market.

However, immense progress has been achieved in the production of cotton during the last few years. After that come sugar-cane, grown mainly in plantations on the Pacific coast, sisal (henequen), balsam, produced between La Libertad and Acajutla and sold at Sonsonate, and lastly—in much smaller quantities —honey and indigo. Maize is the basic food: a little is grown everywhere for home consumption, but chiefly in the regions of Usulutan, Chalatenango and La Libertad. Stock-rearing is also important.

There has been some industrial progress of late. Cement production has increased considerably. Factories have been equipped to produce powdered milk, also oil-cake for cattle. The textile industry has taken root. Two modern shoe factories have been set up. The production of vegetable oils is beginning. A little gold and silver and some copper, lead, zinc and mercury are found, and the government is making efforts to develop the mines. In 1951 an electric plant was completed on the River Lempa; another has just come into operation; a third generating station is under construction.

THE FUTURE OF EL SALVADOR. Agricultural economy is far too dependent on the international market for coffee and cotton; it should be based on products that are of greater use for home consumption and for the maintenance of local industry. It faces the dangers of deforestation and erosion, against which the government has taken preventive measures. At present 52 per cent of the population cannot read, but an intensive campaign against illiteracy has been instituted, which will give the people elementary instruction in agricultural science. El Salvador has begun to develop its industry, especially since the formation of the Central American common market, thus providing more employment for the population.

There are many difficulties in the way of such a transformation: lack of iron, coal and electric power; and traffic and transport problems. Every year, however, new roads are built; the Pan-American highway now crosses the country from the frontier of Guatemala to that of Honduras, over 174 miles. The railroads are shared by the American-financed International Railways of Central America (280 miles), and the British-financed Salvador Railway Company.

San Salvador has a university whose foundation dates from 1841, and possesses an intellectual élite. We may conclude, then, that an improved future can be predicted for the country.

# NICARAGUA

Nicaragua no doubt owes its name to the memory of an Indian chief of that name, with whom the Spaniards had contact when they arrived. It is the largest of the Central American republics (57,143 square miles; population, 1,597,000).

Nicaragua gives the impression of a practically undeveloped contry, yet its natural resources are abundant, and climatic conditions over a large part of the territory are very favourable for agriculture. The government has worked out a plan for developing and stimulating agriculture, this being the sole pursuit of nearly four-fifths of the population. History throws a special light on this situation.

In the pre-Columbian era no Indian civilisation had managed to assert itself. Nicaragua was not an area of any particular importance to the Spanish invaders. It neither lay on a trading route nor was it one of the regions richest in mines. When it gained independence, internal struggles and wars with other states were prejudicial to its economic development. Violent earthquakes occurring at the end of the nineteenth century and the beginning of the twentieth put an end to a plan for cutting a canal there. Recently the vulnerability of the Panama Canal has brought fresh hope to the advocates of this project, which would offer an alternative route between the Pacific and the Atlantic.

*Nicaragua's history.* The territory was peopled by many different tribes in the pre-Columbian era, by the Mosquitos, whose descendants today occupy the Caribbean coast, the Sumos and the Voulvas, the Niquirans in the Rivas isthmus and the island of Omotepec. Other ethnic groups of lesser importance were sprinkled over the country. Farmers and nomads, they were all peace-loving.

The real conquest was achieved in 1722 by Gil Gonzales de Avila and Andres Nuño, who came from Panama. The conquered lands were linked with the San Domingo administration, then with that of Panama, and finally with the *Capitania General de Guatemala.*

At the beginning of the seventeenth century the English understood the strategic value of the coasts and settled on the Atlantic side. In the middle of the eighteenth century the British Admiralty, foreseeing the possibility and the advantage of a navigable route being constructed, created forthwith a little kingdom composed of 10,000 Mosquitos (Indian-Negro half-breeds) which was to be annexed by the Nicaraguan Government in 1894. Nicaragua had proclaimed its autonomy in 1838, but its history, like that of its neighbours, was to be nothing but a succession of wars and insurrections. For the purpose of restoring order, in 1912 American troops were called in and remained until 1934.

The capital, which was in turn Masaya, Leon and then Granada, has been Managua since 1858.

*The three regions of Nicaragua.* Nicaragua is shaped like a triangle between Honduras, the Atlantic Ocean, and the Pacific.

It is very beautiful, with a fertile soil and a climate which in general is varied and temperate because of the proximity of the two oceans and the fairly high altitude. The country on the whole is wet (236 inches of rain at Greytown), which explains the rich pastures of the low-lying regions and the dense forests that clothe the mountain areas. The rains, which in the west follow the rhythm of two well-defined seasons, occur throughout the year in the east. Thus, except for the marshy area of the Atlantic coast, where malaria and yellow fever are rife, the climate over most of the country is not unhealthy.

Nicaragua may be divided into three regions: central, western and eastern.

The central region, formed by a great volcanic plateau, is the most mountainous. It enjoys a mild climate and contains about a quarter of the whole population. It is a stock-rearing area, especially in the Contales, and also has a number of gold and silver mines.

On the Pacific slope, the coast of which extends for 261 miles and is very hot, the most important towns are to be found: Masaya, the most densely populated, with 314 inhabitants to the square mile; Managua, the capital, the home of about one-eighth of the population; Chinandega, Leon and Granada. In the north of this region of low and level lands very suitable for agriculture, where roads and railroads are numerous and where 68 per cent of the population live, there is a long chain of volcanoes. Nicaragua (3,800 square miles), dotted with many islands, islets and volcanic reefs, is the largest lake in Central America. The Tipitapa—with its sulphurous waters—links it with Lake Managua (450 sq. miles).

The western zone produces 80 per cent of the country's rice, 95 per cent of the sesame, 75 per cent of the cotton, 85 per cent of the coffee and some sugar-cane. It is also the industrial centre of Nicaragua. The port of Corinto handles the outflow of 45 per cent of the exports and receives 70 per cent of the imports. A railroad connects it with the capital.

The Atlantic slope is thinly populated. The inhabitants are chiefly Negroes and mulattos, originally from Jamaica. The torrid heat and the torrential rains make the region unhealthy (as in Mosquito Bay); but it is rich in forests and in minerals. The coasts, which extend for about 450 miles, are low and irregular. They are fringed with lagoons and bays, few of which can be turned to account for navigation, although the harbours of Puerto Cabezas, El Bluff and San Juan del Norte deserve mention.

Nicaragua has no fewer than 94 rivers, with 78 affluents; 23 flow into the Atlantic Ocean and only 18 into the Pacific; 45 drain into Lake Nicaragua. The longest river is the Coco, or Segovia, which in its course of 348 miles irrigates three-quarters of the country before emptying into the Atlantic. Large irrigation schemes are under development, based on the Tipitapa and Tuma rivers.

*Rich resources insufficiently exploited.* Nicaragua has a capitalist agriculture whose products are destined for export and a food-producing agriculture which supplies the domestic market. The former is concerned with coffee, cotton, seasame, bananas, sugar-cane, cacao and tobacco; the latter produces maize, beans and rice, which are the staple foods of the people. Eighty per cent of the agricultural production comes from the western region.

Coffee, introduced in 1846 and cultivated mainly on large estates, found a propitious soil and a suitable climate in the western districts. It is the country's principal export, and the United States is the chief purchaser. Cotton, most of it exported to Great Britain, follows closely in importance on coffee; this in turn is followed by sesame. Then come bananas and sugar-cane.

Among the staple food crops maize occupies the first place, before rice and runner beans; it is cultivated all over the country, but above all in the western zone. The wide expanses of pasture encouraged stock-rearing. Breeders have produced an excellent type of cattle, more especially on the Pacific coast. In the plains horses and mules find grass in abundance. Domestic breeding of pigs, sheep and goats is also developed. Nicaragua's exports include leathers and skins.

Forest extends over the mountainous parts, i.e. over 80 per cent of the territory; the timbers, especially cedar and mahogany, might well be a more profitable source of revenue. Many varieties of trees exploited for their fragrant or medicinal properties are also found.

Nicaragua possesses a mineral wealth which is still insufficiently exploited. The gold and silver mines have been known since the colonial era: nearly 1,400 mines are at present officially registered, through six alone supply 90 per cent of the total production. Gold export provides an important percentage of the national revenue. Silver is plentiful. Other minerals —iron, copper, lead, mercury, nickel, zinc, tin and antimony—are also found in large quantities, but are still hardly exploited. The existence of oil, tungsten and uranium deposits was revealed quite recently.

The chief industries include cigarettes, leather, plastics, metal products, cotton, silk and timber. In 1961 there were eleven hydro-electric power units in existence. Exploration for petroleum began off the Pacific and Atlantic coasts in 1965 and a petroleum refining factory has been developed at Managua.

Transport of wood in the countryside north of Leon, an area of many volcanoes and fertile soil; charcoal is practically the only form of fuel for domestic purposes.
The solid-wheeled cart is of a type common in Nicaragua. The inhabitants, most of whom originated in the Iberian peninsula, introduced into Central and South America not only their vehicles, but also their farm implements, notably the swing plough.

PROBLEMS OF THE FUTURE. Natural wealth is therefore still undeveloped, and the average standard of living is low. As in several other Central American countries considerable investment of capital would be necessary to bring about a change. Trade and the highest investment yields favour imports and endanger the economic equilibrium. Lastly, the vast number of illiterates, reaching an average figure of 64 per cent of the population and 80 per cent in some localities, is a disadvantage.

The Government has initiated a general plan for education and equipment. It has made a very special effort to train teachers, and Nicaragua possesses three universities, at Managua, Leon and Granada.

Economic planners have worked out a systematic programme for crops, for increasing variety and production. The country has been divided into six natural regions within which, side by side with products destined for exports, products indispensable for the home food supply, especially rice and maize, will be cultivated.

The rise in price of exported products (cotton, coffee and sugar-cane) calls for very special attention, since it causes dangerous movements of manpower: workers, attracted by higher pay, forsake the production of basic commodities essential for home consumption to find employment in the large concerns working for export.

For many years to come Nicaragua will have difficult problems to solve, but its soil, equally rich on the surface and in underlying strata, will ultimately bring economic improvement to its population.

# COSTA RICA

In a group of nations mainly peopled by poor Indians, living chiefly on agriculture, Costa Rica has a population of 80 per cent Spanish descent, an average annual income per inhabitant of 180 dollars, an agriculture which provides only 34 per cent of the national income, and no armed force, for the Constitution forbids it.

*A favoured country.* A mountain chain runs from northwest to south-east right through central Costa Rica. It falls rapidly to sea level, sometimes in less than twenty miles, as in the plain of Santa Clara. First, in the west, lies the Guanacaste Cordillera, with peaks worn down by erosion and with extinct volcanoes (Orosi, 5,154 feet; Rincon de la Vieja). Next there is a central mesa or table with an average altitude of 3,000 to 5,800 feet and enjoying an exceptionally good climate; seventy-five per cent of the population live there, the density in some places being about 1,000 inhabitants per square mile. It is the centre of the country's economic activity and contains the capital, San José. The mesa is surrounded by the highest peaks of the Central Cordillera: Irazu (11,200 feet) and farther off Turrialba with its four craters (11,350 feet); in the west Barba (9,500 feet) and Poas, concealing a lake in its crater (8,930 feet).

This central plateau of Costa Rica is protected from the north winds by the high mountain ranges and receives an ample share of the softest winds blowing from the Pacific. In the dry period, lasting from December to March, the weather is particularly good. Between the warmest month, March, and the coolest, January, the temperature difference is only 2°C. (5°F.) for a mean temperature of 20°C. (68°F.). Well-cultivated estates grow coffee, flowers and vegetables.

To the east of the central mesa, and bordering on Panama, lies the Talamanca Cordillera, rising to over 1,000 feet and descending to the Atlantic in less than thirty miles.

In the north-east lies the Nicaraguan plain, with the valley of the San Juan River forming the frontier. The valleys leading from the Cordillera to the plains of San Carlos and Santa Clara have all the luxuriance of tropical forest. Around the Rio Frio there are still small, wretched encampments of the Guatuso Indians. This region is rich in valuable timbers, as yet hardly exploited. In contrast, cacao, coffee and sugar-cane are successfully cultivated by the population of Spanish descent.

Along the Atlantic coast there are lowlands, lagoons and fertile alluvial plains bordered by forests. Unhappily the climate is most unhealthy, and diseases such as malaria and yellow fever decimate the population. Torrential rains fall throughout the year; total

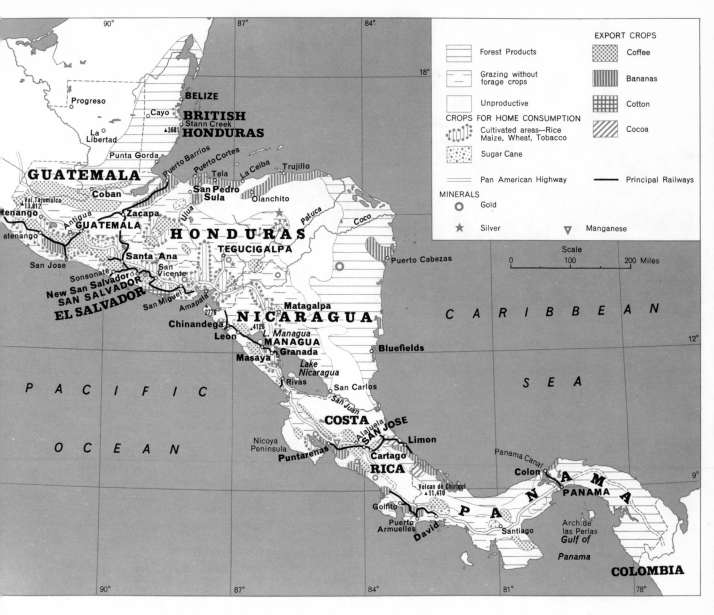

precipitation is over 236 inches on the San Juan River. The fine crops once grown here were ravaged by disease, which came in 1930 from Panama; but luckily it proved possible to substitute cacao to some extent for the banana, and manila-hemp fibre yields substantial profits. Stock-rearing is carried on by the Indians.

Between the Cordillera and the Pacific Ocean lie very fertile areas, with a climate particularly suitable for agriculture. The present small population might with advantage be increased in view of the splendid potentialities there are for stock-rearing as well as for tillage (maize).

*A population of Spanish descent.* In these beautiful and varied surroundings, long before the arrival of the Spaniards, there lived Indian tribes who had attained a certain degree of civilisation, though it was by no means comparable to that of the Mayas, the Aztecs or the Incas.

The peace-loving temperament of the natives made it easy for the Spaniards to occupy the lands they inhabited. The assimilation of the Indian by the white man gained impetus from the heavy immigration of

Europeans early in the twentieth century. During the whole era of Spanish rule Costa Rica was a dependency of the *Capitania de Guatemala.* Its population continued to increase, and by degrees the mestizo element assimilated the Indian.

Costa Rica shared in the great movement for liberation at the beginning of the nineteenth century and in 1848 declared its own absolute autonomy.

*Country of coffee, bananas and cacao.* Coffee met with highly favourable conditions, particularly in the central area of San José, where the volcanic soil, the altitude of 2,200 to 4,600 feet and the climate supply essential requirements. It takes up the greater part of the land under cultivation in the central area and is generally grown on small estates. Its enormous success is due to its high price in comparison with that of other agricultural products, and to the fact that it can be stored easily for a long period. Very up-to-date methods give an excellent yield and extremely good quality.

The production of coffee is of long standing, but cultivation of the banana dates only from the twentieth century, and today it is highly profitable. This crop is

Central America, showing principal crops and mineral resources. The map shows clearly that economic activity is most flourishing along the Pacific coast of Central America, which is drier and healthier than the Caribbean coast, and it is here that most of the cities are situated. The Pan-American Highway, which runs from the Mexico-U.S. border to Chile, passes through the capitals of five Central American republics and serves the Pacific coast region.

Coffee being put through a washing tank in the fertile Orosi valley of Costa Rica. Volcanic soil and a favourable climate in the central region have made coffee a valuable element in the Costa Rican economy. During the washing process unripe beans float to the surface, while the fully ripened beans sink to the bottom of the tank.

# THE
# REPUBLIC OF PANAMA

One might say that after the Spanish conquest the history of Panama revolved around the isthmus, and from the close of the nineteenth century around the Canal, to which it owes its independence as well as its origin.

*The construction of the Panama Canal.* In 1519 Pedro Arias de Avila founded the first city of Panama. Under him the *Nombre de Dios* road was constructed across the isthmus, the only trade thoroughfare during three centuries of colonisation until the railroad was opened in 1885. By this route the precious metals from Peru were transported to the Old World.

Charles V and Philip II were keenly interested in projects for an inter-ocean route. But in 1746 a royal ordinance laid down that Spanish trade should be carried on by the sea route Buenos Aires—Cape Horn—Peru. Panama then sank into a state of lethargy, until the Californian gold rush gave her a new interest a century later; a shipping line connected Panama with San Francisco. The project for cutting a canal remained under discussion.

In the meantime the Spanish colonies had separated from the mother country, and in 1821 Panama joined the new republic of Great Colombia, which included Venezuela, Ecuador and Colombia. In 1903 Panama was proclaimed an independent republic, thanks to the help of the United States, who had been unable to reach agreement with Great Colombia over the creation of the canal.

In 1875 Ferdinand de Lesseps revived the project for the canal from Limon to Panama. And in 1881 the World Company of the Pacific Inter-ocean Canal was founded, with an initial capital of 300,000,000 francs. The operations, directed by de Lesseps, began the following year. The initial plan, which aimed at cutting a 'ditch canal', as at Suez, was very soon abandoned in favour of a 'lock canal', a project less exacting technically and financially.

In spite of the skill and ability of the French engineers, the enterprise was a conspicuous failure, apparently owing to poor organisation of finance and lack of health precautions: 22,000 technicians and workmen died, most of them from malaria. This meant the collapse of de Lesseps's grand project. But by 1898 President McKinley was urging the American Congress to pass a law authorising the Government to build an inter-ocean canal. The advocates of Panama won the day, but agreements with regional authorities still had to be concluded. Colombia refused to pass the United States proposal; this provoked a violent reaction from the Panamanians, and on 27th August 1903 an emissary from Panama went to Washington. On 3rd November 1903 there was a revolt which proclaimed the independence of Panama, while the commander of an American warship anchored in the roadstead prevented Colombia from landing troops to quell the rioting.

Thus the Republic of Panama was born of a canal not yet constructed, and on the 18th November a treaty was signed between Panama and the United States granting to the latter a concession in perpetuity

mainly the concern of foreign companies. Cacao is the third export product. The sugar-cane flourishes also in the area round Cartago, San José and Alajuela. In these regions, too, at a lower altitude, the soil is suitable for tobacco.

All these products ensure considerable foreign payments, but there is no certainty that these make any direct contribution towards raising the standard of living for the people. That is why the Government has been paying special attention to crops of foodstuffs which supply the basic diet of the inhabitants (rice, maize and beans).

Government aid for meat production has yielded excellent results. One of Costa Rica's best sources of wealth is the dairying industry, which flourishes especially to the east of Cartago and in the central area.

There are veins of gold (at Puntarenas), silver and manganese; more recently deposits of copper, iron, lead and oil (at Talamanca) have been discovered.

Industry is hardly developed at all. It is strictly confined to local needs, concentrating on processing foodstuffs.

*An assured future.* The future of Costa Rica looks particularly bright. Limited in area, it has an ever-increasing population. It is making an intelligent effort to stimulate agriculture—which shows excellent returns and can be further expanded—and to develop industry, which is making a sound but slow start. As in all the other countries of Central America, lack of electric power presented a serious obstacle to economic development. But the Costa Rica Electricity Board has established two new power stations, each of 5,000 kW, at San José. A project for a 10,000 kW plant is nearing completion. Lastly, at La Garita, a 30,000 kW hydro-electric plant is to be constructed. Lack of co-ordination between the rail systems remains a handicap. The road system, on the other hand, has been effectively developed.

Finally, Costa Rica is making an exceptional effort in the field of education, to which 19 per cent of the national budget is devoted; illiteracy has dropped from 89 per cent in 1864 to 15 per cent in 1963, which forms the lowest proportion in all Central America.

for construction of the canal. Work began in 1904 and was completed by the Americans in 1914, making extensive use of the work done by de Lesseps.

The United States drove a hard bargain with the young nation. The territorial zone conceded was extended from 6 miles to 10 miles and took in the islands of Naos, Pericos, Flamencos and Culebra; control in health matters was to be exercised solely by the United States, with judicial and policing powers on the same basis; concession of territory and waters essential to the functioning of the canal outisde the zone was without limit.

In 1936 a new treaty granted important concessions to the Republic of Panama. And during the Second World War, in view of the security problems, the Bases Convention was drawn up, bringing considerable gains to the Panamanian Government. When hostilities ended, the United States was reluctant to restore the bases, stressing that the convention implied it would remain in force until the signature of the peace treaty. Panama, however, insisted on their return.

The Panamanians have put forward claims, warranted by the fact that the country's economy is based upon the canal and that the interior offers little scope for native inhabitants. They reproach the Americans for drawing substantial profits from the exploitation of the Canal, while Panama receives a relatively small sum.

However, the Panamanians have derived various benefits from the presence of the Americans: the construction of 186 miles of roads, aid towards the Pan-American Highway, agreements on technical aid, medical supervision, expenditure by American troops stationed in the Canal Zone—all these have contributed greatly to the economic prosperity of the country.

*A mixed population.* The very interesting ethnic past of these territories cannot be ignored.

Long before the arrival of the Spanish conquerors, the Chibchas, coming from the Andes, settled in the west on the Pacific slope. The Caribs made their home in the Atlantic region. Later the Kunas, the Guayamis and the Chocoes formed with them a group of some 35,000 persons. Large numbers were nomads; some who were settled practised collective ownership of land and were organised in clans. Many were familiar with metal-working, particularly in gold.

Originally the result of Indo-Spanish inter-breeding, the population was reinforced as long ago as the sixteenth century by Negro elements and in the nineteenth and twentieth centuries by West Indians, Italians, Greeks, Chinese and Japanese: the isthmus, as the main route between the two oceans, accounts for a race diversity as great as anywhere in the world.

*Strongly contrasting coasts.* Panama, whose underlying rocks are of recent formation, is mainly volcanic and is shaped like a sloping S. This explains the length of its coasts (500 miles on the Caribbean Sea, 870 on the Pacific), which are flanked by countless islands of varying size.

West of the centre is a cordillera whose altitude varies between 2,000 and 5,000 feet. The mean temperature is 20°C. (68°F.), and annual precipitation reaches 94 inches.

In the north, on the Atlantic, lies the rainy area of

tropical forests where precipitation is 134 inches and the mean temperature 30°C. (86°F.)—hot, damp and unhealthy regions that teem with animals and insects. From December to May, the pleasanter season, this area receives the trade winds. The rains, which come from the south, go on from the beginning of June to November.

In the south, on the Pacific, is a region of savannas and marshes (mean temperature 39°C. (86°F.), with average precipitation under 80 inches).

The River Chagres (93 miles), an axis of the country's development, flows along the Atlantic coast. This river helps to feed the Canal and the artificial reservoir of Gatun (165 square miles).

*An economy based on the Canal.* The agriculture of Panama is poor and inadequate. But the economic reforms of 1952, 1953 and 1954 have yielded very encouraging results. Thus the production of rice, the leading crop, had risen sharply from 75,000 tons in 1948 to 516,000 tons in 1962, and of coffee from 2,700 tons in 1945 to 10,800 tons in 1961-2.

Industry employs only 7 per cent of the working population. It suffers from lack of fuel and raw materials. But the underlying rocks appear to be rich in mineral resources; and fishing has been exploited recently on systematic lines. The cement industry, the timber industry, vegetable oils, cigarettes and even paper have developed. The country's economy is based essentially on the Canal and on the capital, Panama, a huge 'head' of 290,000 inhabitants perched on a body of 1,210,000. In 1955, under agreements concluded with the United States. Panama began to take a much greater share in the commercial life of the whole Canal Zone.

Trade across the isthmus remains, as it has always been, the basis of the economy. The Canal dominates the trading pattern of the whole territory and, as a result, a rather artificial economy has developed, relying heavily on goods imported from the United States to supply the needs of the Canal and a variety of related activities. Commercial aviation, which is developing rapidly, is bringing increasing numbers of tourists, and prospects for future development are fairly bright.

Miraflores Lock, Panama Canal Zone.
The original plan was to build a ditch canal, as at Suez, but the mountainous nature of Panama made it necessary to abandon this project in favour of a canal with locks.

# COLOMBIA

Colombia, stretching from the Putumayo, a tributary of the Amazon River, to the Caribbean Sea, from the Orinoco River to the Pacific, is one of the three countries of South America crossed by the Equator. With an area of 439,529 square miles, it has about 1,000 miles of coast on the Atlantic, and 800 miles on the Pacific; unlike the countries in the isthmus, while possessing a double seaboard it also commands a considerable hinterland. Further, lying in the extreme north of South America, Barranquilla is only about 1,100 miles from Miami and about 4,800 miles from Lisbon. The history of the discovery and conquest of Colombia is bound up with its geographical location.

## A LIGHTNING CONQUEST

In 1499 Alonso de Hojeda, Juan de la Cosa and Amerigo Vespucci, who had just explored Lake Maracaibo and named Venezuela, were already passing round the peninsula of Guajira. The crossing of the isthmus and the discovery of the Pacific, in 1513, by Vasco Nuñez de Balboa were to make Colombia the bridgehead and meeting-point for all further enterprises by the conquistadors in South America.

Andagoya had in fact explored the Pacific coast as early as 1522; in 1533 the first governor of Cartagena, Pedro de Heredia, built the most formidable fortress the New World has ever known, Cartagena de Indias, a Spanish monument on American soil. In 1538, Jimenez de Quesada founded the future capital, Santa Fe de Bogota. Of all the Spanish conquests none was to be so complete and so lightning swift, and the twofold aspect of the future Colombia—mountain towns and coastal towns—could be clearly seen from the earliest days of colonisation.

At the time of the Conquest, the cordilleras and the high plateaus of Colombia were occupied by peoples of industrious habits, today called 'peoples of the Chibcha tongue', whose *Zipa*, the 'Golden Prince', was the embodiment of the theocratic constitution. There were probably many *zipas* at the head of as many tribes, for the Chibchas were still far from possessing a centralised political structure. In the northern areas, along the Atlantic coast, the Arawaks, an agricultural people, appear to have been fairly numerous: their descendants, the pure-bred Guajiras, today number about 20,000. The Caribs also—their last remnants in Colombia today are the wild Motilons—occupied part of the coast and the lower valley of the Magdalena.

The mountains were to serve as a springboard for exploration of the savannas and forest in the east. Following penetration to the Orinoco from Santa Fe de Bogota, not only Colombian territory but also contemporary Venezuela owed civil and spiritual allegiance to Bogota. The two countries were to be in close association until after the Wars of Independence, and even after this Great Colombia or the Great Colombian Federation was to remain united under the control of Bolivar until 1830. Venezuela, Colombia and Ecuador—which had joined the Federation in 1822—then regained their autonomy.

## A MOUNTAIN PEOPLE

Colombia is a unified republic of seventeen departments (densely populated Andean and coastal regions), five intendencies or administrative departments and three commissaries or areas under commissioners (vast tracts of savanna and virgin forest in the east and south). The country is governed, with the assistance of a cabinet, by a president who is elected by popular vote for four years. The Chamber of Deputies and the Senate form the National Congress.

The population is very largely Roman Catholic; freedom of worship, however, is assured.

In July 1964 the population of Colombia was estimated at 15,434,000, giving a density of 37 per square mile. Ninety-eight per cent are concentrated in the departments, which cover 45 per cent of the country's area; in contrast the intendencies and the commissaries represent vast tracts uninhabited. A balance is kept in the distribution of population in the mountain area: 70 per cent of the total population live at an altitude of over 3,000 feet. Bogota, Tunja and Pasto lie at about 8,500 feet, Medellin 4,800 feet, Bucaramanga 4,600 feet, Cali nearly 3,300 feet. Among the large cities, only the Atlantic ports of Cartagena, Barranquilla and Santa Marta are in the torrid zone.

The excessive growth of the towns and, above all, the growth of the capital is very much less marked than in any other Latin American country. Fewer than 9 per cent of Colombia's population are collected in Great Bogota.

A colonial past and the African slave trade have produced a stangely mixed population: of every 1,000 Colombians 570 are mestizos (white-Indian), 30 *zambos* (Indian-Negro), 140 mulattos (white-Negro); 200 whites, 20 Indians and 40 pure Negroes.

## THE HYDROGRAPHIC STAR OF COLOMBIA

Of all the Andean countries Colombia has the most complex contours. Between the Equator and latitude 2° N. is the famous shelf or 'node' of Pasto, a plateau with an altitude varying between 7,000 and 10,500 feet, barely 120 miles wide. From it rise the volcanoes Chiles (15,620 feet). Azufral (13,350 feet) and Cumbal (16,043 feet), their tuffs and volcanic ashes filling the hollows. The Pasto plateau is the trunk on which the three ranges of the Andean structure in Colombia are grafted: the Eastern Cordillera or Cordillera of Bogota, the Central Cordillera or Cordillera of Quindio, and the Western Cordillera, or Cordillera of Choco.

These three ranges consist of narrow branches in the south, but spread out in the north between the 4th and 5th parallels, falling steadily till they reach the shores of the Caribbean or the marshy plain of the Lower Magdalena. This star pattern covers an area of something like 117,000 square miles, nearly one-quarter of the whole country; it is not only the source of rivers emptying their waters into the Pacific, the Caribbean Sea, the Orinoco and the Amazon, thus opening up highways, but also exerts a marked influence on the distribution of rainfall by the nature of its contours.

*A great river: the Magdalena.* The valley of the

Magdalena (963 miles) and that of its powerful affluent the Cauca (840 miles) together form the essential arteries of Colombia. Along them low plains lead to the heart of the Andean plateau.

The valleys are deep structural rifts lying between fault lines. The trough of the Magdalena, 370 miles long, and between 20 and 40 miles, wide, is broader and deeper than that of the Cauca. The river flows in it with a relatively slight gradient, the Honda rapids breaking the pressure of water. As a result Honda, a compulsory halting-place on the land and river routes from Cartagena to Bogota or Quito, has become one of the most important trading centres of Spanish America. Inland water transport has gained momentum since the *motonaves,* river vessels propelled by internal combustion engines, have replaced wood-fired steamers. The river ports are departure points for railroutes crossing the Eastern and Central Cordilleras.

The valley of the Magdalena, low-lying and hot, has never been a focus of civilisation. The Cauca, on the other hand, less accessible and barely navigable in its higher reaches offers tracts of upland which even in prehistoric times attracted men to settle there, and here the first conquistadors installed themselves. Between Popayan and Cartago the Cauca depression contains the Popayan plain (average height 5,500 feet), irregular and scrub-covered, and the Cali plain (average altitude 3,300 feet), 120 miles long, 10 to 16 miles wide, flat marshy and commonly known as the 'Cauca Valley'. The aristocracy of sumptuous Popayan formerly had possession of the cattle-rearing *haciendas* throughout the area. Cali, an industrial town, today ranks third in the country. Having rail connections with Buenaventura, the only real port on the Pacific coast, Cali has become a main communications centre. Downstream from Cartago wild gorges opening out on an almost uninhabited marshy plain are dominated by the highly industrialised plateau of Antioquia. The road and the railroad from Medellin to Cali and to Popayan have today practically superseded the difficult navigation of the Cauca.

The Magdalena and the Cauca, emerging from their Andean rift valleys, unite in one vast marshy inland delta with a sprinkling of residual lakes divided by bars, which as a rule resist inundation. The Rio Cesar, flowing from the Santa Marta massif, and the Rio San Jorge, which rises in the Western Cordillera, have both made their contribution to filling up this trough. The lakes, abounding in fish, have attracted many villages of fishing folk, huddled under the palm trees in the midst of the family plantations of banana and sugar-cane. The savanna, with tree clumps here and there, is given up to the rearing of selectively bred cattle.

Downstream the waters of the Magdalena are collected in a single bed until they reach the sea, where they flow out by a bar which for long was impassable. The harbour fairway of Barranquilla (Boca de Ceniza), opened thirty years ago, is maintained at great cost. The progress made by the town and the port since then has been considerable, but to a certain extent this implied the decline of Cartagena and Santa Marta, towns which were traditional rivals of Barranquilla for the Magdalena traffic but have succumbed to competition in recent years.

Bogota is a centre of some considerable importance, particularly since the development of air transport. It has been an archbishopric since 1561 and its preoccupation with learning over many centuries has earned it its reputation as the 'Athens of South America'.

*A ring of coastal rivers.* Among the coastal rivers flowing into the Caribbean Sea are the Sinu (290 miles) and the Atrato (420 miles). Though it runs parallel with the Pacific coast, the Atrato flows out on the eastern shore of the Panama isthmus; it drains the only region of Colombia where there is rain all the year round, the narrow plain of Choco. This is a low-lying forest area, unhealthy and thinly populated, where rainfall is nearly 400 inches annually. The Atrato is said to have a stronger flow in proportion to the area of its basin than any river in the world.

The torrents from the Western Cordillera, which keep up quite a strong flow throughout the year, have short courses into the Pacific. South of Buenaventura Bay the coastal rivers have built up at the base of the Western Cordillera a continuous deltaic bar covered with mangroves. Behind this the channels unite in a meandering course parallel with the coast

Indian on the Rio Yurumangui, at the foot of the western Cordillera. Ethnic and linguistic groups are diverse in Central and South America. They also vary greatly in their degree of civilisation; while a great many Indians wear a woollen poncho, whose origin pre-dates the arrival of Europeans, many still go naked.

and navigable by canoe. Primeval forest extends over all this coastal strip and the mountain sides, and communications are scanty. The port of Buenaventura, however, is connected by road and rail with Cali, as is Quibdo with Medellin and Tumaco with Pasto.

## UNINHABITED EASTERN PLAINS AND FORESTS

On the eastern slope of the Andes massif rise the great rivers which, like the Arauca, the Meta and the Guaviare, pass beyond the savannas to swell the Orinoco, and also those which cross the great forests of the south and flow into the Amazon—the Caqueta and Putumayo and their affluents. Not one is less than 600 miles long; they are the only routes through these solitudes. Other sizable rivers rise in the alluvial plain, like the Vichada, or on the crystalline shelf in the south, like the Inirida and the Guainia, the latter to become the colossal Rio Negro.

The Colombian section of the Orinoco basin covers nearly 125,000 square miles, the Amazon basin 137,000 square miles. The line between grassland and forest does not exactly coincide with the watershed between the two basins, due to both climatic and geological factors. The savannas are exposed to the influence of the north-east trade wind in alternation with the equatorial calms. Thus the dry season, corresponding to that of the trade wind (from November to March), is clearly marked. Farther south, the north-east wind from the northern winter is very uneven in its penetration and the dry season is broken by thunderstorms.

North of the Guaviare the granitic substratum of the Guiana shield reappears, taking the form of a peneplain with short undulations. The many perennial rivers, flowing over this impermeable shelf have encouraged forest growth. Masses of sandstone appear also at the foot of the Eastern Cordillera, with the Vaupes and Apaporis rivers rising just below their eastern end.

Spanish colonisation developed early in the savannas. The *llaneros*—the gauchos of Colombia and Venezuela — carry on extensive stock-rearing in isolated farms and are still using eighteenth-century methods.

In the vast forest area of the south the scattered native populations have never been officially counted. Most of the rivers are broken by rapids, and effective penetration will take a long time. The territories supply little except a few gums—*balatá* or chicle— vegetable fibres such as the *piassava,* or timbers that are difficult to transport. There is, however, a regular service of boats to the Amazon along the Putumayo.

## THE CORDILLERAS

*The Cordillera of Bogota.* The Eastern Cordillera or Cordillera de Bogota, about 750 miles long, is the most important chain in the northern massif of the Andes. From the Central Cordillera at Paramo de las Papas, it dies away in the Guajira peninsula, then serves as the frontier with Venezuela. It culminates in the Sierra de Cocuy at nearly 19,000 feet, being also at its widest there (180 miles); it also forks eastward to form the Venezuelan Cordillera de Merida.

The Eastern Cordillera is a group of parallel folds, with flexures and fractures caused by a vertical movement a considerable breadth long after the folding occurred. Along the Magdalena is a fault whose west side has sunk by 13,000 feet.

Between the parallel secondary chains, the tributaries of the Magdalena have hollowed out deep grooves which by degrees they have filled up. The high plains of accumulation have had the greatest influence on the country's history: to these the Eastern Cordillera owes its emergence as the main centre of Chibcha civilisation, as one of the springboards of Spanish colonisation, and as the cradle of Colombian nationalism. Today, too, these plains feed one-third of the country's population. Parts are covered with marshes, moors, or residual lakes; population and crops are distributed on the periphery, often on the lower mountain slopes.

The most typical development of these high plains is to be found in the plain around Bogota, which in 1,000 square miles has over 2,000,000 inhabitants. The capital is built on the eastern fringe. It is a great hive of industry encroaching on the lower slopes of the twin peaks Montserrat and Guadalupe, each with a famous sanctuary at its summit. Ten-storey concrete blocks rise side by side with monuments and houses of the colonial era. All the great highways of the country converge here.

The altitude of the high plain is suitable for cereals. Maize is cultivated up to 8,800 feet, wheat and barley up to 10,500 feet. Market-gardening has developed considerably in the last few years. Cattle of high quality graze around the marshes in a landscape where willows and poplars are curiously mixed with eucalyptus trees and cactus thickets. The temperature is cool (mean, 14°C.—57°F.); there are two rainy seasons (63 inches yearly), and it is not unusual for two crops to be gathered during the dry seasons, in August and in January. All the high plains are just as carefully turned to account. The warmer middle valleys of the Magdalena's tributaries supply sugar-cane and coffee.

*The Central Cordillera and great volcanoes.* The Central Cordillera, or Cordillera de Quindio, separates the valleys of the Magdalena and the Cauca, rising above them in precipitous and usually well-wooded slopes. About 560 miles long, and very narrow in its southern portion, the Cordillera falls and spreads out north of the 5th parallel to form the Antioquia plateau. The courses of the Magdalena and the Cauca then unite in the plain.

There are twelve great volcanic peaks, five of them under perpetual snow: Huila (18,864 feet), Tolima (18,438 feet), Ruiz (17,716 feet), Quindio (16,896 feet) and Santa Isabel (16,732 feet). The crystalline and schistose-crystalline rocks forming the skeleton of the Cordillera are frequently overlaid by volcanic formations.

Although the native populations were neither as numerous nor as far developed as on the high plains of the Eastern Cordillera, the Caldas and Antioquia departments rank among the most populous today. Medellin, the chief town of Antioquia and second city of Colombia, has 777,000 inhabitants. The peasants of Caldas, though without accessible or easily cultivated land, have made their department the

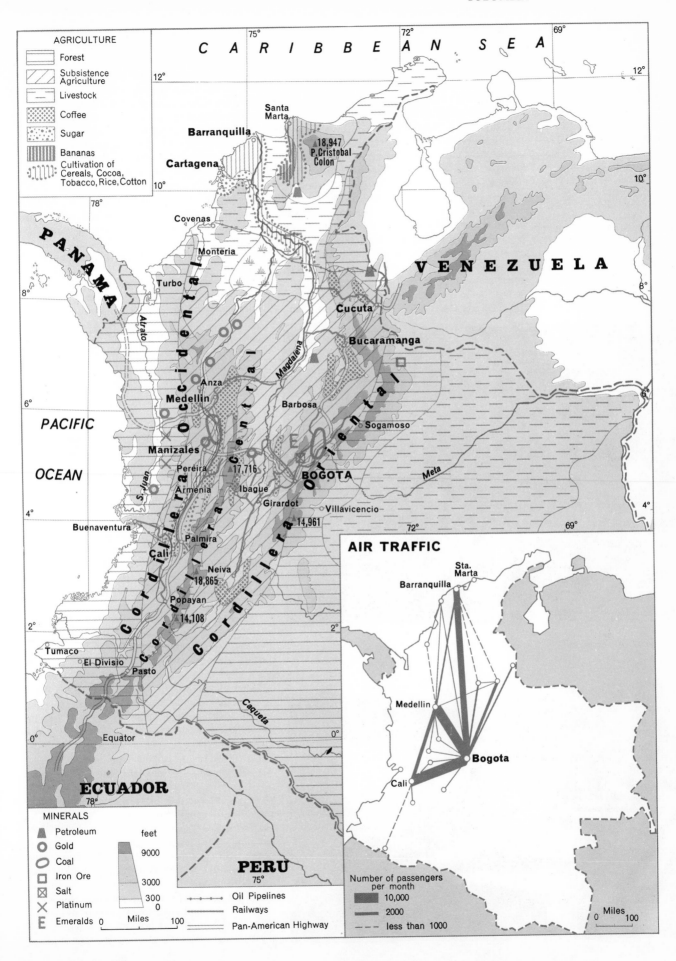

AGRICULTURE
Forest
Subsistence Agriculture
Livestock
Coffee
Sugar
Bananas
Cultivation of Cereals, Cocoa, Tobacco, Rice, Cotton

MINERALS
▲ Petroleum
◎ Gold
◯ Coal
▢ Iron Ore
⊠ Salt
✕ Platinum
E Emeralds

feet
9000
3000
300
0

Miles
0                    100

Oil Pipelines
Railways
Pan-American Highway

CARIBBEAN SEA

PANAMA

PACIFIC

OCEAN

VENEZUELA

Santa Marta
Barranquilla
Cartagena
▲18,947 P. Cristobal Colon
Covenas
Monteria
Turbo
Cucuta
Bucaramanga
Cordillera Occidental
Anza
Medellin
Barbosa
Sogamoso
Cordillera Central
Manizales
Pereira
17,716
Armenia
Ibague
BOGOTA
Meta
Magdalena
Atrato
S. Juan
Cordillera Oriental
Girardot
14,961
Villavicencio
Buenaventura
Palmira
Cali
Neiva
18,865
Popayan
14,108
Tumaco
El Divisio
Pasto
Caqueta
Equator

ECUADOR

PERU

AIR TRAFFIC

Sta. Marta
Barranquilla
Medellin
Bogota
Cali

Number of passengers per month
10,000
2000
less than 1000

Miles
0          100

country's leading producer of coffee, and they sell 2,000,000 bags of it every year.

Antioquia is pre-eminently the industrial department. Spanish colonisation began there in the sixteenth century, attracted by gold-bearing and silver-bearing alluvia of the Rio Nechi and its tributaries. The precious metals, though still exploited, no longer form the main activity of the region. Medellin and its outskirts produce most of the textiles sold in Colombia. With the Casabe deposits the region is also among the foremost in oil production. Rapid developments are taking place in the engineering, chemical and food-producing industries; and Medellin, though its site is rough and rugged, is an important communications centre and remains in the forefront. Despite the lack of good soil, an extremely varied range of agriculture is being fully expanded, profiting by two rainy seasons, which give two crops in the year, notably cereals and potatoes.

*Sierras of Santa Maria and the Choco.* The great isolated massif of Santa Marta, culminating in the Christopher Columbus and Bolivar peaks at 19,000 feet, is the loftiest massif in Colombia. It has been practically uninhabited and almost entirely unknown up to now

The Western Cordillera or Cordillera of the Choco is the direct extension of the Pasto shelf. About 600 miles long, it runs between the Cauca Valley and the Pacific coast and extends to the Atlantic seaboard; its eastern edge (the Cordillera de San Jacinto) fringes the depression of the Lower Magdalena. Not as lofty as the other chains, it rises higher in the north and reaches 12,800 feet at the Paramillo node, then once more makes a rapid drop.

Exposed to winds from the Pacific, the western side of this Cordillera is deeply gullied, criss-crossed by countless hill torrents. From the mangroves of the deltaic coast up to the level of the tree-ferns, the primeval forest stretches unbroken. Groups of Carib Indians are scattered here and there. There are a few gold and platinum placers, and occasionally, in a sheltered valley, a colony of hardy Antioquin pioneers. The eastern flank falls rather abruptly to the fertile valley of the Cauca, and only the upper slopes are forest-clad.

## FROM AGRICULTURAL ECONOMY TO IRON-SMELTING

Diversity of climate, as we have seen, makes possible exceptional variety in food production, and the Colombian economy in this respect is the most self-sufficing in all Latin America. Colombia is the world's second largest producer of coffee, and is the major producer of 'mild coffees'. This crop constitutes 70 per cent of Colombia's exports.

Today priority is being given to road construction. Installation of a rail system and equipment of a network in the full sense demand resources and long-term planning which Colombia has never had. Thanks largely to private initiative, road and air transport, on the other hand, have developed very rapidly in the last few years.

The great problem is energy. Oil production fell sharply during the war, and foreign companies were deterred from making investments by the Government's policy towards them. However, restrictions were lifted in 1950 and annual production is now over 7 million tons. The oil produced at Carabe and at De Marie has to be exported crude, since it is of a quality that demands more developed refining machinery than the Colombians possess. Oil from Barco, however, is refined at Barrancabermeja, but it is insufficient for home consumption. Natural gas has for long an important source of energy.

The coal reserves (probably 40,000 million tons) are by far the most important in all South America, but there is little exploitation. In 1962 the 408 hydroelectric stations produced 459,700 kW. Natural gas has long been used in some parts. There is now a plan to harness one of the tributaries of the Magdalena, the Rio Nare, which rises in the Antioquia plateau, near the great industrial centre of Medellin. But the most ambitious hydraulic plan seems to be the combined project under examination, with the co-operation of North American enterprises, in the Valle del Cauca department, whose chief centre

is Cali (population 813,000). It will, when completed, benefit power production, agriculture and river transport alike.

The opening of the Paz del Rio ironworks in 1955 started Colombia on an era of heavy industry. This is a complete plant, comprising a foundry, steelworks and rolling mills. Its initial capacity is 180,000 tons of rolled steel a year; it also supplies to agriculture, especially coffee producers, 3,000 tons of agricultural lime and nearly 40,000 tons of phosphoric slag. Important further developments are proposed for the future, and the high Sogamoso plain is already witnessing the installation of a host of industries that make use of steel. Paz del Rio is the nucleus of an industry whose growth will lead to expansion, not only of the derivative, accessory or complementary industries, but eventually—with the rise in employment and purchasing power—of trade and agriculture.

# VENEZUELA

With an area of 352,000 square miles, Venezuela, larger than Uruguay, Paraguay and Ecuador put together, is much smaller than the two giants, Argentina and Brazil.

Its seaboard was the first mainland coast sighted by Columbus, who reached the Gulf of Paria in August 1498. In the following year Alonso de Hojeda and Amerigo Vespucci reached, farther west, a gulf extending into an immense lagoon which is known today as Lake Maracaibo. They called the country Venezuela or 'Little Venice'.

## THE FORMATION OF A REPUBLIC

The Spaniards founded Cumana, within easy reach of the richest pearl fisheries, in 1520; Coro, on the isthmus joining the peninsula of Paraguana to the continent, was established in 1523. In the mountainous area bordering the sea, Barquisimeto was not to emerge until 1552, Valencia until 1555. Caracas, though on a fine site, being hemmed in at an altitude of 3,000 feet and having no easy communication with the coast, was not settled until 1567. The Caracas and Teques Indians kept up a fierce struggle there. The forest-clad solitudes of the Guiana shield and the northern confines of Amazonas remained impenetrable for much longer; they are still hardly explored.

Venezuela, at first part of the viceroyalty of Peru, then of New Granada, was given the status of *capitania general* in 1777. United States independence and the French Revolution aroused longings for independence in the controlling class of the creoles (the descendants of non-aboriginal races, born in South America), who were jealous of the prerogatives and privileges enjoyed by the Spaniards. Independence, proclaimed in 1811, was to be established only after the decisive victory of Simon Bolivar at the Carabobo Pass in 1821.

Venezuela is a republic composed of twenty states, one federal district, two federal territories (Delta and Amazonas, the least accessible regions), and island federal dependencies. It is governed by a president who is elected by direct popular vote for five years and assisted by a cabinet. A Chamber of Deputies and a Senate make up the National Congress. The majority of the population are Roman Catholic, but the Constitution provides for freedom of worship. The official language is Spanish.

The population was 8,144,000 in 1963. The annual rate of increase, over 30 per 1,000, is among the highest in Latin America. Foreigners (less than one tenth of the population) are chiefly Spaniards, Portuguese, Italians, and in much smaller numbers Britons, French, German, and Slavs. Even though the Negro population has remained homogeneous in certain coastal villages, cessation of the slave trade over a century ago and the arrival of numbers of Europeans are tending to 'lighten' the population as a whole.

The coastal states include only 16 per cent of the country's area, but contain 60 per cent of the population. The Andean states include 3 per cent of the area and 16 per cent of the population: the density is therefore considerable in the narrow valleys sup-

porting habitation. By contrast, in the vast forest territories of the south (Delta, Bolivar, Amazonas) the population is less than 28,000 over 178,000 square miles.

Drilling in a gold mine at El Callao. This legendary land of El Dorado still produces gold, though iron in the region has proved to be a more reliable source of wealth.

## SOURCES OF THE ORINOCO

In broad outline the relief and the hydrography are very simple: the territory merges, in great measure, into the basin of the chief river, the Orinoco, which flows between the Guiana shield and the great northern arc of the Andes formed by the Andes chain and the Coastal Cordillera. Only the northern slope of this chain and the Anzoátegui terraces empty their waters straight into the Atlantic; the Unare, San Juan and Guanipa are the most important of the coastal rivers.

The Orinoco extends for about 1,350 miles. Along its right bank it winds round the Archaean rocks of the Guiana substratum, which dip beneath the Quaternary alluvia of the Venezuelan and Colombian savannas, to reappear, tilted and folded, over 600 miles to the west in the Cordillera. The building up of the vast alluvial plain (in area over 195,000 square miles) has pushed back the river to the very foot of the Guiana shield.

The massif of the Guianas, or Guiana shield, is really a primitive massif which has never been submerged by sea waters. Formed of igneous rocks (granite, gabbro, etc.) and metamorphic rocks (gneiss, mica schist, etc.), it has been covered by heavy sandstone formations. At their most advanced stage of erosion the mountains look like huge fortified castles whose vertical flanks rise sheer from the great forest.

Exploration of this region is not yet completed. The great watercourses are the only means of access: the complete courses of the Caroni, the Caura and

Ploughing in the Andes. The Andean peasant is frugal and hardworking, with generally only a 7 to 10 acre property to maintain a family of 8 to 12 people. Sugar-cane and coffee are grown on the lower terraces of the mountains, maize on the higher terraces, and wheat on the highest slopes of all.

the Ventuari have only been identified since 1930, the Orinoco since 1951. The Guiana rivers, flowing in contact with the Archaean shelf, are constantly broken by rapids caused by the presence of hard, intrusive rocks.

These solitudes are the home of the 'collector' Indians (living on the wild fruits they pick) and nomads (Guaharibos, Waikas). Some (Piaroas) do rough farming on patches of burnt land; others, such as the Caribs, hold the monopoly in barter trading.

The Brazil-Venezuelan frontier, drawn along the watershed between the Orinoco and Amazon basins, is not yet fully marked out in these remote regions.

## THE CORDILLERAS

*Is the Cordillera still rising?* In the far west of the country the chain of the Venezuelan Andes breaks away from the Eastern Cordillera of Colombia. The tectonic depression of San Cristobal marks a clear break in continuity between the two branches.
The Cordillera extends for some 280 miles from south-west to north-east, then falls away eastward to form the Coastal Cordillera. Its width is nowhere more than about 60 miles. There are no high plateaus and the very steep sides fall sheer into the Maracaibo

depression in the north-west and into the savannas and the Orinoco basin in the south-east.

For the most part the waters of the Andes flow by the Motatan and Chama rivers to Lake Maracaibo. These two hill torrents have opened, on the very back of the Andean anticline, an immense longitudinal furrow. Terraces in four tiers, clinging like giant balconies to the walls of this great central furrow, overhang the Motatan and the Chama. In the valley there is a lower level of terrace formation where the Great Cordillera changes form and rises. Earthquakes are the most noticeable expression of the youth of the Andean chain.

The terraces in the heart of the mountains, alluvial lands with little slope called *mesas* ('tables', provide the only cultivable and habitable regions. The most important villages and even the towns are located on the low terraces, where at the time of the conquest the chief native villages were settled. The Venezuelan Cordillera, like the Colombian Andes, was occupied by tribes using the Chibcha language.

The lower terraces are fertile and well-watered. enriched and often devastated by the frequent river floods. Up to 6,500 feet and sometimes more, this is the sugar-cane and coffee region. On the upper and drier terraces maize in particular is cultivated (up to almost 10,000 feet), and above that wheat, which occupies almost impossible slopes above the last terraces, up to 13,000 feet. Still higher, cattle seek scanty pasture among the erratic blocks of the moraines.

The small property is the rule, and a family of eight to twelve persons often has to subsist on a holding of 7 to 10 acres. The Andean peasant is as frugal as he is hard-working, and has a deep devotion to his own soil, contenting himself every day of the year with the unleavened girdle-cake of wheat or maize, washed down with the raw juice of the sugar-cane. Each house is flanked by its rough cane mill, worked by a donkey or simply by hand. Coffee, introduced towards the end of the eighteenth century, is the only product that brings in a little money for the Andean peasant.

Constructed between 1922 and 1926, the trans-Andean highway, which connects Maracaibo with San Cristobal (almost 400 miles), makes use of the great central furrow. To follow from Barinas the giddy spirals of this road means climbing about 13,000 feet within eighty miles in a car-drive of some four hours. Botanists declare that this short journey offers as many changes in distribution of flora as could be found on a journey from the Antilles to the Arctic Circle.

The Sierra de Santo Domingo and the Sierra Nevada de Merida, towering above the llanos, or grasslands, have the loftiest peaks. The surface area of the perpetual glaciers is probably no more than 5,000 acres, and the lower limit of the perpetual snow does not fall below 15,400 feet on the inner slope, at the side of the great central furrow, while on the eastern slope, facing the llanos and the sea, it drops to 14,800 feet. Falls of snow are exceptional at any altitude below 12,000 feet. The glaciers extend farthest during the summer, which is the rainy season.
*Coastal Cordillera and Inner Cordillera.* The mountainous fringe running along the Caribbean coast is formed by two distinct ranges, largely parallel but

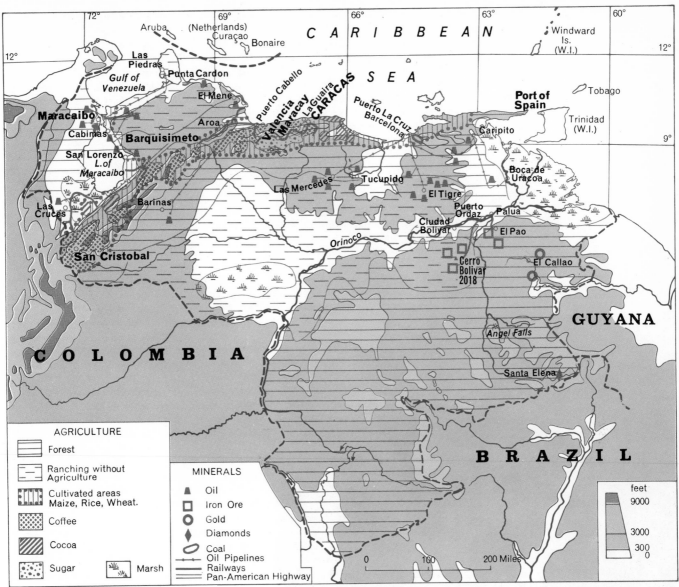

**AGRICULTURE**

Forest

Ranching without Agriculture

Cultivated areas Maize, Rice, Wheat.

Coffee

Cocoa

Sugar    Marsh

**MINERALS**

▲ Oil

□ Iron Ore

○ Gold

◆ Diamonds

Coal

Oil Pipelines

Railways

Pan-American Highway

0    100    200 Miles

feet

9000

3000

300

0

differing in age and structure: the Coastal Cordillera and the Inner Cordillera.

The Coastal Cordillera, which commands the high Caracas plain, is actually the extension of the Andes. From Puerto Cabello to Cape Codera, its gloomy and forbidding wall plunges straight into the Caribbean Sea. The villages, always isolated, lie at the river mouths on alluvial cones, thin strips of land running out into the sea. Las Guaira has become the port of Caracas.

The 'Inner' Cordillera is made up of irregular secondary chains. This mountainous fringe has played a decisive part in the history of the country. The valleys, coinciding with the tectonic depressions extending between the two ranges, represent no more than 780 square miles and the mouths of the coastal torrents about 40. But these lands now contain over a quarter of the whole population, 1,700,000 concentrated on the high Caracas plain, a closed circle of 20 square miles.

When the Spaniards arrived, plantations of manioc, maize and cacao were thriving here. From the end of the sixteenth century settlements multiplied. The sugar-cane, introduced about 1520, was gradually

replacing the indigenous plantations. Lands were portioned out, and these were to be the nucleus of the vast estates which soon gave birth to the trade in Negroes, and whose sole product was to be sugar-cane — always processed on the spot into sugar or rum.

Here, on the Caracas plain, altitude counteracts the trying nature of the tropical climate, and the Spaniards were not out of their element.

The extensive depression of Aragua, whose waters converge towards Lake Tacarigua — now merged with Lake Valencia — lies between the two ranges. Valencia stands where the ways converge and lead eastward to the centre of the depression, northward to the roadstead of Puerto Cabello and southward to Carabobo, the gateway to the llanos. At the other end of the depression, on the road to Caracas, Maracay was to become another gateway. The cities that sprang up on the plain were within riding distance of each other.

Roads serve the principal centres, and one of them, the highway which since 1953 has connected the capital with its port, La Guaira, straddles sheer-sided valleys and plunges under mountains.

Venezuela, showing land use and principal products. Venezuela's economy, once based on export of stock-breeding products, then on the export of oil, is now relying increasingly on the huge iron reserves at Cerro Bolivar, El Pao and El Callao, and products are being used locally in Venezuela's growing industrial enterprises.

## THE 'LLANERO'—MAN OF THE 'LLANOS'

The Jesuit missionaries, following closely on the conquistadors from Bogota, established native convert settlements on the llanos and the army was used to herd recalcitrant natives into these planned settlements. To provide for subsistence and then for the growth of the missions, cattle were brought in. Within a few generations the 'llanero' had appeared; more often than not the offspring of the conquerors and native women, he lived on horseback, subsisting on the great herds wandering free.

The simple, wild spirit of the llanero, formed in the vast, lonely tracts of the llanos, was to animate the horsemen of Paez who offered their services to Bolivar with wooden lances and machetes as their weapons. The llanero of today, still indifferent to money, enjoys spending his leisure time plaiting reins from untanned leather, or dreamily plucking a harp or guitar. Under the wide porch of his palm-roofed house, he will always offer you two nails for your hammock and share with you his traditional menu of dried meat.

No one knows how many cattle there are; all, however, are branded and vaccinated against foot-and-mouth disease. For some years now ring-fences have been put up and selection of animals for breeding has been introduced. An empty plain is scored with dead straight roads furrowed by trucks which replace the cattle-drovers of former days. Heavy cargo aircraft land almost anywhere, often without a landing-strip, quite near the isolated cattle ranch. Cold stores are being built and milk production is contemplated.

Today Venezuela has become self-sufficient in meat and in fruit and vegetables, but still imports wheat and a certain amount of dried milk.

## THE AGE OF OIL AND IRON

From 1925 onward Venezuela was to be swept forward in a headlong rush of modern development, which has reached its peak today. In 1917, on the shores of Lake Maracaibo, oil gushed out for the first time.

Venezuela is now foremost in the production of petroleum in South America. The annual production of crude oil at present is something like 75 million tons. About 70 per cent of this production originates in the tectonic depression of Maracaibo. Five thousand derricks, perched on piles which are often driven to a depth of over 300 feet, spring out of the calm waters of a lake the size of Brittany. The colonial-type town of Maracaibo had in 1920 a population of 7,000; now it is a metropolis with 920,000 inhabitants. The recently dredged channel, $7\frac{1}{2}$ miles wide, which connects the lake with the Gulf of Venezuela and the Caribbean Sea, is navigable today by the largest tankers.

During its development since 1937, the basin of eastern Venezuela has seen the rise of Barcelona, with the outer harbour of Guanta; the latter is connected with the extraction centres by a series of pipelines. The basin extends to the Orinoco delta.

The present world tendency is to develop refining in the country of origin. Venezuela, the first world exporter of oil, did not begin to export refinery products to any great extent until 1950. Over 30 per cent of the output is now processed in the vicinity of the production zones.

Petroleum products cover close on 100 per cent of Venezuela's energy requirements. Every village, every oilfield and every cattle ranch on the llanos has an electricity generating plant sufficient for its own needs. Yet national consumption absorbs only 5 per cent of the production. Notwithstanding the extreme shortage of consumer goods and the increasing volume of equipment imports, the total value of imports is half that of exports. The export surplus ensures the remarkable stability of the currency. Above all it permits the fulfilment of a vast programme of public works, at the same time enabling Venezuela to hope for speedy increase and diversification in its production, especially in agriculture, whereby it may escape the dread of tomorrow: a slump in petroleum.

The Guiana hinterland, the El Dorado of legend, is still the country of gold and diamonds. But iron has also been exploited there for some years now. The

Caracas, capital of Venezuela, a rapidly developing city with many ultra-modern buildings.

Cerro Bolivar, the famous iron mountain several hundred miles south of the Orinoco River. Its iron is 68 per cent dry assay, which is one of the highest concentrations of pure iron in the world.

GUATEMALA: Quiché Indians celebrating pagan rites on the steps of a colonial-style church.     Landscape above Lake Atitlan

more or less tabular hills that fringe the right bank of the Lower Orinoco are composed of ferruginous quartzites, associated with magnetite and hematite. Estimated reserves at present exceed two thousand million tons. Production had reached 15.7 million tons by 1964.

The mines of El Pao and Cerro Bolivar, located on opposite sides of the Caroni, provided the country with the first railroads worthy of the name. On the Orinoco ore transport ships pass frequently, some of them with a tonnage of 45,000 and a draught of 36 feet. Three great arms of the delta, the Caño Mánamo, the Caño Macareo and the Boca Grande, are dredged and marked out.

'*Sowing petroleum.*' It is estimated that from 1946 to 1949, 72 per cent of North American investment in Latin America was absorbed by the petroleum industry in Venezuela. Since 1950, part of these investments has gone towards the prospecting and working of iron. The development of the mining industries is linked, of course, to the needs of American industry. Moreover, it is the occasion for vast imports of consumer goods and equipment.

The lure of the petroleum camps or towns suddenly distended and the enormous inflation of administrative workers (the number of government employees rose from 7,000 in 1936 to over 100,000 in 1955) slowed down agricultural production at the very moment when progress in hygiene and preventive medicine was causing an exceptionally rapid increase in population. Food shortages were accentuated by the improvement in living standards occurring throughout a large section of the population.

More recently, again, the shortages sprang from the changes in ways of life due to contact with European immigrants arriving in large numbers just after the Second World War. It can be said that before the arrival of these post-war immigrants the elementary notion of a 'craft' was hardly conceivable: a mason or a carpenter by trade (always a foreigner) was called *maestro* and supervised a gang of *peones*. This 'technical middle class' is at present causing an upheaval in the towns. It is beginning to design, timidly so far, a new agrarian landscape; in the catchword dear to responsible Venezuelans, the new class is 'sowing petroleum'.

In the rich valley of Aragua, for example, within the traditional framework of the great estate, which has a bias towards single-crop farming, with the aid of mechanisation and use of fertilizers fresh impetus is being given to the growing of crops such as sugarcane, rice, maize, cotton, tobacco, sesame, as well as tomatoes and pineapples intended for bottling or canning and particularly for fruit juices.

Solid tariff structures protect national production of fruit juices and canned goods, of leather, footwear, cotton and sisal yarns and textiles. The paradoxical importation of sugar and chocolate is now no more than a memory.

While one of the major problems is still to increase and diversify production, a no less important objective of Venezuela's political economy is that of adding to the number of export markets (essentially for petroleum) open to the suppliers. Imports from the United States, which in 1946 represented 80 per cent of the total imports, were still as high as 45 per cent in 1961.

THE PROGRESS OF THE PIONEER FRONT. The Venezuelan *campesino* (countryman), living in isolation in some mountain valley or along the rivers of the llanos, tilling his modest family plantation, is an unsettled being. His house is not built to last, and the small clearing, quickly exhausted, is ephemeral.

The example of a true peasant stock was needed, and this could only be introduced from outside Venezuela. South of the historic Carabobo passage the ploughed fields are now encroaching upon the llanos. The first of the agricultural settlements, at Turon, has produced a doubled crop of rice and cotton since 1950. The 650 settlers come from twenty-five different countries. With this encouraging example, other settlements were established in other regions. A pioneer front advances every year, and the agricultural settlements form one of the most promising phenomena in the rapid and fascinating advance of this young country.

Oil derricks on Lake Maracaibo, Venezuela. Many exploration wells have been sunk in the Lake; there is a forest of derricks and a great many wells in full production. An oil centre has come into being at Lagunillas, with its tanks and its workers' city. Almost all the necessary manpower has had to be brought from abroad (Spain, Italy, Cuba). The Maracaibo depression supplies 75 per cent of Venezuelan oil.

# THE GUIANAS

The Guianas, French Guiana, Surinam or Dutch Guiana, and Guyana (British Guiana), cover a vast plateau in the north-east of the South American continent, between latitudes 1°N. and 8°N. and longitudes 54°W. and 63°W.; in the north the plateau dips towards the Atlantic Ocean and in the south is separated from the Amazon basin by a series of mountain blocks.

*Colonisation of the Guianas.* The first explorers of South America did no more than pass along the coasts of this region, which was without any rich Indian empire such as the Andes boasted. At the close of the sixteenth century and early in the seventeenth the Dutch appeared, then the English and the French. It was only from 1814 onward that a series of agreements among the three powers established the present division; arbitration, in 1891, 1899 and 1915, ensured the adjustment of the frontiers.

*Similaries in the three Guianas.* These three territories share many characteristics: the sequence of the geographical zones from the sea towards the interior, and many aspects of climate and population.

COLUMBIA: An exploration oil well in the swamp land of the Middle Magdalena River.     Aerial view of the Cordillera.

The Kaieteur Falls on the Potaro River, a tributary of the great Essequibo River which runs through dense forest in the centre of Guyana. Though such falls reduce the value of the rivers as communication routes, they can be harnessed for hydro-electricity. The waterfall is 300 feet wide and has an initial drop of 741 feet, more than four times that of Niagara Falls.

basins of the Rio Branco, an affluent of the Amazon, and the Essequibo, chief river of Guyana. The Guianas' rivers are navigable only in the coastal region.

Lying in a tropical belt, these territories experience high mean temperatures, 21°C. (70°F.) to 32°C. (90°F.). There is copious rainfall with a long rainy season from April to July, and a short rainy season from November to January; the high humidity is tempered by the prevailing north-east winds.

The population of these territories is very heterogeneous; its chief characteristic is the low proportion of people of European origin. Since the aboriginal Indians, who were few and took to the forest, could not supply enough manpower, it was necessary to import workers of African and Asiatic origin.

## GUYANA

In 1961, British Guiana attained full internal self-government, the British Government being responsible only for defence and external affairs. Five years later, in May 1966, complete independence within the British Commonwealth was attained, and British Guiana reverted to its old name, Guyana.

With its 83,000 square miles Guyana covers an area slightly less than that of Great Britain, but only 0.5 per cent of the land is cultivated along the 240 miles of coast.

This is the most populous of the Guianas, with an average density of 6.5 to the square mile. The population (about 621,000) is increasing rapidly, and includes — besides 13,000 Europeans — 320,000 East Indians, 200,000 Negroes who are descendants of earlier African slaves (slavery was abolished in 1834), 4,000 Chinese and about 24,000 American Indians, existing in a primitive way in the interior. Over a quarter of the population are resident in or around the capital, Georgetown, a port at the mouth of the Demerara River.

The sugar industry is concentrated entirely in the coastal zone. One-third of the wage-earners are employed in it and nearly half the population is dependent on it. The sugar-cane is grown on some 97,000 acres, distributed over about a score of large estates to which the small growers sell their crop. The cane is treated in sixteen factories producing about 317,000 tons of sugar, especially in the form of brown sugar to be sent abroad for refining. Rum and molasses are also exploited.

The bauxite industry employs 2 per cent of the country's manpower and contributes 28 per cent of the national revenue. Guyana has the largest reserves of bauxite known in the world; the deposits are chiefly at Mackenzie, 60 miles from the coast, on the Demerara River.

Among food crops rice, grown on 200,000 acres, is in the first rank; nearly two-fifths of the crop (about 80,000 tons) is exported. Great irrigation and drainage projects now being carried out will add some 75,000 acres to the cultivable area. Coffee and cacao too, offer possibilities; the other crops (maize and potatoes) are adequate for local needs only. Stock-rearing is in process of development, particularly in the Rupununi region.

The forests, which cover 87 per cent of the country, form another important reserve of wealth. Even

Along the coasts there is a narrow strip of flat and marshy land, often below sea level, maintained by a complex system of dykes and canals which the Dutch settlers had established on the model of the polders. Ninety per cent of the population lives in this zone, which is agricultural.

Behind this, over an area some 90 to 130 miles wide, lies a crystalline plateau covered with lateritic clay; it is slightly undulating and has forest and mineral wealth (bauxite, gold and diamonds).

The backbone of the country is composed of a series of well-wooded mountain ranges, separated by very dry savannas. The mountains forming the frontier with Brazil slope downward from west to east.

West of the plateau, along the Venezuelan frontier, a layer of sandstone appears above the crystalline massif, ending in vertical cliffs. This is the highest region in the Guianas (8,530 feet at Mount Roraima, a point common to the frontiers of Venezuela, Brazil and Guyana). In this area is one of the highest single-drop waterfalls in the world, the 820-foot Kaieteur Falls, on the River Potaro. At the foot of Mount Roraima, between this peak and the Acarai Mountains, there is a wide depression which links the

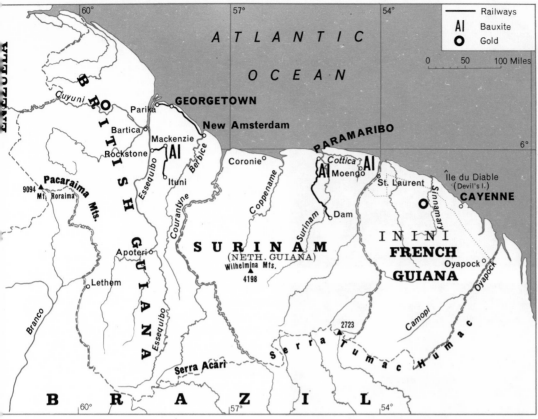

The three Guianas — Guyana, Netherlands and French Guiana — form a physical unity, to which could be added the Venezuelan and Brazilian Guianas. Politically these territories differ in their status, French Guiana being classed since 1947 as an Overseas Department, Surinam being an autonomous part of the kingdom of the Netherlands and Guyana, formerly British Guiana, being a newly independent member of the British Commonwealth.

though some 60,000 square miles could be exploited, mixed stands make exploitation difficult, and only 20 per cent are accessible for profitable working, owing to the lack of means of communication. Nevertheless, there are about 80 sawmills and during the last few years about 50,000 cubic yards of timber have been exported annually.

Finally, export of gold and diamonds also contributes, though to a limited extent, to the country's wealth. An auriferous lode, about sixty miles wide, crosses the country from north-west to south-east. But the production of gold, obtained by gravel-washing, fluctuates sharply and decreases in dry seasons; in recent years it has varied between 3,000 and 18,000 oz. annually. The diamonds come from alluvial sands, notably from the Mazaruni valley; though small, they are of excellent quality and can vie with the Brazilian diamonds; but in general production has declined since 1925.

The country has great potentialities; but means of communication with the interior are poor, although an aviation company ensures internal services. Seven international lines connect Guyana with Europe, the United States, the West Indies and Brazil.

Food products (flour, milk, butter, beer), cotton goods, footwear and medicines have to be imported, and most important — machinery. The main suppliers are Great Britain, the United States and Canada, and the main customers Great Britain, Canada and the United States in that order.

## SURINAM OR NETHERLANDS GUIANA

In accordance with the Constitution of the Netherlands amended in September 1948, Surinam and the Netherlands Antilles form an integral part of the Kingdom of the Netherlands; since 1950 they have enjoyed considerable autonomy, and a charter in force since December 1954 defines the relations of these different territories with one another. The Governor represents the Queen. A Prime Minister and eight Ministers form a Coalition Cabinet and a Legislative Council is elected by popular vote.

This territory, in area (about 55,140 square miles), is more than four times that of the Netherlands, is thinly populated, having about 5 inhabitants to the square mile. The population, estimated at 330,000 at the end of 1962, includes people of European origin, most of them Dutch, Indians (originally from India), Indonesians and Chinese. The Asian workers, arriving on a labour contract, afterwards settled in the country. After the abolition of slavery in 1863, most of the Negroes resumed a primitive existence with the aborigines in the forests; there are about 33,000 Negroes and 5,000 aborigines. The capital, Paramaribo, contains over 35 per cent of the population.

The country's chief industry is the extraction of bauxite. It is found along the Para and Cottica rivers, and exported by sea to the United States; about $3\frac{1}{2}$ million tons are shipped every year.

Timber is also an important item of export (52,000 cubic yards exported from production exceeding 130,000 cubic yards). Balata, a forest product, is being developed (70 tons in 1963). Modern survey methods and mechanisation are the main factors in the industry's growth. There are 45 sawmills and one modern plywood factory.

Agriculture remains the country's great resource. It is concentrated entirely in the coastal zone. The soil and climate are very favourable to the rice crop; the yield is from 1.2 to 2.2 tons of paddy per acre. Coffee production has declined considerably; on the

Street scene in Paramaribo, the
capital of Dutch Guiana.
As in the mother country,
bicycles are a common
means of transport.

A bauxite min at
Mackenzie, Guyana.
The huge machine with its
220-foot boom has to remove
up to 200 feet of over burden
before reaching the bauxite layer.
The reserves of bauxite
in Guyana are the greatest
known deposits in the world.
The industry provides over
a quarter of the country's revenue.

One of the last Oayanas,
aborigines of French Guiana.

other hand, sugar-cane is being grown increasingly. Oranges, grapefruit and lemons also contribute a substantial quota for export, as well as bananas.

The gold industry, which in the past formed the colony's main source of revenue, is now slight.

Means of communication are as inadequate in Surinam as in Guyana. Routes along the rivers serve the bauxite mines and lead to Zandery airport, 30 miles from Paramaribo, a port of call for several airline companies.

The chief suppliers to Surinam, in order of importance, are the United States, the Netherlands and Trinidad. The United States is by far the largest customer, especially for bauxite, plywood and balata; the Netherlands buy mainly fruits, coffee, timber and rice.

## FRENCH GUIANA

Since March 1946, French Guiana has been a French overseas department, enjoying the same administration as a metropolitan department. Since 1957 Inini, the southern portion, has been an 'arrondissement' or administrative district of Guiana. Most of the inhabitants are a mixture of the white and African peoples; only 3,000 are Amerindians and about five per cent are Europeans.

In the 23,000 square miles of this department, roughly one-tenth of the area of France, is a very scattered population of about 33,000, made up, chiefly, of Government officials and West Indians together with a few Chinese and aborigines. Over half the number is concentrated in the capital, Cayenne; the second town, Saint-Laurent, on the River Maroni, has no more than 2,000 inhabitants. The Inini territory (29,000 square miles) has a population of about 3,200. After a long period of declining population, the number of inhabitants is increasing, partly because of immigration, partly because of the spectacularly successful fight against malaria and yellow fever.

Along the 190 miles of coast the waters abound in fish and are dotted with islands.

The country's main industry is gold mining, which is developing rapidly. Bauxite deposits are also being worked.

The forests, which cover about 30,000 square miles, roughly 90 per cent of the territory, are rich but have scarcely been exploited, owing to the lack of roads and the prevalence of mixed stands. Even so, over 10,000 cubic yards are exploited annually — second in value to gold. An essence highly esteemed in perfumery is extracted from rosewood and exported to France.

The soil is fertile, but barely 9,000 acres are under cultivation on the coast; sugar-cane covers about 1,000 acres and annual output is about 15,900 tons; rum is another important export. Rice, maize, manioc, cacao, bananas and tobacco are reserved for local consumption.

There are no railroads, but 170 miles of national highways in the coastal zone; the rivers are navigable in spite of the rapids. Several airlines call at French Guiana.

Most of the trade, both import and export, is with France. There are some exchanges with French and British dependencies in the West Indies, with the United States and with Brazil.

# THE FORESTS,
# CAMPOS AND PAMPAS
# OF SOUTH AMERICA

# BRAZIL

Brazil, discovered in 1500 by Cabral, remained a Portuguese colony until 1822, when it became an independent monarchy ruled by members of the Portuguese royal family; a republic was proclaimed in 1889. It has kept the language and Roman Catholic religion of Portugal.

Brazil is the largest country in South America and the fourth largest in the world. It extends from latitude 33° 45′ S. to latitude 5° 16′ N. and has an area of 3,288,000 square miles, being at its widest in the equatorial region. The prevailing climate is therefore tropical, but the country is so vast that there are inevitably marked differences in climate.

The highest areas are in the east and south-east of the country; when the Portuguese first landed on the Atlantic coast they encountered a barrier of mountains composed of crystalline rocks. Once over this, they found no further topographic obstacle to inland penetration, since most of the area consists of large sedimentary, medium-altitude plateaus. It has always been possible to travel along the Amazon River and its tributaries in the north and the Paraguay River in the west.

The population is predominantly white, since the last survivors of the Indian tribes are hidden in isolated parts of Amazonia or central Brazil and the descendants of African Negro slaves amount to no more than 11 per cent. The Brazilian peasants, or *caboclos*, are of mixed Indian and white origin and there is every degree of intermingling of Portuguese and African blood.

Owing to the fact that Brazil did not become populated suddenly or even smoothly and that successive waves of immigration moved in different directions, the distribution of Indians, Negroes and Whites is uneven and the north-easterners are generally darker than the southerners. Some parts of the country remain almost uninhabited.

A salient feature of the Brazilian scene remains, even today, the concentration of people, farming, mining and industry in the eastern part of the country. In an effort to counteract this tendency, the Brazilian Government has transferred its seat to the interior, to Brasilia, an ultra-modern city specially constructed for the purpose.

After the Portuguese had secured a foothold along the coast by clearing several patches of charcoal-coloured dye-wood, or brazil-wood, they began to move inland. Jesuits settled on the São Paulo plateau; their missionary activities were interrupted in the sixteenth and seventeenth centuries by slave-hunting expeditions against the Indians and in the eighteenth century by gold-prospecting expeditions. The Brazilians call these expeditions *bandeiras* (banners), and the well-known *bandeirantes* were pioneers who took part in them; they were responsible for much of the exploration of Brazil.

The promising future of sugar-cane cultivation along the Atlantic coasts from Recife to Bahia attracted Portuguese planters and traders as well as their Dutch competitors. The planters brought over African slaves to cultivate the land and, in the seventeenth century, the north-eastern countryside and towns became the major centres of the country's economic, political and intellectual life.

In the eighteenth century, the discovery of gold and diamonds in the high lands of Minas Gerais and in central Brazil provided a new magnet for men and wealth.

Towards the middle of the nineteenth century, the growth of the São Paulo coffee areas attracted more immigrants, who then extended the colonisation of the southern states.

The economy has a differentiated regional structure. There was a sugar period during which the north-east was settled; a mining period during the development of Minas Gerais; a brief rubber interlude and an Amazonian period, and the great period of development of São Paulo and of coffee.

## AMAZONIA, LAND OF TREES AND WATER

This region covers 45 per cent of the total area of Brazil, but its population is less than 4 per cent of the whole.

*The great forest.* Amazonia is almost entirely equatorial and consists of a vast area of forests and rivers; the forests constitute a solid mass extending from the Atlantic Ocean to the Andes with fingers stretching along the rivers of Mato Grosso and Goias. They are great, dense forests of giant evergreen trees with many twining lianas and epiphytes and an astonishing variety of botanical species.

There are variations in the general pattern. The damp or marshy *igapo* forest areas along the rivers are overhung with trees inextricably linked, so that even canoes have difficulty in getting through. These trees, which reach heights of about 60 feet, grow on ground where alluvial deposits are constantly being washed away and replenished. The *varzea* forest areas are flooded once a year only, and are therefore less wet and have a more consolidated soil, with very valuable trees such as wild cacao and the famous *Hevea brasiliensis* rubber trees. Since the first explorers who travelled along the rivers found only the *igapo* and *varzea* forests and were constantly surrounded by water, they deduced from this that Amazonia was a great alluvial plain with generally wet soil. Today, however, it is known that it also contains a number of low plateaus above the highest flood levels, on which the so-called *terra firma* forests are situated. Here giant trees rise above a very dense jungle to heights of 60, 100 and even 200 feet or more, and include mahogany and Brazilian rosewood trees as well as the Para chestnut trees, *Bertholletia excelsa*, from which large quantities of fruit are obtained.

Living creatures abound. They include strikingly coloured birds such as aras, humming-birds, flamingoes and egrets; magnificent butterflies; monkeys of every kind; reptiles; wild boars and jaguars; fearsome insects such as voracious ants and malaria-carrying mosquitoes. There are, however, no carriers of sleeping sickness or other African diseases.

There are clearings in some of the drier areas; and in the Rio Branco area, protected from maritime winds by the local relief, there are large savanna patches used as grazing land for the livestock which supplies the urban areas. Elsewhere, and particularly at the mouth of the Amazon River, the slow flow of water contributes to the formation of marshy meadows. Farther on in Maranhão state, the climate is drier, with large plantations of different species of palm trees.

*Rivers of the Amazon basin.* In Brazilian literature, frequent reference is made to the *selva,* or green hell, and the *rio-mar,* or sea river. The forests are impenetrable, but the rivers have made it possible to travel inland, to bring men together in groups and to make use of the forest riches.

The Amazon River is over 4,000 miles long and dramatically impressive in size. Although its source is situated more than 16,000 feet above sea level, it flows at an altitude of only just over 200 feet at the border of Peru and Brazil, 1,800 miles from the ocean. The rate of flow is therefore very slow, in spite of the large volume of water: 3,500,000 cubic feet per second at Obidos and 7,000,000 cubic feet at the mouth of the river, during the floods. The river is about two miles wide when it enters Brazil and four miles wide near Manaus, shrinking to 430 feet at Obidos, where the basin is funnel-shaped owing to a rise in the crystalline bedrock. Downstream, opposite Belem, it is more than eighteen miles wide and looks like a sea. There are a number of islands in this part of the river, which reaches the ocean through variously navigable channels and extends to sea for a distance of about 60 miles.

The Amazon River has many tributaries, which are also large drainage basins; they come from both hemispheres and are subject to alternating floods, thus maintaining a consistent water level. They provide a very fine network for navigation, allowing ocean-going liners to sail 900 miles inland to Manaus and large stamers to reach Iquitos in Peru. There are also many areas of water suitable for seaplanes and, in the near future perhaps, for hovercraft.

Passage along the tributaries themselves is made difficult, however, by the waterfalls and rapids located fairly close to the confluence areas. The exception is the Madeira River, where the local population has developed a surprising number of different types of boat. They include gondolas used for cattle transport, paddle-wheel steamers, *regatãos* used by Brazilian or Syrian traders to carry their goods up-river, and simple canoes that can slither through the narrow waterways filled with lianas, water-lilies and tree trunks.

There is an abundant supply of fish, but fishing is hazardous owing to the presence of poisonous and electric fish and of the voracious *piranhas* which can strip the flesh from an ox in a few minutes. Along the rivers are groups of Indians who live mainly by fishing with nets, spears, bows and arrows.

*Amazonia's part in the Brazilian economy.* Amazonia's share of the Brazilian economy is very small in spite of the reputation of its forests, of its fertile soil and of the gold which is said to be hidden in its subsoil. Although missions were established by Jesuits and Franciscans, at first only the area between Belem and Bragança became inhabited, largely by small farmers who grew manioc, beans, maize, cotton and tobacco. Elsewhere, forest products such as cacao, vanilla, cinnamon and sarsaparilla were picked as they were found; precious woods were also taken. Because looting has continued for three centuries, it has proved impossible to develop a farming mentality or to make men feel close to the land. The latex collectors, for example, worked during the few months of the year when the *hevea* areas were not flooded, and were therefore casual workers who lived badly. They worked in their huts to prepare the large balls of crude rubber which would be taken to the wooden shanties in which their employers lived, from which they would be sold to the wholesalers who lived in the exporting centres of Manaus and Belem. From 1870 to 1912, rubber prices rose continuously, the exporters became rich and the Amazonian towns began to look like cities. When production began in the far eastern plantations, however, there was a crash; the rubber trees had been tapped too heavily and cared for too little; they began to die, so the current rubber harvest does not even provide Brazil with its domestic requirements.

Average monthly temperatures range from 23°C. (73°F.) to 28°C. (82°F.), and are generally consistent,

Yoked oxen, extensively used in the arid north-eastern plains This photograph, taken in the desiccated and sparse forest of Ceara state, shows the drovers' water supply and the thin state of the animals.

The Atlantic coast between Salvador and Recife. This aerial photograph shows a very flat alluvial coast, near which rivers meander between pools and dead river branches. In the foreground is a sandy bar.

while the humidity is very high and the average annual rainfall is between 80 and 120 inches. Amazonia as a whole, however, has months of fairly dry weather, and the winds which blow from the mouth of the river to Manaus are very beneficial. There are also sudden periods of relatively cold weather, the *friagens*, which are due to southerly squalls and can reduce the temperature to below 10°C. (50°F.) in a few hours, with quite serious consequences for human beings. The area is healthier than the Congo although it is much less densely populated.

Amazonia's low population density, therefore, is not entirely due to natural causes. An economy devoted only to the extraction of natural products yields a low standard of living for a population which does not know how to till the soil and which is undernourished.

The situation has been developing favourably, however. Between 1940 and 1950, the population rose by 26 per cent and, in the towns, infant mortality has been declining. The Government is trying to encourage new food crops such as rice, or industrial crops such as jute. North of the mouth of the Amazon, in the Amapa region, the discovery of iron and manganese deposits has led to a marked increase of population. Amazonia nevertheless remains for the time being a dead-weight on Brazil.

## THE DIVIDED NATURE OF THE NORTH-EAST

In the north-east there are two areas with opposite natural characteristics and mutually complementary resources. First, the coastal fringe, which extends from Cape São Roque to the south of Bahia state, and is a damp forest area. Second, the semi-arid inland area or *sertão* which is very similar to the coastal area between Cape São Roque and Maranhão state, and is largely devoted to pastoral farming. This division of the north-east extends beyond the official state limits; it includes Piauí, Ceará, Rio Grande do Norte, Paraiba, Pernambuco, Alagoas, Sergipe and Bahia, and parts of Minas Gerais and Maranhão states.

*The north-east: rain and sugar-cane.* On the coast and a narrow coastal border, rainfall never falls below 35 inches per year and sometimes rises to more than 80 inches. Maximum rainfall occurs in winter from Cape São Roque to the approaches of the Todos os Santos Bay, with 73 per cent of the annual rainfall occurring at Recife between May and August, although farther south there is a better all-year distribution. In both cases, the natural vegetation is or was dense forest.

In general, the coast is flat and has many fine beaches fringed with small dunes. There may be several parallel lagoons, or *restingas,* of which the oldest and best preserved are farthest inland. Off the beaches, there are sandstone reefs similar to that after which Recife is named; beaches and dunes are covered by a magnificent forest of palms — particularly coconut palms. Fishermen live in the shade of the trees, in palm-leaf covered huts, and use light, strong sailing rafts to get around the dangerous reefs and fish on the high seas.

Behind the beaches and coconut plantations there is an old cliff-line which forms the beginning of low plateaus; at Cabo Branco they reach the sea and form a line of steep cliffs which are retreating under the erosive action of the ocean waves. They now have a semi-arid vegetation consisting of brushwood and shrubs.

The landscape changes considerably westward. On the crystalline terrain there are rounded hills in a labyrinth of valleys and, owing to decomposition of granite accelerated by the damp, hot climate, reddish or yellowish clay where tropical forests once existed. In the valleys, alluvial deposits have resulted in very fertile black earth on which sugar-cane is successfully grown. Forests have been extensively cleared by planters, this being one of the tropical areas in which European penetration has brought about the most lasting changes.

Rainfall decreases towards the west, and the Agreste, a transition area of varying extent, shows the change from the wet north-east to the semi-arid lands, from the agricultural to the pastoral areas.

In the rainswept north-eastern coastal strip, the local economy has been and continues to be based chiefly on the production of sugar-cane for export. In the seventeenth century, Brazil was Europe's major source of sugar, and it is through this commodity that urban life developed and became concentrated in the ports in which the Portuguese colony's administrative centres were located. The flourishing sugar industry also attracted the Dutch, who occupied Recife area in the seventeenth century.

The forest area provided the Portuguese with natural conditions favourable to the cultivation of sugar-cane. The virgin *massapé* soil and the small waterways, whose lower reaches were navigable by sailboats and whose waterfalls on the medium reaches could also used, contributed to this development. Indian labour soon proved inadequate, and African slaves were therefore introduced from 1538. Large estates of 1,250 to 2,500 acres were established. Cane-grinding mills and small processing plants were the major components of this sugar empire, in which the plantations were built around the master's house, the slaves' huts being close to the chapel and mill. Tobacco, the only other major crop, was exported to Lisbon or used to buy slaves in Africa; pastureland was barely adequate to feed the oxen used to pull carts or to work the crushing mills. The fruit trees and crops used to feed the workers were so limited in both quantity and quality that the resulting dietary restrictions later developed into and remained genuine taboos for the Africans.

The rivalry of the West Indies put an end to this brilliant Brazilian sugar cycle in the eighteenth century, and the position was later aggravated by the competition of beet-sugar and the abolition of slavery.

Nevertheless, the sugar industry continues and has been modernised. Small factories have disappeared in favour of a few large works owned by individuals or families, equipped with imported machinery and technically efficient. Agricultural techniques remain backward, since the hill slopes are not always suitable for the use of machinery, and the exhausted and eroded soil tends to dry out more quickly during the dry season. Some of the largest factory owners are trying to improve the soil by means of chemical fertilizers and irrigation schemes, but there is some reluctance to do this in view of the expense involved.

Other crops have been introduced and, in the good

earth of the Reconcavo, tobacco is now grown by the descendants of slaves, while in the Agreste cotton and sisal are developing. At Pesqueira there is an immense tomato plantation, with a modern canning factory.

A new area of crop specialisation near the Bahia state coastline, at the far end of the north-eastern coastal strip, is devoted to growing cacao. The local hot, damp climate and the shade provided by the forests are favourable to the growth of cacao trees, and the area has become the second most important cocoa-producing region in the world. The necessary manpower is provided by poor people from the semi-arid areas, and a 'cocoa society' has developed and is characterised by social contrasts, crises and sporadic violence.

There are several permanent characteristics throughout the wet regions in the north-east. These include chronic undernourishment, caused by the poor quality of food crops, as well as the social division which separates the masses from the small number of industrialists, plantation owners and exporters living in the area. Owing to the population density, which reaches 125 or even 250 per square mile and is greater than in most other parts of Brazil, and to the resulting overcrowding, the people of the north-east tend to emigrate.

*The sertão, land of drought and stock-breeding.* In the dry part of the north-east, the *sertao,* which extends inland as well as along the Ceará coast, average rainfall is in places less than 16 inches, and sometimes non-existent, as it may not fall for two or three consecutive years, as in 1951, 1952 and 1953. The natural vegetation which grows on the dry and stony soil is an uneven cover of shrubs with thin, spiny trunks and small grey leaves, as well as many thick-leaved plants, bottle-trees, and a rich variety of cacti.

Throughout its history, the *sertão* has been at the service of the plantation areas to which it has always supplied any necessary livestock, bred in large quantities on considerable areas of land with sparse vegetation. Fields opened up by setting fire to the bushes are sometimes used as pastureland, and the animals graze freely. The cowherds protect themselves and their horses from the thorny trees by means of leather covers.

There is a shifting cultivation of maize, manioc and beans in small fenced-in fields which are abandoned after two or three years, during which they provide the cowherds with their bare subsistence needs only. On the banks of the larger waterways such as the Jaguaribe River, there are large plantations in which there may be many *carnauba* palm trees, whose wax is collected, the leaves being used for fodder. There are a few oases filled with palm trees, banana trees, tropical fruit trees, rice, maize and sugar-cane.

Cotton, grown either as a hardy shrub or as an annual plant, provides the inhabitants with a commodity for barter. Sisal has recently been grown for the local textile industry or for export.

The people of the *sertão* live in fear of drought; when it strikes the crops wither and the animals soon die of thirst. People then emigrate in large numbers to the *zona da mata* (dense forest area) where their arrival is feared, since they are disease carriers and their sufferings have made them violent. The men of the *sertão* are therefore accustomed to be on the move

Cocoa is the chief crop along the coast from Bahia to Ileus. The area devoted to it amounts to about 160,000 acres and output is over 200,000 tons annually. This makes Brazil second only to Ghana as a cocoa producer. In this photograph wet cocoa beans are put into the 'sweating box' to ferment.

The church of São Pedro in Recife, one of the many colonial-style churches in the state of Pernambuco. The north-East was the centre of Brazil's wealth in colonial days and is full of such splendid monuments: the town of Salvador, or Bahia, alone has 365 churches.

and this, coupled with the fact that they are undernourished and therefore tend to be irascible and that they live in constant fear of calamity, naturally disposes them to extremes of behaviour. Many mystics have sprung from the Bahia or Ceará *sertão*, and the north-eastern bandits are familiar figures in Brazilian folklore.

Remedies have long been sought by the federal authorities. Some progress has beeen achieved; dam-reservoirs have been built at great expense in order to increase the size of the irrigated areas to which the peasants come when they are escaping from periods of drought. Only a small part of the total area has, however, been irrigated. Road-building has made more obvious progress; there are also a few rail communications from Bahia, Recife and Fortaleza with a connection between the Bahia and Minas Gerais railroads. Air links, too, are helping to end the isolation of the *sertão* of the north-east. But modern means of communication tend to encourage emigration to the towns.

*The decline and future of the north-east.* The north-east, once the focus of colonial wealth and the centre of intellectual life and political activity, has not been able to withstand competition from the new areas around São Paulo and in the south. In 1872, 30 per cent of the Brazilian population lived in the north-east; by 1950 this figure had been reduced to 24 per cent. The north-east is now a land of emigrants, a buyer of food or manufactured goods and, in consequence, one of the major customers of southern Brazil.

However, this region has now been chosen by ASCOFAM (World Association for the Campaign Against Hunger) as a pilot zone in the struggle against famine. The basic food — manioc flour — has been artificially enriched with proteins and mineral salts, in an attempt to banish endemic disease. Simple techniques have been introduced to inprove food production, and health and educational services. The experiment has already had much success.

Oil and gas deposits have been found in the suburbs of Salvador, and hydro-electric schemes are being implemented. A power plant has been built on the Paulo Afonso Falls, on the lower reaches of the São Francisco River. There are also plans to extend the irrigated areas of the São Francisco valley, where serious consideration has been given to the possibility of inland colonisation. The mining of rare ores such as Bahia quartz found in crystalline rock areas might also be increased, but it is too early to know if these attempts will prove successful.

There is, however, a constant development of urban areas and of industry. From 1940 to 1950, the population of Fortaleza, Salvador and Recife increased by 10,000, 134,000 and 190,000 respectively. Salvador, the city of Negroes and of Afro-Brazilian folklore, is divided by its relief: the lower town, with the port and modern commercial buildings, has been linked with considerable difficulty to the upper town, which has remained typically Portuguese with charming little streets, fine baroque churches and a very picturesque market. Recife, the capital of the sugar area, is the metropolis of the north-east. Established by the Dutch, it is a city of lagoons and bridges, in which old houses built over river inlets stand side by side with a growing number of new skyscrapers, while palm-leaf huts are still being built on the mangrove marshes to accommodate swarms of *sertão*. refugees. Here again are the characteristic conflicts of an old colonial society, and also the antagonism between *zona da mata* and *sertão* The fact that these contrasts co-exist, however, may well be the first indication of the north-east's future.


## MINAS GERAIS

The state of Minas Gerais is essentially a country of highlands; the mountains in places reach a level of more than 5,000 feet. Other types of countryside include the northern areas which are semi-arid, the westernmost part of the state which lies in central Brazil, and the southern part which includes the upper reaches of the Paraná River.

Minas has played a major part in the history and political life of Brazil, as one may deduce from the fine baroque churches, old houses and narrow streets with their very Portuguese appearance which are found in several small towns.

Minas was once an El Dorado; it is now a region of pastoral farming and agriculture. Once a centre for inland colonisation, it is now a centre from which men and capital have been dispersed. In 1872, Minas contained more than 20 per cent of the population total; in 1960 with nearly 10 million people, it contained only 14 per cent.

*The border areas: agriculture and stock-breeding.* The São Francisco River, the only major river whose entire course is through Brazilian soil, has its upper and middle reaches in Minas. Because the river has been a passage from south or north, it has become a symbol of national unity, although its boats with carved prows and its worn-out steamships now have considerable competition from the roads and new rail connections to Bahia. The alluvial plain is dotted with occasional dunes, and bordered by plateaus. This is the semi-arid area where the Brazilian peasants of mixed Indian and Portuguese blood, the *caboclos*, eke out a living.

In the northern part of the state, the Chapada Diamantina is a series of hard ridges which alternate with quite broad valleys. It is named after the diamonds which were discovered there in 1760 and which encouraged settlements. Diamond-seekers still make rare finds today.

The great forest at the borders of the states of Minas Gerais and Espirito Santo has been opened up by people from Minas and by the descendants of Germans who settled in Espirito Santo and followed the Doce River valley. The pioneers are planting maize and manioc and raising pigs, as well as operating a few small cacao plantations and a greater number of coffee plantations.

In the south-west the Minas state border extends between the Grande and Paranaiba rivers which then merge to form the Paraná River. This Minas triangle is a sandstone plateau in which great ravines are cut by fertile valleys, and its inhabitants, influenced by São Paulo, have transformed the bushy savanna into pastureland used to fatten the oxen, which are then sent for slaughter to the cold storage plant at Barretos, in São Paulo state.

The influence of neighbouring states on the outlying areas of Minas Gerais is shown not only by their geographical characteristics but also by the appearance of spas such as Araxà, and by the fact that bauxite, which is mined at Poços de Caldas, is shipped to the aluminium plant at Sorocaba, near the city of São Paulo.

*The heart of Minas Gerais: from gold to iron and steel.* The central part of the state is a plateau of ancient rock, gneiss and mica-schists with an average altitude of about 3,000 feet. Towards the south, this plateau rises uniformly from west to east, culminating in the crests of the Serra da Mantiqueira, whose slopes descend sharply to the Paraiba valley. This range includes the Itatiaia mountain mass (9,260 feet). Here the relief is more rugged, with steep ridges of quartzite, reddish in colour and rocky in appearance. Access to the high lands was facilitated in the days of mule caravans by transverse gaps running in the general direction of the relief, and by the valleys of the São Francisco, Velhas, Doce and Grande rivers, which have also encouraged a spread of population to the outlying areas. The altitude has made the climate more temperate, and in spite of clearing there are some araucaria trees in the Minas mountains, still called a *zona da mata,* or forest area.

Pastoral farming and the cultivation of food crops were established in Minas after a brilliant period of gold mining and of urban development. Tenant farmers pay their rent to the owners of large farmsteads either by providing cartfuls of maize or else by their labour. The owners themselves are hard workers and keen money-makers. Life is frugal, and men can make money from the sale of maize-fed pigs, of cattle, milk and cheese, which are shipped to the large urban areas. Owners of sugar-cane fields use green cane as cattle fodder and make brown sugar and brandy. During the past century, coffee proved an irresistible temptation in the *zona da mata,* although the steep, deforested slopes have not withstood erosion and few plantations survive. Agriculture, pastoral and dairy farming in Minas have the advantage of being within easy reach of the great consumer centres of Rio de Janeiro and São Paulo.

The great mineral riches of Minas Gerais, found chiefly along the rivers, have given the region an economic and industrial uplift. Diamonds and gold found in the alluvial deposits have always attracted many goldwashers, but now one of the deepest gold mines in the world is being operated by an American firm. Iron reserves, estimated to amount to 35,000 million tons, are among the largest in the world. There are whole mountains of iron ore which can be mined quite cheaply, although there are considerable variations in quality. The best deposits are situated in a rectangular area south-east of Belo Horizonte. Mining only began after the Second World War, although output now amounts to more than 10 million tons a year. A large share is processed in Japanese-Brazilian works near the deposits, although the lion's share is sent to the great national iron and steel works at Volta Redonda, in the valley of the Paraiba do Sul.

A number of advantages and drawbacks have affected the development of heavy industry. The wood on the spot, used for blast furnaces, was quickly depleted, and is now being replaced by plantations of quick-growing eucalyptus trees. Communications are unsatisfactory since the railroads cannot cope with the heavy traffic. Manufactured goods can be carried to Rio de Janeiro and São Paulo by road. Domestic capital resources proved inadequate, and Belgium, France, Luxembourg, Germany and Japan have begun to place investments.

Minas also has some textile factories situated in small villages such as Juiz de Fora and Barbacena. Hydro-electric power stations are being constructed and are expected to contribute extensively to industrial development.

The development of the state's mountain area has been shown by the mushroom growth of the capital city of Belo Horizonte, established by decree and inaugurated in 1897. It has become an academic and intellectual centre as well as the seat of increasing commercial and industrial activity. Skyscrapers have sprung up, although the pitiful shanty towns still exist. The fast-growing city had a population of about 693,000 in 1960, and its inhabitants come from every part of the state.

## THE RIO DE JANEIRO AREA

The former national capital, Rio de Janeiro, together with its suburbs and its neighbour Niteroi, which is the capital of the state of Rio de Janeiro, is a conurbation with a population of about 4,000,000, and the largest gathering of white people living on a tropical coast. A few miles from the main streets are rural areas with a low population density, in which archaic customs prevail. Rio is situated in the bay of Guanabara, a famous natural site whose beauty is well known, with its mountainous base and surrounding tropical plains, lagoons and sand spits. In 1960 Brazil inaugurated the new national capital of Brasilia, about 600 miles to the north-west of Rio de Janeiro, in the state of Goias.

*Centuries of control of the land.* The Portuguese city was offiically established in 1565, near the famous Sugar Loaf Mountain and, after years of struggle against the French, the Portuguese won and settled on Castle Hill, which has now been flattened. When the King of Portugal fled from Napoleon in 1808, he took refuge in Brazil and, by establishing his court and administration at Rio, ensured the city's future supremacy.

Sugar-cane plantations were established in the surrounding lowland area of Paraiba do Sul by the Jesuits, who had the Rio marshes drained. When the Jesuits were expelled, in the eighteenth century, these were abandoned in favour of new plantations, farther north near Campos. During the nineteenth century, market-gardening began outside Rio, and coffee plantations appeared on mountain slopes such as Tijuca, now part of the city. As the city's political importance grew, it became an isolated giant surrounded by an area which was virtually unpopulated and often unhealthy.

Since 1930, the situation has completely changed. There are orange and banana plantations and market-gardens, and steps were taken to make the lowlands healthy and to settle a new population there. Farther along, in the mountains, dairy produce and a variety of crops have been developed, and there are many tourists in the summer resorts of Petropolis, Teresopolis and Nova Friburgo.

*A complex area.* There are coastal mountain groups situated within the city itself, and granitic bluffs whose strange silhouettes rise above small alluvial plains which were once marshy and are still filled with lagoons. The coastline consists of alternating rocky headlands and large beaches, which sometimes have dunes, and separate saline marshes such as the Araruama marsh.

Behind these coastal secondary chains, the head of Guanabara Bay consists of mangrove-fringed flat lowlands into which many winding rivers empty. The backdrop is provided by the wall of the Serra do Mar. also called the Serra do Estrela and the Serra dos Orgãos. The first Europeans thought they had discovered the estuary of a major river coming down from the mountains and called it the river of January, or Rio de Janeiro. In fact, this is an old river valley which became filled with water, due to a rise in the sea level. The Serra do Mar is not easy to climb, and railroads and roads have great difficulty in reaching the Paulo Frontin and Barra do Pirai passes. There is a gentler descent to the Paraiba do Sul valley, in which the left bank of the river is dominated by the abrupt rise of the Serra da Mantiqueira. Both the Serra do Mar and the Serra da Mantiqueira are asymmetrical, and turn their more precipitous slopes towards the east. They are parallel to the coast and preceded by a third ridge which is lower and divided into fragments: in effect, these are the coastal secondary mountains.

Communication between the inland sections of the country and the former capital of Brazil is not easy, since even aircraft must fly in between peaks and isolated bluffs to land either on Governador Island in the middle of the bay, or on land recently reclaimed from the sea. The first glimpse of Rio de Janeiro from the air, therefore, shows the isolation of the tropical metropolis and the obstacles which it has had to overcome.

*Rio City.* First, it was necessary to conquer yellow fever, a permanent scourge until the Brazilian scientist, Oswaldo Cruz, found an antidote at the beginning of

neighbourhood is being built at Ipanema beach, since snobbishness and speculation on land and apartments have led the rich to escape from any neighbourhood which begins to be popular.

Rio is not all luxury and beauty: children beg far into the night, and Negro women sell their peppery fried goods and oily cakes on small stands placed on the pavement directly in front of luxury hotels and night clubs. On the bluffs and mountains are shanty towns, consisting of huts made of boarding roofed with zinc, with a sparse water supply and an irregular electricity service. These areas are reached by steep paths, which higher up provide access either to banana plantations or to wild passages along the ocean, only a few minutes from large, richly urbanised avenues. The population here is largely, though not exclusively, Negro, and there are other such neighbourhoods in the low-lying and unhealthy areas. The task of re-housing the population and eliminating these areas remains enormous and difficult to carry out.

The population of the Rio district is constantly increasing. In 1950, Rio had a population of 2,377,451; now it is over 4 million and still growing. This increase is largely due to immigration from other parts of the country.

The political rôle of Rio was responsible for its relationship to the rest of the country. It is a major port serving the hinterland of Minas Gerais, and also becoming a major industrial centre. Industrialisation began with textiles and food and now extends to engineering, shipbuilding, oil refining and chemicals.

Part of Rio de Janeiro and the Bay of Guanabara, from the air. It is a startling contrast of modern and prosperous streets almost next to densely populated slum areas with primitive ways of life. Until recently, Rio was the national capital; but in 1960 the new capital of Brasilia was founded, about 600 miles north-west of Rio.

this century. Secondly, the houses have had to be built in the cramped spaces between the mountains, and additional building land has been reclaimed from the lagoons and sandy spits. Each part of the city is separated by a mountain wall too high to climb; traffic must therefore go through the tunnels which have been built.

The heart of the modern city is Rio Branco Avenue. The neighbouring streets are laid out in straight lines and kept their colonial appearance for many years. To meet the requirements of dense traffic, a direct attack has been made upon this area. The old houses have been torn down, large throughways have been opened and ultra-modern skyscrapers, specially adapted to the climate, have been built.

The city is extending in every direction. There are new working-class neighbourhoods with factories and estate developments in the so-called north zone. Along the ocean, the world-famous Copacabana beach has become, in the space of a very few years, a city which is independent from the great city. A new

## SÃO PAULO: THE LEADING STATE OF BRAZIL

São Paulo is the name of the largest city in Brazil as well as the state of which it is the capital. This prosperous state occupies only 9 per cent of the nation's area; it has 18.3 per cent of the total population and, in 1960, with 6,000,000 people, was the most densely populated state, providing 55 per cent of the national industrial revenue and 40 per cent of the agricultural income. It is therefore the key area in the Brazilian economy.

*A powerful agricultural and industrial unit.* During the latter part of the nineteenth century, the state rapidly achieved its leading position as a result of large-scale production of coffee and pioneer work in clearing the land. It has subsequently become the major industrial centre of Latin America. This great tropcial area, with its white population, is a unique example in Brazil of the integration of the coast with the inland plateaus to form a powerful agricultural and industrial unit.

At the beginning of the sixteenth century the Jesuits established, at an altitude of 2,600 feet and about forty miles from the ocean, the missionary centre of Piritininga, which was to become the city of São Paulo.

Around the middle of the nineteenth century coffee plantations were extended along the slopes of the Mantiqueira and Mar mountains from the Rio de Janeiro hinterland into São Paulo territory. Between about 1870 and 1880 the planters discovered that

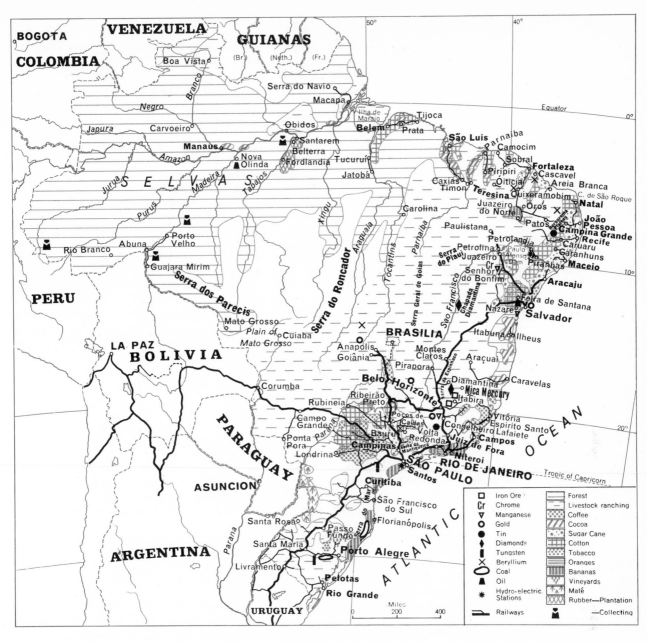

the area around Campianas had a very fertile red-purple soil, or *terra roxa,* due to basalt decomposition. They then cleared the tropical forests, substituting enormous plantations in a carefully laid-out pattern. Coffee, which spread from this area to the north and west, had become the main source of Brazil's wealth by the end of the century. Population figures for São Paulo City increased, the city having grown along with the 'green gold' fever.

The Brazilians obtained ample capital resources from the coffee trade with which to plant and equip their estates, and the plantation owners also organised railroad companies. A rail network stretched in an octopus pattern from São Paulo and Santos, its port, to the inland regions in which the crops were grown. Since both the slave trade and slavery had been abolished, the necessary labour came from free immigration from Spain, Italy and Portugal.

Since the beginning of the twentieth century, the westward advance of both people and coffee has continued. The pace was temporarily slowed down by overproduction crises which occurred in 1905 and 1930. Other crops then began to develop, the leader being cotton. Families arrived from Germany, Poland, Rumania and Hungary after the First World War. After 1930, 130,000 Japanese arrived in São Paulo, and a number of Syrian and Lebanese traders also came. The main influx, of hundreds of thousands of poor people, came from Minas and the north-eastern states.

Land has been continuously cleared towards the Paraná River. When the output of a plantation was reduced and its upkeep became more expensive, it was abandoned in order to 'open up' new plantations, since there was always new land which was cheap and guaranteed to be productive. As the pioneers moved westwards, however, they found less red-purple soil and more sandy soil, which was exhausted even more quickly. The land was abandoned more rapidly, and many barren spaces were left behind.

Because of increasing distances and the danger of frost in the new plantations situated in the north of Brazil, showing land use, principal agricultural and industrial products, power resources, chief cities and railways. The map brings out clearly the great concentration of people and activity in the east of Brazil, in contrast to the almost empty and unused expanses of the west and north. The new capital, Brasilia, was created to encourage westward expansion and to serve as a symbol of Brazil's economic vitality based on vast untapped resources. Manaus, too, after a decline following the collapse of the rubber boom, is now regaining importance as a communications centre.

Paraná state, people began to realise that the advance could not be continued without protecting the rear. Plantations which had been abandoned years before were given a new lease of life by introducing other food crops, sugar-cane, dairy products or even coffee, grown on the basis of the most modern and efficient techniques.

As there are few uncleared forest areas remaining within the state borders, there has been a peaceful invasion of neighbouring states; São Paulo has extended into the north of Paraná state, where more red-purple earth has been found and the town of Londrina was established in 1930. São Paulo has also extended into the southern part of Goiàs state, beyond the Minas triangle, in Mato Grosso state and up to Paraguay.

There are two different areas within the region: the older parts, roughly situated in the east, with a landscape similar to the Rio coastline or to the Minas highlands; and the new western areas, on the western plateaus.

*The old areas.* The older areas show sharper physical differences and greater contrasts in ways of life than the new areas.

The coastal belt consists of a narrow, hot, wet and sparsely populated strip of which the first part, closest to Rio, is a thin fragmented fringe bordered by islands; it includes several little ports which were active in colonial times and are again coming to the fore owing to their new road connections and to tourism. This fringe is followed by a broader area consisting of the alluvial plain of the Cubatão River, on the banks of which the city of Santos is situated. The economy of Santos is based upon its river port and the coffee trade; the city is also becoming a tourist centre for the population of São Paulo. Between the city and the foot of the Serra do Mar, there is a plain of mangroves which has largely been reclaimed for banana plantations. This area is gradually becoming urban following the construction of a large underground hydro-electric power station, a paper mill, an oil refinery and a steel plant.

Beyond Santos, the coastal belt becomes even wider, with long beaches on the ocean front. Poor fishermen, unaffected by the general development of the area, still live and work here. In the Ribeira valley there is a curious mixture of Japanese tea planters and backward peasants.

Along this ocean front of the coffee empire, the Serra do Mar is ever present, though often hidden by fog. It rises to a height of more than 2,500 feet and its relief and vegetation offer fearsome obstacles to penetration, contributing to the isolation of the coast from its hinterland.

The Serra do Mar is drained by rivers which flow away from the ocean towards the west. Large reservoirs have been built to supply the Cubatão power stations through underground tunnels. This is a poor agricultural region and sparsely populated. A second group of highlands consists of the foothills of the Serra de Mantiqueira, which provide shelter for the Paraiba do Sul valley and for the basin in which the city of São Paulo is built. There are still coffee plantations on the Serra da Mantiqueira. The city of São Paulo has encouraged the re-establishment of old plantations, the production of new crops including grapes, fruit trees and vegetables and the introduction of poultry farms.

A wide road runs through the Paraiba do Sul valley from Rio de Janeiro to São Paulo. The fluctuations of the Brazilian economy have had a considerable effect upon the towns and countryside situated along this road, for road transport and, in particular, the Volta Redonda works, have provided a renewal of economic activity. Owing to the increasing number of textile and engineering factories situated in these towns, the former exodus of the local population hs been stopped.

The São Paulo basin is a depression, filled with clay and reddish and dark yellow sand, situated in the heart of the granitic highlands. The Tieté River has moulded this soft soil into hills, and its tributaries have produced deep ravines. The river meanders over a large plain which has had to be protected against possible floods.

The mountain scenery is a reminder of the fact that São Paulo is situated at an altitude of 2,500 feet, although it is a tropical city. The soil is poor and there is little vegetation, the city having developed in a rather uniniviting environment. The site was chosen because it was easily defended against Indian attacks. The Tieté plain had later to be reclaimed and the ravines bridged, and the low-lying area was dried out and used for railroads, stations, factories and working class areas. The city grew in a turbulent and disorderly fashion at a pace which varied according to the fluctuations of the coffee market. In many ways, São Paulo has become the Brazilian counterpart of the North American cities.

São Paulo has recently become industrialised, largely because of the availability of hydro-electric power and because of a large and expanding national market. Industrial development began with textile works which processed cotton produced farther inland, but modern industrial production includes light metals, engineering, automobiles, chemicals, electrical and radio appliances, food, timber and printing. Industrialisation has also encouraged the growth of business and banking firms which have settled near the government offices. Thanks to its wealth, racial diversity and traditions, São Paulo has now become a centre of intellectual and artistic activities. The São Paulo state government was the first to convert its ancient law school into a university. In 1965 it had 13,000 students.

Beyond the granitic secondary mountains of the Mantiqueira there is a crescent-shaped depression with a variety of soils. To the north the savanna and jungle vegetation show a link with central Brazil, while to the south there are subtropical aspects. The richest section is in the centre, where coffee, sugar-cane, cotton and citrus fruits easily grow on patches of *terra roxa*. There is intensive urban activity everywhere, and route and market towns in which industry has gained a foothold have been established at the mountain exits.

*The new areas: the kingdom of coffee.* The eastern limit of these new areas is a steep sandstone and basalt slope, the Serra de Botucatu, whose summit reaches a height of nearly 4,000 feet. It is pierced by rivers which come down from the highlands, while its other side slopes down gently towards the Paraná River in the west. The escarpment is divided by the roughly parallel-flowing rivers into long plateaus, once covered by forests. The easternmost towns were born with the great coffee plantations at the turn of the century, though some newer towns have been established as people moved towards the west. Crops are more varied than in the older areas, and maize, beans, manioc and rice are planted side by side between the rows of coffee or cotton. On the lower terraces and flat patches both coffee and cotton are grown, while the wet lower areas are used as grazing land on which cattle from central Brazil are fattened. The pioneer areas therefore supply food products to the towns, cotton to the textile works and cattle to the canneries, as well as being one of the major sources for the export of coffee.

Large plantations no longer have a monopoly in the new areas, and a good deal of land is farmed by small farm owners or tenant farmers who do not have the necessary means to apply modern agricultural methods or to achieve a balanced economy. Moreover, they tend to be nomadic, and are here today and gone tomorrow.

In the pioneer regions, in addition to the descendants of immigrants from Mediterranean countries, there are people from the Brazilian north-east, Germans, Hungarians, Letts (from Latvia), Poles and Japanese. All these finally become settled inhabitants of São Paulo, although each group keeps some of its former national characteristics.

The railroads are like rivers draining the basin of each plateau; each plateau is named after the railroad company that serves it: for example, the Sorocabana, the area through which the Sorocaba Railroad Company operates. These names show that the inhabitants have not had time to acquire a feeling of kinship with the country, and also that their whole pattern of life is governed by contact with the outside world. Products are all sold to the metropolis, to other Brazilian states, or abroad. The pioneers' major concern is to sell rather than to produce, so their economy is fragile and there is much speculation. However, this is the main contributing factor in the dynamic appraoch of which the people of São Paulo are so proud.

## SOUTHERN BRAZIL

The population of the three southern states, Paraná Santa Catarina and Rio Grande do Sul, has a Portuguese foundation and a majority of European immigrants, so that Brazil becomes increasingly white towards the south. More than 16 per cent of the country's population lives in the three states while, in 1872, the corresponding figure was 10. The increase is due both to immigration and to the high birth rate of the families of German, Italian and Slav extraction.

Physical factors also tend to unify the three southern states. The southern Brazilians are the only ones to be familiar with frost and snow; rain is better distributed throughout the year, although it tends to be heavier during the winter.

The relief consists of a number of plateaus, draining towards the Paraná and Uruguay rivers. In Paraná state, which has a coastal border identical with São

Paulo's, the wooded escarpment of the Serra do Mar reaches a height of almost 6,500 feet; the other side is a crystalline plateau on which the 2,500 foot Curitiba Basin is situated. Farther west, a steep primary sandstone slope (3,800 feet), precedes a second plateau on which rise westward-flowing rivers such as the Iguaçu. Still farther west, sandstone and basalt form the thick strata of the Serra Geral, whose other slope descends to the Paraná valley.

Where the courses of the various rivers cut across the basalt, they have impressive rapids and falls. In Santa Catarina state, the Serra Geral approaches the ocean at Ponta de Torres. It has primary land at its base, with coal deposits possessing a high sulphur content. In Rio Grande, the Serra Geral bends towards the west and skirts the granite hills which are drained by the Jacuí River basin. This is the Campanha, whose grassy vegetation is similar to the Uruguayan vegetation. The Rio Grande coast is fringed with lagoons, behind which the ports are situated.

As a result of the stepping of plateaus in a subtropical area, the vegetation types are correspondingly terraced. Along the coast, tropical crops are still found, including banana plantations and, in Santa Catarina, coffee plantations. Portuguese colonists from the Azores and Madeira who settled here in the seventeenth century are still the core of the population. At 1,600 feet the valleys often experience hoar frosts, which make them unsuitable for tropical crops, but sugar-cane and oranges are grown along the slopes. In the highest areas, temperate-zone plants—fruit trees, cereals such as wheat and barley, and vegetables such as potatoes—are successfully grown.

*Prairies and forests.* The contrast between prairies and forests, as everywhere else in Brazil, has resulted in two different systems of colonisation. More than a

Coffee still accounts for 50-60 per cent of Brazil's foreign earnings despite developments of other products as export commodities. Over-production in the world as a whole has been a recurrent problem to Brazil and research is going on constantly to improve quality and yields. The photograph shows coffee spread in the sun to dry.

quarter of southern Brazil consists of prairies on which grasses grow without any accompanying shrubbery. The prairies have attracted Brazilian breeders of horses, mules and cattle, who have penetrated into the prairies of Paraná Santa Catarina, and, in the eighteenth century, into the pampas of Rio Grande do Sul. The Spaniards and Portuguese fought for possession of these pampas. On the great estates the master still acts in a dictatorial manner when ordering about his noisy gauchos, or mounted herdsmen. They drink a great deal of maté and suck the boiling brew through a tube which is handed from person to person. The great landowners, the gauchos and their customers have played an active part in Brazilian politics. Their influence has been reflected in the results of national elections and in the shift of the centre of gravity of Brazilian politics towards the south of Brazil.

Modern stock-production no longer consists as it once did of hunting semi-wild animals, the herds having been changed and improved by imported British cattle. Dried meat is still produced on a large scale, but a frozen meat industry has also been established at Pelotas and Pôrto Alegre. Sheep are the basis of a well-developed textile industry.

A different type of colonisation took place in the forests which cover the wall of the Serra do Mar and the sandstone and basalt plateau which runs to the edge of the Paraná River. These forests grow on the same fertile *terra roxa* as is found in other parts of the country, and are an extension of the forests cleared by the São Paulo pioneers. They still include many fine tropical trees such as jacaranda and *ipé*, as well as palms, with an edible pith, and plantations of araucaria trees. One of the main assests of southern Brazil is araucaria wood, used for the manufacture of packing-cases.

At the beginning of the nineteenth century, the imperial Brazilian Government decided to establish populated areas in the forests; they wished to eliminate Spanish influence as well as to ensure the safety of caravans of traders and stockmen crossing the wooded mountains under attack from the Indians. Germans, brought over in large numbers, established the colonies of São Leopoldo in 1824 and of Rio Negro in 1829. State and federal governments later continued to implement this policy of settling families on relatively small plots with areas of 60 to 75 acres, a policy which underlines the considerable difference that exists between the people of southern Brazil and those of São Paulo.

The immigrants farthest away have virtually been assimilated; they have taken over the old-fashioned techniques and simple customs of the indigenous peasants, living like the latter on maize, beans and rice and by raising a few pigs. Colonists who were not so remote have been able to sell their wheat, barley and potatoes. They have also added a few cows to the pigs and have built brick houses with beams, directly patterned upon central European styles, instead of wooden huts. Ploughs have replaced hoes although lack of manure and constant repetition of crops on the same soil has exhausted the land. By the second or third generation, these colonists also become native peasants. Near the cities productive crops such as tobacco, clover and vines have made it possible to buy additional cattle and, with the resulting quantities of manure, to ensure soil conservation. It is only in these areas that the standard of living has become adequate and stable.

Most of the farmers have settled on forest soil. The few Russians and Germans who settled on prairie land in Paraná state work harder, and are more successful economically: they can raise livestock, cultivate the soil, and therefore keep the land in good condition.

Owing to the high birthrate, there has been an excessive subdivision of small properties; in addition, the properties tend to produce less and less as time goes on. In the older colonisation areas emigration has resulted in a reduction of the local population and of the available food crops. Wheat has been introduced by small Italian farmers and has now been taken over by the great south-Brazilian landowners. A fair proportion of the local population is now living in pioneer areas, partly westward, but chiefly northward. It is anticipated that the forests of southern Brazil will soon have been completely cleared for agricultural use.

Italian and German colonists have also planted vines. Around Bento Gonçalves and Garibaldi, 15,000,000 vines are grown on 74,000 acres. Tobacco is also grown in this area and cigars are manufactured. But the crops which really distinguish the southern agricultural areas from the rest of Brazil are wheat and rice. The Government is trying to increase wheat production in order to reduce imports from Argentina and North America. Irrigated rice is also produced in Rio Grande do Sul; large quantities are shipped to the north-eastern states, and in Paraná the harvest of mountain-grown rice is increasing, for rice has been planted by pioneers as they cleared each area.

*The cities and industrialisation.* Of the three southern state capitals, only Florianopolis has remained a provincial town, while Pôrto Alegre in Rio Grande do Sul and Curitiba in Paraná have skyscrapers like those of Rio and São Paulo. The population of Pôrto Alegre, which is situated on the Guaiba River, has been stadily increasing, although there has been no immigration: it rose from 394,000 in 1950 to 641,000 in 1960. The Curitiba figures for the same years are 181,000 and 361,000.

Several small towns are also becoming increasingly active, largely through industrial development. Sawmills, textile factories, leather works, frozen meat plants, wine-manufacturing plants, agricultural machinery factories and paper mills have been established. The port of Laguna is being equipped and has recently acquired a new steel plant, situated near the Santa Catarina coal mines.

This part of Brazil, in which there are many small industrial works and a number of crops produced on a relatively small scale, is quite different from the others, in terms of production as well as the population structure. It is estimated that more than one-third of the people of southern Brazil are of recent European extraction and that 52 per cent come from Germany, 34 per cent from Italy and 14 per cent from Poland or the Ukraine. The rate of integration of these immigrants has varied. Portuguese is still not spoken in every home, and the language actually spoken in many rural areas of Rio Grande do Sul and Santa Catarina is a racy mixture of German and

Portuguese. The landscape is often more European than Brazilian or tropical, and country houses are built along central European lines; there are whole streets, in Blumenau for example, which seem to have been lifted directly from a small German town. The differences are superficial, however, since the whole basis of life has become Brazilian, as is shown by the dynamic pace of the cities and the ready adaptation of the foreign pioneers to the ways of life and thinking of the local farmers.

## MATO GROSSO AND GOIAS: THE BRAZILIAN 'FAR WEST'

Goiás and Mato Grosso, which are situated in the centre and west of Brazil, make up an ill-defined, remote, enormous and unfamiliar whole. The area of the two states is over 700,000 square miles, with a population only 3.3 per cent of the Brazilian total and an average population density of 2.4 per square mile. Since the local share of the national income is just over 2 per cent, the general situation is comparable to that of Amazonia. The borders between central and western Brazil and Amazonian Brazil are not clearly defined; the administrative divisions are unrelated to the gradual transition of the climate and of the forest distribution pattern; and so it is customary to select the 12th parallel of latitude as the line of demarcation south of which lies the area of central Brazil.

*The land of pasture and of gold.* Central Brazil consists essentially of sandstone plateaus of low altitude, since the highest point in the Serra dos Pireneus is only 4,500 feet. When the edges of the plateaus are strengthened by basalt layers, they look like steep walls and follow a sinuous pattern similar to that of the mountains in southern Brazil. The finest example of these hilly regions is the Serra de Maracaju which dominates the Paraguay River plain. Where erosion has removed the topsoil, crystalline rocks from the ancient continental platform show through in parallel ridges.

The effects of long dry seasons and the poor quality of the soil are everywhere apparent. Although *Mato Grosso* means 'thick wood', there are very few forests, and these are situated only in the *terra roxa* valleys found particularly in the south-eastern part of Goiàs. Where the plateaus are covered by lateritic crust, there is a jungle to which access is difficult; this is the *campo cerrado* (closed country). Vegetation consists of stunted, twisted bushes and tufts of grass, and despite the lack of rain many of the little trees have large leaves and draw moisture through the fissured lateritic crust. There are also areas of sandy soil and slopes where the soil does not retain moisture, where the vegetation consists of an interrupted carpet of grassy plants. This is the *campo limpo* (clean country), with fine prairies.

In the west of Mato Grosso state, at the Bolivian frontier, is the alluvial plain of the Paraguay River and its tributaries, which extends for more than 750 miles. The main tributary is the Cuiabá River; the area is marshland, although the water is not stagnant, and is called the Pantanal. The Pantanal reaches a height of just over 650 feet in the north and has a very slight gradient and scarcely any relief except for the small Urucum mountain chain. The water spreads out broadly, with a very slow rate of flow; every February, extensive floods over a wide area occur in the north. Farther south they begin in June, continuing until August or even the end of September. After the water has receded, extensive, rich prairies are left.

Because of their remoteness and the scarcity of good agricultural land, Goiás and Mato Grosso have not fully shared in the recent economic expansion of Brazil.

The area is mainly devoted to pastoral farming. A few cowherds on horseback can watch thousands of cattle within the fenced enclosures of very large estates owned by English and French interests as well as Brazilian. The cattle have picturesque but lengthy journeys to São Paulo, all the more exhausting since they take place during the dry season.

Another feature of the area is the presence of gold and diamonds. Gold-seekers come from Bahia and other north-eastern states after hearing fantastic rumours: there is a legend that the Cuiabá branch of the Bank of Brazil is built on a gold placer. Hundreds or even thousands of men arrive in the course of a few weeks to camp miserably in straw or wood huts, many being stricken by malaria. Nothing is planted or picked, not even bananas and oranges; every effort is concentrated on finding gold and diamonds. The ever-present Syrian traders sell whatever is required, at a price. If all else fails, the men can find work in the teams which travel through the 'closed country' looking for *manicoba* rubber trees.

This region has nothing to attract immigrants and the population is small. Scattered along the river banks within the borders of Amazonia are groups of Indians such as the Bororos from the São Lourenço River; the Caduveos, more civilised, live on the large ranches. Many Bolivians and Paraguayans have settled on Brazilian soil; most of them picked maté in the forests of south-western Mato Grosso, though this activity has now virtually come to an end.

Communications were formerly directed towards the La Plata lands by means of the rivers, but since the construction of railroads the trend has been eastwards. São Paulo has had an invigorating influence along the Mato Grosso railroad, and people from São Paulo have given new life to the region around Campo Grande, the main town of Mato Grosso state, which has a population of about 33,000. The state capital, Cuiabá, has a population of only 24,000. Coffee plantations near the Paraguayan frontier, at Dourados, contribute to the area's economic activity.

The isolation of central Brazil is also being ended by trucks; truck drivers are the modern counterparts of the men who used to prance along these tracks on horseback, and they enjoy considerable prestige. Life in this area has been radically altered by air traffic; every great estate now has its own aircraft, its landing strip and two-way radio station. It takes less than an hour, by air, to reach one of the towns with its shops, cinemas, schools and private hospitals where formerly it took days.

*The new capital of Brazil: Brasilia.* The people who live in central and western Brazil have three reasons for looking forward optimistically; the first is the progress achieved in mining copper and, especially, manganese, a small metal works having already begun

BRAZIL: Skyscraper blocks in the centre of Sâo Paulo. Camayura Indian in the Xingu River region of Mato Grosso. Baling water in a diamond mine, Rio Branco territory.

Modern buildings and sculpture in Brasilia, which was inaugurated as capital in April 1960. The buildings house the three branches of Government. The aim of building a new capital in the west was both to encourage and to symbolise the westward expansion of the country's economy which Brazil hopes to bring about.

Cattle on a fazenda in Central Brazil. The region of Goiàs and Mato Grosso is mainly devoted to pastoral farming, and large estates are owned by French and British as well as Brazilian interests.

will no longer be left to cattle-breeders and gold-seekers. By 1960, when Brasilia was inaugurated as the new capital, its population was 141,700. By 1965 the total was 266,000.

THE BRAZILIAN NATION AND ITS HOPES FOR THE FUTURE. There is a very strong national feeling uniting all Brazilians. The continued existence of a few African or European customs does not prevent the people from 'thinking Brazilian', and this unity of feeling is largely based upon the curiously hospitable characteristics of the Portuguese civilisation. The tasks which still await the country, such as the further adaptation of the natural environment to national needs and a general economic development, help to bring the people closer.

Federal power is becoming constantly stronger, and the political parties, in spite of regional overtones, are acquiring an increasingly national character. There is a two-chamber legislature elected by universal suffrage. In addition, every Brazilian man serves in the army, which has traditionally acted as a moderating influence upon presidential excesses.

The strength of this young nation comes from its rate of population increase, which is one of the highest in the world. The population rose by more than 11 million between 1940 and 1950 and by 19 million between 1950 and 1960, to a total population of approximately 71 million. The high birthrate of 43 per 1,000 has resulted in about half the population being under 15 years of age. But there is a lack of balance between the densely populated centres situated near the coast and the sparsely inhabited inland areas, so that every part of this tremendous country is not developing at the same rate. The trend away from the rural areas has been accelerated; Rio de Janeiro and São Paulo have grown too quickly, so that solutions for town planning, housing and food supply problems are difficult and costly.

The increase in population is matched by the country's economic development, and by an improvement in the standard of living.

*Agricultural problems.* Two-thirds of all available manpower is engaged in agriculture. Agricultural exports provide almost 90 per cent of the country's foreign currency resources, and prosperity is still based upon coffee production and world market prices. In 1955, for example, 62 per cent of the country's exports consisted of coffee; by 1962 the proportion had fallen to 53 per cent, and the fact that the coffee position is no longer as strong as it was is largely due to three factors. The first is that the new Paraná plantations are unreliable because of the possibility of frost. The second is that better care of coffee shrubs has led to increased production costs, which can be met only if market prices remain sufficiently high. The third factor is the end of the virtual coffee monopoly which Brazil formerly enjoyed, since American or African suppliers can sell more cheaply or offer better quality. At present, the prices of coffee are being maintained by the Government through every available modern financial device such as bonuses, special exchange rates, etc.; and although the resulting position is satisfactory, it is somewhat artificial.

The other major exports are also mainly agricultural. Cotton constitutes 9.2 per cent of the value of all exports; cocoa, 6.0 per cent; and araucaria wood,

operations at Corumba; the second is the recent rail connection established between the Nordeste line and the Bolivian network; Bolivia has no outlet to the sea and should thus become economically orientated towards Brazil. The third reason is the transfer of the political capital of Brazil from Rio de Janeiro to Brasilia, in the eastern part of Goiás state. The Brazilian Government embarked upon the remarkable venture of creating a capital city in the heart of the country, in one of its least populated areas. This has undoubtedly been inspired by the desire to encourage development in this part of the country and to show that Brazil is now less economically dependent upon foreign countries than upon its own resources.

The first building materials were brought by air and later by road. Sceptics have been confounded by the speed at which ministries, hotels and homes for government officials have been built, all in an advanced style of architecture, in the heart of an area which

3.7 per cent. Citrus fruits, bananas and oils are also exported, but the quantities vary from year to year. Iron ore is now also important, 5.6 per cent by value of total exports.

Sugar-cane is the most widespread crop for domestic consumption; but the great north-eastern plantations must compete with the new, better-equipped plantations in São Paulo state, and can only keep going because of the statutory protection which they are given. Manioc is mainly grown in Amazonia, and maize is the major crop of Minas and of the Brazilians of German origin. Rice and black beans are staple foods everywhere.

Food production cannot satisfy requirements brought about by the increased population and by the newly acquired tastes of city-dwellers. There are many deficiency diseases and, in most of Brazil, the food supply is inadequate in both quantity and quality. More food products must therefore be imported, the most expensive being wheat.

*The industrial impetus.* Industrialisation is growing but it is proving difficult to provide sufficient power; coal deposits in southern Brazil do not convert readily to coking coal, and it is necessary to import this fuel from the United States. There is a tremendous hydro-electric potential, but the best sources of water power are situated in remote areas with the lowest population densities, such as Amazonia and the Paraná basin. A scheme has been put into operation at Paulo Afonso Falls on the São Franciso River, in addition to extensive work carried out in Minas Gerais and around the two major cities of Brazil. In spite of progress made in oil production at Salvador and at Nova Olinda, on the Madeira River, the extent of available oil resources is not yet known. Several refineries have begun operations, however, and a substantial improvement has been recorded.

A second bottleneck arises from the inadequate transport facilities in the country. The waterways are often navigable only between rapids, or else run through economically backward areas, such as Mato Grosso and Amazonia. In spite of spectacular developments in air and road traffic, the railroads still represent the best means of carrying large quantities of goods, but the only satisfactory network is situated south of Minas and São Paulo.

The final barrier to economic expansion is the lack of domestic capital. Brazil has had to call upon American and European banks and industrial concerns for additional capital investments. The Brazilian balance of trade shows the price which has been paid for assistance; in 1962, there was a deficit of $261,000,000. Consequently a strict import tariff was maintained to increase government revenue and protect her industries but these restrictions have largely affected capital goods and therefore restricted industrial expansion.

On the credit side, industrialisation has been encouraged by the availability of mining resources, many of them still untapped, though iron, manganese, chromium, copper, nickel and tungsten ores, monazite sand and rock crystal are all being mined. In spite of bankruptcies or nationalisation, foreign firms have made sufficiently high profits to encourage their programmes of factory building and their continued investment in Brazilian industry. The country's business expansion was also helped by the temporary absence of foreign industrial goods owing to war or economic depressions and, during these same periods, by the arrival of European technical specialists, businessmen and capital.

Another positive factor is the national feeling of the people, who zealously strive to achieve economic independence, and encourage the Government to undertake any activity which may contribute to that independence.

Until the Second World War, industry was almost entirely devoted to the production of consumer goods, beginning with textiles and followed by the assembly of imported automobile and electrical appliance spare parts and, finally, by pharmaceuticals. Today, industry is more varied and Brazilian raw materials are in much greater demand. A major contribution to the production of capital goods, which began during the Second World War, was the establishment of a national iron and steel company. Facilities for the production of iron for export were also provided

General view of the largest iron and steel foundation in Brazil and the most up-to-date in South America, at Colta Redonda in the state of Rio de Janeiro. This factory is sited with easy access to the iron of Minas Gerais and the coal of Santa Catarina. Part of the steel production supplies the new motor industry, which was launched originally in order to cut down on foreign expenditure.

Awati Indians living on the broad plateau of Mato Grosso state in western Brazil. Several tribes of Indians still wander in this relatively unknown and sparsely populated area.

at the time by another government board, and similar facilities were introduced by the Americans for manganese. The old Minas metal industry has been modernised and new plants have been built there. A strong impetus has been given to cement works, rubber plants, ammonia and plastic works, engine and motor factories and engineering works and, during recent years, large foreign firms have begun to operate in Brazil.

This sudden, brilliant and feverish development of industry is reminiscent of some of the older cycles in Brazil's economic history and has similarly enabled many people to 'get rich quick'. It has been accompanied by inflation, which has encouraged speculation. Because the national currency, the *cruzeiro*, has had to be strongly depreciated against the dollar, a remedy has been sought by introducing differential rates of exchange for different categories of imports. Multilateral agreements with a number of European countries have also been signed and, during the worst periods, temporary and carefully measured assistance has been provided by United States loans.

Industrialisation has affected only part of the country. Most factories are situated in the iron-producing areas of Minas, near Rio de Janeiro, in the Paraiba valley and, most of all, in São Paulo, an overall area which is only a small part of Brazil. An important factor in Brazil's development as a whole is the possession of a hydro-electricity potential of 14.5 million kW, which is the fourth largest in the world. Only 6.8 million kW. had been developed by 1964.

The geography of Brazil is characterised by the differences between town and country, between the developed areas and the underdeveloped *sertoes*, and by the anachronistic colonial way of life of the peasants. Many nineteenth-century characteristics still influence the society and economy of the plantation areas, while, at the same time, the great cities closely resemble the largest cities of Europe and the United States. It is these cities, however, that have it in their power to encourage the countryside to develop, so that the whole of Brazil should be able to live at the same stage and level of civilisation.

# PARAGUAY

## A CONTINENTAL TROPICAL STATE

Paraguay and Bolivia are the only land-locked countries in South America. Paraguay, whose capital city, Asuncion, is situated on the banks of the Paraguay River, has a strategic position which led to a brilliant beginning when the area was first discovered in the sixteenth century. The Spanish conquerors decided that the Paraguay and Plate rivers would offer favourable transport for the ores discovered in the Andes. Asuncion, established in 1536, was the first city in the Plate River area, and became a major port of exit for the Peruvian mines, since sailing vessels could reach it without difficulty. Vineyards were planted, wheat was sown and herds of cattle were grazed.

However, by the beginning of the seventeenth century the country's importance began to decline and it was finally left to its own devices. This great river crossroads has remained the most sparsely populated and least developed country on the continent and in 1965 had a population of about two million giving a population density of 11.5 per square mile in an area of 157,048 square miles.

Paraguay is crossed at its widest part by the Tropic of Capricorn, and it is therefore tropical, although owing to the fact that it is about 600 miles from the nearest sea coast, it is also continental. Powerful Atlantic winds bring rain and magnificent natural drainage, so that although the country does include a desert area it has within its boundaries one of the world's great rivers, the Paraná with its tremendous tributary, the Paraguay River. These rivers are surrounded by large plains which easily turn into marshland or *esteros* since the rivers flow at an altitude of only 200 feet above sea level and the mouth of the Paraguay River is over 900 miles distant.

There are three distinct areas, characterised by different patterns of rainfall. Towards the Brazilian frontier the annual rainfall is more than 80 inches, and a great tropical forest or *selva* spreads out on the sandstone plateau of the Paraná. In the centre, along the left bank of the Paraguay River, which has an average rainfall of less than 60 inches, is the *campo*, consisting of former prairies with varying amounts of woodland, now used for both grazing and agriculture. On the right bank of the river, the western part of the country has a rainfall of less than 40 inches. This is the Chaco, which turns into savanna or even semi-desert during long dry seasons.

*Selva, campo, Chaco*. The economic life of Paraguay is determined by this division into *selva, campo* and Chaco. The forest area or *selva* is uhinhabited, although there are some Indians, such as the Guayakis, who hunt for honey there, and a few plantations of precious woods such as mahogany or *lapacho*. Maté is also grown in this area and is one of the country's major exports. Another valuable export is the essence made from unripe bitter oranges and used in perfumes.

The central *campo* or prairies, on which four-fifths of the population is concentrated in an area of barely 40,000 square miles, or one-quarter of the total area, are the richest and most productive in the country. Even in this area, however, the population density is less than 26 per square mile. There is a variety of crops grown on a small scale: maize, manioc, rice, castor-oil plants and oranges, and extensive pastoral farming. A curious system of settlements prevailed here in the seventeenth century, consisting of what might be called collective farms organised by the Jesuit fathers. They were established in order to protect the Indians from outside attacks and to convert them to Roman Catholicism. As a result, there is still a large Indian population in Paraguay. After 1767, when the Jesuit order was suppressed, the population began to mingle with the first Spanish colonists and more than 80 per cent of the modern population are therefore mestizos, or Spanish-Indian half-breeds. The Guarani language has remained one of the country's two officially recognised languages, the other being Spanish.

New animal species such as zebus and new vegetable species such as groundnuts (peanuts) have been introduced. There are large estates in this area, which also has the only railroads, towns and made-up roads

*Maps opposite:* Paraguay, Uruguay, Argentina and Chile, showing vegetation and agriculture, mineral resources and industries, and population growth from 1890 to 1959. *Inset right:* the Santiago and Concepcion areas in Chile.

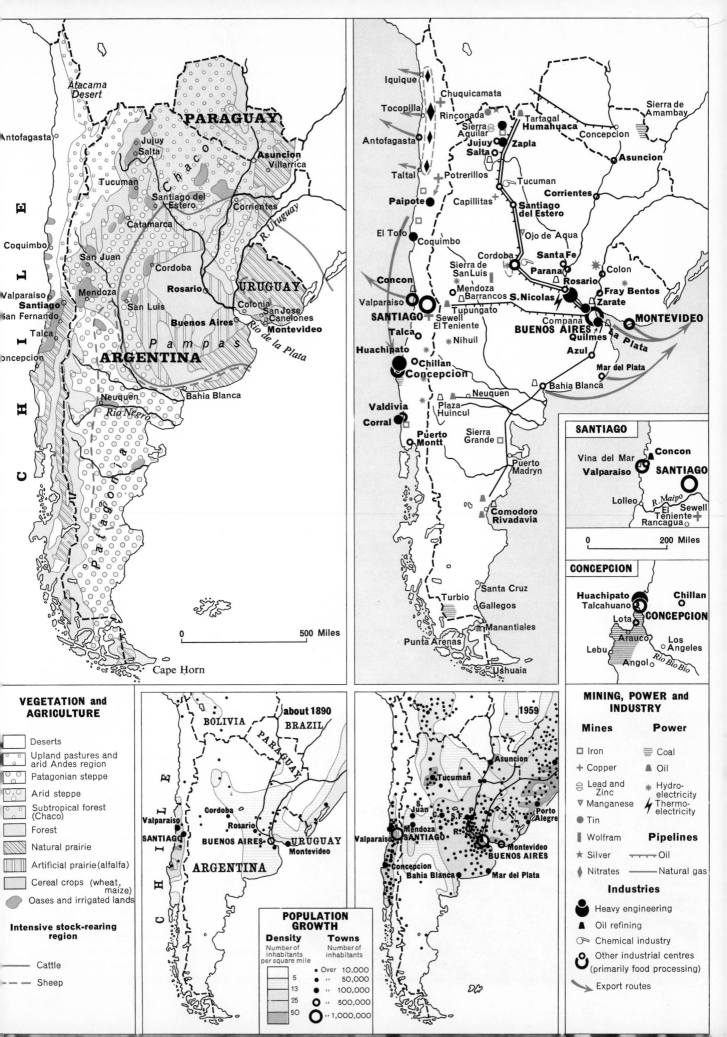

in the country. Asuncion, the capital, has a population or more than 305,000.

The thorny jungle of the Chaco includes more than 60 per cent of the country's area, and has some regions virtually unknown and inhabited by nomadic Indian tribes. There are immense pastoral areas from which herds of almost wild animals move away at flood times. Quebracho is cut along the banks of the Paraguay River and sent to Argentina for tannin extraction. A few isolated groups of farmers have settled in the region, one of them being German and Russian Mennonites, most of whom have come from Canada.

THE FUTURE OF PARAGUAY. Paraguay has become in spite of its central position an 'end of the world' state which its great neighbours have tried to dominate. After a bitter war fought from 1865 to 1870 against Argentina, Brazil and Uruguay, Paraguay was left with almost no able-bodied men, the ratio of women to men being then estimated at 28 to 1. Most of the country's trade has to pass through Argentina, in which the Paraguay River's only outlet is situated, and to which there is a railway connection, involving a journey of fifty hours.

Paraguay is today regaining some of its importance as a central continental country since its airport is one of the most important junctions in South America; the Brazilian railroads now extend to its borders; it has a national merchant fleet, which is gradually freeing the country from the monopoly formerly held by Argentinian shipping companies; and efforts are also being made to attract foreign immigration.

Food supplies are inadequate: 60 per cent of the population live by agriculture on about 5 per cent of the total area (the Asuncion region) while most of the rest of the country is used only for stock-raising and forestry. It was evident that land reform must be the basis of improvement. A law passed in 1953 laid down that ranches would be colonised systematically, the former owners remaining in possession. Minimum price guarantees were made by the Government for certain vital crops such as maize, manioc, cotton, sugar-cane and peanuts. As a result the area under cultivation rose from 606,692 acres in 1940 to 3,829,000 acres in 1960. But despite favourable soil and climate this is a small proportion of the total cultivable area of 101 million acres.

The country has been hampered in its development by the high rate of illiteracy for which wars and revolution can be largely blamed. Poor diet and lack of medical care have weakened and reduced the population. Since 1942 the United States has been supplying both medical and technical aid. It also financed a system of agrarian credit to help small farmers to improve their holdings. Further aid came from the United States after 1950 under the Point Four programme, from the Agency for International Development and the International Bank for Reconstruction and Development in order to buy agricultural as well as other machinery, road-building equipment and trucks.

In agriculture, tobacco and orange growing are developing and the zebu has been introduced into pastoral farming. There is even some industrial development, although little ore is being mined and there is a limited power supply. There are prospects of oil extraction, however. The isolation and decline of Paraguay are probably due to man rather than to nature, and it appears that this vigorous and deserving nation can expect a better future.

# URUGUAY

Uruguay, with an area of 72,133 square miles, is one of the smallest countries in South America. During the colonial struggle between the Spaniards in Argentina and the Portuguese in Brazil, a buffer state was almost established along the banks of the Paraná River. The conflict was not settled until Europe had intervened and Britain, anxious to have the great estuary of the River Plate controlled by a small independent state between the Brazilian and Argentinian giants, had acted as arbitrator. As a result, the Oriental Republic of Uruguay was recognised in 1828, its inhabitants still referring to themselves as 'orientals'. The region was originally settled by Spanish adventurers who came from the interior of the continent to the 'orient' or east, after crossing the Paranà and Uruguay rivers. The capital of Uruguay, Montevideo, is situated east-south-east of Buenos Aires.

The 'shore' area to which the first settlers came is not situated on the Atlantic Ocean but inland, along the banks of the Uruguay River, which forms the frontier with Argentina. Montevideo was founded in 1726, and a transfer to the coast became firmly established at the time of the country's independence. Recently there has been a revival of the shoreline activity, mainly concentrated on the port of Paysandu, which it is hoped to make into the main inland maritime port.

Uruguay is a republic without a president, being governed by a college or National Council, elected by the population on a direct ballot for a four-year period, and assisted by a Chamber of Representatives and a Senate. Although the prevailing religion is Roman Catholic, Church and State are separated. The country's language is Spanish.

A pause in the reed-cutting for a refreshing drink of 'Paraguay tea' infused from the leaves of the maté, a shrub related to the holly.

The population has not increased quickly as there is a low birthrate—less than 20 per 1,000—although, against this, the death rate of 8 per 1,000 is the lowest in the Americas. The people are almost all of European extraction; about one-fifth are foreign-born, consisting mainly of Spaniards and Italians.

## A COUNTRY OF GRASS

The country is situated within the large crystalline rock area known as the Brazilian shield, and consists of a broad continental platform which rises on its oceanic side and dips gradually towards the interior. Like the Brazilian rivers, most of the Uruguayan rivers, which include the Rio Negro and its tributaries, the Yi, Arapey, Queguay and others, flow away from the ocean towards the west, into the centre of the continent, where they join the Uruguay River trough.

The highest areas are in the south-east, along the Atlantic Ocean. The highest mountain, the Sierra de las Animas, is only 1,600 feet high. The uplands are long and monotonous ridges with granite outcrops, rounded towards the south; to the north, beyond the Rio Negro, there are tablelands with surface basalt. The valleys are very shallow, frequently marshy and easily flooded, owing to the slight slope and irregular rates of flow. They are filled with a scrub of hirsute plants which forms fingers of forest-land, while the hills are covered by extensive prairies.

The *pampero* blows from a south-westerly direction, and has distributed over the entire southern part of Uruguay a layer of eolian and sometimes volcanic deposits similar to the deposits on the pampas, which encourage the growth of grass and prevent the growth of trees. This ocean of grass is broken by only a few thickets of eucalyptus trees, known as 'islands'. It is not, however, steppe-like: in contrast to the Argentinian pampas where there is virtually no water, here there is enough rainfall to maintain the headwaters of a number of rivers and to provide fairly abundant but irregular moisture. Uruguay is an undulating plain drained by many rivers.

## THE BIRTH OF A PASTORAL NATION

However, men were also to take advantage of the climate, and this was the last area to be developed in South America. Until the Europeans came it was populated only by a few Indians including the Chanas and the cruel Charruas. The country had not yet discovered its potential assests, although only the presence of animals was needed to transform the magnificent grasslands into grazing land.

Cattle were first released beyond the Uruguay River in 1611 and quickly multiplied; the eastern strip became a large, rich cattle-farm which, like the precious metals found in the Andean countries, gave rise to violent envy.

When men had settled in Uruguay, they used the cattle only for their leather, since this was the only product which could then be shipped out. Competition became fiercer when it was found that the meat could be dried and salted. During the eighteenth century, demand rose sharply as large amounts of meat were required to feed the new mining communities of Peru and the increasing number of slaves employed on sugar plantations along the tropical coast of Brazil and in the West Indies. The animals still ran wild in herds, each with its own leader and its own particular grazing area. The first cattle-owners based their herds on these natural groups. Their settlements were highly scattered; the stockmen, or *gauchos*, who lived on horseback and ate only grilled meat, would mark the animals rather than the land in order to indicate ownership.

*Sheep and wire*. In the nineteenth century sheep were introduced and new immigrants came to watch over them. Since sheep had a greater tendency to wander, the grazing land had to be fenced in and wire was used because there was no wood available. The fencing was a revolution in pastoral farming.

With the new enclosures, gauchos were no longer necessary; they became a kind of 'cattle proletariat', living in earthen hovels in miserable hamlets on the edges of the estates.

Cattle on the range in Uruguay. These are a cross between Herefords and Shorthorns. New breeds had to be introduced when beef began to be frozen rather than salted; in addition, the main customer, Britain, began to demand young, tender beef. The grasslands of Uruguay owe their richness to the proximity of the ocean. They have been further improved in some places by the creation of artificial prairies.

Taming a wild horse. Note the baggy trousers and leather aprons of the gauchos.

The immense herds of sheep in the country were the basis of Uruguay's textile industry. This is, however, now becoming less specialised; the photograph shows warping cotton in a modern textile mill near Montevideo.

Aerial view of the modern city of Montevideo. About one third of the country's population lives in the capital, which has grown in size and importance owing to its exceptionally fine site on a peninsula overlooking the entrance to the Rio de la Plata. It provides a safe harbour for ocean-going liners and, in winter, for deep-sea fishing vessels.

*Cold storage.* Further revolutionary changes occured in the twentieth century, when cold storage techniques were developed. After 1905, four refrigerating plants, employing more than 15,000 workers, began to operate along the northern bank of the River Plate, whose importance as a 'meat coast' increased. The cold storage plants gradually began to process beef, which had formerly been used only by a few salt meat plants. England, the main customer, insisted on having young, tender 'baby beef', so that the herds and the grazing had to be improved. Artificial prairies were planted, and the large estate owners even brought in a few farm labourers.

*Pastoral and agricultural areas.* Although livestock were becoming more important, the population density in the rural areas remained low, with an average of 5 to 8 per square mile. There was even some emigration, since the larger herds required fewer men to look after them. The animal markets did not lead to settlements, as they were organised by dealers in uninhabited areas and were only temporary.

The only part of Uruguay to have a higher population density, amounting to 78 per square mile, is in the south, along the banks of the River Plate. Around Colonia, Canelones and San José, there is some agriculture and also new types of estates in which cereals, vegetables, fruit maize, tobacco, groundnuts (peanuts), sunflower seeds and linseed are produced, as well as wine. Rice is cultivated in lagoons situated close to the Brazilian frontier, and there is extensive dairy-farming around Montevideo.

## MONTEVIDEO

Montevideo is situated within this more densely populated coastal area; it is an urban monster, holding almost one-half of the country's population, or more than 1,204,000 out of the total of 2,59,000. Thanks to its enormous capital city, Uruguay has the highest average population density in South America: 37 per square mile. The city increased its population tenfold between 1860 and 1910. The next largest cities, Paysandu and Salto, each have a population of only about 60,000.

The tremendous estuary of the River Plate, which is the main outlet for the temperate regions of South America, is a delta in course of formation, clogged by large quantities of alluvium from the Paraná River. On the south shore, along the Argentinian pampas, alluvial banks make access to Buenos Aires very difficult. The north Uruguayan shore, on the other hand, is partly protected from alluvial deposits by the confluence with the River Uruguay, a river of clear water flowing from the Brazilian crystalline plateaus. Ships sail along the northern shore and pass the little granitic island of Martin Garcia, which has been taken over by Argentina, in spite of Uruguay's protest, because it controls the only good passage of the great Argentinian river.

A fine gulf, created by the advance of the sea, is protected at its entrance by a granite mound, the Cerro, which dominates Montevideo, the only good natural port in the estuary, with a depth of more than thirty feet. Large ships often call there and unload a large cargo before going on to Buenos Aires.

Montevideo is the fourth largest city in South America. It is very attractive, with a fine maritime façade extended to the east by the long, well arranged beaches of Atlantida and Punta del Este. In addition to the factories associated with pastoral farming, which include cold storage plants, tanneries and canneries, there are textile, shoe and chemical factories and other works which have enabled Uruguay to produce most of its requirements in manufactured goods.

THE COUNTRY'S PROBLEMS AND THE FUTURE. Unfortunately, Uruguay has neither fuel nor metals. Power comes from coal imported from England, from Venezuelan oil, and from the growing number of hydroelectric dams situated on the inland rivers. There is new industrial activity in leather, wool-carding, the manufacture of cold storage equipment, etc.

More than 70 per cent of Uruguay's exports, including wool, meat, hides and leather, come from her livestock. The remainder consists of goods sent to Argentina, including large quantities of granite and marble which are wholly lacking on the pampas.

Normally the balance of trade is slightly in favour of exports. The disastrous spring floods of 1959 covered approximately one-third of the country, and there was widespread destruction of livestock and crops. The economy suffered a reverse, increased in 1960 when many farming areas were affected by drought. Until the Second World War, the bulk of Uruguay's trade was with Great Britain, but today the United States is in the lead, with West Germany and the great neighbouring states of Brazil and Argentina. The country has a relatively extensive road network and a modern airport at Carrasco, twelve miles from Montevideo.

Uruguay is distinguished from most other South American republics by its tradition of democratic government; it has been one of the world's pioneers in government-sponsored social welfare. It is one of the most highly literate countries in the world. Government aid is given in illness subject to a means test. Further reforms envisaged are minimum diet provisions for rural workers and the introduction of a shared-profits system in government-owned corporations.

It is generally recognised that the social welfare system has led to a top-heavy Civil Service and hence to some rigidity. Centralised government has also led to the relative overdevelopment of Montevideo. The problem for the future will be to counterbalance this tendency and to extend social benefits to rural workers. A start has been made by building more factories in provincial towns and provision of more electric power in rural areas, and improvement of transport and communications.

# THE REPUBLIC OF ARGENTINA

The republic of Argentina, which is situated at the southern end of South America, is one of the largest countries in the world (1,084,120 square miles). The only countries with larger areas in the Americas are Canada, Brazil and the United States. This impressive figure would rise to 1,554,321 if Argentina's claim to the part of Antarctica situated between longitudes 25° and 74° west were recognised.

Argentina was originally the Viceroyalty of the Rio de la Plata, established in 1776 by Charles III of Spain to counter the Portuguese threat. It included present-day Bolivia, Paraguay and Uruguay and an outlet on the Pacific through the Potosi intendancy.

It started to break up shortly after the beginning of the liberation movement. Paraguay was separated from the main unit in 1811, followed by Bolivia in 1825, and Uruguay in 1828.

The Indians still ruled large areas during the nineteenth century and whole sections of the Pampa, of Patagonia and of the Chaco remained virtually closed to the whites, who had to be on their guard and live in small forts in the border areas. The struggles against the Indians gradually ended with the 'desert conquest' expeditions undertaken in the Pampa and Patagonia in 1879 and the later Chaco expeditions.

Argentina is approximately 2,300 miles long from north to south and extends from latitude 21° 46′ at Jujuy to 53° 3′ at Tierra del Fuego. The country is narrow towards the south and is 750 miles wide at its broadest.

## THE COUNTRY AND ITS PEOPLE

*Mountains to the west, plains to the east.* Relief divides Argentina into two distinct regions: mountains to the west and plains to the east. This division is broken only by a few mountain ranges which stand out from the Ventana, Tandil and Central Pampa plains.

The eastern area has as its foundation two great crystalline plateaus: the Brazilian shield and Patagonia. The first of these is a region of subsidence and soil accumulation and its plains include an undulating 'Mesopotamia', stretching between the Paraná and Uruguay rivers; the Chaco woodland plain, extending monotonously as far as Paraguay and Bolivia in the north and becoming lost south of the Saldo River; and, most important of all, the enormous treeless plain of the Pampa, which becomes increasingly arid

in the west. In the southern area, the Patagonian plateaus are unaffected by moisture from the adjoining Atlantic Ocean, and have a desert appearance and steppe-like vegetation.

The western area is mountainous, and consists mainly of the Cordillera of the Andes. The Pampas Sierras are situated along the edges of the plains after which they are named. A pre-cordillera which runs from Catamarca down to Mendoza is separated from the cordillera by broad longitudinal valleys. In the north-western corner of the country there is a tremendous basin at an altitude of 12,500 feet, called the Puna. It is closed to the west by mountains of volcanic origin including the 22,146-foot Llullaillaco volcano and, to the east, by the Salta and Jujuy pre-cordillera mountain ranges running from north to south.

The arid Andes, which have no vegetation, are situated north of Mendoza. They include Aconcagua and Ojos del Salado, respectively 23,080 and 22,586 feet high and the highest peaks in America. The snowline north of Mendoza is 19,400 feet high. These

Road leading across the empty pampas from the Argentine lake district in the Andes to the Atlantic. Nothing grows on this arid steppe but short grass and a few bushes.

mountains contrast with the Patagonian Andes, where the peak of the Lanin volcano reaches only 12,382 feet and the snowline starts at a level of 9,850 feet in the north and falls to 2,600 feet in the Straits of Magellan. The beauty of the southern Andes is further heightened by many glaciers, woods and lakes. In the far south there are ice-fields remaining from Quaternary glaciation.

*The battle between Atlantic and Pacific climates.* The atlantic and Pacific major anticyclonic areas both exert an influence in Argentina. The Atlantic high pressure centre, between 25° and 35° S., moves a little to the north during the southern hemisphere winter, while the Pacific centre is situated at slightly higher latitudes. In addition, Argentina is an area of almost constant low pressure; this is most marked in the central region, largely owing to the local relief. In the northern section the precipitation, almost of monsoon type, owing to the influence of the Atlantic anticyclone, gradually decreases towards the west. Rain falls only on the eastern slopes of the north-western mountain ranges, while west of these the climate is arid. Large flat or undulating grassy stretches and closed depressions in the pampas mountain ranges hinder the passage of moisture-laden maritime winds. The Pacific anticyclone, on the other hand, penetrates in the south by virtue of the lower altitude and transverse structure of the Patagonian Andes. Its influence brings a cold and dry wind, the *pampero,* which sweeps across the plateaus and accounts for the desert appearance of the Patagonian plateaus.

*The distribution of forests and steppes.* The climate accounts for the existence of the Misiones forest, near the Tropic of Capricorn in the north-east. This has an annual rainfall of more than 60 inches. A subtropical mountain forest is situated on the eastern mountains from Tucuman to Bolivia, but the main woodland concentration is found in western Patagonia and in Tierra del Fuego, which has a cold, temperate climate. West of Formosa, in the Chaco area, there is less woodland. The xerophilous vegetation, adapted to a hot, dry climate, marks a transition to the Chilean Atacama Desert. In the temperate zone of the pampas, the eastern herbaceous steppe is gradually replaced by xerophilous, slightly arborescent formations, while to the south the Patagonian steppe has shrubs.

To sum up, there is an arid diagonal strip with an annual rainfall of 4 to 20 inches, north-west to south-east. Agriculture and pastoral farming have flourished in the wet eastern zone, in which there are woodland and herbaceous areas; to the west, the lack of rainfall is offset by the melting Andean snow, and this has led to the formation of many rich oases in the provinces closest to the cordillera and of a few poor oases in the centre. The east, with the Paraná, Uruguay, Paraguay, Iguaçu and other rivers, contrasts sharply with the semi-arid areas in which the streams flow into lagoons or into lakes that have no outflow, and with the arid areas situated around the centre and in the west.

*A mainly white population.* There is virtually no aboriginal population in Argentina, since people of mixed Indian and white blood constitute less than two per cent of the population. There is no Negro population at all. When the Spaniards arrived, the area in which agriculture was furthest developed was the north-west, where the Diaguitan Indians, who had been influenced by the Incas, used fairly advanced irrigation techniques. Tribes of hunters and fishermen elsewhere were not as advanced, although the Guaranis were an exception. Their language is still spoken in the northern part of Entre Rios province, and two other native languages are still spoken, Araucan in the Neuquen cordillera and in the Rio Negro area, and Quechua in the western Chaco. Spanish in the official language.

Most of the existing population is white and of European origin, since it consists of descendants of the Spaniards. Argentina is now largely a country of immigrants and their descendants: the latest census figures show that 84.7 per cent of the people are native-born whites and of these more than four-fifths had foreign parents. These parents were 83 per cent of European origin, 66 per cent being Latins. Of the total population 44 per cent are of Italian and 31 per cent of Spanish extraction.

## ECONOMIC ACTIVITY

*Prevalence of pastoral farming.* In pre-Columbian South America, there was a limited exploitation of some animals, among which only the llamas were herded and used as beasts of burden. The entire stock of cattle, sheep and horses which are the glory of Argentinian pastoral farming was imported by the conquerors. Pedro de Mendoza, who founded Buenos Aires in 1535, had brought with him 72 mares and horses which reproduced surprisingly well: in 1549 Nuflo de Chaves brought the first Peruvian sheep to Paraguay. Cattle followed a route which ran from the Brazilian coast to Paraguay through Misiones. The livestock thrived in the propitious climate and satisfactory soil conditions which prevailed, particularly in the eastern Pampa.

During the first stage of development of pastoral farming, in the seventeenth and eighteenth centuries, organised groups of gauchos slaughtered ownerless animals for the sole purpose of obtaining leather, the major commodity required for their extensive smuggling activities. This exploitation almost resulted in extermination of the livestock and, on several occasions, protective measures had to be introduced.

During this first stage, pastoral farms were being established. Their size varied considerably, since they were usually based on gifts of land made to conquering colonists in the neighbourhoods of new settlements and towns. Livestock wandered everywhere and made agriculture impossible. During the latter part of the eighteenth century, factories began to produce salt meat for export, mainly to Brazil and Cuba, where it was used to feed the slaves.

Pastoral farming's second stage of development began in 1844, when Ricardo Newton introduced barbed wire fencing. Selection of livestock was developed, in the new enclosures the quality of the herds was considerably improved, and the way was open for a much larger meat production.

In 1882 the first cold storage plant, financed by Argentinian capital, was opened at San Nicolas, After England had banned livestock imports in 1900, production of canned meats began and, at the same time, there were extensive English and North American captial investments in the meat trade.

Agricultural production, which had begun after barbed wire enclosures had been introduced, also increased towards the end of the nineteenth century. The resulting competition between pastoral farming and agriculture, influenced by the availability of export markets, led to an extensive redistribution of regional activity. Meat-producing cattle remain on the best and most expensive grazing land, situated near the ports of embarkation, where the favourable climate, soil and economic pattern are conducive to breeding high-quality herds. Lincoln sheep (producing both wool and meat) have similarly replaced the merino wool-producing sheep, which are now concentrated in the tremendous uncultivated areas of Patagonia, to which other minor livestock have also been relegated. Wool is one of the country's major exports, and as it does not have to be clipped near the ports of embarkation, there has been a trend in sheep-farming away from Buenos Aires.

Stock-breeding is such an important component of the Argentinian economy that agricultural development in the pastoral areas became subordinate to it, and the acreage devoted to lucerne or alfalfa rose considerably.

*The development of agriculture in the nineteenth century.* Agriculture became generally developed only in the second half of the nineteenth century, despite the fact that the local Indians had developed irrigation schemes and improved crops in a number of difficult agricultural areas, including the north-west.

In colonial times, anyone who tilled the soil was treated with contempt and, in 1774, Buenos Aires had only thirty-three farmers out of a total population of 10,000.

A number of factors, in addition to field enclosure, contributed to the development of agriculture after 1850, and as a result Argentina had become one of the world's leading agricultural producers by the beginning of the twentieth century. The first agricultural colonies were established through organised immigration. This was accompanied by a spontaneous influx of European agricultural migrants and, whenever there was a rise in inmigration, the acreage under cultivation also increased. The 'desert conquest' schemes introduced in 1880 made it possible to extend the agricultural acreage to the entire fertile Pampa region and this was facilitated by the construction between 1880 and 1890 of a network of railroutes.

From 1881 to 1930, 3,700,000 immigrants came to Argentina and the area under cultivation rose from 3 million to 66 million acres. This was followed by a period of stagnation or even of reduction in the acreage as a result of the worldwide depression, the Government's restrictive immigration policy and the Second World War. But the figure had risen to about 74 million by 1959-60, almost 90 per cent of the cultivated area being situated in the eastern Pampa.

The major characteristic of Argentinian agriculture is the high proportion of cereals. Because the population is not very dense, there has always been a surplus for export, which has won the country its reputation as a granary to the world.

There is a marked difference between the two types of agricultural crops produced. Cereals and fodder crops are generally grown in the eastern Pampa and the southern plains of Entre Rios and are intended for export, while in other parts of the country there are industrial crops such as sugar-cane and vines which are sold on the domestic market.

Both the wet Pampa area and southern Entre Rios have fertile black earth, a wet and temperate climate and a good distribution of rain throughout the year. These conditions have encouraged the growth of wheat, maize, oats, barley, rye, flax (for linseed) and fodder plants. In addition, during the past twenty years, sunflowers have been increasingly successful. The products which have given Argentina a major share in international trade, however, are wheat, maize and flax.

Owing to the length of Argentina from north to south, to the irregular distribution of rainfall and to the different climates found in the country, it has been possible to grow a variety of crops, different areas specialising in different commodities. Vines and sugar-cane have been grown since colonial times, but cotton, tobacco, fruit trees, rice, tea and *yerba mate* are more recent.

Sheep in pens outside a 'frigorifico', a slaughter house connected with cold-storage plant in which the meat is frozen for export.

These giant cacti sometimes reach a height of 50 feet in the arid upland deserts of north-western Argentina. Water is stored in the thick fleshy stems and branches.

Argentina, together with Paraguay and southern Brazil, is the leading world consumer of·maté. The north-eastern province of Misiones provides the required temperatures and moisture for growing this plant. Because production soon exceeded consumer demand, maté cultivation has been restricted. In the Misiones area and in the north-east of Corrientes, tea and tung-oil (obtained from the tung-oil tree) are produced, and the output of these commodities and of rice, mainly grown on easily flooded land in Corrientes, near the Rio Uruguay, is adequate for domestic requirements. The country's tobacco production also meets domestic needs; the Lerma valley, in Salta, favours Virginia tobacco, of which production has increased during the past twenty years.

The main cotton area is west of the Rio Paraguay. Large-scale production did not begin until 1920; by 1961 it covered an area of 1,622,250 acres, 75 per cent of which is in Chaco province.

Sugar had been produced at the beginning of the colonial period and, after a period of decline, was re-

Forest exploitation includes the red quebracho trees found in the eastern Chaco. Because of their high tannin content (quebracho extract is used for tanning leather), the trees were ruthlessly cut—a dangerous policy in view of their slow growth. Quebracho extract has thus lost a great deal of its economic importance.

Single-crop specialisation, which is characteristic of the prevailingly speculative nature of the country's economy, has led to crises due to bad weather or to business recessions which have harmed the balance of trade and internal economy. Attempts have therefore been made to develop industrial production.

*The ideal of economic independence.* Industry did not get under way until the twentieth century. Foreign sources of supply were no longer available during the First World War and, in order to satisfy domestic demand, Argentina was compelled to build a number of factories, many of which continued operations after the war. The same situation arose in 1939 and provided an impetus to industrial development, so that industry is now the major national activity in terms of output and of manpower, and the industrial index for every branch has been rising continuously.

Argentina has ample supplies of animal and vegetable raw materials and is now trying to diversify industry. Some manufacturing industries have grown tremendously, including the twenty-two large cold storage plants for meat, in which a number of products and by-products are also made. There are, too, nearly one hundred factories which produce pig meat and tinned meats and process a large number of animals. The textile industry is also developing fast, mainly in wool and cotton, since raw materials are plentiful, and production has met with a favourable consumer response.

There is a leather industry, a dairy industry which supplies the urban areas with milk, and flour mills. In addition, Tucuman and Mendoza have become the major centres for agricultural industry through sugar and wine production.

Unfortunately, there is a scarcity of available fuel and iron for the expansion of heavy industry and heavy engineering. One of the most favourable developments in recent years has been the rise in oil production and the discovery of six new oilfields. The country now has four major oil-producing areas, the largest of which is situated at Comodoro Rivadavia. Production, of which eighty per cent is government controlled, reached 16,100,000 tons in 1961, and by 1964 met all Argentina's increasing requirements.

There are valuable deposits of lead, mixed with silver and zinc, and of tin in Jujuy, of copper at Capillitas, in Catamarca, and of wolfram in the San Luis mountains. There are also large reserves of peat in Tierra del Fuego and, in various parts of the country, salt mines, saline marshes and sulphur deposits. Iron and coal mining are still in their early stages. although it is estimated that there will soon be enough iron and coal to supply the major industries. Mining of the Jujuy iron reserves of over a million tons began in 1945; coal mining in the Turbio river basin began in 1943, and it is estimated that deposits amount to 350 million tons. However, operations in this basin are complicated by the need to transport the coal to the Atlantic Ocean, which is about 150 miles away.

A farm worker's home near Tucuman. Solid yet severely simple, such dwellings are typical of the agricultural pioneers who opened up the Argentinian desert.

introduced in 1821. The highest yields were obtained in Salta and Jujuy, where they averaged 18 tons per acre against the Tucuman average of 14 tons. Many people come from neighbouring provinces for the sugar harvest, and the population has tended to congregate around the plants in which sugar-cane is processed industrially.

Viticulture is concentrated in the Andean provinces of Mendoza and San Juan, which began to make wine in colonial times. Immigration, the construction of railroads and irrigation schemes brought a remarkable increase in the number of acres cultivated in Mendoza. The conditions of soil and climate in the vine areas have also been favourable to the extension of olive orchards, established thirty years ago.

Argentinian agricultural production also includes citrus fruits, grown in Entre Rios and Salta; pears in San Juan and Mendoza; citrus fruits, peaches and apples in the Paraná delta and pears and apples in a few Patagonian valleys, particularly in the upper valley of the Rio Negro.

A railroad has been constructed to carry coal from Turbio to the Atlantic coast at Rio Gallegos. The iron deposits situated in the Rio Negro territory are estimated to hold more than 100 million tons.

In spite of the uncertain situation, heavy and light engineering have grown considerably. Recently a steel plant with a scheduled capacity of 560,000 tons was built at San Nicolas, and this helped to raise the total steel production in 1964 to 1,000,000 tons. FUTURE PROSPECTS. *The shortage of power.* Argentina is caught in a vicious circle, since there is not enough power to develop means of transport and not enough means of transport to carry the power resources. Between 1947 and 1949, one of the longest natural-gas pipelines in the world was built between Comodoro Rivadavia and Buenos Aires, 1,050 miles away. Gas and oil will shortly be carried by pipelines to be distributed amongst the country's other major industrial centres.

Argentina has immense resources of waterpower, but they are very remote from the producing and consuming centres. An additional problem is that foreign capital is required, and in 1958 a new law gave foreign investors the same terms and privileges as Argentinian investors. In 1959 about one-third of the foreign capital invested in Argentina went towards the manufacture of chemicals and pharmaceuticals, and one-third towards motor-vehicle and tractor manufacture.

*Regional imbalance.* Buenos Aires, which in 1960 had a population of 2,967,000, is the most densely populated urban centre in South America, since, if the suburbs which completely encircle the city are included, its population is more than 6 million. The other Argentinian cities are much smaller, though Rosario, Cordoba, La Plata, Tucuman, Santa Fe, Mar del Plata, Bahia Blanca and Mendoza all have populations of more than 100,000.

The spectacular growth of Buenos Aires is easy to understand (from 177,787 in 1869 to 2,982,580 in 1947). The city is situated along the River Plate at the end of a depression which marks the limit of the 'undulating Pampa', and provides the principal link between the inland areas and the ouside world. It is built like other Spanish-American cities, in a chequerboard pattern, particularly in the centre. An attempt has been made to solve the heavy traffic problem by means of the Nueve de Julio Avenue, which is 460 feet wide and runs through the heart of the city.

Owing to its disproportionate size, Buenos Aires is the cause of major population and economic imbalance which has affected the entire country. In 1947, 29 per cent of the country's population lived in the city on 0.06 per cent of the total area, with a population density of 6,478 per square mile.

Buenos Aires and the coast govern the development of the entire country. This leadership was established 50 years ago, when areas which had had large populations in colonial times, particularly those in the north-west, lost their former importance. In 1946, an industrial census showed that 68.7 of the country's factories, 60.5 of its industrial workers and 73.9 of its industrial investment were concentrated in the capital and in Buenos Aires and Santa Fe provinces.

Most of the country's agricultural and pastoral assets are situated in the pampas and, in general, the country

becomes poorer in its remote areas. Industrialisation has to some extent changed this pattern. The Peron policy of promoting economic self-sufficiency led to some positive gains: the development of the Andean regions, particularly of their mineral resources; the building of roads where the rail system was inadequate; and the development of engineering and other industries in many provincial centres, such as Cordoba.

Under Peron, most of Argentina's trade was with overseas countries. Subsequent efforts to promote trade with other South American countries and to reduce tariffs resulted in the signing in 1960 of a Free Trade Association agreement between Argentina, Brazil, Chile, Mexico, Paraguay, Peru and Uruguay.

When Argentina has overcome its domestic difficulties and is able to implement long-term plans vital to its development, it will undoubtedly have a great future, since it has a sizable internal market, its natural resources are abundant and its population, benefiting from advanced social welfare legislation, has the will to make the most of the country's wealth.

A village street in Santa Victoria, northern Argentina, where the mule is the only form of transport.

# ANDEAN AMERICA

# ECUADOR

Ecuador, situated along the Pacific Ocean on either side of the Equator, lies between Colombia and Peru and is an area of transition between the two countries, although it has highly original geographic characteristics. The frontier with Colombia, to the north, follows the course of several rivers, some flowing into the Pacific while others, tributaries of the Amazon River, empty into the Atlantic Ocean. The eastern frontier with Peru is an artificial line cutting across the Amazon tributaries; although determined by means of a protocol signed at Rio de Janeiro on 29th January, 1942, it is still in dispute.

## FROM THE INCA EMPIRE
## TO THE PRESENT DAY

What is now Ecuador had been a Spanish province, Quito, conquered and completely assimilated into the Inca empire during its final expansion, fifty years before it fell. Later, Quito was included within the Spanish Peruvian administration, in which it achieved a fair degree of autonomy. It was included in 1822 within greater Colombia as its liberator, Simon Bolivar, had hoped, and later (1830) became the independent state called Ecuador.

The country's lively history and the constant disputes over the determination of some of its frontiers have had a marked effect on its politics. There are two dominant factors which have influenced the present position. The first is the fear of losing part of the nation's territory to Peru. This has contributed to a spirit of cohesion which has counteracted the tendency to division and to localised interests, which the country's great diversity of geographical conditions and earlier lack of adequate communications have fostered.

The second factor is the rise to power of the new industrialists and businessmen in Guayaquil, who are beginning to counterbalance the traditional strength of the landed aristocracy of the sierras.

## GEOGRAPHIC ORIGINALITY
## AND DIVERSITY

It is customary to distinguish four areas in Ecuador —the Galapagos Islands and three continental areas: the coast, the Sierra, and the Oriente or Amazon region.

*The Galapagos Islands and the coastal plain.* The Galapagos Islands, about 650 miles west of the coastline, consist of 14 islands and more than 60 islets and rocks, and are strategically important. The surrounding water is filled with a large number of fish which attract fishermen from as far as Japan and California.

Continental Ecuador includes a section which is exceptional on the Pacific American coast: a coastal plain with a width of two degrees of longitude and a length of four degrees of latitude, interrupted by a few high areas. The plain is crossed by three river networks which come down from the cordillera and are partly navigable. They include the Santiago and Esmeraldas rivers and, most important, the Guayas River, along which ocean-going ships can reach the port of Guayaquil, which is situated about thirty miles inland.

Three relatively narrow inlets surround a number of low islands and penetrate far inland, thus providing a natural shelter. The first is the bay of Limones, where the port of San Lorenzo is to be established; the second is the Estero Salado, in which a new port has been built for Guayaquil trade, and the third, which is protected by Jambeli Island and already carries a good deal of traffic, is situated near the Peruvian frontier, at Puerto Bolivar.

The cold Humboldt Current reduces the temperature considerably here, helped by the steep rise of the western slope of the Andes. The coastal strip becomes subtropical towards the south, especially by the time it reaches the Peruvian frontier. The Santa Helena peninsula is semi-desert. The Guayaquil area, at the foot of the cordillera, has a savanna-like vegetation broken by fingers of forest; it is much wetter, although it has a marked dry season. The Humboldt Current moves away from the coast towards the north where the rainfall is more abundant and regular and the climate is equatorial. This has led to the development of the great forests in Esmeraldas province, reaching to the Colombian border.

*The Sierra.* The western cordillera is not as high or as massive as the eastern, although it includes the highest peak, Chimborazo (over 20,000 feet). There are a number of volcanoes in both ranges, some of them still active. These are often situated above the 16,000-foot snowline; they surround the inter-Andean depression where life and activity are concentrated at altitudes of 6,500 to 10,000 feet. This depression is cut off by high plateaus. The southern area is low and dry and the northern is higher and wetter. There are several valleys, all with individual characteristics and different climates owing to their elevation and to their eastern or western orientation, which determines whether they are influenced by the Atlantic Ocean or by the Pacific. The Chota River valley, which runs down towards the Pacific Ocean, includes a small, typical desert area, situated about 30 miles north of the Equator; 20 miles south of the Equator there is a region of cool climate and a virtually constant year-round temperature. The capital city, Quito, is situated within this area. In the Sierra and coastal areas, the climate varies from subtropical to equatorial, with temperate or cold climates at high altitudes.

*The Oriente.* The Oriente, or eastern slope of the cordillera, descends fairly gently, and the herbaceous vegation of the plateaus gradually gives way to forests. Many large rivers flow into the Amazon, including the Putumayo, which forms the boundary with Colombia, the Napo, Pastaza, the Santiago, and the Maranon, along which the Peruvian frontier runs

The territorial losses sustained by the protocol of 1941 mean that Ecuador has no outlet eastwards, for the Peruvian frontier cuts across the Amazon tributaries upstream of their navigable stretches. Because of difficulties of access and lack of roads the Oriente is largely undeveloped. Extensive exploration for oil proved fruitless and in 1937 was abandoned. The population is estimated at only 46,000; it consists mainly of three Indian tribes among whom the Jivaro tribe has a language distinctly its own.

## POPULATION AND ECONOMY

Population distribution is uneven. The total population is estimated at about 4,396,000; with a total area of 119,870 square miles, density is 37 per square mile. However, more than 57 per cent of the population lives in the Sierra where the average density is 78 per square mile, and 40 per cent along the coast with an average density of 52. Thirty-nine per cent is Indian, 41 per cent of mixed Indian and other blood, 10 per cent white, 5 per cent Negro and mulatto, and 5 per cent other races. More than 70 per cent of the population is rural, and more than half of the urban population lives in Quito, the capital (314,000) and in the country's major port, Guayaquil (about 450,000)' Quito tends to be more administrative and cultural, Guayaquil more commercial and industrial.

*The Sierra: an economic and cultural centre.* The country's prosperity came in Spanish times from the Sierra. Quito was then a flourishing kingdom thanks to its temperate crops, the cotton and sugar-cane grown in its tropical valleys, sheep-raising, and the skill of its textile and wood craftsmen.

Only about half of the Sierra region is cultivable, and the available land has been impoverished over the years by the system of land tenure: the large plantations have been wastefully exploited for quick profits. Only rye, potatoes and barley are increasing in output. The remaining land, owned by Indians, has been divided into increasingly small plots cultivated either in 'free agricultural communities' dating from colonial times, which are generally steep, heavily eroded plots made to yield only by the Indians' perseverance, or in still smaller plots known as *minifundia,* which are too small to support a family. As a result, the million Sierra Indians are available as a cheap source of labour. They have considerable constitutional rights. The richest among them are the artisans, and the poorest those living near the great plantations. Little has been done about land reform in the past, but legislation was enacted in 1964.

The Sierra is now producing cereals such as maize, the country's staple food, and wheat and barley. Potato crops are being extensively developed along the borders of the plateaus; cotton has virtually disappeared. Sugar-cane is still flourishing, but there are fewer sheep, and the country is not self-sufficient in wool. Milk production has risen considerably during the past few years, although the beef-producing potential has not followed a similar upward trend. The recent introduction of pyrethrum crops has also been successful, but the growing population pressure in the Sierra is resulting in soil exhaustion and this has restricted the area's development. Due to the country's relative isolation and to the nature of domestic production, which is mainly intended for local consumption, Ecuador has inclined towards a high degree of self-sufficiency.

*The coastal exporting centre.* At the beginning of the twentieth century cocoa production and exports changed the coastal area into an important contributor to the nation's economy. After 1922, plant diseases and world market fluctuations reduced output drastically and led to a major economic and financial depression. Production has again risen but is still far from its former level. During the Second World War, the demand from a number of countries led to a rapid development of rice production for export; annual production rose to an all-time high of 110,000 tons in 1947, followed by a sharp drop in production to about 70,000 tons; exports are now 2,000 tons.

Banana production has also risen steeply. Ecuador has become the leading world exporter of bananas. The value of the banana exports was $61,700,000 in 1962. Coffee production has had a more constant rate of growth, and in recent years has been second in value among exports Sugar-cane is also grown, and output has increased in recent years and some is exported. Other crops include castor beans and cotton. Forest products are of lesser importance; they include corozo nuts and balsa wood, which is prized because of its lightness. Little has been done, however, in pastoral farming, although the conditions are favourable.

Jivaro Indians. These head-hunters originated on the Upper Maranon (Peru). Today their main prey is wild boar, which they attack with blowpipes and arrows tipped with curare, a paralysing poison.

Cotopaxi, in northern Ecudor, the highest active volcano in the world; its snow-covered peak is 19,344 feet high. In the foreground stretches the scrubland of the high inter-Andean depression. Cotopaxi is one of a series of volcanoes running through Central and South America.

ECUADOR: Quito, the capital city, situated high in the Sierra.

The coastal region suffers as a whole, by comparison with the Sierra, from a lack of manpower. Though the Guayaquil businessmen are gradually gaining political power at the expense of the Sierra landed aristocracy, the latter are unwilling to release their great labour force for work in the rival coastal area.

*Industrial development.* Existing industries are largely devoted to consumer goods, the textile industry, which is based upon an established tradition in the Sierra, being the most important. Industrial development is hampered by the small size of the available market, by lack of power and by the scarcity of non-agricultural raw materials. Mining activity consists mainly of the production of oil in the Santa Elena peninsula. Ecuador also imports some crude oil and owing to shortage of refining capacity, some refined products. Small quantities of gold and silver are also produced. Development of the Sierra's extensive water power resources is at the present time only in the initial stages.

The Sierra is developing effectively and has a stable, relatively limited economy mainly intended to meet local needs. Skilled manpower is available to the new industries. The coastal population, on the other hand, has a dynamic approach, a remarkably flexible economy and a willingness to take risks encouraged by the continued availability of natural resources, particularly in the north and in the region of fertile volcanic ash along the cordillera.

A better balance and co-ordination between the country's two major areas would make it possible to develop the coastal area more fully; this would lead to expansion of the Sierra market and make more effective use of highland resources. The future will largely depend upon achieving economic union and the development of a communications network. A railroad runs between Guayaquil and Quito and has recently been extended northwards to the Pacific Ocean to reach San Lorenzo, near the Colombian frontier. The Pan-American Highway runs through Ecuador from north to south, and many roads between the Sierra and various coastal ports have been built. The first stages in the construction of roads to link Ecuador with the navigable parts of the major Amazonian rivers are in progress and, although implementation of this programme requires a major effort, it is essential to the country's economic prosperity and growth.

# PERU

## FROM THE SPANISH CONQUEST TO INDEPENDENCE

The total area of Peru is 496,222 square miles, and it is the third largest country in South America. With a population of 10,857,000, the density is only 21 per square mile.

The region occupied by Peru today had already been inhabited for many centuries and seen a number of civilisations by the time it became part of the Inca empire, well before the arrival of the Spaniards. Francisco Pizarro first landed at Tumbes in 1527; he returned in 1532 with three ships, 200 men and 27 horses and established Spanish rule. The country remained a Spanish viceroyalty for almost three centuries. Independence was first proclaimed at Lima in July 1821 by José de San Martin, the liberator of Argentina, but the country was not finally liberated until Bolivar and Sucre had won the battles of Junin and Ayscucho in 1824.

## THE GEOGRAPHIC AREAS OF PERU

Peru consists of three more or less parallel regions running from north to south, between which communications are very difficult. The coastal area is a desert with a number of cultivated oases gradually rising towards the cordillera. The Sierra has a cold climate and bristles with the highest mountains in the country. Finally, there is the Montaña, which includes both the eastern slope of the cordillera and the dense tropical rain forest area.

*Oases in the coastal area.* The coastal area is a narrow strip along the entire 1,600-mile coastline, never wider than about 90 miles, sometimes shrinking almost to nothing when the foothills of the Sierra come near the ocean. Rain falls on this sandy area only once every 3 or 4 years; crops can be grown by means of irrigation schemes, introduced well before the arrival of the Spaniards. Although about fifty small waterways flow down from the Sierra, only about ten of them are filled with water throughout the year, and a great deal of complicated work has therefore been carried out in order to find sources of water. Tunnels have been dug beneath the watershed in order to make use of the rivers which flow into the Amazon basin, major works of this kind having been carried out in the Chiclayo and Piura areas. More than 1,350,000 acres of land are now irrigated and there are about 40 oases which have rich and fertile soil.

There are three large oases situated in the north, between the frontier with Ecuador and the mouth of the Santa River. This is the longest river emptying into the Pacific, flowing for 180 miles after rising in Lake Conococha at an altitude of 13,500 feet above sea level. The Piura oasis is established around a town which was founded by Pizarro three years before Lima; the Chiclayo oasis lies south of the large Sechura desert. Farther south again is the oasis of Trujillo, Peru's sixth largest city. Large quantities of rice, sugar-cane and cotton, as well as a little wheat, are produced in these oases; 75 per cent of the country's rice is produced in Chiclayo and Piura, and 56 per cent of its sugar grows in the Trujillo area. These cities are linked to their respective ports by short railroads, the bulk of their production being shipped, although the cities are now connected by the Pan-American Highway.

South of this rich area the Sierra approaches the sea, and between Pativilca and Lima there is only a narrow strip of arable land. Sugar-cane, cotton and vegetables for the capital are grown here, although there is less sunshine than in the northern areas. Between Lima and Ica there is a fairly rich agricultural area including the Canete, Chincha and Pisco oases, in which cotton, some sugar-cane, and large quantities of vines and fruit are grown. Between this area and the Chilean border aridity is more marked, though

Cotton is Peru's most
important cash crop.
The plant is indigenous
and is grown in the fertile
coastal valleys of the central
region and around Piura
in the north. Here, an Indian
family is harvesting the crop.

Landscape in the Sierra.
The principal wealth of this
mountainous area is its mineral
deposits. The main products
are lead and zinc. Mining
and the metallurgical industry
employ 35,000 Indians,
the only people able to work at
an altitude of more than
16,000 feet.

here, too, there are a few oases such as Arequipa, the
third largest city in Peru, and Moquegua, with their
ports at Mollendo and Ilo and their magnificent
vineyards.

In the north, near the Ecuador frontier, there are
large oil wells which have sprung up in the middle
of the desert and enjoy excellent road connections to
the refinery situated at the port of Talara. In 1956 a
steel plant was built at the mouth of the Santa River
to process ore which is mined 250 miles south of
Lima, near Ica, and is shipped to the plant through
the small port of Chimbota. Power comes from hydro-
electric stations that have been built in the picturesque
Santa River valley, enclosed between the Black and
White Cordilleras. Copper mining necessitated the
construction of 105 miles of railroads, completed in
1959, to carry the ore to the port of Ilo. There are
many spinning and weaving mills and knitting
factories.

The islands of Foca, San Lorenzo, San Francisco,
Lobos de Tierra and Lobos de Afuera are situated off
the coast, washed by the cold Humboldt Current.
Here fish are plentiful and have given rise to a new
and rapidly expanding industry. Thousands of birds

which nest in the islands also feed on the fish, and
their droppings provide 300,000 tons of guano each
year, used to fertilise the oases. The guano works
are a state monopoly. The prevailing maritime winds
are so dry that moisture tends to condense only in
winter, from May to October, when it forms a mist.
It provides enough moisture for the oases and the
Sierra foothills where there is grass to feed livestock
brought down from the mountains. Around Christmas, a warm current sometimes comes from the
Equator to heat the water. The fish depart and many
birds starve to death, but the current brings beneficial
rains to the desert.

It is thought that this coastal area was inhabited as
far back as 3000 B.C. In pre-Christian times, the
'Chavin' civilisation flourished in the upper Santa
River valley. It was replaced, around A.D. 300, by
several others distributed along the coast. To the
north, the 'Mochica' culture has left fine pottery
and the ruins of the 'Huaca de Sol' temple in the
Viru valley, while, in the centre, the 'Paracas' culture produced interesting materials and tapestries in
which mummies were wrapped. In the south beautiful
ceramics have been left by a culture still unidentified.
The Tiahuanaco empire then developed an advanced
civilisation around Lake Titicaca and extended its
control over the southern coastal area about A.D. 1000,
while, in the north, the Chimu empire ruled over an
area extending from the neighbourhood of what is
now Lima to the frontier with Ecuador. During the
thirteenth century the Incas took over all these coastal
civilisations, and the ruins of the great Inca coastal
city of Pachacamac still stand twelve miles south
of Lima.

*The capital city: Lima.* Cuzco, the capital of the Inca
empire, was too far inland for Pizarro; he therefore
founded Lima, in January 1535. The city grew considerably during the sixteenth century and continued
to be the real capital of the Spanish possessions in
South America until independence had been won. The
university of San Marcos was founded in 1551, to be
followed shortly after by the establishment of the
southern continent's first printing works, and the first
theatre opened in 1563. The city reached its peak in
the eighteenth century, when it had a rich and lively
population of 80,000. It has adapted itself to changing
times and has been growing steadily during the
twentieth century. It is the fifth largest city in the
whole of South America, with a population of
1,800,000.

The geographical situation of Lima, and of its port,
Callao, accounts for their remarkable growth; the
city is built along both banks of the Rimac, on
broad terraces 650 feet above sea level, and provides
an outlet for the mines located nearly 100 miles away
in the Sierra. There is an extensive air network connecting it to other parts of the country as well as to
the world's major cities. Although situated 12 degrees
south of the Equator, between the ocean and the
mountains, Lima enjoys a moderate climate in which
there is no rain; the sea mist, supplemented by irrigation, provides sufficient moisture for the valley
crops and grazing land. Callao handles 75 per cent
of all imports and 20 per cent of all exports.

*The Sierra and its mines.* The Sierra area consists of a
very extensive high plateau, the Altiplano, with an

average altitude of about 13,000 feet, broken by deep valleys. The cordillera ranges rise from this plateau and run roughly parallel, south-south-east to north-north-west.

In the south, two chains come from Chile and Bolivia to form a large oval area around Lake Titicaca, meeting again north of the lake in the Vilcanota region, where the water divides between the Amazon tributaries and the interior basin of Lake Titicaca. Farther north, the chains again meet in the Pasco region, from which the Maranon and Huallaga rivers begin to flow north and the Mantaro River flows south. The parallel chains then extend towards the north-west, their highest peaks being situated in the White Cordillera which overlooks the Santa River valley. Beyond, the mountains drop again near the Ecuador frontier. The Maranon River crosses the eastern heights and then bends towards the east, while in the Montaña area tributaries flow from the mountains of Ecuador to the left bank of the Maranon; others come from the Peruvian mountains to its right bank. There are more than ten peaks with altitudes of 19,500 feet or higher in the central area of the Sierra, and several volcanoes in the south.

The Sierra's principal wealth lies in the exploitation of its mineral resources, which is particularly well developed in the centre and on its western slopes. There are tremendous untapped ore reserves, usually of mixed lead, zinc, copper, silver and gold; the ore is usually processed *in situ* or else in the neighbouring area, where there are foundries, concentrating plants and refineries. The main products today are lead and zinc. Copper is mined mainly around Oroya and Cerro de Pasco. Peru also has a rich vanadium mine at Minaragra, west of Cerro de Pasco, and antimony and tungsten are also mined. Fourteen per cent of the country's exports are provided by the mining and metallurgical industry. It employs 35,000 Indians, who are irreplaceable since they are the only people who are able to work at an altitude of more than 16,000 feet.

Stock-breeding and agriculture are highly dependent upon the climate, which varies from area to area. The western slope is dry, while the eastern slope and the northern area, covered with forests up to a height of 11,500 feet, have a heavy rainfall from October to April. Between the forest edges and the snowline, which is at 16,500 feet above sea level in the latitude of Lima and 18,700 feet farther south, there are immense areas of treeless grazing land on which a few thorny shrubs grow. Alpacas, llamas, sheep and some cattle graze more than 46,000 square miles. The wool is clipped by the Indians, who use it to weave their clothing and blankets and sell the surplus production on the Arequipa market. Their food is provided by the animals and the few vegetables which they grow, with some difficulty, around their homes. Llamas are used as beasts of burden, and their dung provides fuel.

Some crops are grown in the valleys at heights between about 9,000 and 14,000 feet, on terraces along steep slopes. Coca is grown almost everywhere and its leaves are chewed by the Indians. Some valleys have become prosperous through agricultural production: wheat, corn, barley and potatoes.

*Cuzco and Inca remains.* Cuzco, the capital of the Inca empire, is situated at an altitude of 11,380 feet in the Sierra area. Both archaeological finds and legend indicate that the Inca tribes came from the shores or islands of Lake Titicaca and settled in the broad Cuzco valley around the eleventh century, after which the Inca, or supreme chief, gradually extended his rule over extensive areas of land well beyond the existing frontiers of Peru.

Cuzco still has a population of 70,000 which is predominantly Indian, although it was seriously shaken by an earthquake which occured in 1950 and was almost as severe as the famous earthquake of 1650. The entire region is densely populated, particularly in the Urubamba valley, and the main crops are cereals and tobacco. There are Inca ruins everywhere, and the high degree of civilisation of the Incas is shown by a fine road network discovered and studied by means of aerial photographs in 1952-53, and the great number of terraced areas on which crops were grown by means of irrigation.

*The underdeveloped Montaña area.* The Montaña extends from the eastern slopes of the Sierra to the frontiers of Peru with Ecuador, Colombia, Brazil and Bolivia. This region is covered with dense, tropical forests crossed in the north by the Maranon, Huallaga and Ucayali rivers. In the southern part of the Montaña, rivers from the eastern cordillera come to swell the Madre de Dios River, which is a tributary of the Madeira River, itself a tributary of the Amazon. The population is concentrated along the river banks, where a number of towns have recently developed. The largest town in the area is Iquitos, which is situated on the Upper Amazon and has thus a direct connection with the Atlantic Ocean through Brazil.

The forests are filled with many cedar, oak and mahogany trees, as well as with varieties ranging from hardwoods such as ironwood to softwood such as balsa, which is used by the natives to build their boats. After the trees are felled they are usually floated along the rivers to sawmills at Tingo Maria and Pucallpa; timber is exported through Iquitos, which also trades in other forest products such as medicinal plants and rubber.

The Canzo Azul oil wells, situated about 25 miles south of Pucallpa, meet all of the area's requirements and the oil is transported to the town by pipeline.

Peaks of the Cordillera Blanca Range. With peaks reminiscent of the Alps, these ranges form part of the Andes, the backbone of South America.

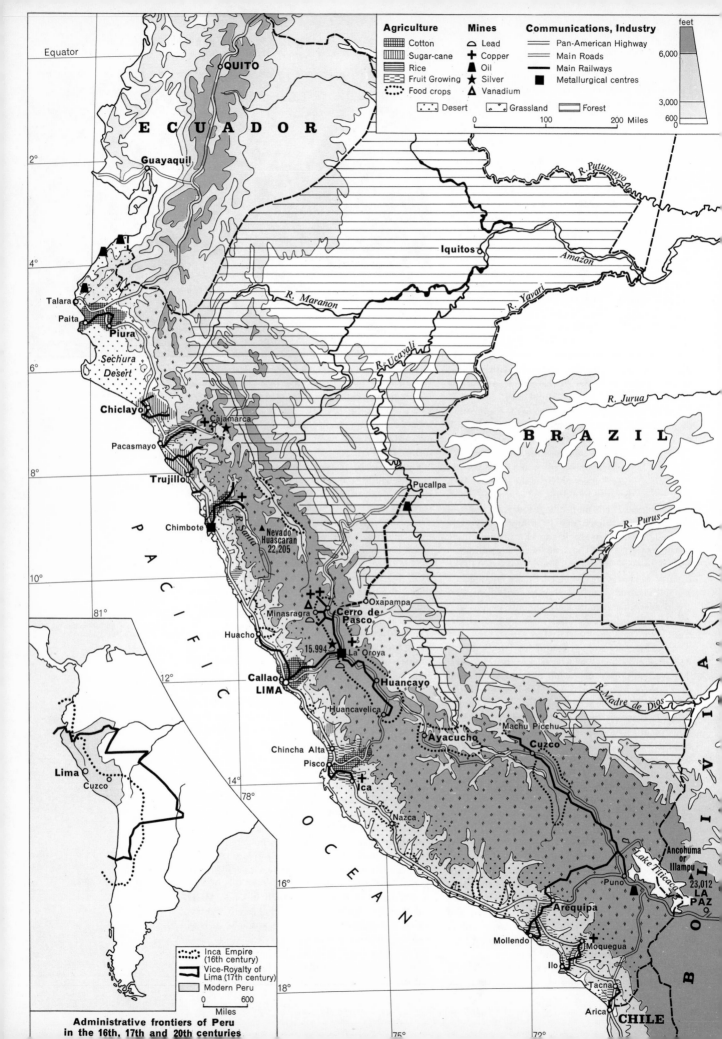

**Agriculture**
- Cotton
- Sugar-cane
- Rice
- Fruit Growing
- Food crops

**Mines**
- Lead
- Copper
- Oil
- Silver
- Vanadium

**Communications, Industry**
- Pan-American Highway
- Main Roads
- Main Railways
- Metallurgical centres

Desert  Grassland  Forest

0        100        200 Miles

feet
6,000
3,000
600

Equator

**E C U A D O R**

QUITO

Guayaquil

2°

4°

Iquitos

R. Putumayo

R. Marañon

R. Yavari

Amazon

Talara

Paita

Piura

Sechura Desert

6°

R. Ucayali

Chiclayo

Cajamarca

Pacasmayo

8°

Trujillo

Chimbote

R. Santa

Pucallpa

**B R A Z I L**

R. Jurua

R. Purus

Nevado Huascaran 22,205

10°

Oxapampa

Minasragra

Cerro de Pasco

Huacho

15,994

La Oroya

Callao
LIMA

12°

Huancayo

Huancavelica

R. Madre de Dios

Machu Picchu

Ayacucho

Cuzco

**B O L I V I A**

Chincha Alta

Pisco

Ica

14°

Nazca

81°

Lima

Cuzco

78°

P A C I F I C

Ancohuma or Illampu 23,012

LA PAZ

Lake Titicaca

Puno

16°

Arequipa

O C E A N

Mollendo

Moquegua

Ilo

Inca Empire (16th century)
Vice-Royalty of Lima (17th century)
Modern Peru

0        600
Miles

Tacna

Arica

**CHILE**

18°

**Administrative frontiers of Peru in the 16th, 17th and 20th centuries**

75°        72°

There are only about 500,000 acres of arable land along the waterways, where bananas, sugar-cane, coca and tea are grown, while coffee has been planted in upper valleys of the Ucayali River tributaries.

This rich area is just beginning to develop, and its economic expansion is being greatly facilitated by the provision of new means of transport.

## COMMUNICATIONS, RESOURCES AND ACTIVITIES

*Difficult communications.* From time immemorial the ocean has been used to connect the cities situated in the coastal area. It was not, however, until the twentieth century that communications between the country's three areas were substantially improved.

In spite of this late start, Peru was the first South American country to have a railroad. It started to operate in 1851 along an 8 mile track between Callao and Lima. In 1907 the central railroad began to function. This is considered to be one of the wonders of the continent in view of the many structures which had to be built along its 250-mile length, including 68 tunnels, 55 bridges and 22 reversal points.

There are only 1,700 miles of railroad in Peru, but during the past thirty years road construction has been extensive, and there are now more than 24,000 miles of carriageable roads. Secondary roads provide connections between the main highway and the coastal sugar and cotton producing areas as well as the Sierra mines, thus facilitating trade between producers and consumers or exporters.

In addition to rail and road transport, air travel has been extensively developed. Peru has many international air connections with the outside world, and a large internal network linking the coastal cities with each other and with the Sierra and Montaña. It now takes only three hours to fly from Lima to Iquitos, whereas the journey formerly lasted three weeks and was difficult and dangerous, involving constant changes from one means of transport to another. There is no road running through Peru from Lima to Iquitos, although the latter can easily be reached through Brazil, via the Amazon River. Aircraft also provide a rapid means of transport for machinery and spare parts to isolated areas.

AGRICULTURE AND RICH MINING RESOURCES Sixty-two per cent of the active population are engaged in agriculture, stock-breeding and forestry, which together provide about one-third of the national income. Land reforms of 1962 aim at juster distribution of holdings and modernisation of methods.

Cotton and sugar, once the most important exports, now account respectively for only 13 and 11 per cent of the total. Their place has been rapidly taken by the vastly expanded fishing industry, with 25 per cent, mostly in the form of fishmeal and oil. Copper accounts for 14.6 per cent and silver, lead, zinc, iron ore and oil for 27 per cent. Peru imports foodstuffs such as cereals, meat and wine in addition to machinery, vehicles and manufactured goods. The United States and Canada buy 30 per cent of all exports and provide 40-45 per cent of imports; there are also exports to the United Kingdom and Chile. The country's balance of trade is now favourable.

Plans are being made to improve Peru's economic position, and schemes are being implemented to cultivate and irrigate large areas in the coastal region of the Montaña. Ultimately these should bring relief from the grinding poverty that is the lot of the Indian masses. Foreign capital, mainly American, has contributed to the rapid development of mining and a national electrification plan has been launched, while the International Bank is financing railroad modernisation and the construction of port facilities at Callao.

*Map opposite:* Peru, showing agriculture, mineral resources and industry.

Balsa rafts, tortora reeds, clear skies and exhilarating air are the idyllic features of Lake Titicaca.

Callao, which serves Lima, is one of the most important harbours on the South Pacific coast.

# BOLIVIA

Bolivia, which has an area of 415,000 square miles, has a population of 3,462,000, giving a density of only 8 per square mile.

*From the Spanish conquest to independence.* The area was originally inhabited by the Aymara Indians who had settled around Lake Titicaca, but it was taken over by the Cuzco Incas, who ruled from the thirteenth century until the beginning of Spanish control, six years after the arrival of Pizarro on the Peruvian coast. Sucre, which is still Bolivia's official capital, was established in 1538. In 1559 the country became part of the Lima viceroyalty. In 1777 it was incorporated into the La Plata viceroyalty. In 1825 General Sucre entered La Paz and proclaimed the independence of Bolivia. The state was named after General Bolivar.

Since that time, Bolivia has been sorely tried by wars, frontier disputes and revolutions, and after the unfortunate Pacific War (1879-83) over the Atacama Desert nitrate deposits, it lost all direct access to the ocean by being stripped of its small coastal area on the Pacific Ocean and the little port of Cobija, which has since disappeared. The frontier with Chile

La Paz, the seat of Bolivia's Government and an important business centre, situated at a height of 12,200 feet in a hollow 1,500 feet below the level of the Altiplano, or high plateau of the Andes.

was agreed by the peace treaty of 1904, and by a protocol signed in May 1907, in accordance with which Chile built a railroad from Arica to La Paz, in exchange for some of Bolivia's rich nitrate deposits. In September 1953 Arica became a free port and Bolivia was granted customs and storage facilities there. The frontier with Argentina was determined in 1925. Part of the Chaco was conceded to Argentina, in exchange for which that country also built a railroad to Bolivia. Similarly, when Brazil received the Acre territory by a treaty signed in November 1903, it, too, undertook to build a railroad. A frontier agreement with Peru was reached in 1912, but the

section concerned with the Copocaban peninsula on Lake Titicaca has only recently been ratified. The worst frontier dispute was with Paraguay and concerned the Chaco. It led to fighting between 1928 and 1930 as well as between 1933 and 1935, when the League of Nations intervened, and a peace treaty was eventually signed in July 1938. Paraguay was given three-quarters of the Chaco and Bolivia obtained access to the Paraguay River, near Corumba.

Owing to these internal difficulties and to the lack of government stability resulting from the Chaco War, there was a revolution in 1952 — the 178th since 1825. The social structure of the country was radically altered; the great tin mines were expropriated and nationalised, and agrarian reform led to a break-up of the large estates. The Government is now endeavouring to give the country a more varied economy and to combat inflation, with the aid of technical assistance missions from the International Labour Organisation and the Food and Agriculture Organisation as well as with the financial support of the International Monetary Fund and of the United States.

## CONTRASTING GEOGRAPHICAL AREAS

There are three sharply contrasting geographical areas in Bolivia, the first being the Altiplano, a high plateau bordered by two very high mountain chains. It includes the centre of the country from Lake Titicaca to the Argentinian frontier and is the home of 75 per cent of the country's population. The second geographical region consists of valleys situated along the eastern slope of the eastern cordillera, and the third of tropical plains which stretch north, east and south to the borders of Peru, Brazil and Paraguay. These occupy 70 per cent of the total area, but are sparsely populated.

*The Altiplano and the mines.* The Altiplano is a harsh, treeless, windswept area, uniformly grey except for a few green patches found where there is rainfall. But rain occurs infrequently and is concentrated during December and January, when the water is rapidly absorbed by the spongy soil. The air is always clear and bright; average temperature is 8°C. (46°F.), although at night this can fall to –20°C. (–4°F.). The area is densely populated in the north, near Lake Titicaca, but becomes increasingly arid and deserted towards the south.

In actual fact, the Altiplano is a large corridor about 80 miles wide and more than 500 miles long, an inland basin flanked by the two cordilleras. The Desaguadero River, the outlet of Lake Titicaca, which is situated at an altitude of 12,517 feet, runs through increasingly arid and uninhabited areas to Lake Poopo, 190 miles to the south. This salt lake, which has an area of 1,080 square miles, overflows in turn into another salt lake situated fifty miles to the southwest, the Salar de Coipasa.

Thanks to adequate rainfall and an average temperature of 11°C. (52°F.), a few crops can be grown in the valleys running into Lake Titicaca as well as on terraces which project from the mountain slope. Production is limited to potatoes and oats and is barely sufficient for local requirements, despite Government attempts to organise agriculture in the area. In other

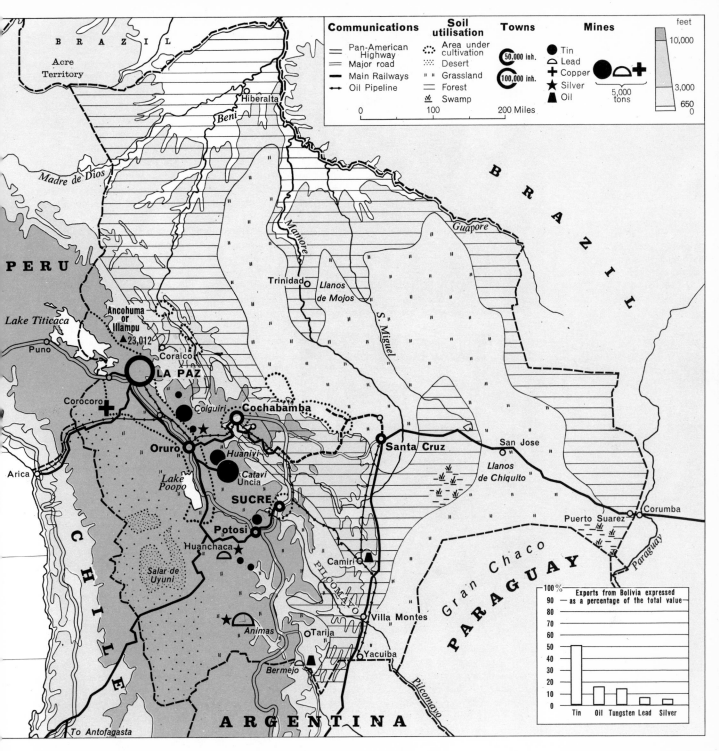

Communications
Pan-American Highway
Major road
Main Railways
Oil Pipeline

Soil utilisation
Area under cultivation
Desert
Grassland
Forest
Swamp

Towns
50,000 inh.
100,000 inh.

Mines
● Tin
△ Lead
+ Copper
★ Silver
▲ Oil

5,000 tons

feet
10,000
3,000
650
0

0    100    200 Miles

Exports from Bolivia expressed as a percentage of the total value

Tin   Oil   Tungsten   Lead   Silver

parts of this region the only crops are potatoes and *ocas*, which are local tubers, and very nourishing cereals, *canahui* and *quinoa*, the latter being used to make the fermented beverage known as *chicha*. Llamas and alpacas are found throughout the region as well as a few sheep whose dried and salted meat is very popular, and vicunas, which are highly prized for their fleece.

The frontier with Chile is formed by the western cordillera, a series of peaks of volcanic origin, separated by gaps or mountain passes through which communication can be made to the Pacific Ocean. There are twelve peaks higher than 16,500 feet, and

five over 19,500 feet high. There is virtually no rainfall on this cordillera, which is almost uninhabited and has only one river, the Loa.

The western cordillera, or Royal Cordillera of the Andes, is the chief foundation of Bolivia's economy. This steep continuous chain has the highest peaks in the country, including Ancohuma which is 23,012 feet high. Towards the south the chain gradually loses height, though there are a number of peaks higher than 16,500 feet. These mountains divide the waters of the Altiplano inland basin from the basins of various tributaries of the Amazon and the Rio de la Plata.

Physical and economic map of Bolivia. The importance of the Altiplano is evident: towns, communications and mines are most numerous in this region. Roads and railroads diverge from it linking this coastless country to the Pacific and Atlantic.

A mine in the massive central plateau of Bolivia, where the average altitude is 12,500 feet. The principal resource of Bolivia is mining, chiefly of tin, though many other minerals are also exploited. Most of the mines are concentrated on the western flank of the Cordillera Real.

A Chola Indian woman selling fruit in a street of La Paz. She wears the check shawl and bowler hat typical of Bolivian Indian women, and reads a newspaper as she waits. Since the nationalisation of the mines the living standards of the Bolivian people have risen. The International Labour Organisation has done much to improve conditions and stamp out illiteracy.

Since 1545, when the Spaniards discovered the Cerro Rico, which is a compact mass of silver, tin, bismuth and tungsten ores, the western slopes of the Royal Cordillera and a few isolated areas to the east have constituted the country's major source of wealth. The tin ore or cassiterite is found in small veins at altitudes which range from 11,000 to 16,000 feet. Although there is a small refinery at Oruro, the ore concentrates are usually exported to the United States and Great Britain is the only tin producing country in South America and is the world's third largest producer. Silver is also mined, notably at Huanchaca, where one of the largest mines in the world is situated, lead and zinc at Potosi, and at Corocoro south of La Paz bismuth and antimony, together with copper.

Although the mining industry employs only 4 per cent of the population, it provides about 90 per cent of the country's exports by value, as well as the foreign currency needed to import foodstuffs.

In spite of the relative cheapness of Bolivian man-

power, transport to export centres is expensive, notwithstanding the Altiplano's reasonably adequate communications network.

*The real capital of Bolivia: La Paz.* Although Sucre is still the judiciary capital and the seat of the High Court, the real capital of the country is La Paz, situated at an altitude of 12,000 feet at the bottom of a basin about 1,500 feet below the level of the Altiplano. This city, which has a population of over 350,000, was founded in 1548 by the Spaniards. There is often frost at night, but the average temperature is 10°C. (50°F.). In addition to administrative and residential areas, a number of small industries have been developed, including wool and cotton spinning mills, cement works, etc. These constitute more than 50 per cent of the country's industries — all hampered by still insufficient power supplies.

*The valleys.* The valleys which descend from the tropical plains north, east and south of the Royal Cordillera and of its eastern foothills are called *yungas*. Their appearance varies considerably from region to region.

North and east of La Paz, the rather steep wooded slopes of the eastern side are deeply cut by the tributaries of the Beni River, itself a tributary of the Madeira River. These fertile valleys produce coffee, cocoa, sugar-cane, coca and tropical fruits as well as most of the vegetables needed for the capital city. Transportation is difficult, however, since the only possible road clings to the vertical mountain walls, and has to rise 11,000 feet along fifty miles of bends, passing through every possible type of vegetation, in order to cross a 15,000-foot mountain pass seven miles from the capital. The most lucrative activity of the valleys is the production of coca leaves which are dried and sold to the Altiplano Indians.

Between these northern *yungas* and the Argentine border, the eastern slopes of the Royal Cordillera are less steep, and descend gently to the tropical plains along the Puna Plateau. This plateau has been formed by the Rio Grande tributaries, which flow to the Amazon basin, and by the tributaries of the Pilcomayo River, which flows through the Chaco to the Rio de la Plata. The valleys are well cultivated and enjoy a semi-tropical climate. They have a very dense population which consists mainly of mestizos, though there are also some Europeans.

Transport to the Altiplano towns and cities is difficult. The line which branches off from the central railroute at Oruro to go to Cochabamba must cross the Puna and the Cuesta Colorada at a height of 13,450 feet before descending 5,500 feet into the valley. The roads which have been laboriously built to Cochabamba have made this city, which is the second largest in the country and has a population of 90,000, one of the main gateways to the eastern tropical plains. Farther south is the Tarija basin, at an altitude of only 6,000 feet; when better transport is available this area will be able to produce all the country's food requirements. At present there is a road between Tarija and Potosi and another to Villa Montes, a pastoral and cotton industry centre. A new railway line now crosses the Pilcomayo River and is connected to Argentina's rail network.

*The tropical plains or 'llanos'.* These plains cover most of the country from the *yungas* to the frontiers of

Peru, Brazil, Paraguay and Argentina, and gradually descend from 1,600 feet to 650 feet above sea level. In the north are the Madre de Dios, Beni and Mamore Rivers; in the south-east are the tributaries of the Paraguay River.

The north has abundant seasonal rainfall, with alternating floods and periods of drought. The climate is hot, with average temperatures of 25°C. (77°F.) to 27°C. (81°F.), but it is sometimes moderated by the south wind. Towards the south there is less rainfall. In the north and east there are more than 1,250,000 acres of tropical forests containing the same varieties as the Peruvian Montaña; but timber production is limited and does not meet domestic requirements owing to transport difficulties. A great deal of rubber was produced during the rubber boom, but there are now almost no exports; medicinal barks such as cinchona, from which quinine is made, are still produced in the Beni River forests. Stock-breeding tends to be concentrated in the Beni department, in the Mojos llanos, where there are more than a million head of livestock, some half-wild; the area is producing a growing proportion of the meat consumed at La Paz, Oruro and Cochabamba. The Santa Cruz department is the largest in Bolivia and has the richest natural resources in the country. Although another 15,000 tons must be imported, 15,000 tons of rice are produced every year around San José de Chiquitos. This department produces sugar-cane, oil-yielding plants, maize, cotton and citrus fruits. Its capital is Santa Cruz, founded in 1595 by the Spaniards. A 312-mile motor highway between Santa Cruz and Cochamba, in use since late 1953, is now open throughout the year and has substantially reduced transportation costs. In 1954, a railroad 420 miles long was built through the jungle to Corumba, on the Paraguay River, where it connects with the Brazilian network to reach Santos on the Atlantic. Santa Cruz is also linked to the Argentine network.

There are almost no communications facilities on the remaining llanos. Some parts of the rivers are navigable, but there is no connection to the Amazon basin because of the Porto Velho rapids on the Madeira river; however, Brazil hopes soon to improve the Porto Velho-São Paulo road. Links with the Altiplano have been improved by aviation. In addition to passenger flights, large quantities of freight are carried, mainly fresh and dried meat, cocoa, hides and timber. The economic potential of the llanos, however, depends largely upon the further growth of their population.

All of Bolivia's food requirements should, in future, be produced on these broad plains, and a systematic policy of surveying may also show the existence of further resources. Iron deposits have already been found at Mutum, near Puerto Suarez, about sixty miles from Corumba on the Paraguay River, which can be used as an exporting centre. Gold has also been found in some river sand, and oil prospecting has begun.

### NEW TRENDS

*The search for oil.* It would appear that, thanks to the geological structure of Bolivia, there are rich oil deposits throughout a large section of the country, extending along the foot of the eastern cordillera from Trinidad, 250 miles north-east of La Paz, through Santa Cruz to the Argentine frontier. Output meets all the country's requirements except for aviation fuels and some oil is now exported.

Following the decline of traditional ore exports, notably of cassiterite, the Bolivian government has tried to interest foreign firms in its oil deposits. They were given extensive guarantees by means of an oil Code in 1956 and, by the beginning of 1959, more than ten firms had been granted licences to prospect about 27 million acres, while the state firm retained control of about 12,000,000 acres. A very extensive network of pipelines carries oil from the extraction and refinery areas to consumer and export centres.

FUTURE OF THE BOLIVIAN ECONOMY. Since the 1952 revolution, the economic development of the country has been undertaken together with a struggle against inflation, which was a legacy of the Chaco War. A number of technical missions from the United Nations and its specialised agencies, as well as from the United States, have contributed to the advancement of the economic programme.

Although Bolivia still imports wheat, flour and livestock, further development of the valleys and tropical plains and the improvement of agriculture and methods of transport should enable it to become self-sufficient in food products in the near future; it may even be able to export some food. In this country without iron or coal and where water-power resources are untapped, industry is still in its infancy and manufactured goods and a few industrial raw materials constitute 50 per cent of its imports.

Bolivia's importing capacity is based upon its ore-exporting potential, particularly tin ore. Ores make up 95 per cent of all exports, 75 per cent of these being tin ore. Owing to mining difficulties, to the poor tin content and costly transport, the Bolivian mining industry cannot compete favourably in the world market. Oil gives room for hope of a considerable improvement in the economy.

# CHILE

'Chile' is an old Aymara Indian word which can be translated as 'land's end'. Chile clings to the western slopes of a continent which tapers towards the south; it continues to the southernmost end of this continent, into the solitary southern seas. Valparaiso is situated to the south of a subtropical belt of land but itself has a Mediterranean climate; a little farther south are areas of greenness and freshness worthy of England or Switzerland. Chile is at once the remotest and most familiar looking of South American countries for Europeans and North Americans.

### MOUNTAINS AND INSULARITY

The isolation of Chile is not due to distance only. The country is bounded by the ocean to the south and west, by the desert to the north, by a double barrier of mountains (almost 23,000 feet high) and of aridity to the east. The arid belt delimits and isolates Chile's Mediterranean and oceanic greenery.

A maritime strip with virtually no hinterland, Chile

is like an island or, since it is 2,500 miles long, a sub-continent. In the Santiago and Valparaiso areas, the Pacific Ocean beaches are barely 120 miles from the inaccessible, icy heights of the Argentine border.

The longitudinal pattern of Chile's relief is well known. On the Argentine frontier is the impressive barrier of the Andes, bristling with volcanoes and devoid of valleys. The massive mountains rise sheer, with passes situated at great heights, so that the road and railroute to Buenos Aires cross the frontier at an altitude of 13,000 feet. The coastal cordillera, on the Pacific Ocean side, is much lower, and has only a few peaks reaching a height of 6,500 feet. It is an interrupted chain, less precipitous and more varied than the eastern cordillera. Between these two mountain groups, a line of tectonic weakness is shown where subsidence has taken place over long stretches: the pampas of the great northern desert in which nitrates, copper, and sulphur are found, and the temperate longitudinal valley of Chile, in which the country has developed with a high degree of insularity throughout the centuries.

The Andes drop quickly south of Santiago and are then easier to cross. Climate, however, rather than these breaks in the physical structure, creates the differences and contrasts between the country's various natural regions.

Since Chile extends from latitudes 17° to 53°S. it has a wide range of climates; transitions over the range are almost imperceptible, but every climate characteristic of a continental west coast is included. In the far north there is virtually no rainfall and the area is a desert. In central Chile the climate is Mediterranean: Santiago has an annual rainfall of about 14 inches but is absolutely dry in summer, 86 per cent of the total rainfall being concentrated into five months of the year. In this area there are sections of steppe that are yellow-grey in summer and a rich green in winter, alternating with heathland filled with shrubs and tough-leaved evergreen trees. In the south there is a maritime climate completely different from the others, since from Chillan or Concepcion southwards there are more and larger rivers in which the water is clear and green and no longer filled with silt and mud; a number of impenetrable forests dominate the landscape, though some have now been cleared. There is ample evidence of the abundant and consistent rainfall, which amounts to 98 inches annually at Valdivia and 110 inches at Puerto Aysen.

In spite of the diversity of climate, largely arising from the amount and distribution of rainfall, there are also certain resemblances. Temperatures vary with changes of latitude but the ocean has a moderating effect, as the great west winds bring relatively tepid water to the south coast and reduce the severity of winter, while the Humboldt Current brings cold water from the ocean depths to protect the centre and north from excessive summer heat. As a result, differences in temperature within the country are never greater than 13°C. (23°F.) and there is little seasonal variation.

In view of the climate and relief, there is only a limited amount of useful land, and the only rich and attractive areas are situated in the middle latitudes where they are restricted to the longitudinal depression and to the valleys.

## THE GENESIS OF A NATION

*The colonial period.* The Spanish conquistadors did not find large areas of available land as in North America, Brazil and Argentina, and the local Indians were not easy to conquer. The territory and population of modern Chile have therefore been established only after centuries of patient work, influenced by the existence of natural frontiers and by a policy of more or less conscious assimilation.

The main feature of the entire colonial period was the resistance of the Araucanians. These people were relative newcomers to the area at the time of the Spanish conquest, having arrived around 1400 from the Argentine pampas or else from southern Brazil. Although this was an entirely new environment for them, they were able to develop a fairly original civilisation within a short period, based upon agriculture, pastoral farming and extensive use of the forests. The rapid adaptation of the Araucanians to the geographic situation was undoubtedly one of the major factors in their resistance to the Incas and the Spaniards. Although the latter were better organised, they were unfamiliar with the wet forest areas in which they had to fight the warlike Araucanians. The Spaniards had to evacuate the settlements they had established immediately after the conquest south of the Bio-Bio River. The resulting 'frontier' lasted with few changes for another three hundred years.

Colonial Chile was therefore blocked to the south, and in determining its eastern frontier was compelled to choose between mountains and aridity. It was from Santiago that the trans-Andean province of Cuyo was colonised; its capital was established at Mendoza, cut off from the Plate River lands by the Monte sub-desert. In 1778 it became part of the Buenos Aires viceroyalty and the frontier was moved back to the Andean peaks.

Colonial Chile then became a definite entity, with nominal authority extending to the southernmost part of the continent, including Patagonia from the Atlantic to the Pacific Ocean. Araucanian resistance, however, wedged Chile between the Andes and the ocean and limited it for practical purposes to the areas with a Mediterranean climate.

The Chilean nation emerged in this restricted but clearly defined and relatively homogeneous area. Little is known about the native components of the population. Between the Araucanian, Atacamena and Diaguitas civilisations, the Spaniards found the Picunches, the northern section of a large group of peoples which had originally lived between the edges of the desert and the Chiloe area and had been separated from each other by the Araucanians. After the Incas had left, the Picunches had virtually no political organisation, so that it was relatively easy for the Spaniards to mix with them. The first settlers lived in towns surrounded by native villages and hamlets. They supervised work in the gold mines and were able to use local Indians as labourers in return for making armed contributions to the country's defence system.

By the end of the sixteenth century, mining had gradually been replaced by pastoral farming. Land concessions led to the establishment of great estates whose owners assumed leadership of the colony.

Mixed marriages became a commonplace in the rural areas. In the eighteenth century, the development of agriculture led to a gradual change in the types of workers and social structure and to the introduction of a characteristic form of land tenure which still exists today.

At the end of the colonial period, Chile looked like one of the more remote provinces of Spain itself. The Indians had been so extensively assimilated and had intermarried over so long a period that they could no longer be identified as a separate ethnic group.

*The Republic of Chile.* After independence was achieved in 1818, a new stage of development began, the major characteristic of which was a tremendous increase in the country's area. In the north, as a result of the war against Bolivia and Peru, Chile acquired part of Antofagasta and Arica provinces. In the south, Araucanian resistance was finally overcome after a campaign which lasted from 1880 to 1890. The natural frontier policy was then fully carried out, although it took many years of hard work before it was completely implemented. In Patagonia, both sides of the cordillera had been explored and colonised from Chile, since the relief had not been as difficult to overcome as the climate. The frontier was finally drawn along the ridges after arbitration by the King of England; Chile acquired its present-day form, an elongated strip of land between the mountains and the sea.

Since 1940 it has been claiming jurisdiction over the sector of Antarctica between longitudes 53° and 90°W. This sector would overlap by 27° with the territory claimed by Britain between 20° and 90° W. Chile has four bases in Antarctica, set up in 1947, 1948 and 1951.

During the last stage of development Chile's population rose considerably in areas which had remained outside Spanish colonisation. Although there were no large waves of immigration, Germans began to arrive in 1850 and were encouraged by the government to settle around Valdivia and Lake Llanquihue, and after the 'frontier' had been wiped out, the Germans were followed by numbers of French, Swiss and additional German settlers. Recently, some Japanese have settled, chiefly in the regions of Punta Arenas and Antofagasta.

The population is now over 8 million, with a density of 28 per square mile; 20 per cent lives in the Santiago conurbation, and 63 per cent lives in the eleven provinces of central Chile, where the density is over 90 per square mile.

The increase in population has been slow but steady (the birthrate is 34.6 per 1,000, the death-rate 11.7 per 1,000). Immigration has never been extensive, as is shown by the fact that 97.4 per cent of the present population is of Chilean origin. About 130,000 Araucanians now live a poverty-stricken existence on their reservations.

There is undoubtedly some relationship between social position and colour of skin, although the whole situation is in a constant state of flux. Santiago is a melting-pot. A contributory factor to the mixture of the people is provided by large numbers of Chilean itinerant workers who take jobs in mining, road-building and harvesting, and by the Chilote lumber-men and boatmen who also move about a great deal in the southernmost areas of the country. As a result, Chile may soon lose all trace of the varied origins of its people and retain only a few local differences such as are found in European countries.

## RURAL CHILE AND ITS PEOPLE

Agriculture was introduced into Chile on a commercial basis in colonial times. It was easy to introduce European crops into the country, however, and in colonial times agriculture produce was exported in large quantities. In the seventeenth century, Chile sold tallow and hides, and in the eighteenth century cereals to Lima. In the nineteenth century ships sailed up and down the Pacific coasts, finding new customers for their wheat cargoes in California, Australia and the French settlements in Oceania, until England offered the advantage of a larger and more regular market.

Although this trade is now reduced and new products have been added, immediately outside Santiago,

Santiago, the capital of Chile, a sprawling city at the foot of the Andes, seen in the distance. It has a population of 2,012,000 and is constantly growing. Most of the major roads and rail lines converge on the city, and it is its favourable geographic position which has largely determined its rôle as administrative, cultural and economic capital of Chile.

Paine Falls, with the 10,650-foot Mount Paine in the background. Mount Paine is situated in Magellanes province, at the southern tip of Chile.

Valparaiso and Concepcion, Chile is still a rural country imbued with old landed traditions. This is the *campo chileno,* the area in which Spanish colonisation made its greatest inroads, and which enjoys a Mediterranean climate. North of La Serena, the country is arid and there are only a few scattered areas of arable land along the waterways, while south of che Bio-Bio River, where the climate is maritime-temperate, the land is still relatively under-developed.

Although the summer is not very hot, the Mediterranean area is completely lacking in rain; but water is provided by melting snow from the ice-covered peaks of the cordillera, through large canals and a complex network of irrigation ditches. The crops are of European origin with the exception of maize, beans, potatoes and melons; Europe has also provided the livestock and the rows of poplars, weeping willows and bramble hedges.

From the Santiago area to San Fernando and Talca in the south there are dry crops only along the coast; there is a sharp contrast between the irrigated lowlands and the barren uplands at the foot of which crops and houses abruptly disappear.

Until 1950 farming systems were similar to those which prevailed in colonial times and still prevail in a number of other South American countries. Except for the area around Santiago and a few old and poor areas in which land was divided into small plots, there were everywhere large estates of hundreds or thousands of acres, farmed by tenants who received advantages in kind, such as a small house, 2 to 5 acres of farming land and grazing rights for 5 or 6 cows, as well as a very low wage in return for working for the owner from sunrise to sunset.

The tenant farmers were accustomed to living on a subsistence basis; neither they nor the small landowners, foremen and estate managers, could hope for much improvement in their way of life until the introduction of land reform legislation in 1960. But now, gradually, their economic situation is being transformed.

Food consists mainly of meat, soups and vegetables, though in summer there is plenty of magnificently cooked maize, tomatoes and melons of every variety.

The tenant farmers' houses line the roads which surround the large and rustic houses of the estate-owners; they consist of adobe walls and corrugated iron roofs with two or three separate rooms built around open verandas covered in greenery and flowers in summer. Life is monotonous and peaceful. Variety is provided by holidays and ceremonies; though most of the peasants are Roman Catholics, their lives are often governed by superstition.

The country's agricultural problems arise from the farmers' poverty as well as from low production levels. They are particularly acute in the huge wheat fields at the 'frontier', where the forests have been replaced by flat plains undermined and ravaged by soil exhaustion; they are less severe in the southern pastoral areas, which although well organised are surrounded by forests and too remote from consumer markets.

Neither agricultural products nor pastoral farming meet domestic requirements. There were 83 cattle per 100 inhabitants in 1907: today the proportion is 37 to 100, and the total of 2,800,000 cattle may even be dropping slightly. There is a similar downward trend for sheep, so that a chronic meat scarcity necessitates imports from Argentina. Since 1957 wheat production has been raised, and imports have been reduced. At the same time, the demand for wheat continues to grow.

Of the country's total area 60 per cent is unusable and another 20 per cent consists of woodland. Agricultural production and pastoral farming are therefore limited to one-fifth of the area, although some regions are mountainous and poor, consisting only of scanty grazing land and scrub. There remain only 15 million acres of arable land with varying degrees of fertility. Moreover, cultivated areas do not extend over more than 2,500,000 acres, and thousands of acres of good arable land are used only for grazing. Crop yields are much lower than they should be.

This situation is due to the survival of traditional farming practices. On the very large estates modernisation is usually hampered by lack of capital as well as by absentee ownership, although the output is usually higher than on the small, poorly equipped and backward farmsteads. The system of tenant-farming by poor labourers who are usually paid miserably in kind is a major impediment to development, and is most marked in the northern and central provinces. The tenant-farmers are not only badly paid but also underfed, and cannot work hard enough to shake off their established routine. Government policy did very little to help agriculture or to encourage its more profitable activities, in spite of low agricultural taxation, until the agrarian reforms of 1960.

Today, a number of changes are being made. An agricultural colonisation board is carrying out a positive programme of land redistribution, although the results have not always been conclusive. Near the cities and, in particular, around Santiago, there is greater specialisation; estates have been divided spontaneously and 'Californian' vegetation has been introduced. Advanced techniques and high outputs are also found in the south, where Germans settled. A major asset is the variety of climates in the country, conducive to a great flexibility in production; consequently both private and Government endeavours to introduce a large variety of crops are being made. The old combination of wheat and native crops is on the wane and, from north to south, olive trees, flax, sugar-beet and milk products are being added to the older fruits, market-garden produce and vines.

## MINING AND THE COUNTRY'S ECONOMY

Agricultural production is concentrated in the central, most densely populated areas near the capital and other urban centres. It is not exported, nor does it make a significant contribution to the national income, although it supplies food to the urban areas. It allows the concentrated rural population, which is the most stable component of the Chilean people, to earn its livelihood.

Mining, until recently, was peripheral in terms of geographical situation, ownership and place in the nation's economy. Geographically, the mines are concentrated in the desert or desert border areas; the exception is El Teniente, situated in a remote spot in the Rancagua mountain range at a height of over 9,000 feet. Until 1964 the mines belonged almost wholly to North American and other foreign companies, who shipped the products directly from the desert to European or North American industrial centres. Only copper was refined locally, owing to the low copper content of the ore.

Taxes, royalties and duties on mining provided 20 per cent of the country's tax revenue; mining accounts for 86 per cent of exports and governs the hard currency position on which the domestic currency is based. The national income is therefore largely dependent upon fluctuating world market prices for copper.

Chile is accustomed to uncertainty in connection with its mining resources, since these were long subjected to a pattern of random spectacular discoveries and rapid exhaustion of mines. After the Pacific War, 75 per cent of Chile's exports consisted of nitrates, although large investments in copper mining made by France and the United States resulted in the existing division of importance between copper and nitrate production.

This division is not consistent, because nitrate production is in a permanent state of crises. Output was maintained until recently at about 1,500,000 tons per annum; in 1963, however, it had fallen to 1,106,000 tons. In copper production Chile is second only to the United States and produces over 500,000 tons each year, constituting 62 per cent of its exports.

In 1964 the Chilean President announced the policy of 'association', whereby the State was to have a greater share in ownership of the mines, which would thus constitute an investment for the future of the country. Thus Chile now has 25 per cent interests in existing mines at Chuquicamata (which are the largest in the world) and at Potrerillos, and will have a one-third interest in any new mines. It now holds 51 per cent of the stock at El Teniente. All these are held in partnership with their North American developers. Small and medium mines, supplying the State-controlled Ventanas foundry, have increased output.

A more or less floating population of miners has been attracted to the desert by copper, nitrates, iodine, sulphur, iron and manganese. After copper and nitrates, iron ore is by far the most important of these, and is quickly overtaking nitrates as the country's second mineral; in 1963 the output reached 8,510,000 tons. The *oficinas* or factories of the nitrate companies are situated along the pampas, wrapped in clouds of dust. In the desert, at Chuquicamata, a gigantic amphitheatre has been carved out of the light-coloured ore at a height of nearly 10,000 feet; two large foundries have been built, and a private town where 20,000 people live.

*The growth of industry.* Industrial development has recently been added to mining and agriculture, sponsored by both Government and private capital resources during the past fifteen years.

With the exception of Brazil, Chile is undoubtedly the country which has achieved the most spectacular industrial progress in South America. Manufacturing is now the leading branch of production, providing 22 per cent of the national income.

Industry began to develop on a small scale during the First World War, when imported manufactured goods were in short supply, and continued to grow between the wars with the exception of the depression years, 1930 to 1932. The government gave various forms of assistance, and the Chilean Development Corporation began, in 1939, to organise previously isolated industrial efforts. During the Second World War the economy became wealthier, the national income rose by 28 per cent and refugee capital began to pour in.

At the same time, access to Chile became easier. The European war and the availability of new means of transport brought many people to South America; tourists were attracted by Chile's magnificent snow-fields in August (the southern winter), by the Mediterranean summer of Viña del Mar in December, by the glacial trout-filled lakes, the countryside and the mountain ranges. The vanguard of tourists consisted of wealthy businessmen, who became interested in making capital investments in the country.

Intangible psychological influences have also helped, including a jealous wish to achieve economic

A stony mountain-road flanked by cactus plants leading in the direction of Chusmiza into the interior of the Iquique region, the most northerly of Chile. The region once had a flourishing guano industry, but now derives its economic importance from its nitrate deposits.

A herd of cattle near Linares, in central Chile.

The Chiquicamata copper mine in the Atacama Desert, the largest copper mine in the world. The huge amphitheatre stands at an altitude of 9,850 feet and is carved out of the pale ore. Chile is the second largest copper producing country in the world after the United States; copper accounts for 60 per cent of its exports.

*Opposite:* A colony of Adelie penguins at Gourlay Peninsula, Signy Island, one of the South Orkney Islands.

An iceberg frozen in the sea off Louber Coast, south-west Graham Land. On top of the iceberg stands an expedition member with three husky dogs.

independence and a spirit of continental competition. Materially, the situation is not completely favourable to industry owing to the lack of power resources and of raw materials. Coal reserves amount to over 2,000 million tons, but it is mostly low grade. Up to 2 million tons of poor quality coal are produced annually at Concepcion and Arauco; low-grade lignite comes from Magellanes, which is too remote. Oil was discovered in Magellanes in 1945, and output in 1960 was more than ten times higher than in 1950. Hydro-electric prospects are also encouraging, since it is estimated that a minimum of 12 million kW could be provided by water power.

There are similar variations in raw materials. Iron ore available in the provinces of Atacama and Co-quimbo has an iron content of 40 to 60 per cent. The known reserves, estimated at over 1,000 million tons, will be adequate for a great number of years. Other relatively plentiful raw materials include the various ores mined in the desert, wool from the south (including Tierra del Fuego) and timber, although there are not enough conifers in the natural forests to supply a large paper industry. At present, about 20 per cent of Chile's entire imports consist of raw materials.

The human factor is, however, both the greatest strength and the greatest weakness of Chilean industrialisation. Its strength lies in a labour market still not very demanding, and its weakness in a limited outlet for consumer goods. Industrial specialisation is therefore difficult, and industry is forced to export against stiff competition from abroad.

Industry consists of two very different groups, the first of which includes a small number of large firms sponsored by the Chilean Development Corporation and mostly devoted to the production of capital goods; the second consists of a large number of privately owned factories and workshops of various sizes. One of the leading members of the first group is the Compania de Acero del Pacifico with its iron and steel works at Huachipato, where 600,000 tons of pig-iron and about 480,000 tons of steel are partially processed. This is more than enough for the Chilean market, so that this new iron and steel industry is

already experiencing difficulties in finding markets. Nevertheless, a new cold rolling mill was started at Huachipato in 1960, and there were discussions with Brazil on the possible exchange of steel products.

The Chilean Development Corporation is also responsible for the establishment of a copper foundry at Paipote and for the great oil refinery at the mouth of the Aconcagua River, at Cancon. Here again, capacity is greater than Chile's requirements.

The second group (private industrial developments) is much smaller and has no definite pattern of organisation except for its geographical concentration: in Santiago, Valparaiso and Concepcion, where the main manpower resources are available, the consumer market has a more even distribution. The textile industry is the largest in this group.

## THE URBAN CENTRES

The development of manufacturing industries has been accomplished by a spectacular growth of towns and cities: 60 per cent of the total population of Chile is now urban as against 50 per cent in 1930. The availability of labour has contributed to industrial development and even made it a necessity.

Santiago's population has doubled every 20 or 25 years since the 1865 census, and is now almost 2,012,000. Fifty per cent of the increase is due to the annual surplus of births over deaths. Even if the rise in the city's population is the result of intensive centralisation, the capital is still oddly sited: it lies inland in a long narrow country mainly situated along the ocean; in addition, it is no longer, as it was when it was founded, in the centre of Chile, but somewhat north of centre. However, it is near the agricultural and mining areas, easily reached through the longitudinal depression and the Aconcagua transverse valley, and close to the fine port of Valparaiso.

Major rail connections run from the capital. Three are of standard gauge and provide comfortable and rapid connections with Valparaiso, San Antonio, Concepcion and Puerto Montt in the south, while there is also a railroad from Santiago to the Argentine border and to Buenos Aires, and another from the capital to the north and the mining desert.

The road network more or less follows the railroads, and also centres on Santiago. Modern roads run from Santiago to Valparaiso and San Antonio, the Pan-American Highway serves most parts of the country, and there is also a good road along the Aconcagua valley.

The prosperity of Santiago is therefore based upon its geographical situation, upon the Chilean pattern of centralisation, the concentration of roads and railroads, the rate of growth of its population and upon the development of its industry. It sprawls at the foot of the Andes, consisting mainly of low-built houses. The centre, however, is full of ten- and twelve-storey buildings and there are many new residential suburbs.

The other Chilean cities are much smaller. The conurbation of Valparaiso and Viña del Mar has a population of only 420,000. Valparaiso lost much of its importance for shipping when the Panama Canal was opened. The mineral ports deprived it of its former export supremacy. It remains the leading port of arrival for imports despite competition from San Antonio, and is now also a major industrial centre.

Concepcion, the third largest city in Chile, has a population of 190,000 including its suburbs. It has an active port, a growing fishing industry and various activities of a regional character, and is increasingly dependent upon the industrial development at Hauchipato. Antofagasta, with a population of 93,500, is becoming the capital of the mining desert because of its port.

Chilean imports often consist of goods needed for basic requirements and there have thus been several devaluations of the currency which have led to a rise in the cost of living and to acute social difficulties. Santiago is crowded with a floating population which lives on a hand-to-mouth basis. The Chilean system of social legislation is, nevertheless, one of the most progressive in Latin America, and the country's standard of living, on a per capita basis, one of the highest.

The country also enjoys a completely democratic system, the Chileans being rightly proud of their relatively peaceful history and their respect for governmental institutions, a sentiment that pervades their political life. The smooth development of the country's institutions has also influenced other fields. Several international organisations have located their South American headquarters in Chile, and it has become a cultural centre with an influence throughout Latin America. Engineers, doctors and agronomists trained in Chilean universities can hold their own against colleagues from the finest European and North American universities.

# ANTARCTICA

In a book primarily devoted to human and economic geography, the empty continent of Antarctica must, nevertheless, be included for three reasons. The first is the rich biological environment provided by the southern seas, to which men have been attracted by the large number of cetacea that feed there and are an extensive and profitable source of animal oil. The second reason is the economic potential of Antarctica, which, in the distant future, may be covered by mining areas and linked by an air network stretching across the tips of the three southern continents, despite recent disappointments in this last direction. The third reason is scientific interest: Antarctica provides a magnificent natural laboratory in which atmospheric circulation, ice in every shape and form, the sea, and marine biology may be studied.

Antarctica is in the southern hemisphere, which differs fundamentally from the northern hemisphere. In the latter, temperate lands have been settled by millions of human beings and by the original and powerful civilisations of Europe, Asia, the Soviet Union and the United States; the temperate lands of the southern hemisphere have had no such advantages. Continents in the northern hemisphere broaden out

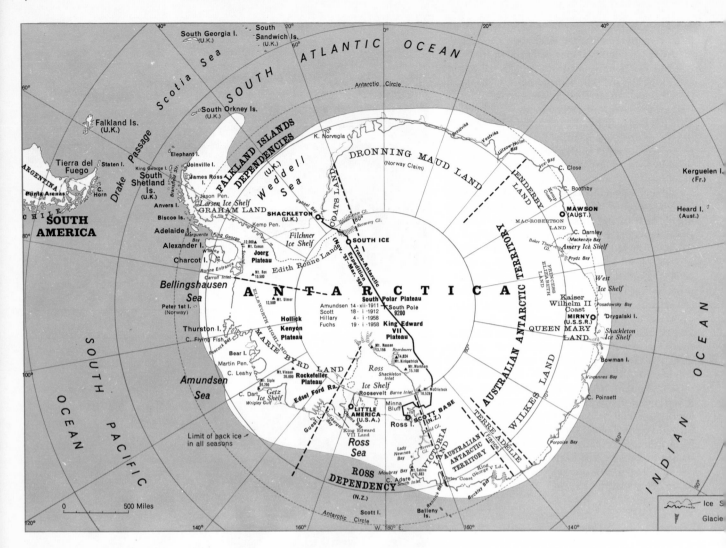

Antarctica: routes of
recent expeditions and stations
set up during the International
Geophysical Year. This was the
last continent to be discovered
(and exploration is by no
means complete yet) but it is the
first continent to be
used exclusively for peaceful
projects — as a laboratory of
international science and
collaboration.

as they near the pole; in the southern hemisphere they
become narrower and finally disappear together with
any permanent settlements of human beings, though
south of the continental masses about 20,000 people are
found temporarily on the islands, on whaling ships
of the southern seas and in Antarctica. In the northern
hemisphere are Canada, Europe and northern Asia;
but the corresponding part of the southern hemisphere
is the largest maritime belt on earth. Our planet is
thus remarkably assymmetrical, though this is not
generally understood owing to the customary distortion found in atlas maps. This lack of symmetry is a
disadvantage to the south.

## DISCOVERING ANTARCTICA

POLITICAL, SCIENTIFIC AND ECONOMIC ASPECTS. Antarctica is divided into sections over which sovereignty is
claimed in theory, if not held in actual fact, by a
number of governments, on the basis of principles
which are sometimes mutually contradictory. The
oldest principle is the right of first discovery, which
has been claimed by the British and Australians in the
widest section, by the Norwegians in Queen Maud
Land, and by the French in Adélie Land. Another
principle is maritime reconnaissance, though this has
not been claimed by the Germans and Belgians as a

result of their journey at the turn of the century, by
the French in connection with Charcot's expedition
or by the Americans, despite their work in the Ross
Sea from their base at Little America. It has, however,
been claimed by the Soviet Union following its expeditions to the Antarctic seas. Finally, claims based on
geographical proximity are made by Argentina, Chile
and New Zealand. Attempts to find an international
solution to the problem were symbolised by Admiral
Byrd, of the United States, who flew over the South
Pole in February 1947, and dropped a bundle of
United Nations flags.

Since 1945, the major purpose of every expedition
to the Antarctic has been scientific study. During the
Antarctic summer of 1946-47, the United States organised a very large-scale air and sea operation, while
from 1949 to 1952 three French polar expeditions
explored Adélie Land, and Anglo-Swedish-Norwegian
expeditions Queen Maud Land. At the beginning of
1954, the Australians settled at Mawson in Mac-
Robertson Land, and there are also permanent stations
maintained by Argentina, Chile and Great Britain in
Graham Land.

The only possible activities in this inhospitable land
are scientific. Antarctica has an area of nearly 6 million square miles, twice as large as Australia; it is a
cold desert in which there is virtually no plant life

and animal life is seasonal only and concentrated on the outer borders. So it would be almost impossible to subsist on agriculture, hunting and fishing. However, it appears that the ancient continental platform of eastern Antarctica contains precious or semi-precious ores and is covered by coal seams. The only finds made lie inland from the eastern coast of the Ross Sea. In this area, however, which is the beginning of western Antarctica, with its folded 'Andean' structure and peaks more than 15,000 feet high, the mining resources are almost entirely buried under ice.

*The ice and polar circulation.* The tremendous frozen hump of the South Pole is the symmetrically opposite counterpart of the maritime basin of the North Pole. The Antarctic ice sheet is very thick; the thickness varies, however, in a pattern which is still not fully known, in spite of recent seismic probes. In Queen Maud Land valleys in the continental platform have been detected next to buried mountains, while further on, peaks over 9,000 feet high break through the ice sheet. In eastern Antarctica, it is likely that the ice runs from a ridge line of which the highest known peak has a height of 13,800 feet; this glacial divide is roughly parallel to the steepest shore of the Ross Sea, along which are situated Victoria Land, the volcanoes Mounts Erebus and Terror, and Mount Markham (15,020 feet). The glacial divide runs across the continent much closer to the Ross Sea than to the distant shore, so that the polar ice-cap is not symmetrically convex. On one side of the topographic axis there is the hollow basin of the South Pole, where an American base has been established at an altitude of 8,900 feet, and on the other there is the area in which the Soviet Union has its Vostok and Sovietskaya bases (11,500 and 12,200 feet respectively) and which was, until recently, generally regarded as the pole of inaccessibility.

The ice consists of huge monotonous plateaus, often pitted by sastrugi, extending towards the shores. More work has been done near these shores than inland. In Adélie Land, for example, a series of soundings perpendicular to the coast has shown that the ice, 9,500 feet thick, rises gradually inland up to an altitude of 7,900 feet at the Charcot station and beyond. The rocky continental platform has a height which varies between +1,650 feet and –2,000 feet; the variations occur over a distance of 300 miles with a gentle slope of less than 4°, so that the continental platform is almost horizontal. This ice-covered peneplain extends over most of eastern Antarctica, but our knowledge of it is very incomplete. In the centre, it is likely that the ice-cap has a thickness of 13,000 feet, and there is a similar area on the other side, in western Antarctica, where the ice reaches heights of nearly 10,000 feet and covers land with greater relief. At the shore, the ice consists of walls 300 feet high, or of platforms extending along inlets of the continental shelf.

Several different methods have been used by expeditions going inland from coastal stations. Before 1914, men travelled over distances of hundreds of miles either by hauling their sledges themselves, or by having them pulled by dogs, and this method is still in use today. Later came caterpillar-tracked vehicles, used extensively by Byrd in 1933 to 1935 when he established the advanced inland station in which he wintered alone, and almost died. The position and size of any advance post established by means of tracked land transport only are governed by the performance of the vehicles used; the classic example is the Weasel, a small caterpillar tractor that can haul a load of one or two tons. More recent vehicles have a high load capacity and in 1956 a train of caterpillar tractors enabled 350 tons of equipment to be brought to the Byrd station, 600 miles from Little America at the far end of the Ross Sea. The fuel consumption is very high, sometimes allowing only 3 miles per gallon, while speeds are limited to 12 to 15 m.p.h., so that any large-scale mechanised inland operations will increasingly be dependent on assistance from the air.

Since 1929, when the first flight was made, every expedition has had at least limited assistance from aircraft. Flights take place in summer only, though atmospheric conditions are always uncertain and landing near the coast is difficult. Aircraft are also used for reconnaissance and photographic work where it is possible to determine the relief by using stereoscopic techniques in conjunction with astronomical bearings and altimeter readings.

*Antarctic settlements, bad weather and isolation.* Polar ships are engaged in a race against both ice and time; finding safe berths from which their passengers and cargo can land is a very difficult operation, since there is no possibility as yet of establishing permanent ports or airfields. Ships continue to play a vital part in polar expeditions, and must be provided with adequate shelter if they are to be bases for semi-permanent occupation of areas in which continuous observations are to be made over periods of several years.

The main permanent bases on the continent are situated at Graham Land, the northernmost part of Antarctica, while the other coastal stations were occupied for a few winters only by Scott, Shackleton and Amundsen on the Ross Sea before 1914, by Mawson at Cape Denison and by explorers today at Port Martin, Maudheim and Mawson. Coastal bases were also established during the 1957-59 period, as well as the first inland settlements. An example of the unstable conditions which affect Antarctic stations is provided by Little America. This base was almost as large as a town when it was established by the Americans in 1929 on the Bay of Whales in the Ross Sea, and was found to be in perfect condition though completely buried under snow in 1934, when it was cleared, enlarged and used by a wintering party. In 1940-41 Byrd returned to Little America. In January 1955, however, after a reconnaissance voyage by the ice-breaker *Atka*, it was reported that Little America had disappeared and that part of the great shelf on which it was built had drifted out to sea.

Antarctic bases must be built to withstand rigorous weather conditions and total isolation for a period of eleven months, and every item needed to provide shelter, food and facilities for scientific observation must be landed during the few weeks of summer. To make possible rapid construction in icy or rocky and uneven terrain, most building components must be prefabricated. Buildings must be well insulated and perfectly blizzard-proof as well as able to withstand the strongest winds, so they must be designed with air locks and very few doors.

*The polar climate and blizzard squalls.* Mean temperatures are always below 0°C. (32°F.). But owing to the considerable difficulties experienced in penetrating to the central plateau in winter and in reaching the innermost continental section of eastern Antarctica, it is likely that the coldest temperatures existing on the continent have not yet been encountered. Average winter temperatures of –30°C. (–22°F.) have been observed, but minimum temperatures have ranged from –45°C. (–49°F.) in Queen Maud Land, to –74°C. (–101°F.) at the American Amundsen-scott station on the South Pole and –87°C. (–125°F.) at the Russian Sovietskaya station, over 3,000 feet higher than the South Pole base. The highest temperatures observed have been recorded at the outer edges during the short southern summer, when there is sunshine and extensive melting of the ice. The midnight sun then shines over almost all Antarctica, and the long summer days are very pleasant. By February freezing is well under way, while in March birds and penguins return to their winter quarters on the pack, apart from a few Emperor penguin rookeries along the coast. By April, the continent is once more surrounded by ice, temperatures have dropped and the sun sets.

Winds of gale force which sweep up ice dust and blow at speeds greater than 120 m.p.h. are the most frequent. They rise and fall suddenly and may blow for weeks on end; the resulting blizzards increase and become colder owing to the slope of the plateau and the existence of coastal inlets. The influence of polar winds is felt beyond Antarctica, since they force the pack-ice well out to sea during the December and January break-up. In the distant future, it may prove possible to use the refrigerating potential to cool down torrid areas and to store surplus crops, while the temperature differential between the continent and the free-flowing sea water under the pack could be exploited to supply thermo-electro stations. Alternatively, the winds could provide an inexhaustible supply of eolian energy.

## THE SOUTHERN SEAS AND ISLANDS

*The pack and the southern seas.* Precursors of Antarctica are seen long before the continent is reached. Flat-topped icebergs, reaching a record size of 1,600 square miles, are known to have broken away from the ice barriers of the Ross Sea, Weddell Sea and Shackleton Shelf. There are also smaller and more complex-shaped floes, formed when the glaciers flow down to the sea or when ice breaks off from ice cliffs and walls. These all drift out to latitude 60° S. or beyond before melting and disappearing; they are more interesting than dangerous to encounter, since navigation in these areas is usually restricted to the long summer days, and collisions are prevented by radar. During the break-up these individual bergs are surrounded by thousands of ice fragments from the melting pack, which drifts slowly out to sea. In winter, the surface of the sea consists of a virtually impenetrable mass of ice which may be more than 6 feet thick and extend out from the coast to a distance of 400 to 1,000 miles. This reaches its maximum extent in September and October, when it may reach latitude 55°S. on the Atlantic side, although it does not go beyond latitude 65° on the eastern Pacific side. By the end of January the pack has sometimes completely disappeared; but usually it remains tight, extending far north until the end of February, when the surface begins to freeze again and the new pack is formed around the remains of the old pack.

When a ship sails to Antarctica, it is impossible to know in advance what type of pack will be encountered. It may be open, with 'pancake ice' and large pools of ice-free water, or it may be more or less closed. In either case, navigation is difficult.

Once the pack has been crossed there are very extensive stormy areas. The cold southern seas become more temperate after the Antarctic convergence but, because the west to east circulation of sea and air encounters no obstructions, the weather is always bad and there are constant storms with the world's worst waves and swells. The southern seas are situated in the temperate region, where a constant flow of air from west to east carries a stream of depressions around the globe. The 'brave west winds' enabled sailing vessels to round Cape Horn and sail all over the world, and depending upon the latitudes in which they blow, they are known by various names: the *roaring forties, furious fifties and screeching sixties.*

*The islands.* The sub-Antarctic islands are all quite small and, whether situated in temperate or in cold temperate latitudes, have a strongly maritime climate. Depending upon how far south they are situated, they are either Antarctic precursors such as Heard, Macquarie and Bouvet Islands, or else monotonously clement such as New Amsterdam Island. In the Kerguelen Islands, for example, there is only 5°C. (8°F.) between the winter mean of 2.6°C. (37°F.) and the summer mean of 7.4°C. (45°F.), but there are ten to fifteen periods of bad weather every month.

Vegetation is scanty, and only crayfish are found — around a few of the warmer islands. Approach to the islands is hazardous owing to the stormy climate, high, wave-beaten western cliffs, belts of smooth rocks and algae (*macrocystis*). There are virtually no mineral resources on the islands and the only available fuel is peat.

These little isolated islands are therefore unattractive and often unpopulated. Indeed, their sole use seems to be scientific investigation. Like Antarctica, the islands were investigated during the International Geophysical Year. They are also occasionally used as ports of call on the way to the South Pole, and were formerly used by whaling ships. Whale factory-ships no longer need to refuel in the sub-Antarctic region, however.

*Navigation and whales.* Although the southern seas are scarcely attractive, they provide an excellent breeding ground for cetacea, which feed on krill, a type of phosphorescent shrimp which is found there. Antarctic navigation was therefore largely begun by whalers, which penetrated the pack.

There are now both polar ships and whalers on the southern seas and, in 1949-50, 10,726 men sailed on whale factory-ships and whalers, which are mainly Norwegian. In these waters large numbers of blue and rorqual whales can be found for periods which last from a few days to a few months. The catch is, however, limited by international agreement to 15,000 'Blue Whale Units' per year. In order to ensure survival of the whale species, an International Whaling Convention was signed at Washington in 1946, and a rigid control of areas, periods of whaling and authorised catches per species is carried out by an annual whaling conference. Both Norway and the Netherlands have since withdrawn from the convention. Production from the southern seas amounts to 300,000 to 400,000 tons of oil every year.

The size of each scientific expedition governs the size of the ships which it uses and, correspondingly, the method used to penetrate the pack. Small ships built of metal and armoured to provide the best defence against ice force their bows against the loosest floes and follow zig-zag courses through pools of open water.

Small ships can no longer deal with the amount of material which must be carried by even the smallest expedition, and ship tonnage has therefore been increased. An excellent example of the newest ships is the Danish 1,200-ton *Kista Dan,* built specially for the purpose, whose shape and manoeuvring capacity enable it to 'work' the ice like a small ice-breaker and to crush the floes instead of pushing them aside. Large ice-breakers are also used, but they are expensive and their surplus power requirements reduce their cargo capacity.

Regardless of the type of ship used, transport is always very costly. Owing to the difficulty of getting through the pack, the remoteness of starting bases and the need to bring every item of food and equipment to Antarctica, it is still very difficult to establish permanent bases there. The exception is Graham Land, which is more accessible. There are neither economic nor strategic reasons to justify the expenditure involved, but every possible means of ensuring navigation, traffic and accommodation in the Antarctic region has been employed to further a major international scientific programme.

## THE INTERNATIONAL GEOPHYSICAL YEAR

The International Geophysical Year, in 1957-58, represented an unprecedented investment in Antarctica which involved 13 nations and 740 explorers in a major scientific programme of investigation into areas that were already known or hitherto unexplored. Bases were actually established in 1956 and some still exist, since many countries have a continuing interest in Antarctica.

A number of countries have established permanent bases both in Graham Land, which is also called the Palmer Archipelago, San Martin Land or O'Higgins Land depending upon the country concerned, and in the South Shetland Islands. Argentina, Chile and Great Britain have six, four and nine stations respectively while there are, in addition, two British bases at the far side of the Weddell Sea and another set up on the plateau during the trans-Antarctic expedition. Each of the countries traditionally associated with the exploration of a given area has set up an additional coastal station on it: Belgium in Princess Astrid Land; Norway in Queen Maud Land; and France in Adélie Land. Most of the countries nearest to Antarctica tend to concentrate on given geographical areas. Thus, Argentina has two new stations at the far side of the Weddell Sea. Australia has two stations in the southern part of the Kerguelen Islands and New Zealand has a base on the Ross Sea and another in the same area, in conjunction with the United States. There are two American bases on the Ross Sea, and another temporary base on the Weddell Sea, but the United States has concentrated on the previously unknown area of Marie Byrd Land and on the South Pole itself. Four newcomers have entered the field: Japan, which has a station in Prince Harald Land; the Soviet Union, which has three stations along the Indian Ocean coast, and a network of stations on the immense, unexplored plateau of eastern Antarctica, along which the pole of inaccessibility and the cold pole were reached; Poland, which recently took over the Soviet 'oasis' station in Knox Land; and the Union of South Africa, which has established three stations on sub-Antarctic islands. France, Great Britain, Australia, New Zealand and Argentina have a total of eight additional stations on these islands. Scientific work sponsored by the International Geophysical Year is therefore continuing at 57 Antarctic stations, including 11 on the islands, 19 in Graham Land and 27 in the continent proper. These stations are tiny outposts, hundreds or even thousands of miles apart.

Attempts at simultaneous international scientific research in the polar regions had already been made in 1881 and 1932 but the aim of the International Geophysical Year, first proposed by the International Union of Geodesy and Geophysics, was much wider: it lasted from July 1957 to the end of 1958, and was organised and implemented on a world scale. The Antarctic programme was the study of upper atmosphere phenomena. It involved so many material and operational problems necessitating co-ordination, such as the provision of radio links, centralised meteorological information, support and rescue services, and information on suitable methods and equipment, that the countries involved introduced machinery for special co-ordination.

The first agreement on international co-operation in science and disarmament, the Antarctic Treaty, was signed at Washington in December 1959. It marked the end of the International Geophysical Year and the beginning of a new stage of development, although a number of problems remain outstanding, such as the claims and counter-claims to parts of Antarctica, which were not considered in the treaty. Future meetings are planned to work out ways and means of implementing both the treaty and the agreement reached on the principle of banning nuclear explosions or deposits of radioactive waste in Antarctica. The treaty, which has been signed by twelve countries including all those mentioned above apart from Poland, is open to acceptance by any other country without restrictions if it is a member of the United Nations Organisation, or with the agreement of the other signatories if it is not. It is a paradox that Antarctica, which has no population, is the first area in the world in which total demilitarisation has been agreed internationally. Thanks to the Antarctic Treaty, Antarctica and the surrounding oceans extending to latitude 60°S. are to be neutral and devoted to peaceful and disinterested scientific activity.

733

Illustrations were drawn from the following sources: 13 Mauritius. 14 Hasonbild. 15 L: Rapho, R: Barnaby's. 16 Hasonbild. 17 Mauritius. 18 J. Allan Cash. 19 National Travel Ass. of Denmark. 20 T: Danish Embassy, C: Ullstein, B: J. Allan Cash. 21 Danish Tourist Office. 22 Barnaby's. 23 T: Mauritius, B: J. Scheerboom. 24 T, C: J. Allan Cash, B: T. Schneiders. 25 T: Magnum-Photo, C: Mauritius, B: Norsk Polarinstitutt. 27 T: Bowater Paper Corpn., B: Swedish Tourist Association. 28 TL: T. Schneiders, TR, B: Hasonbild. 29 T. Schneiders. 31 Finnish Embassy. 32 Finnish Embassy. 33 Rapho. 34 T: Finnish Embassy, B: A. Ehrhardt. 37 T: Rapho, C: H. Schlenker, B: Ullstein. 38 J. Scheerboom. 40 T: J. Allan Cash, C: Fairey Air Surveys Ltd, B: J. Bowden. 41 T: J. Allan Cash, B: Coleman & Hayward. 42 L: I. L. Gibbs, R: M. Busselle. 43 T: J. Allan Cash, C: Sunday Telegraph, B: J. Allan Cash. 44 L. Sansom. 45 T: J. Allan Cash, B: L. & M. Gayton. 47 T: R. Gee, C: C. Douglas Milner, B: A. Gregory. 48 T: R. Gee, B: R. Lowden. 49 T, B: R. Gee. 50 J. Bulmer. 51 T: J. Allan Cash, B: L. & M. Gayton. 52 T: Eagle Photos, C: J. Allan Cash, B: L. & M. Gayton. 55 L: Richard Thomas & Baldwins Ltd, R: British Nylon Spinners Ltd. 56 T: L. Sansom, C: I.C.I., B: Barnaby's. 57 T: D. Innes, C: J. Topham Ltd, B: Scotsman Photos. 58 L: J. Allan Cash, R: Nat. Coal Board. 59 T. Weir. 60 T: Fox Photos, C: Scotch Whisky Ass., B: Eagle Photos. 63 Dr H. Winch. 64 T: Gov. of N. Ireland, B: J. Allan Cash. 65 Arthur Guinness Son & Co. Ltd. 68 L: W. F. van Heemskerck Düker, R: Belgian State Tourist Office. 70 T: J. Allan Cash, B: K.L.M. 72 L: E. Schleinitz, R: J. Roubier. 73 J. Roubier. 75 L: Belgian State Tourist Office, R: W. Lüden. 76 L: Sabena, R: Camera Press. 77 Société Industrielle Belge des Pétroles. 79 R. Delvert. 80 T: P. Almasy, C: G. Finlayson, B: P. Jovet. 81 S. Presser. 83 T: Lapie, C: A. Martin, B: R. Delvert. 84 R. Delvert. 86 T: French Ministry of Agriculture, C: J. Roubier, B: Mirrorpic. 89 J. Topham Ltd. 90 T: S. Presser, C: R. Delvert, B: Charbonnages de France. 91 L: Yan, R: French Embassy. 94–5 R. Delvert. 97 J. Allan Cash. 98 T: Camera Press, C: Portuguese State Office, B: L. Sansom. 99 T: L. Sansom, B: J. Allan Cash. 100 D.Z.F. 101 W. Lüden. 102 T: M. Busselle, B: Swiss Nat. Tourist Office. 103 L: Coleman & Hayward, R: Swiss Nat. Tourist Office. 104 P. Almasy. 108 T: Swiss Nat. Tourist Office, C: W. Lüden, B: Swiss Nat. Tourist Office. 110 T, C: Swiss Nat. Tourist Office, B: Ullstein. 111 Austrian Embassy. 113 T: M. Busselle, B: E. Schleinitz. 114 M. Busselle. 115 T: Austrian Embassy, B: Boudot-Lamotte. 116 T: Bundesbildstelle, Bonn, B: W. Lüden. 117 W. Lüden. 118 Mauritius. 119 Ullstein. 120 T: W. Lüden, B: J. Roubier. 122 W. Lüden. 123 D. Z. F. 125 L: Mauritius, R: Inter Nationes. 126 T: Bundesbildstelle, Bonn, C, B: Mirror Features. 128 T: Mauritius, B: W. Lüden. 130 Deutsche Fotothek, Dresden. 131 London Express News. 132 Czechoslovak Embassy. 133 S. Presser. 134 Ullstein. 136 L: Camera Press, R: Czechoslavak Chamber of Commerce. 138, 141 Hungarian News and Information Service. 142 Ullstein. 143 Mauritius. 144–5–7 Hungarian News and Information Service. 149 C. A. F. 150 L: G. Gravett, R: C. A. F. 151 C. A. F. 152 Deutsche Fotothek, Dresden. 155–6 Camera Press. 159 Deutsche Fotothek, Dresden. 161 Camera Press. 162 Rumanian Legation. 163 Bulgarian Legation. 164 T: E. Hosking, C: Bulgarian Legation, B: Ullstein. 165 Camera Press. 166 J. Allan Cash. 168 Yugoslav Information Service. 169 Yugoslav National Tourist Office. 172 Rapho. 173 V. Zuber. 174 J. Allan Cash. 176–7 M. Grcevic. 178 V. Zuber. 181 V. Zuber. 183 J. Kanapa, Atlas-Photo. 185–6 Camera Press. 187 T: B. Clark, B: J. Baker. 188 T: P. Almasy, C: N. Tozer, B: Popper. 189 S. Harrison. 190 T: S. Harrison, C, B: A. Bolt. 191 J. Allan Cash. 193 Italian State Tourist Office. 194 PAF International Ltd. 195 Italian State Tourist Office. 196 T: Mauritius, C: C. Douglas Milner, B: Boudot-Lamotte. 197 E. Schleinitz. 198 E.N.I.T. 200 T: E.N.I.T., B: Mauritius. 203 S. Presser. 204 Fiat. 205 T: Mauritius, B: Esso Standard. 206 T: P. Belzeaux, B: Publifoto, Milan. 207 T: Publifoto, Milan, B: M. Busselle. 209 T: Mauritius, B: Mirrorpic. 210 T: Planet News, C: R. Viollet, B: Monaco Tourist Office. 211 G. Finlayson. 212 A. Bolt. 214 J. Roubier. 215 T: R. Herzog, B: J. Allan Cash. 216 Spanish Nat. Tourist Office. 219 T: J. Allan Cash, B: D. Pike. 220 J. Allan Cash. 221 J. Rufus. 225 T: A. Bolt, C: Mauritius, B: D. Pike. 226 J. Allan Cash. 227 Mauritius. 230 Paisajes Espanoles. 234 P. Almasy. 235 T: E. Schleinitz, B: Moroccan Nat. Tourist Office. 237 Moroccan Nat. Tourist Office. 238–9 Boudot-Lamotte. 243 R. Delvert. 245 E. G. Schleinitz. 246 Tunisian Embassy. 247 T: P. Almasy, B: Moroccan Nat. Tourist Office. 248–9 Moroccan Nat. Tourist Office. 250 L, R: Popper. 253 T: London Express News, B: R. Delvert. 255 T: Esso Photograph, B: S. Presser. 259 T: Middle East Marketing Services, B: Esso Photograph. 260 Middle East Marketing Services. 261 Esso Photograph. 262 T: G. Gravett, B: Middle East Marketing Services. 263 Esso Photograph. 264 T: R. Herzog, B: J. Baker. 265 B.O.A.C. 266 T: J. Allan Cash, B: P. Almasy. 268 United Nations. 269 R. Herzog. 270 H. Müller-Feldmann. 271 Camera Press. 272 P. Almasy. 273 T. Schneiders. 274 United Nations. 275 T. Schneiders. 276 E. Aubert de la Rüe. 279 J.F.E. Bloss. 280 W. Suschitzky. 282 T: W. Suschitzky, B: Central Press Photos Ltd. 283 J. Allan Cash 284 T: W. Suschitzky, B: J. Allan Cash. 286 P. Almasy. 288 United Africa Co. Ltd. 290 J. Allan Cash. 293 T: D. Pike, C: United Africa Co. Ltd, B: Popper. 294 J. Allan Cash. 295 T: J. Allan Cash, C: Ghana High Commission. B: D. Pike. 297 United Africa Co. Ltd. 298 P. Almasy. 299 T: Mauritius, B: P. Almasy. 300–4 P. Almasy. 306–8 Ministère de la France d'Outre-Mer. 311 Ministère de la France d'Outre-Mer. 312 P. Almasy. 316 T: Bell Howarth Ltd, B: Popper. 317–8 Popper. 319 A. Gregory. 312 P. Almasy. 322 P. Almasy. 323 Portuguese State Office. 324 London Express News. 325 S.P.G. 326 Agencia Geral do Ultramar. 327 L: Camera Press, R: E. Schleinitz. 328 Ullstein. 330 T, C: A. Gregory, B: Kenya Information Services. 332 J. Allan Cash. 333–4 E. African Railways & Harbours. 335 Tanganyika Public Relations Dept. 336 T, B: J. Allan Cash. 337 T, C: C.O.I., B: Popper. 338 Rhodesian Selection Trust Ltd. 339 Bell Howarth Ltd. 342–3 Ministry of Home Affairs, Rhodesia & Nyasaland. 344 T: A. Morath, B: Ministry of Home Affairs, Rhodesia & Nyasaland. 345 Ministry of Home Affairs, Rhodesia & Nyasaland. 346 State Information Office, Pretoria. 347 South African Information Service. 348 Bell Howarth Ltd. 349 State Information Office. 352 T: J. Allan Cash, B: Johnson, Matthey & Co. Ltd. 353 J. Allan Cash. 354 E. Schleinitz. 355 F. Perret. 356 French Embassy. 358 F. Perret. 362 G. Gravett. 364 Coleman & Hayward. 365 London Express News. 366 J. Allan Cash. 367–8 Popper. 369 Orient Press Photo Co. 370 Litvinoff. 371 Mauritius. 372 Ullstein. 373 E. Aubert de la Rüe. 374 P. Almasy. 375 D. Pike. 379 B.O.A.C. 380 R. Viollet. 381 P. Almasy. 382 Ullstein. 383 T: Mauritius, B: Middle East Marketing Services. 384 Middle East Marketing Services. 385 Barnaby's. 386 Iraq Petroleum Co. Ltd. 387 British Petroleum Co. 388 P. Almasy. 389 T: Esso Photograph, B: Kuwait Oil Co. Ltd, 390 G. Gravett. 391 A. Janata. 393 L: A. Janata, R: Kuwait Oil Co. Ltd. 394 Kuwait Oil Co. Ltd. 397 Mauritius. 398 E. Scheidegger. 399 J. C. Inglis. 400 R. Herzog. 401 Mauritius. 402 P. Almasy. 403 T: W. Suschitzky, B: P. Almasy. 406 D. Pike. 407 W. Suschitzky. 409 T: Information Service of India, B: W. Suschitzky. 410 Mauritius. 411 R. Herzog. 412 Camera Press 416 A. Gregory. 417 T: Mauritius, B: A. Gregory. 418 E. Scheidegger. 419 P. Almasy. 420 G. Gravett. 422 A. Gregory. 424 P.I.A. 425 T: Middle East Marketing Services, B: Pakistan High Commission. 426 D. Pike. 427 S.P.G. 428 W. Suschitzky. 430 T: Popper, B: E. Scheidegger. 432 T: S.P.G., B: Popper. 433 Dunlop Rubber Co. Ltd. 435 D. Pike. 437 Popper. 438 Ministry of Culture, Singapore. 439 Popper. 440 London Express News. 441 Popper. 442 R. Viollet. 433 P. Almasy. 445 Royal Embassy of Cambodia. 447 Royal Embassy of Cambodia. 448 Popper. 449 United Nations. 451–2 P. Almasy. 454 London Express News. 455 N. Vietnam Government. 457 P. Almasy. 458 T: P. Almasy, B: N. Vietnam Government. 459 London Express News. 460 P. Almasy. 461 Popper. 463–4 P. Almasy. 465 Z.P.A. 467 W. Suschitzky. 469 T: Crown Copyright, B: Indonesian Embassy. 471 Caltex Pacific Oil Co. 472 B.O.A.C. 473 Sarawak Information Service. 474 J. Bulmer. 475 T. Saulnier. 476 T: Popper, B: Camera Press. 477 P. Almasy. 478 Popper. 481 High Commissioner for N. Zealand. 483 T. Saulnier. 484 P. Almasy. 485 Camera Press. 486 J. Bulmer. 487–9 High Commissioner for N. Zealand. 489 Australian News and Information Bureau. 491 R. Burks. 492 T: Barnaby's, B: W. Suschitzky. 493 A. Poignant. 495 Australian News and Information Bureau. 496 W. Suschitzky. 497 Australian News and Information Bureau. 500 Popper. 501 T: Japanese Embassy, B: Japan Tourist Ass. 503 E. Scheidegger. 504 A. Zucca. 507–8 Japan Tourist Ass. 509 Mitsubishi Shipbuilding Co. Ltd. 511 T: Japan Tourist Ass., B: O.S.K. 512 Camera Press. 516 T: Camera Press, B: Korean Society for Cultural Relations with Foreign Countries. 517 Ullstein. 518 Camera Press. 519 T: Camera Press, B: Popper. 520 Camera Press. 521 T: E. Landau, B: Popper. 522 E. Landau. 523 Popper. 524 Camera Press. 526–8 Camera Press. 529 T: Camera Press, B: J. Allan Cash. 534–5 Camera Press. 537 T: Popper, B: J. Allan Cash. 538 E. Landau. 539 B.S.F. 541 T: S.C.R., C: Camera Press, B: S.C.R. 544–5 S.C.R. 548 T: Popper, B: Tass. 550 S.C.R. 551 Mirrorpic. 552–63 S.C.R. 557 B.S.F. 564 Nat. Film Board of Canada. 565–6 Polar Photos. 568 T: J-J. Languepin, B: A. Ehrhardt. 569 Popper. 570 Hunting Survey Corpn. Ltd. 571 G. Gravett. 574 T: J. Allan Cash, B: U.S.I.S. 575 Nat. Film Board of Canada. 576 Canada House. 577 Bowater Paper Corpn. 580 T: Canada House B: Hunting Survey Corpn. Ltd. 581 Nat. Film Board of Canada. 583 T: Nat. Film Board of Canada, B: Canadian Nat. Railways. 584 Canada House. 586 T: High Commissioner for Canada, B: Aluminium Co. of Canada. 587 T: Camera Press, B: Nat. Film Board of Canada. 589 T: London Electrotyping Agency, B: State of California: Div. of Beaches & Parks. 590 L: U.S.I.S., R: S. Dakota State Highway Commission. 591 L: N. Y. State Dept of Commerce, R: London Electrotype Agency. 593 London Electrotype Agency. 594 Wide World Photos. 599 T: Pictorial Press, B: Pan American. 602 U.S.I.S. 603 U. S. Information Agency. 604 Delaware State Development Dept. 605 Port of N. Y. Authority. 607–8 London Electrotype Agency. 610 Arizona Photographic Associates. 611 Florida State News Bureau. 612 U.S.I.S. 617 Ullstein. 619 U. S. Dept of Interior: Bureau of Reclamation. 621 T: Keystone Press Agency Ltd, B: E. Schleinitz. 622 T: Sunkist Photo, B: State of Ohio, Dept of Industrial and Agricultural Development. 623 London Electrotype Agency 625 T: U.S.I.S., C: A. Morath, B: Utah Tourist & Publicity Council. 626 L: Monsanto Chemical Co., R: Bethlehem Steel Corpn. 628 E. Schleinitz. 629 G. Strouvé. 630 E. Aubert de la Rüe. 632 Mauritius. 633 Pan American Coffee Bureau. 634 Popper. 638 A. Bolt. 640 A. Bolt. 641 T: M. Teague, B: J. Murphy Ltd. 642 Camera Press. 644 T: Elders & Fyffes Ltd, B: Shell Photo. 645 A. Bolt. 647 Mauritius. 648 A. Bolt. 651 T: Popper, B: Camera Press. 654 Bell Howarth Ltd. 656 Pan American World Airways. 657 Mauritius. 659 T: Bell Howarth Ltd, B: E. Aubert de la Rüe. 662 T: Colombian Embassy, B: Popper. 663 A. Bolt. 664 Mauritius. 666 T: A. Bolt, B: Ministry of Development, Venezuela. 669 Creole Petroleum Corpn. 670 A. Bolt. 672 T: Aluminium (Canada) Ltd, C: Popper, B: Mauritius. 673 P. Almasy. 675 E. Aubert de la Rüe. 677 T: Bureau of Commerce, Brazil, B: C. Arapoff, 680 Rapho. 683 Popper. 688 J. Allan Cash. 689 T: Camera Press, B: Popper. 692 P. Almasy. 693 T: P. Almasy, B: J. Allan Cash. 694 T: British Council, B: J. Allan Cash. 695 J. Allan Cash. 697 T: Popper, B: J. Allan Cash. 698 P. Almasy. 699–700 Popper. 702 Shell Photos. 706 T: A. Gregory, B: Popper. 707 A. Gregory. 709–10 Bell Howarth Ltd. 712 T: Foto Thorlichen, B: J. Frank. 715 T: E. Stockins, B: R. Viollet. 717 T: P. Almasy, B: E. Stockins. 718 E. Aubert de la Rüe. 719 F.I.D.S.

Colour plates:

Frontis E. J. O. Stone. 35 T: T. Schneiders, B: Z.F.A. 36 T: Z.F.A., B: D. Pike. 53 T: A. Taylor, BL: Z.F.A., BR: P. Almasy. 54 Shell Photo. 87 W. F. Davidson. 88 T, B: P. Almasy. 105 T: Owczarzak, B: G. Cubitt. 106 W. F. Davidson. 139 W. F. Davidson. 140 R.S.W. (PRASA). 157 T: N. Tozer, B: G. Cubitt. 158 T: A. Genalis, B: H. Maier. 223 W. Benser. 224 T: G. Cubitt, B: A. Bolt, BR: D. Pike. 241 T, BL: S. Harrison, BR: H. Seymour Davies. 242 T: H. Roer, B: W. Swaan. 291 E. J. O. Stone. 292 T: W. Benser, BL: P. Keen, BR: W. Benser. 309 Rhodesian Selection Trust Group of Companies. 310 T: C.O.I. B: Rhodesian Selection Trust Group of companies. 359 Anglo-American Corpn. of South Africa. 360 T: A. Cash, B: G. Cubitt. 377 Kuwait Oil Co. 378 T: Novack, B: D. Pike. 395 W. Suschitsky. 396 T: A.E.I., BL: A. Gregory, BR: D. Pike. 413 Ministry of Culture 414 T: Aubert de la Rüe, B: D. Pike. 479 New Zealand High Commissioner. 480 A. Poignant. 513 Z.F.A. 514 T: D. Pike, B: J. Lauwerys. 531 P. Keen. 532 Gulf Oil Corpn. 597 T: Shostal, B: Chromoslide. 598 T: Nilsson, B: H. Seymour Davies. 615 W. Benser. 616 T: S. Harrison, B: Gratwohl. 649 A. Bolt. 650 T: H. Seymour Davies, B: A. Bolt. 667 T, B: S. Harrison. 668 T: Shell Photo, B: Hartmann. 685 A. Morath. 686 T: Z.F.A., B: J. Moore. 703 J. Moore. 704 T: Z.F.A., B: A. Cash.